standard catalog of

INDEPENDENTS

The Struggle to Survive Among Giants

Edited by Ron Kowalke

Published by

700 E. State Street • Iola, WI 54990-0001
Telephone: 715/445-2214

Please call or write for our free catalog of automotive publications.
Our toll-free number to place an order or obtain a free catalog is 800-258-0929 or please use our regular business telephone 715-445-2214 for editorial comment and further information.

Library of Congress Catalog Number: 98-84631
ISBN: 0-87341-569-8
Printed in the United States of America

FOREWORD

It is always exciting to debut another volume in the long-running and popular *Standard Catalog* series, published by Krause Publications. This, the first edition of *Standard Catalog of Independents*, covers a select group of automakers that, although never achieving the business longevity and ensuing financial success of the "Big Three" (Chevrolet, Chrysler and Ford), were nonetheless instrumental in the automobile's evolution from its rudimentary beginning at the turn of the 20th century to the sophisticated chariot of luxury and dependability it became in the late-1980s. This is when the final surviving automaker recognized as being an "independent," American Motors Corp., was purchased by Chrysler Corp., and the AMC name relegated to the history books.

The true history of independent automobile manufacture involves thousands of automakers. Many of these were in business for only a short while, with only one or two vehicles to show as their contribution to the auto industry. Obviously, in a book such as this limited to 400 pages, the select number of automakers included in this first edition represent those felt to have made the biggest impact on the industry. Loosely, the factors behind this "impact" include: number of continuous years of production, product acceptance in the marketplace and how well the automobiles these makers produced held up to the test of time—i.e.: collector car status. As with the other Krause Publications' *Standard Catalogs*, future updates of this catalog will allow for the addition of more manufacturers not included in this first volume due to space constraints.

Also, as with any first edition, there are areas of incomplete information in this book—many marked with the N/A (not available) symbol. This is where you, the loyal readers, can be of help. Should anyone have access to expanded information that could be included in future editions of this catalog, please contact the automotive editors in care of: Krause Publications, 700 E. State St., Iola, WI 54990. Every effort will be made to include additional information and/or corrections in future editions.

CONTENTS

PHOTO CREDITS

AA - Applegate & Applegate
A-C-D - Auburn-Cord-Duesenberg Museum
BCAM - Briggs Cunningham Auto Museum
FR - Fred Roe
HAC - Henry Austin Clark, Jr.
HET - Hudson-Essex-Terraplane Club
JAC - John A. Conde
LIAM - Long Island Auto Museum
OCW - *Old Cars Weekly*
WLB - William L. Bailey

Catalog Staff

Editor: Ron Kowalke
Cover design: Allen West
Color section design: Jon Stein
Book design: Ethel Thulien

Explanation of Vehicle Condition Scale Ratings in Pricing Section

1) **Excellent:** Restored to current maximum professional standards of quality in every area, or perfect original with components operating and appearing as new. A 95-plus point show vehicle that is not driven.

2) **Fine**: Well-restored, or a combination of superior restoration and excellent original. Also, an extremely well-maintained original showing very minimal wear.

3) **Very Good**: Completely operable original or "older restoration" showing wear. Also, a good amateur restoration, all presentable and serviceable inside and out. Plus, combinations of well-done restoration and good operable components or a partially restored vehicle with all parts necessary to complete and/or valuable NOS (new old stock) parts.

4) **Good**: A driveable vehicle needing no or only minor work to be functional. Also, a deteriorated restoration or a very poor amateur restoration. All components may need restoration to be "excellent," but the vehicle is mostly useable "as is.

5) **Restorable**: Needs complete restoration of body, chassis and interior. May or may not be running, but is not weathered, wrecked or stripped to the point of being useful only for parts.

6) **Parts Vehicle**: May or may not be running, but is weathered, wrecked and/or stripped to the point of being useful primarily for parts.

HOW TO USE THIS CATALOG

APPEARANCE AND EQUIPMENT: Word descriptions identify cars by styling features, trim and (to a lesser extent) interior appointments. Most standard equipment lists begin with the lowest-priced model, then enumerate items added by upgrade models and option packages. Most lists reflect equipment available at model introductions.

I.D. DATA: Information is given about the Vehicle Identification Number (VIN) found on the dashboard. VIN codes show model or series, body style, engine size, model year and place built. Beginning in 1981, a standardized 17 symbol VIN is used. Earlier VINs are shorter. Locations of other coded information on the body and/or engine block may be supplied. Deciphering those codes is beyond the scope of this catalog.

SPECIFICATIONS CHART: The first column gives series or model numbers. The second gives body style numbers revealing body type and trim. Not all cars use two separate numbers. Some sources combine the two. Column three tells number of doors, body style and passenger capacity ('4-dr Sed-6P' means four-door sedan, six-passenger). Passenger capacity is normally the maximum. Cars with bucket seats hold fewer. Column four gives suggested retail price of the car when new, on or near its introduction date, not including freight or other charges. Column five gives the original shipping weight. The sixth column provides model year production totals or refers to notes below the chart. In cases where the same car came with different engines, a slash is used to separate factory prices and shipping weights for each version. Unless noted, the amount on the left of the slash is for the smallest, least expensive engine. The amount on the right is for the least costly engine with additional cylinders. 'N/A' means data not available.

ENGINE DATA: Engines are normally listed in size order with smallest displacement first. A 'base' engine is the basic one offered in each model at the lowest price. 'Optional' describes all alternate engines, including those that have a price listed in the specifications chart. (Cars that came with either a six or V-8, for instance, list the six as 'base' and V-8 'optional'). Introductory specifications are used, where possible.

CHASSIS DATA: Major dimensions (wheelbase, overall length, height, width and front/rear tread) are given for each model, along with standard tire size. Dimensions sometimes varied and could change during a model year.

TECHNICAL DATA: This section indicates transmissions standard on each model, usually including gear ratios; the standard final drive axle ratio (which may differ by engine or transmission); steering and brake system type; front and rear suspension description; body construction; and fuel tank capacity.

OPTIONAL EQUIPMENT LISTS: Most listings begin with drivetrain options (engines, transmissions, steering/suspension and mechanical components) applying to all models. Convenience/appearance items are listed separately for each model, except where several related models are combined into a single listing. Option packages are listed first, followed by individual items in categories: comfort/convenience, lighting/mirrors, entertainment, exterior, interior, then wheels/tires. Contents of some option packages are listed prior to the price; others are described in the Appearance/Equipment text. Prices are suggested retail, usually effective early in the model year. ('N/A' indicates prices are unavailable.) Most items are Regular Production Options (RPO), rather than limited-production (LPO), special-order or dealer-installed equipment. Many options were available only on certain series or body types or in conjunction with other items. Space does not permit including every detail.

HISTORY: This block lists introduction dates, total sales and production amounts for the model year and calendar year. Production totals supplied by auto-makers do not always coincide with those from other sources. Some reflect shipments from the factories rather than actual production or define the model year a different way.

HISTORICAL FOOTNOTES: In addition to notes on the rise and fall of sales and production, this block includes significant statistics, performance milestones, major personnel changes, important dates and places and facts that add flavor to this segment of America's automotive heritage.

1979 AMC

CONCORD — SERIES 01 — FOUR/SIX/V-8 — Front end styling changed appreciably on the compact, luxurious Concord, with wide clear parking/signal lights setting below quad rectangular headlamps. The restyled formal grille was considerably taller, with seven vertical bars. Bright aluminum bumpers had black end caps and guards. Standard engine remained the 232 cu. in. six, but a 258 six, 304 V-8 and 121 four were all optional. Four-speed manual floor shift was standard; column-shift automatic transmission optional.

I.D. DATA: The 13-symbol Vehicle Identification Number (VIN) again was embossed on a metal plate riveted to the top left surface of the instrument panel, visible through the windshield. Coding was the same as 1976-78. Model year code (symbol two) changed to '9' for 1979. Series code (symbol four) now included: '0' Concord; '4' Spirit/AMX; '7' Limited; and '9' AMX.

SPIRIT SERIES 40

Series No.	Body/Style No.	Body Type & Seating	Price Four/Six	Shipping Weight	Prod. Total
40	7943-7	2-dr Lift-4P	3999/4049	2545/2762	Note 1
40	7946-7	2-dr Sed-4P	3899/3949	2489/2706	Note 1

FACTORY PRICE AND WEIGHT NOTE: Figure before the slash is for six-cylinder engine, after slash for V-8 engine: except Spirit, which is four-cylinder and six-cylinder.

ENGINES: BASE FOUR (Spirit); OPTIONAL (Concord hatchback/sedan): Inline. Overhead cam. Four-cylinder. Cast iron block; cast aluminum alloy head. Displacement: 121 cu. in. (2.0 liters). Bore & stroke: 3.41 x 3.32 in. Compression ratio: 8.2:1. Brake horsepower: 80 at 5000 R.P.M. Torque: 105 lb.-ft. at 2800 R.P.M. Five main bearings. Solid valve lifters.

CHASSIS DATA: Wheelbase: (Spirit/AMX) 96 in.; (Pacer) 100 in.; (Concord) 108 in. Overall length: (Spirit/AMX liftback) 168.5 in.; (Spirit sedan) 166.8 in.; (Pacer hatchback) 172.7 in.; (Pacer wagon) 177.7 in.; (Concord) 186 in. Height: (Spirit/AMX) 51.6 in.; (Pacer hatch) 52.8 in.; (Pacer wagon) 53.1 in.; (Concord) 51.1-51.6 in. Front Tread: (Spirit/AMX) 58.1 in.; (Pacer) 61.2 in.; (Concord) 57.6 in. Rear Tread: (Spirit/AMX/Concord) 57.5 in.; (Pacer) 60.0 in. Standard Tires: (Spirit) C78 x 14; (AMX) ER60 x 14 Flexten belted radial OWL; (Pacer) P195/75R14 GBR; (Concord) D78 x 14 except Limited, P195/75R14 GBR.

TECHNICAL: Four-speed manual transmission with floor shift was standard. Three-speed available on Spirit. Column-shift automatic available on Spirit/Concord/Pacer. Floor-shift automatic available on Spirit/AMX/Pacer.

SPIRIT/CONCORD/AMX CONVENIENCE/APPEARANCE OPTIONS: Spirit liftback GT package ($469); with Limited ($200-$469). Spirit liftback GT rally tuned suspension package ($99). Extra quiet insulation package: Concord ($48). Protection group: Concord ($87); Concord DL ($21); AMX ($27). Convenience group incl. headlight on buzzer, intermittent wipers, dual vanity mirrors ($75).

HISTORY: Introduced: September 19, 1978. Model year production (U.S.): 169,439 (1.8 percent of the industry total). Calendar year production: 184,636 cars, including 88,581 Concords. Calendar year sales by U.S. dealers: 162,057 (1.9 percent of industry total). Concords sold the best (85,432), Pacers the worst (only 8,168).

HISTORICAL FOOTNOTES: Record-breaking profits highlighted AMC's year, along with a strengthened tie to Renault, the French-owned automaker. Renault paid $200 million for an interest in AMC, carrying forward the agreement that had begun the previous year. Plans were made to begin assembling Renault autos at Kenosha for the 1982 model year, with Renault supplying the engines and transmissions.

INTRODUCTION

In 1931, automobiles were displayed on two levels at Edwards Motors, an Auburn-Cord dealer in Chicago. A new Cord L-29 front-drive sedan and an Auburn 8-98 sedan are parked out front, while an Auburn 8-98 phaeton is visible in the second story window. (Photo courtesy of Auburn-Cord-Duesenberg Museum)

The role of the independent automobile manufacturer has been an important one throughout much of automotive history. Smaller makers have often set trends in the industry which the so-called "Big Three" (Chrysler, Ford and General Motors) have found themselves following.

Before delving into the histories of these automakers, the term independent should be defined.

When the automotive industry was in its infancy in this country before the turn of the century, virtually all of the companies, partnerships and tinkerers could be considered independent manufacturers. As with any new industry, leaders emerge. Oldsmobile and Rambler were among the early makers to go into production and enjoy strong sales.

However, before the first decade of the new century was in the books, two of the eventual three major manufacturers were on their way: Ford Motor Co. and General Motors Corp. Ford, under the direction of Henry Ford, became the industry leader in volume by the mass production of one basic vehicle, the Model T. Prices came down, sales went up. A different approach at getting big was orchestrated by William Crapo (Billy) Durant. He used financial instead of mechanical know-how to meld together Buick, Oldsmobile, Cadillac and Oakland by 1909 to form General Motors. The combination of brands, factors and sales organizations made GM a major player from then on.

There were, of course, several attempts by other manufacturers to copy Durant, including a couple by Durant himself. He lost control of GM, shortly after forming it, but parlayed his new Chevrolet brand into controlling General Motors for a second time, only to lose it again. Finally, Durant put together his own brand, Durant, with Locomobile, Star, Eagle (Flint) and Mason trucks in yet another attempt to be a major player, but this time his magic failed him.

The final of the "Big Three" to be organized and stand the test of time was Chrysler Corp. Walter P. Chrysler was hired by Maxwell/Chalmers in 1923 to get the Maxwell on its feet. Fresh from Willys, he was able to get the Willys six rights and made it the first Chrysler for 1924. Maxwell died shortly after, but the Chrysler was the first of a long line of successful cars. In 1928, Walter Chrysler bought Dodge Brothers cars and Graham Brothers trucks, and brought out two more nameplates: Plymouth in the low-priced field and DeSoto in the low-medium field.

Ford balanced his low-priced Ford by buying luxury Lincoln in 1922 and added the medium-priced Mercury in 1939.

With the Big Three in place by the end of the 1920s, only then could the term independents truly start to evolve.

Unfortunately, with the Great Depression just around the corner, many automakers that had survived to that point, began to unravel. Relatively few made it past World War II.

Since it was virtually impossible to tell at the outset which makes would be bound to the "Big Three" and which would be independents, the histories of the latter must be looked at from their beginnings and we find many highlights along the way.

With reasons ranging from less bureaucracy to get fresh ideas through, to desperation to stay afloat, the independents continually brought new vehicles and concepts to market that covered the price and functionality spectrum. Among the economy standouts were the 1927 Whippet from Willys-Overland, the 1939 Studebaker Champion and the instigator of the postwar compact car revolution, the 1950 Nash Rambler. There was even a lesson on how to shorten a standard-sized car into a compact, the 1959 Studebaker Lark.

At the other end of the dollar scale, who could dispute the prestige of 1929-37 Duesenberg Model J, 1929-32 Cord L-29 or Packard V-12-powered Senior cars of 1932-39.

Performance has waxed and waned as a sales tool over the past century, but when it came to speed, most of the stronger independents were raced and offered performance models that could compete with the best. Just a few examples include the 1912 and later Stutz Bearcats, raw performance machines from the start; 1932-38 Terraplanes from Hudson, which set many records; stock car champion 1951-54 Hudson Hornet; supercharged 1957-58 Studebaker Golden Hawks and later 1963-64 Avanti; and two-passenger 1968-70 AMX from American Motors.

Styling success is in the eye of the beholder, but when it came to futuristic designs, independents produced some stunners, such as the 1929 Auburn Cabin Speedster, 1933 Pierce-Arrow Silver Arrow, 1936 Cord 810 and 1953 Studebaker Starliner and Starlight coupes. The 1947 Kaiser and Frazer designs were the first mass-produced postwar cars featuring envelope styling (no separate fenders).

The list could go on and on. Other features common today such as hydraulic valves (Pierce-Arrow, 1933), air conditioning (Packard, 1940), unitized construction on a U.S. mass-produced car (Nash 600, 1941), seat belts (Nash, 1950), split master cylinder (Rambler, 1962) and much more started in or was popularized by independent brands.

Independent-produced automobile marques number in the hundreds, each multiplied by different models and years, some few, some numerous.

In the coming pages we take a look at the most significant of the independents in automotive history. They range from single make, single purpose vehicles such as Checker to the Rambler/Jeffrey/Nash/American Motors timeline that started among the earliest and lasted the longest.

Pre-World War II standouts such as Auburn-Cord-Duesenberg, Stutz and Pierce-Arrow are included, along with postwar flash Kaiser-Frazer as are long distance runners Packard, Studebaker, Willys/Overland and Hudson

Auburn/Cord/Duesenberg

If there would have been just a small fraction of the high esteem of today for the cars from Auburn, Cord and Duesenberg in the dark days of the 1930s, then the last car to come from that hallowed combination, a Cord 812, would not have been built in 1937.

As has been the case for some time, there is wide appreciation for the cars that set new standards in racing, style, performance and mechanical components. The former headquarters in Auburn, Indiana, has been restored and converted into a museum that is the center for a major collector car gathering every Labor Day weekend, as well as for other events during the year.

The story of A-C-D is one not unlike some aspects of the "Big Three." Auto manufacturers and other industries were drawn together for strength and survival, but unfortunately neither turned out too well, at least as far as the production of passenger cars was concerned.

From the car standpoint, three main elements were brought together, the medium-priced Auburn, the ultra-luxury Duesenberg and a combination salesman, promoter and financial wizard, Errett Lobban Cord. The Cord car was only made in two basic models on an on-and-off basis.

Auburn, out of the Indiana city by the same name, dates back farthest of the three, to 1900. Its early years were not spectacular in product or production. It was a solid medium-priced car. Changes were in the offing when Cord was named general manager in 1924. Two-tone color combinations, Lycoming eight-cylinder engines and zooming sales all followed, as did Cord's takeover of the firm.

Trying to sort out the automotive exploits of Fred and Augie Duesenberg takes patience, lots of words and a juggler or two. To way oversimplify it, they built race cars, engines and finally luxury passenger cars starting in 1920—but they kept on building engines and race cars. In 1926, E.L. Cord bought the company. The last of the initial Duesenbergs, the Model A, was made in 1927.

Cord brought out the new Model J chassis for 1929 and took the Duesenberg name to a new, higher level. Power (265 horses of it) came from a double overhead cam straight eight with four valves per cylinder. The chassis alone was $8,500. Bodies came from several of the best builders.

To help fill the gap between the Auburn and Duesenberg a new nameplate was added for 1929, the Cord L-29. Far from ordinary, it featured front-wheel drive and the first industry use of X-bracing in the frame.

While front-wheel drive was not new, it was rare. Among the domestics, only the also-new Ruxton shared it. The buying public had been prepped by the design's success in race cars and proponent Harry Miller was among the advisors on the project.

A Lycoming straight eight provided power. Cord also owned the engine company by this time. Coachbuilders and Cord provided bodies. The Depression helped end production, after just over 5,000 cars had been made by late 1931—and leftovers were sold as 1932s. It would be four years before the next Cord was ready.

To describe all the classics turned out by A-C-D in the 1930s and what made them great makes for interesting reading, as you will see, but suffice it to say each brand was well rewarded. Auburn got a boattail speedster in 1931, V-12 for 1932 and perhaps its most memorable car, the 851, which could be supercharged, for 1935. Unfortunately it also got the ax after the 1936 models.

Duesenberg Model Js lasted until 1937. Starting in 1932, supercharging was available, but by fall of 1935, only about three dozen were made.

Cord's final appearance came with the Gordon Buehrig-designed 810 for 1936. With front-wheel drive, a Lycoming V-8, no runningboards, disappearing headlights and the famed "coffin nose," the Cord convertible and Beverly sedan were probably two of the most forward-looking and most significant automotive designs of all times. Production problems prevented it from saving the crumbling A-C-D empire. Only 1,764 were made for 1936 and the little-changed 1937 812 generated 1,066 copies before its production line stopped for good in August. The 810-812 did have a couple of reincarnations by Hupp and Graham, but numbers were less than Cord's.

While various elements of the A-C-D businesses did go on for many years, building complete cars was done.

Revivals of the A-C-D names, various models and combinations thereof surfaced in the specialty industry from the 1960s on and some were quite good. However, at least from manufacturers in this country, we may never see the aura, the essence or the likes of Auburn, Cord or Duesenberg again.

Checker

Checker was unique among the independents in that it had one primary purpose, to produce taxicabs, and it was able to do so over a span of 60 years. The first Checker was made on July 12, 1922, and the last July 12, 1982. Excursions into limousines, passenger cars for the public and even buses never deterred management from its mission of durable, passenger-friendly vehicles for the rugged task of taxi operation.

Checker remained independent of other manufacturers, except for a brief period in the 1930s when it was controlled by Errett Lobban Cord of Auburn-Cord-Duesenberg as part of a stock deal that helped founder Morris Markin eventually regain control of his company.

Through 1959, Checkers were primarily sold to taxi operators, though vehicles were sold to private individuals from time to time. In 1931 and 1932, the Suburban Utility was produced as a combination station wagon and limousine.

After World War II, a series of taxis were produced that were rather stylish at the start, but looked dated when production ended in the mid-1950s. There were civilian versions available, but were little publicized. The cabs were the A2, A4, and A6, while the limousines/public models were labeled A3, A5, and A7.

That brings us to the A8, which introduced (for Checker) modern styling and was used to the end. Cars went on sale to the public, with fanfare, and dealers in late 1959 as 1960 models. A new station wagon was in the lineup, which would remain through the 1974 model year. A unique feature of the wagon was a power rear seat.

Power shifted from Continental engines to Chevrolet, with some Chrysler powerplants used in the extended wagon aerobuses before also converting to Chevy.

In later years, civilian Checker sales averaged about 1,000 annually. Federal standards, especially for fuel economy, threatened the old, heavy models being produced. Checker also had (and still has) a successful stamping business for other manufacturers and the decision to pull the plug after the 1982 models was made.

Today, while a good number of civilian Checkers and some later taxis survive, many of the earlier models are long gone. They were used up and scrapped well before there was any collector interest. Even the postwar A2 through A7 models are extremely rare today.

Hudson/Essex/Terraplane

Hudson Hornet dominance of national championship stock car racing from 1951 through 1954 is cited as one of the high points of performance history for the independents. For Hudson it may have been a notable accomplishment as well, but it was by no means rare. Starting with the Model 20 in 1909, Hudsons were entered in performance contests by factory personnel and others, usually with bragging rights being the result.

Throughout its history, Hudsons, as well as lower priced Essex and Terraplane models, relied on balance to achieve performance. A combination of dependable engines, solid chassis and well-designed suspension produced the desired results.

The Hornets, like so many Hudsons, relied on the L-head six engine for power, which by the time it was introduced was considered obsolete. However, the Hudson also had "Step-Down" design, which combined a unitized chassis, lower center of gravity, and an understanding of heavy-duty and speed parts that the competition was years behind in utilizing. Hudsons won.

Using a name and money from department store owner Joseph L. Hudson, the leadership of aggressive auto executive Roy D. Chapin and a host of talent, the first Hudson, the 1910 Model 20 was built in 1909. Sales success, speed records and six-cylinder engines followed with a claim by 1915, of being the world's largest manufacturer of sixes. A speed record of 102.5 mph at Daytona Beach, Florida, in 1916 didn't hurt, either.

An early campaign for Hudson was selling the closed car in volume. This came when the touring (open) car accounted for most of the models and sales. Sedans were traditionally higher priced, often by several hundred dollars. Hudson claimed to sell more sedans than Ford or Chevrolet for 1916, and gradually reduced the price of its closed cars to less than that for the open models. It was a major factor in the closed car becoming the most popular during the 1920s.

Hudson's reliance on six-cylinder engines became well established in its mid-priced class. To reach out to buyers in lower price segments, the Essex was introduced for 1919. It was a separate make. First available in open models, later sedans were added. Powering them was an F-head four. Of course, the Essex sales campaign was kicked off by running a specially prepared example for 50 hours on a racetrack. The average speed topped 60 mph.

Essex was an immediate hit and remained a lower priced companion to Hudson into the 1930s. It became a six for 1926. Its last appearance was 1932.

While F-head design disappeared from the Essex, it was used from 1927 through 1929 on the Hudsons, some of which were fitted with Biddle & Smart bodywork.

L-head power returned for 1930 Hudsons, but this time on the new eight-cylinder engines. Hudsons would exclusively use eights through 1932. A six was again offered for 1933 and through 1952, there was a choice of L-head six or eight engines in Hudsons, depending on the model.

To induce excitement into its lower priced line, Hudson brought out the Essex Terraplane in July 1932. Aimed at Chevrolet and Ford, it featured light weight and performance, at first from just a six, but starting in 1933 (when the Essex name was dropped) also as an eight. Hudson claimed six dozen speed and hill climb records as part of its promotion.

Terraplanes came in a variety of body styles, were sleekly styled and today are highly valued by Hudson collectors. In November of 1935, Hudson claimed to have the first all-steel top, just ahead of GM.

Despite the success, the Terraplane drew closer to the regular Hudsons. For 1938, it was billed as the Hudson Terraplane and was no longer a separate make. For 1939, it was gone, replaced by the rather nondescript label, 112. A Pacemaker came along mid-year and also helped out.

Hudsons were redesigned for 1940 and again, for the most part for 1941. That body carried through to 1947. Two new designs bowed in the 1948 line, the all-new Frank Spring-designed "Step-Down" body and a new engine. Getting, by far, the most attention, though, was the new car, which featured a low overall height and passenger footwells between the frame rails. On a 124-inch wheelbase it provided good handling and a low center of gravity, which the competition would come around to nearly a decade later. The engine, on the other hand, was the new Super Six, a flathead of 262 cubic inches. This was at a time when the "Big Three" were working on overhead valve V-8s.

Sedans and coupes came at first, with a convertible mid-year. Styling remained relatively stable, but for 1951, the six was enlarged to 308 cubic inches and the Hornet series was born. It was not intended as a race car, but independent stock car racers, led by garage owner Marshall Teague, combined the handling of the chassis and torque of the 308 and threw in some speed parts to make the "Fabulous Hudson Hornet". The factory listened, put the parts in its catalogs and the rest is history. Hudson's racing story is a book in itself.

A two-door Hollywood hardtop joined the lineup mid-year for 1951. Despite winning races, having desirable body styles and decent performance, Hudson sales were declining fast. To counter this, two things happened and neither turned out good for Hudson.

Instead of a tool-up for much needed new styling or V-8 power, dollars went for a new compact car. The slab-sided Jet used two-thirds of the discontinued eight. It was a fine performer on the road, but not in sales.

The second event was a merger with Nash-Kelvinator. Nash, too, was singing the independents blues, but was in better shape than Hudson. On May 1, 1954, American Motors Corp. was formed. By the end of October, production of Hudsons from the Detroit factory ended. An Italia sports model built in Italy was near stillborn with only 25 made.

For three more model years, Hudson nameplates would be attached to a variety of Nash products. The big cars were different in some styling features—which proved more negative than positive. Hudson badges on Ramblers and Metropolitans were only for the dealers, not the heritage of the White Triangle. It was all over after the last of the 1957 models.

Kaiser/Frazer

If there was any such thing as a right time to enter the domestic automotive industry after it was well established, directly after World War II was probably as close as it got. Pent-up demand for automobiles was far beyond supply and the majority of the cars to come to market wore warmed-over prewar styling.

Such was the entry point of Kaiser-Frazer Corp. It combined the names, talents and some finances of shipbuilder Henry J. Kaiser and Joseph W. Frazer of Graham-Paige Motors Corp.

The differing backgrounds, personalities and philosophies of these two men could fill many pages, but they did combine to bring two lines of freshly styled sedans to market ahead of any other domestic mass producer of standard-sized cars. The medium-priced Kaiser and somewhat upmarket Frazer featured envelope styling by Howard "Dutch" Darrin.

Introduction of the 1947 lines started in August of 1946. Engineering was entirely conventional with Continental flathead six-cylinder engines and rear-wheel drive, and would remain so throughout the entire runs for the full-size cars of both makes. Prototype Kaisers featured front-wheel drive, but the concept never advanced beyond that stage.

As other modernly styled cars such as the 1947 Studebaker and 1948 Hudson came out, Kaiser and Frazer styling looked less radical, but it did not mean there was no room for innovation. Three variations on the basic four-door body all were interesting, if not popular with the buying public. They were in the Kaiser line.

There was a minor face lift for 1949. To help counter falling sales, a new hatchback called the Traveler was added. It featured a fold-down rear seat; fixed left rear door; heavy-duty suspension and the ability to be used as a sedan or semi-wagon. In the low-priced Special series, its Deluxe series counterpart was the Vagabond.

A four-door hardtop-looking mid-year model was the Virginian, which featured slim, chromed door frames and a trimmed glass centerpost. It was not a true four-door hardtop, but looked like one. Late in the model year, a four-door convertible with similar side window setup was produced in small numbers. There were also a few Frazer four-door convertibles made.

There was a short 1950 model run using retitled 1949 models. Sales had nose-dived and "Big Three" pressure was immense.

For the 1951 model year, two approaches were used. Kaiser was all-new with truly advanced styling. Frazer returned to market for its final year with the purpose of using up the leftover 1949-50 Kaiser and Frazer bodies, many of which were hatchbacks (Vagabonds). There were also four-door convertibles and hardtops.

For 1951, there was also the new Henry J compact. That lasted through 1954 as did a version for Sears & Roebuck, named the Allstate, which started as a 1952 model.

Kaiser styling for 1951 was well advanced over the competition. It came in both two- and four-door sedans, including Traveler hatchbacks. A mid-year Dragon option enhanced interior trim, which would be a Kaiser strong suit, right to the end. Despite the enhanced styling, mechanicals remained sedate, as did sales. Retitling of the previous year's models became a way of life in the final years. These years were, however, not without a few more highlights.

On May 28, 1953, Kaiser-Frazer purchased Willys-Overland and moved its headquarters from Michigan to Willys in Toledo, Ohio. The move would keep the Kaiser name associated with motor vehicles in one way or another for the next 17 years.

For 1954, to counter the competition's V-8 engines and the horsepower race, a McCulloch supercharger was fitted to the Kaiser six, producing a claim of 140 horsepower.

Also announced in late 1953 as a 1954 model was the Kaiser-Darrin, a fiberglass sports car with contemporary styling and the novel feature of forward sliding doors. It was mounted on a Henry J frame and had a 161-cubic inch Willys six-cylinder engine for power. At least it looked fast! Only 435 were made before the plug was pulled. Darrin himself bought up unused bodies and sold the sports cars in later years, most with Cadillac engines.

Kaiser the car came to an end during the 1955 model year. There was an order for Argentina that took up most of the production run. When it was completed, the dies were taken out of Toledo and shipped to that country, where the design was eventually produced from 1958-62.

Willys passenger car production ended at the same time. However Willys Jeeps continued to grow in popularity and eventually took on the name Kaiser Jeep before being sold to American Motors Corp. in 1970.

Rambler/Jeffery/Nash/AMC

When American Motors Corp. was swallowed by Chrysler Corp. in 1987, it brought to an end the independent mass production automobile manufacturer era in the United States. While AMC's right and wrong decisions over its 33 years will no doubt be debated for the next third of a century, its heritage cannot. Its bloodlines can be traced back to 1897 when bicycle manufacturer Thomas B. Jeffery experimented with the gasoline automobile. The start of manufacturing of Rambler cars in Kenosha, Wisconsin, in 1902, began an 85-year history that went by several names, but turned out to be among the longest-lived continuums in the country.

Though later Nash, Rambler and AMC automobiles always seemed to be a few steps behind on the respect curve, a surprising number of firsts and significant models were turned out of Kenosha and other company plants before it was all over.

Moving to a large factory in Kenosha paid off and Rambler was second in sales (Oldsmobile was first) for 1902. Swiftly, Rambler moved up in price and could be considered in the medium field.

Thomas B. Jeffery died in 1910, and in 1914, the Rambler name was replaced by Jeffery. That proved short-lived as ex-General Motors and Buick boss Charles W. Nash bought the company in 1916. Starting mid-year 1917, the cars produced wore Nash badges.

For 1918, cars were Nash designed and that meant an overhead valve six. Overhead valve engines would remain a Nash feature on higher priced models right through to the V-8 era in the 1950s. Rubber engine mounts in four-cylinder-powered 1922 models was an industry first for Nash, as was the option of an electric clock in the dash for 1924.

An unsuccessful quest for higher priced market share with the Lafayette of 1920-24 was balanced by a low-priced foray with the Ajax of 1925 and 1926. The latter became the Nash Light Six after that.

While a cylinder race was heating up, Nash doubled up on spark plugs with twin ignition available for its overhead valve sixes in the 1929 models. Twelve spark plugs became 16 with the introduction of the Series 490 Twin Ignition Eight for 1930. A flathead eight came along for 1931.

While Nash weathered the onset of the Depression better than most, a low-priced line was needed. That came for 1934 with the resurfacing of the Lafayette name and a flathead six-cylinder engine. It helped boost production. This time the Lafayette was listed as a Nash series and not as a separate make as was the earlier luxury version.

An option for 1936, the Double Bed Conversion for the Lafayette and 400 would be the first of a long line of sleep-oriented features that would distinguish Nashes and successors from the competition, especially in the 1950s and early 1960s.

A merger of a different sort took place in 1937 when Nash Motors and Kelvinator Corp. became Nash-Kelvinator Corp. and took on the dual role as automobile and appliance manufacturer. For those thinking Nash produced rather stodgy cars during the period, one only has to look at the Alexis de Sakhnoffsky customized Ambassador Eight cabriolet with its cut-down doors and chopped windshield. Once in awhile, things like this did come out of the conservative Nash door.

Model year 1940 was the last for the Lafayette and the body style it used. Nashes were all-new for 1941. Although they looked similar, there was a big difference between the 1941 low-priced 600 and medium Ambassador. Most significant was the 600, which featured unitized construction, a 172.6-cubic inch flathead six and 20-gallon gas tank. It weighed more than 800 pounds less than the Ambassador eight. A claim of up to 30 mpg from a 20-gallon tank resulted in the 600 nomenclature. With a 112-inch wheelbase—nine inches less than the Ambassador—the 600 foretold of economy, intermediate-size cars of the postwar period with the room of a full-size car.

1941 turned out to be the last for twin ignition and the war-shortened 1942 run marked the end of the Nash straight eight.

Postwar Nashes, like most of the "Big Three" competition, started with face-lifted prewar bodies. Two stand out for collectors, the 1946-47 Ambassador Suburban four-door sedan with wood bodywork and the mid-year 1948 Ambassador convertible, of which only 1,000 were made.

For 1949, controversy and an attempt at aerodynamics collided in Airflyte styling. Fastback bodies, enclosed wheels (front and back) and smooth flowing lines front to back set Nashes apart from the competition, but so did their descriptions as "inverted bathtubs" by detractors.

Minor changes marked the 1950 models and one of them was dropping the 600 series tag and replacing it with Statesman. Revised grilles and raised rear fenders were added for 1951. While Airflyte styling may not have pleased everyone, the 1950 sales of 191,665 turned out to be Nash's all-time best.

Of course, that total included another innovation, the Rambler. Reviving the original name used on the production cars in 1902 by Thomas B. Jeffery, Nash, guided by George Mason, brought out a 100-inch wheelbase compact. While short wheelbase compacts were nothing new, Mason's approach was. Ramblers did not start as strippers built down to a price. Rather, the first model was a fully equipped convertible (with fixed sides). Later came an upscale wagon and a two-door hardtop. Delivery vehicles and cheaper sedans and wagons came in later years.

Longer wheelbase (108 inches) four-door sedans and wagons joined the Rambler lineup during the 1954 model year and the first body died, or so it appeared, after the 1955 models were released. Meanwhile, the big Nash was fully restyled for its Golden Anniversary in 1952. Big, wide, smooth riding cars were aimed at the traveler. Power still came from sixes: flatheads in Statesman models and overhead valve units in Ambassadors. The latter picked up an optional LeMans dual-carburetor setup that was used on the Nash-Healey sports car Nash imported from 1951 through 1954.

Like the other independents, Nash realized there were troubled times ahead. Mason wanted to combine his firm with Hudson, Packard and Studebaker to rival the "Big Three." It did not happen, but he did merge with Hudson, from a point of strength, to form American Motors.

Officially formed on May 1, 1954, American Motors sought to consolidate Nash and Hudson production under the control of Nash in Kenosha. Hudson dealers would get the Rambler instead of their slow-selling Jet compact and the imported Metropolitan that Nash dealers were just starting to sell. Hudson lasted three years in the American Motors harness before it was killed at the end of the 1957 run. It did not die alone, however, as Nash went to the grave with it.

An all-new 108-inch wheelbase Rambler bowed for 1956 with four-door models only. It would take awhile to catch on, but it was right for the times. At first it was powered by an overhead valve conversion of the Statesman six. For 1957, Rambler was sold as a separate make. A new V-8 that came out in mid-year 1956 Nash and Hudsons was made available in 1957 Ramblers. Offering mild performance with 250 cubic inches, it was a start. Mid-year, the 327-cubic inch V-8 from the big cars was put in the Rambler, called the Rebel. This combination turned out to be one of the hottest cars of the year. Only 1,500 were made and how they got that one by economy/compact crusader AMC President George Romney remains one of life's mysteries.

Originally, the Nash and Hudson names were to be applied to a stretched (117-inch wheelbase), face-lifted 1958 Rambler called the Ambassador. Some were built that way before the decision to drop the names was made. The car carried a 270-hp 327 V-8 and put AMC into the intermediate/luxury compact business before the competition even knew what that meant.

Romney preached, Ramblers sold and the "Big Three" rushed compacts from the drawing board into production as the 1950s closed. One compact that did not come off the drawing board was the 1958 Rambler American. Tooling for the 1955 two-door sedan was dusted off and put back into production with minor modifications. Even the old L-head six came back. It was joined by the two-door wagon for 1959 and a four-door sedan that modified the 100-inch wheelbase pieces for 1960.

American got a new outer shell for 1961, kept some of its basic innards, the 100-inch wheelbase and just to show off, came in a convertible, this time without the side frames. Romney left American Motors in 1962 to run for governor of Michigan (which he won) and the company and Rambler began a period of lack of focus and eventually, declining sales.

Rambler (now called Classic) and Ambassador were all-new for 1963. Two-door hardtops were added for 1964 and convertibles for 1965. American, after a one-year fling with a new two-door hardtop in 1963, got an all-new body for 1964 with a 106-inch wheelbase. Mid-year 1966, it was first to get the new AMC

V-8 rated at 290 cubic inches. To meet the fastback fashion craze mid-year in 1965, one was grafted onto a 112-inch wheelbase Classic and called the Marlin. Some were wild over it, but most were not, preferring the Tarpon dream car, which was American-based. Even a change to the Ambassador chassis for 1967, its final year, did nothing to make the Marlin anything but an automotive footnote.

New management, all-new bodies for the bigger cars and new power, with 343 cubic inches now tops, marked the 1967 cars. Classics were now Rebels and only they and the Americans carried the Rambler name. Interest in racing may have been shocking for AMC fans in 1967, but that was nothing compared to 1968 when the Javelin pony car and then mid-year two-passenger AMX came along. The V-8 was up to 390 cubic inches and red, white and blue AMC race cars were seemingly everywhere.

AMX turned out to be one of the most collectible American Motors products of all-time. Though the two-passenger cars' production run only lasted through the 1970 model year, the name popped up a few more times on other AMC models that were aimed at performance buyers.

The Rambler name was considered to be a bad part of the past in the late 1960s and for 1968, only the American carried it. For 1969, the American tag was gone and it was just plain Rambler. However, it did not go without a final splash. With the help of Hurst, a two-door hardtop with a 390 V-8 stuffed in, wild hood scoop and bold red, white and blue paint job was offered as a muscle car below $3,000. Its name? The SC/Rambler. Its collector status: immediate and continuing. A not-quite-so-radical Rebel two-door hardtop used a similar formula: The Machine. There may have been some 1971 cars optioned that way.

Replacing the Rambler for 1970 was an all-new compact called the Hornet. There was no Twin-H power, but for 1971 there was a low-key performance model, the SC/360. Compared to what would follow, it turned out to be a balanced and worth-saving performer.

The 1970s was a turn-down decade for all makes and AMC was no exception. A shortened Hornet gave AMC a jump on the "Big Three" sub-compacts and it would come in handy during the so-called "fuel crisis" of 1973-74. Production of the Javelin ceased in 1974, as did the long-running Ambassador. Just before the gas lines got long a new 1974 Matador coupe hit the market and the racetrack. How much better it could have done at both is a matter of speculation, but it did win some racing events. It died with the rest of the Matador line after the 1978 run.

Cited as being everything from well ahead of its time (cab-forward design) to the stupidest looking car ever made was the 1975 Pacer, which came out mid-year. It was wide, heavy and radical. It sold well at first, but not for long and despite a wagon version being added to the hatchback sedan for 1977, it helped drag AMC down.

For 1980, another innovation, somewhat better received, was the Eagle, which adapted Jeep four-wheel drive components to first Concord and later shorter Spirit passenger cars. The Eagle came out the year AMC no longer offered V-8 power in its passenger car lines. Never a large seller, it did help popularize the concept that today sells so many Subarus.

Government-owned Renault of France bought into AMC, first as an outlet in AMC plants in Kenosha, producing first the Alliance and later the Encore. AMC lines such as Concord and Spirit were dropped in 1983 and only the Eagle soldiered on, being made in Canada. After a flash of popularity, Renault sales declined and the home company wanted out. That came in 1987, when Chrysler Corp. bought AMC. Chrysler wanted the Jeep. It had been building some of its cars in Kenosha under contract.

When Chrysler took over, it killed the small Renaults immediately. After a few 1988 AMC Eagles were made, that too was axed. The Eagle name was then used for a line of passenger cars that included new larger Renaults, imports and eventually Mitsubishi-built cars from Illinois. Eagle officially died after the 1998 model run.

Packard

Few automotive advertising slogans are remembered for more than a few weeks or months after their use. Indeed, some slogans don't even ring a bell *during* their campaigns. One slogan that defies that trend—and even merits a feeling of deep reverence when spoken—is "Ask the man who owns one," referring to the Packard, which dates back to 1899.

While today just asking a man such a question may seem sexist, there are still plenty of them to ask. This, despite the fact that the last mass produced domestic car to carry the Packard nameplate left the factory more than 40 years ago, in 1958. Packard remains one of the most fervently respected and collected automobiles today, from the early Brass era, through the Classics of the 1920s and '30s, right up to the flashy final efforts of the 1950s. Indeed, you can get in quite an argument if you ask a Senior Packard owner of the 1930s if the One-Tens and One-Twenties of the era were full-fledged Packards or if they were the start of the downfall of the company.

Likewise, suggesting the Clippers of the 1940s and '50s were the near equals of their larger and more expensive brethren can bring spirited responses, to put it mildly. And do not even think of espousing the merits of the 1957 and 1958 Studebaker-based Packards, which were the last of the make.

The bottom line is Packard still very much means many things to many people, from custom-bodied Twin Sixes, to exciting Darrin specials to station wagons to basic family sedans to even taxicabs. Packard even produced trucks, buses and well-respected aircraft engines in addition to its better-known passenger car lines.

While analysis of why Packard went from the traditional luxury sales leader to a death as a near-badge-engineered Studebaker has been going on for decades and will likely continue for many more. An appreciation for Packard's contributions to automotive history, engineering, styling and prestige is easy to come by and hard to let go.

Dissatisfaction with the purchase of a motor car led the Packard Brothers to build a better one, with five constructed in 1899. Building it better quickly put Packards among America's finest produced cars. The Gray Wolf set a record of 77.6 mph in Daytona Beach, Florida, in 1903. By 1916, the Packard Twin Six was the first 12-cylinder automobile put into mass production worldwide. The engine lasted through the 1923 models. A Single Eight replaced it for 1924, but that did not deter custom coachbuilders, which by 1926 were selecting the Packard chassis in impressive numbers to carry their work.

Despite the onslaught of the Depression, a wide variety of Packard body styles were offered. The Twin Six returned for 1932 and despite small numbers, remained at the top of the Senior Packard ladder through 1939. It was simply called the Twelve from 1933 on. While the Twelve contributed to Packard's reputation, it contributed less than 1,000 sales to the 1934 model year tally of only about 8,000. Several old line makes were failing; would Packard be another?

To answer that question and lead to several more, there was the 1935 One-Twenty. A medium-priced car starting under $1,000, it offered contemporary styling, a straight eight engine, independent front suspension and hydraulic brakes. The public responded with nearly 25,000 orders to a little over one-third of that for the rest of the line. Yes, it helped save Packard. It and the six (later One-Ten) that came along for 1937 provided sufficient sales to keep Packard out of danger and able to continue to make the Senior cars, but did the smaller cars dilute the Packard image? Well, the Lincoln Zephyr and the

LaSalle (which did not carry a Cadillac nameplate) did serve the same purpose for the competition, but the debate, then as now, was spirited.

Sales success at the lower end did not translate into neglect of the Senior Packards. Witness the Custom Super Eight Darrin convertible victoria of 1940 and 1941. No runningboards, Darrin-dipped doors and even a landau roof in the latter year, it made for one of the most desirable Packards of all time.

New Clipper styling bowed in the short-run 1942 line on a couple of One-Sixty models. It would preview the only bodies to return after the war. Indeed, after the war, all Packards were initially based on the Clipper, leaving cries that the prestige of the Senior Packards was not carried through. Eights and sixes provided power. A clever face lift of the Clipper provided new styling for 1948 and sixes were restricted to taxis, but at this time rival Cadillac was poised to take over sales leadership.

Real all-new bodies arrived for 1951. While styling could be considered contemporary if not outstanding, engines continued to be L-head straight eights, at a time when the competition was switching to overhead valve V-8s. Packard would be saddled with the long eights through the 1954 model run. The newly styled cars were not without their share of attractions. A series of show cars based on production bodies, such as the Pan American, Balboa and Panther, caught the fancy of the luxury car set. The production 1953 and 1954 Caribbean Custom convertible translated some of the styling cues, such as hood scoop, full wheel cutouts and spoked wheels, to the showroom floor.

It was in 1954 that Packard joined the consolidation trend among independents and took over Studebaker, which was also struggling with decreased sales. Packard's last hurrah (for some) were the 1955 and 1956 models, which featured heavily face-lifted 1951-54 bodies, modern V-8 power and radical Torsion-Level Ride. The latter featured a full torsion bar suspension with electric motors in the system to keep the cars level despite loads. Also, 1956 models had an electric push-button system for the Twin Ultramatic transmission. "Star" for those two years and among collectors today were the Caribbeans. There were convertibles both years and a two-door hardtop for 1956. Also for 1956, three-tone color combinations were offered as were reversible seat cushions.

Poor sales (less than 29,000 for the 1956 models), a takeover by Curtiss-Wright and lack of cash brought Packard production and plans for all-new 1957 models to an end. There were 1957 models, but they turned out to be face-lifted Studebakers from South Bend, Indiana. A sedan and wagon were offered, with superchargers offered as standard equipment. Finned 1958 Packards of the same persuasion followed, plus a new two-door hardtop design, minus the supercharger. That went into the Packard Hawk, a flat-nosed version of the Studebaker model.

While the 1957 and 1958 models make fine special interest cars, calling them Packards does not sit well with the majority of the red hexagon armada. The 1958s were the final Packard passenger cars. Some export trucks carried the name, as did some later custom offerings by non-related builders, but it was over. On April 26, 1962, Studebaker-Packard Corp. became just Studebaker Corp.

Pierce-Arrow

For a prime example of how a low production, independent manufacturer can make major contributions to automotive history with innovative engineering and styling—all while providing high-end luxury—look no further than Pierce-Arrow.

Starting with the one-cylinder Pierce Motorette in 1901, the Buffalo, New York, firm started its upmarket climb with the four-cylinder Great Arrow in 1904 and six-cylinder version in 1907. Two years later, the full Pierce-Arrow became the brand and company name. By 1910, the four-cylinders were gone and a reliance on the six would be legendary, despite competition with more cylinders from Cadillac, Packard and others. Perhaps the best-known Pierce-Arrow trademark, fender-mounted headlights, came in 1913, though the self-standing drum units would be available through 1932. Another forward looking feature appeared in the 1924 models, vacuum-assisted power brakes—on all four wheels. It would be decades before they would be widely available from other manufacturers.

Not all the crystal ball vision was devoted to style and mechanics. Seeing that independent manufacturers would have a hard time making it in the future, Pierce-Arrow merged with Studebaker in 1928. Unlike many that took place later, Pierce-Arrow kept its factory and its autonomy.

A new straight eight replaced the six for 1929, ending the Pierce-Arrow holdout against more cylinders. It was a Buffalo design. The new engine and Studebaker's help did boost production to an all-time high of 8,422 for that year. Despite the Depression, the eight was supplanted at the top of the Pierce-Arrow engine chain by a V-12 for 1932, again designed inhouse. Though collectors prize the Model 51 and 53 V-12 cars, total production for all series for 1932 was down to 2,692.

Significant things happened for 1933. Hydraulic tappet lifters were introduced, again well ahead of their common use. Second, a Silver Arrow show car appeared that featured aerodynamic styling that was both futuristic and stunning. Only five were produced. Finally, Studebaker went into receivership, starting the path to regain independence for Pierce-Arrow. Some of the Silver Arrow features were added to the mildly changed 1934 models, but this action did not help and sales continued a death spiral that ended with Pierce-Arrow's assets being sold in 1938.

Today many of the features Pierce-Arrow pioneered are taken for granted. Pierce-Arrows that survive bring high collector dollars, but the independent company that made these magnificent automobiles was just another that did not survive the Depression and the tough years that followed.

Studebaker

After making a name in the horse-drawn wagon building business before the turn of the 20th century, the Studebaker brothers gradually turned to powered vehicles, starting with electric cars in 1902. As the years progressed, a series of solid, but less than spectacular cars emerged from South Bend, Indiana, management with factory entrants in the Indianapolis 500 in the early 1930s about as exciting as it got. Okay, naming a car the Dictator as late as 1937 did take some bravado, with Hitler gathering power in Europe!

It was after World War II that Studebaker's moves were the most controversial, as it embraced radical, for its time, styling in its 1947 lineup, 1953 lineup and 1963 Avanti models. Studebakers in those and subsequent years looked different from the competition and in some ways foretold the future. The "which way is it going" 1947s sold well. The long, low 1953s did not, and the 1963 Avanti was too late.

Historians make great sport today of what killed Studebaker, as radical styling and all, the last Studebakers made came from Canada in 1966. In a world of jellybean cars today, being different would seem to be welcomed, but automotive history is filled with examples that were different and failures, nearly simultaneously. However, instead of bemoaning how unkind history was to Studebaker, it is far more fun to appreciate some of the innovative and just plain good looking cars that were built before and during its final years.

Early Studebaker-powered vehicles took a variety of forms starting with electrics in 1902, Garford-chassised gasoline cars in 1903 and the marketing of Everitt-Metzger-Flanders Co. (E-M-F) cars in 1905. Studebaker took over E-M-F in 1911 and formed Studebaker Corp. From 1913 on, all cars carried the Studebaker name, but that would change with the lower-priced Erskine of 1927-30 (named for Studebaker's president), the merger with Pierce-Arrow in 1928, and the ill-fated Rockne of 1932-33. The latter lasted about a year and was named just as famed Notre Dame coach Knute Rockne died.

A bit of upmarket exploration came at Studebaker's quarter-century mark with the introduction of the President Big Six as a 1927 model. It was further enhanced for 1928 with a new straight eight powerplant. Going through several body changes, the President Eight would remain atop the Studebaker line-up through the 1942 model run.

Success at the other end of Studebaker's price reach came in mid-1939 when the Champion six filled the bottom notch. Falling below the Commander it featured a 78-hp, 164.3-cubic inch flathead six and 110-inch wheelbase. This compared to the Commander's 226-cubic inch six and 116.5-inch stretch. Prices started at $660, over $200 below the Commander.

In six months, Champion production nearly hit 34,000 compared to almost 52,000 for the Commanders and Presidents for a full year. Studebaker's AAA record of 27.25 mpg in an economy trial was helpful in establishing Champion's reputation as an economy car in 1939 and for years to come.

All-new Raymond Loewy styling of the 1941 models proved a forerunner of postwar things-to-come with crisp lines being ahead of their times. While most have forgotten—or never knew about—the first postwar Studebaker, the short-lived Skyway Champion, which used the 1941-42 body, few will pass by the 1947 models and their derivatives without a second look. The Raymond Loewy-Virgil Exner-styled lineup included sedans (with center-opening doors), convertibles and coupes with a wraparound rear window called the Starlight. The latter helped prompt the saying, "Which way is it going?" Champion and Commander sixes were offered with a stretched version of the latter replacing the President, called the Land Cruiser.

A face lift for 1950 may seem a bit strange today, but the nose that looked like it was lifted from a jet fighter aircraft was quite up-to-date back then. Despite being on its fourth year with the same body, the 1950 sales topped 320,000. Something must have been right. For 1951, a new V-8 engine came along. Its overhead valve design and oversquare dimensions were modern, but its weight and limited room for growth from its 232.6 cubic inches would hurt in the future. The new Starliner two-door hardtop for 1952 was nothing compared to the all-new 1953 models, which were especially striking in the Starliner hardtops and Starlight coupes. Getting quality and enough of them to the showrooms proved a problem and the momentum was lost.

In June of 1954, Studebaker merged with Packard to form Studebaker-Packard Corp. At first, Packard had the upper hand but after yet another takeover by Curtiss-Wright in 1956, Studebaker would dominate to its 1966 demise. The rather heavy-handed face lift of 1955 produced two Studebaker milestones: the return of the President name and the mid-year Speedster Coupe in that series that gave early signs of the Hawk sporting series that was to follow.

Updating the 1953 coupe and hardtop designs with squared off grilles and for some models, fiberglass fins, the 1956 Studebaker Hawks hit right on in the horsepower performance race. Topping the quartet was the Golden Hawk hardtop with a 352-cubic inch, 275-hp Packard V-8. Mild fin restyling and a switch to a supercharged Studebaker 275-hp, 289-cubic inch V-8 kept the Golden Hawk in the forefront for 1957. It was accompanied by the non-supercharged Silver Hawk coupe. There was a repeat for 1958, after which only the coupe survived for a trio of model years.

Brooks Stevens restyled the Hawk into a formal-roofed hardtop on the cheap for 1962 and production lasted into the ultra-short 1964 run, which stopped when assembly plants in South Bend closed down. Studebaker was also playing the economy game with its Champion holding down the fort through 1958. For 1957 and 1958, it was joined by the Champion Scotsman, which gave new meaning to the term plain Jane or stripper. All that changed for 1959 when the compact car challenge was met by introducing the Lark, which used the old 1953-based bodies with shortened ends and a combination of 108- and 113-inch wheelbases. A variety of models with six and V-8 power were offered and a profit was shown briefly, but eventually terminal problems engulfed the former wagon maker from South Bend.

The last blast was the fiberglass Avanti for 1963. Mounted on a Lark convertible chassis and powered by Studebaker V-8 engines, including supercharged versions, the Avanti was easily one of the most collectible Studebakers of all time. Unfortunately production and financial problems prevented many new buyers from collecting them. There were also a handful of 1963 and 1964 supercharged Larks and Hawks made that also are considered valuable today.

Production of cars in the United States ended in December of 1963, with some models being shifted to a small plant in Canada. The Hawk and Avanti were not among them. The Avanti was, however, saved and was produced in small numbers, with Chevrolet power, into the 1990s. Chevrolet power also motivated the 1965 and 1966 model Studebakers from Canada. Despite the fact that the Hamilton, Ontario, plant was making a small profit, the company directors voted to pull the plug on auto production and such was done in March of 1966.

Stutz

In production for not much more than two decades, Stutz cast a long shadow in automotive history that included the raw performance of the Bearcat, pure luxury LeBaron-bodied town cars, the elegant speed of the Black Hawk and the engineering sophistication of the double overhead cam, 32-valve straight eight DV-32, good for 156 horsepower. Born of the racetrack and killed by the Great Depression, the Stutz Motor Car Co. of Indianapolis, was like the street fighter that acquired expensive tastes, but led a short life.

Harry C. Stutz entered a car in the first Indianapolis 500 in 1911 with his new transaxle design. It finished 11th and was billed as "The car that made good in a day." A line of 1912 models bowed with four- and six-cylinder power and were extensively raced. The most famous among them—and from Stutz for that matter—was a two-place Bearcat, which was a sports car of its day and featured minimal bodywork and creature comforts.

Stutz started building its own four-cylinder engines around 1917 and used them exclusively through 1923 when a new overhead valve six replaced the four.

Harry Stutz lost control of his company via stock transactions in 1916 and left before the decade ended. A variety of leadership changes ended with a new president in 1925, who looked upmarket. The last Bearcat (for awhile) was a 1924 model and a new Vertical Eight replaced the six for 1926. A combination of luxury and performance was to be the Stutz signature and for 1928, a long list of models with European names bowed. Most famous was the Black Hawk Speedster, which went on to win the AAA stock championship and set a 106.5 mph record at Daytona Beach, Florida.

Confusion, no doubt, abounded when Stutz brought a lower priced marque to market for 1929, the Blackhawk (one word) six. There was also a 1930 Blackhawk before it was added to the Stutz line for 1931 as the LA series, still with a six for power.

The Depression hit hard, dropping Stutz production from 2,320 in 1929 to 1,038 in 1930 and a mere 310 for 1931. The 1932 models were exciting, in catalogs if not in real numbers. Revived was the Bearcat, followed by the Super Bearcat on a shortened wheelbase. With 156 horsepower from the DV-32 eight, speed on the road was assured. The same highlights were in the 1933 portfolio as well, but production was sad with only 206 of all models being made for 1932 and 80 for 1933.

A full slate of models was again announced for 1934, but a mere half dozen were called for. Some 1935 and 1936 models could also be had, but the firm turned toward a light commercial vehicle for survival. Insolvency came in 1937 and the end in 1939.

Over the years, the Stutz name has been applied to specially built cars and probably there will be more. The magic of the Stutz name is far from being used up.

Willys-Overland

er cars spanned
offerings by the
ans for its auto-
ysler was hired
n 1919. He was
. He left in 1921
s and was able
r eventually be-
Chrysler Corp.
hen Willys won
e U.S. Govern-
World War II is
ve history. The
cars and after
r today.
ur decades are
reproduced and
77 coupes and
with racers and
ylinder engines,
ant to be econ-
envisioned their
. However help-
not what Willys-
out economical
t.
obile manufac-
yed small until
th Willys came
over. It was re-
st Willys brand-
4.

CHAPTERS
Chapters Store 770
Dalhousie Station S.C.
5005 Dalhousie Dr.N.W. Unit 195
Calgary, Alberta T3A 5R8
(403) 202-4600 Fax:(403) 202-1234

106300 Reg 7 ID 319 6:04 pm 25/08/01

S LACE	1 @	1.00	1.00
S 2877142833			
S GREEN IGUANAS & O	1 @	.01	.01
S 0793802725			
S RAT SNAKES	1 @	.01	.01
S 0793802563			
S ART OF MAGIC	1 @	.01	.01
S 1575440369			
S BOOK CLEARANCE	1 @	4.97	4.97
S X91			
S JOSEPHINE BAKER &	1 @	.01	.01
S 0810927721			
S ZIEGFELD TOUCH	1 @	.01	.01
S 0810939665			
S STANDARD CATALOG	1 @	.01	.01
S 0873415698			
S BOOK CLEARANCE	1 @	9.97	9.97
S X91			
SUBTOTAL			16.00
TAX: GST - 7%			1.12
TOTAL SALES TAX			1.12
TOTAL			17.12
CASH PAYMENT			20.12
CHANGE			3.00

Returns or exchanges within 14 days
with Proof of Purchase
No returns on magazines/newspapers/
opened software/music/audio/video/dvd
GST# R897152666

A trademark of J.N. Willys was to have a low-priced economy car in the lineup. For awhile Overland filled that role, but production ended in 1926. From late 1926 to 1931 the Willys-Overland economy entry was the Whippet. Billed as America's smallest car at introduction, it came as a 100-inch wheelbase four or 109-inch wheelbase six. It offered low prices ($545 for the four), decent performance (it held speed records) and it sold well (110,000 the first year). Moreover, the four-cylinder engine went on to long use, including in World War II and later Jeeps.

Replacing the Whippet was the task of the 1933 Willys 77 with four-cylinder power and a 100-inch wheelbase. From 1934 through 1936, the 77 was all Willys-Overland built. New streamlined styling marked the 1937 models and, using a variety of names, the four-cylinder, short wheelbase formula continued through the end of production in 1942.

Concentration on launching civilian Jeeps set back the passenger car timetable after the war. Willys did not return to the market until the Aero line was introduced for 1952. The 108-inch wheelbase featured unitized construction, compact dimensions and conservative styling. Power was a variety of six-cylinder units. Performance, economy and sales were all moderate.

Independence for Willys-Overland ended on April 28, 1953, when also-struggling Kaiser-Frazer took over and made Willys a subsidiary. Headquarters were moved to Willys' home in Toledo, Ohio, and Willys cars and trucks quickly got access to Kaiser's 226-cubic inch flathead six, but for the cars it was too late. The mildly and somewhat flashy face-lifted 1955s were the last. Dies were shipped to Brazil where the Willys enjoyed a long production life.

Of course, the Jeeps also enjoyed a long life (and many owners) right in Toledo.

Summary

ist against the
ed out to be a
y the wayside
by their own

ession helping
to chew up some of the survivors including grand names such as Stutz, Pierce-Arrow, Auburn, Cord and Duesenberg.

After World War II, there was prosperity for all due to the shortage of cars and pent-up demand. Once the hard facts of competition set in the 1950s, consolidation was seen as the key to being able to stay in business. Kaiser-Frazer and Willys-Overland joined, so did Nash and Hudson and Studebaker and Packard. Even with all this teaming up, only three nameplates were around after the 1958 model year, Rambler, Studebaker and limited production Checker. Studebaker expired during the 1966 season. The Kaiser-Willys combo stayed very much alive making Jeeps, but that heritage was folded into American Motors in 1970. Checker's last cars were 1982 models and five years later, AMC was absorbed into the Chrysler Corp. mix. The mass production independents were gone.

That is not the end of the story, however, as in 1998, Chrysler Corp. merged with Daimler-Benz of Germany to form a new German company, DaimlerChrysler AG. Is it now the "Big Two?" Will similar fates involve General Motors and Ford? Are independents forever gone? As the second hundred years of the automobile unfold so do questions brought on by the first hundred.

AUBURN

AUBURN — Auburn, Indiana — (1900-1936) — Charles Eckhart was a wheelwright who worked awhile for the wagon-building Studebaker brothers in South Bend, moving to Auburn in 1874 to establish his own Eckhart Carriage Company. He retired in 1893, leaving the business to his sons Frank and Morris. In 1900 the Eckhart brothers built their first single-cylinder, solid-tired, tiller-steered automobile and started the Auburn Automobile Company. The firm was capitalized at $2,500. Though the Eckharts affixed an $800 price tag to their efforts, it does not appear they sold many, if any, of them. In-house experimentation continued for two years. Following the Chicago Automobile Show of 1903 the brothers went into manufacture in earnest. The car remained the same chain-drive runabout, but now with pneumatic tires and tonneau and touring variations. In 1905 a two-cylinder touring followed; in 1909 there was an Auburn four, in 1912 a six. Through the World War I years, things looked good for Auburn, on the outside. The Eckharts boasted that their secret of success was the fact that there "had been no change in ownership or officers" in their company since its inception, but the truth was they were not very successful, and that secret was out in 1919 when the Eckharts sold controlling interest in Auburn to a group of Chicago businessmen including William Wrigley, Jr., who made chewing gum. The immediate result was the Auburn Beauty-SIX introduced in 1919, which any beholder could see was a prettier car than its predecessors. But it hit the postwar recession head-on and in the four years following, just 15,717 were sold. By 1924, Auburn was producing six units a day, which was more than meeting the demand. Hundreds of unsold touring cars stood forlornly in the company parking lot the day Errett Lobban Cord visited Auburn to see what he could do. Cord, who cheerfully admitted to having made and lost $50,000 three times in a variety of businesses on the West Coast, all before reaching age 21, had become the hotshot salesman of Moon cars for Chicago's Quinlan Motor Company, subsequently acquiring an interest in the firm and a nestegg of $100,000 that was now burning a hole in his pocket. In 1924, he became Auburn's general manager, at modest salary and with the option of buying control if he could save the company. A little stylish nickel plating and some flashy repainting, and the unsold Auburns began to sell. In 1925, Cord contracted for some Lycoming straight-eight engines, had chief engineer James Crawford fit them into the old six-cylinder Auburn chassis, and introduced the result to the Auburn range as the Auburn 8-63 and 8-88. Two-tone color schemes and a beltline gracefully sweeping over the top of the hood distinguished these Auburns, styling so modish that it would be effectively retained until 1930. In three consecutive years Cord doubled sales, and by the middle of the third one — 1926 — he was president of the Auburn Automobile Company. In 1927, because the demise of Mercer had left Stutz without any apparent challenger, Cord took his Auburn 8-88 racing and record-breaking, renting the Atlantic City Speedway in July so three Auburns could break all speed marks for fully equipped stock cars from 5 to 5,000 miles. In 1928, the more powerful 8-115 had hydraulic instead of the former mechanical four-wheel brakes and Bijur lubrication, a rarity for a car in the medium-price class. And it was given a boattail speedster variation styled by Al Leamy that was Cord's answer to the famous Stutz Black Hawk. That year, Wade Morton drove an Auburn 8-115 speedster 108.46 mph over the measured mile at Daytona, 2,033 miles in 24 hours for a record 84.7 mph average at Atlantic City, and set a new record at Pikes Peak. Though the Stutz Black Hawk admittedly was a slightly faster car, its Bearcat speedster sold for almost $5,000. An Auburn 8-115 speedster could be had for about $2,000. The 8-120 Auburn followed in 1929, the 8-125 in 1930. Prior to Cord, Auburn dealers had been mostly garage owners with perhaps one demonstration car; with Cord's arrival, a vast distribution network was set up, with carloads of Auburns systematically being sent to dealers. In 1929, Auburn stock on hand averaged a car and a half per showroom; dealers couldn't get Auburns fast enough. By now, with Auburn doing nicely, Cord had begun to build his empire. He acquired Ansted Engine Company, Lexington Motor Car Company, Central Manufacturing, and a lot of property in nearby Connersville; he bought Lycoming (Williamsport, Pennsylvania), Limousine Body (Kalamazoo, Michigan), and Duesenberg Motors (Indianapolis). Nineteen twenty-nine was Cord's best year yet. The aerodynamic Auburn Cabin Speedster was the sensation of the New York Automobile Show. Cord introduced the Model J Duesenberg, as well as a new front-wheel-drive Cord L-29, and gathered all of the diverse companies he had bought into a new one called Cord Corporation. He barely noticed that the stock market crashed. Though Auburn sales fell in the immediate wake of the Great Depression, they more than doubled for 1931; profit that year equaled the previous peak of 1929. And there were a thousand new Auburn dealers, most of them abandoning the franchises of other marques to join up. Auburn production was concentrated on a single straight-eight, the 8-98, with engine by Lycoming, the first center X-bracing ever offered in a rear-drive car, Lovejoy hydraulic shock absorbers, Bijur lubrication, semi-elliptic suspension front and rear, and the L.G.S. Free Wheeling unit. At $1,195-$1,395 ($945-$1,195 less freewheeling), the new Auburn was reported by *Fortune* magazine to be "the biggest package in the world for the price," by *Business Week* as "more car for the money than the public has ever seen." In 1932, Cord outdid even himself with a new V-12 by Lycoming that sold for less than a thousand dollars, certainly the cheapest 12-cylinder automobile ever marketed. New that year, too, on all Auburns was the two-speed rear axle of the Columbia Axle Company, that firm yet another Cord acquisition for his empire. A fully equipped Auburn Twelve speedster put up a flurry of records at Muroc dry lake that summer, many of which would stand until after World War II. But now things began falling apart. The slight business upswing the nation had enjoyed was followed by the "depression within the depression," and Auburn sales plummeted. The V-12 and eight-cylinder lines were reduced, a cheaper six-cylinder line reinstated. Cord's automotive interests now included Checker Cab, and he was into shipbuilding and aviation, too. Auburn was being neglected and it was in trouble. There was a final blaze of glory, and it was the Auburn 851, with Lycoming straight-eight engine supercharged by Kurt Beier of Schwitzer-Cummins, and boattail speedster body conjured largely from parts on hand by Duesenberg designer Gordon Buehrig. A hundred miles an hour was guaranteed, and the speedster driven by Ab Jenkins at Bonneville became the first fully equipped American stock car to exceed 100 mph for a 12-hour period. About 500 speedsters were built and sold at $2,245, Auburn losing money on each one. The car's purpose was to attract showroom traffic and sales for the bread-and-butter 851 eights and the cheaper sixes. Sales did rise 20 percent, but not enough for a profit. A diesel-powered Auburn airport limousine was rumored for 1936, but it was lost amid the excitement of a brand-new car called the Cord 810. The Auburn line for 1936 was virtually unchanged from 1935. No Auburns appeared at all at the beginning of 1937, though they were announced to be on the way. They never arrived. In August, under heavy scrutiny by both the Bureau of Internal Revenue and the Securities and Exchange Commission for his business dealings, Errett Lobban Cord sold out his holdings. In October of 1937, "informed Wall Street sources" reported that the Auburn, Cord, and Duesenberg automobiles would be discontinued. The sources were well informed.

AUBURN PRODUCTION: 1900 8; 1901 25; 1902 72; 1903 120; 1904 144; 1905 160; 1906 189; 1907 197; 1908 356; 1909 1,018; 1910 1,365; 1911 954; 1912 1,605; 1913 1,554; 1914 1,094; 1915 2,113, 1916 2,686; 1917 2,307; 1918 1,374; 1919 6,062, 1920 5,034; 1921 3,306; 1922 2,408; 1923 2,443; 1924 2,474; 1925 4,044; 1926 7,138, 1927 14,515; 1928 12,899; 1929 23,509; 1930 12,985; 1931 34,228; 1932 11,145; 1933 5,038; 1934 7,770; 1935 6,316; 1936 1,263.

1903

Model A, 1-cyl., 6 hp

Model No.	Body Type & Seating	Factory Price	Shipping Weight	Prod. Total
—	Rbt-2P	800	1150	Note 1
A	Tr-4P	1000	1500	Note 1

Note 1: Auburn production for 1903 totaled 120 with no breakout available.

1904

Model A, 1-cyl., 10 hp

Model No.	Body Type & Seating	Factory Price	Shipping Weight	Prod. Total
A	Tr-4P	1250	1600	144

1905

Model B, 2-cyl., 18 hp

Model No.	Body Type & Seating	Factory Price	Shipping Weight	Prod. Total
B	Tr-5P	1250	1750	160

1906

Model C, 2-cyl., 20 hp

Model No.	Body Type & Seating	Factory Price	Shipping Weight	Prod. Total
C	Tr-5P	1250	1750	189

1902 Auburn, runabout, A-C-D

1904 Auburn, Model A, rear entrance tonneau, A-C-D

1906 Auburn, Model C, touring, WLB

1907 Auburn, Model D, touring, WLB

1911 Auburn, Model M, roadster, WLB

1911 Auburn, Model Y, touring, WLB

1913 Auburn, Model 33L, touring, HAC

1907

Model D, 2-cyl., 24 hp

Model No.	Body Type & Seating	Factory Price	Shipping Weight	Prod. Total
D	Tr-5P	1250	N/A	Note 1

Model F, 2-cyl., 24 hp

Model No.	Body Type & Seating	Factory Price	Shipping Weight	Prod. Total
F	Rbt-2P	1150	N/A	Note 1

Note 1: Auburn production for 1907 totaled 197 with no breakout available. Auburn also offered a Model E touring, which was essentially the Model D with more equipment.

1908

Model G, 2-cyl., 24 hp

Model No.	Body Type & Seating	Factory Price	Shipping Weight	Prod. Total
G	Tr-5P	1350	1800	Note 1

Model H, 2-cyl., 24 hp

Model No.	Body Type & Seating	Factory Price	Shipping Weight	Prod. Total
H	Tr-5P	1400	N/A	Note 1

Model K, 2-cyl., 24 hp

Model No.	Body Type & Seating	Factory Price	Shipping Weight	Prod. Total
K	Rbt-2P	1250	1700	Note 1

Note 1: Auburn production for 1908 totaled 356 with no breakout available.

1909

Model G, 2-cyl., 24 hp

Model No.	Body Type & Seating	Factory Price	Shipping Weight	Prod. Total
G	Tr-5P	1250	N/A	Note 1

Model H, 2-cyl., 24 hp

Model No.	Body Type & Seating	Factory Price	Shipping Weight	Prod. Total
H	Tr-5P	1300	N/A	Note 1

Model K, 2-cyl., 24 hp

Model No.	Body Type & Seating	Factory Price	Shipping Weight	Prod. Total
K	Rds-2P	1150	N/A	Note 1

Model B, 4-cyl., 30 hp

Model No.	Body Type & Seating	Factory Price	Shipping Weight	Prod. Total
B	Tr-5P	1400	N/A	Note 1

Model C, 4-cyl., 30 hp

Model No.	Body Type & Seating	Factory Price	Shipping Weight	Prod. Total
C	Rds-4P	1350	N/A	Note 1

Model D, 4-cyl., 30 hp

Model No.	Body Type & Seating	Factory Price	Shipping Weight	Prod. Total
D	Rds-3P	1300	N/A	Note 1

Note 1: Auburn production for 1909 totaled 1,018 with no breakout available.

1910

Model G, 2-cyl., 24 hp

Model No.	Body Type & Seating	Factory Price	Shipping Weight	Prod. Total
G	Tr-5P	1250	2350	Note 1

Model H, 2-cyl., 24 hp

Model No.	Body Type & Seating	Factory Price	Shipping Weight	Prod. Total
H	Tr-5P	N/A	N/A	Note 1

Model K, 2-cyl., 24 hp

Model No.	Body Type & Seating	Factory Price	Shipping Weight	Prod. Total
K	Rds-2P	1150	2300	Note 1

Model B, 4-cyl., 40 hp

Model No.	Body Type & Seating	Factory Price	Shipping Weight	Prod. Total
B	Tr-5P	1400	N/A	Note 1

Model X, 4-cyl., 40 hp

Model No.	Body Type & Seating	Factory Price	Shipping Weight	Prod. Total
X-40	Tr-5P	1650	2500	Note 1

Model R, 4-cyl., 40 hp

Model No.	Body Type & Seating	Factory Price	Shipping Weight	Prod. Total
R-40	Baby Tonn-4P	1650	2450	Note 1

Model S, 4-cyl., 40 hp

Model No.	Body Type & Seating	Factory Price	Shipping Weight	Prod. Total
S-40	Rds-3P	1650	2400	Note 1

Note 1: Auburn production for 1910 totaled 1,365 with no breakout available.

1911

Model G, 2-cyl., 24 hp

Model No.	Body Type & Seating	Factory Price	Shipping Weight	Prod. Total
G	Tr-5P	1000	N/A	Note 1

Model K, 2-cyl., 24 hp

Model No.	Body Type & Seating	Factory Price	Shipping Weight	Prod. Total
K	Rds-2P	1000	N/A	Note 1

Model F , 4-cyl., 30 - 40 hp

Model No.	Body Type & Seating	Factory Price	Shipping Weight	Prod. Total
F-30	Baby Tonn-4P	1400	N/A	Note 1

Model L, 4-cyl., 30 - 40 hp

Model No.	Body Type & Seating	Factory Price	Shipping Weight	Prod. Total
L-30	Tr-5P	1400	2340	Note 1

Model M, 4-cyl., 30 - 40 hp

Model No.	Body Type & Seating	Factory Price	Shipping Weight	Prod. Total
M-40	Rds-3P	1700	2650	Note 1

Model N, 4-cyl., 30 - 40 hp

Model No.	Body Type & Seating	Factory Price	Shipping Weight	Prod. Total
N-40	Tr-5P	1750	2700	Note 1

Model T, 4-cyl., 30 - 40 hp

Model No.	Body Type & Seating	Factory Price	Shipping Weight	Prod. Total
T-40	Baby Tonn-4P	1700	2650	Note 1

Model Y, 4-cyl., 30 - 40 hp

Model No.	Body Type & Seating	Factory Price	Shipping Weight	Prod. Total
Y-40	Tr-5P	1700	2650	Note 1

Note 1: Auburn production for 1911 totaled 954 with no breakout available.

1912

Model 40H, 4-cyl., 40 hp

Model No.	Body Type & Seating	Factory Price	Shipping Weight	Prod. Total
40H	Tr-5P	1650	N/A	Note 1

Model 40M, 4-cyl., 40 hp

Model No.	Body Type & Seating	Factory Price	Shipping Weight	Prod. Total
40M	Rds-2P	1750	N/A	Note 1

Model 40N, 4-cyl., 40 hp

Model No.	Body Type & Seating	Factory Price	Shipping Weight	Prod. Total
40N	Tr-5P	1750	N/A	Note 1

Model 30L, 4-cyl., 35 hp

Model No.	Body Type & Seating	Factory Price	Shipping Weight	Prod. Total
30L	Rds-2P	1100	N/A	Note 1
30L	Tr-5P	1100	N/A	Note 1

Model 35L, 4-cyl., 35 hp

Model No.	Body Type & Seating	Factory Price	Shipping Weight	Prod. Total
35L	Tr-5P	1400	N/A	Note 1

Model 6-50, 6-cyl., 50 hp

Model No.	Body Type & Seating	Factory Price	Shipping Weight	Prod. Total
6-50	Tr-7P	3000	N/A	Note 1

Note 1: Auburn production for 1912 totaled 1,605 with no breakout available.

1913

Model 33M, 4-cyl., 33 hp

Model No.	Body Type & Seating	Factory Price	Shipping Weight	Prod. Total
33M	Rds-2P	1150	N/A	Note 1

Model 33L, 4-cyl., 33 hp

Model No.	Body Type & Seating	Factory Price	Shipping Weight	Prod. Total
33L	Tr-5P	1150	N/A	Note 1

Model 37L, 4-cyl., 37 hp

Model No.	Body Type & Seating	Factory Price	Shipping Weight	Prod. Total
37L	Tr-5P	1400	N/A	Note 1

Model 40A, 4-cyl., 40 hp

Model No.	Body Type & Seating	Factory Price	Shipping Weight	Prod. Total
40A	Rds-2P	1650	N/A	Note 1

Model 40L, 4-cyl., 40 hp

Model No.	Body Type & Seating	Factory Price	Shipping Weight	Prod. Total
40L	Tr-5P	1650	N/A	Note 1

Model 6-45, 6-cyl., 45 hp

Model No.	Body Type & Seating	Factory Price	Shipping Weight	Prod. Total
45	Twn Cr-5P	2500	N/A	Note 1

Model 6-45B, 6-cyl., 45 hp

Model No.	Body Type & Seating	Factory Price	Shipping Weight	Prod. Total
6-45B	Rds-2P	2000	N/A	Note 1
6-45B	Tr-5P	2000	N/A	Note 1
6-45B	Limo-7P	3200	N/A	Note 1

Model 6-50, 6-cyl., 50 hp

Model No.	Body Type & Seating	Factory Price	Shipping Weight	Prod. Total
6-50	Tr-7P	3000	N/A	Note 1

Note 1: Auburn production for 1913 totaled 1,554 with no breakout available.

1914

Model 4-40, 4-cyl., 40 hp

Model No.	Body Type & Seating	Factory Price	Shipping Weight	Prod. Total
4-40	Rds-2P	1490	N/A	Note 1
4-40	Tr-5P	1490	N/A	Note 1
4-40	Cpe-2P	1690	N/A	Note 1

Model 4-41, 4-cyl., 40 hp

Model No.	Body Type & Seating	Factory Price	Shipping Weight	Prod. Total
4-41	Tr-6P	1590	N/A	Note 1

Model 6-45, 6-cyl., 45 hp

Model No.	Body Type & Seating	Factory Price	Shipping Weight	Prod. Total
6-45	Rds-2P	2000	N/A	Note 1
6-45	Tr-5P	2000	N/A	Note 1

Model 6-46, 6-cyl., 45 hp

Model No.	Body Type & Seating	Factory Price	Shipping Weight	Prod. Total
6-46	Tr-6P	2100	N/A	Note 1

Note 1: Auburn production for 1914 totaled 1,094 with no breakout available.

1915

Model 4-36, 4-cyl., 36 hp

Model No.	Body Type & Seating	Factory Price	Shipping Weight	Prod. Total
4-36	Rds-2P	1075	2650	Note 1
4-36	Tr-5P	1075	2700	Note 1
Model 4-43, 4-cyl., 43 hp				
4-43	Rds-2P	1500	2760	Note 1
4-43	Tr-6P	1500	2850	Note 1
Model 6-40, 6-cyl., 50 hp				
6-40	Rds-2P	1550	3100	Note 1
6-40	Tr-5P	1550	3150	Note 1
Model 6-47, 6-cyl., 47 hp				
6-47	Rds-2P	2000	3700	Note 1
6-47	Tr-7P	2000	3800	Note 1

Note 1: Auburn production for 1915 totaled 2,113 with no breakout available.

1916

Model 4-38, 4-cyl., 38 hp

Model No.	Body Type & Seating	Factory Price	Shipping Weight	Prod. Total
4-38	Rds-2P	985	2800	Note 1
4-38	Tr-5P	985	2850	Note 1
Model 6-38, 6-cyl., 40 hp				
6-38	Rds-2P	1050	2850	Note 1
6-38	Tr-5P	1050	2900	Note 1
Model 6-40A, 6-cyl., 48 hp				
6-40A	Rds-2P	1375	3200	Note 1
6-40A	Tr-7P	1375	3250	Note 1
6-40A	Limo-7P	2700	N/A	Note 1
Model (Union) 4-36, 6-cyl., 36 hp				
4-36	Rds-2P	895	2560	Note 1
4-36	Tr-5P	895	2600	Note 1

Note 1: Auburn production for 1916 totaled 2,686 with no breakout available. The Union 4-36 was a companion car to the Auburn and replaced the 4-38 line midyear.

1917

Model 6-39, 6-cyl., 39 hp

Model No.	Body Type & Seating	Factory Price	Shipping Weight	Prod. Total
6-39	Rds-3P	1195	2850	Note 1
6-39	Tr-5P	1195	2900	Note 1
Model 6-44, 6-cyl., 44 hp				
6-44	Rds-4P	1635	3100	Note 1
6-44	Tr-7P	1635	3350	Note 1
Model 4-36U, 4-cyl., 36 hp				
4-36U	Rds-2P	895	2560	Note 1
4-36U	Tr-5P	895	2600	Note 1

Note 1: Auburn production for 1917 totaled 2,307 with no breakout available. The Union name was not used this year (just the letter 'U' and the 4-36U line was dropped completely before the end of the model year.

1918

Model 6-39, 6-cyl., 43 hp

Model No.	Body Type & Seating	Factory Price	Shipping Weight	Prod. Total
6-39	Tr-5P	1445	2900	Note 1
6-39	Rds-4P	1445	2850	Note 1
6-39	Spt Tr-5P	1545	3100	Note 1
Model 6-44, 6-cyl., 55 hp				
6-44	Tr-7P	1785	3500	Note 1
6-44	Rds-4P	1685	3100	Note 1
6-44	Spt Tr-7P	2085	3450	Note 1
6-44	Sed-7P	2550	3600	Note 1

Note 1: Auburn production for 1918 totaled 1,374 with no breakout available.

1919

Model 6-39, 6-cyl., 43 hp

Model No.	Body Type & Seating	Factory Price	Shipping Weight	Prod. Total
6-39H	Tr-5P	1695	2950	Note 1
6-39K	Smart Trstr-4P	1695	2940	Note 1
6-39R	Rds-2P	1695	2885	Note 1
6-39	Cpe-4P	2375	3195	Note 1
6-39	Sed-5P	2375	3245	Note 1

Note 1: Auburn production for 1919 totaled 6,062 with no breakout available.

1920

Model 6-39, 6-cyl., 43 hp (revised midyear to 55 hp)

Model No.	Body Type & Seating	Factory Price	Shipping Weight	Prod. Total
6-39H	Tr-5P	1795	2950	Note 1
6-39K	Trstr-4P	1795	2940	Note 1
6-39R	Rds-2P	1845	2885	Note 1
6-39	Sed-5P	2775	3245	Note 1
6-39	Cpe-4P	2775	3195	Note 1

Note 1: Auburn production for 1920 totaled 5,034 with no breakout available.

1921

Model 6-39, 6-cyl., 55 hp

Model No.	Body Type & Seating	Factory Price	Shipping Weight	Prod. Total
6-39H	Tr-5P	1695	2950	Note 1
6-39K	Trstr-4P	1695	2940	Note 1
6-39R	Rds-2P	1715	2885	Note 1
6-39	Tr Sed-5P	N/A	N/A	Note 1
6-39	Sed-5P	2795	3245	Note 1
6-39	Cpe-4P	2795	3195	Note 1

Note 1: Auburn production for 1921 totaled 3,306 with no breakout available. Prices listed were mark-downs from original prices ($200 higher) at the beginning of the model year, due to recession.

1922

Model 6-51, 6-cyl., 55 hp (revised midyear to 58 hp)

Model No.	Body Type & Seating	Factory Price	Shipping Weight	Prod. Total
6-51H	Tr-5P	1475	3110	Note 1
6-51S	Tr-7P	1545	3140	Note 1
6-51R	Rds-2P	1575	2960	Note 1
6-51	Spt Tr-4P	1995	3300	Note 1
6-51	Sed-7P	2345	3430	Note 1
6-51	Cpe-4P	2275	3380	Note 1

Note 1: Auburn production for 1922 totaled 2,408 with no breakout available. Prices listed were mark-downs from original prices ($200 higher) at the beginning of the model year, due to recession. The 6-51 sedan introduced at the beginning of the model year was rebodied midyear resulting in increased passenger capacity from five to seven.

1923

Model 6-43, 6-cyl., 50 hp

Model No.	Body Type & Seating	Factory Price	Shipping Weight	Prod. Total
6-43	Tr-5P	1165	2550	Note 1
6-43	Sed-5P	1535	2830	Note 1
Model 6-63, 6-cyl., 58 hp				
6-63	Tr-5P	1725	3165	Note 1
6-63	Spt Tr-4P	1985	3375	Note 1
6-63	Brgm-4P	2045	3390	Note 1
6-63	Sedan-7P	2345	3620	Note 1
Model 6-51, 6-cyl., 58 hp				
6-51	Tr-5P	1275	3110	Note 1
6-51	Tr-7P	1345	3140	Note 1
6-51	Spt Tr-4P	1895	3340	Note 1
6-51	Sed-7P	2245	3430	Note 1
6-51	Brgm-4P	1965	3300	Note 1

Note 1: Auburn production for 1923 totaled 2,443 with no breakout available. The 6-51 line was offered for only three months before being phased out and replaced by the 6-63 models, also called the Auburn Six Supreme line. In the 6-43 line, a Chesterfield touring was available for $1,275.

1914 Auburn, Model 6-46, touring, HAC

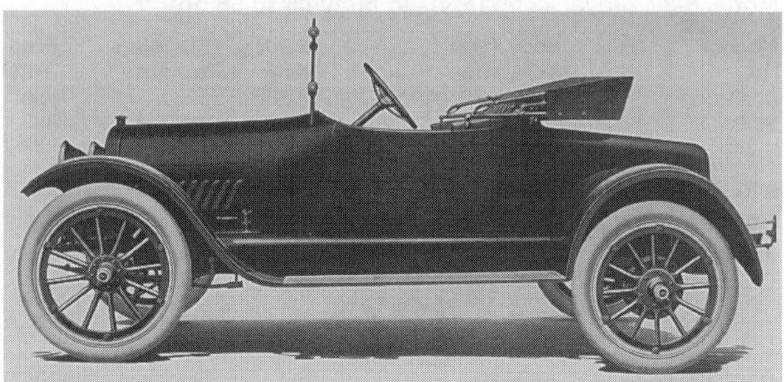
1916 Auburn, Model 4-38, roadster, HAC

1921 Auburn, Model 6-39, Beauty six sedan, HAC

1924 Auburn, Model 6-43, sport touring, WLB

1926 Auburn, Model 8-88, touring, JAC

1915 Auburn, Model 4-36, touring, HAC

1918 Auburn, Model 6-39, sport touring, WLB

1922 Auburn, Model 6-51, Beauty six roadster, HAC

1925 Auburn, Model 6-43, sport phaeton, HAC

1927 Auburn, Model 8-77, sport sedan, HAC

1924

Model No.	Body Type & Seating	Factory Price	Shipping Weight	Prod. Total
Model 6-43, 6-cyl., 50 hp				
6-43	Stnd Tr-5P	1095	2550	Note 1
6-43	Spt Tr-5P	1365	2760	Note 1
6-43	Special Tr-5P	1295	2610	Note 1
6-43	Sed-5P	1695	2825	Note 1
6-43	English Coach-5P	1895	2900	Note 1
6-43	Tr Cpe-5P	1595	2825	Note 1
Model 6-63, 6-cyl., 58 hp				
6-63	Tr-5P	1695	3165	Note 1
6-63	Spt Tr-4P	1935	3390	Note 1
6-63	Sed-7P	2445	3562	Note 1
6-63	Brgm-5P	2245	3572	Note 1

Note 1: Auburn production for 1924 totaled 2,474 with no breakout available. The 6-63 Brougham model was rebodied as a four-door model instead of the two-door version the year previous. Passenger capacity was increased from four to five.

1925

Model No.	Body Type & Seating	Factory Price	Shipping Weight	Prod. Total
Model 8-63, 8-cyl., 62 hp				
8-63	Tr-5P	1895	3280	Note 1
8-63	Brgm-5P	2395	3550	Note 1
8-63	Sed-7P	2550	3550	Note 1
8-63	English Coach-5P	2650	3550	Note 1
Model 6-43, 6-cyl., 50 hp				
6-43	Special Tr-5P	1395	2610	Note 1
6-43	Spt Tr-5P	1465	2760	Note 1
6-43	Special Sed-5P	1595	2885	Note 1
6-43	English Coach-5P	1945	2900	Note 1
Model 6-66, 6-cyl., 48 hp				
6-66	Rds-2/4P	1495	2850	Note 1
6-66	Brgm-5P	1595	3020	Note 1
6-66	Sed-5P	1795	3070	Note 1
Model 8-88, 8-cyl., 68 hp				
8-88	Rds-3/6P	1975	3180	Note 1
8-88	Sed-5P	2350	3450	Note 1
8-88	Sed-7P	2550	3750	Note 1
8-88	Brgm-5P	2250	3380	Note 1

Note 1: Auburn production for 1925 totaled 4,044 with no breakout available. The 6-43 line's Coupe and Sedan from the year previous were carried over unchanged to 1925 and priced, respectively, at $1,695 and $1,795. These two models were phased out two months into the model year.

1926

Model No.	Body Type & Seating	Factory Price	Shipping Weight	Prod. Total
Model 4-44, 4-cyl., 42 hp				
4-44	Tr-5P	1145	2740	Note 1
4-44	Rds-2/4P	1145	2740	Note 1
4-44	Cpe-2P	1175	2720	Note 1
4-44	Sed-5P	1195	2960	Note 1
Model 6-66, 6-cyl., 48 hp				
6-66	Rds-2/4P	1395	2850	Note 1
6-66	Tr-5P	1295	2860	Note 1
6-66	Brgm-5P	1495	3020	Note 1
6-66	Sed-5P	1695	3070	Note 1
6-66	Cpe-2P	1445	2830	Note 1
Model 8-88, 8-cyl., 88 hp, 129" wb				
8-88	Rds-2/4P	1695	3180	Note 1
8-88	Tr-5P	1695	3200	Note 1
8-88	Cpe-3P	1745	3210	Note 1
8-88	Brgm-5P	1795	3380	Note 1
8-88	Sed-5P	1995	3450	Note 1
8-88	Sed-7P	2095	3750	Note 1
Model 8-88, 8-cyl., 88 hp, 146" wb				
8-88	Sed-7P	2495	4200	Note 1

Note 1: Auburn production for 1926 totaled 7,138 with no breakout available.

1927

Model No.	Body Type & Seating	Factory Price	Shipping Weight	Prod. Total
Model 6-66, 6-cyl., 66 hp				
6-66	Rds-2/4P	1095	2850	Note 1
6-66	Tr-5P	1145	2860	Note 1
6-66	Spt Sed-5P	1195	3070	Note 1
6-66	Cabr-4P	1295	3020	Note 1
6-66	Sed-5P	1295	3070	Note 1
Model 8-77, 8-cyl., 77 hp				
8-77	Rds-2/4P	1395	3005	Note 1
8-77	Tr-5P	1445	3005	Note 1
8-77	Spt Sed-5P	1495	3270	Note 1
8-77	Cabr-4P	1595	3170	Note 1
8-77	Sed-5P	1695	3270	Note 1
Model 8-88, 8-cyl., 88 hp, 129" wb				
8-88	Tr-5P	2045	3200	Note 1
8-88	Rds-2/4P	1995	3440	Note 1
8-88	Cabr-4P	2095	3600	Note 1
8-88	Sed-5P	2195	3625	Note 1
8-88	Spt Sed-5P	2095	3625	Note 1
Model 8-88, 8-cyl., 88 hp, 146" wb				
8-88	Sed-7P	2595	4080	Note 1
8-88	Tr-7P	2295	3790	Note 1

Note 1: Auburn production for 1927 totaled 14,515 with no breakout available.

1928

Model No.	Body Type & Seating	Factory Price	Shipping Weight	Prod. Total
Model 6-66A, 6-cyl., 66 hp				
6-66A	Rds-2/4P	1095	2850	Note 1
6-66A	Tr-5P	1145	2860	Note 1
6-66A	Cabr-4P	1295	3020	Note 1
6-66A	Sed-5P	1295	3070	Note 1
6-66A	Spt Sed-5P	1195	3070	Note 1
Model 8-77, 8-cyl., 77 hp				
8-77	Rds-2/4P	1395	3005	Note 1
8-77	Tr-5P	1445	3005	Note 1
8-77	Spt Sed-5P	1495	3270	Note 1
8-77	Cabr-4P	1595	3170	Note 1
8-77	Sed-5P	1695	3270	Note 1
Model DL8-88, 8-cyl., 88 hp				
DL8-88	Rds-2/4P	1995	3440	Note 1
DL8-88	Tr-5P	2045	3200	Note 1
DL8-88	Cabr-4P	2095	3600	Note 1
DL8-88	Sed-5P	2195	3625	Note 1
DL8-88	Spt Sed-5P	2095	3625	Note 1
Model DL8-88, 8-cyl., 88 hp, 136" wb				
DL8-88	Sed-7P	2595	4080	Note 1
DL8-88	Tr-7P	2295	3790	Note 1
SECOND SERIES				
Model 76, 6-cyl., 60 hp				
76	Rds-2/4P	1195	2980	Note 1
76	Tr-5P	1195	3070	Note 1
76	Cabr-2/4P	1395	3125	Note 1
76	Sed-5P	1395	3300	Note 1
76	Spt Sed-5P	1295	3300	Note 1
Model 88, 8-cyl., 88 hp				
88	Spds-2P	1695	3245	Note 1
88	Tr-5P	1495	3380	Note 1
88	Rds-2/4P	1495	3265	Note 1
88	Cabr-4P	1695	3410	Note 1
88	Sed-5P	1695	3590	Note 1
88	Spt Sed-5P	1595	3590	Note 1
88	Phae Sed-5P	1895	3600	Note 1
Model 115, 8-cyl., 115 hp				
115	Spds-2P	2195	3590	Note 1
115	Rds-2/4P	1995	3665	Note 1
115	Cabr-2/4P	2195	3880	Note 1
115	Sed-5P	2195	3995	Note 1
115	Spt Sed-5P	2095	3995	Note 1
115	Phae Sed-5P	2395	3990	Note 1

Note 1: Auburn production for 1928 totaled 12,899 with no breakout available. The Second Series Auburns were introduced at the New York Auto Show in January 1928.

1929

Model No.	Body Type & Seating	Factory Price	Shipping Weight	Prod. Total
Model 76, 6-cyl., 60 hp				
76	Rds-2/4P	1195	2980	Note 1
76	Tr-5P	1395	3070	Note 1
76	Cabr-2/4P	1395	3125	Note 1
76	Vic-4P	1395	3295	Note 1
76	Sed-5P	1395	3300	Note 1
76	Spt Sed-5P	1295	3300	Note 1
Model 88, 8-cyl., 88 hp				
88	Rds-2/4P	1495	3265	Note 1
88	Cabr-2/4P	1695	3410	Note 1

1929 Auburn, Model 115, victoria (with optional wire wheels), AA

1930 Auburn, Model 125, sport sedan, AA

1931 Auburn, Model 8-98A, Custom boattail speedster, AA

1932 Auburn, Model 8-100A, Custom brougham, AA

1932 Auburn, Model 12-160A, Custom boattail speedster, AA

1933 Auburn, Model 12-161A, Custom phaeton sedan, OCW

Model No.	Body Type & Seating	Factory Price	Shipping Weight	Prod. Total
88	Sed-5P	1695	3590	Note 1
88	Sed-7P	1945	3835	Note 1
88	Spt Sed-5P	1595	3590	Note 1
88	Phae Sed-5P	1895	3600	Note 1
88	Vic-4P	1695	3590	Note 1
Model 115, 8-cyl., 125 hp				
115	Spds-2P	2195	3590	Note 1
115	Rds-2/4P	1995	3665	Note 1
115	Cabr-2/4P	2195	3880	Note 1
115	Sed-5P	2195	3995	Note 1
115	Spt Sed-5P	2095	3995	Note 1
115	Phae Sed-5P	2395	3990	Note 1
115	Vic-4P	2195	3995	Note 1

SECOND SERIES

Model No.	Body Type & Seating	Factory Price	Shipping Weight	Prod. Total
Model 6-80, 6-cyl., 70 hp				
6-80	Tr-5P	995	3070	Note 1
6-80	Cabr-2/4P	1095	3125	Note 1
6-80	Vic-4P	1095	3295	Note 1
6-80	Sed-5P	1095	3300	Note 1
6-80	Spt Sed-5P	995	3300	Note 1
Model 8-90, 8-cyl., 100 hp				
8-90	Spds-2P	1495	3245	Note 1
8-90	Tr-5P	1395	3380	Note 1
8-90	Cabr-2/4P	1495	3410	Note 1
8-90	Phae Sed-5P	1695	3600	Note 1
8-90	Vic-4P	1495	3590	Note 1
8-90	Sed-5P	1495	3590	Note 1
8-90	Spt Sed-5P	1395	3590	Note 1
Model 120, 8-cyl., 125 hp				
120	Spds-2P	1895	3590	Note 1
120	Cabr-2/4P	1895	3800	Note 1
120	Phae Sed-5P	2095	3990	Note 1
120	Vic-4P	1895	3995	Note 1
120	Sed-5P	1895	3995	Note 1
120	Sed-7P	2145	4185	Note 1
120	Spt Sed-5P	1795	3995	Note 1

Note 1: Auburn production for 1929 totaled 23,509 with no breakout available. The Second Series Auburns were introduced December 2, 1928.

1930

Model 6-85, 6-cyl., 70 hp

Model No.	Body Type & Seating	Factory Price	Shipping Weight	Prod. Total
6-85	Cabr-2/4P	1095	3125	Note 1
6-85	Sed-5P	1095	3300	Note 1
6-85	Spt Sed-5P	995	3300	Note 1
Model 8-95, 8-cyl., 100 hp				
8-95	Cabr-2/4P	1295	3410	Note 1
8-95	Phae Sed-5P	1395	3600	Note 1
8-95	Sed-5P	1295	3590	Note 1
8-95	Spt Sed-5P	1195	3590	Note 1
Model 125, 8-cyl., 125 hp				
125	Cabr-2/4P	1595	3800	Note 1
125	Phae Sed-5P	1695	3990	Note 1
125	Sed-5P	1595	3995	Note 1
125	Spt Sed-5P	1495	3995	Note 1

Note 1: Auburn production for 1930 totaled 12,985 with no breakout available.

1931

Model 8-98, 8-cyl., 98 hp, Standard, 127" wb

Model No.	Body Type & Seating	Factory Price	Shipping Weight	Prod. Total
8-98	Spds-2P	945	3320	Note 1
8-98	Cabr-2/4P	1045	3540	Note 1
8-98	Phae Sed-5P	1145	3650	Note 1
8-98	Cpe-2P	995	3460	Note 1
8-98	Brgm-5P	945	3580	Note 1
8-98	Sed-5P	995	3700	Note 1
Model 8-98, 8-cyl., 98 hp, Standard 136" wb				
8-98	Sed-7P	1195	3990	Note 1
Model 8-98A, 8-cyl., 98 hp Custom, 127" wb				
8-98A	Spds-2P	1395	3370	Note 1
8-98A	Cabr-2/4P	1245	3590	Note 1
8-98A	Phae Sed-5P	1345	3700	Note 1
8-98A	Cpe-2P	1195	3510	Note 1
8-98A	Brgm-5P	1145	3630	Note 1
8-98A	Sed-5P	1195	3750	Note 1
Model 8-98A, 8-cyl., 98 hp, Custom 136" wb				
8-98A	Sed-7P	1395	4040	Note 1

Note 1: Auburn production for 1931 totaled 34,228 with no breakout available.

1932

Model 8-100, 8-cyl., 100 hp, Standard, 127" wb

Model No.	Body Type & Seating	Factory Price	Shipping Weight	Prod. Total
8-100	Spds-2P	845	3345	Note 1
8-100	Cabr-2/4P	795	3495	Note 1
8-100	Phae Sed-5P	845	3675	Note 1
8-100	Cpe-2P	675	3485	Note 1
8-100	Brgm-5P	725	3605	Note 1
8-100	Sed-5P	775	3725	Note 1
Model 8-100, 8-cyl., 100 hp, Standard, 136" wb				
8-100	Sed-7P	875	4040	Note 1
Model 8-100A, 8-cyl., 100 hp, Custom Dual Ratio, 127" wb				
8-100A	Spds-2P	975	3435	Note 1
8-100A	Cabr-2/4P	925	3585	Note 1
8-100A	Phae Sed-5P	975	3765	Note 1
8-100A	Cpe-2P	805	3575	Note 1
8-100A	Brgm-5P	855	3695	Note 1
8-100A	Sed-5P	905	3815	Note 1
Model 8-100A, 8-cyl., 100 hp, Custom, 136" wb				
8-100A	Sed-7P	1005	4105	Note 1
Model 12-160, 12-cyl., 160 hp, Standard				
12-160	Spds-2P	1145	4135	Note 1
12-160	Cabr-2/4P	1095	4285	Note 1
12-160	Phae Sed-5P	1145	4465	Note 1
12-160	Cpe-2P	975	4275	Note 1
12-160	Brgm-5P	1025	4395	Note 1
12-160	Sed-5P	1075	4515	Note 1
Model 12-160A, 12-cyl., 160 hp, Custom Dual Ratio				
12-160A	Spds-2P	1275	4235	Note 1
12-160A	Cabr-2/4P	1225	4385	Note 1
12-160A	Phae Sed-5P	1275	4565	Note 1
12-160A	Cpe-2P	1105	4375	Note 1
12-160A	Brgm-5P	1155	4495	Note 1
12-160A	Sed-5P	1205	4615	Note 1

Note 1: Auburn production for 1932 totaled 11,145 with no breakout available.

1933

Model 8-101, 8-cyl., 100 hp, Standard, 127" wb

Model No.	Body Type & Seating	Factory Price	Shipping Weight	Prod. Total
8-101	Spds-2P	945	3345	Note 1
8-101	Cabr-2/4P	895	3495	Note 1
8-101	Phae Sed-5P	945	3675	Note 1
8-101	Cpe-2P	745	3485	Note 1
8-101	Brgm-5P	795	3605	Note 1
8-101	Sed-5P	845	3725	Note 1
Model 8-101, 8-cyl., 100 hp, Standard, 136" wb				
8-101	Sed-7P	945	4015	Note 1
Model 8-101A, 8-cyl., 100 hp, Custom Dual Ratio, 127" wb				
8-101A	Spds-2P	1095	3435	Note 1
8-101A	Cabr-2/4P	1045	3585	Note 1
8-101A	Phae Sed-5P	1095	3765	Note 1
8-101A	Cpe-2P	895	3575	Note 1
8-101A	Brgm-5P	945	3695	Note 1
8-101A	Sed-5P	995	3815	Note 1
Model 8-101A, 8-cyl., 100 hp, Custom Dual Ratio, 136" wb				
8-101A	Sed-7P	1095	4105	Note 1
Model 8-105, 8-cyl., 100 hp, Salon Dual Ratio				
8-105	Spds-2P	1195	3510	Note 1
8-105	Cabr-2/4P	1145	3640	Note 1
8-105	Phae Sed-5P	1195	3835	Note 1
8-105	Sed-5P	1095	3920	Note 1
Model 12-161, 12-cyl., 160 hp, Standard				
12-161	Spds-2P	1345	4135	Note 1
12-161	Cabr-2/4P	1295	4285	Note 1
12-161	Phae Sed-5P	1345	4465	Note 1
12-161	Cpe-2P	1145	4275	Note 1
12-161	Brgm-5P	1195	4395	Note 1
12-161	Sed-5P	1245	4515	Note 1
Model 12-161A, 12-cyl., 160 hp, Custom Dual Ratio				
12-161A	Spds-2P	1495	4235	Note 1
12-161A	Cabr-2/4P	1445	4385	Note 1
12-161A	Phae Sed-5P	1495	4565	Note 1
12-161A	Cpe-2P	1295	4375	Note 1
12-161A	Brgm-5P	1345	4495	Note 1
12-161A	Sed-5P	1395	4615	Note 1
Model 12-165, 12-cyl., 160 hp, Salon Dual Ratio				
12-165	Spds-2P	1745	4440	Note 1
12-165	Cabr-2/4P	1695	4570	Note 1
12-165	Phae Sed-5P	1745	4710	Note 1
12-165	Brgm-5P	1595	4715	Note 1
12-165	Sed-5P	1645	4870	Note 1

Note 1: Auburn production for 1933 totaled 5,038 with no breakout available.

1934

Model 652X, 6-cyl., 85 hp, Standard

Model No.	Body Type & Seating	Factory Price	Shipping Weight	Prod. Total
652X	Cabr-2/4P	795	3175	Note 1
652X	Brgm-5P	695	3215	Note 1
652X	Sed-5P	745	3260	Note 1

Model 652Y, 6-cyl., 85 hp, Custom

Model No.	Body Type & Seating	Factory Price	Shipping Weight	Prod. Total
652Y	Cabr-2/4P	895	3245	Note 1
652Y	Phae Sed-5P	945	3345	Note 1
652Y	Brgm-5P	795	3245	Note 1
652Y	Sed-5P	845	3355	Note 1

Model 850X, 8-cyl., 100 hp, Standard

Model No.	Body Type & Seating	Factory Price	Shipping Weight	Prod. Total
850X	Cabr-2/4P	1045	3605	Note 1
850X	Brgm-5P	945	3625	Note 1
850X	Sed-5P	995	3670	Note 1

Model 850Y, 8-cyl., 115 hp, Custom Dual Ratio

Model No.	Body Type & Seating	Factory Price	Shipping Weight	Prod. Total
850Y	Cabr-2/4P	1175	3655	Note 1
850Y	Phae Sed-5P	1225	3775	Note 1
850Y	Brgm-5P	1075	3690	Note 1
850Y	Sed-5P	1125	3755	Note 1

Model 1250, 12-cyl., 160 hp, Salon Dual Ratio

Model No.	Body Type & Seating	Factory Price	Shipping Weight	Prod. Total
1250	Cabr-2/4P	1495	4570	Note 1
1250	Phae Sed-5P	1545	4710	Note 1
1250	Brgm-5P	1395	4715	Note 1
1250	Sed-5P	1445	4870	Note 1

Note 1: Auburn production for 1934 totaled 7,770 with no breakout available.

1935

Model 653, 6-cyl., 85 hp, Standard

Model No.	Body Type & Seating	Factory Price	Shipping Weight	Prod. Total
653	Cabr-2/4P	945	3180	Note 1
653	Phae Sed-5P	995	3250	Note 1
653	Cpe-2P	835	3105	Note 1
653	Brgm-5P	745	3215	Note 1
653	Sed-5P	795	3280	Note 1

Model 653, 6-cyl., 85 hp, Custom Dual Ratio

Model No.	Body Type & Seating	Factory Price	Shipping Weight	Prod. Total
653	Cabr-2/4P	1050	3280	Note 1
653	Phae Sed-5P	1100	3350	Note 1
653	Cpe-2P	940	3200	Note 1
653	Brgm-5P	850	3320	Note 1
653	Sed-5P	950	3390	Note 1

Model 653, 6-cyl., 85 hp, Salon Dual Ratio

Model No.	Body Type & Seating	Factory Price	Shipping Weight	Prod. Total
653	Cabr-2/4P	1100	3430	Note 1
653	Phae Sed-5P	1180	3500	Note 1
653	Cpe-2P	990	3370	Note 1
653	Brgm-5P	930	3470	Note 1
653	Sed-5P	980	3535	Note 1

Model 851, 8-cyl., 115 hp, Standard

Model No.	Body Type & Seating	Factory Price	Shipping Weight	Prod. Total
851	Cabr-2/4P	1225	3415	Note 1
851	Phae Sed-5P	1275	3565	Note 1
851	Cpe-2P	1085	3395	Note 1
851	Brgm-5P	995	3475	Note 1
851	Sed-5P	1095	3580	Note 1
851	Sed-7P	1595	3750	Note 1

Model 851, 8-cyl., 115 hp, Custom Dual Ratio

Model No.	Body Type & Seating	Factory Price	Shipping Weight	Prod. Total
851	Cabr-2/4P	1315	3510	Note 1
851	Phae Sed-5P	1370	3665	Note 1
851	Cpe-2P	1175	3495	Note 1
851	Brgm-5P	1090	3575	Note 1
851	Sed-5P	1190	3680	Note 1
851	Sed-7P	1690	3850	Note 1

Model 851, 8-cyl., 115 hp, Salon Dual Ratio

Model No.	Body Type & Seating	Factory Price	Shipping Weight	Prod. Total
851	Cabr-2/4P	1360	3640	Note 1
851	Phae Sed-5P	1450	3815	Note 1
851	Cpe-2P	1220	3645	Note 1
851	Brgm-5P	1170	3725	Note 1
851	Sed-5P	1270	3835	Note 1
851	Sed-7P	1770	4005	Note 1

Model 851, 8-cyl., 150 hp, Supercharged Dual Ratio

Model No.	Body Type & Seating	Factory Price	Shipping Weight	Prod. Total
851	Spds-2P	2245	3705	Note 1
851	Cabr-2/4P	1675	3635	Note 1
851	Phae Sed-5P	1725	3715	Note 1
851	Cpe-2P	1545	3565	Note 1
851	Brgm-5P	1445	3655	Note 1
851	Sed-5P	1545	3390	Note 1

Note 1: Auburn production for 1935 totaled 6,316 with no breakout available.

1936

Model 654, 6-cyl., 85 hp, Standard

Model No.	Body Type & Seating	Factory Price	Shipping Weight	Prod. Total
654	Cabr-2/4P	945	3180	Note 1
654	Phae Sed-5	995	3250	Note 1
654	Cpe-2P	835	3105	Note 1
654	Brgm-5P	745	3215	Note 1
654	Sed-5P	795	3280	Note 1

Model 654, 6-cyl., 85 hp, Custom Dual Ratio

Model No.	Body Type & Seating	Factory Price	Shipping Weight	Prod. Total
654	Cabr-2/4P	1050	3280	Note 1
654	Phae Sed-5P	1100	3350	Note 1
654	Cpe-2P	940	3200	Note 1
654	Brgm-5P	850	3320	Note 1
654	Sed-5P	900	3390	Note 1

Model 654, 6-cyl., 85 hp, Salon Dual Ratio

Model No.	Body Type & Seating	Factory Price	Shipping Weight	Prod. Total
654	Cabr-2/4P	1050	3430	Note 1
654	Phae Sed-5P	1100	3350	Note 1
654	Cpe-2P	940	3370	Note 1
654	Brgm-5P	850	3470	Note 1
654	Sed-5P	900	3535	Note 1

Model 852, 8-cyl., 115 hp, Standard

Model No.	Body Type & Seating	Factory Price	Shipping Weight	Prod. Total
852	Cabr-2/4P	1225	3415	Note 1
852	Phae Sed-5P	1275	3565	Note 1
852	Cpe-2P	1085	3395	Note 1
852	Brgm-5P	995	3475	Note 1
852	Sed-5P	1095	3580	Note 1
852	Sed-7P	1595	3750	Note 1

Model 852, 8-cyl., 115 hp, Custom Dual Ratio

Model No.	Body Type & Seating	Factory Price	Shipping Weight	Prod. Total
852	Cabr-2/4P	1315	3510	Note 1
852	Phae Sed-5P	1370	3665	Note 1
852	Cpe-2P	1175	3495	Note 1
852	Brgm-5P	1090	3575	Note 1
852	Sed-5P	1190	3680	Note 1
852	Sed-7P	1690	3850	Note 1

Model 852, 8-cyl., 115 hp, Salon Dual Ratio

Model No.	Body Type & Seating	Factory Price	Shipping Weight	Prod. Total
852	Cabr-2/4P	1360	3640	Note 1
852	Phae Sed-5P	1450	3815	Note 1
852	Cpe-2P	1220	3645	Note 1
852	Brgm-5P	1170	3725	Note 1
852	Sed-5P	1270	3835	Note 1
852	Sed-7P	1770	4005	Note 1

Model 852, 8-cyl., 150 hp, Supercharged Dual Ratio

Model No.	Body Type & Seating	Factory Price	Shipping Weight	Prod. Total
852	Spds-2P	2245	3705	Note 1
852	Cabr-2/4P	1675	3730	Note 1
852	Phae Sed-5P	1725	3880	Note 1
852	Cpe-2P	1545	3695	Note 1
852	Brgm-5P	1445	3810	Note 1
852	Sed-5P	1545	3915	Note 1
852	Sed-7P	2045	4090	Note 1

Note: This was the final year for Auburn automobile production, which totaled 1,263 with no breakout available.

This 1935 Auburn Salon Eight five-passenger sedan featured full wheel covers and "Unitype" body construction—welded steel mounted directly to the frame.

1935 Auburn, Model 6-653, Standard coupe, AA

1935 Auburn, Model 6-653, Standard sedan, AA

1935 Auburn, Model 8-851, Salon brougham, AA

1935 Auburn, Model 8-851, Standard sedan, AA

1936 Auburn, Model 6-654, Salon sedan, AA

1936 Auburn, Model 8-852, Super-Charged sedan, AA

CORD

CORD L-29 — Auburn & Connersville, Indiana — (1929-1932)/CORD 810-812 — (1936-1937) — There were two front-wheel-drive American motorcars announced in 1929, and they were produced by two of the most dynamic and colorful entrepreneurs in the American automobile industry at the time. Errett Lobban Cord managed to get his L-29 into the marketplace faster than Archie Andrews did his Ruxton, and initially this worked to Cord's advantage. The rationale for the car was certainly a viable one: Cord needed something to fill the price gap in his Cord Corporation between the popularly priced Auburn and the grand Model J Duesenberg he had just introduced — and, although the front-wheel-drive idea had languished in America since Walter Christie failed commercially before the First World War, it was now enjoying public attention because of its successful application in several race cars for the Indianapolis 500. Race car engineers Harry Miller and Cornelius Van Ranst, as well as Indy driver Leon Duray, would be advisers to the L-29 project. Auburn chief engineer Herb Snow would devise the industry's first X-frame bracing for the new Cord, this after E.L. Cord himself had driven the ladder-framed prototype over a plowed field behind his home in Auburn, and all the doors popped open. Fix it, he said. Powering the L-29 was a 298.6-cubic inch 125 hp L-head eight supplied by Lycoming (a company Cord owned), and the car was priced at $3,095 for sedan and brougham, $3,295 for cabriolet and phaeton. These were uncommonly lovely cars; indeed, many connoisseurs today consider the L-29 the best-looking American car of the period. Front-wheel-drive made for a much lower and more rakish silhouette than the norm, and the L-29 proved particularly attractive to master coachbuilders on both sides of the Atlantic. A blue coupe designed by Alexis de Sakhnoffsky took the prestigious Concours d'Elegance in Monaco by storm in 1930, this but one of dozens of "beauty contest" victories the car won throughout Europe. Two months after the introduction of the L-29, however, the crash on Wall Street effectively killed its chances for commercial success. Prices were lowered to the $2,395-$2,595 range for 1931, but it didn't help; for the 1932 model year the L-29 engine was bored out one-eighth inch for 322 cubic inches and 132 hp, which didn't help either. Interestingly, the total production run of the L-29 — 5,010 units — was almost precisely what Cord had scheduled for the car from the beginning. Five thousand L-29s had been the plan, with the car thereafter to be followed by the improved L-30. When the Depression saw to it that the L-30 would never happen, many of the changes committed for it (i.e., the larger engine) were incorporated into the last L-29s built. Production ceased December 31, 1931, the last 157 cars titled as 1932 models. And that, seemingly, was that. Four years later, however, the front-drive Cord was back, with modern "coffin nose" styling by Gordon Buehrig. Perhaps the single most instantly recognizable car in the history of the American automobile, the Cord 810 happened almost by accident. By this time E.L. Cord's automotive empire was faltering, and Cord himself was devoting considerably less time to it than to many of his other activities. But he recognized that the "specialty merchandise field" was where his automobile company belonged, and the 810 Cord was his last attempt to put it there. Originally designed as a "baby Duesenberg," the car became a Cord when front-wheel-drive was decided upon in order to make for a lower silhouette. And the decision was made quickly, with just 15 weeks to build enough cars for presentation at the November automobile shows. There was a Keystone Kops semblance to the entire operation, but the cars made it to the shows, where they received a rousing reception — and then the problems moved to the production line, where haste made further waste, and though the kinks were worked out as the cars were being built, it was not before unflattering rumors spread. The 810 of 1936 was powered by Lycoming's 125 hp V-8, which did not change for the 812 models in 1937, though a supercharger did become available, which boosted horsepower to 170. "Specialty merchandise" that it was, the $2,000-$3,000 price range for the cars was not the 810/812's undoing. Nor were the teething problems of the car, since most new cars had those. Errett Lobban Cord's exit from the automobile industry in 1937 was. On August 7th that year, after the production of not quite 3,000 810/812s, the assembly line stopped. Auburn production had already ceased. So had Duesenberg. The last car to come from the Cord empire, fittingly, was a Cord.

1930

Series L-29, 8-cyl., 125 hp, 137.5" wb

Model No.	Body Type & Seating	Factory Price	Shipping Weight	Prod. Total
—	Sed-5P	3095	4530	Note 1
—	Brgm-5P	3095	4500	Note 1
—	Cabr-2/4P	3295	4300	Note 1
—	Phae Sed	3295	4500	Note 1

Note 1: Cord production for 1930 totaled 1,873 with no breakout available. Production of Cord automobiles began midyear in 1929, but all cars were officially designated 1930 models for registration purposes.

1931

Series L-29, 8-cyl., 125 hp, 137.5" wb

Model No.	Body Type & Seating	Factory Price	Shipping Weight	Prod. Total
—	Sed-5P	2395	4530	Note 1
—	Brgm-5P	2395	4500	Note 1
—	Cabr-2/4P	2495	4300	Note 1
—	Phae Sed-5P	2595	4500	Note 1

Note 1: Cord production for 1931 totaled 1,243 with no breakout available.

1932

Series L-29, 8-cyl., 125 hp, 137.5" wb

Model No.	Body Type & Seating	Factory Price	Shipping Weight	Prod. Total
—	Sed-5P	2395	4560	Note 1
—	Brgm-5P	2395	4560	Note 1
—	Cabr-2/4P	2495	4300	Note 1
—	Phae Sed-5P	2595	4500	Note 1

Note 1: Cord production for 1932 totaled 58 with no breakout available.

(No Manufacturing of Cord automobiles took place in 1933-34-35)

1936

Model 810, 8-cyl., 125 hp, 125" wb

Model No.	Body Type & Seating	Factory Price	Shipping Weight	Prod. Total
810	Westchester Sed-5P	1995	3715	Note 1
810	Beverly Sed-4P	2095	3740	Note 1
810	Sportsman-2P	2145	3815	Note 1
810	Conv Phae Sed-5P	2195	3864	Note 1

Note 1: Cord production for 1936 totaled 1,764 with no breakout available.

1937

Model 812, 8-cyl., 125 hp, 125" wb

Model No.	Body Type & Seating	Factory Price	Shipping Weight	Prod. Total
812	Westchester Sed	2445	3715	Note 1
812	Sportsman-2P	2595	3835	Note 1
812	Conv Phae Sed-5P	2645	3900	Note 1
812	Beverly Sed-5P	2545	3740	Note 1
Model 812, 8-cyl., 125 hp, 132" wb				
812	Cus Beverly-5P	2960	4090	Note 1
812	Cus Berline-5P	3060	4115	Note 1
Model 812, supercharged 8-cyl., 170 hp, 125" wb				
812	Westchester Sed	2860	3895	Note 1
812	Sportsman-2P	3010	3950	Note 1
812	Conv Phae Sed-5P	3060	4005	Note 1
812	Beverly Sed-5P	2960	3925	Note 1
Model 812, supercharged 8-cyl., 170 hp, 132" wb				
812	Cus Beverly-5P	3375	4175	Note 1
812	Cus Berline-5P	3575	4190	Note 1

Note 1: 1937 was the final year for Cord production, which totaled 1,066 with no breakout available.

1930 Cord, L-29, sedan, AA

1930 Cord, L-29, cabriolet, AA

1930 Cord, L-29, brougham, AA

1930 Cord, L-29, cabriolet (Indianapolis 500 pace car with Cord sales manager Wade Morton at the wheel), AA

1930 Cord, L-29, convertible sedan, AA

1931 Cord, L-29, sedan, A-C-D

1932 Cord, L-29, convertible sedan, A-C-D

1936 Cord, 810, convertible coupe, AA

DUESENBERG

DUESENBERG — Indianapolis, Indiana — (1920-1937) — In the March 1903 issue of *Cycle and Automobile Trade Journal,* in the column titled "Injunctions, Lawsuits, Fires, Judgments, Failures, Etc.," it was revealed that one F.S. Duesenberg, a bicycle builder from Iowa, had filed a petition in bankruptcy, reporting assets of $1,075.50 and liabilities of $2,115.95. This little-known historic fact is insignificant, perhaps, but mentioned for a reason. If but one of all the automobiles ever built in America had to be singled out as the most glorious achievement in this country's automotive history, that car would have to be the Duesenberg. It transcended the ordinary in full measure, created legends in its wake, which will live forever, and became a literal metaphor — "It's a Duesy" — for anything unrelentingly superlative. And yet, just as the man who built it might fail insignificantly in his career, the Duesenberg had its insignificant failings, too. But they scarcely mattered in the overall scheme of what the Duesenberg was. Following the bankruptcy of his bicycle business, Fred Duesenberg remained in Iowa where the first car he designed and raced was the Mason. By 1913, in partnership with his brother Augie, he relocated in St. Paul, Minnesota, where the Duesenberg Motor Company was organized and where manufacture of auto and marine engines was commenced. The horizontal-valve rocker-arm (or "walking-beam") engine he had designed for the Mason race cars was continued in competition cars that bore the Duesenberg name from 1914. Their success was wonderful; Ralph Mulford and Eddie Rickenbacker drove Duesenbergs to commanding victories on Midwest board tracks. Eddie O'Donnell largely saw to the car's triumphs on the West Coast. The Duesenberg name became famous, and investment capital in the brothers' activities came easier. It is significant that the Duesenbergs never owned but instead were merely employees in their various enterprises. Duesenberg Motors Corporation, a $1.5 million venture, was organized in 1916 by New York capitalists, with construction of a huge factory in Elizabeth, New Jersey, following. The war on, and racing largely over for the duration, the Duesenbergs undertook production there of aero engines (and some artillery tractor units) under government contract. The war over, the brothers found themselves with a big factory and nothing commercially significant to manufacture, except their four-cylinder auto engine for a number of new budding automotive manufacturers who had asked for it. This prospect didn't tantalize, since the Duesenbergs by now believed the four passé and were anxious to move into eight-cylinder development. The New York capitalists behind the Duesenbergs seemed unenthused. Consequently, the rights to the Duesenberg four were sold to Rochester Motors Company, Inc. (which ultimately marketed developed versions to Biddle, Roamer, ReVere, Richelieu, Meteor, Kenworthy, and Argonne). Duesenberg Motors Corporation and the Elizabeth plant were acquired by Willys. This left the brothers free to continue development in nearby Newark on the single-overhead-camshaft, inline eight-cylinder racing engine the development of which they had begun about the time of the Armistice. Interestingly, the prototype of the Duesenberg Model A passenger car that was introduced at the Hotel Commodore in November 1920 was fitted with a horizontal-valve, rocker-arm straight-eight, though even by the time it appeared, Fred Duesenberg had decided that production cars would use the overhead camshaft design. Hydraulic four-wheel brakes — a first for America — had been fitted to the prototype, however. By now the Duesenbergs were part of a new $1.5 million company in Indianapolis: the Duesenberg Automobile and Motors Corporation. The new Model A created a sensation at its debut. Unfortunately, two problems ensued: first, Fred Duesenberg's decision to switch to the ohc design for production meant initially delayed deliveries (indeed, it would be the 1922 model year before the car was available); second, the people who were backing the venture, though businessmen of standing, had scant experience in managing an automobile company. (The Duesenbergs themselves had always been pretty much lackluster in administrative matters.) The Indiana venture was reorganized as Duesenberg Motors Company in 1925, but fared little better. More than 600 Model As were built in five years, but not profitably, and the car has since been practically forgotten, or consigned to bridesmaid's status to the later Model J. The Model A Duesenberg is that rarity: a great car that still remains overlooked. Impossible to overlook during the period it was produced, however, was the phenomenal success the brothers enjoyed in competition. There were two great names in American racing during the Twenties: one was Duesenberg, the other was Miller. Meanwhile, one day in 1926, Auburn President Errett Lobban Cord strode into Duesenberg history, acquired the company (subsequently renamed Duesenberg, Inc.) and instructed Fred Duesenberg to build a super car that could stand alongside — and hopefully surpass — the world's most magnificent automobiles. That took time, of course, and in the interim the Model X — which had been a shoestring attempt by Fred Duesenberg to revamp the Model A — was produced during 1927. Only about a dozen cars were built, the number for which parts had been on hand at the time Cord bought the Duesenberg company. On December 1, 1928, at the New York Automobile Salon, the mighty Model J moved center stage in Duesenberg history. It was big, it was fast, it was gorgeous, it was expensive. How big and how fast has since become a subject of conjecture. Its race-inspired engine (twin overhead camshafts operating four valves per cylinder) was said to develop 265 hp, which it probably did on the dynamometer though doubtless not in the heroically-sized (142-1/2 and 153-1/2 wheelbase inches) car itself. Still, whatever the figure, it was perhaps twice that of any other American car on the road. Likewise, the speed of 116 mph in high that was achieved in tests at Indianapolis Motor Speedway was probably not approached by those production cars that tipped the scales at 5,000 pounds. But what did it matter; the Duesenberg was still king of the American road. "He drives a Duesenberg" was the only copy in many company advertisements. Owning a Duesenberg was an expensive proposition, of course. The chassis price was $8,500 (about $2,000 more than the price tag of a Model A with open car coachwork), and although the epic length and low stance of the Duesenberg chassis made it a favorite among coachbuilders on both sides of the Atlantic for special one-off efforts, the Duesenberg company itself preferred selling its own car complete, either with the superb in-house bodies designed by Gordon Buehrig or the limited series productions of approved coachbuilders. Tragically, in July 1932, Fred Duesenberg died following an automobile accident. Already he had designed the centrifugal supercharger that boosted horsepower of the J to 320 and with the later ram's horn — developed by brother Augie who took over as chief engineer — to perhaps almost 400. A supercharged J convertible coupe was purportedly tested at the Indy Speedway at 129 mph, and in 1935 Ab Jenkins sped 152.1 mph in an hour and averaged 135.5 for 24 hours at Bonneville, Utah, in the supercharged Duesenberg Special. But by now the end was near for the Duesenberg. About 500 cars for the first production run had been the figure agreed upon by E.L. Cord and Fred Duesenberg at the outset, with no parameters regarding the timespan in which they would be built. Certainly neither of them foresaw the stock market crash at that time, and obviously its aftermath affected the Duesenberg's fortunes as it did everything else. By the end of 1931, approximately 360 cars had been produced. From May of 1932 through October of 1935, about 36 supercharged Js were built. There were 10 JNs (by Rollston, distinguished by wider, dropped bodies and deeper doors than the Duesenberg norm), and two SSJs (not an official designation, but an apt one to describe the pair of supercharged Js built on a shortened 125-inch wheelbase chassis, one for Clark Gable, the other for Gary Cooper). The approximate total Duesenberg J production was 480 cars. Of these, probably more were delivered to people with famous (sometimes infamous) names than a likewise percentage of any other American manufacturer's production. The Duesenberg was more than a status symbol; it was status pure and simple, whether the owner was a maharajah, movie star, politician, robber baron, gangster or evangelist. In 1937, the Duesenberg was no more, discontinued with the Auburn and Cord following E.L. Cord's sale of his corporation. Probably few would cavil that the Duesenberg is the single most sought after car in America today.

1922

Model A, 8-cyl., 88 hp, 134" wb

Model No.	Body Type & Seating	Factory Price	Shipping Weight	Prod. Total
A	Tr-4P	6500	N/A	N/A
A	Tr-5P	6500	N/A	N/A
A	Rds-2/4P	6500	N/A	N/A
A	Tr-7P	6750	N/A	N/A
A	Sed Limo-7P	7800	N/A	N/A
A	4-dr Special Cpe-4P	7800	N/A	N/A
A	Twn Brgm-5P	8800	N/A	N/A

1923

Model A, 8-cyl., 88 hp, 134" wb

Model No.	Body Type & Seating	Factory Price	Shipping Weight	Prod. Total
A	Spt Tr-4P	5750	N/A	N/A
A	Tr-5P	5500	N/A	N/A
A	Rds-2P	5750	N/A	N/A
A	Tr-7P	5900	N/A	N/A
A	Sed Limo-7P	7500	N/A	N/A
A	4-dr Cpe-4P	7250	N/A	N/A
A	Twn Brgm-5P	7800	N/A	N/A
A	Dlx Limo-7P	7500	N/A	N/A

1924

Model A, 8-cyl., 88 hp, 134" wb

Model No.	Body Type & Seating	Factory Price	Shipping Weight	Prod. Total
A	Phae-5P	6250	N/A	N/A
A	Phae-7P	6750	N/A	N/A
A	Rds-2P	6500	N/A	N/A
A	4-dr Cpe-4P	7500	N/A	N/A
A	Spt Phae-4P	6500	N/A	N/A
A	Twn Brgm-5P	7800	N/A	N/A

Model A, 8-cyl., 88 hp, 141" wb

A	Imperial Sed-7P	7800	N/A	N/A
A	Dlx Limo-7P	7800	N/A	N/A

1925

Model A, 8-cyl., 88 hp, 134" wb

Model No.	Body Type & Seating	Factory Price	Shipping Weight	Prod. Total
A	Phae-5P	6500	N/A	Note
A	Rds-2P	6850	3640	Note
A	Rds-2/4P	N/A	N/A	Note
A	Spt Phae-4P	6850	3700	Note
A	Phae-7P	6850	3985	Note
A	Twn Brgm-5P	N/A	4245	Note
A	Sed-5P	7700	N/A	Note

Model A, 8-cyl., 88 hp, 141" wb

A	Sed Limo-7P	8300	4350	Note

Note: Duesenberg production for 1925 totaled 129 with no breakdown available.

1926

Model A, 8-cyl., 88 hp, 134" wb

Model No.	Body Type & Seating	Factory Price	Shipping Weight	Prod. Total
A	Rds-2P	6850	3920	N/A
A	Rds-2/4P	6850	3970	N/A
A	Tr-5P	6650	4000	N/A
A	Spt Tr-4P	6850	4045	N/A
A	Sed-5P	7700	N/A	N/A

Model A, 8-cyl., 88 hp, 141" wb

A	Sed-7P	8300	N/A	N/A
A	Tr-7P	6850	N/A	N/A

1927

Model A, 8-cyl., 88 hp, 134" wb

Model No.	Body Type & Seating	Factory Price	Shipping Weight	Prod. Total
A	Rds-2P	6850	3920	N/A
A	Rds-2/4P	6850	3970	N/A
A	Tr-5P	6650	4000	N/A
A	Spt Tr-4P	6850	4045	N/A
A	Sed-5P	7700	N/A	N/A

Model A, 8-cyl., 88 hp, 141" wb

A	Sed-7P	8300	N/A	N/A
A	Tr-7P	6850	N/A	N/A

Priced at around $6,500, this custom-bodied 1924 Duesenberg roadster was one of the fastest automobiles on the road in its time.

1927

Model X, 8-cyl., 100 hp, 135" & 141" wb (see accompanying list)

1929-1937

Model J, 8-cyl., 265 hp, 142-1/2" & 153-1/2" wb (see accompanying list)

All of the following automobiles were custom built. Chassis price at introduction was $8,500, later increased to $9,500.

Phaeton
All-Weather Cabriolet
Enclosed Drive Sedan
Sedan-5P
Convertible Sedan
Convertible Roadster
Tourster
Convertible Berline
Convertible Victoria
Convertible Roadster
Beverly
Limousine
Prince of Wales Sedan
Coupe
Town Limousine
Town Car
Town Sedan
Coupe-4P
Convertible Phaeton
Town Limousine
Arlington
All-Weather Landau
Formal Town Car

Body Styles By Coachbuilder

LeBaron Double Cowl Phaeton (sweep panel)—1929-1930.
LeGrande Double Cowl Phaeton (sweep panel)—1930-1934.
Murphy Convertible Coupe—1929-1932
Murphy Convertible Sedan—1929-1932
Murphy Clear Vision Sedan—1929-1932
Murphy Beverly Sedan—1930-1932
Murphy Double Cowl Phaeton—1930-1931
Murphy Boattail (Torpedo) Convertible Coupe—1930-1932.
Derham Five-Passenger Sedan (Arlington)—1929-1932
Holbrook Five-Passenger Sedan—1929-1930
Weymann Five-Passenger Sedan—1930-1931
Holbrook Town Car—1929-1930
Murphy Town Car—1930-1932
Rollston Town Car—1930-1934
Willoughby Limousine—1930-1934
Willoughby Berline—1930-1934
Judkins Limousine—1930-1934
Derham Tourster—1930-1934
Rollston Convertible Coupe (JN)—1933-1936
Rollston Convertible Sedan (JN)—1933-1936
Rollston Sport Sedan (JN)—1933-1936
LaGrande Torpedo Phaeton—1934-1936
LaGrande Convertible Coupe—1934-1936
LaGrande Convertible Berline—1930-1933
Rollston Convertible Victoria—1930-1933

1922 Duesenberg, Model A, roadster, FR

1923 Duesenberg, Model A, town car, FR

1924 Duesenberg, Model A, roadster, JAC

1925 Duesenberg, Model A, touring, JAC

1927 Duesenberg, Model X, Locke dual cowl phaeton, AA

1929 Duesenberg, Model J, Willoughby four-window sedan-limousine, AA

1929 Duesenberg, Model J, Weymann St. Cloud sport sedan, OCW

1929 Duesenberg, Model J, Derham "cabriolet" town car, AA

1930 Duesenberg, Model J, LeBaron dual-cowl "barrel side" phaeton, AA

1931 Duesenberg, Model J, Rollston limousine (with luggage roof rack), OCW

1931 Duesenberg, Model J, Murphy Beverly semi-formal berline, AA

1931 Duesenberg, Model J, Franay long wheelbase town car, AA

1932 Duesenberg, Model SJ, Fernandez & Darrin convertible victoria, AA

1933 Duesenberg, Model SJ, Rollston "Twenty Grand" torpedo sedan, JAC

1934 Duesenberg, Model SJ, Murphy town car, JAC

1935 Duesenberg, Model J, D'leteren Freres convertible coupe, LIAM

1935 Duesenberg, Model SSJ, La Grande sports roadster, BCAM

1935 Duesenberg, Model SJ, Bohman & Schwartz convertible coupe, FR

1936 Duesenberg, Model SJ, Rollston convertible sedan, AA

1936 Duesenberg, Model SJ, Rollston convertible sedan, AA

CHECKER 1960-1982

Checker Motors Corp. can be traced back to the DeSchaum Automobile Co. of Buffalo, N.Y., which began building automobiles in 1908. Later, in 1910, DeSchaum became the Suburban Motor Car Co. of Detroit, Mich. In turn, Suburban evolved into the Partin Manufacturing Co. and finally the Checker Cab Manufacturing Co. was founded in 1923. This company absorbed the factories of Dort and Handley-Knight in Kalamazoo, Mich. Checker was engaged, exclusively, in the building of taxicabs from 1923 until 1959. Then it launched a line of modified taxicabs for passenger car use. At one period the firm was a part of the automobile empire put together by E.L. Cord.

By G. Marshall Naul

The company name was changed to Checker Motors Corp. in 1958. The business of manufacturing passenger cars was conducted on a modest scale, at least by Detroit standards, until the early 1980s.

However, the manufacture of Checker taxis and passenger cars continually declined from its high point of production, in 1962. Finally, Checker was forced to announce that it would cease building passenger cars in July 1982.

The Checker passenger cars, which were first offered to the public late in 1959, were based on the Model A8 taxi, which appeared as early as 1956. With only a few exterior changes, the four-door sedan remained essentially unchanged from 1960 to 1982.

Small modifications were made to provide a station wagon. Later, in 1963, a stretched version of the sedan provided the chassis for an eight-passenger Custom Limousine and Deluxe Sedan.

The major changes in Checkers over the years 1960-1975 have been in the powerplants used. Checker passenger car engine applications began with an 80-hp L-head six. Gradually, the marque switched to V-8s. Overhead valves appeared by the 1970s. Continental engines were originally used for the early six and a later overhead valve version of the L-head. In 1964, Chevrolet Motor Division became the source for Checker engines, with both overhead valve sixes and V-8s being available. In the period 1963-1964, a number of Checker cars were provided with Chrysler V-8 engines.

The Checker never claimed to be the vision or victim of automotive stylists, but rather, maintained a reputation as a utilitarian vehicle with a reputation for longevity, endurance and a lack of obsolescence. This is evidenced in Checker's resistance to yearly appearance changes. Gradual improvements were made, though.

The fact that the basic design was offered for 22 years and grew old-fashioned can't be denied. If the company had adopted a Ghia-designed Checker prototype of 1970, it's likely the nameplate would have remained around for some time.

1960

SUPERBA STANDARD/SPECIAL—(6-CYL) — SERIES A10 — The Superba was based on the Checker taxicab, Model A8 of 1956, with the dual headlamps of the 1959 Model A9 included. The Special series had extra trim and script on the side and an upgraded interior. The four-door station wagon used a dash panel controlled switch to lower the rear seat, a feature that was unique to Checker. The L-head six-cylinder engine, which had been a mainstay with Checker cabs, was essentially the same obsolescent design that had been used in Kaisers and Frazers a decade earlier. It was built by Continental Motors Co. For station wagon attachments, the engine builder converted this engine to a six with pushrod-operated overhead valves. This gave slightly more power to move around the 370 pound heavier wagons.

CHECKER I.D. NUMBERS: Serial numbers and engine numbers were found on the upper firewall. Serial and engine codes had three parts. The first identified the model; the second part the production order and the third part the chassis or serial numbers. Serial numbers for 1960 were 37396 and up. Although true style numbers were not used, the first part of the serial number served this purpose and a 'W' was added to identify station wagons.

SUPERBA STANDARD/SPECIAL SERIES

Model No.	Body/Style No.	Body Type & Seating	Factory Price	Shipping Weight	Prod. Total
STANDARD LINE					
A10	A10	4-dr Sed-6P	2542	3410	Note 1
A10	WA10	4-dr Sta Wag-6P	2896	3780	Note 1
SPECIAL LINE					
A10	A10	4-dr Sed-6P	2650	3410	Note 1
A10	WA10	4-dr Sta Wag-6P	3004	3780	Note 1

Note 1: Production total for all models combined is estimated at 1,050.

SEDAN ENGINE: Inline. L-head Six. Cast iron block. Displacement: 226 cid. Bore and stroke: 3-5/16 x 4-3/8 inches. Compression ratio: 7.3:1. Brake hp: 80 at 3100 rpm. Four main bearings. Solid valve lifters. Carburetor: Carter Type AS one-barrel Model 2858S.

STATION WAGON ENGINE: Inline. Six. Overhead valve. Cast iron block. Displacement: 226 cid. Bore and stroke: 3-5/16 x 4-3/8 inches. Compression ratio: 8.0:1. Brake hp: 122 at 4400 rpm. Four main bearings. Solid valve lifters. Carburetor: Carter Type AS one-barrel Model 2858S.

CHASSIS FEATURES: Wheelbase: 120 inches. Overall length: 199.5 inches. Front tread: 60 inches. Rear tread: 62-1/2 inches. Overall width: 76 inches. Tires: 6.70 x 15.

OPTIONS: Power steering ($64). Power brakes ($33). Air conditioning ($411). Overdrive ($108). Overhead valve engine ($57). Single range automatic transmission ($222). Dual-range automatic transmission ($248).

HISTORICAL FOOTNOTES: This was the first year Checkers were sold in the private car market. The firm's contribution was small and was not recorded in regular industry publications such as *Ward's Automobile Yearbook*. In fact, the 1961 edition of *Ward's* did not even list Checker output under its catch-all category, "Others." The company's plant was in Kalamazoo, Mich.

1961

CHECKER SUPERBA — (6-CYL) — SERIES A10 — In 1960, Checker Motors Corp.'s total output was 6,980 cars, of which an estimated 1,050 went to private buyers. The balance were sold to the taxicab trade. Production for the private sector was considered sufficient to continue marketing cars for this purpose in 1961. The Superba Special was renamed the Marathon and considered a separate series. The standard Superba was the base line this year. The main styling difference between the two was in the placement of front parking lamps. The standard Superba had them mounted on a panel housed within the outboard vertical division of the cross-hatched grille insert. Dual headlamps were used on both cars. The sedan was fitted with 14-inch tires to make it ride lower. Standard equipment included full instrumentation, padded interior and an extra large rear seating compartment with a flat floor and folding jump seats.

CHECKER I.D. NUMBERS: Serial numbers and engine numbers were found on the upper firewall. Serial and engine codes had three parts. The first identified the model; the second part the production order; and the third part the chassis or serial numbers. Serial numbers for 1961 were determined by the year appearing on the registration for each car. Numbers for 1961 began in September 1960. Style numbers were changed as indicated on charts below.

CHECKER SUPERBA SERIES

Model No.	Body/Style No.	Body Type & Seating	Factory Price	Shipping Weight	Prod. Total
A10	W/10L	4-dr Sed-6P	2542	3410	Note 1
A10	W/A10	4-dr Sta Wag-6P	2896	3670	Note 1

Note 1: A total of 5,683 Checkers were built this year including taxicabs. Of this total, an estimated 860 were private passenger cars or station wagons. This estimate includes both Superbas and Marathons.

CHECKER MARATHON — (6-CYL) — SERIES A10 — The Marathon had the parking lamps outside the grille, below the headlights, and a strip of chrome on the front fenders and doors. A few small extras were included as standard equipment.

CHECKER MARATHON SERIES

Model No.	Body/Style No.	Body Type & Seating	Factory Price	Shipping Weight	Prod. Total
A10	W/10L	4-dr Sed-6P	2650	3410	Note 1
A10	W/A10	4-dr Sta Wag-6P	3004	3720	Note 1

Note 1: A total of 5,683 Checkers were built this year including taxicabs. Of this total, an estimated 860 were private passenger cars or station wagons. This estimate includes both Superbas and Marathons.

SEDAN ENGINE: Inline. L-head Six. Cast iron block. Displacement: 226 cid. Bore and stroke: 3-5/16 x 4-3/8 inches. Compression ratio: 7.3:1. Brake hp: 80 at 3100 rpm. Four main bearings. Solid valve lifters. Carburetor: Carter Type AS one-barrel Model 2858S.

STATION WAGON ENGINE: Inline. Six. Overhead valve. Cast iron block. Displacement: 226 cid. Bore and stroke: 3-5/16 x 4-3/8 inches. Compression ratio: 8.0:1. Brake hp: 122 at 4000 rpm. Four main bearings. Solid valve lifters. Carburetor: Carter Type AS one-barrel Model 2858S.

CHASSIS FEATURES: Wheelbase: 120 inches. Overall length: 199.5 inches. Front tread: 60 inches. Rear tread: 62-1/2 inches. Overall width: 76 inches. Tires: (sedans) 6.70 x 14; (station wagons) 6.70 x 15.

OPTIONS: Power steering ($64). Air conditioning ($411). Power brakes ($33). Single range automatic transmission ($222). Dual range automatic transmission ($248). Overdrive ($108). Overhead valve W/A10 engine ($57).

HISTORICAL FOOTNOTES: Kalamazoo, Mich.'s, largest automaker remained rather obscure this year. In fact, a special 1961 statistical issue of *Automotive News* ran a list of all known automakers past and present. Marathon Motor Works (of Cincinnati, circa 1912) was on it, but the builder of the 1961 Marathon was not. The same publication did, however, have both monthly and yearly production totals for 1960 Checkers, plus a short publicity release of the current models. The car in the press photo had a two-tone finish.

1962

CHECKER SUPERBA — (6-CYL) — SERIES A10 — Checkers were like Volkswagens in one regard; they weren't compacts, but they didn't change much from year to year. Therefore, the 1962 models were nearly identical to the previous cars in all regards, right down to price. There may have been a number of small detail changes, but the only one that is easily documented was a switch to a Zenith one-barrel carburetor in place of the former Carter type. Even this had no effect as far as the horsepower rating went. Also, the station wagon became an eight-passenger model.

CHECKER I.D. NUMBERS: Serial numbers and engine numbers were found on the upper firewall. Serial and engine codes had three parts. The first identified the model; the second part the production order and the third part the chassis or serial numbers. Serial numbers for 1962 were determined by the year appearing on the registration for each car. Numbers for 1962 began in September 1961. Style number changes are reflected on charts below.

CHECKER SUPERBA SERIES

Model No.	Body/Style No.	Body Type & Seating	Factory Price	Shipping Weight	Prod. Total
A10	W/10L	4-dr Sed-6P	2542	3410	Note 1
A10	W/A10	4-dr Sta Wag-8P	2896	3670	Note 1

Note 1: A total of 8,173 Checkers were built this year including taxicabs. Of this total, an estimated 1,230 were non-taxicabs, including all series models.

CHECKER MARATHON — (6-CYL) — SERIES A10 — The 1962 Marathon changed about as much as the new Superba, which is to say very little. And the variations between the two cars were the same as the previous season, mainly different grille treatments and the chrome side spear used to embellish the front fenders and both doors of Marathons.

CHECKER MARATHON SERIES

Model No.	Body/Style No.	Body Type & Seating	Factory Price	Shipping Weight	Prod. Total
A10	W/10L	4-dr Sed-6P	2650	3410	Note 1
A10	W/A10	4-dr Sta Wag-8P	3004	3720	Note 1

Note 1: A total of 8,173 Checkers were built this year including taxicabs. Of this total, an estimated 1,230 were non-taxicabs, including all series models.

SEDAN ENGINE: Inline. L-head Six. Cast iron block. Displacement: 226 cid. Bore and stroke: 3-5/16 x 4-3/8 inches. Compression ratio: 7.3:1. Brake hp: 80 at 3100 rpm. Four main bearings. Solid valve lifters. Carburetor: Zenith 0-12469 one-barrel.

STATION WAGON ENGINE: Inline. Six. Overhead valve. Cast iron block. Displacement: 226 cid. Bore and stroke: 3-5/16 x 4-3/8 inches. Compression ratio: 8.0:1. Brake hp: 122 at 4000 rpm. Four main bearings. Solid valve lifters. Carburetor: Zenith 0-12469 one-barrel.

CHASSIS FEATURES: Wheelbase: 120 inches. Overall length: 199.5 inches. Front tread: 60 inches. Rear tread: 62-1/2 inches. Overall width: 76 inches. Tires: (sedans) 6.70 x 14; (station wagons) 6.70 x 15.

OPTIONS: Power steering ($64). Air conditioning ($411). Power brakes ($33). Single range automatic transmission ($222). Dual range automatic transmission ($248). Overdrive ($108). Overhead valve W/A10 engine ($57).

HISTORICAL FOOTNOTES: Checker Motors Corp. had a good year, with sales climbing 1,500 units. This inspired the company to plan some "big" changes in 1963. A Town Limousine with eight-passenger seating was developed and a new front bumper was redesigned. It should be noted that Checker did not adhere to annual model year alterations. New features and models were introduced as a running production change and, therefore, some standard reference sources date the above changes to 1962, since they came in that particular calendar year.

1963

CHECKER SUPERBA — (6-CYL) — SERIES A12 — Instead of a straight across, wraparound bumper with two vertical guards placed in front of the Superba parking lights, 1963 models had a more sculptured wraparound bumper with a dip in the center and no bumper guards. The parking lamps remained mounted inside the grille on panels that filled the space between the grille surround and the outboard vertical dividers. As in the past, this gave the appearance of the Superba having a narrower grille with only four vertical segments compared to six on the Marathon. Dual headlamps continued on both lines. A new Rochester two-barrel carburetor was supplied in those Checkers with overhead valve Continental engines. Two engines continued to be offered, the basis for attachment being changed. The 80-hp L-head six was now standard in all models; the overhead valve six, with its new 141-hp rating, was optional in all Checkers at $57 extra. Three-speed manual transmission was standard with both powerplants. Overdrive was optionally available. A single range automatic transmission could be ordered with the L-head Six. Dual-range Hydra-Matic was optional with the 141-hp two-barrel six. A padded dashboard, heater and defroster and heavy-duty battery were standard equipment with the more powerful drivetrain. As in the past, the sedan came with a flat rear floor and folding jump seats.

CHECKER I.D. NUMBERS: Serial numbers and engine numbers were found on the upper firewall. Serial and engine codes had three parts. The first identified the model; the second part the production order and the third part the chassis or serial numbers. Serial numbers for 1963 were determined by the year appearing on the registration for each car. Numbers for 1963 began in September 1962. The series number was changed to A12 for conventional models and A19E for the long wheelbase limousine. The 'E' may have indicated 'Extended Wheelbase'.

CHECKER SUPERBA SERIES

Model No.	Body/Style No.	Body Type & Seating	Factory Price	Shipping Weight	Prod. Total
A12	A12	4-dr Sed-6P	2642	3485	Note 1
A12	A12W	4-dr Sta Wag-8P	2991	3625	Note 1

Note 1: A total of 7,050 Checkers were built this year including taxicabs. Of this total, an estimated 1,080 were not taxicabs.

CHECKER MARATHON — (6-CYL) — SERIES A12 — The Marathon continued with its wide grille look, the rectangular parking lamps being placed in a horizontal plane midway between the dual headlamps and the horizontally grooved outer grille extensions. The new bumper, with a dip in the center and no guards, was seen. A straight chrome molding ran across the fender sides, above the front wheel opening, and continued back over the doors. Above this molding on the front fenders was wording that read "Checker" in underlined block letters and, on a lower level, "Marathon" in script. Small, black rubber gravel guards were placed ahead of the front wheel openings. Jump seats were used in the sedan and the station wagon continued as an eight-passenger rated model. Rear decorative treatments included a bumper that looked identical to the front unit. The taillamp treatment consisted of a protruding oblong red lens placed above a round white lens, both of which were set upon a vertically positioned oblong chrome plate. This, then, was mounted on a vertical, paddle-shaped panel that ran from the top of the fender to the bottom.

CHECKER MARATHON SERIES

Model No.	Body/Style No.	Body Type & Seating	Factory Price	Shipping Weight	Prod. Total
A12	A12	4-dr Sed-6P	2793	3485	Note 1
A12	A12W	4-dr Sta Wag-8P	3140	3625	Note 1

Note 1: A total of 7,050 Checkers were built this year including taxicabs. Of this total, an estimated 1,080 were not taxicabs.

CHECKER MARATHON TOWN CUSTOM — (6-CYL) — SERIES A19E — The new Town Custom Limousine was on a long 129-inch wheelbase. It had the Marathon grille and trim treatment. Photos of this model seem to indicate the use of extra chrome outside window frame moldings. Two folding jump seats were standard equipment. A glass driver's partition and power-operated accessories were featured. For a Checker product, the price was high and the production is believed to have been extremely low. The car did have a certain market niche, however, since many limousine buyers of this era were dissatisfied with the low styling contemporary to other early 1960s cars.

CHECKER MARATHON TOWN CUSTOM

Model No.	Body/Style No.	Body Type & Seating	Factory Price	Shipping Weight	Prod. Total
A19E	A19E	4-dr Limo-8P	4638	3525	Note 1

Note 1: A total of 7,050 Checkers were built this year including taxicabs. Of this total, an estimated 1,080 were not taxicabs.

BASE ENGINE: Inline. L-head Six. Cast iron block. Displacement: 226 cid. Bore and stroke: 3-5/16 x 4-3/8 inches. Compression ratio: 7.3:1. Brake hp: 80 at 3100 rpm. Four main bearings. Solid valve lifters. Carburetor: Zenith 0-12469 one-barrel.

OPTIONAL ENGINE: Inline. Six. Overhead valve. Cast iron block. Displacement: 226 cid. Bore and stroke: 3-5/16 x 4-3/8 inches. Compression ratio: 8.0:1. Brake hp: 141 at 4400 rpm. Four main bearings. Solid valve lifters. Carburetor: Rochester two-barrel Model 7023096.

CHASSIS FEATURES: Wheelbase: (Limousine) 129 inches; (other models) 120 inches. Overall length: (Limousine) 208 inches; (other models) 199.3 inches. Front tread: 60 inches. Rear tread: 62-1/2 inches. Tires: (Limousine) N/A; (sedan) 6.70 x 15; (station wagon) 7.10 x 15.

OPTIONS: Power brakes ($33). Power steering ($64). Air conditioning ($382). Whitewall tires. Full wheel discs. Padded dash. Heater and defroster. Heavy-duty battery. Single range automatic transmission ($222). Dual range automatic transmission ($248). Overdrive transmission ($108). Overhead valve engine in sedan ($57).

HISTORICAL FOOTNOTES: Last year for six-cylinder engines only. The November 1962 edition of *Motor Trend* magazine carried an article on page 57 about the 1963 Checker line.

1964

CHECKER MARATHON — (6-CYL) — SERIES A12 — The Superba name was dead for 1964 — or was it? There is no disputing the fact that the only standard wheelbase Checker left was the Marathon, but according to at least one source the L-head engine was still referred to as the "Superba Six." This engine was the base powerplant in both the Marathon sedan and station wagon. Styling and equipment features reflected no changes over 1963. Jump seats still came in the sedan, even though it was rated for only six passengers. The station wagon came with three seats for eight place seating. Prices for both cars were 'adjusted' in stages. The sedan was introduced at the same price as 1963, then later increased by $21. The station wagon also started the year with carryover retail prices, then jumped $20. Identification features included the high, front-side molding and a twin-level Checker/Marathon nameplate on the fender, aside the cowl.

CHECKER I.D. NUMBERS: Serial numbers and engine numbers were found on the upper firewall. Serial and engine codes had three parts. The first identified the model; the second part the production order and the third part the chassis or serial numbers. Serial numbers for 1964 were determined by the year appearing on the registration for each car. Numbers for 1964 began in September 1963. The Series number was changed to A12 for conventional models and A19E for the long wheelbase limousine. The 'E' may have indicated 'Extended Wheelbase'. An interesting fact was that for the 1965 model year (beginning September 1964) all new Checkers or 1964 models left in stock with serial numbers higher than 20,000 were made 1965 models.

CHECKER MARATHON SERIES

Model No.	Body/Style No.	Body Type & Seating	Factory Price	Shipping Weight	Prod. Total
A12	A12	4-dr Sed-6P	2793	3485	Note 1
A12	A12W	4-dr Sta Wag-8P	3140	3625	Note 1

Note 1: A total of 6,310 Checkers were built this year including taxicabs. Of this total, an estimated 960 were not taxicabs.

Note 2: Factory retail prices of $2,814 for the sedan and $3,160 for the station wagon seem to have gone into effect in midyear. Cars with overhead valve attachments (optional) were approximately 95 pounds heavier than base models listed above.

CHECKER MARATHON TOWN CUSTOM — (6-CYL) — SUB-SERIES A12E — The Town Limousine was again available on the extended, 129-inch wheelbase Checker chassis. Styling and equipment features paralleled those of the previous season. A front fender script, attached above the horizontal molding, identified the model. A glass driver's partition and several standard options were included. While specifics are not available, collectors will have no problem spotting one of these extra-long cars. And, if the serial number is under 20,000, it can be pinpointed as a 1963 or 1964 edition.

CHECKER MARATHON TOWN CUSTOM

Model No.	Body/Style No.	Body Type & Seating	Factory Price	Shipping Weight	Prod. Total
A12	A12E	4-dr Limo-8P	4638	3525	Note 1

Note 1: A total of 6,310 Checkers were built this year including taxicabs. Of this total, an estimated 960 were not taxicabs.

SUPERBA SIX ENGINE: Inline. L-head Six. Cast iron block. Displacement: 226 cid. Bore and stroke: 3.31 x 4.38 inches. Compression ratio: 7.3:1. Brake hp: 80 at 3100 rpm. Four main bearings. Solid valve lifters. Carburetor: Zenith Type 'O' one-barrel Model 12469. Engine manufactured by Continental Motors Corp., Muskegon, Mich. Exhaust valve diameter: 1.328 inches. Intake valve diameter: 1.515 inches. Chrome piston rings with 0.0020 inch skirt clearance. Durex 100 bearings with babbitt overlay. Exhaust pipe: two inch diameter. Tailpipe: 1.74 inch diameter. Electrical system: 12-volt negative ground. Spark setting: four degrees Before Top Dead Center. Fuel pump pressure: 3 psi. Spark plugs: Champion 18mm Model UD-16. Autolite generator.

MARATHON OPTIONAL ENGINE: Inline. Six. Overhead valve. Cast iron block. Displacement: 266 cid. Bore and stroke: 3-5/16 x 4-3/8 inches. Compression ratio: 8.0:1. Brake hp: 141 at 4400 rpm. Four main bearings. Solid valve lifters. Carburetor: Rochester Type 2GC Model 7023096. Engine manufactured by Continental Motors Corp., Muskegon, Mich. Exhaust valve diameter: 1.422 inches. Intake valve diameter: 1.781 inches. Chrome piston rings with 0.0015 inch skirt clearance. Durex bearings. Exhaust pipe and tailpipe same as L-head six. Electrical system: 12-volt negative ground. Spark setting: same as L-head six. Fuel pump pressure: 3 psi. Spark plugs: Champion 14mm Model N-8. Autolite generator.

CHASSIS FEATURES: Wheelbase: (Town Custom) 129 inches; (Marathon) 120 inches. Overall length: (Town Custom) 208.3 inches; (Marathon) 199.3 inches. Front tread: 60 inches. Rear tread: 62-1/2 inches. Tires: (Town Custom) N/A; (sedan) 6.70 x 15; (station wagon) 7.10 x 15. Standard transmission: Warner Gear three-speed manual with nonsynchromesh first gear. Ten-inch Auburn coil clutch. Standard rear axle gear ratio: 3.73:1. Brakes: Eleven-inch front and rear drum type with 311 square inch swept area. Manual steering ratio: 26.9:1. Turns lock-to-lock: 5.8. Suspension: (front) coil spring; (rear) 2.50 x 56.0 inch leaf.

OPTIONS: Power steering ($65). Air conditioning ($382). Power brakes ($33). White sidewall tires. Full wheel discs. Padded dashboard. Heater and defroster. Heavy-duty battery. NOTE: Padded dashboard, heater/defroster and power brakes are standard on overhead valve models. Two-speed Hydra-Matic (Neutral-Drive-Low-Reverse), with L-head engine only ($222). Dual-Range Hydra-Matic (Park Reverse/Neutral/Drive 1/Drive 2/Low), with overhead valve engine only ($248). Overhead valve engine, specifications listed below ($57). Overdrive transmission ($108). Available rear axle ratio: (automatic) 3.31:1; (overdrive) 4.09:1; (other) 3.54:1. Limited slip differential.

HISTORICAL FOOTNOTES: The April 1964 issue of *Car Life* magazine had a 16-page specifications chart giving details on all U.S. cars, including standard wheelbase Checker models. It provided such obscure facts as the timing chain pitch and the weight of the crankshaft. For Checkers, it is generally hard to obtain this type of information. One Checker model that is generally outside the scope of this catalog deserves mention in relation to a 1964 change. This is the station wagon-like eight-door (nine including tailgate) Aerobus, which was designed for airport transportation service. It came with front fender clearance lights, full length air foil/luggage rack roof 'fins' and a twin-level Checker/Aerobus fender script. Through the end of 1964, all Aerobuses were built with Chrysler V-8 attachments. In 1965, the Aerobus switched to Chevrolet V-8 power. This year was also the last season for the 226-cid Continental Six as Checkers came with Chevrolet sixes or V-8s from 1965 on. The November 1963 issue of *Motor Trend* had a Checker article.

1965

CHECKER MARATHON — (6-CYL) — SERIES A12 — In a rather strange sounding statement, Checker Motors Corp. announced that all new and unused cars sold after Sept. 1, 1964, with serial numbers larger than 20,000 would be considered 1965 models. Outwardly there was no change in the product. Below the hood, Chevrolet powerplants were new. The base engine was 230-cid overhead valve six and a 283-cid V-8 was optional. Although not really a physical revision the sedan was now marketed separately with two seating configurations. Standard six-passenger models came with front and rear bench seats and the year's lowest price tag. Carrying a higher retail was the six-/eight-passenger version with two folding jump seats. Marathons were unchanged insofar as styling or identification features and continued to be built on a sturdy X-frame with five heavy crossmembers. Use of the lighter Chevrolet engine reduced weight by 125 pounds for sedans; 175 pounds for station wagons. Checkers continued with a basically boxy look and plenty of headroom. The overall height of the sedan was 62.8 inches. The 6.3-inch ground clearance was more than on all U.S. cars, except the Kaiser Jeep. Surprisingly front hip room was only average and rear hip room of 52.5 inches was less than all standard domestic cars. In fact, rear hip room in Mustangs was only slightly less; in Buick Rivieras just slightly more. So there wasn't all that much more space in a Checker, but it was arranged somewhat differently than in other makes.

CHECKER I.D. NUMBERS: Serial numbers and engine numbers were found on the upper firewall. Serial and engine codes had three parts. The first identified the model; the second part the production order and the third part the chassis or serial numbers. Serial numbers for 1965 were determined by the year appearing on the registration for each car. The series number was A12 for conventional models and A19E for the long wheelbase limousine. The 'E' may have indicated 'Extended Wheelbase'. The beginning 1965 serial number was 20001 and the ending number was 26636.

CHECKER MARATHON SERIES

Model No.	Body/Style No.	Body Type & Seating	Factory Price	Shipping Weight	Prod. Total
A12	A12	4-dr Sed-6P	2874	3360	Note 1
A12	A12	4-dr Sed-6/8P	3567	3406	Note 1
A12	A12W	4-dr Sta Wag-6P	3075	3400	Note 1

Note 1: A total of 6,136 Checkers were built this year including taxicabs. Of this total, an estimated 930 were not taxicabs, including all models in both series.

Note 2: The new 'jump seat' sedan had the same price differential as the 1966 Deluxe Sedan and must have been the same model, although not officially called a Deluxe. This would explain the over $300 spread between it and the regular sedan, which the addition of jump seats alone would not warrant. When equipped with optional jump seats, the station wagon weighed 3,450 pounds.

CHECKER MARATHON TOWN CUSTOM — (6-CYL) — SERIES A12E — The Marathon Town Custom limousine was now available on special order only. It increased noticeably in both price and weight, suggesting the inclusion of additional standard features. Styling was the same as in 1964. Power steering and brakes were standard equipment.

CHECKER MARATHON TOWN CUSTOM SERIES

Model No.	Body/Style No.	Body Type & Seating	Factory Price	Shipping Weight	Prod. Total
A12	A12E	4-dr Limo-6P	5491	4640	Note 1

Note 1: A total of 6,136 Checkers were built this year including taxicabs. Of this total, an estimated 930 were not taxicabs.

CHECKER MARATHON ENGINE: Inline. Six. Overhead valve. Cast iron block. Displacement: 230 cid. Bore and stroke: 3.88 x 3.25 inches. Compression ratio: 8.5:1. Brake hp: 140 at 4400 rpm. Seven main bearings. Hydraulic valve lifters. Carburetor: Carter Model 3933 one-barrel or Rochester Type BC one-barrel Model 7028230.

OPTIONAL ENGINE: V-8. Overhead valve. Cast iron block. Displacement: 283 cid. Bore and stroke: 3.88 x 3.00 inches. Compression ratio: 9.25:1. Brake hp: 195 at 4800 rpm. Five main bearings. Hydraulic valve lifters. Carburetor: Rochester Type 2GC two-barrel Model 7028230.

CHASSIS FEATURES: Wheelbase: (Town Custom) 129.5 inches; (Marathons) 120 inches. Overall length: (Town Custom) 208.3 inches; (Marathons) 199.3 inches. Front tread: 60 inches. Rear tread: 62-1/2 inches. Tires: (Town Custom) 9.00 x 15; (Marathons) 7.10 x 15. Overall width: 76 inches.

OPTIONS: Power steering, standard on eight-passenger sedan and Town Custom ($76). Power brakes, standard on above models ($41). Air conditioning ($354). Power-operated forward folding rear seat. Auxiliary jump seats. Station wagon rooftop luggage carrier. Power tailgate. Full wheel discs. White sidewall tires. Heavy-duty shock absorbers. Two-tone paint finish. Chevrolet V-8 engine ($110). A Warner Gear three-speed manual transmission with non-synchromesh first gear was standard equipment. Overdrive transmission was optional ($108). Two-speed Turbo-Hydramatic transmission was optional ($248). A Power-Lok limited slip differential was optional. Available rear axle gear ratios: (standard) 3.73:1; (overdrive) 4.09:1; (Hydramatic) 3.31:1.

HISTORICAL FOOTNOTES: The 12-passenger Aerobus on the 129-inch wheelbase continued to be offered for commercial use. An article about Checkers appeared in the November 1964 issue of *Motor Trend* on page 63.

1966

CHECKER MARATHON — (6-CYL) — SERIES A12 — The 1966 Checkers continued to look just like the 1963 models outside. An engineering addition was the optional availability of a 327-cid Chevrolet V-8, plus the 230-cid six (base) or 283-cid V-8 (option). A new tire size was used for standard models. Power brakes and steering were standard on Deluxe sedans.

CHECKER I.D. NUMBERS: Serial numbers and engine numbers were found on the upper firewall. Serial and engine codes had three parts. The first identified the model; the second part the production order and the third part the chassis or serial numbers. Serial numbers for 1966 were determined by the year appearing on the registration for each car. The series number was A12 for all models. The beginning 1966 serial number was 26637.

CHECKER MARATHON SERIES

Model No.	Body/Style No.	Body Type & Seating	Factory Price	Shipping Weight	Prod. Total
A12	A12	4-dr Sed-6P	2874	3360	Note 1
A12	A12E	4-dr DeL Sed-6P	3567	3800	Note 1
A12	A12W	4-dr Sta Wag-6P	3075	3500	Note 1

Note 1: A total of 5,761 Checkers were built this year including taxicabs. Of this total, an estimated 1,056 were not taxicabs.

CHECKER MARATHON ENGINE: See 1965 Checker Marathon series engine data.

CHECKER MARATHON TOWN CUSTOM — (6-CYL) — SERIES A12E — The Marathon Town Custom Limousine was reinstated as a regularly listed model. There were no changes other than the new optional V-8 and the use of a more expensive optional air conditioning system on this model. On all 'E' suffix models power brakes and power steering were standard equipment.

CHECKER MARATHON TOWN CUSTOM SERIES

Model No.	Body/Style No.	Body Type & Seating	Factory Price	Shipping Weight	Prod. Total
A12	A12E	4-dr Limo-6P	4541	3800	Note 1

Note 1: A total of 5,761 Checkers were built this year including taxicabs. Of this total, an estimated 1,056 were not taxicabs.

Note 2: Since the Deluxe sedan was built on the standard wheelbase, the 'E' suffix no longer indicated use of the extended wheelbase chassis.

CHASSIS FEATURES: Same as 1965 except that an overall length of 211 inches is noted for the Limousine and 8.15 x 15 tires are fitted to standard wheelbase Checkers.

POWERTRAIN OPTIONS: Chevrolet 195 horsepower V-8 ($108). Chevrolet 250 horsepower V-8 ($194). See specifications below. Turbo-Hydramatic transmission.

OPTIONAL ENGINE: V-8. Overhead valves. Cast iron block. Displacement: 283 cid. Bore and stroke: 3.88 x 3.00 inches. Compression ratio: 9.25:1. Brake horsepower: 195 at 4800 rpm. Five main bearings. Hydraulic valve lifters. Carburetor: Rochester Type 4GC four-barrel.

OPTIONAL ENGINE: V-8. Overhead valves. Cast iron block. Displacement: 327 cid. Bore and stroke: 4.00 x 3.25 inches. Compression ratio: 10.5:1. Brake horsepower: 250 at 4400 rpm. Five main bearings. Hydraulic valve lifters. Carburetor: Rochester Type 4GC four-barrel.

CONVENIENCE OPTIONS: Air conditioning in Town Custom ($450). Air conditioning in other models ($346). Power brakes, standard in 'E' models ($41). Power steering, standard in 'E' models ($74). Power side windows. Radio. Dash clock. Backup lights. Parking brake warning light. Safety four-way flashers. Station wagon rooftop luggage rack. Power tailgate window. Wheel discs. Power folding rear seat. Jump seats. White sidewall tires. Heavy-duty shock absorbers. Two-tone paint.

HISTORICAL FOOTNOTES: A short article about Checkers appeared in the November 1965 issue of *Motor Trend* on page 87. A Checker road test appeared in the September 1965 issue of *Motor Trend* on pages 45-47. Morris Markin, who had founded the Checker Motors Corp. as a taxicab builder, over 40 years earlier, was still in charge of the firm.

1967

CHECKER MARATHON — (6-CYL) — SERIES A12 — There were no physical or technical changes in the 1967 Checker Marathon. The three Chevrolet engines remained available, with the six as base powerplant. The sedan had a 12.2 cubic foot trunk capacity and both models carried 23 gallon gas tanks. The steering system was, however, slightly modified for 1967. With manual steering 6.14 turns lock-to-lock were required, as opposed to 5.80 the previous year. With power assist, the respective figures moved in the opposite direction to 4.12 from 5.80. The turning circle stayed the same at 37.5 feet. Also, brake swept area decreased to 276 square inches (from 311 square inches previously). In Chevrolets, the horsepower rating of the four-barrel 327-cid V-8 climbed to 275 hp this year, but it appears that this did not affect Checker immediately. The company probably had 250-hp engines in stock. As far as the model lineup, the 'E' suffix models were either dropped or converted into a special order choice. They do not appear in standard reference sources for 1967.

CHECKER I.D. NUMBERS: Serial numbers and engine numbers were found on the upper firewall. Serial and engine codes had three parts. The first identified the model; the second part the production order and the third part the chassis or serial numbers. Serial numbers for 1966 were determined by the year appearing on the registration for each car. The series number was A12 for all models. The beginning 1967 serial number was 26637. New and unused cars sold after Sept. 1, 1966, with serial numbers larger than (6000) 28923 were considered 1967 models.

CHECKER MARATHON SERIES

Model No.	Body/Style No.	Body Type & Seating	Factory Price	Shipping Weight	Prod. Total
A12	A12	4-dr Sed-6P	2874	3400	Note 1
A12	A12W	4-dr Sta Wag-6P	3075	3500	Note 1

Note 1: A total of 5,822 Checkers were built this year including taxicabs. Of this total, an estimated 950 were not taxicabs.

BASE ENGINE: Inline. Six. Overhead valve. Cast iron block. Displacement: 230 cid. Bore and stroke: 3.88 x 3.25 inches. Compression ratio: 8.5:1. Brake hp: 140 at 4400 rpm. Seven main bearings. Hydraulic valve lifters. Carburetor: Carter Model 3933 one-barrel or Rochester Type BC one-barrel Model 7028230 (Chevrolet manufacture).

OPTIONAL ENGINE: V-8. Overhead valve. Cast iron block. Displacement: 283 cid. Bore and stroke: 3.88 x 3.00 inches. Compression ratio: 9.25:1. Brake hp: 195 at 4800 rpm. Five main bearings. Hydraulic valve lifters. Carburetor: Rochester Type 2GC two-barrel Model 7028230 (Chevrolet manufacture).

OPTIONAL ENGINE: V-8. Overhead valves. Cast iron block. Displacement: 327 cid. Bore and stroke: 4.00 x 3.25 inches. Compression ratio: 10.5:1. Brake hp: 250 at 4400 rpm. Five main bearings. Hydraulic valve lifters. Carburetor: Rochester Type 4GC four-barrel (Chevrolet manufacture).

CHASSIS FEATURES: Wheelbase: (Marathons) 120 inches. Overall length: (Marathons) 199.3 inches. Front tread: 60 inches. Rear tread: 62-1/2 inches. Tires: (Marathons) 8.15 x 15. Overall width: 76 inches.

OPTIONS: Air conditioning ($346). Power brakes ($41). Power steering ($74). Power side windows. Radio. Dash clock. Back-up lights. Parking brake warning light. Safety four-way flashers. Station wagon rooftop luggage rack. Power tailgate window. Wheel discs. Power folding rear seat. Jump seats. White sidewall tires. Heavy-duty shock absorbers. Two-tone paint. Chevrolet 195-hp V-8 ($108). Chevrolet 250-hp V-8 ($194).

1968

CHECKER MARATHON — (6-CYL) — Like other manufacturers in America, the Kalamazoo cab maker was forced to bow to Federal Government safety and emissions control regulations this year. Round side marker lamps were added to the front fenders, ahead of the wheel opening. Padded dashboards, outside rearview mirror, windshield washers, front seat headrests, front safety belts, dual master cylinder braking system and four-way safety flashers became part of the standard safety equipment assortment. The standard wheelbase Deluxe sedan was reinstated in the Marathon model lineup. The 327 cid/275 hp Chevrolet V-8 found its way to the Checker stockroom for the 1967 model year. The former 283-cid V-8 was bored and stroked to 307 cid. Otherwise, things were much the same as before.

CHECKER I.D. NUMBERS: Serial numbers and engine numbers were found on the upper firewall. Serial and engine codes had three parts. The first identified the model; the second part the production order and the third part the chassis or serial numbers. New and unused cars sold after Sept. 1, 1967, with serial numbers larger than 1364-8001 were considered 1968 models.

CHECKER MARATHON SERIES

Model No.	Body/Style No.	Body Type & Seating	Factory Price	Shipping Weight	Prod. Total
A12	A12	4-dr Sed-6P	3221	3390	Note 1
A12	A12W	4-dr Sta Wag-6P	3491	3480	Note 1
A12	A12E	4-dr DeL Sed-8P	3915	3700	Note 1

Note 1: A total of 5,477 Checkers were built this year including taxicabs. Of this total, 992 were not taxicabs.

BASE ENGINE: Inline. Six. Overhead valve. Cast iron block. 230 cid. Bore and stroke: 3.88 x 3.25 inches. Compression ratio: 8.5:1. Brake hp: 140 at 4400 rpm. Seven main bearings. Hydraulic valve lifters. Carburetor: Carter one-barrel Model 3933 or Rochester Type BC one-barrel Model 7028230 (Chevrolet manufacture).

OPTIONAL ENGINE: V-8. Overhead valve. Cast iron block. Displacement: 307 cid. Bore and stroke: 3-7/8 x 3-1/4 inches. Compression ratio: 9.0:1. Brake hp: 200 at 4600 rpm. Five main bearings. Hydraulic valve lifters. Carburetor: Rochester two-barrel.

OPTIONAL ENGINE: V-8. Overhead valve. Cast iron block. Displacement: 327 cid. Bore and stroke: 4.00 x 3.25 inches. Compression ratio: 10.5:1. Brake hp: 250 at 4400 rpm. Five main bearings. Hydraulic valve lifters. Carburetor: Rochester Type 4GC four-barrel (Chevrolet manufacture).

CHASSIS FEATURES: Wheelbase: (Marathons) 120 inches. Overall length: (Marathons) 199.3 inches. Front tread: 60 inches. Rear tread: 62-1/2 inches. Tires: (Marathons) 8.15 x 15. Overall width: 76 inches.

OPTIONS: Air conditioning ($346). Power brakes ($41). Power steering ($74). Power side windows. Radio. Dash clock. Back-up lights. Parking brake warning light. Safety four-way flashers. Station wagon rooftop luggage rack. Power tailgate window. Wheel discs. Power folding rear seat. Jump seats. White sidewall tires. Heavy-duty shock absorbers. Two-tone paint. Chevrolet 195-hp V-8 ($108). Chevrolet 250-hp V-8 ($194).

HISTORICAL FOOTNOTES: A road test of a Checker was done by *Road & Track* magazine in its August 1968 issue (pages 73-76).

1969

CHECKER MARATHON — (6-CYL) — What Uncle Sam had wrought, mere men could not throw asunder. Neither could Checker Motors Corp., so the round fender side markers and safety equipment remained in 1969. So did the limousine, being grouped in a separate Deluxe series with the Deluxe sedan. Both Deluxes were, in fact, now on the 129-inch wheelbase and had Deluxe front fender scripts. The 327-cid V-8 was de-tuned and robbed of 40 hp, but a 350-cid Chevrolet engine was new and put out 300 hp, a high for Checker. The base engine was a new 250-cid Chevrolet six-cylinder.

CHECKER I.D. NUMBERS: The numbers looked like the following sample: A12E 2134 90001. The first group of symbols was the Body/Style Number; the second group the Production Number and the third group the Chassis Number.

CHECKER MARATHON SERIES

Model No.	Body/Style No.	Body Type & Seating	Factory Price	Shipping Weight	Prod. Total
A12	A12	4-dr Sed-6P	3290	3390	Note 1
A12	A12W	4-dr Sta Wag-6P	3560	3480	Note 1

Note 1: A total of 5,417 Checkers were built this year including taxicabs. Of this total, 760 were not taxicabs.

CHECKER DELUXE — (6-CYL) — The new Deluxe series had two long wheelbase models averaging $1,000 in price over Marathons. Both cars had richer appointments and more regular equipment than the standard series entries. The word Deluxe appeared in script on the fenders. Most were sold with optional V-8 power and many accessories. They still had appeal to more conservative limousine buyers, plus people with large families. Both were priced way below the cheapest Cadillacs or Lincolns. Jump seats were standard in these cars.

CHECKER DELUXE SERIES

Model No.	Body/Style No.	Body Type & Seating	Factory Price	Shipping Weight	Prod. Total
A12	A12E	4-dr Sed-6/8P	3984	3590	Note 1
A12	A12E	4-dr Limo-6/8P	4969	3802	Note 1

Note 1: A total of 5,417 Checkers were built this year including taxicabs. Of this total, 760 were not taxicabs.

BASE ENGINE: Inline Six. Overhead valve. Cast iron block. Displacement: 250 (249.9) cid. Bore and stroke: 3-7/8 x 3-17/32 inches. Compression ratio: 8.5:1. Brake hp: 155 at 4200 rpm. Seven main bearings. Hydraulic valve lifters. Carburetor: Rochester Type MV two-barrel.

OPTIONAL ENGINE: V-8. Overhead valve. Cast iron block. Displacement: 327 cid. Bore and stroke: 4 x 3-1/4 inches. Compression ratio: 9.0:1. Brake hp: 235 at 4800 rpm. Five main bearings. Hydraulic valve lifters. Carburetor: Rochester four-barrel.

OPTIONAL ENGINE: V-8. Overhead valve. Cast iron block. Displacement: 350 cid. Bore and stroke: 4 x 3-15/16 inches. Compression ratio: 10.25:1. Brake hp: 300 at 4800 rpm. Five main bearings. Hydraulic valve lifters. Carburetor: Rochester four-barrel.

CHASSIS FEATURES: Wheelbase: (Marathon) 120 inches; (Deluxe) 129 inches. Overall length: (Marathon) 202 inches; (Deluxe) 211 inches. Front tread: 63.6 inches. Rear tread: 63 inches. Tires: 8.25 x 15.

OPTIONS: Air conditioning ($346). Power brakes ($41). Power steering. Automatic transmission. Optional 327-cid V-8 ($108). Optional 350-cid V-8 ($195).

HISTORICAL FOOTNOTES: An article about Checker appeared in *Car and Driver* magazine June 1969 (pages 59-61, 88). In addition, an article about a Ghia-modified Checker appeared in *Road & Track* in January 1969.

1970

CHECKER MARATHON — (6-CYL) — SERIES A-12 — In 1970, Morris Markin, Checker's founder, died. His son David took over as president of the firm with R.E. Oakland as executive vice-president and treasurer. Only one optional engine, the 350-cid V-8, was offered and its power was down by 17 percent. Two lines were available again: the standard 120-inch wheelbase Marathon and the Marathon Deluxe series, with a nine-inch longer stance. All cars were one inch longer, due to minor bumper changes.

CHECKER I.D. NUMBERS: Vehicle Identification code locations were on the dash under hood and on top of the instrument panel. Serial numbers for 1970 were again a three part code referring to the model, production order and chassis or serial number. Example: A-12-403-00001.

CHECKER MARATHON SERIES

Model No.	Body/Style No.	Body Type & Seating	Factory Price	Shipping Weight	Prod. Total
A-12	A-12	4-dr Sed-6P	3671	3268	Note 1
A-12	A-12W	4-dr Sta Wag-6P	3941	3470	Note 1

Note 1: An estimated 4,000 Checkers were built this year including taxicabs. Of this total, 397 were not taxicabs, including all models in both series.

CHECKER MARATHON DELUXE — (6-CYL) — SERIES A-12E — The long wheelbase models were now called Marathon Deluxes. There were no styling changes to speak of. The cars were one inch longer, which was probably due to a new bumper mounting system. Disc brakes were a new option this year. Jump seats, power steering and power brakes were standard on the big cars.

CHECKER MARATHON DELUXE

Model No.	Body/Style No.	Body Type & Seating	Factory Price	Shipping Weight	Prod. Total
A-12	A-12E	4-dr Sed-8P	4364	3378	Note 1
A-12	A-12E	4-dr Limo-8P	5338	3578	Note 1

Note 1: An estimated 4,000 Checkers were built this year including taxicabs. Of this total, 397 were not taxicabs, including all models in both series.

BASE ENGINE: Inline. Six. Overhead valve. Cast iron block. Displacement: 250 cid. Bore and stroke: 3.88 x 3.53 inches. Compression ratio: 8.5:1. Brake hp: 155 at 4200 rpm. Seven main bearings. Hydraulic valve lifters. Carburetor: Rochester Type MV two-barrel.

OPTIONAL ENGINE: V-8. Overhead valve. Cast iron block. Displacement: 350 cid. Bore and stroke: 4.00 x 3.48 inches. Compression ratio: 9.0:1. Brake hp: 250 at 4500 rpm. Five main bearings. Hydraulic valve lifters. Carburetor: Rochester four-barrel.

CHASSIS FEATURES: Wheelbase: (Marathon) 120 inches; (Deluxe) 129 inches. Overall length: (Marathon) 203 inches: (Deluxe) 212 inches. Front tread: 63.6 inches. Rear tread: 63 inches. Tires: (Marathon) 8.25 x 15.

OPTIONS: Power brakes ($41). Power steering. Air conditioning. Disc brakes ($64). Power windows. Three-speed manual transmission was standard. Overdrive transmission. Automatic transmission. 350 cid/250 hp four-barrel V-8 engine ($108). Positive traction rear axle.

HISTORICAL FOOTNOTES: The 1970 Checkers were introduced Sept. 1, 1969. David Markin became the chief executive officer of the firm this year, replacing his father Morris, who died. Morris Markin had founded Checker in 1921. The company's address was 2016 N. Pitcher St., Kalamazoo, MI 49007. The 12-passenger Aerobus continued in production as a commercial vehicle.

1971

CHECKER MARATHON — (6-CYL/V-8) — SERIES A-12 — Checker attempted to market its cars separately as sixes and V-8s after the 1971 model year began. This had the effect of doubling the number of 'models,' although it was not really a true expansion of the line. All Checkers grew another inch in length and G78-15 tires were used. They were unchanged otherwise. Round side marker lamps were seen on both the front and rear fenders of all models.

CHECKER I.D. NUMBERS: The numbering system and code locations were the same as for previous models. Checkers continued with a three-part code. The first group of symbols referred to the model; the second group indicated production order number and the third group formed the chassis or serial numbers. Example: A-12-403-10001. In the final group of symbols the first digit '1' designated the 1971 model year. Official Body/Style Numbers were not used, although the A-12, A-12W and A-12E codes served the same purpose.

CHECKER MARATHON SERIES

Model No.	Body/Style No.	Body Type & Seating	Factory Price	Shipping Weight	Prod. Total
SIX					
A-12	A-12	4-dr Sed-6P	3843	3400	Note 1
A-12	A-12W	4-dr Sta Wag-6P	4113	3600	Note 1
V-8					
A-12	A-12	4-dr Sed-8P	3956	3500	Note 1
A-12	A-12W	4-dr Sta Wag-6P	4228	3700	Note 1

Note 1: Total output, including taxicabs, was approximately 4,500 vehicles.

CHECKER MARATHON DELUXE — (6-CYL/V-8) — SERIES A-12E — The long wheelbase cars were also marketed as sixes and V-8s. They grew an inch and used the new sized tires. No styling or standard equipment changes can be discerned.

CHECKER MARATHON DELUXE SERIES

Model No.	Body/Style No.	Body Type & Seating	Factory Price	Shipping Weight	Prod. Total
SIX					
A-12	A-12E	4-dr Sed-8P	4536	3700	Note 1
A-12	A-12E	4-dr Limo-8P	5510	3700	Note 1
V-8					
A-12	A-12E	4-dr Sed-8P	4651	3800	Note 1
A-12	A-12E	4-dr Limo-8P	5626	3800	Note 1

Note 1: Total output, including taxicabs, was approximately 4,500 vehicles.

MARATHON SIX SERIES ENGINE: Inline. Six. Overhead valve. Cast iron block. Displacement: 250 cid. Bore and stroke: 3.88 x 3.53 inches. Compression ratio: 8.5:1. Brake (SAE NET) hp: 145 at 4200 rpm. Seven main bearings. Hydraulic valve lifters. Carburetor: Rochester Type MC two-barrel.

MARATHON EIGHT SERIES ENGINE: V-8. Overhead valve. Cast iron block. Displacement: 350 cid. Bore and stroke: 4 x 3-15/32 inches. Compression ratio: 9.0:1. Brake hp: 245 at 4800 rpm. Five main bearings. Hydraulic valve lifters. Carburetor: Rochester Type four-barrel.

CHASSIS FEATURES: Wheelbase: (Marathon) 120 inches; (Marathon Deluxe) 129 inches. Overall length: (Marathon) 204 inches; (Marathon Deluxe) 213 inches. Front tread: (All models) 63.6 inches. Rear tread: (All models) 63 inches. Tires: (All models) G78-15.

OPTIONS: Power brakes. Power steering. Air conditioning ($364). Three-speed manual transmission was standard. Overdrive transmission. Automatic transmission. Positive traction rear axle. Heavy-duty clutch.

HISTORICAL FOOTNOTES: The 1971 Checkers were introduced Sept. 1, 1970. David R. Markin was the chief executive officer of the company again this year. A graduate of Bradley University, Markin had entered the auto industry with Checker Motors Corp. in 1948. He had worked in every phase of the business until assuming the presidency upon his father's passing.

1972

CHECKER MARATHON — (6-CYL/V-8) — SERIES A-12 — Once again, Checker styling and post 'Federal' era trim features were the same. Automatic transmission and power-operated disc brakes were made standard equipment this year. The firm continued to market sixes and V-8s as separate models. A total of 5,325 miscellaneous marque ("non-Big Three") gas-powered cars were manufactured in the United States this year and the majority of these were Checkers.

CHECKER I.D. NUMBERS: The numbering system and code locations were the same as for previous models. They took the form: A-12E-2134-20001. The first group of symbols designated the Body/Style Number. The second group of symbols designated the Production Number. The third group of symbols designated the Chassis Number. The '12E' designation indicates a Deluxe 129-inch wheelbase model. The '2' in the Chassis Number indicates a 1972 model.

CHECKER MARATHON SERIES

Model No.	Body/Style No.	Body Type & Seating	Factory Price	Shipping Weight	Prod. Total
SIX					
A-12	A-12	4-dr Sed-6P	3654	3522	Note 1
A-12	A-12W	4-dr Sta Wag-6P	3910	3725	Note 1
V-8					
A-12	A-12	4-dr Sed-6P	3769	3623	Note 1
A-12	A-12W	4-dr Sta Wag-6P	4025	3616	Note 1

Note1: Estimated production of non-taxicab Checkers was 850 units.

CHECKER MARATHON DELUXE — (6-CYL/V-8) — SERIES A-12E — The limousine was dropped for the 1972 model year. Available on the 129-inch wheelbase was the Deluxe sedan. It had the same styling, with an extra wide rear door and rear side window. Jump seats were included, too, but the driver's partition was not. Deluxe script was attached to the front fenders, above the straight, horizontal trim molding.

CHECKER MARATHON DELUXE SERIES

Model No.	Body/Style No.	Body Type & Seating	Factory Price	Shipping Weight	Prod. Total
SIX					
A-12	A-12E	4-dr Sed-8P	4312	3722	Note 1
V-8					
A-12	A-12E	4-dr Sed-8P	4427	3823	Note 1

Note 1: Estimated production of non-taxicab Checkers was 850 units.

MARATHON SIX ENGINE: Inline. Overhead valve. Cast iron block. Displacement: 250 cid. Bore and stroke: 3.88 x 3.53 inches. Compression ratio: 8.5:1. Brake hp: 145 at 4200 rpm. Seven main bearings. Hydraulic valve lifters. Carburetor: Rochester Type MV two-barrel.

MARATHON V-8 ENGINE: Overhead valve. Cast iron block. Displacement: 350 cid. Bore and stroke: 4 x 3-15/32 inches. Compression ratio: 9.0:1. Brake hp: 345 at 4800 rpm. Five main bearings. Hydraulic valve lifters. Carburetor: Rochester Type 4GC four-barrel.

CHASSIS FEATURES: Wheelbase: (Marathon) 120 inches; (Marathon Deluxe) 129 inches. Overall length: (Marathon) 203 inches; (Marathon Deluxe) 212 inches. Front tread: (All models) 63.6 inches. Rear tread: (All models) 63 inches. Tires: (All models) G78-15.

OPTIONS: Power steering ($71). Air conditioning ($362). Dual air conditioning ($624). Full wheel discs. White sidewall tires. Vinyl top. Radio. Station wagon roof top luggage carrier. Power side windows. Power tailgate window. Jump seats. Power rear seat in station wagon. Automatic transmission was standard. Positive traction rear axle was available at extra cost.

HISTORICAL FOOTNOTES: The full-size Checkers were introduced Sept. 1, 1971. David Markin was the chief executive officer of the company this year. R.E. Oakland was first vice-president. Taxicabs and the 12-passenger Aerobus were also produced. General Motors supplied Checker engines (Chevrolet Division) and released both brake and net horsepower ratings for its powerplants in 1972. The six had an output of 110 SAE net hp. The V-8 was rated at 165 SAE net hp.

1973

CHECKER MARATHON — (6-CYL/V-8) — SERIES A-12 — Checker sales climbed to 5,900 vehicles in 1973, with taxicabs included. It is estimated that private sector deliveries went up by about 50 cars. Tough new federal emissions standards were met in the General Motors powerplants by reducing compression ratios and adding an exhaust gas recirculating system (EGR) developed by Rochester Products Division. Also, it appears that slightly more oval-shaped parking lamp housings were substituted at about the same time. Not much else was in variance with the past. These changes added $299 to the Marathon's price and 100 pounds more weight.

CHECKER I.D. NUMBERS: The numbering system and code locations were the same as for previous models. They took the form A-12W-2134-30001. The first group of symbols designated the Body/Style Number. The second group of symbols designated the Production Number. The third group of symbols designated the Chassis Number. The '12W' designation indicates a station wagon. The '3' in the Chassis Number indicates a 1973 model.

CHECKER MARATHON SERIES

Model No.	Body/Style No.	Body Type & Seating	Factory Price	Shipping Weight	Prod. Total
SIX					
A-12	A-12	4-dr Sed-6P	3955	3622	Note 1
A-12	A-12W	4-dr Sta Wag-6P	4211	3825	Note 1
V-8					
A-12	A-12	4-dr Sed-6P	4070	3723	Note 1
A-12	A-12W	4-dr Sta Wag-6P	4326	2916	Note 1

Note 1: A total of 5,900 Checkers were built including taxicabs. Of this total, an estimated 900 were not taxicabs including models in all series.

CHECKER MARATHON DELUXE — (6-CYL/V-8) — SERIES A-12E — The 129-inch wheelbase Deluxe eight-passenger sedan also got a less powerful 'clean air' engine and oval-shaped parking lamps. Its price climbed an even $300 and weight went up 100 pounds. Automatic transmission and power disc brakes were used as standard equipment on all Checker products, including taxicabs. Power steering was now standard as well.

CHECKER MARATHON DELUXE SERIES

Model No.	Body/Style No.	Body Type & Seating	Factory Price	Shipping Weight	Prod. Total
SIX					
A-12	A-12E	4-dr Sed-6P	4612	3822	Note 1
V-8					
A-12	A-12E	4-dr Sed-8P	4727	3923	Note 1

Note 1: A total of 5,900 Checkers were built including taxicabs. Of this total, an estimated 900 were not taxicabs including models in all series.

MARATHON SIX ENGINE: Inline. Overhead valve. Cast iron block. Displacement: 250 cid. Bore and stroke: 3.88 x 3.53 inches. Compression ratio: 8.25:1. SAE net hp: 100 at 3600 rpm. Seven main bearings. Hydraulic valve lifters. Carburetor: Rochester two-barrel.

MARATHON V-8 ENGINE: Overhead valve. Cast iron block. Displacement: 350 cid. Bore and stroke: 4 x 3-15/32 inches. Compression ratio: 8.5:1. SAE net hp: 145 at 4000 rpm. Five main bearings. Hydraulic valve lifters. Carburetor: Rochester four-barrel.

CHASSIS FEATURES: Wheelbase: (Marathon) 120 inches: (Marathon Deluxe) 129 inches. Overall length: (Marathon) 203 inches (Marathon Deluxe) 212 inches. Front tread: (All models) 63.6 inches. Rear tread: (All models) 63 inches. Tires: (All models) G78-15.

OPTIONS: Air conditioning ($362). Dual air conditioning ($624). Full wheel discs. White sidewall tires. Vinyl top ($121). Radio. Station wagon rooftop luggage carrier. Power side windows. Power tailgate window. Jump seats. Power rear folding seat in station wagon. Automatic transmission was standard. Positive traction rear axle was available at extra cost.

HISTORICAL FOOTNOTES: The full-sized Checkers were introduced Sept. 1, 1972. Model year production peaked at 5,900 units. Calendar year sales of 6,297 cars and taxicabs were recorded. David Markin was the chief executive officer of the company this year. All Checkers had automatic transmissions. A total of just 662 Checkers were manufactured with V-8s. Sixes were employed in 5,259 cars. Discs brakes were standard equipment on all and combined with power assist. Also, all of these cars featured power steering. Twenty-six percent of production, or 1,770 cars, left the factory with air conditioning. A rare option was a vinyl top. Rather surprising is the fact that just a few hundred cars each year had radios installed at the factory. Apparently, most Checker taxicabs weren't delivered with regular radios. The Aerobus remained available.

1974

CHECKER MARATHON — (6-CYL/V-8) — SERIES A-12 — There were substantial increases in both price and weight this year, as Checker struggled to keep up with a myriad of new government regulations. For the 1973 model year, other manufacturers, who produced in larger numbers, were forced to install front bumpers capable of withstanding five mile per hour crash barrier impact tests. Now, it was Checker's turn to comply with the new regulation. Shunning elaborate polyurethane nose treatments and such the Kalamazoo company adopted a bulky, shelf-like bumper that looked like something lifted straight from taxicab specifications. The important thing was that it did the job. Pricing and weight jumped substantially and overall length increased by two inches. Styling and standard equipment were basically unaffected. Ornamentation resembled the past. Both model year output and calendar year sales took a dip, although market share increased by 0.01 percent to a whopping 0.07 percent of industry output. The factory installed only 230 radios and added a mere 34 vinyl roofs on 1974 Checkers. The price of the Marathon V-8 station wagon climbed to over $5,000.

CHECKER I.D. NUMBERS: The numbering system and code locations were the same as for previous models. They took the form A-12-2134-40001. The first group of symbols designated the Body/Style Number. The second group of symbols designated the Production Number. The third group of symbols designated the Chassis Number. The 'A-12' designation indicates the base Marathon sedan. The '4' in the chassis code indicates a 1974 model.

CHECKER MARATHON SERIES

Model No.	Body/Style No.	Body Type & Seating	Factory Price	Shipping Weight	Prod. Total
SIX					
A-12	A-12	4-dr Sed-6P	4716	3720	Note 1
A-12	A-12W	4-dr Sta Wag-6P	4966	3925	Note 1
V-8					
A-12	A-12	4-dr Sed-6P	4825	3723	Note 1
A-12	A-12W	4-dr Sta Wag-6P	5074	3916	Note 1

Note 1: A total of 5,880 Checkers were built this year including taxicabs. Of this total, an estimated 900 were not taxicabs, including all models in both series.

CHECKER MARATHON DELUXE — (6-CYL/V-8) — SERIES A-12E — This was the last year for the long wheelbase cars, which measured two inches more end-to-end because of the new "Federal' bumpers. With the recently emasculated engine, that was a lot of car to get out of its own way when it couldn't. As usual, there was little change in body styling or trim other than the new cowcatcher bumper up front. Prices increased an average of $779.

CHECKER MARATHON DELUXE SERIES

Model No.	Body/Style No.	Body Type & Seating	Factory Price	Shipping Weight	Prod. Total
SIX					
A-12	A-12E	4-dr Sed-8P	5394	3920	Note 1
V-8					
A-12	A-12E	4-dr Sed-8P	5503	3923	Note 1

Note 1: A total of 5,880 Checkers were built this year including taxicabs. Of this total, an estimated 900 were non-taxicabs, including all models in both series.

MARATHON SIX ENGINE: Inline. Six. Overhead valve. Cast iron block. Displacement: 250 cid. Bore and stroke: 3.83 x 3.53 inches. Compression ratio: 8.25:1. SAE net hp: 100 at 3600 rpm. Seven main bearings. Hydraulic valve lifters. Carburetor: Rochester two-barrel.

MARATHON V-8 ENGINE: V-8. Overhead valve. Cast iron block. Displacement: 350 cid. Bore and stroke: 4 x 3-15/32 inches. Compression ratio: 8.5:1. SAE net hp: 145 at 3800 rpm. Five main bearings. Hydraulic valve lifters. Carburetor: Rochester four-barrel.

CHASSIS FEATURES: Wheelbase: (Marathon) 120 inches; (Marathon Deluxe) 129 inches. Overall length: (Marathon) 205 inches; (Marathon Deluxe) 212 inches. Front tread: (all models) 63.6 inches. Rear tread: (all models) 63 inches. Tires: (all models) G78-15.

OPTIONS: Air conditioning ($362). Dual air conditioning ($592). Vinyl roof ($145). Radio. Full wheel discs. Whitewall tires. Luggage carrier. Power windows. Power tailgate. Jump seats. Power folding seat in station wagon. Automatic transmission was standard. Positive traction rear axle was available at extra cost.

HISTORICAL FOOTNOTES: The full-sized Checkers were introduced Sept. 1, 1973. Model year production peaked at 5,830 units. Calendar year sales of 5,229 cars and taxicabs were recorded. David Markin was the chief executive officer of the firm this year. No executive changes had been made since 1972. Checkers advertising agency was Baker and Brichta, Inc. of Chicago, Illinois. Equipment having 100 percent installation rates included automatic transmission, power steering and power brakes. A total of 662 cars had V-8 engine installed. Air conditioners were ordered by only 882 Checker buyers this season. Radios were put into 230 production units. A mere 34 Checkers wore vinyl tops.

1975

CHECKER MARATHON — (6-CYL/V-8) — SERIES A-12 — In 1975, General Motors cars were fitted with catalytic converters. Since Checkers had Chevrolet motors, they received this change, too. As a consequence, both prices and weights increased again. The model and series lineup was also rearranged. The Marathon station wagon was dropped. The Deluxe series nomenclature also disappeared and the long wheelbase models were dropped. A Deluxe Marathon V-8 sedan on the standard platform replaced it. It was over $700 more expensive than the big car. Styling stayed the same.

CHECKER I.D. NUMBERS: The numbering system and code locations were the same as for previous models. The A-12W Body Style code was no longer used. Serial numbers took the form A-12E-2134-50001. The first group of symbols designated the Body/Style Number. The second group of symbols designated the Production Number. The third group of symbols designated the Chassis Number. The "A-12E" designation indicates a Deluxe sedan. The '5' in the chassis code indicates a 1975 model.

CHECKER MARATHON SERIES

Model No.	Body/Style No.	Body Type & Seating	Factory Price	Shipping Weight	Prod. Total
SIX					
A-12	A-12	4-dr Sed-6P	5394	3774	Note 1
V-8					
A-12	A-12	4-dr Sed-6P	5539	3839	Note 1
A-12	A-12E	4-dr DeL Sed-6P	6216	4137	Note 1

Note 1: A total of 3,005 Checkers were built in the 1975 calendar year including taxicabs. Of this total, 450 were estimated to be non-taxicabs including all models above.

MARATHON SIX ENGINE: Inline. Six. Overhead valve. Cast iron block. Displacement: 250 cid. Bore and stroke: 3.63 x 3.53 inches. Compression ratio: 8.25:1. SAE net hp: 100 at 3600 rpm. Seven main bearings. Hydraulic valve lifters. Carburetor: Rochester two-barrel.

MARATHON V-8 ENGINE: V-8. Overhead valve. Cast iron block. Displacement: 350 cid. Bore and stroke: 4 x 3-15/32 inches. Compression ratio: 8.5:1 SAE net hp: 145 at 3800 rpm. Five main bearings. Hydraulic valve lifters. Carburetor: Rochester four-barrel.

CHASSIS FEATURES: Wheelbase: (all models) 120 inches. Overall length: (all models) 205 inches. Front tread: (all models) 63.6 inches. Tires: (all models) G78-15.

OPTIONS: Air conditioning ($362). Dual air conditioning ($592). Vinyl roof ($145). Radio. Full wheel discs. Whitewall tires. Jump seats. Two-tone paint. Automatic transmission was standard. Positive traction rear axle was available at extra cost.

HISTORICAL FOOTNOTES: The full-sized Checkers were introduced Sept. 1, 1974. Model year production totals were not reported. Calendar year sales of 3,005 cars and taxicabs were recorded. David R. Markin was the chief executive officer of the company this year. No top executives were changed. Checker's share of the U.S. auto market dropped to 0.04 percent. In the first 12 months of the 1975 model year, 3,171 Checkers were registered in the U.S. In December 1975, another 306 units were registered. This compares to respective figures of 4,892 and 230 in the 1974 model year. The company did not report optional equipment installment rates. The Environmental Protection Agency (EPA) gave the Checker with automatic transmission and 250-cid six a fuel economy rating of 17 city/23 highway/19 combined.

1976

MARATHON - SERIES A-12 - SIX/V-8 - Founded in 1922 by Morris Markin, a Russian immigrant, Checker soon established itself as a builder of durable vehicles that stood aside from the whims of change. The company prevailed in its rivalry with John Hertz of Yellow Taxi through the Chicago gangland days. The familiar "slabsided" Checker body, introduced as the A8 taxicab in 1956, was first offered to private passenger-car buyers in late 1959 as the Superba. Changes were minimal through the next decade-and-a-half: not much more than five mph bumpers, a switch from round to square turn signal lenses, catalytic converters (starting in 1975), and federally-mandated reflectors. First offered with Continental engines, Checker switched to Chevrolet powerplants (inline six and V-8) in 1965. The station wagon body style was dropped in 1975, leaving only four-door sedans. Built for rugged use, Checkers featured a double-channel X-frame with five X-members, as well as reinforced body center posts. That kind of construction meant a heavyweight car, with the lightest model approaching three tons. Rear floors were virtually flat, rooflines high to allow great headroom. Body parts (bolt-on fenders, grillework, side panels) could be replaced in minimum time. Front and rear bumpers were interchangeable. The standard Model A12, on a 120-inch wheelbase, came with a 250 cu. in. inline six-cylinder engine. The long-wheelbase Al2E carried a standard 350 cu. in. V-8, which was also optional on the smaller model. (Model A11 and A11E designations were for taxicabs.) Most engine parts were readily accessible. Complete data on the 1976 model is not available, but similar to the '77; see next listing for standard equipment and appearance details.

I.D. DATA: Not available.

MARATHON (SIX)

Model No.	Body/Style No.	Body Type &Seating	Factory Price	Shipping Weight	Prod. Total
A-12	N/A	4-dr. Sed-6P	5749	3775	Note 1

MARATHON (V-8)

Model No.	Body/Style No.	Body Type &Seating	Factory Price	Shipping Weight	Prod. Total
A-12	N/A	4-dr. Sed-6P	N/A	3839	Note 1
A-12E	N/A	4-dr. DeL Sed-6P	6736	4137	Note 1

Note 1: A total of 4,790 Checkers (private and taxi) were built in 1976.

ENGINE DATA: BASE SIX (Standard model): Inline, overhead valve six-cylinder. Cast iron block and head. Displacement: 250 cu. in. (4.1 liters). Bore & stroke: 3.88 x 3.53 in. Compression ratio: 8.2:1. Brake horsepower: 105 at 3800 R.P.M. Torque: 186 lb.-ft. at 1200 R.P.M. Seven main bearings. Hydraulic valve lifters. Carburetor: 1Bbl. Rochester 17056014. Chevrolet-built. BASE V-8 (DeLuxe model): 90-degree, overhead valve V-8. Cast iron block and head. Displacement: 350 cu. in. (5.7 liters). Bore & stroke: 4.00 x 3.48 in. Compression ratio: 8.2:1. Brake horsepower: 145 at 3800 R.P.M. Torque: 250 lb.-ft. at 2200 R.P.M. Five main bearings. Hydraulic valve lifters. Carburetor: 2Bbl. Rochester 17056114. Chevrolet-built.

CHASSIS DATA: Wheelbase: 120 in. (DeLuxe, 129 in.). Overall Length: 204.8 in. (DeLuxe, 213.8 in.). Height: 62.8 in. Width: 76 in. Front Tread: 64.5 in. Rear Tread: 63.3 in. Wheel size: 6 x 15 in. Standard Tires: G78 x 15.

TECHNICAL: Transmission: Turbo Hydramatic 400 three-speed automatic standard. Gear ratios: (1st) 2.48:1; (2nd) 1.48:1; (3rd) 1.00:1; (Rev) 2.07:1. Standard final drive ratio: 3.31:1. Steering: Recirculating ball. Suspension: Front coil springs with control arms and anti-sway bar; rigid rear axle with semi-elliptic leaf springs. Brakes: Front disc (11.75 in. dia.), rear drum. Ignition: Delco-Remy HEI. Body construction: Separate body and box-type ladder frame. Fuel Tank: 21.6 gal.

OPTIONS: Limited-slip differential. Air conditioning. Auxiliary rear seats. HR78 x 15 tires. Note: Other options similar to 1977; see next listing.

MANUFACTURER: Checker Motors Corp., Kalamazoo, Michigan. Established 1922. David R. Markin, chairman/president. 600 workers.

HISTORY: Calendar year sales: 4,681 (mainly taxis).

1977

MARATHON - SERIES A-12 - SIX/V-8 - "Being practical is never out of style." That was the strongest selling point for Checker in the 1970s. As the factory brochure proclaimed, "It's functional. It's spacious. It's sensible .... A tribute to the common sense of its owner." Only a small fraction of those owners were private, however: typically at least 90 percent of Checkers were destined for taxi use. Base engine for the short-wheelbase Model A12 was again Chevrolet's 250 cu. in. inline six, but the Al 2E switched from a 350 V-8 to a 305. The 350 remained optional, however, in both models. A Turbo Hydramatic 400 transmission was standard. So were power steering and brakes. Checkers had coil spring front suspension and five-leaf semi-elliptic rear springs. Checkers had a winged emblem at the front of the hood and quad round headlamps, with amber parking lamps just below. 'Marathon' script stood on the cowl. Round amber marking lamps were on front fenders. The wide, bright grille kept the same look year after year. Vertical-style taillamps each consisted of two round lenses, one above the other. Standard equipment included G78 x 15 bias-belt L/RB blackwall tires; two-speed electric wiper/washers; heater/defroster; front side vent windows; rubber fender shields; door-ajar warning light; four sets of lap belts; two sets of shoulder harnesses and lap belt combination; rear door pull handles; inside day/night mirror; padded instrument panel; and dual padded sunvisors. Directional signals included a lane-change feature. The step-on parking brake had a warning light. Body paint was DuPont acrylic enamel in 94 color choices. Chair-high seats came with vinyl upholstery in a wide variety of colors. Square forward-facing auxiliary seats were optional in Model A12E, for nine-passenger capacity. Also optional: covered rear quarter windows.

I.D. DATA: Not available.

MARATHON (SIX)

Model No.	Body/Style No.	Body Type & Seating	Factory Price	Shipping Weight	Prod. Total
A-12	N/A	4-dr. Sed-6P	N/A	3775	Note 1

MARATHON (V-8)

Model No.	Body/Style No.	Body Type & Seating	Factory Price	Shipping Weight	Prod. Total
A-12	N/A	4-dr. Sed-6P	N/A	N/A	Note 1
A-12E	N/A	4-dr. DeL Sed-6P	N/A	4137	Note 1

Note 1: A total of 5,377 Checkers were built in the model year; all but 337 were taxicabs.

ENGINE DATA: BASE SIX (Standard model): Inline, overhead valve six-cylinder. Cast iron block and head. Displacement: 250 cu. in. (4.1 liters). Bore & stroke: 3.88 x 3.53 in. Compression ratio: 8.3:1. Brake horsepower: 110 at 3800 R.P.M. Torque: 195 lb.-ft. at 1600 R.P.M. Seven main bearings. Hydraulic valve lifters. Carburetor: 1Bbl. Rochester 17057014. Chevrolet-built. BASE V-8 (DeLuxe model): 90-degree, overhead valve V-8. Cast iron block and head. Displacement: 305 cu. in. (5.0 liters). Bore & stroke: 3.74 x 3.48 in. Compression ratio: 8.5:1. Brake horsepower: 145 at 3800 R.P.M. Torque: 245 lb.-ft. at 2400 R.P.M. Five main bearings. Hydraulic valve lifters. Carburetor: 2Bbl. Rochester 17057108. Chevrolet-built. OPTIONAL V-8 (both models). 90-degree, overhead valve V-8. Cast iron block and head. Displacement: 350 cu. in. (5.7 liters). Bore & stroke: 4.00 x 3.48 in. Compression ratio: 8.5:1. Brake horsepower: 170 at 3800 R.P.M. Torque: 270 lb.-ft. at 2400 R.P.M. Five main bearings. Hydraulic valve lifters. Carburetor: 4Bbl. Rochester 17057202. Chevrolet-built.

CHASSIS DATA: same as 1976.

TECHNICAL: same as 1976.

OPTIONS: 305 two-barrel or 350 four-barrel V-8. Trac-Lok rear axle. Trunk-mounted battery and shield. Six-leaf rear springs. Heavier shocks. Transmission oil cooler. Heavy-duty coolant. Air conditioning. Power rear door locks. Tinted glass. Auxiliary under-seat heater. Rear defogger. Spotlight. AM or AM/FM radio. Two-way radio antenna. Undercoating. Auxiliary seats. Front armrests. Driver's card case. Life-Guard partition. Full wheel covers. Whitewalls. HR78 x 15 Firestone 500 SBR tires. Roof lamp. Taxi lettering details.

MANUFACTURER: Checker Motors Corp., Kalamazoo, Michigan. David R. Markin, chairman/president.

HISTORY: Calendar year sales: 4,568 (mainly taxis).

Historical Footnotes: Checker also made a 15-passenger limousine called the Aerobus 15.

1978

MARATHON - SERIES A-12 - SIX/V-8 - Checkers changed little in appearance or equipment, except that a 90-horsepower inline six was used in California models.

I.D. DATA: Not available.

MARATHON (SIX)

Model No.	Body/Style No.	Body Type & Seating	Factory Price	Shipping Weight	Prod. Total
A-12	N/A	4-dr. Sed-6P	6419	3765	Note 1
MARATHON (V-8)					
A-12	N/A	4-dr. Sed-6P	N/A	3862	Note 1
A-12E	N/A	4-dr. DeL Sed-6P	7472	4062	Note 1

Note 1: A total of 5,503 Checkers were built in model year 1978 (only 307 for private sale).

ENGINE DATA: BASE SIX (Standard model): Inline, overhead valve six-cylinder. Cast iron block and head. Displacement: 250 cu. in. (4.1 liters). Bore & stroke: 3.88 x 3.53 in. Compression ratio: 8.1:1. Brake horsepower: 110 at 3800 R.P.M. Torque: 190 lb.-ft. at 1600 R.P.M. Seven main bearings. Hydraulic valve lifters. Carburetor: 1Bbl. Rochester 17058020. Chevrolet-built. BASE V-8 (DeLuxe model); OPTIONAL (Standard model): 90-degree, overhead valve V-8. Cast iron block and head. Displacement: 305 cu. in. (5.0 liters). Bore & stroke: 3.74 x 3.48 in. Compression ratio: 8.4:1. Brake horsepower: 145 at 3800 R.P.M. Torque: 245 lb.-ft. at 2400 R.P.M. Five main bearings. Hydraulic valve lifters. Carburetor: 2Bbl. Rochester 17058108B. Chevrolet-built. OPTIONAL V-8 (both models): 90-degree, overhead valve V-8. Cast iron block and head. Displacement: 350 cu. in. (5.7 liters). Bore & stroke: 4.00 x 3.48 in. Compression ratio: 8.2:1. Brake horsepower: 160 at 3800 R.P.M. Torque: 260 lb.-ft. at 2400 R.P.M. Five main bearings. Hydraulic valve lifters. Carburetor: 4Bbl. Rochester 17058504A. Chevrolet-built.

CHASSIS DATA: same as 1976-77.

TECHNICAL: Transmission: Turbo Hydramatic 400 three-speed automatic standard. Gear ratios: (1st) 2.48:1; (2nd) 1.48:1; (3rd) 1.00:1; (Rev) 2.07:1. Standard final drive ratio: 3.07:1 w/six, 2.72:1 w/V-8. Steering: Recirculating ball. Suspension: Front coil springs with control arms and anti- sway bar; rigid rear axle with semi-elliptic leaf springs. Brakes: Front disc (11.75 in. dia.), rear drum. Ignition: Delco-Remy HEI. Body construction: Separate body and box-type ladder frame. Fuel Tank: 21.6 gal.

OPTIONS: 305 cu. in. V-8 engine ($179). 350 cu. in. V-8 ($322) except ($145) for A12E. Trac-Lok differential ($71). Front air conditioning ($475). Dual air cond. ($855). Rear defogger ($46). Auxiliary heater ($83). Auxiliary rear seats ($75); DeLuxe ($257). Power rear door locks ($75); all doors ($138). AM radio ($99); AM/FM radio ($165). Vinyl roof ($194). Tinted glass. Heavy-duty shocks. HR78 x 15 Firestone 500 tires.
Note: Complete option list not available, but similar to 1979; see next listing.

MANUFACTURER: Checker Motors Corp., Kalamazoo, Michigan. David Markin, chairman/president.

1979

MARATHON - SERIES A-12 - SIX/V-8 - Appearance and equipment changed little, as usual. Standard equipment included the Chevrolet 250 cu. in. six-cylinder engine; dual master cylinder brake system with power front disc brakes; power steering; three-speed automatic; two-speed electric wiper/washers; 63-amp generator; 80-amp battery; rear door pull handles; full wheelcovers; rubber fender shields; and day/night mirror. P215/75 blackwall tires rode on 15 in. wheels, replacing the former G78 x 15 size. The Marathon DeLuxe A12E, on 129 in. wheelbase, had a 305 V-8 and vinyl roof, and required P225 radial tires.

I.D. DATA: Not available.

MARATHON (SIX)

Model No.	Body/Style No.	Body Type & Seating	Factory Price	Shipping Weight	Prod. Total
A-12	N/A	4-dr. Sed-6P	7314	3740	Note 1
MARATHON (V-8)					
A-12	N/A	4-dr. Sed-6P	7515	3862	Note 1
A-12E	N/A	4-dr. DeL Sed-6P	8389	3999	Note 1

Note 1: A total of 5,231 Checkers were built in the model year (all except 270 were taxicabs).

ENGINE DATA: same as 1978.

CHASSIS DATA: Wheelbase: 120 in. (DeLuxe, 129 in.). Overall Length: 204.8 in. (DeLuxe, 213.8 in.). Height: 62.8 in. Width: 78 in. Front Tread: 64.5 in. Rear Tread: 63.3 in. Wheel size: 15 x 6 in. Standard Tires: P215/75R15 Firestone 721 blackwall SBR.

TECHNICAL: same as 1978.

OPTIONS: 305 cu. in. V-8 engine ($201). 350 cu. in. V-8, required in Calif. ($322) except on A12E ($121). Aux. transmission oil cooler ($92). Trac-Lok axle ($78.50). Firm ride shocks ($14). Skid bar ($6.50). 145-pound rear springs ($29.50). Rear helper springs ($38). Optional cooling ($58). Front air cond. ($520). Dual air cond. ($921). Auxiliary floor heater ($89.50). Rear electric door locks only ($76.50). Tinted glass ($51.50); windshield ($24.50). Left-hand spotlight ($63). Right mirror ($10.50); left one standard. AM radio ($101.50). AM/FM radio ($171). Rear speaker ($43.50). Vinyl roof, A12 ($209). Two-tone paint ($46). Metallic paint ($197). Elimination of quarter window ($131.50); vinyl roof required on A12. Chrome fender shields ($48). California pkg. for six ($276). Aux. rear seats ($84); DeLuxe ($292). Front carpet ($45). Additional ashtrays ($10 each). P215 whitewall tires ($50). P225 blackwall tires ($63). P225 whitewall tires ($113).

MANUFACTURER: Checker Motors Corp., Kalamazoo. Michigan. David Markin, chairman/president. 1,000 workers.

1980

MARATHON - SERIES A-12 - V-6/V-8 - Checkers came with new, smaller engines this year. A 229 cu. in. V-6 replaced the former inline six as base engine in Model A12, while a 267 cu. in. V-8 replaced the 305. The 305 engine remained available in California (rated at 155 horsepower), but the 350 cu. in. V-8 was gone. Also available was a new diesel powerplant. Standard equipment included three-speed Turbo Hydramatic transmission, heater/defroster. P215/75R15 tires, two-speed wiper/washers, power front disc brakes, power steering, safety day/night mirror, and front side vent windows. Rear carpeting, rubber fender shields, rear door pull handles, full wheel covers, and rear-mounted battery with shield also were standard. Long-wheelbase Model A12E came with the 267 cu. in. V-8 engine and vinyl roof, and required P225/75R15 tires. Fenders and grille were bolt-on type; front and rear bumpers interchangeable.

I.D. DATA: Not available.

MARATHON (V-6)

Model No.	Body/Style No.	Body Type & Seating	Factory Price	Shipping Weight	Prod. Total
A-12	N/A	4-dr. Sed-6P	8118	3680	Note 1
MARATHON (V-8)					
A-12	N/A	4-dr. Sed-6P	N/A	N/A	Note 1
A-12E	N/A	4-dr. DeL Sed-6P	9192	3999	Note 1

Note 1: A total of 2,574 Checkers were built in the model year. Price Note: Diesel-engine models cost $10,473 and $11,310, respectively. As usual, taxi models were cheaper ($7,597 for A11 and $8,321 for A11E).

ENGINE DATA: BASE V-6 (Standard model): 90-degree, overhead valve V-6. Cast iron block and head. Displacement: 229 cu. in. (3.8 liters). Bore & stroke: 3.74 x 3.48 in. Compression ratio: 8.6:1. Brake horsepower: 115 at 4000 R.P.M. Torque: 175 lb.-ft. at 2000 R.P.M. Four main bearings. Hydraulic valve lifters. Carburetor: 2Bbl. Rochester 1780130. BASE V-8 (DeLuxe model); OPTIONAL (Standard model): 90-degree, overhead valve V-8. Cast iron block and head. Displacement: 267 cu. in. (4.4 liters). Bore & stroke: 3.50 x 3.48 in. Compression ratio: 8.3:1. Brake horsepower: 120 at 3600 R.P.M. Torque: 215 lb.-ft. at 2000 R.P.M. Five main bearings. Hydraulic valve lifters. Carburetor: 2Bbl. Rochester 17080138. OPTIONAL V-8 (both models): 90-degree, overhead valve V-8. Cast iron block and head. Displacement: 305 cu. in. (5.0 liters). Bore & stroke: 3.74 x 3.48 in. Compression ratio: 8.6:1. Brake horsepower: 155 at 4000 R.P.M. Torque: 230 lb.-ft. at 2400 R.P.M. Five main bearings. Hydraulic valve lifters. Carburetor: 2Bbl. OPTIONAL DIESEL V-8 (both models): 90-degree, overhead valve V-8. Cast iron block and head. Displacement: 350 cu. in. (5.7 liters). Bore & stroke: 4.06 x 3.39 in. Compression ratio: 22.5:1. Brake horsepower: 125 at 3600 R.P.M. Torque: 225 lb.-ft. at 1600 R.P.M. Five main bearings. Hydraulic valve lifters. Fuel injection.

CHASSIS DATA: Wheelbase: 120 in. (DeLuxe, 129 in.). Overall Length: 204.8 in. (DeLuxe, 213.8 in.). Height: 62.8 in. Width: 76 in. Front Tread: 64.5 in. Rear Tread: 63.3 in. Wheel size: 15 x 6 in. Standard Tires: P215/75RI5 except (A12E) P225/75R15.

TECHNICAL: Transmission: Turbo Hydramatic 400 three-speed automatic standard. Gear ratios: (1st) 2.48:1; (2nd) 1.48:1; (3rd) 1.00:1; (Rev) 2.07:1. Standard final drive ratio: 2.72:1. Steering: Recirculating ball. Suspension: Front coil springs with control arms and anti-sway bar; rigid rear axle with semi-elliptic leaf springs. Brakes: Front disc (11.86 in. dia.), rear drum. Ignition: Delco-Remy HEI. Body construction: Separate body and box-type ladder frame. Fuel Tank: 21.6 gal.

OPTIONS: 267 cu. in. V-8 engine ($237). 305 cu. in. V-8; required in Calif. ($214) except on A12E ($677). 105-amp alternator ($217). Trac-Lok axle ($86). Aux. transmission oil cooler ($97). Firm ride shocks ($14.50). Skid bar ($12). 145-pound rear springs ($29.50). Rear helper springs ($38). Optional cooling ($58). Front air cond. ($579). Dual air cond. ($1007). Auxiliary floor heater ($97.50). Rear defogger ($53.50). Four electric door locks ($171). Rear electric door locks only ($92). Tinted glass ($68.50); windshield ($25). Left-handed spotlight ($68). Right mirror ($11). AM radio ($114). AM/FM radio ($192). Rear speaker ($46). Vinyl roof, A12 ($230). Two-tone paint ($55). Metallic paint ($230). Elimination of quarter window ($131.50); vinyl roof required on A12. Chrome fender shields ($55.50). Aux. rear seats ($98.50); DeLuxe ($329). Front carpet ($48.50). Additional ashtrays ($11 each). P215 whitewall tires ($79). P225 blackwall tires ($75.50). P225 whitewall tires ($115).

MANUFACTURER: Checker Motors Corp., Kalamazoo, Michigan. David Markin, chairman/president.

1981

MARATHON - SERIES A-12 - V-6/V-8 - Appearance and equipment were similar to 1980. Prices jumped considerably this year, as they had in 1980.

I.D. DATA: Not available.

MARATHON (V-6)

Model No.	Body/Style No.	Body Type & Seating	Factory Price	Shipping Weight	Prod. Total
A-12	N/A	4-dr. Sed-6P	9632	3680	Note 1
MARATHON (V-8)					
A-12	N/A	4-dr. Sed-6P	9869	N/A	Note 1
A-12E	N/A	4-dr. DeL Sed-6P	10706	3999	Note 1

Note 1: A total of 2,950 Checkers were produced in the model year (private and taxi).

ENGINE DATA: BASE V-6 (Standard model): 90-degree, overhead valve V-8. Cast iron block and head. Displacement: 229 cu. in. (3.8 liters). Bore & stroke: 3.73 x 3.48 in. Compression ratio: 8.6:1. Brake horsepower: 110 at 4200 R.P.M. Torque: 170 lb.-ft. at 2000 R.P.M. Four main bearings. Hydraulic valve lifters. Carburetor: 2Bbl. Rochester 1780130. BASE V-8 (DeLuxe model); OPTIONAL (Standard model): 90-degree, overhead valve V-8. Cast iron block and head. Displacement: 267 cu. in. (4.4 liters). Bore & stroke: 3.50 x 3.48 in. Compression ratio: 8.3:1. Brake horsepower: 115 at 4000 R.P.M. Torque: 200 lb.-ft. at 2400 R.P.M. Five main bearings. Hydraulic valve lifters. Carburetor: 2Bbl. Rochester 17080138. OPTIONAL V-8 (both models): 90-degree, overhead valve V-8. Cast iron block and head. Displacement: 305 cu. in. (5.0 liters). Bore & stroke: 3.74 x 3.48 in. Compression ratio: 8.6:1. Brake horsepower: 150 at 3800 R.P.M. Torque: 240 lb.-ft. at 2400 R.P.M. Five main bearings. Hydraulic valve lifters. Carburetor: 2Bbl. Rochester 17080502. OPTIONAL DIESEL V-8 (both models): 90-degree, overhead valve V-8. Cast iron block and head. Displacement: 350 cu. in. (5.7 liters). Bore & stroke: 4.06 x 3.38 in. Compression ratio: 22.5:1. Brake horsepower: 105 at 3200 R.P.M. Torque: 200 lb.-ft. at 1600 R.P.M. Five main bearings. Hydraulic valve lifters. Fuel injection.

CHASSIS DATA: same as 1980.

TECHNICAL: same as 1980.

OPTIONS: 267 cu. in. V-8 engine ($237). 305 cu. in. V-8 ($343); Calif. ($914). Front air cond. ($711). Dual air cond. ($1211). Rear defogger ($62). Four electric door locks ($198); rear only ($104). AM radio ($145); AM/FM radio ($231). Vinyl roof ($269).

Note: Complete option list not available, but similar to 1980.

MANUFACTURER: Checker Motors Corp., Kalamazoo. Michigan. David Markin, chairman/president.

1982

MARATHON - SERIES A-12 - V-6/V-8 - Appearance and equipment were similar to 1980-81. Once again, prices jumped sharply.

I.D. DATA: Not available.

MARATHON (V-6)

Model No.	Body/Style No.	Body Type & Seating	Factory Price	Shipping Weight	Prod. Total
A-12	N/A	4-dr. Sed-6P	10950	3680	Note 1
MARATHON (V-8)					
A-12	N/A	4-dr. Sed-6P	11187	N/A	Note 1
A-12E	N/A	4-dr. DeL Sed-6P	12025	3839	Note 1

Note 1: A total of 2,000 Checkers were produced in this final model year (private and taxis).

ENGINE DATA: BASE V-6 (Standard model): 90-degree, overhead valve V-8. Cast iron block and head. Displacement: 229 cu. in. (3.8 liters). Bore & stroke: 3.73 x 3.48 in. Compression ratio: 8.6:1. Brake horsepower: 110 at 4200 R.P.M. Torque: 170 lb.-ft. at 2000 R.P.M. Four main bearings. Hydraulic valve lifters. Carburetor: 2Bbl. Rochester 1780130. BASE V-8 (DeLuxe model); OPTIONAL (Standard model): 90-degree, overhead valve V-8. Cast iron block and head. Displacement: 267 cu. in. (4.4 liters). Bore & stroke: 3.50 x 3.48 in. Compression ratio: 8.3:1. Brake horsepower: 115 at 4000 R.P.M. Torque: 205 lb.-ft. at 2400 R.P.M. Five main bearings. Hydraulic valve lifters. Carburetor: 2Bbl. Rochester 17080138. OPTIONAL DIESEL V-8 (both models): 90-degree, overhead valve V-8. Cast iron block and head. Displacement: 350 cu. in. (5.7 liters). Bore & stroke: 4.06 x 3.38 in. Compression ratio: 22.5:1. Brake horsepower: 105 at 3200 R.P.M. Torque: 200 lb.-ft. at 1600 R.P.M. Five main bearings. Hydraulic valve lifters. Fuel injection.

CHASSIS DATA: Wheelbase: 120 in. (DeLuxe, 129 in.). Overall length: 201.6 in. (DeLuxe, 210.6 in.). Height: 62.8 in. Width: 78 in. Front Tread: 64.5 in. Rear Tread: 63.3 in. Wheel size: 15 x 6 in. Standard tires: P215/75R15 except (A12E) P225/75R15.

TECHNICAL: same as 1980-81.

OPTIONS: 267 cu. in. V-8 engine ($237). Propane 229 cu. in. V-6 ($275). Tilt steering ($127). Front air cond. ($750). Dual air cond. ($1315). Rear defogger ($68). Floor heater ($132). Four electric door locks ($211); rear only ($119). AM radio ($152). Vinyl roof ($290). Oval opera windows ($342). Aux. rear seats: A12 ($121). DeLuxe aux. rear seats: Al2E ($415).

Note: Complete option list not available, but similar to 1980 listing:

MANUFACTURER: Checker Motors Corp., Kalamazoo, Michigan. David Markin, chairman/president.

Historical Footnotes: A completely different kind of Checker was anticipated for 1983. Thoughts about a replacement for the antiquated, three-decades-old design stretched back a dozen years. There had been a Ghia-designed prototype in 1970. A proposal from a Michigan design/engineering company had been rejected in 1975. Ed Cole, who had joined Checker after retiring as GM president in the mid-1970s, naturally envisioned a further connection with General Motors, the longtime supplier of Checker's drivetrains. Some thought was given to making the new Checker a stretched version of GM's X body, but obstacles shunted aside that prospect. It would definitely be front-drive, in any case. *Motor Trend* magazine reported that the next choice was a GM mid-size chassis, with special independent rear suspension (dubbed "Marsh Mellow") developed by Jerry Marsh of Firestone. Amid speculation that three wheelbases would be offered on that platform, the company instead went out of business. After six decades of production, the final Checker automobile was built on July 12, 1982.

What better vehicle for an afternoon of scenic motoring than a 1966 Checker Marathon. An option in that year was Chevrolet power under the hood, including a bowtie-built 327-cid V-8.

1960 Checker, Superba Special, four-door sedan, OCW

Above and below, 1963 Checker, Marathon, four-door sedan, OCW

1970 Checker, Marathon, four-door sedan, OCW

1970 Checker, Marathon, station wagon, OCW

1962 Checker, Marathon, station wagon, OCW

1964 Checker, Marathon, four-door sedan, OCW

1966 Checker, Marathon, station wagon, OCW

1970 Checker, Marathon Deluxe, nine-passenger four-door sedan, OCW

1975 Checker, Marathon Deluxe, four-door sedan, OCW

HUDSON 1910-1942

HUDSON — Detroit, Michigan — (1910-1942 et. seq.) — The first advertisement appeared in *The Saturday Evening Post* on June 19, 1909, the first car left the factory on July 8th, by the following July more than 4,000 Hudsons had been sold for the biggest first-year business yet recorded in the automobile industry. It was an auspicious beginning. But it wasn't really surprising. The men behind the Hudson were Roy D. Chapin and Howard E. Coffin, veterans of Olds Motor Works, who had just recently built the Thomas-Detroit and the Chalmers-Detroit. Joining them in partnership in 1908 were George W. Dunham and Roscoe B. Jackson, also graduates of Olds. Putting up the money was Joseph L. Hudson, probably the only member of the venture who had any misgivings, but his niece was Roscoe Jackson's wife, and gentle family pressure combined with the fact that $90,000 wasn't an outlandish sum for the man who owned Detroit's most successful department store proved ultimately persuasive. On February 24, 1909, the Hudson Motor Car Company had been organized with a capital stock of $100,000, by spring the firm had bought the Selden patent license of the defunct Northern and had moved into the factory of the defunct Aerocar, and by summer the company was in business. The car that enjoyed that record-breaking first year success was a 20 hp four good for 50 mph, priced at $900 and offered only as a racy and brassy little roadster on a 110-inch wheelbase. It was introduced as a 1910 model. Though it carried the soon-to-be-famous Hudson triangle, the emblem was brass on the Model 20. It turned white with the introduction of the Model 33 for 1911, a larger monobloc four on a 114-1/2-inch wheelbase with prices now edging upwards of $1,000 and with a spartan but speedy new two-seater called the Mile-a-Minute Roadster — and guaranteeing that — available in 1912. All this was but a prelude, however, for already Coffin (the engineering genius of the Hudson group) was working on the car that would transform Hudson's auspicious beginning into a long-term solid industry success. By now the company had moved into its brand-new Albert Kahn-designed factory at the corner of Jefferson and Conner Avenues in Detroit, and it was there that the prototype of the first Hudson six was completed in July of 1912. It was introduced for the 1913 model year, promising 65 mph in touring trim for $2,450, and was followed in 1914 by a lightweight six offering similar performance for only $1,550. Prior to Hudson, fast-paced sixes had primarily been the preserve of luxury car manufacturers. By 1914, all Hudsons were sixes, with over 10,000 built that year, over 12,000 the year following as the company began advertising itself as the "world's largest manufacturer of six-cylinder cars." At the New York Automobile Show in January 1916, the Super Six arrived — and it was that, an entirely new L-head engine with improved cylinder head design for a 5.0:1 compression ratio on standard fuel and a puissant 76 bhp at 3000 rpm. In April at Daytona, Ralph Mulford drove a Super Six to a new one-mile straightaway stock car record of 102.5 mph; in May at Sheepshead Bay the 24-hour stock speed record was taken at a 75.8 mph average, a mark that would stand for 15 years; in August Mulford's climb up Pikes Peak in 18 minutes-25 seconds represented a new class record to stand for eight years; in September Mulford with co-drivers Vincent and Patterson got into a Super Six seven-passenger touring car in San Francisco.

Hudson Data Compilation by Robert C. Ackerson

Five days-three hours-31 minutes later they were in New York City to break the Marmon's previous cross-country record, then they turned around and drove back to San Francisco to establish America's first ever double-transcontinental. Hudson sales doubled that year, too—to more than 25,000 cars. The Super Six would remain the solid rock around which Hudson fortunes revolved for a decade, followed in 1928 by the 91 hp Special Six, an F-head that was an amalgam of the meritorious engineering features of the Essex four- and six-cylinder engines as well as the venerable Hudson unit. The Essex, introduced for 1918, was Hudson's low-priced companion car and by the mid-Twenties had forcefully carried forward the Hudson focus on closed car production (begun in 1916 when the company sold more sedans than either Ford or Chevrolet) with the offering of a closed coach for less than a touring car, heretofore unheard of in the industry. Be they open or closed models, some Hudsons of the later Twenties and early Thirties carried custom bodies, initially from Biddle & Smart, later Murray, Briggs and occasionally LeBaron. In 1930, in the chassis on which these—and all Hudsons—were built was a straight-eight, which was essentially the Essex six with two cylinders added. It was called the Great Eight, though at 80 hp, it was less powerful than the big six. It became heftier in horses subsequently, and a big six was soon returned to the line. In 1931, Frank Spring, formerly of Murphy, joined the company as styling director. By now most of the original team members who had started Hudson had retired or died, save for Roy Chapin who had a short sojourn in Washington as President Hoover's Secretary of Commerce but who returned to Hudson in 1933. His company's hottest car now was the Terraplane, which would spur sales immeasurably, but like every other business in America, Hudson's financial outlook was lukewarm at best. The strain of keeping the company afloat hastened his death at age 56 in February 1936. Taking over now were A.E. Barit as president, who had begun as a stenographer for the company in 1910; and Stuart G. Baits as engineering vice-president, who had entered Hudson as a draftsman in 1915. Hudsons for 1934 had seen introduction of "Axle-Flex," a semi-independent front suspension; and 1935 brought the "Electric Hand," a vacuum-powered automatic gearshift built by Bendix and not a particularly good idea. Though beauty be in the proverbial beholder's eye, the look of the 1936 and later Hudsons was perhaps not a good idea either, though the appearance of the 1940 line ("symphonic styling," the company said) was nice and tidy. Tidy, too, were records resulting at Bonneville by a stock 1940 model—now with fully independent front suspension—driven by John Cobb to capture virtually every AAA Class C closed car record from one mile to 3,000 kilometers, and from one hour to 12, the half-day completed at a terrific 91.29 mph. Despite the vagaries of the Depression, the Hudson Motor Car Company had survived the Thirties in good order. In 1941, the company made a profit of $3,756,000. On February 5, 1942, Hudson ceased building cars, for the duration of the war its factories turning out machine guns and aircraft components. Hudson's best prewar year had been 1929, with over 300,000 cars produced, a figure the company would never approach again. Although there would be some interesting and spirited cars built postwar, the glory years of the Hudson were already behind it.

1910

HUDSON — MODEL 20 — FOUR: The Model Twenty roadster was an extremely handsome automobile that Hudson advertised as "Strong — Speedy — Roomy — Stylish." In the first public announcement the Twenty was touted as an automobile that was far and away superior to its competitors. Included in its initial price were two headlamps, generator, side oil lamps, a tool set and a horn. Both the Hudson's appointments and design belied its low $900 price. The early models were finished in maroon with black striping and fenders. The interior was blue-black leather. The radiator, steering column, side lamp brackets, hubcaps and side control levers were finished in brass and the entry step plate was of aluminum. Hudson pointed with pride to the features the Twenty shared with far more expensive automobiles. For example, its sliding gear transmission was "such as you find on the Packard, Peerless, Pierce, Lozier and other high grade cars." The Hudson engine was described as "the Renault type and Renault Motors are the pride of France." The larger 110-inch wheelbase foredoor roadster and touring models were less graceful than the roadster but their body styles enabled Hudson to expand its share of the market. By the end of 1910 it ranked 17th in U.S. automobile sales.

I.D. DATA: Serial numbers found in two locations, on plate on front seat riser and on right side of frame. Starting: 1. Ending: 7100. Engine number location: NA. Starting: NA. Ending: NA

Note: Initially the Twenty was powered by an engine supplied by the Atlas Motor Company of Indianapolis. As production increased the Buda company of Harvey, Illinois, also supplied engines.

Model 20

Model No.	Body Type & Seating	Factory Price	Shipping Weight	Prod. Total
20	Open Rds.-3P	900	1800	4000
20	2-dr. Rds.-3P	1200	1800	1000
20	2-dr. Tr. Car-5P	1150	2000	2099

Note 1: Beginning in January 1910 the price of the Model 20 open roadster was increased to $1,000.

Note 2: The Model 20 two-door roadster differed from the open roadster by having two small doors. However, that on the right side was not operational due to the position of the outside controls!

1910 Hudson, Model 20, touring, OCW

1910 Hudson, Model 20, open roadster, OCW

1911 Hudson, Model 33, touring, OCW

1915 Hudson, Model 6-40, touring, OCW

1913 Hudson, Model 54, touring, OCW

Note 3: Production total on Model 20 open roadster included approximately 1,100 cars built in 1909 but announced as 1910 models by Hudson.

Note 4: Price on the Model 20 two-door touring included three oil lamps, two gas lamps, generator, horn, tire repair kit, tools and jack.

ENGINE: Inline Four. Cast iron block. B & S: 3-3/4 x 4-1/2 in. Disp. 198.8 cu. in. Brake H.P.: 20. A.L.A.M./H.P.: 22.5. Main bearings: two. Valve lifters: mechanical. Carb.: Holley, Mayer and Stromberg Model B carburetors were used.

CHASSIS: [Model 20 roadster] W.B.: 100 in. Tires: 32 x 3 front; 32 x 3-1/2 rear. [Model 20 fore-door roadster] W.B.: 110 in. Tires: 32 x 3-1/2. [Model 20 touring] W.B.: 110 in. Tires: 32 x 3-1/2.

***Note** — There was only one series — Model 20 — but the three different body types warrant identification. After January 1910, the Twenty designation was abandoned and the three Hudsons were advertised as either the roadster, touring car or fore-door roadster.

TECHNICAL: Sliding gear transmission. Speeds: 3F/1R. Floor shift controls. Leather-faced cone clutch. Shaft drive. Semi-floating rear axle. Overall ratio: NA. Mechanical brakes on two wheels. Wood wheels. Rim size: 32 in.

OPTIONS: Bosch magneto, top, Presto-O-Lite tank, rumbleseat available as a group option for the roadster, priced at $150. "Zig-Zag" windshield ($40). Rumbleseat or 25 gallon fuel tank (fore-door roadster) (NA).

HISTORICAL: Introduced June 1909. October 1909 preliminary (10-lap Massapequa Cup) to Vanderbilt Cup race, set fastest lap, finished fourth. Hudson offered a competition model, the Express, which won a 24-hour race held at Seattle, Washington. From July 1909 through December 1909 1,108 cars were shipped. Calendar year production: 7,100 cars. Hudson made 4,556 shipments to dealers during the 1910 calendar year. Model year production approximately 8,200. The president of Hudson was Roy D. Chapin.

1911

HUDSON — MODEL 33 — FOUR: The Model 33 was an entirely new Hudson designed by Howard E. Coffin. As such it is usually accepted as the first of the true Hudson automobiles. Its monobloc engine had its intake and exhaust valves on opposite sides of the cylinder head and they were completely enclosed. The Model 33's clutch with its cork facings was enclosed in an oil-filled unit along with its disc. This was expensive to manufacture but it soon gave the Model 33 a deserved reputation for smooth operation. The Model 33's styling was conventional with high crowned fenders, exposed controls and suspension components. However the distinctive shape of its radiator with the already well-known triangular Hudson crest and the large letters spelling HUDSON across its surface made it easy to pick out a Model 33 from the competition.

HUDSON — MODEL 20 — FOUR: No changes were made in the Model 20 for 1911.

I.D. DATA: Car number on front seat riser plate and on right side of frame: Starting: [Model 20] 7101, [Model 33] 7501. Ending: [Model 20] 9000, [Model 33] 15000. Engine numbers on right front of cylinder block. Starting: NA. Ending: NA.

Note: Model 20 engine built by Buda Company. The Model 33 engine was manufactured by the Continental Motor Manufacturing Company of Muskegon, Michigan. During 1911 a new plant was built by Continental in Detroit and it then became Hudson's only supplier of engines.

Model 20

Model No.	Body Type & Seating	Factory Price	Shipping Weight	Prod. Total
20	Rds.	1000	1800	400
20	Fore Dr. Rds.-3P	1200	1800	NA
Model 33				
33	2-dr. Tr.-5P	1250	2250	1500
33	3-dr. Fore Dr. Tr.-5P	1600	2250	500
33	2-dr. Pony Ton.	1300	2360	3500
33	3-dr. Torpedo Tr.-5P	1350	2460	2000

ENGINE: [Model 20] Inline Four. Cast iron block. B & S: 3-3/4 x 4-1/2 in. Disp. 198.8 cu. in. Brake H.P.: 26. N.A.C.C. H.P.: 22.5. Main bearings: two. Valve lifters: mechanical. Carb.: Stromberg Model B. [Model 33] Inline Four. Cast iron block. B & S: 4 x 4-1/2 in. Disp.: 226 cu. in. Brake H.P.: 33. N.A.C.C. H.P.: 26.6. Main bearings: two. Valve lifters: mechanical. Carb.: Stromberg.

CHASSIS: [Model 20] W.B.: 110 in. Tires: 32 x 3-1/2. [Model 33] W.B.: 114 in. Tires: 34 x 3-1/2.

TECHNICAL: Sliding gear transmission. Speeds: 3F/1R. Floor shift controls. Leather-faced clutch. [Model 20] cork insert, wet clutch [Model 33]. Shaft drive. Semi-floating rear axle. Overall ratio: NA. Mechanical brakes on two wheels. Wood wheels. Rim size: [Model 20] 32 in. [Model 33] 34 in.

OPTIONS: Front bumper. Rear bumper. Double rumbleseat — Model 20. 25-gallon fuel tank.

HISTORICAL: Introduced October 1910. Hudson made 6,486 shipments to dealers during the 1911 calendar year. Model year production was approximately 7,900. The president of Hudson was Roy D. Chapin.

1912

HUDSON — MODEL 33 — FOUR: The Model 20 was dropped from the 1912 line and all Hudsons were Model 33s. There were no major mechanical or styling changes but a total of seven body types was available including the 60 mph, Mile-A-Minute Roadster. Unlike the standard roadster this two-seater was fitted with 32-inch wheels and was not equipped with doors or a windshield. An interesting piece of standard equipment was a 100 mph speedometer. Hudson continued to tout the engineering virtues of the Model 33 in 1912. Potential customers were warned to "Beware of unsafe motor car purchases" that were out of date due to rapid engineering advances. In contrast the Model 33 was depicted as a car that possessed more advanced features than any other automobile. In mid-model year the Disco self starter built by the Disco Company of Grand Rapids, Michigan, became standard equipment for the Model 33. With a weight of just 4-1/2 pounds and only 12 moving parts, it was an appropriate addition to the Model 33, which Hudson claimed had "approximately 1,000 fewer parts" than the average car.

I.D. DATA: Car number on front seat riser plate and right side of frame. Starting: 15001. Ending: 27200 upward. Engine number on left side of front motor mount.

Note: Hudson continued to use Continental built engines.

Model 33

Model No.	Body Type & Seating	Factory Price	Shipping Weight	Prod. Total
33	3-dr. Tr.-5P	1600	2757	NA
33	3-dr. Torp.-4P	1600	2737	NA
33	Mile-A-Minute Rds.-2P	1600	NA	NA
33	2-dr. Comm. Rds.-2P	1600	2631	NA
33	4-dr. Limo.-7P	2750	NA	NA
33	2-dr. Cpe.-2P	2250	NA	NA
33	3-dr. Torp.-5P	1600	2737	NA

ENGINE: Inline. Four-cylinder. Cast iron block. B & S: 4 x 4-1/2 in. Disp. 226 cu in. Brake H.P.: 33. N.A.C.C. H.P.: 26.6. Main bearings: two. Valve lifters: mechanical. Carb. Stromberg.

CHASSIS: [Model 33] W.B.: 144-1/2 in. Frt./Rear Tread: 56 in. Tires: 34 x 4.

TECHNICAL: Sliding gear transmission. Speeds: 3F/1R. Floor shift controls. Cork inserts, wet clutch. Shaft drive. Semi-floating rear axle. Mechanical brakes on two wheels. Wood wheels. Rim size: 34 in.

OPTIONS: Front bumper. Rear bumper. All Model 33s with exception of the Mile-A-Minute Roadster were delivered with a top, windshield, Bosch dual ignition Prest-O-Lite gas tank or generator as standard equipment.

HISTORICAL: Introduced July 1911. Hudson made 5,708 shipments to dealers during the 1912 calendar year. The president of Hudson was Roy D. Chapin.

1913

HUDSON — MODEL 37 — FOUR: 1913 Hudsons were easily identified by their lack of an externally mounted crank. However, a crank was packed in with the Hudson's standard equipment tool kit. In addition, the longer wheelbase of the Model 37 set it apart from the older Model 33. The most stylish Hudson in either the Model 37 or Model 54 lines was the torpedo. Compared to the touring car body, its cowl was extended slightly and a shorter windshield was installed. The front seat and steering wheel were also repositioned slightly further back.

HUDSON — MODEL 54 — SIX: The Model 54 introduced Hudson's new six-cylinder engine. Its success enabled Hudson to both proclaim itself "the world's largest producer of six-cylinder automobiles" and declare in August 1913 a stock dividend of 100 percent. The six-cylinder Hudson's top speed was approximately 65 mph and it could reach 58 mph in 30 seconds. With the 127-inch wheelbase the Model 54 was easily set apart from the Model 37 line. Both Model 37 and Model 54 were equipped with a Delco starting system in place of the older and less-efficient Disco acetylene-gas unit.

I.D. DATA: Car number on front seat riser plate and on right side of frame. Starting: [Model 37] 30001, [Model 54] 45001. Ending: [Model 37] 39200, [Model 54] 56000. Engine number on left side of cylinder block [Model 54], right front of cylinder block [Model 37].

Note 1: The Model 37 engine was supplied by Continental, which gave it a Model C designation.

Model 37

Model No.	Body Type & Seating	Factory Price	Shipping Weight	Prod. Total
37	2-dr. Rds.-2P	1875	3173	NA
37	3-dr. Torpedo-5P	1875	3350	NA
37	3-dr. Tr. Car-5P	1875	3390	NA
37	2-dr. Cpe.-3P	2350	3408	85
37	3-dr. Limo.-7P	3250	3680	41
Model 54				
54	2-dr. Rds.-2P	2450	3588	NA
54	3-dr. Torpedo-5P*	2450	3748	NA
54	3-dr. Tr. Car-7P	2600	3870	NA
54	3-dr. Tr. Car-5P	2450	3823	NA
54	3-dr. Limo.-7P	3750	4110	59
54	2-dr. Cpe.-3P	2950	3933	15

* Re-designated the phaeton in February 1913.

ENGINE: [Model 54] Inline. Six-cylinder. Cast iron block. B & S: 4-1/8 x 5-1/4 in. Disp.: 421 cu. in. Brake H.P.: 54 @ 1500 R.P.M. N.A.C.C. H.P.: 40.84. Main bearings: three. Valve lifters: mechanical. [Model 37] Inline. Four-cylinder. Cast iron block. B & S: 4-1/8 x 5-1/4. Disp. 280.6 cu. in. Brake H.P.: 37 @ 1500 R.P.M. N.A.C.C. H.P.: 27.23. Main bearings: three. Valve lifters: mechanical.

CHASSIS: [Model 37] W.B.: 118 in. Frt/Rear Tread: 56 in. Tires: 34 x 4. [Model 54] W.B.: 127 in. Frt/Rear Tread: 56 in. Tires: 36 x 4-1/2.

TECHNICAL: Sliding gear transmission. Speeds: 3F/1R. Floor shift controls. Cork insert, wet clutch. Shaft drive. Semi-floating rear axle. Mechanical brakes on two wheels. Wood wheels. Rim size: 34 in. [Model 37] 36 in. [Model 54].

OPTIONS: Front bumper. Rear bumper. Standard equipment both of the Model 37 and Model 54 was extensive, including electric starting and lights, illuminated dash, mohair top, side curtains, "rain vision" windshield, speedometer, clock and demountable rims. Jump seats for touring car models ($40).

HISTORICAL: Introduced July 1912 — Model 37, August 1912 — Model 54. Innovations: Delco starting system. Hudson made 6,404 shipments to dealers during the 1913 calendar year. The president of Hudson was Roy D. Chapin.

1914

HUDSON — MODEL SIX-40 — SIX: Hudson was strictly a manufacturer of six-cylinder automobiles in 1914 and while the new Six-40 Series was larger than the four-cylinder models they replaced, their prices were reduced. The new engine's dimensions of 3-1/2 inch bore and 5 inch stroke pointed towards future American practice and offered both better fuel economy and more power than the old four. Appearance changes included enclosed hinges on all models and a reshaped radiator with smooth curves.

HUDSON — MODEL SIX-54 — SIX: Hudson's senior six series, the Six-54 now had a long 135-inch wheelbase and featured, along with the Six-40, new styling. The Hudson grille still carried the familiar triangular logo but its rounded form joined the more gently curved fenders and the smooth lines of the cowl as clear indicators that the Hudson was abandoning the angular appearance of earlier models. Also adding to the Hudson's visual appeal was its windshield, which for the first time was designed as a fully integrated part of its body.

I.D. DATA: Car number on front seat riser plate and on right side of frame. Starting: [Six-40] 63001, [Six-54] 565001. Ending: [Six-40] 77201, [Six-54] 62500. Engine number on left side of cylinder block.

Note: The Six-54 engine was a Continental 6C model. The Six-40 engine was designated 7N by Continental.

Model SIX-40

Model No.	Body Type & Seating	Factory Price	Shipping Weight	Prod. Total
Six-40	2-dr. Rds.-2P	1750	2822	NA
Six-40	4-dr. Phae.-6P	1750	2977	NA
Six-40	2-dr. Cabr.-2P	1950	2976	NA
Six-40	4-dr. Tr.-5P	1750	2968	NA
Six-40	4-dr. Tr.-5P (right-hand drive)	1750	2974	NA
Six-40	4-dr. Phae.-7P	2250	3939	NA
Model SIX-54				
Six-54	2-dr. Sed.-5P	3100	4100	NA

ENGINE: [Model Six-40] Inline. Six-cylinder. Cast iron block. B & S: 3-1/2 x 5 in. Disp. 288.5 cu. in. Brake H.P.: 40. S.A.E. H.P.: 29.4. Main bearings: three Valve lifters: mechanical. [Model Six-54] Inline. Six-cylinder. Cast iron block. B & S: 4-1/8 x 5-1/4 in. Disp.: 421 cu. in. Brake H.P.: 54 @ 1500 R.P.M. N.A.C.C. H.P.: 40.84. Main bearings: three. Valve lifters: mechanical.

CHASSIS: [Model Six-40] W.B.: 123 in. Frt/Rear Tread: 56 in. Tires: 34 x 4. [Model Six-54] W.B.: 135 in. Frt/Rear Tread: 56 in. Tires: 36 x 4-1/2.

TECHNICAL: Sliding gear transmission. Speeds: 4F/1R, 3F/1R (Model Six-40). Floor shift controls. Cork insert, wet clutch. Shaft drive. Semi-floating rear axle. Mechanical brakes on two (rear) wheels. Artillery type wood wheels. Rim size: 36 in., 34 in. (Model Six-40).

OPTIONS: Front bumper. Rear bumper. Wire wheels, radiator cap with Hudson triangle identification.

HISTORICAL: Introduced August 1913 — Six-54. November 1913 — Six-40. Hudson made 10,261 shipments to dealers during the 1914 calendar year. The president of Hudson was Roy D. Chapin.

1915

HUDSON — MODEL SIX-40 — SIX: The new Hudson models were externally identified by their honeycomb type radiators (previous models were fitted with horizontal-finned versions) and higher mounted headlamp tie-bar. All models also had a smoother radiator/hood line. Open cars (roadster and phaeton) had a new non-folding two-piece windshield design whose upper portion pivoted from the top of the side brackets. On the Six-40 models a revamped interior arrangement placed the gas pedal between the brake and clutch pedals. A new electric horn was activated by the steering wheel center mounted button. Mechanically the Six-40 for 1915 had a new tubular driveshaft and a tapered frame that allowed for a slightly shorter turning radius. Other improvements to the Six-40 for 1915 included a horsepower increase to 42, a cast enbloc manifold, more efficient pre-heating of carburetor air and a hollow rather than solid driveshaft.

HUDSON — MODEL SIX-54 — SIX: Changes in the Six-54 were limited to the use of the honeycomb radiator and smoother radiator/hoodline as adopted by the Six-40.

I.D. DATA: Car number on front seat riser plate and on right side of frame. Starting: [Six-40] 73501, [Six-54] 59001. Ending: [Six-40] 90000, [Six-54] 62000. Engine number on left side of cylinder block.

Model SIX-40

Model No.	Body Type & Seating	Factory Price	Shipping Weight	Prod. Total
Six-40	2-dr. Rds.-3P	1550	2772	NA
Six-40	4-dr. Phae.-7P	1550	2922	NA
Six-40	2-dr. Cabr.-3P	1750	2946	NA
Six-40	2-dr. Cpe.-4P	2150	3162	NA
Six-40	4-dr. Limo. Landaulet-7P	2700	3432	NA
Six-40	4-dr. Limo-7P	2550	3362	NA
Six-40	4-dr. R.H. Phae.-7P	1550	2922	NA
Model SIX-54				
Six-54	4-dr. Phae.-7P	2350	3965	NA
Six-54	2-dr. Sed.-5P	3100	NA	NA
Six-54	4-dr. Limo.-7P	3500	4226	NA

ENGINE: [Model Six-40] Inline. Six-cylinder. Cast iron block. B & S: 3-1/2 x 5 in. Disp.: 288.5 cu. in. Brake H.P.: 42. N.A.C.C. H.P.: 29.4. Main bearings: four. Valve lifters: mechanical. [Model Six-54] Inline. Six-cylinder. Cast iron block. B & S: 4-1/2 x 5-1/4 in. Disp.: 421 cu. in. Brake H.P.: 55 @ 1500 R.P.M. N.A.C.C. H.P.: 40.84. Main bearings: three. Valve lifters: mechanical.

CHASSIS: [Model Six-40] W.B.: 123 in. Frt/Rear Tread: 56 in. Tires: 34 x 4. [Model Six-54] W.B. 135 in. Frt/Rear Tread: 56 in. Tires: 36 x 4-1/2.

TECHNICAL: Sliding gear transmission. Speeds: 4F/1R, 3F/1R (Model Six-40). Floor shift controls. Cork insert, wet clutch. Shaft drive. Semi-floating rear axle. Mechanical brakes on two rear wheels. Artillery-type wood wheels. Rim size: 36 in., 34 in. (Model Six-40).

1915 Hudson, Model 6-40, limo landaulet, OCW

1921 Hudson, Super Six, four-passenger coupe, OCW

1922 Hudson, Super Six, touring, OCW

1926 Hudson, Super Six, coach, OCW

OPTIONS: Front bumper. Rear bumper. Wire wheels.

HISTORICAL: Introduced June 1914. Hudson made 12,864 shipments to dealers during the 1915 calendar year. The president of Hudson was Roy D. Chapin.

1916

HUDSON — MODEL SIX-40 — SERIES G-SIX: The Six-40's model run was a short one, lasting from June 1915 to January 1916 when it, as well as the unchanged Six-54, was replaced by the Super Six. The Six-40 featured both styling and engineering changes. The beltline was given a gentle curve to further enhance the "yacht-line" styling that had been an advertised feature since 1913, and both entry into and riding in a Hudson became a bit more enjoyable due to wider doors and a roomier interior. On open models the upper portion of the beltline was leather-covered. Hudson also touted its new "Ever-Lustre" finish, which in a veiled reference to rust and corrosion, it noted "combats as never before the main cause of depreciation." In preparation for the new Super Six and a change of philosophy regarding annual model changes Hudson identified the last of the Six-40s as Series G.

I.D. DATA: Car number on front seat riser plate and on right side of frame. Starting: [Series G] G10001. Ending: [Series G] G40000. Engine number on left side of cylinder block.

Series G

Model No.	Body Type & Seating	Factory Price	Shipping Weight	Prod. Total
Series G	2-dr. Rds.-3P	1350	2900	NA
Series G	4-dr. Phae.-7P	1350	3033	NA
Series G	2-dr. Cabr.-3P	1650	3009	NA
Series G	2-dr. Cpe.-4P	2000	3240	NA
Series G	2-dr. Tr.Sed.-7P	1875	3330	NA
Series G	4-dr. Limo.-7P	2450	3535	NA
Series G	4-dr. Twn. Car-7P	—	3370	NA

ENGINE: Inline. Six-cylinder. Cast iron block. B & S: 3-1/2 x 5 in. Disp.: 288.5 cu. in. C.R.: 5.0:1. Brake H.P.: 42. N.A.C.C. H.P.: 29.4. Main bearings: four. Valve lifters: mechanical.

CHASSIS: [Model Six-40] W.B.: 123 in. Frt/Rear Tread: 56 in. Tires: 34 x 4.

TECHNICAL: Sliding gear transmission. Speeds: 3F/1R. Floor shift controls. Cork insert, wet clutch. Shaft drive. Semi-floating rear axle. Mechanical brakes on two (rear) wheels. Artillery-type wood wheels. Rim size: 34 in.

OPTIONS: Front bumper. Rear bumper. Wire wheels.

HISTORICAL: Introduced June 1916. Hudson made 25,772 shipments to dealers during the 1916 calendar year. The president of Hudson was Roy D. Chapin.

HUDSON — SUPER SIX — SERIES H — SIX: Hudson made motoring history with the introduction of the Super Six. Not only was this car powered by the first Hudson-built engine but it established a new benchmark by which the performance of production automobiles would be measured. The Super Six four-bearing crankshaft was fitted with eight counterweights, for which Hudson received a patent. Other notable advancements included larger valves, a high 5.0:1 compression ratio and excellent porting. With considerable justification Hudson called the Super-Six "the greatest motor built." In production until 1926 it established Hudson as a manufacturer whose six-cylinder engines made a mockery of performance claims made by producers of far more expensive automobiles.

I.D. DATA: Car numbers on front seat riser plate and on right side of frame. Starting: [Series H] H-1. Ending: [Series H] H-99999. Engine number on left side of cylinder block.

Series H

Model No.	Body Type & Seating	Factory Price	Shipping Weight	Prod. Total
Series H	2-dr. Rds.-2P	1375	3170	NA
Series H	4-dr. Phae.-7P	1375	3385	NA
Series H	2-dr. Cabr.-3P	1675	3310	NA
Series H	4-dr. Tr. Sed.-7P	1900	3600	NA
Series H	4-dr. Limo.-7P	2500	3750	NA
Series H	4-dr. Limo.-Landaulet-7P	2750	—	NA
Series H	4-dr. Twn. Car-7P	2500	3660	NA
Series H	4-dr. Twn. Car Landaulet-7P	2750	—	NA
Series J	4-dr. Phae.-4P	1750	3180	NA

ENGINE:Inline. Six-cylinder. Cast iron block. B & S: 3-1/2 x 5 in. Disp.: 289 cu. in. C.R.: 5.00:1. Brake H.P.: 76 @ 2450 R.P.M. N.A.C.C. H.P.: 29.4. Main bearings: four. Type of valve lifters: mechanical. Carb.: Hudson-built, side draft.

CHASSIS: [Series H] W.B.: 125-1/2 in. Frt/Rear Tread: 56 in. Tires: 35 x 4-1/2.

TECHNICAL: Sliding gear transmission. 3F/1R. Floor shift. Cork inserts, wet clutch. Shaft drive. Semi-floating rear axle. Mechanical brakes on two (rear) wheels. Artillery-type wood wheels. Rim size: 34 in.

OPTIONS: Front bumper. Rear bumper. Wire wheels, spare tire. The Series H phaeton had disc wheels and moto-meter as standard equipment.

HISTORICAL: Introduced January 16, 1916, following a series of Super Six speed runs made on a Long Island (New York) track in December 1915. Series H shipments to dealers were included in the 25,772 total for the 1916 calendar year. The president of Hudson was Roy D. Chapin. The Super Six set a new, transcontinental, San Francisco-New York record of 5 days, 3 hours, 31 minutes. After an eight-hour rest, the car, a stock touring car and its four-man crew headed back and arrived in San Francisco 5 days, 17 hours, 32 minutes later. At Daytona Beach on April 10, 1916, Ralph Mulford drove a Super-Six with a competition body to a new stock car chassis speed record of 102.53 mph. Mulford also set a new Pikes Peak record with a Super Six of 18 minutes, 24 seconds. Mulford's Daytona Beach record car also established a 24-hour mark for stock chassis automobiles at Sheepshead Bay, New York. His average of 74.8 mph for 1,819 miles stood for 15 years before it was eclipsed by a 16-cylinder Marmon.

1917

HUDSON — SUPER SIX — SERIES J — SIX: Beginning on December 1, 1916, the Series H Super Six was superseded by the Series J and 4J with a built-in radiator shutters and a Boyce moto-meter radiator cap. In addition, a different upholstery pattern was used on open phaetons, and the limousine version had a straight, instead of curved front door line and squared off window edges.

I.D. DATA: Car numbers on front seat riser plate and on right side of frame. Starting: [Series J] J-1, [Series 4J] 4J-75000. Ending: [Series J] J-96499, [Series 4J] 4J-97999. Engine number on left side of cylinder block.

Series J

Model No.	Body Type & Seating	Factory Price	Shipping Weight	Prod. Total
Series J	4-dr. Phae.-4P	1750	3180	NA
Series J	4-dr. Phae.-7P	1650	3220	NA
Series J	4-dr. Tr. Sed.-7P	2175	3450	NA
Series J	2-dr. Cabr.-3P	1950	3195	NA
Series J	4-dr. Limo.-7P	2925	3715	NA
Series J	4-dr. Limo. Lan.-7P	3025	3760	NA
Series J	4-dr. Twn. Car-7P	2925	3530	NA
Series J	4-dr. Twn. Car Lan.-7P	3025	3585	NA
Series J	2-dr. Tr. Sed.-5P	NA	NA	NA
Series J	2-dr. Rbt. Lan.	2350	3250	NA
Series 4J	4-dr. Sed.-7P	NA	3700	NA
Series 4J	4-dr. Tr. Limo.-4P	3150	3655	NA
Series 4J	4-dr. Full-Folding Lan.-4P	NA	NA	NA

ENGINE: Inline. Six-cylinder. Cast iron block. B & S: 3-1/2 x 5 in. Disp.: 289 cu. in. C.R.: 5.00:1. Brake H.P.: 76 @ 2450 R.P.M. N.A.C.C. H.P.: 29.4. Main bearings: four. Type of valve lifters: mechanical. Carb.: Hudson-built, side draft.

CHASSIS: [Series J] W.B.: 125-1/2 in. Frt/Rear Tread: 56 in. Tires: 35 x 4-1/2.

TECHNICAL: Sliding gear transmission. 3F/1R. Floor shift. Cork inserts, wet clutch. Shaft drive. Semi-floating rear axle. Mechanical brakes on two (rear) wheels. Artillery-type wood wheels. Rim size: 34 in.

OPTIONS: Front bumper. Rear bumper. Wire wheels, spare tire.

HISTORICAL: Introduced December 1, 1916. Calendar year shipment of Hudsons to dealers totaled 20,976. The president of Hudson was Roy D. Chapin. The Super Six continued its winning ways, with a four-car team enjoying numerous racing victories during 1917.

1918

HUDSON — SUPER SIX — SERIES M — SIX: Changes in the Super Six format were limited. The rear doors on phaeton models now were rear hinged and closed models were not equipped with external windshield visors.

I.D. DATA: Car number on front seat riser plate and on right side of frame. Starting: [Series M] M5000. Ending: [Series M] M97499. Engine number on left side of cylinder block/motor mount.

Series M

Model No.	Body Type & Seating	Factory Price	Shipping Weight	Prod. Total
Series M	4-dr. Phae.-4P	2050	3180	NA
Series M	4-dr. Phae.-7P	1950	3400	NA
Series M	2-dr. Rbt. Lan.-2P	2350	3250	NA
Series M	2-dr. Cabr.-3P	2650	3500	NA
Series M	2-dr. Cpe.-4P	2850	3450	NA
Series M	4-dr. Sed.-7P	2750	3700	NA
Series M	4-dr. Limo.-7P	3400	3715	NA
Series M	4-dr. Limo. Lan.-7P	3500	3760	NA
Series M	4-dr. Twn. Car-7P	3400	3605	NA
Series M	4-dr. Full-Folding Lan.-4P	4250	3765	NA
Series M	4-dr. Tr.Limo.-7P	3150	NA	NA
Series M	4-dr. Twn. Car Lan.-7P	3500	NA	NA

ENGINE: Inline. Six-cylinder. Cast iron block. B & S: 3-1/2 x 5 in. Disp.: 289 cu. in. C.R.: 5.0:1. Brake H.P.: 76 @ 2450 R.P.M. N.A.C.C. H.P.: 29.4. Main bearings: four. Valve lifters: mechanical. Carb.: Hudson-built, side draft.

CHASSIS: [Series M] W.B.: 125-1/2 in. Tires: 35 x 4-1/2*

*Four-passenger phaeton and runabout landau used 32 x 4-1/2 tires. The town car landaulette, town car and limousine landaulette were fitted with 33 x 5 tires.

TECHNICAL: Sliding gear transmission. 3F/1R. Floor shift. Cork inserts, running in oil. Shaft drive. Semi-floating rear axle. Mechanical brakes on two (rear) wheels. Wheels: 10 spoke wooden front, 12 spoke wooden rear. Rim size: 34 in.

OPTIONS: Front bumper. Rear bumper. Wire wheels. Windshield mounted spotlight. Runningboard mats. Leather top for runabout landaulette.

HISTORICAL: Introduced December 1917. Hudson made 12,526 shipments to dealers during the 1918 calendar year. The president of Hudson was Roy D. Chapin. The Hudson racing team was disbanded in August 1917.

1919

HUDSON SUPER SIX — SERIES O — SIX: All closed body Series O Hudsons had large external sun visors, and their front doors were now rear-hinged. Common to all Hudsons were new 12-spoke front wheels. Major chassis revision included larger seven-inch side frame rails, a larger and sturdier rear axle plus brakes with measurements of 2-1/2 x 15 inches. The Hudson's single taillight was moved from its left rear fender location on Series M to the rear cross member on Series O. Also identifying the Series O Hudsons were their higher gearshift and four-hinge doors. The Model M doors had three hinges.
Note 1: Hudson regarded the Series M Super Six as a 1919 model until the Series O was introduced in May 1919.

I.D. DATA: Car number on front seat riser plate and on right side of frame. Starting: [Series O] 5000. Ending: [Series O] 90999. Engine number of left side of cylinder block/motor mount.

Series O

Model No.	Body Type & Seating	Factory Price	Shipping Weight	Prod. Total
Series O	4-dr. Phae.-4P	2075	3320	NA
Series O	4-dr. Phae.-7P	1975	3475	NA
Series O	2-dr. Cabr.-3P	2450	3500	NA
Series O	2-dr. Cpe.-4P	2950	3530	NA
Series O	4-dr. Sed.-7P	2775	3775	NA
Series O	4-dr. Tr. Limo.-7P	3300	3730	NA
Series O	4-dr. Limo.-7P	3650	3800	NA
Series O	4-dr. Limo. Lan.-7P	NA	NA	NA
Series O	4-dr. Twn. Car-7P	NA	NA	NA
Series O	4-dr. Twn. Car Lan.-7P	NA	NA	NA

ENGINE: Inline. Six-cylinder. Cast iron block. B & S: 3-1/2 x 5 in. Disp. 289 cu. in. C.R.: 5.0:1. Brake H.P.: 76 @ 2450 R.P.M. N.A.C.C. H.P.: 29.4. Main bearings: four. Valve lifters: mechanical. Carb.: Hudson-built, side draft.

CHASSIS: [Series O] W.B.: 125-1/2 in. Frt/Rear Tread: 56 in. Tires: 34 x 4-1/2.

TECHNICAL: Sliding gear transmission. 3F/1R. Floor shift. Cork inserts, running in oil. Shaft drive. Semi-floating rear axle. Mechanical brakes on two (rear) wheels. Wood spoke wheels. Rim size: 34 in.

OPTIONS: Front bumper. Rear bumper. Wire wheels. Windshield mounted spotlight. Runningboard mats. Leather top for runabout landau.

HISTORICAL: Introduced May 1919. Hudson made 18,175 shipments to dealers during the 1919 calendar year. The president of Hudson was Roy D. Chapin. Six old Hudson racers attempted to qualify for the 1919 Indianapolis 500. Ira Vail's Hudson qualified at 94.1 mph and finished eighth. Just behind was car #21, a Hudson driven by Denny Hickey who averaged 80.22 mph for the 500 miles. Another Hudson, driven by Ora Haibe started in 26th position and was credited with 14th place at the race's end. Car #5, which was powered by a modified Hudson engine and had a qualifying average of 99.80 mph, was placed in the 14th position for the race's start. However it was out on lap 14 with a broken connecting rod.

1920

HUDSON — SUPER SIX — SERIES 10-0, SERIES 11-0, SERIES 12-0 — SIX: Hudson produced the Super Six in three series yet they were little changed from 1919. Most models were slightly heavier than their year-old counterparts. Although not used throughout the entire model run, a new front tie-bar was introduced that positioned the headlights notably higher.

I.D. DATA: Car number on front seat riser plate and on right side of frame. Starting: 5000. Ending: 91999. Engine number on left side of cylinder block/motor mount.

Super Six

Model No.	Body Type & Seating	Factory Price	Shipping Weight	Prod. Total
NA	4-dr. Phae.-4P	2600	3405	NA
NA	4-dr. Phae.-7P	2600	3575	NA
NA	2-dr. Cabr.-2P	NA	3550	NA
NA	2-dr. Cpe.-4P	3575	3620	NA
NA	4-dr. Tr.Limo.-7P	3925	3840	NA
NA	4-dr. Limo.-7P	4275	3860	NA
NA	4-dr. Sed.-7P	3400	3815	NA

Note: During the year Hudson made substantial price cuts.

ENGINE: Inline. Six-cylinder. Cast iron block. B & S: 3-1/2 x 5 in. Disp.: 289 cu. in. C.R.: 5.0:1. Brake H.P.: 76 @ 2450 R.P.M. N.A.C.C. H.P.: 29.4. Main bearings: four. Valve lifters: mechanical. Carb.: Hudson built, side draft.

CHASSIS: [Series 10-0] W.B.: 125-1/2 in. Frt/Rear Tread: 56 in. Tires: 34 x 4-1/2. [Series 11-0] W.B.: 125-1/2 in. Frt/Rear Tread: 56 in. Tires: 34 x 4-1/2. [Series 12-0] W.B.: 125-1/2 in. Frt/Rear Tread: 56 in. Tires: 34 x 4-1/2.

TECHNICAL: Sliding gear transmission. 3F/1R. Floor shift. Multiple disc, cork inserts, running in oil. Shaft drive. Semi-floating rear axle. Mechanical brakes on two (rear) wheels. Wood spoke wheels with detachable rims.

OPTIONS: Front bumper. Rear bumper. Wire wheels. Spotlight. Runningboard mats.

HISTORICAL: Introduced December 1919. Hudson made 22,268 shipments to dealers during the 1920 calendar year. The president of Hudson was Roy D. Chapin.

1921

HUDSON — SUPER SIX — SIX: From 1921 through 1923 Hudson annually produced, in effect two separate lines of automobiles. For example the initial 1921 models were essentially carryovers from 1920. Then in September revamped models also regarded as 1921 models were introduced. In turn these became 1922 models until May 1922 when new versions, also regarded as 1922 vintage debuted. The second run of 1921 models were identified by a revamped interior featuring a new steering wheel and instrument panel that placed all the instruments in a panel center mounted on the dash. In addition the classic H-shaped shifting gate was replaced with a rotating ball arrangement. Hudson also rearranged its foot controls by moving the accelerator from its position between the clutch and brake to the more logical location adjacent to the right side of the brake. External styling revisions of the second series Hudsons included heavier fenders with a more pronounced overlap and the installation of splash shields beneath the radiator.

I.D. DATA: Car number on front frame channel, dash and frame side. Starting: 100000. Ending: 499999 (serial number range 1921-23). Engine number on left side of cylinder block/motor mount.

Super Six

Model No.	Body Type & Seating	Factory Price	Shipping Weight	Prod. Total
NA	4-dr. Phae.-4P	NA	3405	NA
NA	4-dr. Phae.-7P	NA	3575	NA
NA	2-dr. Cabr.-2P	NA	3550	NA
NA	2-dr. Cpe.-4P	3275	3620	NA
NA	4-dr. Tr. Limo.-7P	3625	3840	NA
NA	4-dr. Limo.-7P	4000	3860	NA
NA	4-dr. Sed.-7P	3400	3815	NA

Note 1: Hudson reduced the prices of its automobiles twice during 1921, in June and August.

ENGINE: Inline. Six-cylinder. Cast iron block. B & S: 3-1/2 x 5 in. Disp.: 289 cu. in. C.R.: 5.0:1. Brake H.P.: 76 @ 2450 R.P.M. N.A.C.C. H.P.: 29.4. Main bearings: four. Valve lifters: mechanical. Carb.: Hudson-built, side draft.

CHASSIS: No series identification used during 1921-23. W.B.: 125-1/2 in. Frt/Rear Tread: 56 in. Tires: 34 x 4-1/2.

TECHNICAL: Sliding gear transmission. 3F/1R. Floor shift. Multiple disc, cork inserts, running in oil. Shaft drive. Semi-floating rear axle. Mechanical brakes on two (rear) wheels. Wood spoke wheels with detachable rims.

OPTIONS: Front bumper. Rear bumper. Spotlight. Wire wheels. Runningboard mats. Radiator shutters.

HISTORICAL: Introduced December 1, 1920, revamped models introduced September 1921. Hudson made 13,721 shipments to dealers during the 1921 calendar year. The president of Hudson was Roy D. Chapin. A competition-prepared Hudson won the Penrose trophy at the Pikes Peak hill climb with a time of 19 minutes, 16.1 seconds.

1922

HUDSON — SUPER SIX SERIES — SIX: Hudson moved out of the postwar sales depression in a strong fashion. In July price reductions ranging from $50 to $100 were announced and company president Roy D. Chapin reported that "the volume of shipment is now so great that certain savings have been effected in costs, and the public is to be given the benefit." Stockholders also received a share of Hudson's renewed prosperity since in September a dividend of 50 cents per share in non-par and $2.50 per share on par capital stock was declared. Although the new Essex coach captured the bulk of the public's attention, Hudson also introduced this new body style. During the first portion of the model year new drum-shaped headlights were adopted. Among the second line of Super Sixes for 1922, which debuted in May 1922, was a sedan with a Biddle & Smart body. Its styling, far more elegant than the Fisher-built body it replaced, pointed toward the classic Biddle & Smart-bodied Hudsons yet to come. Improvements to Hudson's long-lived Super Six included the adoption of aluminum pistons and a Morse timing chain in place of the older helical gear drive. Second series Hudsons had their batteries placed under the front seat.

I.D. DATA: Car number on front frame channel, dash and frame side. Starting: 100000. Ending: 499999 (series numbers range 1921-23). Engine number on left side of cylinder block/motor mount.

Super Six

Model No.	Body Type & Seating	Factory Price	Shipping Weight	Prod. Total
NA	4-dr. Phae.-4P	1695	3395	NA
NA	4-dr. Phae.-7P	1745	3445	NA
NA	2-dr. Cabr.-2P	2295	3550	NA
NA	2-dr. Cpe.-4P	2570	3620	NA
NA	2-dr. Cch.-5P	1625	3435	NA
NA	4-dr. Sed.-7P	2650	3785	NA
NA	4-dr. Tr. Limo.-5P	2920	3870	NA
NA	4-dr. Limo.-7P	3495	3860	NA
NA	4-dr. Spds.-4P	1525	3310	NA
NA	4-dr. Phae.-7P	1575	3455	NA
NA	4-dr. Sed.-7P*	2295	3720	NA

Note 1: *four-door sedan-seven-passenger: Biddle & Smart body.

ENGINE: Inline. Six-cylinder. Cast iron block. B & S: 3-1/2 x 5 in. Disp. 289 cu. in. C.R.: 5.0:1. Brake H.P.: 76 @ 2450 R.P.M. N.A.C.C. H.P.: 29.4. Main bearings: four. Valve lifters: mechanical. Carb.: Hudson-built, side draft.

CHASSIS: No series identification used 1921-23. W.B. 125-1/2 in. Frt/Rear Tread: 56 in. Tires: 34 x 4-1/2.

TECHNICAL: Sliding gear transmission. Speeds: 3F/1R. Floor shift controls. Multiple disc, cork inserts, running in oil. Shaft drive. Semi-floating rear axle. Mechanical brakes on two (rear) wheels. Wood spoke wheels with detachable rims.

OPTIONS: Front bumper. Rear bumper. Wire wheels. Runningboard mats. Radiator shutters.

HISTORICAL: Introduced December 1921, second version — May 1922. Hudson made 28,242 shipments to dealers during the 1922 calendar year. The president of Hudson was Roy D. Chapin. Hudsons finished first at Pikes Peak in hill climb with a time of 20 minutes, 5 seconds.

1923

HUDSON — SUPER SIX — SIX: Except for minor detail modifications that were incorporated as running changes during the year the 1923 Hudsons were virtually identical to the 1922 models. Among these revisions were the use of McKee "Spreadlight" headlight lenses, plus an extended length, 28-inch gearshift. This was an extremely profitable year for Hudson. Its fiscal year profits totaled nearly $14.5 million, up from the $12.6 million level of the previous year. Twice during the year the company declared an extra 25 cent dividend in addition to the regular 50 cent dividend. The Hudson Motor Car Company also made some significant changes in its top level management structure. Roy D. Chapin, after serving as president for 13 years became chairman of the board. His successor was Roscoe B. Jackson. Replacing Jackson as vice-president and treasurer was William J. McAneeny.

I.D. DATA: Car number on front frame channel, dash and frame side. Starting: 100000. Ending: 499999 (serial number range 1921-23). Engine number on left side of cylinder block.

Super Six

Model No.	Body Type & Seating	Factory Price	Shipping Weight	Prod. Total
NA	4-dr. Spds.-4P	1295	3395	NA
NA	4-dr. Phae.-7P	1350	3445	NA
NA	2-dr. Cch.-5P	1375	3433	NA
NA	2-dr. Cpe.	2570	3620	NA
NA	4-dr. Sed.-5P	1895	3620	NA
NA	4-dr. Sed.-7P	2095	3720	NA

Note 1: Four-door sedan-five-passenger: Biddle & Smart body.

Note 2: Two-door coupe and four-door sedan-seven-passenger: These two bodies were phased out of production during 1922.

ENGINE: Inline. Six-cylinder. Cast iron block. B & S: 3-1/2 x 5 in. Disp.: 289 cu. in. C.R.: 5.0:1. Brake H.P.: 76 @ 2450 R.P.M. N.A.C.C. H.P.: 29.4. Main bearings: four. Valve lifters: mechanical. Carb.: Stewart Warner.

CHASSIS: No series identification used 1921-23. W.B.: 125-1/2 in. Frt/Rear Tread: 56 in. Tires: 34 x 4-1/2.

TECHNICAL: Sliding gear transmission. Speeds: 3F/1R. Floor shift controls. Multiple disc, cork inserts, running in oil. Shaft drive. Semi-floating rear axle. Mechanical brakes on two (rear) wheels. Wood spoke wheels with detachable rims.

OPTIONS: Front bumper. Rear bumper. Spotlight. Steel disc wheels ($25.00). Spare wheel. Under seat heater. Radiator shutters.

HISTORICAL: Introduced December 1922. Hudson made 46,337 shipments to dealers during the 1923 calendar year. The president of Hudson was Roscoe B. Jackson.

1924

HUDSON — SUPER SIX — SIX: The initial line of Hudson Super-Six automobiles was virtually unchanged from those offered in the latter part of 1923. In mid-June they were replaced by significantly altered models. Styling changes included windshields with a curved lower edge and a raised hood line from radiator to cowl. A new fender crease line began to take Hudson away from the more rigid look of the early Twenties. A longer, 127.5-inch wheelbase also contributed to this effect. Mechanical changes were also extensive. New, smaller 33-inch wheels were fitted with new "balloon" type, 33 x 6.20 tires. To accom-

1926 Hudson, Super Six, sedan, OCW

1930 Hudson, Model U, touring sedan, OCW

1931 Hudson, Series T, Murray-bodied sport roadster, OCW

1932 Hudson, Major (Series L), brougham, OCW

1933 Hudson, Pacemaker (Series T), Standard coupe, OCW

1935 Hudson, Special (Series HT), business coupe, OCW

1935 Hudson, Special (Series HT), suburban sedan, OCW

modate this change the Hudson's steering and suspension were modified. Although its horsepower rating of 76 remained unchanged, the Super Six engine now had a separate intake manifold mounted on the right side. Previously the manifold had been on the opposite side of the engine and cast integrally with the block. The Hudson-made side draft carburetor was also replaced by a Detroit Lubricator model.

I.D. DATA: Car number on front frame channel, dash and frame side. Starting: 500001. Ending: 562016. Engine number on left side of cylinder block.

Super Six

Model No.	Body Type & Seating	Factory Price	Shipping Weight	Prod. Total
NA	4-dr. Sed.-5P	1895	3590	NA
NA	4-dr. Sed.-7P	2145	3675	NA
NA	4-dr. Sed.-5P	2145	3605	NA
NA	4-dr. Spds.-4P	1400	3275	NA
NA	4-dr. Phae.-7P	1500	3400	NA
NA	4-dr. Sed.-5P	2150	3585	NA
NA	2-dr. Cch.-5P	1395	3385	NA
NA	4-dr. Sed.-7P	2250	3640	NA

Note: Four-door sedan-five-passenger and four-door sedan-seven-passenger: Biddle & Smart body.

ENGINE: Inline. Six-cylinder. Cast iron block. B & S: 3-1/2 x 5 in. Disp. 289 cu. in. C.R.: 5.0:1. Brake H.P. 76 @ 2450 R.P.M. N.A.C.C. H.P.: 29.4. Main bearings: four. Valve lifters: mechanical. Carb.: Detroit Lubricator.

CHASSIS: No series designation used. W.B. 127-1/2 in. Tires: 33 x 6.20.

TECHNICAL: Sliding gear transmission. Speeds: 3F/1R. Floor shift controls. Multiple disc, cork inserts, running in oil. Shaft drive. Semi-floating rear axle. Mechanical brakes on two (rear) wheels. Wood spoke wheels with detachable rims.

OPTIONS: Front bumper. Rear bumper. Spotlight. Auxiliary seats & carpeting (sedan) ($115.00). Steel Tuarc disc wheels. Wire wheels. Radiator shutters.

HISTORICAL: Introduced December 1923 — new models introduced June 1924. Hudson made 59,427 shipments to dealers during the 1924 calendar year. The president of Hudson was Roscoe B. Jackson.

1925

HUDSON — SUPER SIX — SIX: Hudson did not make any significant changes in the appearance of its automobiles for 1925. However, beginning in June 1925 a handsome Biddle & Smart-bodied brougham model became available and proved to be the most popular Biddle & Smart Hudson ever offered. Hudson also revised its coach model during 1925 by reshaping its body to accept thinner side pillars and a windshield with a curved lower edge. In January a shift from 33 x 6.20 to 33 x 6.00 tires was announced. A total output of 269,474 Hudson and Essex automobiles put the Hudson Motor Car Company in third position behind Chevrolet and Ford for the 1925 calendar year.

I.D. DATA: Car number on front frame channel, dash and frame side. Starting: 562017. Ending: 672227. Engine number on left side of cylinder block/motor mount.

Super Six

Model No.	Body Type & Seating	Factory Price	Shipping Weight	Prod. Total
NA	2-dr. Cch.-4P	1345	3385	NA
NA	2-dr. Cch.-4P (A)	1165	3385	NA
NA	4-dr. Sed.-5P (B)	1695	3585	NA
NA	4-dr. Sed.-7P (B)	1650	3640	NA
NA	4-dr. Brgm.-4P (B)	1450	3425	NA
NA	4-dr. Phae.-7P	1200	3400	NA

Note 1: (A) This coach replaced the older coach in March 1925. Its Biddle & Smart body was constructed of aluminum.

Note 2: (B) Biddle & Smart body.

ENGINE: Inline. Six-cylinder. Cast iron block. B & S: 3-1/2 x 5 in. Disp. 289 cu. in. C.R.: 5.0:1. Brake H.P.: 76 @ 2450 R.P.M. N.A.C.C. H.P.: 29.4. Main bearings: four. Valve lifters: mechanical. Carb.: Detroit Lubricator.

CHASSIS: No series designations assigned. W.B. 127-1/2 in. Tires: 33 x 6.20 — replaced by 33 x 6.00 starting January 1925.

TECHNICAL: Sliding gear transmission. Speeds: 3F/1R. Floor shift controls. Multiple disc, cork inserts, running in oil. Shaft drive. Semi-floating rear axle. Mechanical brakes on two (rear) wheels. Wood spoke wheels with detachable rims.

OPTIONS: Front bumper. Rear bumper. Auxiliary seats and carpeting (sedan). Steel Tuarc disc wheels. Wire wheels. Radiator shutters.

HISTORICAL: Introduced December 1924. Hudson made 109,840 shipments to dealers during the 1925 calendar year. The president of Hudson was Roscoe B. Jackson.

1926

HUDSON — SUPER SIX — SIX: Although Hudson carried the style and design of its 1925 models in 1926, it was nonetheless an important year for Hudson. Recognition of the role Hudson had played in automotive history in developing the Essex coach came from *The New York Times* (January 10, 1926), which noted, "The flood of new, small closed sixes is one of the outstanding features of the year ... That the light, economical six makes a definite and potent appeal cannot be doubted. Indeed the Hudson and Essex organization has one of the most remarkable achievements of 1925 to its credit in the production of 250,000 cars both makes, almost entirely closed models." Hudson also moved boldly to expand its corporate base in 1926 with the opening of its new, three million dollar body plant whose first product was a revised coach for both Hudson and Essex. Mechanical changes consisted of revamped carburetor and intake manifold that Hudson said would improve fuel consumption by two mpg.

I.D. DATA: Car number on front frame channel, dash and frame side. Starting: 672228. Ending: 713809*. Engine number on left side of cylinder block/motor mount.

* In a letter to its dealers dated September 10, 1926, Hudson explained that it was instituting a yearly model classification starting with definite serial numbers. Thus the following cars were considered 1927 models, Hudson coach beginning with serial number 713810, sedans starting with serial number 714674 and broughams starting with serial number 716440.

Super Six

Model No.	Body Type & Seating	Factory Price	Shipping Weight	Prod. Total
NA	4-dr. Brgm.-4P	1450	3425	NA
NA	4-dr. Brgm.-5P	1395	3495	NA
NA	4-dr. Sed.-7P	1650	3640	NA
NA	4-dr. Tr. Car-7P	1300	3395	NA
NA	2-dr. Cch.-4P	1165	3470	NA
NA	2-dr. Cch. Sp.	1150	3440	NA

Note 1: Four-door brougham-five passenger: Biddle & Smart body replaced the older brougham mid-way through the model year.

Note 2: The four-door town car-seven passenger had the Biddle & Smart body.

Note 3: The two-door coach special was fitted with a Hudson-built body approximately two inches lower than the older version.

ENGINE: L-head. Inline. Six-cylinder. Cast iron block. B & S: 3-1/2 x 5 in. Disp.: 289 cu. in. C.R.: 5.0:1. Brake H.P.: 76 @ 2450 R.P.M. N.A.C.C. H.P.: 29.4. Main bearings: four. Valve lifters: mechanical. Carb.: Detroit Lubricator.

CHASSIS: No series designation used. W.B.: 127-1/2 in. Tires: 33 x 6.00.

TECHNICAL: Sliding gear transmission. Speeds: 3F/1R. Floor shift controls. Multiple disc, cork inserts, running in oil. Shaft drive. Semi-floating rear axle. Mechanical brakes on two (rear) wheels. Wood spoke wheels with detachable rims.

OPTIONS: Front bumper. Rear bumper. Spotlight. Radiator shutters.

HISTORICAL: Introduced December 1925. Hudson made 70,261 shipments to dealers during the 1926 calendar year. The president of Hudson was Roscoe B. Jackson.

1927

HUDSON — MODEL O & S — SIX: Hudsons for 1927 were radically changed automobiles. They were fitted with new 18-inch wheels, four wheel brakes, new rear suspension and styling that featured a higher radiator-hood line and fenders of full crown design. Headlamps were bullet-shaped and contributed along with a four-inch reduction in height to Hudson's attractive styling. Hudson also offered new exterior color choices to take full advantage of its new look and on models offered after late June a full-length beltline molding painted in a contrasting body color dramatically improved Hudson's appearance. The Model S Hudsons were mounted on a 118-inch wheelbase, while the Model O cars continued the 127-3/8 inch wheelbase. A startling development was the replacement of the veteran Super Six engine with a six-cylinder engine of F-head design. Also breaking with previous practice was the adoption of a single-plate clutch in place of the older multi-disc unit. Hudson had spent some $7 million to expand output of its factory to 1,800 cars per nine-hour day and Hudson chairman Roy D. Chapin understandably looked to the future with optimism. He noted however that "Buyers are now insistent that cars shall excel in appearance and convenience as well as in the fundamental qualities. The demand for improved performance is widespread and is being met by better design, material and workmanship."

I.D. DATA: Car numbers on front frame channel, dash and frame side. Starting: [Model O] 750000, [Model S] 1001. Ending: [Model O] 803568, [Model S] 12269. Starting: 713810 (carryover 1926 cars sold as 1927 models). Engine numbers on left side of cylinder block/motor mount. Starting: 438230. Ending: NA.

Model O

Model No.	Body Type & Seating	Factory Price	Shipping Weight	Prod. Total
O	Standard 2-dr. Cch.-5P	1285	3505	NA
O	Standard 4-dr. Sed.-5P	1385	3620	NA
O	Custom 2-dr. Rds.-2P	1500	3480	NA
O	Custom 4-dr. Sed.-5P	1750	3755	NA
O	Custom 4-dr. Phae.-7P	1600	3565	NA
O	Custom 4-dr. Sed.-7P	1850	3870	NA
O	Custom 4-dr. Brgm.-4P	1575	3660	NA
Model S				
S	Standard 2-dr. Cch.-5P	1175	3510	NA
S	Standard 4-dr. Sed.-5P	1285	3590	NA

Note 1: All Model O Custom Hudsons had Biddle & Smart bodies.

ENGINE: F-head. Inline. Six-cylinder. Cast iron block. B & S: 3-1/2 x 5 in. Disp. 288.5 cu. in. C.R.: 5.0:1. Brake H.P.: 92 @ 3200 R.P.M. N.A.C.C. H.P.: 29.4. Main bearings: four. Valve lifters: mechanical. Carb.: Marvel 1-1/4 in.

CHASSIS: [Model O] W.B. 127-3/8 in. O.L: 188 in. Tires: 31 x 6.00. [Model S] W.B. 118 in. O.L.: 178-1/2 in. Tires: 31 x 6.00.

TECHNICAL: Sliding gear transmission. Speeds: 3F/1R. Floor shift controls. Single disc, cork inserts, running in oil. Shaft drive. Semi-floating rear axle. Overall ratio: 4.09:1 — Model S, 4.45:1 — Model O. Bendix mechanical brakes on four wheels. Wood spoke wheels with detachable rims. Rim size: 19 x 4-1/2 in.

OPTIONS: Trunk. Bumpers — front and rear. Radiator shutters.

HISTORICAL: Introduced January 1927. Innovations: new F-head engine, four wheel brakes. Hudson made 66,034 shipments to dealers during the 1927 calendar year. The president of Hudson was Roscoe B. Jackson. The Hudson's F-head official rating of 92 hp has been regarded as conservative by Hudson historians. This is especially true of a revised version that became available in July 1927, which had new manifolding, altered head design and relocated spark plugs and intake valves. Claims of a 100 mph top speed for the 1927 Hudson were not uncommon and Barney Oldfield drove a 1927 coach for 1,000 miles at the Culver City, California, track at a speed in excess of 76 mph.

1928

HUDSON — MODEL O & S — SIX: The 1928 Hudsons were handsome automobiles. The use of a higher and more slender radiator, vertical engine louvers and larger, parabolically shaped headlights gave them a stately, almost aristocratic appearance. With the motometer moved to the dash, a sculptured hood ornament took its place and small "saddle lamps" were now mounted on the cowl. An industry first was Hudson's new steering wheel constructed of a hard rubber shell and a solid steel core. Formed with finger scallops it was colored ebony black to match the finish of the instrument panel. The spark, throttle, light and horn controls were placed at the steering wheel's center. In place of the transmission lock previously used, the Hudson was now equipped with an Electrolock ignition system. Although the Hudson's basic chassis structure was unchanged, two tubular cross-members were added. During 1928 a number of Hudsons were fitted with custom-built bodies by Murphy Body of Pasadena, California, that were extremely handsome. Murphy was also responsible for the basic design of two of the most attractive Hudson production models, the victoria and landau sedan. The Model S line Hudsons were mounted on a 118-1/2-inch wheelbase and were available in standard and custom form. The Model O versions also had standard and custom styles and a 127-3/8-inch wheelbase.

I.D. DATA: Car numbers on front frame channel, dash and frame side. Starting: [Model S] 12270, [Model O] 803569. Ending: [Model S] NA, [Model O] 825406. Engine numbers on left motor mount, side of cylinder block.

Model S

Model No.	Body Type & Seating	Factory Price	Shipping Weight	Prod. Total
S	Standard 2-dr. Cpe.-2P	1295	3525	NA
S	Standard 2-dr. Cch.-5P	1250	3575	NA
S	Standard 4-dr. Sed.-5P	1325	3645	NA
S	Custom 2-dr. Rds.-3P	1295	3355	NA
Model O				
O	Standard 4-dr. Sed.-5P	1450	3720	NA
O	Custom 4-dr. Phae.-7P	1650	3630	NA
O	Custom 2-dr. Vic.-4P	1650	3710	NA
O	Custom 4-dr. Lan. Sed-5P	1650	3780	NA
O	Custom 4-dr. Sed.-7P	1950	3945	NA

ENGINE: F-head. Inline. Six-cylinder. Cast iron block. B & S: 3-1/2 x 5 in. Disp.: 288.5 cu. in. C.R.: 5.0:1. Brake H.P.: 92 @ 3200 R.P.M. N.A.C.C. H.P.: 29.4. Main bearings: four. Valve lifters: mechanical. Carb.: Marvel, 1-1/4 in.

CHASSIS: [Model O] W.B.: 127-3/8 in. O.L.: 188 in. Tires: 31 x 6.00. [Model S] W.B.: 118-1/2 in. O.L.: 178-1/2 in. Tires: 31 x 6.00.

TECHNICAL: Sliding gear transmission. Speeds: 3F/1R. Floor shift controls. Single disc, cork inserts, running in oil. Shaft drive. Semi-floating rear axle. Overall ratio: 4.09:1 — Model S, 4.45:1 — Model O. Bendix mechanical brakes on four wheels. Wood spoke wheels with detachable rims. Rim size: 18 in.

OPTIONS: Front bumper. Rear bumper. Leather upholstery. Triplex shatterproof windshield glass. Trunk. Radiator shutters. Sidemounts (single & dual).

HISTORICAL: Introduced January 1928. Hudson made 52,316 shipments to dealers during the 1927 calendar year. The president of Hudson was Roscoe B. Jackson.

1929

HUDSON — MODEL R — SIX: In a move that undoubtedly upset old line Hudson fans but apparently did not harm sales, Hudson abandoned the time-honored "Super Six" label and instead identified its 1929 offering "The Greater Hudson." All Hudsons had bodies approximately four inches longer with the Model R versions having a 122.5-inch wheelbase. Among Hudson's 1929 styling highlights were larger windshields of shatterproof glass and narrower cornerposts. The landau sedan and victoria Model R Hudsons had Biddle & Smart bodies.

HUDSON — MODEL L — SIX: The 139-inch wheelbase Model L chassis was used exclusively for custom-built bodies supplied by Biddle & Smart. All Model L Hudsons were fitted with five wire wheels as standard equipment. All Hudsons had a higher radiator, cowl and hoodline plus larger diameter headlights. Included in the list of 64 improvements Hudson claimed for 1929 were hydraulic, double-action shock absorbers, self-energizing brakes and "silenced roof construction." Hudsons were delivered with a long list of standard equipment such as an electric gas and oil gauge, windshield wiper, rear view mirror and the electrolock anti-theft device.

I.D. DATA: Car numbers on front frame channel, dash and frame side. Starting: [Model R] 825407, [Model L] 41384. Ending: [Model R] 893401, [Model L] 46598. Engine numbers on left side of cylinder block/motor mount.

Model R

Model No.	Body Type & Seating	Factory Price	Shipping Weight	Prod. Total
R	2-dr. Phae.-5P	1350	3495	NA
R	2-dr. Conv. Cpe.-3P	1450	3580	NA
R	4-dr. Std. Sed.-5P	1175	3785	NA
R	2-dr. Cpe.-3P	1195	3610	NA
R	2-dr. Cch.-5P	1095	3680	NA
R	4-dr. Twn. Sed.-5P	1375	3795	NA
R	2-dr. Vic.-5P	1500	3795	NA
R	4-dr. Lan. Sed.-5P	1500	3825	NA
R	2-dr. Rds.-2P	NA	NA	NA
Model L				
L	4-dr. Clb. Sed.-5P	1850	4140	NA
L	4-dr. Limo.-7P	2100	4290	NA
L	4-dr. Sed.-7P	2000	4260	NA
L	4-dr. Spt. Phae.-4P	2200	3795	NA
L	4-dr. Phae.-7P	1600	3760	NA

ENGINE: F-head Inline. Six-cylinder. Cast iron block. B & S: 3-1/2 x 5 in. Disp. 288.5 cu. in. Brake H.P.: 92 @ 3200 R.P.M. Taxable/A.L.A.M./N.A.C.C. H.P.: 29.4. Main bearings: four. Valve lifters: mechanical. Carb.: Marvel 1-1/4 in.

CHASSIS: [Model R] W.B.: 122.5 in. Frt/Rear Tread: 56/57.5 in. Tires: 31 x 6.50. [Model L] W.B.: 139 in. Frt/Rear Tread: 56/57.5 in. Tires: 31 x 6.0.

TECHNICAL: Sliding gear transmission. Speeds: 3F/1R. Floor shift controls. Single disc, cork insert, running in oil. Shaft drive. Semi-floating rear axle. Bendix mechanical brakes on four wheels. Wood spoke wheels with detachable rims. Rim size: 19 in.

OPTIONS: Front bumper. Rear bumper. Eight-day clock. Cigar lighter. Spotlight. Five wire wheels. Twelve spoke demountable wood wheels (10 spoke standard). Radiator shutters. Trunk. Special trunk with fitted luggage. Ball-jointed tire mount mirrors. Protectahood. Lap robes. Spring covers. Window awnings. Spare tire locks. Sidemounts (single & dual).

HISTORICAL: Introduced January 1929. Hudson made 71,179 shipments to dealers during the 1929 calendar year. 139-inch wheelbase models with Biddle & Smart bodies only. The president of Hudson was William J. McAneeny.

1930

HUDSON — MODEL T — EIGHT: Styling changes for 1930 were limited to details such as the use of hood doors instead of louvers and a thinner radiator shell with a simulated cap. In addition the headlights were now mounted on a curved bar. The Model T Hudsons were mounted on a 119-inch wheelbase and were highlighted by the new Sun sedan body that provided the open-air motoring pleasure of a phaeton with the comfort of a two-door, five-passenger closed car. Its interior featured special upholstery without pleats. Common to all 1930 Hudsons were wider fenders, chrome-plated trim, beaded body beltline, a lower overall height and runningboard shields.

HUDSON — MODEL U — EIGHT: The Model U wheelbase at 126 inches was a full 13 inches shorter than that of the 1929 Model L. But far more controversial was Hudson's decision to drop its F-head six and replace it with an L-head straight eight. This engine was to be the only eight-cylinder engine ever offered by Hudson and it would remain in production until 1952. Perhaps in anticipation of the controversy, this move would cause Hudson to call its 1930 offering the Hudson Great Eight. Although with 80 hp it was less powerful than the old F-head six, it was installed in an automobile that was significantly lighter. Thus explained Hudson, "It strikes off the shackles of bulk and useless weight."

I.D. DATA: Car numbers on front frame channel, dash and frame side. Starting: [Model T] 893402, [Model U] 46599. Ending: [Model T] 914292, [Model U] 57114. Engine numbers on left side of cylinder block.

Model T

Model No.	Body Type & Seating	Factory Price	Shipping Weight	Prod. Total
T	2-dr. Cpe.-2P	885	3010	NA
T	4-dr. Phae.-5P	965	2940	NA
T	2-dr. Rds.-4P	995	2870	NA
T	2-dr. Cpe. w/R/S-4P	925	3060	NA
T	4-dr. Std.Sed.-5P	1025	3200	NA
T	2-dr. Sun.Sed.-5P	1045	3100	NA
T	2-dr. Cch.-5P	895	3080	NA
Model U				
U	4-dr. Phae.-7P	1160	3080	NA
U	4-dr. Brgm.-5P	1195	3210	NA
U	4-dr. Tr. Sed.-5P	1145	3270	NA
U	4-dr. Sed.-7P	1295	3385	NA

Note: During 1930 Hudson made significant price reductions in an effort to spur sales, the prices cited represent the lowest levels reached.

ENGINE: L-head. Inline. Eight-cylinder. Cast iron block. B & S: 2-3/4 x 4-1/2 in. Disp.: 213.8 cu. in. C.R.: 5.78:1. Brake H.P.: 80 @ 3400 R.P.M. N.A.C.C. H.P.: 24.2. Main bearings: five. Valve lifters: mechanical. Carb.: Marvel 10-776.

CHASSIS: [Model T] W.B.: 119 in. Tires: 18 x 5.50. [Model U] W.B.: 126 in. Tires: 18 x 5.50.

TECHNICAL: Sliding gear transmission. Speeds: 3F/1R. Floor shift controls. Single disc, cork insert, running in oil. Shaft drive. Semi-floating rear axle. Bendix mechanical brakes on four wheels. Wood spoke wheels with steel rims.

OPTIONS: Spotlight. Sidemounts (single & dual). Trunk. Spare tire. Radiator shutters.

HISTORICAL: Introduced January 1930. A car known as the Marr Special, consisting of an Essex chassis and a Hudson Eight engine qualified for the 1930 Indianapolis 500 at a speed of 106.185 mph. Its driver was Chet Miller. Starting in 15th position, Miller finished a respectable 10th, averaging 89.58 mph. This was the last Hudson-engined car to complete the 500-mile Indianapolis race. A Hudson also won the 1930 Tour de France. Hudson made 36,674 shipments to dealers during the calendar year. The president of Hudson was William J. McAneeny.

1931

HUDSON — SERIES T — EIGHT: The Series T version of the "Hudson Greater Eight," as the 1931 Hudsons were advertised, had a 119-inch wheelbase. Although styling changes were not extensive they were sufficient to represent another evolutionary step away from the severe angular lines characteristic of the 1920s. The grille insert was now a fine mesh and a new front headlight tie-rod gave the headlights both a free-standing appearance and a lower position. The fenders were more deeply flanged and at the front swept downward to further enclose the wheels. Also redesigned for 1931 were the Hudson's bumpers, hubcaps, runningboards and exterior hardware. At the rear a new rectangular window was used. Also identifying the 1931 Hudson were belt moldings that extended the full length of the hood to the radiator shell and at the rear, were positioned higher than previously.

HUDSON — SERIES U — EIGHT: The Series U Hudson had a 126-inch wheelbase and was easily identified by its standard left front fender spare tire well. The hood louvers on all models were placed higher than in 1930. A sure sign of the times was Hudson's decision to discontinue standard radiator shutters. They were still available as an accessory where there were extremely cold winters. However, Hudson noted that they had "been virtually useless, as evidenced by the fact that few and particularly the newer members of the Hudson family ever made use of them." Interior revisions common to all 1931 Hudsons included a handbrake lever with a pawl and ratchet design that Hudson promised was "rattleproof." Hudson offered new choices of Bedford cord, flat fabrics, mohairs and velour interiors and all models had walnut finishes on the dash and side garnish moldings. Rear seat occupants enjoyed at least two inches of additional leg room in the 1931 Hudsons with some sedan models offering as much as five more inches. Freewheeling was introduced as a $35 option in June and was operated by a small lever placed just behind the gearshift.

I.D. DATA: Car numbers on front frame channel, dash and frame side. Starting: [Series T] 914293, [Series U] 57115. Ending: [Series T] 930769, [Series U] 62883. Engine numbers on left side of cylinder block.

Series T

Model No.	Body Type & Seating	Factory Price	Shipping Weight	Prod. Total
Series T	4-dr. Phae.-5P	1095	2865	NA
Series T	2-dr. Cpe.-2P	875	2865	NA
Series T	2-dr. Cpe. R/S-2/4P	925	2955	NA
Series T	2-dr. Sp. Cpe. R/S-2/4P	1065	3145	NA
Series T	2-dr. Cch.-5P	895	2975	NA
Series T	4-dr. Twn. Sed.-5P	945	3055	NA
Series T	4-dr. Std. Sed.-5P	995	3115	NA
Series T	2-dr. Spt. Rds.-2P	995	2675	NA
Series U				
Series U	4-dr. Phae.-7P	1295	3055	NA
Series U	4-dr. Tr. Sed.-5P	1145	3190	NA
Series U	4-dr. Family Sed.-7P	1195	3230	NA
Series U	4-dr. Sp. Sed.-5P	1325	3430	NA
Series U	4-dr. Sed.-7P	1450	3375	NA
Series U	4-dr. Clb. Sed.-5P	1445	3235	NA
Series U	4-dr. Brgm.-5P	1225	3190	NA
Series U	4-dr. Brgm. Del.-5P	1375	3480	NA

ENGINE: L-head. Inline. Eight-cylinder. Cast iron block. B & S: 2-7/8 x 4-1/2 in. Disp. 233.7 cu. in. C.R.: 5.8:1. Brake H.P.: 87 @ 3600 R.P.M. N.A.C.C. H.P.: 26.4. Main bearings: five. Valve lifters: mechanical. Carb.: 1-1/2 in. Marvel 10-951.

CHASSIS: [Series T] W.B.: 119 in. Tires: 18 x 5.50. [Series U] W.B.: 126 in. Tires: 18 x 5.50.

TECHNICAL: Sliding gear transmission. Speeds: 3F/1R. Floor shift controls. Single disc, cork insert, running in oil. Shaft drive. Semi-floating rear axle. Bendix mechanical brakes on four wheels. Wood spoke wheels. Freewheeling ($35.00). Startix.

OPTIONS: Heater. Chrome windshield frame. Dual windshield wipers. Twin taillights. White sidewall tires. Spare tire cover. Wire wheels. Sidemounts (single & dual).

HISTORICAL: Introduced November 1930. In August 1931, the Hudson and Essex became the first American cars available with Startix. This device automatically started and if needed restarted the car after the driver turned the ignition key to the "on" position. Clutch plate now constructed from duralumin. Hudson made 17,487 shipments to dealers during the 1931 calendar year. The president of Hudson was William J. McAneeny. The Marr Special averaged 89.58 mph to finish 10th at Indy. The driver was Chet Miller.

1932

HUDSON — SERIES T (STANDARD) — EIGHT: The 1932 "Greater Eight" Hudsons were easily identified by their elegant vee-shaped grille with prominent vertical bars, single-piece bumper and triangular-shaped head, cowl and taillights. Frank Spring, who was to influence the appearance of virtually every future Hudson, gave the 1932 models a fresh look by the use of gracefully sweeping fenders and gentler body curves. All new Hudsons had a new instrument panel with larger gauges and a knob allowing the driver to adjust the ride control of the shock absorbers. The Standard models had a 119-inch wheelbase and were equipped with a single windshield wiper and taillight. A choice of either painted wood or wire wheels was offered.

HUDSON — SERIES U (STERLING) — EIGHT: Sterling Series Hudsons were mounted on a 126-inch wheelbase and were equipped with standard dual wipers, taillights, and white sidewall tires.

HUDSON — SERIES L (MAJOR) — EIGHT: The 132-inch wheelbase Hudson had the same standard features of the Series U. Thus customers had a choice of either natural-finish wood wheels or wire wheels.

I.D. DATA: Car numbers on front frame channel, dash and frame side. Starting: [Series T] 930770, [Series U] 62884, [Series L] 25001. Ending: [Series T] 936702, [Series U] 68332, [Series L] 25116. Engine numbers on left side of cylinder block.

Series T

Model No.	Body Type & Seating	Factory Price	Shipping Weight	Prod. Total
Series T	Std. 2-dr. Sp. Cpe. R/S-4P	1115	3215	NA
Series T	Std. 4-dr. Twn. Sed.-5P	1050	3270	NA
Series T	Std. 2-dr. Conv. Cpe.-2P	1195	3085	NA
Series T	Std. 2-dr. Cch.-5P	1025	3190	NA
Series T	Std. 4-dr. Std. Sed.-5P	1095	3285	NA
Series T	Std. 2-dr. Cpe.-2P	995	3145	NA
Series T	Std. 2-dr. Cpe. R/S-4P	1045	3175	NA
Series U				
Series U	Sterling 2-dr. Sub.-5P	1275	3350	NA
Series U	Sterling 4-dr. Sp. Sed.-5P	1295	3415	NA
Series L				
Series L	Major 4-dr. Tr. Sed.-5P	1445	3475	NA
Series L	Major 4-dr. Clb. Sed.-5P	1495	3555	NA
Series L	Major 4-dr. Brgm.-5P	1495	3560	NA
Series L	Major 4-dr. Sed.-7P	1595	3590	NA

ENGINE: Inline. Eight-cylinder. Cast iron block. B & S: 3 x 4-1/2 in. Disp.: 254.4 cu. in. C.R.: 5.8:1. Brake H.P.: 101 @ 3600 R.P.M. Main bearings: five. Valve lifters: mechanical. Carb.: 1-1/2 in. Marvel 10-996.

CHASSIS: [Series T] W.B.: 119 in. [Series U] W.B.: 126 in. Tires: 17 x 6.00. [Series L] W.B.: 132 in. Tires: 17 x 6.50.

TECHNICAL: Sliding gear transmission. Speeds: 3F/1R. Floor shift controls. Single disc, cork inserts, running in oil. Shaft drive. Semi-floating rear axle. Overall ratio: 4.64:1 (5.1:1 opt.). Bendix mechanical brakes on four wheels. Wood artillery wheels. Drivetrain options: Free-wheeling and selective automatic clutch.

OPTIONS: Sidemount cover(s) metal, fabric. Clock. Radio antenna. Wire wheels. Chrome grille cover. Chrome hood doors. Shatterproof glass. Leather upholstery. Locking glovebox. Whitewall tires. Trunk (and trunk rack). Double stop and taillights. Side and center rear arm-rests. Sidemounts (single & dual).

HISTORICAL: Introduced January 1932. Hudson made 7,777 shipments to dealers during the 1932 calendar year. The president of Hudson was William J. McAneeny. Two Hudson Specials were entered at Indy. Chet Miller's car qualified at 111.053 mph, Al Miller's at 110.129. Neither car finished. The Chet Miller car was out on lap 125, that of Al Miller on lap 66.

1933

HUDSON — SUPER SIX — SERIES E — SIX: The Super Six Hudson was essentially the 1932 Essex Pacemaker. Distinguishing it from other Hudsons for 1933 were triangular-shaped headlights and single row of hood louvers. The first six-cylinder Hudson since 1923 featured a two-piece aluminum and iron cylinder head with either a 6.2:1 or 7.1:1 compression ratio.

HUDSON — STANDARD EIGHT — SERIES T — EIGHT: The Standard Eight Hudson was mounted on a 119-inch wheelbase and retained door-type hood ventilators.

HUDSON — MAJOR EIGHT — SERIES L — EIGHT: Production of Hudsons reached its nadir in 1933. Only 2,401 were assembled in spite of more attractive styling and significant engineering improvements. The Series L on a 132-inch wheelbase had a more luxurious interior than the Standard Eight. Aside from their greater length the Major Eight Hudsons were distinguished from the Standard Eights by wide runningboard trim and dual chromed horns mounted on each side of the grille. After losing $5,429,350 in 1932, Hudson experienced another loss of $4,409,903 on sales of $23,521,458 in 1933.

I.D. DATA: Car number on dash, right rear frame crossmember. Starting: [Series E] 1300501, [Series T] 936703, [Series L] 251117. Ending: [Series E] 1301462, [Series T] 938029, [Series L] 251679. Engine number on left side of cylinder block opposite number one cylinder.

Series E — Hudson Super Six

Model No.	Body Type & Seating	Factory Price	Shipping Weight	Prod. Total
Series E	2-dr. Cpe.-4P	735	2845	NA
Series E	2-dr. Bus. Cpe.-2P	695	2780	NA
Series E	2-dr. Cch.-5P	695	2900	NA
Series E	4-dr. Sed.-5P	765	2980	NA
Series E	2-dr. Conv. Cpe. R/S-4P	845	2800	NA
Series E	4-dr. Phae.-5P	835	NA	NA
Series T — Hudson Pacemaker Standard Eight				
Series T	2-dr. Cpe. R/S-4P	995	3190	NA
Series T	2-dr. Cch.-5P	975	3245	NA
Series T	4-dr. Sed.-5P	1045	3345	NA
Series T	2-dr. Conv. Cpe. R/S-4P	1145	3145	NA
Series L — Hudson Pacemaker Major Eight				
Series L	4-dr. Tr. Sed.-5P	1250	3485	NA
Series L	4-dr. Clb. Sed.-5P	1350	3630	NA
Series L	4-dr. Sed.-7P	1350	3605	NA
Series L	4-dr. Brgm.-5P	1350	3650	NA

ENGINE: [Series T & L] Inline. Eight-cylinder. Cast iron block. B & S: 3 x 4-1/2 in. Disp.: 254.4. C.R.: 5.8:1. Brake H.P.: 101 @ 3600 R.P.M. Main bearings: five. Valve lifters: mechanical. Carb.: updraft Marvel 10-1535. Optional engine: Inline. Eight-cylinder. Cast iron block. B & S: 3 x 4-1/2 in. Disp. 254.4. C.R.: 7.1:1. Brake H.P.: 110 @ 3600 R.P.M. Main bearings: five. Valve lifters: mechanical. Carb.: updraft Marvel 10-1535.

ENGINE: [Super Six] Inline. Six-cylinder. Cast iron block. B & S: 2-15/16 x 4-3/4 in. Disp.: 193.1 cu. in. C.R.: 6.2:1. Brake H.P.: 73 @ 3200 R.P.M. Main bearings: three. Valve lifters: mechanical. Carb.: updraft Marvel 10-1532. Optional Engine: Inline. Six-cylinder. Cast iron block. B & S: 2-15/16 x 4-3/4 in. Disp.: 193.1 cu. in. C.R.: 7.1:1. Brake H.P.: 80 @ 3200 R.P.M. Main bearings: three. Valve lifters: mechanical. Carb.: updraft Marvel 10-1532.

CHASSIS: [Series E] W.B.: 113 in. Tires: 18 x 5.25. (17 x 5.50 opt.). [Series L] W.B.: 132 in. Tires: 17 x 6.50. [Series T] W.B.: 119 in. Tires: 17 x 6.00.

TECHNICAL: Sliding gear transmission. Speeds: 3F/1R. Floor mounted shift controls. Single plate, cork inserts, running in oil. Shaft drive. Semi-floating rear axle. Overall ratio: 4.64:1 (5.1:1 opt.). Bendix mechanical on four wheels. Wire spoke wheels. Rim size: Super Six — 18 in., Std Eight — 17 in., Major Eight — 17 in. Drivetrain options were automatic clutch [Super Six]. 17 x 5.50 tires, 17 in. wheels [Super Six].

OPTIONS: Wire wheels. Chrome grille cover. Chrome hood doors. Shatterproof glass. Leather upholstery. Locking glovebox. Whitewall tires. Trunk, trunk rack. Double stop and taillights. Side and center rear armrests. Sidemounts (single & dual).

HISTORICAL: Introduced January 1933. Innovations: standard equipment on all Hudsons was freewheeling, Startix and adjustable steering column. Hudson made 2,401 shipments to dealers during the 1933 calendar year. The president of Hudson was William J. McAneeny. Four cars powered by Hudson engines qualified at Indianapolis. Car #29 driven by Gene Haustein qualified in 28th position. It retired after 197 laps and was credited with a 15th place finish. Car #28 was driven by Chet Miller. Qualifying at 112.025 mph it began the race in 32nd position. Just after Miller was relieved by Shorty Cantlon, it fell by the wayside with a broken connecting rod. Al Miller's Car #19 started 24th and also retired with a blown connecting rod on lap 161. It was placed 20th in the final standing. A fourth Hudson-powered car, #59, was qualified by Ray Campbell at 108.65 mph. Starting the race in 37th position, it retired after 24 laps with an oil leak.

1934

HUDSON — STANDARD EIGHT — SERIES LL (123-inch wheelbase models) — EIGHT: The 1934 Hudsons had all-new styling with wide flowing fenders, longer hoods and in sedans and coaches a reverse curve rear section that allowed the spare tire to be stored within the body. Hudson described this new look as "Streamlined in Wind-Sculptured Steel." For the first time Hudson offered a factory-installed radio and a no-cost option, the "AxleFlex," semi-independent front suspension. Other improvements included a new dash panel that placed the instruments closer to the driver, an improved interior ventilation system and an improved synchromesh for the three-speed transmission. An interesting innovation was the use of three-beam headlights. The third beam was intended to serve as a cornering light and was controlled along with the usual high and low beams by a toe switch. Although sales rebounded strongly during 1934, Hudson reported a loss of $3,239,201 for the year. Hudson Standard Eight models in the LL series had Bedford cord interiors.

HUDSON — DELUXE EIGHT — SERIES LLU — EIGHT: The LLU models were distinguished from the LL versions by their broadcloth upholstery, and front fender side lamps. Both types had six hood doors, fender striping, brightwork trim around the windshield and front door vent panes.

HUDSON — EIGHT — SERIES LT — EIGHT: The LT models lacked front fender parking lights. Their windshields were given bright molding trim and front door vent panes were fitted. The sport roadster model was equipped with dual horns and taillights in a chrome finish. In addition they had two windshield wipers while other models carried a single wiper for the driver.

HUDSON — DELUXE EIGHT — SERIES LU — EIGHT: The DeLuxe models were equipped with dual front fender sidelamps, dual chrome-finish taillights, dual windshield wipers and horns.

HUDSON — CHALLENGER — SERIES LTS — EIGHT: These ultra-low priced models were introduced in June. They were identified by their three hood doors and lack of front door vent panes. They were fitted with a manual rather than automatic clutch and lacked such features as an interior sun visor.

I.D. DATA: Car numbers on firewall, right rear frame crossmember. Starting: [Series LT & LU] 950000, [Series LTS] 964463, [Series LL & LLU] 252000. Ending: [Series LT & LU] 968679, [Series LTS] 968679, [Series LL & LLU] 256158. Engine numbers on left side of cylinder block opposite number one cylinder.

Series LT — 116" wheelbase, 8-cyl.

Model No.	Body Type & Seating	Factory Price	Shipping Weight	Prod. Total
Series LT	2-dr. Cpe.-4P	775	2795	NA
Series LT	2-dr. Bus. Cpe.-2P	695	2720	NA
Series LT	2-dr. Cpe.-2P	725	2750	NA
Series LT	2-dr. Conv. Cpe. R/S-4P	835	2815	NA
Series LT	2-dr. Spt. Rds. R/S-4P	NA	2845	NA
Series LT	2-dr. Cch.-5P	745	2855	NA
Series LT	2-dr. Vic.-5P	785	2850	NA
Series LT	4-dr. Sed.-5P	805	2905	NA
Series LT	2-dr. Compartment Sed.-5P	845	2930	NA
Series LT	2-dr. Cch. with built-in trunk-5P	745	NA	NA
Series LT	2-dr. Sed. with built-in trunk-5P	805	NA	NA

Series LTS — 116" wheelbase, 8-cyl.

Model No.	Body Type & Seating	Factory Price	Shipping Weight	Prod. Total
Series LTS	4-dr. Sed.-5P	765	2910	NA
Series LTS	2-dr. Cpe.-2P	685	2720	NA
Series LTS	2-dr. Cpe. R/S-4P	735	2765	NA
Series LTS	2-dr. Conv. Cpe.-4P	800	2785	NA
Series LTS	2-dr. Cch-5P	705	2800	NA

Note 1: Series LTS four-door sedan-five-passenger was manufactured after August with built-in trunk at no price change.

Series LL — 123" wheelbase, 8-cyl.

Model No.	Body Type & Seating	Factory Price	Shipping Weight	Prod. Total
Series LL	4-dr. Tr. Sed.-5P	970	2950	NA
Series LL	4-dr. Compartment Tr. Sed.-5P	1000	2975	NA

Series LLU — 123" wheelbase, 8-cyl.

Model No.	Body Type & Seating	Factory Price	Shipping Weight	Prod. Total
Series LLU	4-dr. Clb. Sed.-5P	1070	3080	NA
Series LLU	4-dr. Compartment Clb. Sed.-5P	1125	3110	NA
Series LLU	4-dr. Brgm.-5P	1145	3075	NA
Series LU	2-dr. Cpe. R/S-4P	855	2850	NA
Series LU	2-dr. Cpe.-2P	815	2805	NA
Series LU	2-dr. Conv. Cpe. R/S-4P	900	2835	NA
Series LU	4-dr. Sed.-5P	895	2930	NA
Series LU	4-dr. Compartment Sed.-5P	935	2955	NA
Series LU	2-dr. Cch.-5P	835	2870	NA
Series LU	2-dr. Compartment Vic.	875	2895	NA
Series LU	4-dr. Sed. w/built-in trunk	895	NA	NA
Series LU	2-dr. Cch. w/built-in trunk	835	NA	NA

Note 1: Production ceased June 1935 for Series LTS four-door sedan-five passenger and two-door coach-five passenger: Series LU four-door Compartment sedan-five passenger and two-door Compartment Victoria.

Note 2: Series LU four-door sedan w/built-in trunk and two-door coach w/built-in trunk were introduced in August 1935.

ENGINE: [Series LL & LLU] L-head. Straight. Eight-cylinder. Chrome alloy block. B & S: 3 x 4-1/2 in. Disp. 254.4 cu. in. C.R.: 6.25:1. Brake H.P.: 113 @ 3800 R.P.M. Taxable/A.L.A.M./N.A.C.C. H.P.: 28.8. Main bearings: five. Valve lifters: mechanical. Carb.: Carter downdraft one-barrel 2825. Optional engine: L-head. Straight. Eight-cylinder. Chrome alloy block. B & S: 3 x 4-1/2. Disp. 254.4. C.R.: 7.0:1. Brake H.P.: 121 @ 3800 R.P.M. Taxable/A.L.A.M./N.A.C.C. H.P.: 28.8. Main bearings: five. Valve lifters: mechanical. Carb.: Carter Downdraft one-barrel 2825.

ENGINE: [Series LT, LTS, & LU] L-head. Straight. Eight-cylinder. Chrome alloy block. B & S: 3 x 4.5 in. Disp.: 254.4. C.R.: 5.75:1. Brake H.P.: 108 @ 3800 R.P.M. Taxable H.P.: 28.8. Main bearings five. Valve lifters: mechanical. Carb.: Carter downdraft one-barrel 2825. Optional engine: L-head. Straight. Eight-cylinder. Chrome alloy block. B & S: 3 x 4.5 in. Disp. 254.4. C.R.: 7.0:1. Brake H.P.: 121 @ 3800 R.P.M. Taxable/A.L.A.M./N.A.C.C. H.P.: 28.8. Main bearings: five. Valve lifters: mechanical. Carb. Carter downdraft one-barrel 2825.

CHASSIS: [Series LL] W.B.: 123 in. O.L.: 197 in. Frt/Rear Tread: 56/57.5 in. Tires: 16 x 6.50. [Series LT] W.B.: 116 in. O.L.: 194 in. Frt/Rear Tread 56/56 in. Tires: 16 x 6.25. [Series LU] W.B.: 116 in. O.L.: 194 in. Frt/Rear Tread: 56/56 in. Tires: 16 x 6.25. [Series LLU] W.B.: 123 in. O.L.: 197 in. Frt/Rear Tread: 56/57.5 in. Tires: 16 x 6.50. [Series LTS] W.B.: 116 in. O.L.: 194 in. Frt/Rear Tread: 56/56 in. Tires: 16 x 6.25.

TECHNICAL: Sliding gear transmission. Speeds: 3F/1R. Floor shift controls. Single plate, cork insert, running in oil. Shaft drive. Semi-floating rear axle. Overall ratio: 4.11:1. Bendix mechanical brakes on four wheels. Steel artillery wheels. Rim size: 16 in. Drivetrain options: Hill-holder. Automatic clutch.

OPTIONS: Dual sidemount (except for Challenger). Bumper guards front and rear ($2.15 pair). Radio. Heater (standard 12.50, DeLuxe 15.50). Electric clock (13.50). Cigar lighter (1.25, 2.00). Stainless steel wheel moldings (5.00, 9.00). Underhood battery charger (9.75). Chrome plated exhaust extension (1.95). Luggage rack (9.50). Right side tail & stop light (6.00). Twin horns (10.00 pair). Dual windshield wipers (10.00). Inside right side visor. Trunk light. Fender skirts (9.50 pair in primer). Hill-holder (32.50). Fitted luggage (9.75 to 22.50). Vacuum clutch (15.00). 7:1 cylinder head (18.00).

HISTORICAL: Introduced January 1934. Innovations: Axle-flex three-beam headlights. Hudson made 27,130 shipments to dealers during the 1934 calendar year. The president of Hudson was Roy D. Chapin. Freewheeling was discontinued. The Martz Special powered by a 257-cid Hudson engine was qualified for the Indianapolis 500 by Gene Haustein at 109.426 mph. The car started in 31st position and was credited with finishing in 30th place after being wrecked in an accident in lap 13. Another Hudson-powered car, #13, was the first alternate to the qualifiers but it didn't race.

1935

HUDSON CUSTOM EIGHT — HHU — EIGHT: Although the styling of the 1935 Hudson was similar to the 1934 model, there were many improvements that have prompted Hudson historians to regard the 1935s as the first modern Hudsons. The most dramatic advancement was the industry's first all-steel body, which Hudson introduced prior to General Motor's Turret Top. The most predominant external changes aside from the steel roof were the new bullet-shaped headlight shells, larger rear windows and narrow hood louver panels. The use of flatter rear leaf springs enabled overall height to be lowered 1.5 inches. On July 8, 1935, the Hudson Motor Car company celebrated its 26th anniversary with the production of its 2,262,810th automobile. Also during 1935, Roy Chapin established the "Twenty Year Club" for Hudson employees with that number of years of service. Members received a solid gold pin with a Hudson 20 engraved on one side and their name on the other. January 5, 1935, was the 25th anniversary of Roy D. Chapin's election to the presidency of Hudson. The Custom Eight had the exterior features of the DeLuxe Eights plus chrome trim for the runningboards and three chrome stripes on the trailing edge of the front fenders. Interior trim appointments were also upgraded. Standard equipment included the Electric Hand transmission.

HUDSON SPECIAL EIGHT — HT — EIGHT: The Special 8 was Hudson's lowest priced line of eight-cylinder. models and had a 117-inch wheelbase. They had painted headlights shells and single windshield wipers.

HUDSON DELUXE EIGHT — SERIES HU — EIGHT: The DeLuxe 8 models shared the 117-inch chassis with the Special 8 series. However they were equipped with dual windshield wipers and chrome-plated headlight shells.

HUDSON SPECIAL COUNTRY CLUB EIGHT — SERIES HTL — EIGHT: This series combined the painted headlight shells and single windshield wiper of the Special Eight series with the long, 124-inch wheelbase of the DeLuxe Eight models. Wood spoke wheels were optional at no extra cost.

HUDSON DELUXE COUNTRY CLUB EIGHT — SERIES HUL — EIGHT: The HUL series shared their chromed headlight shells with the HU models but were given a higher quality interior. Wire wheels were standard, wood spoke wheels optional at no extra cost.

HUDSON BIG SIX — SERIES GH — SIX: The Hudson Six was easily identified by its grille mesh with its horizontal inserts.

I.D. DATA: Car numbers on dash, right rear frame crossmember. Starting: [Series GH] 53101, [Series HHU] 56101, [Series HT] 54101, [Series HU] 55101, [Series HTL] 57101, [Series HUL] 58101. Ending: [Series GH] 537724, [Series HHU] 561560, [Series HT] 547250, [Series HU] 553197, [Series HTL] 571066, [Series HUL] 58221. Canadian built cars inserted a "C" between series and serial number (i.e., 53C60432). Engine numbers on left rear side of cylinder block. Starting: 70000. Ending: 78999.

Series HHU — 124" wheelbase, 8-cyl.

Model No.	Body Type & Seating	Factory Price	Shipping Weight	Prod. Total
Series HHU	4-dr. Clb. Sed.-5P	1025	3130	--
Series HHU	4-dr. Sub. Sed.-5P	1057	3145	--
Series HHU	4-dr. Brgm.-6P	1095	3055	--
Series HHU	4-dr. Tr. Brgm.-6P	1127	3070	720*

Series HU — 117" wheelbase, 8-cyl.

Model No.	Body Type & Seating	Factory Price	Shipping Weight	Prod. Total
Series HU	2-dr. Cch.-5P	875	2880	--
Series HU	2-dr. Tr. Brgm.	907	2895	--
Series HU	Sed.	935	2945	--
Series HU	4-dr. Sub. Sed.-5P	967	2960	--
Series HU	Bus. Cpe.-2P	845	2790	--
Series HU	Cpe. R/S-4P	895	2855	--
Series HU	2-dr. Conv. Cpe. R/S-2P	955	2805	3096*

Series HTL — 124" wheelbase, 8-cyl.

Model No.	Body Type & Seating	Factory Price	Shipping Weight	Prod. Total
Series HTL	2-dr. Tr. Brgm.-5P	812	2855	--
Series HTL	2-dr. Cch.-5P	780	2840	--
Series HTL	4-dr. Sed.-6P	840	2890	--
Series HTL	4-dr. Sub. Sed.-6P	872	2905	965*

Series HUL — 124" wheelbase, 8-cyl.

Model No.	Body Type & Seating	Factory Price	Shipping Weight	Prod. Total
Series HUL	4-dr. Sub. Sed.-5P	1007	3030	--
Series HUL	4-dr. Clb. Sed.-5P	975	3015	--
Series HUL	4-dr. Brgm.-5P	1025	3055	--
Series HUL	4-dr. Tr. Brgm.-5P	1052	3070	9923*

Series GH — 116" wheelbase, 6-cyl.

Model No.	Body Type & Seating	Factory Price	Shipping Weight	Prod. Total
Series GH	2-dr. Cpe. R/S-3P	740	2665	--
Series GH	2-dr. Bus. Cpe.-2P	695	2600	--
Series GH	4-dr. Sed.-5P	770	2780	--
Series GH	2-dr. C'ch.-5P	710	2720	--
Series GH	4-dr. Sub. Sed.-5P	802	2795	--
Series GH	2-dr. Conv. Cpe.	790	2640	--
Series GH	2-dr. Tr. Brgm.	742	2735	7623*

Series HT — 117" wheelbase, 8-cyl.

Model No.	Body Type & Seating	Factory Price	Shipping Weight	Prod. Total
Series HT	2-dr. Cch.-5P	780	2840	--
Series HT	2-dr. Tr. Brgm.	812	2855	--
Series HT	Sed.	840	2890	--
Series HT	4-dr. Sub. Sed.-5P	872	2905	--
Series HT	Bus. Cpe.-2P	760	2740	--
Series HT	Cpe. R/S-4P	810	2810	--
Series HT	2-dr. Conv. Cpe. R/S-2P	860	2765	7149*

Note: * Applies to total series production not model production.

ENGINE: [Hudson Eight] (This engine used for all Hudson Eight models). L-head. Inline. Eight-cylinder. Chrome alloy block. B & S: 3 x 4.5 in. Disp.: 254. cu. in. C.R.: 6.0:1. Brake H.P.: 113 @ 3800 R.P.M. Taxable H.P.: 28.8. Main bearings: five. Valve lifters: mechanical. Carb.: Carter 330S. Optional engine: L-head. Straight eight. Chrome alloy block. B & S: 3 x 4.5 in. Disp.: 254 cu. in. C.R.: 7.0:1. Brake H.P.: 124 @ 4000 R.P.M. Main bearings: five. Valve lifters: mechanical. Carb.: Carter 330S.

ENGINE: [Hudson Six] L-head. Inline. Six-cylinder. Chrome alloy block. B & S: 3 x 5 in. Disp.: 212 cu. in. C.R.: 6.25:1. Brake H.P.: 93 @ 3800 R.P.M. Taxable H.P.: 21.6. Main bearings: three. Valve lifters: mechanical. Carb.: Carter 329S. Optional engine: L-head. Inline. Six-cylinder. Chrome alloy block. B & S: 3 x 5 in. Disp.: 212. cu. in. C.R.: 7.0:1. Brake H.P.: 100 @ 3800 R.P.M. Main bearings: three. Valve lifters: mechanical. Carb.: Carter 329S.

CHASSIS: [Series HHU] W.B.: 124 in. Tires: 16 x 6.50. [Series HU] W.B.: 117 in. Tires: 16 x 6.25. [Series HTL] W.B.: 124 in. Tires: 16 x 6.50. [Series HUL] W.B.: 124 in. Tires: 16 x 6.50. [Series HT] W.B.: 117 in. Tires: 16 x 6.25. [Series GH] W.B.: 116 in. Tires: 6.00 x 16.

TECHNICAL: Manual, sliding gear transmission. Speeds: 3F/1R. Floor shift controls. Single disc, cork insert, running in oil. Shaft drive. Semi-floating rear axle. Overall ratio: 4.19:1. Mechanical, "Rotary Equalizer" brakes on four wheels. Steel wheels. (Wood spokes on 124-inch wheelbase models). Drivetrain options: Electric hand (std. on Custom Eights, optional on all other Hudsons and Terraplanes) ($20.42). AxleFlex independent front suspension. Adjustable steering column. Automatic clutch (10.21). Automatic clutch and Electric hand (28.08).

OPTIONS: Radio ($51.81). High compression cylinder head (six-cylinder) (18.50). High compression cylinder head (eight-cylinder) (22.00). Startix (8.50). Luggage carrier (10.00). Tune up kit (4.50). Zenith radio (44.00). Twin air horns (11.50). Front and rear seat covers (7.50). Leather upholstery (18.81). Sidemounts (single and dual).

HISTORICAL: Introduced December 1934. Rotary-equalized brakes. Optional Electric Hand. Pre-selector shifting mechanism. Hudson made 29,476 shipments to dealers during the 1935 calendar year. The president of Hudson was Roy D. Chapin. Two Hudson-powered cars were entered in the Indy 500 but neither qualified. In February 1935, Sir Malcolm Campbell set seven new records at Daytona Beach with a Hudson sedan. These included the flying mile at 88.207 mph, flying kilometer at 88.207 mph, flying 5 miles at 88.051 mph, flying 5 kilometers at 88.105 mph and the standing start mile at 68.18 mph. In April, 36 new AAA records were captured by a Hudson 8 sedan at Muroc Dry Lake in California. Among these records set by Wilbur Shaw, Babe Stapp and Al Gordon was a 93.03 mph speed for five miles and an average of 85.8 mph for 1,000 miles. In addition the Hudson captured every record in its engine displacement up to 3,000 kilometers as well as four unlimited class records for closed cars.

1936

HUDSON — CUSTOM SIX — SERIES 63 — SIX: A new styling motif for Hudson with rounded surfaces, highly domed fenders and an ornate front grille design was introduced in 1936. All series had longer wheelbases and body widths. An important technical advance was Hudson's adoption of a hydraulic braking system that incorporated a mechanical unit operating on the rear wheels. If the front pedal traveled beyond the 3/4 point of its maximum distance, this system would function. Replacing the AxleFlex system as Hudson's answer to General Motors' independent front suspension system was Radial Safety Control. A solid front axle was continued but two radius arms attached to the axle and pivoted to the frame side members controlled its move-

1936 Hudson, Deluxe (Series 64), brougham (with optional chrome wheelcovers and rear wheel shields), OCW

1939 Hudson, Country Club (Series 95), convertible brougham, OCW

1939 Hudson, Pacemaker (Series 91), touring sedan, OCW

1938 Hudson (112), Series 89, brougham, OCW

1940 Hudson, Series 44, touring sedan, OCW

1940 Hudson, Traveler (Series 40T), coupe, OCW

ment. This allowed softer leaf springs to be used and the result was steady steering and a smooth ride. Net profits for the year totaled $3,305,616. All Custom models (six- or eight-cylinder) had chrome wheelcovers and front fender medallions. Standard upholstery texture was worsted boucle with a green-gray color.

HUDSON — CUSTOM EIGHT — SERIES 65 & 67 — EIGHT: With the exception of their wheelbases these two series of Custom Eight Hudson were identical. Full size wheelcovers with Hudson Eight lettering were standard. Standard equipment on the Custom Eight included a radio with its antenna positioned under the car.

HUDSON — DELUXE EIGHT — SERIES 64 & 66 — EIGHT: The DeLuxe Eight shared both of its 120- and 127-inch wheelbase chassis with the Custom Eight Series. Their small standard hubcaps made them easy to identify.

I.D. DATA: Car number on dash, right rear frame crossmember. Starting: [Series 63] 63101, [Series 64] 64101, [Series 66] 66101. Ending: [Series 63] 639820, [Series 64] 645456, [Series 66] 663543. Engine number on left side of cylinder block. Car number on plate mounted on firewall. Starting: [Series 65] 65101, [Series 67] 67101. Ending: [Series 65] 652514, [Series 67] 675004. Engine numbers on left side of cylinder block. Starting: 79000 — six cylinder. 1008 — eight cylinder. Ending: 89999 — six cylinder. 17634 — eight cylinder. Canadian-built cars included letter "C".

Series 63 — 120" wheelbase, 6-cyl.

Model No.	Body Type & Seating	Factory Price	Shipping Weight	Prod. Total
Series 63	2-dr. Cpe. R/S-3-5P	755	7810	NA
Series 63	2-dr. Bus. Cpe.-3P	710	2730	NA
Series 63	2-dr. Conv. Cpe.-3P	810	2870	NA
Series 63	2-dr. Brgm.-6P	730	2830	NA
Series 63	2-dr. Tr. Brgm.-6P	755	2830	NA
Series 63	4-dr. Sed.-6P	785	2880	NA
Series 63	4-dr. Tr. Sed.-6P	810	2880	NA
Series 64 — 120" wheelbase, 8-cyl.				
Series 64	2-dr. Bus. Cpe.-3P	760	2865	NA
Series 64	2-dr. Cpe. R/S-3-5P	810	2965	NA
Series 64	2-dr. Conv. Cpe.-3P	875	3000	NA
Series 64	2-dr. Brgm.-6P	790	2985	NA
Series 64	2-dr. Tr. Brgm.-6P	815	2985	NA
Series 64	4-dr. Sed.-6P	830	3045	NA
Series 64	4-dr. Tr. Sed.-6P	855	3045	NA
Series 66 — 127" wheelbase, 8-cyl.				
Series 66	4-dr. Sed.-6P	855	3110	NA
Series 66	4-dr. Tr. Sed.-6P	880	3110	NA
Series 65 — 120" wheelbase, 8-cyl.				
Series 65	2-dr. Bus. Cpe.-3P	845	2915	NA
Series 65	2-dr. Cpe. R/S-3-5P	895	3000	NA
Series 65	2-dr. Conv. Cpe.-3-5P	970	3045	NA
Series 65	2-dr. Brgm.-6P	885	3030	NA
Series 65	2-dr. Tr. Brgm.-6P	910	3030	NA
Series 65	2-dr. Sed.-6P	925	3075	NA
Series 65	4-dr. Tr. Sed.-6P	950	3075	NA
Series 67 — 127" wheelbase, 8-cyl.				
Series 67	4-dr. Sed.-6P	950	3140	NA
Series 67	4-dr. Tr. Sed.-6P	975	3140	NA

ENGINE: This engine used for all Hudson eight cylinder models. L-head. Inline. Eight-cylinder. Chrome alloy block. B & S: 3 x 4.5 in. Disp.: 254. cu. in. C.R.: 6.0:1. Brake H.P.: 113 @ 3800 R.P.M. Taxable H.P.: 28.8. Main bearings: five. Valve lifters: mechanical. Carb.: Carter 330S. Optional engine: L-head. Straight. Eight-cylinder. Chrome alloy block. B & S: 3 x 4.5 in. Disp.: 254 cu. in. C.R.: 7.0:1. Brake H.P.: 124 @ 4000 R.P.M. Main bearings: five. Valve lifters: mechanical. Carb.: Carter 330S. [Custom Six] L-head. Inline. Six-cylinder. Chrome alloy block. B & S: 3 x 5 in. Disp.: 212 cu. in. C.R.: 6.25:1. Brake H.P. 93 @ 3800 R.P.M. Taxable H.P.: 21.6. Main bearings: three. Valve lifters: mechanical. Carb.: Carter 329S. Optional engine: L-head. Inline. Six-cylinder. Chrome alloy block. B & S: 3 x 5 in. Disp. 212 cu. in. C.R.: 7.0:1. Brake H.P.: 100 @ 3800 R.P.M. Main bearings: three. Valve lifters: mechanical. Carb.: Carter 329S.

CHASSIS: [Series 63] W.B.: 120 in. Tires: 16 x 6.00. [Series 64] W.B.: 120 in. Tires: 16 x 6.25. [Series 65] W.B.: 120 in. Tires: 16 x 6.25. [Series 66] W.B.: 127 in. Tires: 16 x 6.25. [Series 67] W.B.: 127 in. Tires: 16 x 6.25.

TECHNICAL: Sliding gear transmission. Speeds: 3F/1R. Floor shift controls. Single disc, cork insert, running in oil. Shaft drive. Semi-floating rear axle. Overall ratio: 4.19:1. Hydraulic brakes on four wheels. Pressed steel wheels. Rim size: 16 in. Drivetrain options: Electric hand preselector transmission.

OPTIONS: Bumper guards. Radio. Heater. Mohair upholstery. Fender skirts. Full wheel covers. High compression cylinder heads. Startix. Luggage carrier. Tune up kit. Zenith radio. Twin air horns. Front and rear seat covers. Leather upholstery. Sidemounts (single & dual).

HISTORICAL: Introduced November 1935. Innovations: radial safety control front suspension, hydraulic brakes. Hudson made 25,409 shipments to dealers during the 1936 calendar year. The president of Hudson was A. Edward Barit (elected president, February 1936 following the death of Roy D. Chapin).

1937

HUDSON CUSTOM SIX — SERIES 73 — SIX: The Custom Six wheelbase was extended to 122 inches for 1937. Appearance of the Custom Six was identical to that of the DeLuxe and Custom Eight models. The only exception was the Hudson 6 identification on the Custom Six grille. All the restyled Hudsons were described by their manufacturer as possessing "useful beauty" with interiors of "Drawing room luxury." Overall body width was increased by five inches and wheelbases of all series was lengthened by two inches, while overall height was reduced by the same amount. These new dimensions were accompanied by the use of a stronger 7-1/4 inch deep double drop frame. In addition to their greater size, the 1937 Hudsons were set apart from previous models by their front hinged front doors, reshaped hood louvers and simpler grille design. In place of the rumbleseat on coupe models was a transversely-mounted jump seat. Detail changes included placement of the battery within the engine compartment and improvements in Hudson's Radial Safety front suspension and Electric Hand gearshift mechanism. The downturn in the nation's economy had a negative impact upon Hudson sales and at year's end Hudson's profit was a slim $670,716.

HUDSON DELUXE EIGHT — SERIES 74 & 76 — EIGHT: DeLuxe Eight models carried front fender medallions, runningboard trim strips and Hudson 8 identification on the front grille. The Series 74 Hudsons had a 122-inch wheelbase while that of the Series 76 models extended to 129 inches.

HUDSON CUSTOM EIGHT — SERIES 75 & 77 — EIGHT: Custom Eight models were externally identical to DeLuxe Eights. However their interiors differed significantly. That of the Custom Eight had a knobby twist upholstery (leather was used for all Hudson convertible interiors), standard equipment radio, cigarette lighter and electric clock. With the exception of its 129-inch wheelbase, the Series 77 Hudson was identical to the Series 75.

I.D. DATA: Car numbers on plate mounted on firewall. Starting: [Series 73] 73101, [Series 74] 74101, [Series 75] 75101, [Series 76] 76101, [Series 77] 77101. Ending: [Series 73] 736913, [Series 74] 745728, [Series 75] 753374, [Series 76] 761197, [Series 77] 773752. Canadian-built chassis serial number have a C after the first two digits that identify the series. Engine numbers on left side of cylinder block. Starting: 90000 — six-cylinder, 18000 — eight-cylinder. Ending: 97082 — six-cylinder, 31693 — eight-cylinder. Canadian-built cars included letter "C".

Series 73 — 122" wheelbase, 6-cyl.

Model No.	Body Type & Seating	Factory Price	Shipping Weight	Prod. Total
Series 73	2-dr. Vic. Cpe.-4P	765	2865	—
Series 73	2-dr. Bus. Cpe.-3P	695	2760	—
Series 73	2-dr. Cpe.-3P	720	2805	—
Series 73	2-dr. Brgm.-5P	740	2925	—
Series 73	2-dr. Tr. Brgm.-5P	765	2925	—
Series 73	2-dr. Conv. Cpe.-4P	820	2870	—
Series 73	4-dr. Sed.-6P	790	2990	—
Series 73	4-dr. Tr. Sed.-6P	815	2990	—
Series 73	2-dr. Conv. Brgm.-6P	900	2945	—
Series 74 — 122" wheelbase, 8-cyl.				
Series 74	2-dr. Conv. Brgm.-6P	965	3124	—
Series 74	2-dr. Conv. Cpe.-4P	885	3020	—
Series 74	2-dr. Brgm.-5P	800	3105	—
Series 74	2-dr. Tr. Brgm	825	3105	—
Series 74	4-dr. Tr. Sed.-6P	865	3135	—
Series 74	4-dr. Sed.-6P	840	3135	—
Series 74	2-dr. Cpe.-3P	770	3010	—
Series 74	2-dr. Vic. Cpe.-4P	820	3055	—
Series 74	4-dr. Sed.-6P	865	3205	—
Series 74	4-dr. Tr. Sed.	890	3205	—
Series 76 — 129" wheelbase, 8-cyl.				
Series 76	4-dr. Sed.-6P	865	3205	—
Series 76	4-dr. Tr. Sed.-6P	890	3205	—
Series 77 — 129" wheelbase, 8-cyl.				
Series 77	4-dr. Closed CoupledSed.-6P	965	3260	—
Series 77	4-dr. Closed Coupled Tr. Sed.-6P	990	3260	—

Series 75 — 122" wheelbase, 8-cyl.

Model No.	Body Type & Seating	Factory Price	Shipping Weight	Prod. Total
Series 75	2-dr. Vic. Cpe.-4P	905	3085	—
Series 75	2-dr. Conv. Cpe.-4P	980	3070	—
Series 75	2-dr. Cpe.-3P	855	3055	—
Series 75	2-dr. Conv. Brgm.-6P	1060	3160	—
Series 75	2-dr. Brgm.-6P	895	3135	—
Series 75	2-dr. Tr. Brgm.-6P	920	3135	—
Series 75	4-dr. Tr. Sed.-6P	965	3195	—
Series 75	4-dr. Sed.	940	3195	—

Note: Prices increased later in the model year.

ENGINE: [Custom Six] L-head. Inline. Six-cylinder. Chrome alloy block. B & S: 3 x 5 in. Disp.: 212 cu. in. C.R.: 6.25:1. Brake H.P.: 161 @ 4000 R.P.M. Taxable H.P.: 21.6. Main bearings: three. Valve lifters: mechanical. Carb.: two-barrel Carter. Optional engine: L-head. Inline. Six-cylinder. Chrome alloy block. B & S: 3 x 5 in. Disp.: 212 cu. in. C.R.: 7.0:1. Brake H.P.: 107 @ 4000 R.P.M. Taxable H.P.: 21.6. Main bearings: three. Valve lifters: mechanical. Carb.: two-barrel Carter. [This engine used in all DeLuxe and Custom Eight models.] L-head. Straight. Eight-cylinder. Chrome alloy block. B & S: 3 x 4-1/2 in. Disp.: 254.47 cu. in. C.R.: 6.25:1. Brake H.P.: 122 @ 4200 R.P.M. Taxable H.P.: 28.8. Main bearings: five. Valve lifters: mechanical. Carb.: two-barrel Carter.

CHASSIS: [Series 73] W.B.: 122 in. O.L.: 199 in. Tires: 16 x 6.00 (15 x 7.00 opt.). [Series 74] W.B.: 122 in. O.L.: 199 in. Tires: 16 x 6.25 (15 x 7.00 opt.). [Series 76] W.B.: 129 in. O.L.: 203 in. Tires: 16 x 6.25 (15 x 7.00 opt.). [Series 75] W.B.: 122 in. O.L.: 199 in. Tires: 16 x 6.25 (15 x 7.00 opt.). [Series 77] W.B.: 129 in. O.L.: 203 in. Tires: 16 x 6.25 (15 x 7.00 opt.).

TECHNICAL: Manual synchromesh transmission. 3F/1R. Floor shift. Single plate, cork inserts, running in oil. Shaft drive. Semi-floating rear axle. Overall ratio: 4.11:1. Hydraulic brakes on four wheels. Steel drop center type wheels. Drivetrain options: "Hydraulic Hill Hold." The Electric Hand (pre-selector).

OPTIONS: Single sidemount. Dual sidemount. Fender skirts. Bumper guards. Radio. Heater. Clock (standard on Custom Eight). Cigar lighter. Seat covers. Spotlight. Twin air horns. Vacuum-assist fuel pump.

HISTORICAL: Introduced November 1937. Under AAA supervision Hudson broke all existing Class C, closed stock car records from 10 to 2,000 miles and from 1 to 24 hours. In addition new records were set in the unlimited class for all distances from 500 to 2,000 miles and from 6 to 24 hours. In the latter run the Hudson DeLuxe Eight Brougham covered 2,104.22 miles in 24 hours at an average speed of 87.67 mph. The Hudson's speed of 93.03 mph across the Muroc Dry Lake was the fastest speed a closed, Class C car had ever attained in a five-mile run. In addition to the 38 new stock car records set on this outing, Hudson had earlier claimed seven additional new marks in speed at Daytona Beach. Hudson made 19,848 shipments to dealers during the 1937 calendar year. The president of Hudson was Abraham Edward Barit.

1938

HUDSON 112 — SERIES 89 — SIX: The Hudson 112 was introduced in January 1938. Standard and DeLuxe models were available on a 112-inch wheelbase. The more expensive DeLuxe version had a walnut grain finish on the dash and window moldings, in place of the painted finishes found on the Standard models. In addition stainless steel trim was used for the DeLuxe interior. A more attractive upholstery with a pleated surface was also used. Both versions were powered by a 175-cid six-cylinder engine. At Bonneville the Hudson 112, which was also the pace car for the Indianapolis 500, set numerous Class D records including 80.50 mph for one hour and a 12-day, 20,327 mile run at 70.58 mph.

HUDSON CUSTOM SIX — SERIES 83 — SIX: All 1938 Hudsons featured a new grille with larger horizontal bars divided by a single vertical bar. This arrangement was less complicated than the form used in 1937. The Custom Six displayed a new front bumper with a center indentation that gave it a two piece appearance.

HUDSON CUSTOM EIGHT — SERIES 85 & 87 — EIGHT: The Custom Eight was with the exception of its engine identical to the Custom Six. The only difference was represented by the two Custom Eight Series 87 Country Club models that used a 129- rather than 122-inch wheelbase.

HUDSON DELUXE EIGHT — SERIES 84 — EIGHT: The DeLuxe Eight shared its 122-inch chassis with the Custom Six and Eight Series. In addition its interior appointments were those of the Custom Six.

I.D. DATA: Hudson 112: car numbers on plate mounted on firewall. Starting: 8928566. Ending: 8956040. Engine numbers on left side of cylinder block. Starting: same as serial numbers. Hudson Six: car numbers on right front door post. Starting: 83131. Ending: 8356040. Engine numbers on top right side of cylinder block. Starting: same as serial numbers. Hudson DeLuxe Eight: car numbers on right front door post. Starting: 84101. Ending: 8456040. Engine numbers on top right side of cylinder block. Starting: same as serial numbers. Hudson Custom Eight Country Club: car numbers on right front door post. Starting: 87161. Ending: 8756040. Engine numbers on top right side of cylinder block. Starting: same as serial numbers. Note: Starting engine numbers were 360000 for all series until car number 11630 when engine number began matching serial number.

Series 89 — 112" wheelbase, 6-cyl.

Model No.	Body Type & Seating	Factory Price	Shipping Weight	Prod. Total
Std.	2-dr. Cpe.-3P	694	2500	NA
Std.	2-dr. Vic. Cpe.-4P	740	2540	NA
Std.	2-dr. Conv. Brgm.-6P	886	2610	NA
Std.	4-dr. Sed.-6P	755	2620	NA
Std.	4-dr. Tr. Sed.-6P	775	2625	NA
Std.	2-dr. Conv. Cpe.-3P	835	2545	NA
Std.	2-dr. Brgm.-6P	724	2595	NA
Std.	2-dr. Tr. Brgm.-6P	743	2600	NA
DeL.	2-dr. Cpe.-3P	704	2500	NA
DeL.	2-dr. Vic. Cpe.-4P	750	2540	NA
DeL.	2-dr. Conv. Brgm.-6P	891	2610	NA
DeL.	4-dr. Sed.-6P	765	2620	NA
DeL.	4-dr. Tr. Sed.-6P	785	2625	NA
DeL.	2-dr. Conv. Cpe.-3P	840	2545	NA
DeL.	2-dr. Brgm.-6P	734	2595	NA
DeL.	2-dr. Tr. Brgm.-6P	753	2600	NA

Note 1: The Standard models comprised the initial 112 offerings. After May 1 they were designated as "Standard" models when the DeLuxe version with walnut grain finished instrument panels and interior trim were introduced.

Custom Six — Series 83 — 122" wheelbase, 6-cyl.

Model No.	Body Type & Seating	Factory Price	Shipping Weight	Prod. Total
Series 83	2-dr. Cpe.-3P	909	2825	NA
Series 83	2-dr. Conv. Cpe.-3P	1041	2895	NA
Series 83	2-dr. Vic. Cpe.-5P	995	2880	NA
Series 83	2-dr. Conv. Brgm.-6P	1104	2975	NA
Series 83	2-dr. Brgm.-6P	948	2935	NA
Series 83	2-dr. Tr. Brgm.-6P	968	2940	NA
Series 83	4-dr. Sed.-6P	984	3005	NA
Series 83	4-dr. Tr. Sed.-6P	1005	3010	NA

DeLuxe Eight — Series 84 — 122" wheelbase, 8-cyl.

Model No.	Body Type & Seating	Factory Price	Shipping Weight	Prod. Total
Series 84	2-dr. Vic. Cpe.-5P	1031	3060	NA
Series 84	2-dr. Cpe.-3P	990	3010	NA
Series 84	2-dr. Conv. Cpe.-3P	1121	3060	NA
Series 84	2-dr. Conv. Brgm.-6P	1185	3140	NA
Series 84	4-dr. Sed.-6P	1060	3155	NA
Series 84	4-dr. Tr. Sed.-6P	1080	NA	NA
Series 84	2-dr. Brgm.-6P	1028	3115	NA
Series 84	2-dr. Tr. Brgm.-6P	1049	3120	NA

Custom Eight — Series 85 — 122" wheelbase, 8-cyl.

Model No.	Body Type & Seating	Factory Price	Shipping Weight	Prod. Total
Series 85	2-dr. Cpe.-3P	1080	3020	NA
Series 85	2-dr. Vic. Cpe.-5P	1131	3080	NA
Series 85	2-dr. Brgm.-6P	1134	3140	NA
Series 85	2-dr. Tr. Brgm.-6P	1155	3145	NA
Series 85	4-dr. Sed.-6P	1171	3190	NA
Series 85	4-dr. Tr. Sed.-6P	1191	3195	NA

Custom Eight Country Club — Series 87 — 129" wheelbase, 8-cyl.

Model No.	Body Type & Seating	Factory Price	Shipping Weight	Prod. Total
Series 87	4-dr. Sed.-6P	1199	3270	NA
Series 87	4-dr. Tr. Sed.-6P	1219	3275	NA

ENGINE: [All Hudson Eights used this engine.] L-head. Straight. Eight-cylinder. Chrome alloy block. B & S: 3 x 4.5 in. Disp.: 254 cu. in. C.R.: 6.25:1. Brake H.P.: 122 @ 4200 R.P.M. Taxable H.P.: 28.8. Main bearings: five. Valve lifters: mechanical. Carb.: two-barrel, downdraft Carter WDO 402S. [Hudson 112] L-head. Inline. Six-cylinder. Chrome alloy block. B & S: 3 x 4-1/8 in. Disp.: 175 cu. in. C.R.: 6.50:1. Brake H.P.: 83 @ 4000 R.P.M. Taxable H.P.: 21.6. Main bearings: three. Valve lifters: mechanical. Carb.: Carter 411S (early), 417S (late). [Hudson Six] L-head. Six-cylinder. Chrome alloy block. B & S: 3 x 5 in. Disp.: 212 cu. in. C.R.: 6.25:1. Brake H.P.: 101 @ 4000 R.P.M. Taxable H.P.: 21.6. Main bearings: three. Valve lifters: mechanical. Carb.: two-barrel Carter WDO downdraft. Optional engine: L-head. Six-cylinder. Chrome alloy block. B & S: 3 x 5 in. Disp.: 212 cu. in. C.R.: 7.0:1. Brake H.P.: 107. Main bearings: three. Valve lifters: mechanical. Carb.: Dual Downdraft Carter WDO 397S.

CHASSIS: [Series 89 (112)] W.B.: 112 in. O.L.: 186 in. Height: 70 in. Frt/Rear Tread: 56/59 in. Tires: 16 x 5.50. [Series 85 (Hudson Custom Eight)] W.B.: 122 in. O.L.: 197-3/4 in. Frt/Rear Tread: 56/59 in. Tires: 16 x 6.00 (15 x 7.00 opt.). [Series 83 (Hudson Custom Six)] W.B.: 122 in. O.L.: 197-3/4 in. Frt/Rear Tread: 56/59 in. Tires: 16 x 6.00 (15 x

7.00 opt.). [Series 84 (Hudson DeLuxe Eight)] W.B.: 122 in. O.L.: 197-3/4 in. Frt/Rear Tread: 56/59 in. Tires: 16 x 6.00 (15 x 7.00 opt.). [Series 87 (Hudson Custom Eight Country Club)] W.B.: 129 in. Frt/Rear Tread: 56/59 in. Tires: 16 x 6.00 (15 x 7.00 opt.).

TECHNICAL: Sliding gear, synchromesh transmission. 3F/1R. Floor shift. Single disc cork insert, running in oil. Shaft drive. Semi-floating rear axle. Overall ratio: 4.11:1. Bendix Hydraulic brakes on four wheels. Steel disc wheels. Drivetrain options: Selective automatic shift. Automatic clutch.

OPTIONS: DeLuxe heater. Custom radio (seven tubes) Hudson-RCA Victor DB38. DeLuxe radio (six tubes) Hudson-RCA Victor SA-38. Custom hot water heater. Hydraulic hill-hold. Dual sidemounts (last year of availability). Fender skirts. Fog and spotlights. 15 x 7.00 tires.

HISTORICAL: Introduced January 1938. Hudson made 51,078 shipments to dealers during the 1938 calendar year. Terraplanes carried the Hudson name in sales literature and on hubcaps (see Terraplane section). The president of Hudson was A.E. Barit.

1939

HUDSON 112 — SERIES 90 — SIX: The Hudson 112 was the only Hudson model for 1939 that retained the side-hood mounted headlights of earlier years. Artificial catwalk grille panels were new, as was the steering column mounted shift lever.

HUDSON PACEMAKER — SERIES 91 — SIX: The Pacemaker Series was introduced in March 1939 and is often regarded as the successor to the Terraplane. As were other Hudsons, the Pacemaker's suspension was equipped with Auto-Poise Control. This consisted of a bar attached to the frame across the front of the chassis. Its ends were angled backward to form arms that attached to the wheel spindles. The result was a torsional effect that pulled the wheels back to a center location whenever they moved away from a straight-ahead position.

HUDSON SIX — SERIES 92 — SIX: Interior and dash appointments of the Series 92 were of a higher quality than those of the Series 91. Both series shared painted catwalk grilles, narrow body beltline trim and a relatively short hood ornament. In common with all Hudsons, the Six was equipped with the forward hinged hood introduced in 1938 on the Hudson 112.

HUDSON COUNTRY CLUB SIX — SERIES 93 — SIX: Standard equipment on all Country Club and convertible models were Airfoam latex rubber cushions. Exterior appointments included chrome catwalk grilles, front fender chrome spears placed above the headlights, wider beltline molding and small arrowhead shaped lights in the leading edge of the side hood trim.

HUDSON COUNTRY CLUB EIGHT — SERIES 95 — EIGHT: These Hudsons were identical to the Series 93 versions with the exception of their front bumper center section that carried a plate reading "Hudson Eight." Those on the Series 93 read "Hudson."

HUDSON COUNTRY CLUB EIGHT — SERIES 97 — EIGHT: The two models in this series were mounted on the 109-inch wheelbase chassis and were distinguished by their taupe cashmere cloth interiors.

I.D. DATA: Car number on plate mounted on firewall. Starting: [Series 90] 90101, [Series 91] 9132576, [Series 92] 92101. Ending: [Series 90] 9054902, [Series 91] 9154902, [Series 92] 9254902. Engine numbers on right side of cylinder block. Starting: same as serial numbers. Car numbers on plate mounted on firewall. Starting: [Series 93] 93101, [Series 95] 95101, [Series 97] 97101. Ending: [Series 93] 9354902, [Series 95] 9554902, [Series 97] 9754902. Engine numbers on right side of cylinder block. Starting: same as serial numbers. Canadian-built cars included letter "C".

Series 90 — 112" wheelbase, 6-cyl.

Model No.	Body Type & Seating	Factory Price	Shipping Weight	Prod. Total
Series 90	2-dr. Cpe.-3P	745	2587	NA
Series 90	2-dr. Conv. Cpe.-3P	886	2627	NA
Series 90	2-dr. Conv. Brgm.-6P	936	2732	NA
Series 90	2-dr. Tr. Brgm.-6P	775	2682	NA
Series 90	4-dr. Tr. Sed.-6P	806	2712	NA
Series 90	2-dr. Vic. Cpe.-4P	791	2622	NA
Series 90	2-dr. Util. Cpe.-3P*	750	2714	NA
Series 90	2-dr. Trav. Cpe.-3P*	695	2544	NA
Series 90	2-dr. Util. C'ch.-6P*	725	2634	NA
Series 90	4-dr. Sta. Wag.-6P*	931	2880	NA

Note 1: The two-door utility coupe-three passenger, two-door travel coupe-three passenger, two-door utility coach-six passenger, and four-door station wagon-six passenger were classified as Series 90 — Business Car.

Pacemaker Series 91 — 118" wheelbase, 6-cyl.

Model No.	Body Type & Seating	Factory Price	Shipping Weight	Prod. Total
Series 91	4-dr. Tr. Sed.-6P	854	2867	NA
Series 91	2-dr. Tr. Brgm.-6P	823	2832	NA
Series 91	2-dr. Vic. Cpe.-4P	844	2752	NA
Series 91	2-dr. Cpe.-3P	973	2717	NA
Series 92 — 118" wheelbase, 6-cyl.				
Series 92	2-dr. Cpe.-3P	823	2757	NA
Series 92	2-dr. Vic. Cpe.-5P	869	2787	NA
Series 92	2-dr. Conv. Cpe.-3P	872	2782	NA
Series 92	2-dr. Conv. Brgm.-6P	1032	2892	NA
Series 92	2-dr. Tr. Brgm.-6P	856	2847	NA
Series 92	4-dr. Tr. Sed.-6P	898	2897	NA
Country Club Series 93 — 122" wheelbase, 6-cyl.				
Series 93	2-dr. Cpe.-3P	919	2848	NA
Series 93	2-dr. Vic. Cpe.-5P	967	2893	NA
Series 93	2-dr. Conv. Cpe.-3P	1052	2898	NA
Series 93	4-dr. Tr. Sed.-6P	995	3023	NA
Series 93	2-dr. Conv. Brgm.-6P	1115	2083	NA
Series 93	2-dr. Tr. Brgm.-6P	960	2968	NA
Country Club Series 95 — 122" wheelbase, 8-cyl.				
Series 95	2-dr. Vic. Cpe.-5P	1051	3053	NA
Series 95	2-dr. Conv. Cpe.-3P	1138	3033	NA
Series 95	2-dr. Conv. Brgm.-6P	1201	3123	NA
Series 95	2-dr. Tr. Brgm.-6P	1049	3138	NA
Series 95	4-dr. Tr. Sed.-6P	1079	3193	NA
Custom Series 97 — 129" wheelbase, 8-cyl.				
Series 97	4-dr. Cust. Sed.-6P	1175	3268	NA
Series 97	4-dr. Cust. Sed.-7P	1430	3378	NA

ENGINE: [Series 95 and 97] L-head. Straight. Eight-cylinder. Chrome alloy block. B & S: 3 x 4-1/2 in. Disp.: 254 cu. in. C.R.: 6.25:1. Brake H.P.: 122 @ 4200 R.P.M. Taxable H.P.: 28.8. Main bearings: five. Valve lifters: mechanical. Carb.: Carter two-barrel, downdraft WDO 402S. [Series 93] L-head. Straight. Six-cylinder. Chrome alloy block. B & S: 3 x 5 in. Disp.: 212 cu. in. C.R.: 6.25:1. Brake H.P. 96 @ 3600 R.P.M. Main bearings: three. Valve lifters: mechanical. Carb.: two-barrel Carter downdraft WDO. [Series 91] L-head. Straight Six. Chrome alloy block. B & S: 3 x 5 in. Disp. 212 cu. in. C.R.: 6.25:1. Brake H.P.: 96 @ 3900 R.P.M. Main bearings: three. Valve lifters: mechanical. Carb.: one-barrel Carter. [Series 92] L-head. Straight Six. Chrome alloy block. B & S: 3 x 5 in. Disp.: 212 cu. in. C.R.: 6.25:1. Brake H.P.: 96 @ 3900 R.P.M. Main bearings: three. Valve lifters: mechanical. Carb.: one-barrel Carter. Optional engine: L-head. Straight Six. Chrome alloy block. B & S: 3 x 5 in. Disp.: 212 cu. in. C.R.: 6.25:1. Main bearings: three. Valve lifters: mechanical. Carb.: two-barrel Carter WDO downdraft. [Series 90] L-head. Straight Six. Chrome alloy block. B & S: 3 x 4-1/2 in. Disp.: 175 cu. in. C.R.: 6.5:1. Brake H.P.: 86 @ 4000 R.P.M. Taxable H.P.: 21.6. Main bearings: three. Valve lifters: mechanical. Carb.: one-barrel Carter WDO.

CHASSIS: [Series 90] W.B.: 112 in. O.L.: 187-7/8 in. Frt/Rear Tread: 50/59-1/2 in. Tires: 6.00 x 16. [Series 91] W.B.: 118 in. O.L.: 193-7/16 in. Frt/Rear Tread: 56/59-1/2 in. [Series 93] W.B.: 122 in. O.L.: 199 in. Frt/Rear Tread: 56/59-1/2 in. Tires: 6.25 x 16. [Series 92] W.B.: 118 in. Frt/Rear Tread: 56/59-1/2 in. [Series 95] W.B.: 122 in. O.L.: 199 in. Frt/Rear Tread: 56/59-1/2 in. Tires: 6.50 x 16. [Series 97] W.B.: 129 in. O.L.: 206 in. Frt/Rear Tread: 56/59-1/2 in. Tires: 6.50 x 16.

TECHNICAL: Sliding gear transmission. Speeds: 3F/1R. Steering column controls. Single disc, cork inserts, running in oil. Shaft drive. Semi-floating rear axle. Overall ratio: 4.11:1. Bendix hydraulic brakes on four wheels. Steel, drop center type wheels. Rim size: 16 in. Selective automatic shift. Automatic clutch.

OPTIONS: Single sidemount. Heater (Custom and DeLuxe). Custom radio. DeLuxe radio. Foglights. Air electric horns. Side mirrors. Seat covers.

HISTORICAL: Introduced November 1938. Innovations: Airfoam seat cushions, Auto-Poise Control, interior hood release. Hudson made 82,161 shipments to dealers during the 1939 calendar year. The president of Hudson was A.E. Barit.

1940

OVERVIEW — Hudson's styling was extensively revised for 1940. The almond-shaped headlights of 1939 gave way to circular sealed beam units although the shape of the headlight frame and the positioning of the parking lights directly below the main lamps gave both arrangements a similar appearance. The Hudson's grille form, which had been steadily evolving towards a strictly horizontal design for several years, took another strong step in that direction as a two-section arrangement with horizontal bars was adopted. Additional horizontal bars ran the length of the body adding an impression of low built and fleetness. At the rear a larger, single-piece window was adopted. All models were offered with or without runningboards at no extra cost. Leading the list of Hudson mechanical and technical improvements was a full independent front suspension consisting of coil springs, unequal length A-arms and hydraulic shock absorbers. Also new were longer by five inches, rear semi-elliptic springs with a total length of 60 inches and as an option, the semi-electric Warner overdrive feature that replaced Selective Automatic Shift. Hudson's "Fluid Cushioned" automatic clutch was available with or without overdrive. The Hudson 112 series was dropped for 1940 with a new line of four Hudson Six Travelers taking its place. Hudson produced 86,865 automobiles but losses still totaled $1,507,780.

HUDSON SUPER SIX — SERIES 41 — SIX: Super Six models carried Hudson lettering on the sides of the hood along with the small triangular lights of the Series 43 and 44 models. In addition their greater length made it easy to separate them from the Series 40T and 40P.

HUDSON SIX TRAVELER SIX — SERIES 40T — SIX: As with all Hudsons the Series 40T models were equipped with sealed beam headlamps. Since this line was Hudson's least expensive it was fitted with sliding glass. Its interior featured taupe worsted boucle. The Traveler was easily set apart from other Hudsons by its lack of front vent panes.

HUDSON DELUXE SIX — SERIES 40P — SIX: The higher price of the Series 40P compared to the Traveler Six was justified by its higher quality brown taupe stripe broadcloth upholstery and roll-down windows.

HUDSON EIGHT — SERIES 44 — EIGHT: The Series 44 Hudsons were identical in appearance to the Series 41, Super Six models.

HUDSON EIGHT DELUXE — SERIES 45 — EIGHT: The two models in this series had a higher quality interior than the Series 44.

HUDSON COUNTRY CLUB EIGHT — SERIES 47 — EIGHT: These Hudsons were identified by their added length, wider door (front) and distinctive front grille with a rectangular opening in its center section. The front fenders were crowned with chrome strips and the taillights were given added chrome trim. Included as standard equipment were directional signals.

HUDSON COUNTRY CLUB SIX — SERIES 43 — SIX: These three Hudsons were with the exception of their engine and running gear identical to the Country Club Eight. Interior features included a standard two-tone brown and tan Hockanum woolen upholstery. Door panels were fitted with chrome scruff plates and the pleated sections of the seats and door panels had horizontal dividers.

I.D. DATA: Car numbers on plate mounted on firewall. Starting: [Series 40] 40101, [Series 41] 41250, [Series 43] 43370, [Series 44] 44294, [Series 45] 451752, [Series 47] 47167. Ending: [Series 40] 4089192, [Series 41] 4189192, [Series 43] 4389192, [Series 44] 4489192, [Series 45] 4589192, [Series 47] 4789192.

* Includes 40T, 40P and 40C (commercial cars).

Engine numbers on right side of cylinder block. Starting: Series 40 same as serial numbers, [Series 41 & 43] 43101, [Series 44 & 45] 45101. Ending: Series 40 same as serial numbers, [Series 41 & 43] 4389192, [Series 44 & 45] 4589192. Canadian-built cars included letter "C".

Traveler Series 40T — 113" wheelbase, 6-cyl.

Model No.	Body Type & Seating	Factory Price	Shipping Weight	Prod. Total
Series 40T	2-dr. Cpe.-3P	670	2800	NA
Series 40T	2-dr. Vic. Cpe.-4P	750	2830	NA
Series 40T	2-dr. Tr. Sed.-6P	735	2895	NA
Series 40T	4-dr. Sed.-6P	763	2940	NA

DeLuxe Series 40P — 113" wheelbase, 6-cyl.

Model No.	Body Type & Seating	Factory Price	Shipping Weight	Prod. Total
Series 40P	2-dr. Cpe.-3P	745	2840	NA
Series 40P	2-dr. Vic. Cpe.-4P	791	2865	NA
Series 40P	2-dr. Conv. Cpe.-5P	930	2860	NA
Series 40P	2-dr. Tr. Sed.-6P	775	2930	NA
Series 40P	2-dr. Conv. Sed.-6P	955	2920	NA
Series 40P	4-dr. Tr. Sed.-6P	806	2965	NA

Super Series 41 — 118" wheelbase, 6-cyl.

Model No.	Body Type & Seating	Factory Price	Shipping Weight	Prod. Total
Series 41	2-dr. Cpe.-3P	809	2950	NA
Series 41	2-dr. Vic. Cpe.-5P	860	2980	NA
Series 41	2-dr. Conv. Cpe.-5P	1087	2980	NA
Series 41	2-dr. Conv. Sed.-6P	1030	3020	NA
Series 41	2-dr. Tr. Sed.-6P	839	3020	NA
Series 41	4-dr. Tr. Sed.-6P	870	3050	NA

Country Club Series 43 — 125" wheelbase, 6-cyl.

Model No.	Body Type & Seating	Factory Price	Shipping Weight	Prod. Total
Series 43	4-dr. Tr. Sed.-6P	1018	3240	NA
Series 43	4-dr. Sp. Tr. Sed.-6P	1044	3240	NA
Series 43	4-dr. Sed.-8P	1230	3355	NA

Series 44 — 118" wheelbase, 8-cyl.

Model No.	Body Type & Seating	Factory Price	Shipping Weight	Prod. Total
Series 44	2-dr. Cpe.-3P	860	3040	NA
Series 44	2-dr. Vic. Cpe.-4P	942	3075	NA
Series 44	2-dr. Conv. Sed.-6P	1122	3130	NA
Series 44	2-dr. Conv. Cpe.-5P	1087	3065	NA
Series 44	2-dr. Tr. Sed.-6P	942	3185	NA
Series 44	4-dr. Tr. Sed.-6P	952	3185	NA

DeLuxe Series 45 — 118" wheelbase, 8-cyl.

Model No.	Body Type & Seating	Factory Price	Shipping Weight	Prod. Total
Series 45	2-dr. Tr. Sed.-6P	942	3185	NA
Series 45	4-dr. Tr. Sed.-6P	976	3215	NA

Country Club Series 47 — 125" wheelbase, 8-cyl.

Model No.	Body Type & Seating	Factory Price	Shipping Weight	Prod. Total
Series 47	4-dr. Tr. Sed.-6P	1118	3285	NA
Series 47	4-dr. Sp. Tr. Sed.-6P	1144	3285	NA
Series 47	4-dr. Sed.-8P	1330	3400	NA

ENGINE: [Series 40T and 40P] L-head. Straight. Six-cylinder. Chrome alloy block. B & S: 3 x 4-1/8 in. Disp.: 175 cu. in. C.R.: 6.5:1. Brake H.P.: 92 @ 4000 R.P.M. Main bearings: three. Valve lifters: mechanical. Carb.: Carter 430 SV (early), 461S (late). Optional engine: L-head. Straight. Six-cylinder. Chrome alloy block. B & S: 3 x 5 in. Disp.: 212 cu. in. C.R.: 6.5:1. Brake H.P.: 102 @ 4000 R.P.M. Main bearings: three. Valve lifters: mechanical. Carb.: Carter 430SV (early), 461S (late). [Series 41 and 43] L-head. Inline. Six-cylinder. Chrome alloy block. B & S: 3 x 5 in. Disp.: 212 cu. in. C.R.: 6.5:1. Brake H.P.: 102 @ 4000 R.P.M. Main bearings: three. Valve lifters: mechanical. Carb.: two-barrel Carter 454S. [Series 44, 45 and 47] L-head. Inline. Eight-cylinder. Chrome alloy block. B & S: 3 x 4-1/2 in. Disp.: 254.4 cu. in. C.R.: 6.5:1. Brake H.P.: 128 @ 4200 R.P.M. N.A.C.C. H.P.: 28.8. Main bearings: five. Valve lifters: mechanical. Carb.: two-barrel Carter 455S. Note: cars with the 3 x 5 in. engine were designated by the letter "L" placed between series and serial number.

CHASSIS: [Series 40T, 40P] W.B.: 113 in. O.L.: 190-3/8 in. Height: 70.5 in. Frt/Rear Tread: 56-1/4/59-1/2 in. Tires: 16 x 5.50 — 40T, 16 x 6.00 — 40P, 15 x 7.00 opt. [Series 41] W.B.: 118 in. O.L.: 195-3/8 in. Height: 70.5 in. Frt/Rear Tread: 56-1/4/59-1/2 in. Tires: 16 x 6.00, 15 x 7.00 opt. [Series 43] W.B.: 125 in. O.L.: 202-3/8 in. Height: 70.5 in. Frt/Rear Tread: 56-1/4/59-1/2 in. Tires: 16 x 6.25, 15 x 7.00 opt. [Series 44] W.B.: 118 in. O.L.: 195-3/8 in. Height: 70.5 in. Frt/Rear Tread: 56-1/4/59-1/2 in. Tires: 16 x 6.00, 15 x 7.00 opt. [Series 45] W.B.: 118 in. O.L.: 195-3/8 in. Height: 70.5 in. Frt/Rear Tread: 56-1/4/59-1/2 in. Tires: 16 x 6.00, 15 x 7.00 opt. [Series 47] W.B.: 125 in. O.L.: 202-3/8 in. Height: 70.5 in. Frt/Rear Tread: 56-1/4/59-1/2 in. Tires: 16 x 6.50, 15 x 7.00 opt.

TECHNICAL: Sliding gear transmission. 3F/1R. Column controls. Single disc, cork inserts, running in oil. Shaft drive. Semi-floating rear axle. Overall ratio: Series 40T and 40P — 4.55:1; all others 4.11:1. Bendix hydraulic brakes on four wheels. Steel, drop center type wheels. Drivetrain options: Overdrive. Automatic clutch.

OPTIONS: Turn signals (standard only on Country Club models). Air-foam cushions (optional on Hudson Six models — standard in all others). Weather-Master Fresh Air and Heat Control.

HISTORICAL: Introduced September 1939. 1940 was the first year for Hudson's fully independent suspension. Hudson made 87,900 shipments to dealers during the 1940 calendar year. The president of Hudson was A.E. Barit. From August 23 to August 27, just prior to the introduction date of the 1940 Hudson both the Hudson Six and Hudson Eight set numerous new AAA speed records. The Hudson Six established 58 new Class D endurance marks plus 23 unlimited records for stock cars regardless of size or price. Equipped with overdrive and the optional 3.88:1 rear axle the Hudson averaged 70.5 mph for 10,000 miles. The Hudson Eight with the optional 7.0:1 cylinder head, overdrive and 3.88:1 rear axle was used by John Cobb to set additional Class D records including a 10-mile run at 92.89 mph and a flying mile record of 93.89. Both cars also participated in economy runs. The Hudson Six finished a 1,000-mile run at an average of 29.88 mph with a fuel consumption of 32.66 mpg. The Hudson Eight averaged 27.12 mpg for 1,000 miles at a constant speed of 29.31 mph.

1941

OVERVIEW — The 1941 Hudsons were substantially redesigned automobiles, sharing only the front fender sheet metal and driveline components with the 1940 models. All wheelbases were increased three inches and overall height was reduced by two inches due to a flatter roof line. Overall body length was extended by 5-1/2 inches. The handsome, horizontal grille format was continued from 1940 but nine rather than seven grille bars were used and their greater length reduced the size of the center grille divider. Rear deck changes included taillights moved from the fenders to the quarter panels and externally mounted chrome trunk hinges. Convertible models were now equipped with a power top and a new three-speed synchromesh transmission with helical-cut gears was also introduced. In a break with tradition, Hudson introduced Symphonic Styling for 1941, which at no extra cost offered the customer a wide selection of interior color combinations that harmonized with the car's exterior color. Although shipments to dealers dropped to 79,529, Hudson's profit was a respectable $3,756,418.

HUDSON TRAVELER, SIX DELUXE — SERIES 10T, SERIES 10P — SIX: The 10T and 10P shared the same chassis, wheelbase and engines. Both series were equipped with a single taillight and sun visor but the 10P was fitted with many other features. These included larger 16 x 6.00 standard tires, gray or tan colored broadcloth upholstery (in place of the 10T's taupe worsted boucle), wood grained dash and garnish moldings, front window vent panes, rear anti-sway bar, spring covers, bumper guards, rear seat ashtrays and assist plus front armrests.

HUDSON SUPER SIX — SERIES 11 — SIX: The Super Six was powered by the same cylinder engine as the Commodore Six and shared the 121-inch wheelbase chassis with both the Commodore Six and Eight. Externally it was identified by the Super Six nameplates positioned on each side of the hood near the windshield's base. Its standard equipment was identical to that of the DeLuxe Six but the Super Six interior featured Hockanum Tweed in either tan, gray or green and the instrument panel and garnish molding was painted to match one of these colors.

HUDSON COMMODORE SIX — SERIES 12 — SIX/COMMODORE EIGHT — SERIES 14 — EIGHT: The Commodore Six and Commodore Eight were, except for their engine and accompanying mechanical modifications, identical automobiles. The only exceptions were their hood identifications that read either Commodore Six or Commodore Eight. Both cars had a 121-inch wheelbase and crowning their front fenders were long chrome bars that trailed away from the parking lights. The front bumpers had large "guard wings" at either end with similar gravel deflectors mounted on the rear bumpers. The Commodore interior featured Hockanum Twill Cord upholstery in gray, tan or green and the finish of the instrument panel matched that of the upholstery. The front and rear seat backs and armrests were leather finished and a deluxe, 18-inch steering wheel with a chrome horn ring was fitted. Among the Commodore's standard equipment were airfoam seats, twin horns and taillights, large hubcaps and on sedans a rear dome light. In addition, the Commodores were offered in special, two-tone exterior color combinations.

HUDSON COMMODORE CUSTOM EIGHT — SERIES 15 & 17 — EIGHT: The Commodore Custom Eights were offered in either coupe (121-inch wheelbase) or sedan (128-inch wheelbase) models. They were identified by such external features as the center bar placed between the front bumper guards, wheel trim rings, hood identification script, inward pointed, triangular taillights and similarly shaped rear deck emblem. In addition to the equipment supplied to the Commodore Series the Custom Eight's standard appointments included two cigarette lighters, radio and front and rear center armrests. Their Hockanum Fancy Bedford Cord upholstery in green, gray or tan covered double thickness airfoam cushions. Additional leather trim was also installed on the interior door edges and front seat corners.

I.D. DATA: Car numbers on plate positioned on right front door hinge pillar post. Starting: [Series 10T] T10101. [Series 10P & 10C] P10101, [Series 11 & 12] 11101. [Series 14 & 15] 14101. [Series 17] 17101. Ending: [Series 10T] T1092988, [Series 10P & 10C] P1092988, [Series 11 & 12] 1192988, [Series 14 & 15] 1492988. [Series 17] 1792988. Engine number on stamping on top of the cylinder block between numbers one and two exhaust manifold flanges. Starting: [Series 10T] T10101. [Series 10P & 10C] C10101. [Series 11 & 12] 12101. [Series 14 & 15] 15101. [Series 17] NA. Ending: [Series 10T] T1092988. [Series 10P & 10C] C1092988. [Series 11 & 12] 1292988. [Series 11 & 12] 11292988.[Series 14 & 15] 1592988. [Series 17] NA. "C" included in Canadian cars.

Traveler Series 10T — 116" wheelbase, 6-cyl.

Model No.	Body Type & Seating	Factory Price	Shipping Weight	Prod. Total
Series 10T	2-dr. Clb. Cpe.-6P	788	2840	NA
Series 10T	2-dr. Cpe.-3P	695	2790	NA
Series 10T	2-dr. Tr. Sed.-6P	765	2850	NA
Series 10T	4-dr. Tr. Sed.-6P	793	2900	NA

DeLuxe Series 10P — 116" wheelbase, 6-cyl.

Model No.	Body Type & Seating	Factory Price	Shipping Weight	Prod. Total
Series 10P	2-dr. Clb. Cpe.-6P	848	2895	NA
Series 10P	2-dr. Cpe.-3P	801	2840	NA
Series 10P	2-dr. Tr. Sed.-6P	822	2900	NA
Series 10P	4-dr. Tr. Sed.-6P	856	2950	NA
Series 10P	2-dr. Conv. Sed.-6P	1063	2980	NA

Super Series 11 — 121" wheelbase, 6-cyl.

Model No.	Body Type & Seating	Factory Price	Shipping Weight	Prod. Total
Series 11	2-dr. Clb. Cpe.-6P	936	2980	NA
Series 11	2-dr. Cpe.-3P	881	2935	NA
Series 11	2-dr. Tr. Sed.-6P	901	3000	NA
Series 11	4-dr. Tr. Sed.-6P	932	3050	NA
Series 11	2-dr. Conv. Sed.-6P	1156	3125	NA
Series 11	4-dr. Sta. Wag.-8P	1383	3400	NA

Commodore Series 12 — 121" wheelbase, 6-cyl.

Model No.	Body Type & Seating	Factory Price	Shipping Weight	Prod. Total
Series 12	2-dr. Clb. Cpe.-6P	997	3045	NA
Series 12	2-dr. Cpe.-3P	935	3000	NA
Series 12	2-dr. Conv. Sed.-6P	1204	3160	NA
Series 12	2-dr. Tr. Sed.-6P	966	3050	NA
Series 12	4-dr. Tr. Sed.-6P	994	3100	NA

Commodore Series 14 — 121" wheelbase, 8-cyl.

Model No.	Body Type & Seating	Factory Price	Shipping Weight	Prod. Total
Series 14	2-dr. Clb. Cpe.-6P	1040	3210	NA
Series 14	2-dr. Cpe.-3P	978	3135	NA
Series 14	2-dr. Conv. Sed.-6P	1254	3350	NA
Series 14	2-dr. Tr. Sed.-6P	1003	3210	NA
Series 14	4-dr. Tr. Sed.-6P	1035	3260	NA
Series 14	4-dr. Sta. Wag.-8P	1383	3400	NA

Commodore Custom Series 15 — 121" wheelbase, 8-cyl.

Model No.	Body Type & Seating	Factory Price	Shipping Weight	Prod. Total
Series 15	2-dr. Clb. Cpe.-6P	1127	3235	NA
Series 15	2-dr. Cpe.-3P	1064	3185	NA

Commodore Custom Series 17 — 128" wheelbase, 8-cyl.

Model No.	Body Type & Seating	Factory Price	Shipping Weight	Prod. Total
Series 17	4-dr. Tr. Sed.-6P	1232	3400	NA
Series 17	4-dr. Sed.-8P	1438	3440	NA

ENGINE: [Series 11 and 12] L-head. Inline. Six-cylinder. Chrome alloy block. B & S: 3 x 5 in. Disp.: 212 cu. in. C.R.: 6.25:1. Brake H.P.: 102 @ 4000 R.P.M. Taxable H.P.: 21.6. Main bearings: three. Valve lifters: mechanical. Carb.: Carter Duplex Downdraft 501S. [Series 10T and 10P] L-head. Inline. Six-cylinder. Chrome alloy block. B & S: 3 x 4-1/2 in. Disp.: 175 cu. in. C.R.: 7.25:1. Brake H.P.: 92 @ 4000 R.P.M. Taxable H.P.: 21.6. Main bearings: three. Valve lifters: mechanical. Carb.: Carter Single Downdraft. Optional engine: L-head. Inline. Six-cylinder. Chrome alloy block. B & S: 3 x 5 in. Disp.: 212 cu. in. C.R.: 6.5:1. Brake H.P.: 102 @ 4000 R.P.M. Taxable/A.L.A.M./N.A.C.C. H.P.: 21.6. Main bearings: three. Valve lifters: mechanical. Carb.: Carter Duplex Downdraft. [Series 14, 15 and 17] L-head. Inline. Eight-cylinder. Chrome alloy block. B & S: 3 x 4-1/2 In. Disp. 254.4 cu. in. C.R.: 6.5:1. Brake H.P.: 128 @ 4200 R.P.M. Taxable H.P.: 28.8. Main bearings: five. Valve lifters: mechanical. Carb.: two-barrel Carter 502S.

CHASSIS: [Series 10T] W.B.: 116 in. O.L.: 195-1/4 in. Height: 68 in. Frt/Rear Tread: 56-1/4/59-1/2 in. Tires: 16 x 5.5 (16 x 6.00 optional). [Series 10P] W.B.: 116 in. O.L.: 195-1/4 in. Height: 68 in. Frt/Rear Tread: 56-1/4/59-1/2 in. Tires: 16 x 6.00. [Series 11] W.B.: 121 in. O.L.: 200-1/4 in. Height: 68-3/4 in. Frt/Rear Tread: 56-1/4/59-1/2 in. Tires: 16 x 6.00 (16 x 6.50 or 15 x 7.00 optional). [Series 12] W.B.: 121 in. O.L.: 203-1/4 in. Height: 68-3/4 in. Frt/Rear Tread: 56-1/4/59-1/2 in. Tires: 16 x 6.25 (16 x 6.50 or 15 x 7.00 optional). [Series 14] W.B.: 121 in. O.L.: 203-1/4 in. Height: 68-3/4 in. Frt/Rear Tread: 56-1/4/59-1/2 in. Tires: 16 x 6.25 (16 x 6.50 or 15 x 7.00 optional). [Series 15] W.B.: 121 in. O.L.: 203-1/4 in. Height: 68-3/4. Frt/Rear Tread: 56-1/4/59-1/2 in. Tires: 16 x 6.25 (16 x 6.50 or 15 x 7.00 optional). [Series 17] W.B.: 128 in. O.L.: 210-1/4 in. Height: 68-3/4 in. Frt/Rear tread: 56-1/4/59-1/2 in. Tires: 16 x 6.50 (15 x 7.00 optional).

TECHNICAL: Sliding gear transmission. Speeds: 3F/1R. Column controls. Single disc, cork inserts, running in oil. Shaft drive. Semi-floating rear axle. Overall ratio: 4.11, 4.55 optional — except series 10T and 10P. Standard axle with overdrive 4.55, 4.11 optional. Bendix hydraulic brakes on four wheels. Steel wheels. Rim size: 16 in. (15 in. optional). Vacumotive Drive (automatic clutch) ($27.50). Overdrive (62.50).

OPTIONS: DeLuxe radio ($49.75). Custom heater (includes defroster) (26.00). Clock (13.50). Spotlight (17.00). Junior radio (29.50). Custom radio (67.50). Power radio antenna (6.75). Weathermaster heater and defroster (36.00). Directionals (17.50, 19.50). Seat covers (7.25). Chrome outside window moldings (7.25, 13.00). DeLuxe 18-inch steering wheel (13.95). Special runningboard moldings (2.25). Airfoam seats. Large hubcaps (6.75). Twin horn.

HISTORICAL: Hudson made 79,529 shipments to dealers during the 1941 calendar year. The president of Hudson was A.E. Barit. Hudson emphasized its economic operation rather than performance in 1941. In the Gilmore Oil Grand Canyon a DeLuxe Six was a class winner with a 24.6 mpg mark. Also a class champion was the Commodore Eight at 20.18 mpg. *Safety Engineering* magazine presented Hudson with its Safety Engineering trophy for the 1941 models' safety and engineering excellence. In each of 14 categories the Hudson received a perfect score.

1941 Hudson, Super Six (Series 11), station wagon, OCW

1942 Hudson, Super Six (Series 11), club coupe, OCW

1942 Hudson, Deluxe (Series 20P), club sedan, OCW

1948 Hudson, Commodore (Series 484), club coupe, OCW

1950 Hudson, Pacemaker (Series 500), sedan (with optional outer bumper guards and rear wheel cover panels), OCW

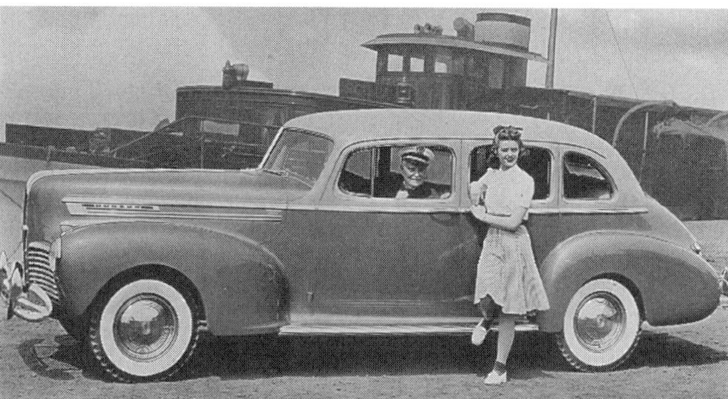

1941 Hudson, Commodore Custom (Series 17), touring sedan, OCW

1942 Hudson, Super Six (Series 11), convertible sedan, OCW

1946 Hudson, Commodore (Series 54), sedan, OCW

1948 Hudson, Commodore (Series 484), convertible brougham, OCW

1951 Hudson, Hornet (Series 7A), convertible brougham, OCW

1942

OVERVIEW — The last of the prewar Hudsons received a fairly substantial face lift. The lower body section now flared out to conceal the remnants of the runningboard and pointing the way to the full width grille arrangements common to most postwar American cars were the chrome strips running full width of the body and extending around the first few inches of the front fender. Also given greater width was the Hudson's grille. To accommodate these changes new front and rear fenders were used. Overall height was reduced by 1.5 inches due to altered rear spring and frame design. The Hudson's profile also carried new trim consisting of a single long bright strip with shorter stripes at either extremity. However, December 31, 1941, was the end of chrome plating trim for U.S. cars with the only external components exempt being bumpers. After that date Hudson's trim consisted of metal pressings covered with plastic. Hudson's production of its 1942 models began on July 21, 1941, and by February 5, 1942, when it came to an end, a total of 40,661 were assembled.

I.D. DATA: Car numbers on plate mounted on firewall. Starting: [Series 20T] T-20101. [Series 20P] P-20101, [Series 21] 21101. [Series 22] 22101. Ending: [Series 20T] T2041232. [Series 20P] P2041232. [Series 21] 2141232. [Series 22] 2241232. Engine numbers stamped on top of the cylinder block between numbers one and two exhaust manifold flanges. Starting: same as serial numbers. Car numbers on plate mounted on firewall. Starting: [Series 24] 24101. [Series 25] 25101. [Series 27] 27101. Ending: [Series 24] 2441232. [Series 25] 2541232. [Series 27] 2741232. Engine number stamped on top of the cylinder block between numbers one and two exhaust manifold flanges. Starting: same as serial numbers. Canadian-built cars included letter "C".

Commodore Series 22 — 121" wheelbase, 6-cyl.

Model No.	Body Type & Seating	Factory Price	Shipping Weight	Prod. Total
Series 22	2-dr. Clb. Cpe.-6P	1239	3090	NA
Series 22	2-dr. Cpe.-3P	1176	2995	NA
Series 22	2-dr. Clb. Sed.-6P	1216	3090	NA
Series 22	4-dr. Sed.-6P	1246	3145	NA
Series 22	2-dr. Conv. Sed.-6P	1481	3280	NA

Commodore Series 24 — 121" wheelbase, 8-cyl.

Model No.	Body Type & Seating	Factory Price	Shipping Weight	Prod. Total
Series 24	2-dr. Clb. Cpe.-6P	1282	3205	NA
Series 24	2-dr. Cpe.-3P	1220	3130	NA
Series 24	2-dr. Clb. Sed.-6P	1252	3230	NA
Series 24	4-dr. Sed.-6P	1291	3280	NA
Series 24	2-dr. Conv. Sed.-6P	1533	3400	NA

Commodore Custom Series 25 — 121" wheelbase, 8-cyl.

Model No.	Body Type & Seating	Factory Price	Shipping Weight	Prod. Total
Series 25	2-dr. Clb. Cpe.-6P	1380	3235	NA
Series 25	2-dr. Cpe.-3P	1318	3160	NA

Commodore Series 27 — 128" wheelbase, 8-cyl.

Model No.	Body Type & Seating	Factory Price	Shipping Weight	Prod. Total
Series 27	4-dr. Sed.-8P	1510	3395	NA

Traveler Series 20T — 116" wheelbase, 6-cyl.

Model No.	Body Type & Seating	Factory Price	Shipping Weight	Prod. Total
Series 20T	2-dr. Clb. Cpe.-6P	965	2845	NA
Series 20T	2-dr. Cpe.-3P	893	2795	NA
Series 20T	2-dr. Clb. Sed.-6P	945	2895	NA
Series 20T	4-dr. Sed.-6P	973	2940	NA

DeLuxe Series 20P — 116" wheelbase, 6-cyl.

Model No.	Body Type & Seating	Factory Price	Shipping Weight	Prod. Total
Series 20P	2-dr. Clb. Cpe.-6P	1034	2900	NA
Series 20P	2-dr. Cpe.-3P	981	2845	NA
Series 20P	2-dr. Clb. Sed.-6P	1012	2935	NA
Series 20P	4-dr. Sed.-6P	1045	2975	NA
Series 20P	2-dr. Conv.-6P	1292	3140	NA

Super Series 21 — 121" wheelbase, 6-cyl.

Model No.	Body Type & Seating	Factory Price	Shipping Weight	Prod. Total
Series 21	2-dr. Clb. Cpe.-6P	1159	3010	NA
Series 21	2-dr. Cpe.-3P	1102	2950	NA
Series 21	2-dr. Clb. Sed.-6P	1132	3035	NA
Series 21	4-dr. Sed.-6P	1162	3080	NA
Series 21	2-dr. Conv. Sed.-6P	1414	3200	NA
Series 21	4-dr. Sta. Wag.-6P	1486	3315	NA

ENGINE: [Series 24, 25, 27] L-head. Inline. Eight-cylinder. Chrome alloy block. B & S: 3 x 4-1/2 in. Disp.: 254.4 cu. in. C.R.: 6.5:1. Brake H.P.: 128 @ 4200 R.P.M. Taxable H.P.: 28.8. Main bearings: five. Valve lifters: mechanical. Carb.: two-barrel downdraft Carter 502S. [Series 21, 22] L-head. Inline. Six-cylinder. Chrome alloy block. B & S: 3 x 5 in. Disp.: 212 cu. in. C.R.: 6.25:1. Brake H.P.: 102 @ 4000 R.P.M. Taxable H.P.: 21.6. Main bearings: three. Valve lifters: mechanical. Carb.: Carter Duplex Downdraft 501S. [Series 20T, 20P] L-head. Inline. Six-cylinder. Chrome alloy block. B & S: 3 x 4-1/2 in. Disp.: 175 cu. in. C.R.: 7.25:1. Brake H.P.: 92 @ 4000 R.P.M. Taxable H.P.: 21.6. Main bearings: three. Valve lifters: mechanical. Carb.: Carter Single Downdraft 454S. Optional engine: L-head. Inline. Six-cylinder. Chrome alloy block. B & S: 3 x 5 in. Disp.: 212 cu. in. C.R.: 6.5:1. Brake H.P.: 102 @ 4000 R.P.M. Taxable H.P.: 21.6. Main bearings: three. Valve lifters: mechanical. Carb.: Carter Duplex Downdraft 501S.

CHASSIS: [Series 20T] W.B.: 116 in. O.L.: 198-1/4 in. Frt/Rear Tread: 56-5/16/59-1/2 in. Tires: 16 x 5.50 (16 x 6.00 optional). [Series 20P] W.B.: 116 in. O.L.: 200-1/2 in. Frt/Rear Tread: 56-5/16/59-1/2 in. Tires: 16 x 6.00 (16 x 6.50 optional). [Series 21] W.B.: 121 in. O.L.: 207-3/8 in. Frt/Rear Tread: 56-5/16/59-1/2 in. Tires: 16 x 6.00 (16 x 6.50, 15 x 7.00 optional). [Series 22] W.B.: 121 in. O.L.: 207-3/8 in. Frt/Rear Tread: 56-5/16/59-1/2 in. Tires: 16 x 6.00 (16 x 6.50, 15 x 7.00 optional). [Series 24] W.B.: 121 in. O.L.: 207-3/8 in. Frt/Rear Tread: 56-5/16/59-1/2 in. Tires: 16 x 6.25 (16 x 6.50, 15 x 7.00 optional). [Series 25] W.B.: 121 in. O.L.: 207-3/8 in. Frt/Rear Tread: 56-5/16/59-1/2 in. Tires: 16 x 6.25 (16 x 6.50, 15 x 7.00 optional). [Series 27] W.B.: 128 in. O.L.: 214-3/8 in. Frt/Rear Tread: 56-5/16/59-1/2 in. Tires: 15 x 6.50 (15 x 7.00 optional).

TECHNICAL: Sliding gear transmission. Speeds: 3F/1R. Steering column controls. Single disc, cork inserts, running in oil. Shaft drive. Semi-floating rear axle. Overall ratio: Series 20T, 20P — 4.55:1, all others 4.11:1. With overdrive: Series 20T, 20P — 4.87:1, all others 4.55:1. Bendix hydraulic brakes on four wheels. Steel drop center type wheels. Drivetrain options: Drive-Master transmission. Overdrive.

OPTIONS: White sidewall tires. Full chrome hubcaps. Bumper wing guards (standard on Commodore). Sleeper kit.

HISTORICAL: Introduced August 1941. Innovations: Drive-Master, which was a combination of vacumotive plus an additional power unit that shifted gears by intake manifold vacuum. Cars with this feature had an instrument panel switch with three push buttons. The "Off" button allowed the car to function in the conventional manner. The "VAC" button put Vacumotive Drive into action. For full Drive-Master operation, the "HDM" button was pushed. Model year production: 40,661 cars. The president of Hudson was A.E. Barit.

HUDSON 1946-1957

Founded by Roy D. Chapin and financed by J.L. Hudson, the Hudson Motor Car Co. pioneered modestly-priced closed cars since its creation in 1909. The company made a small profit during World War II building airplanes and landing craft engines and re-entered the automobile market, in 1946, with face-lifted prewar models.

Hudson retained both its L-head six and eight engines with the Super Six accounting for two-thirds of Hudson's 1946 production. The wheelbase remained unchanged at 121 inches, but optional transmissions included Drive Master, Vacumotive Drive and overdrive. Except for minor exterior and interior changes, models were unchanged for 1947 and Hudson registered profits in both years.

For 1948, Hudson introduced one of the great postwar designs with its unit-body Hudson, which was to continue through 1954. Being low and sleek, it had a low center of gravity and handled exceptionally well. Its dropped floorpan earned it the nickname Step-Down. It was offered in four models —Commodore Six and Eight and Super Six and Eight —and sat on a 124-inch wheelbase. That same year, Hudson introduced a new engine, the 262-cid Super Six, which developed 121 hp at 4000 rpm. In 1951, this same engine evolved into the '308' Hornet powerplant that, from 1951 through 1954, was the king of stock car racing.

Although the Step-Down proved to be one of America's most roadable cars from 1948-1954, Hudson lacked sufficient funds to add new models to the series, and combined with a lack of innovation, principally the lack of a V-8 engine in subsequent years, found sales dropping through the early 1950s.

Hudson introduced a Pacemaker model in 1950, which used a destroked version of the flathead Super Six and sold over 60,000 units. Mention should be made of Pacemaker's five-inch shorter wheelbase and tighter turning radius. The Commodore Six and Eight were continued and all models offered optional Drive Master, Supermatic Drive and overdrive transmissions. Hydra-Matic was an option from 1951 on.

Carrying the same pricetag as the Commodore Eight, the legendary Hudson Hornet was introduced in 1951. Available in four body styles, the Hornet's six-cylinder powerplant produced 145 hp at 3800 rpm in stock form. In the hands of skilled tuners, though, it was capable of considerably more and the most noted of these, Marshall Teague, achieved 112 mph from a NASCAR-certified stock Hornet. In 1953, Hudson also offered factory severe-usage options that were designed for racing applications. Racing items were listed as "Export" options! These included 'Twin H-Power' for improved breathing and a '7-X' racing engine that combined Twin H-Power with other high-performance options to produce about 210 hp.

Tim Flock was the 1952 NASCAR champion in a Hornet. In 1953, Marshall Teague's Hornet won 12 of 13 AAA stock car events and drivers Herb Thomas, Dick Rathmann, Frank Mundy and Al Keller drove Hornets to 65 NASCAR victories through 1954. Although Hudson added and subtracted series throughout this period, its inability to add new body styles hurt sales. When the Hornet and the Hollywood hardtop were added in 1951, Hudson dropped the standard Pacemaker and Super Eight. In 1952, the Wasp replaced the Super Six and all the Commodores were dropped the next year. A new Hornet Special of 1954 failed to increase sales.

Data compiled by
Jack Miller and Charles Liskow
of Hudson-Essex-Terraplane Club
Introduction by Linda Clark

Hudson's ill-fated compact Jet appeared in 1953 and the luxurious Jet Liner of 1954 sold poorly. However, it inspired a two-passenger Grand Turismo, built on the Jet chassis and called the Italia. It was designed by Hudson's Frank Spring and built by Carrozzeria Touring of Milan, Italy. Powered by a 114-hp Jet engine, the Italia had an aluminum body with a wraparound windshield, doors cut into the roof, fender scoops for brake cooling, flow-through ventilation and a leather interior. In addition to the prototype, 25 production Italias were made, plus a four-door 'X-161' that was built on the Hornet's 124-inch wheelbase chassis.

By late 1953, Hudson sales were slumping and the company merged with Nash and moved production to Kenosha, Wis., after closing its Detroit plant on Oct. 30, 1954. The all-new 1955 Hudson was really a restyled Nash using Hudson's 1954 dashboard instruments. Hudson front suspension components and Dual-Safe brakes were retained. Wasps were powered by the former '202' Jet engine and the big six was retained for the Hornet. The Hornet V-8 used a Packard 208-hp engine and a line of Ramblers and Metropolitans was offered.

In 1956, American Motors introduced its own 190-hp V-8 for the Hornet Special and a line of Hudson Ramblers, but modest styling and engineering advances contributed to decreasing sales. The 1957 Hornets were two inches lower and used 14-inch wheels and the new 327-cid AMC V-8 with a four-barrel carb and dual exhaust. Cars so-equipped were excellent performers. Like other Hudsons, they also carried price reductions, but it was still to be Hudson's last year. AMC decided to drop Hudson and Nash to concentrate on Rambler.

1946

HUDSON SUPER —SERIES 51 SIX —SERIES 53 EIGHT —Hudson's big 1946 change was a new grille in the old postwar body. It now had a massive upper bar housing a Hudson badge. There were wide indentations at the center of each of the horizontal blades. The nose was smooth and no longer had a molding between the mascot and the grille, though a strip of chrome did run from the windshield base to the mascot. Nameplates alongside the rear of the hood revealed the model identity. The standard list was long, including dual brake system; dual carburetion; Auto Poise control; chrome alloy engine block; oil-cushioned clutch; center point steering; rear lateral stabilizer; teleflash signals; push-button starting; safety locking hood; hand-rubbed lacquer finish; Duo-Flo oiling; high-compression engine; large trunk; and Long Life spark plugs. The basic equipment assortment for all models comprised left-hand front door armrests; twin air horns; dashboard and rear ashtrays; woodgrain instrument panel; spring covers; front and rear stabilizers; twin wipers; stoplights; locking glovebox; windshield and rear window reveal moldings; new oval headlamp rims with sealed beam bulbs; front door locks; pile carpet; and, for sedans, envelope-type front seatback pockets. Supers were trimmed in blue and gray boucle waffle weave cloth.

HUDSON I.D. NUMBERS: Serial numbers were on the right door post. Engine numbers were the same and were found on a boss near the top left side of the cylinder block and also between the first two manifold flanges. The first symbol was a '3' in 1946. The second symbol corresponded to the second number in the series model code. The following group of symbols designated production sequence. Super Sixes were numbered 31101 to 3195099; Commodore Sixes 32101 to 3295062, Super Eights 33101 to 3395085 and Commodore Eights 34101 to 3495100. Body/Style Numbers were not used through 1955. First columns in charts below show six-cylinder model numbers; second columns show eight-cylinder model numbers.

HUDSON SUPER SIX (SERIES 51)/SUPER EIGHT (SERIES 52)

Model No.	Model No.	Body Type & Seating	Factory Price	Shipping Weight	Prod. Total
51	53	4-dr Sed-6P	1555/1668	3085/3235	Note 1
51	N/A	2-dr Brghm-6P	1511/—	3030/—	Note 1
51	53	2-dr Clb Cpe-6P	1553/1664	3015/3185	Note 1
51	N/A	2-dr Cpe-3P	1481/—	2950/—	Note 1
51	N/A	2-dr Conv Brghm-6P	1879—	3195/—	Note 1

Note 1: Series production was 61,787 Super Sixes/3,961 Super Eights with no breakouts.

Note 2: Approximately 1,037 Super Six Convertible Broughams were built.

Note 3: Only the Sedan and Club Coupe came as Super Eights.

Note 4: Data above slash for six/below slash for eight.

HUDSON COMMODORE —SERIES 52 SIX —SERIES 54 EIGHT — All basic features and Super series equipment were standard on Commodores plus blue gray plain cloth upholstery; air foam seat cushions; carpet insert front floor covering; crank-type ventipanes; door step courtesy lights; black filled etched aluminum scuff plates; luggage compartment rubber floor mats; and vertical rear window bars. In addition, Deluxe level appointments included interior hardware; taillamps; passenger assist straps and door handles. Gold finish was used on Commodore instrument dial letters and dash panel finish plates. Chrome-nickel plating brightened the steering column, shift lever, brake hand grip and glove locker box. An 18-inch custom steering wheel with horn ring was used and so were right-hand sun visors and electric clocks. A quick look at the Commodore exterior would reveal front and rear bumper bar extensions; front fender lamps with chrome extension moldings; oversize tires with large hubcaps (wheel covers); wide body moldings with wheel color stripes and an extra chrome strip above the belt moldings. Sedans had rear seat center armrests, leather robe hangers and rear dome lamps.

HUDSON COMMODORE SIX (SERIES 52)/COMMODORE EIGHT (SERIES 54)

Model No.	Model No.	Body Type & Seating	Factory Price	Shipping Weight	Prod. Total
52	54	4-dr Sed-6P	1699/1774	3150/3305	Note 1
52	54	2-dr Clb Cpe-5/6P	1693/1760	3065/3235	Note 1
N/A	54	2-dr Conv Brghm-6P	—/2050	—/3410	Note 1

Note 1: Series production was 17,685 Commodore Sixes and 8,193 Commodore Eights with no breakouts.

Note 2: Approximately 140 Commodore Eight Convertible Broughams were built.

Note 3: Convertible Broughams came only as Commodore Eights.

Note 4: Data above slash for six/below slash for eight.

ENGINES:

(SIX-CYLINDER) Inline. L-head six-cylinder. Chrome alloy block. Displacement: 212 cid. Bore and stroke: 3 x 5 inches. Compression ratio: 6.5:1. Brake hp: 103 at 4000 rpm. Three main bearings. Solid valve lifters. Carburetor: Carter two-barrel WDO type Model 501S.

(EIGHT-CYLINDER) Inline. L-head eight-cylinder. Chrome alloy block. Displacement: 254 cid. Bore and stroke: 3 x 4-1/2 inches. Compression ratio: 6.5:1. Brake hp: 128 at 4200 rpm. Five main bearings. Solid valve lifters. Carburetor: Carter two-barrel WDO type Model 502S.

CHASSIS FEATURES: Wheelbase: 121 inches. Overall length: 207-3/8 inches. Front tread: 56-5/16 inches. Rear tread: 59-1/2 inches. Tires: (Supers) 6.00 x 16; (Commodores) 6.50 x 15.

OPTIONS: Commodore front and rear seat cushions ($17); front only ($9). Commodore front and rear bumper bar extensions ($20). Commodore electric clock ($14). Commodore fender lamps ($16). Commodore horn ring with standard steering wheel ($6). Large hubcaps ($9). Custom 18-inch steering wheel with horn ring ($19). Right side visor ($3). Oversize 6.50 x 15 tires with four large hubcaps ($28). Right front door armrest ($4). Direction indicator for Supers ($26). Red or cream wheel color (no cost). Police car and taxi equipment ($11). Radio ($77). Heavy scale front and rear springs for sixes (no cost). Heavy scale rear springs (no cost). Weather Master heater ($50). Chrome wheel trim rings ($13). Three-quarter leather trim ($32-$53 depending on body style). Three-quarter leather grain trim ($25-$41 depending on body style). Vacumotive Drive ($40). Drive-Master, including Vacumotive Drive ($98). Oil bath air cleaner ($3). Power Dome with eight-cylinder engine ($10). Overdrive transmission ($88). Combination fuel and vacuum pump ($7). Rear axle with 4.11:1 gear ratio (no cost). Rear axle with 4.55:1 gear ratio (no cost). Factory delivered prices included leather-grain trims. Police/ Taxi package included: larger clutch; heavy rear springs; 11-inch brakes; and heavy construction seats. Convertible Broughams included full-length trim, air foam seats, oversize tires and extra sun visors. Blue-gray Shadow Weave Cloth (Supers) or blue-gray Bedford Cloth (Commodores) were used in combination with special three-quarter trim options. Note: First 10 equipment items listed above standard on Commodore, optional on Super.

HISTORICAL FOOTNOTES: Production of 1946 Hudsons began on August 30, 1945. Dealer introductions were held Oct. 1, 1945. The company displayed a 1909 Hudson at the Automotive Golden Jubilee in Detroit this year. Model year sales hit 95,000 units. Calendar year deliveries peaked at 93,870 cars. Hudson held ninth place on the industry's sales charts. The trunk emblem used in 1946 was made of plastic. Nine standard colors, two extra cost hues and four two-tone combinations were provided for 1946 Hudsons. Royal red finish was $23 extra and Nepal ivory was $60 extra. Two-tone selections were all priced at $18 extra. Eight tire size and construction options were offered at exchange prices between $15 and $72, but whitewalls were not available. A unique Cab Pick-up, with passenger car-type sheet metal, was marketed in 1946 and 1947.

1947

HUDSON SUPER —SERIES 171 SIX —SERIES 173 EIGHT —Minor styling changes and equipment revisions were seen on 1947 Hudsons. Plastic trunk emblems were replaced with bright metal types and the corporate logo badge, centered in the upper grille bar was ever so slightly modified to a larger size. Standard features of Supers included diagonal check Boucle upholstery; single adjustable hinged sun visor; 30-hour wind-up clock; woodgrain window finish moldings; black rubber front floor covering; carryall luggage compartment with vertically housed spare tire; felt trunk mats; cord robe hangers in sedans; new hoodside ornaments; 17-inch steering wheel; latch-type front ventipanes; twin standard taillamps; sliding pane rear quarter glass in sedans; and stationary rear quarter glass in Club Coupes.

HUDSON I.D. NUMBERS: Serial numbers were on the right door post. Engine numbers were the same and were found on a boss near the top left side of the cylinder block and also between the first two manifold flanges. The numbering system was basically the same as in 1946, with numbers running in single consecutive order, regardless of series. The first three symbols were comprised of the new series/model codes, followed by a group of numbers beginning at 101. Super Sixes were numbered 171101 to 17195100. Commodore Sixes 172101 to 17295099; Super Eights 173101 to 17394992; and Commodore Eights 174101 to 17495088. Body/Style Numbers were not used through 1955. First columns in charts below show six-cylinder model numbers; second columns show eight-cylinder model numbers.

HUDSON SUPER SIX (SERIES 171)/SUPER EIGHT (SERIES 173)

Model No.	Model No.	Body Type & Seating	Factory Price	Shipping Weight	Prod. Total
171	173	4-dr Sed-6P	1749/1862	3110/3260	Note 1
171	N/A	2-dr Brghm-6P	1704/—	3055/—	Note 1
171	173	2-dr Clb Cpe-6P	1744/1855	3040/3210	Note 1
171	N/A	2-dr Cpe-3P	1628/—	2975/—	Note 1
171	N/A	2-dr Conv Brghm-6P	2021/—	3220/—	Note 1

Note 1: Series production was 49,276 Super Sixes and 5,076 Super Eights with no breakouts.

Note 2: Approximately 1,462 Super Six Convertible Broughams were built.

Note 3: Only the Sedan and Club Coupe came as Super Eights.

Note 4: Data above slash for six/below slash for eight.

HUDSON COMMODORE —SERIES 172 SIX —SERIES 174 EIGHT —Standard equipment for Commodores included herringbone weave upholstery; electric clock; air foam seat cushions; rear seat center armrest in sedans; cigarette lighter; chrome window finish moldings; instrument dial dimmer (also used 1946); carpet insert rubber front floor mats; rubber trunk mat; leather robe hangers in sedans; side window reveal moldings; rear window bars; auxiliary belt moldings; new hood top ornament with plastic crest; hoodside ornaments; bumper bar wing extensions for front and rear; 18-inch Deluxe steering wheel with horn ring; crank-type ventipanes; carryover window glass construction; Deluxe-type twin taillamps; and front fender lamps. Commodores also used the new chrome trunk medallion and heavier molding around the grille top medallion. They again came standard with 6.50 x 15 tires and large hubcaps, which were optional equipment on Supers.

COMMODORE SIX (SERIES 172)/COMMODORE EIGHT (SERIES 174)

Model No.	Model No.	Body Type & Seating	Factory Price	Shipping Weight	Prod. Total
172	174	4-dr Sed-6P	1896/1972	3175/3330	Note 1
172	174	2-dr Clb Cpe-6P	1887/1955	3090/3260	Note 1
N/A	174	2-dr Conv Brghm-6P	—/2196	—/3435	Note 1

Note 1: Series production was 25,138 Commodore Sixes and 12,593 Commodore Eights with no breakouts.

Note 2: Approximately 361 Commodore Eight Convertible Broughams were built.

Note 3: Convertible Broughams came only as Commodore Eights.

Note 4: Data above slash for six/below slash for eight.

ENGINES:

(SIX-CYLINDER) Inline. L-head six-cylinder. Chrome alloy block. Displacement: 212 cid. Bore and stroke: 3 x 5 inches. Compression ratio: 6.5:1. Brake hp: 103 at 4000 rpm. Three main bearings. Solid valve lifters. Carburetor: Carter two-barrel WDO type Model 501S.

(EIGHT-CYLINDER) Inline. L-head eight-cylinder. Chrome alloy block. Displacement: 254 cid. Bore and stroke: 3 x 4-1/2 inches. Compression ratio: 6.5:1. Brake hp: 128 at 4200 rpm. Five main bearings. Solid valve lifters. Carburetor: Carter two-barrel WDO type Model 502S.

CHASSIS FEATURES: Wheelbase: 121 inches. Overall length: 207-3/8 inches. Front tread: 56-5/16 inches. Rear tread: 59-1/2 inches. Tires: (Supers) 6.00 x 16; (Commodores) 6.50 x 15.

OPTIONS: Air foam seat cushions, front and rear ($17); front only ($9). Front and rear bumper bar extensions ($20). Electric clock ($14). Fendertop lamps ($16). Horn ring with standard 17-inch steering wheel ($6). Large hubcaps ($9). Custom 18-inch steering wheel with horn ring ($19). Right side inside sun visor ($3). Oversize 6.50 x 15 tires with four large hubcaps ($28). Right fender door armrest ($4). Directional indicators for Super ($26). Red or cream wheel colors (no cost). Police and taxi equipment including large clutch; heavy rear springs; 11-inch brakes and heavy construction seats ($11). Radio ($77). Heavy scale front and rear springs for sixes (no cost). Heavy scale rear springs (no cost). Weather Master heater ($50). Chrome wheel trim rings ($13). Three-quarter leather trim ($32-$53 extra per body style). Three-quarter leather grain trim ($25-$41 per body style). [Note: Above trim options include special blue-gray Shadow Weave Cloth on Supers or special blue-gray Bedford Cloth on Commodores.] Full leather upholstery with Air Foam seat cushions and an extra sun visor was standard in convertibles. Factory Town delivered prices included three-quarter leather grain trim. Royal red finish ($23). Nepal Ivory finish ($60). Two-tone finish ($18). Eight tire options were available at exchange prices from $14.60 to $72.80. Available sizes included 6.00 x 16 and 7.00 x 15 and all could be had in four- or six-ply construction on specific body styles and models. Many tire options included four large hubcaps. Whitewall tires reappeared late in the year. Vacumotive Drive ($40). Drive-Master, including Vacumotive Drive ($98). Oil bath air cleaner ($3). Eight-cylinder Power Dome ($10). Overdrive manual transmission ($88). Combination fuel and vacuum pump ($7). Rear axle with 4.11:1 gear ratio (no cost). Rear axle with 4.55:1 gear ratio (no cost). Note: First 10 equipment items listed above standard on Commodore, optional on Super.

HISTORICAL FOOTNOTES: Sales of the 1947 Hudson line began in December 1946. Model year totals peaked at approximately 95,000 units. Calendar year sales were 100,393 cars. Hudson was rated the 13th largest producer in the United States. The company built its 3,000,000th car this season, which was proudly displayed and photographed besides a 1909 Hudson, which was part of the factory's antique car collection. This latest Hudson milestone was a fancy Commodore Eight convertible photographed wearing white sidewall tires. Six prototype wooden bodied station wagons were built for special use on the factory grounds.

1948

HUDSON SUPER —SERIES 481 SIX —SERIES 483 EIGHT —In November of 1947, Hudson introduced a completely new line of slab-sided cars with the famous 'Step Down' design. They were sleek, low and aerodynamic with unit-body construction and many advanced body engineering features. Standard equipment for Super series models included striped Bedford Cord upholstery; gray salt and pepper carpet-like rubber front floor mats; rear carpeting; cord robe hangers in sedans; dark mahogany woodgrain dash on 1948 Super models; window garnish moldings; 30-hour wind-up clocks; 17-inch steering wheel; adjustable sun visors; armrests at ends of all seats; latch-type ventipanes; wing-type rear quarter windows in sedans; side window reveal moldings; full opening rear quarter windows in Club Coupes; front parking lamps; twin standard taillamps; carryall trunk with horizontal mount spare tire; luggage compartment floor mat; and hubcaps on Supers.

HUDSON I.D. NUMBERS: Serial numbers were on the right front door post. Engine numbers were the same and were found on the upper front right-hand side of six-cylinder blocks or between the first and second exhaust manifold flanges on eight-cylinder blocks. The first three symbols corresponded to the series/model code, followed by a group of numbers beginning at 101. Super Sixes were numbered 481101 to 481117300; Commodore Sixes 482101 to 482117301; Super Eights 483101 to 48311786 and Commodore Eights 484101 to 484117256. Body/Style Numbers were not used through 1955. First columns in charts below show six-cylinder model numbers; second columns show eight-cylinder model numbers.

HUDSON SUPER SIX (SERIES 481)/SUPER EIGHTS (SERIES 483)

Model No.	Model No.	Body Type & Seating	Factory Price	Shipping Weight	Prod. Total
481	483	4-dr Sed-6P	2222/2343	3500/3535	Note 1
481	N/A	2-dr Brghm-6P	2172/—	3470/—	Note 1
481	483	2-dr Clb Cpe-6P	2219/2340	3480/3495	Note 1
481	N/A	2-dr Clb Cpe-3P	2069/—	3460/—	Note 1
481	N/A	2-dr Conv Brghm-6P	2836/—	3750—	Note 1

Note 1: Series production was 49,388 Super Sixes and 5,338 Super Eights with no breakouts.

Note 2: Approximately 86 Super Six Convertible Broughams were built.

Note 3: Only the Sedan and Club Coupe came as Super Eights.

Note 4: Data above slash for six/below slash for eight.

HUDSON COMMODORE —SERIES 482 SIX —SERIES 484 EIGHT —Standard specifications for the new 'Step Down' Commodores included Broadcloth upholstery (tan with green stripes or gray with blue stripes); air foam seat cushions; taupe colored carpet-like rubber front floor mats; rear compartment carpeting; cloth covered sedan robe hangers; 16-inch rear seat center armrest in Club Coupe; cigarette lighter; dark walnut and blonde grained instrument panel (two-tone); instrument panel dial dimmer; walnut grain window garnish moldings; twin adjustable swiveling sun visors; plastic rimmed 18-inch Deluxe steering wheel with horn ring; electric clock; side window reveal moldings; crank-type front door ventilating wings; wing-type rear quarter window ventilation in sedans; full-opening rear quarter windows in Club Coupe; rubber trunk mat and Deluxe twin taillamps; and front parking lamps.

HUDSON COMMODORE SIX (SERIES 482)/COMMODORE EIGHT (SERIES 484)

Model No.	Model No.	Body Type & Seating	Factory Price	Shipping Weight	Prod. Total
482	484	4-dr Sed-6P	2399/2514	3540/3600	Note 1
482	484	2-dr Clb Cpe-6P	2374/2490	3550/3570	Note 1
482	484	2-dr Brghm Conv-6P	3057/3138	3780/3800	Note 1

Note 1: Series production was 27,159 Commodore Sixes and 35,315 Commodore Eights with no breakouts.

Note 2: Approximately 49 Commodore Six convertibles and 65 Commodore Eight convertibles were built.

Note 3: Data above slash for six/below slash for eight.

ENGINES:

(SIX-CYLINDER) Inline. L-head six-cylinder. Chrome alloy block. Displacement: 262 cid. Bore and stroke: 3-9/16 x 4-3/8 inches. Compression ratio: 6.5:1. Brake hp: 121 at 4000 rpm. Four main bearings. Solid valve lifters. Carburetor: Carter two-barrel WDO type Model 647S.

(EIGHT-CYLINDER) Inline. L-head eight-cylinder. Chrome alloy block. Displacement: 254 cid. Bore and stroke: 3 x 4-1/2 inches. Compression ratio: 6.5:1. Brake hp: 128 at 4200 rpm. Five main bearings. Solid valve lifters. Carburetor: Carter two-barrel WDO type Model 647S.

CHASSIS FEATURES: Wheelbase: 124 inches. Overall length: 207-1/2 inches. Front tread: 58-1/2 inches. Rear tread: 55-1/2 inches. Tires: 7.10 x 15.

OPTIONS: Red or cream wheel covers (no cost). Front fender ornaments on Supers ($6). Front bumper guard on Supers ($13). Convertible Brougham top rear window glass ($21). Rear window reveal moldings on Supers ($4). Weather Control heater ($64). Radio ($84). Foam rubber front seat back ($16). Directional indicators ($20). Commodore steering wheel on Supers ($20). Foam rubber seat cushions on Supers ($28). Wheel trim rings ($13). Hydraulic window regulators on Super Six convertibles ($63). Large hubcaps ($10). Foam rubber front seat cushions on Supers ($14). Electric clock on Supers ($17). Leather trim options for closed cars were available at prices between $83 and $145, with the cost depending on body style. Leather trims came in Russet gray or dark red colors. Convertible Broughams came standard with 7.60 x 15 tires, antique grain Maroon leather trim and hydraulic window regulators (except Super Six). Brown cloth and maroon leather or gray cloth and maroon leather trims were no cost convertible options. Convertible tops came in black, gray or maroon. Specific upholstery trim and top colors were recommended with certain exterior body colors although variations were possible. Note: Equipment choices specifically listed above as Super series options were standard on Commodores. Tire options included white sidewalls, oversize 7.60 x 15 tires, and extra-ply construction. Six-cylinder aluminum cylinder head ($11). Eight-cylinder aluminum cylinder head ($13). Vacumotive Drive ($44). Drive-Master, including Vacumotive Drive ($112). Oil bath air cleaner, Six ($6); Eight ($8). Overdrive manual transmission ($101). Vacuum booster pump ($9). Standard rear axle gear ratio was 4.11:1 on all models. Optional 4.55:1 or 4.30:1 gear ratios were available at no extra cost. With Overdrive transmission, the 4.55:1 rear axle was standard and 4.11:1 or 4.30:1 axles were no cost options. The 4.11:1 gear ratio rear axle was used in conjunction with DriveMaster.

HISTORICAL FOOTNOTES: The new styling introduced on 1948 models was created by a group of Hudson designers under the direction of Frank Spring. The 1948 line was offered for sale in December 1947. Model year sales hit the 117,200 unit level while calendar year sales peaked at 142,454 cars. Hudson was ranked as America's 11th largest maker this season. The Vacumotive system automatically controlled the operation of the clutch. The DriveMaster system automatically controlled both clutching and gear shifting operations. Hudson dealers in New York City began one of the first television automobile advertising campaigns in 1947. Some body styles were not available at the beginning of the season. Four-door sedans, Brougham sedans and Club Coupes appeared first in late 1947. The Convertible Brougham did not show up until August 1948.

1949

HUDSON SUPER —SERIES 491 SIX —SERIES 493 EIGHT —There were minor annual revisions in the 1949 Hudson models and all were found inside the cars. The Super series standard equipment list included all previous features plus non-glare dashboard top finish and leather-grained trim on the following items: valance panels under windows; kick pads on all doors; rear quarter panels of Broughams and Club Coupes; recessed panel shelves; and top of armrests. Cloth covered robe hangers were now used in all models, except the three-passenger coupe. A new, ribbed-type front rubber floor mat with simulated carpet pattern was seen.

HUDSON I.D. NUMBERS: Serial numbers were on the right front door post. Engine numbers were the same and were found on the upper front right-hand side of six-cylinder blocks or between the first and second exhaust manifold flanges on eight-cylinder blocks. The first three symbols changed to correspond to new model numbers. Super Sixes were numbered 491-101 to 491-159201; Commodore Custom Sixes 492-101 to 492-159081; Super Eights 493-101 to 493-15919 and Commodore Custom Eights 494-101 to 494-159159. Body/Style Numbers were not used through 1955. First columns in charts below show six-cylinder model numbers; second columns show eight-cylinder model numbers.

HUDSON SUPER SIX (SERIES 491)/SUPER EIGHT (SERIES 493)

Model No.	Model No.	Body Type & Seating	Factory Price	Shipping Weight	Prod. Total
491	493	4-dr Sed-6P	2207/2296	3555/3565	Note 1
491	493	2-dr Brghm-6P	2156/2245	3515/3545	Note 1
491	493	2-dr Clb Cpe-6P	2203/2292	3480/3550	Note 1
491	N/A	2-dr Cpe-3P	2053/—	3485/—	Note 1
491	N/A	2-dr Conv Brghm-6P	2799/—	3750/—	Note 1

Note 1: Production was 91,333 Super Sixes and 6,365 Super Eights with no breakouts.

Note 2: Approximately 1,868 Super Six Convertible Broughams were built.

Note 3: Coupe and Convertible Brougham only came as Super Sixes.

Note 4: Data above slash for six/below slash for eight.

HUDSON COMMODORE CUSTOM —SERIES 492 SIX —SERIES 494 EIGHT —Upper series models were now called Commodore Customs and looked identical to 1948 Commodores on the outside. The standard equipment list was essentially the same, with the following minor changes: a new brown front floor mat was made of rubber and had a ribbed simulated carpet pattern. Non-glare finish was used on top of the instrument panel. Envelope-type pockets were now used on the front seatbacks of convertibles instead of only on sedans. Leather graining was seen on the door kick pads and rear quarter panels of Broughams and Club Coupes. Two large parcel compartments with locks were now incorporated at each side of the Commodore Custom dashboard, the left-hand locker being new. As usual, Commodore Customs had such distinguishing features as bumper guards, metal hand rails on back of front seat; rear window reveal moldings; and 18-inch Deluxe steering wheel with full circle horn ring. Much of this could be ordered, as optional equipment, on Supers.

COMMODORE CUSTOM SIX (SERIES 492)/COMMODORE CUSTOM EIGHT (SERIES 494)

Model No.	Model No.	Body Type & Seating	Factory Price	Shipping Weight	Prod. Total
492	494	4-dr Sed-6P	2383/2472	3625/3650	Note 1
492	494	2-dr Clb Cpe-6P	2359/2448	3585/3600	Note 1
492	494	2-dr Conv Brghm-6P	2952/3041	3780/3800	Note 1

Note 1: Series production was 32,715 Commodore Custom Sixes and 28,687 Commodore Custom Eights with no breakouts.

Note 2: Approximately 656 Commodore Custom Six convertibles and 596 Commodore Custom Eight convertibles were built.

Note 3: Data above slash for six/below slash for eight.

ENGINES:

(SIX-CYLINDER) Inline. L-head six-cylinder. Chrome alloy block. Displacement: 262 cid. Bore and stroke: 3-9/16 x 4-3/8 inches. Compression ratio: 6.5:1. Brake hp: 121 at 4000 rpm. Four main bearings. Solid valve lifters. Carburetor: Carter two-barrel WDO type Model 647S.

(EIGHT-CYLINDER) Inline. L-head eight-cylinder. Chrome alloy block. Displacement: 254 cid. Bore and stroke: 3 x 4-1/2 inches. Compression ratio: 6.5:1. Brake hp: 128 at 4200 rpm. Five main bearings. Solid valve lifters. Carburetor: Carter two-barrel WDO type Model 647S.

CHASSIS FEATURES: Wheelbase: 124 inches. Overall length: 207-1/2 inches. Front tread: 58-1/2 inches. Rear tread: 55-1/2 inches. Tires: 7.10 x 15.

OPTIONS: Red or cream wheel covers (no cost). Front fender ornaments on Supers ($6). Front bumper guard on Supers ($13). Convertible Brougham top rear window glass ($21). Rear window reveal moldings on Supers ($4). Weather Control heater ($64). Radio ($84). Foam rubber front seatback ($16). Directional indicators ($20). Commodore steering wheel on Supers ($20). Foam rubber seat cushions on Supers ($28). Wheel trim rings ($13). Hydraulic window regulators on Super Six convertibles ($63). Large hubcaps ($10). Foam rubber front seat cushions on Supers ($14). Electric clock on Supers ($17). Leather trim options for closed cars were available at prices between $83 and $145, with the cost depending on body style. Leather trims came in Russet, gray or dark red colors. Convertible Broughams came standard with 7.60 x 15 tires, antique grain Maroon leather trim and hydraulic window regulators (except Super Six). Brown cloth and maroon leather or gray cloth and maroon leather trims were no cost convertible options. Convertible tops came in black, gray or maroon. Specific upholstery trim and top colors were recommended with certain exterior body colors although variations were possible. Note: Equipment choices specifically listed above as Super series options were standard on Commodore Customs. Tire options included white sidewalls, oversize 7.60 x 15 tires, and extra-ply construction. Six-cylinder aluminum cylinder head ($11). Eight-cylinder aluminum cylinder head ($13). Vacumotive Drive ($44). DriveMaster including Vacumotive Drive ($112). Oil bath air cleaner, Six ($6); Eight ($8). Overdrive manual transmission ($101). Vacuum booster pump ($9). Standard rear axle gear ratio was 4.11:1 on all models. Optional 4.55:1 or 4.30:1 gear ratios were available at no extra cost. With Overdrive transmission, the 4.55:1 rear axle was standard and 4.11:1 or 4.30:1 axles were no cost options. The 4.11:1 gear ratio rear axle was used in conjunction with DriveMaster.

HISTORICAL FOOTNOTES: The 1949 Hudson line was introduced to the public in November 1948. Hudson retained its 11th rank in industry with model year sales of 159,100 cars and calendar year sales of 142,462 units. The firm celebrated its 40th anniversary this season.

1950

HUDSON PACEMAKER —SERIES 500 —SERIES 50A DELUXE — A shorter Hudson was Hudson's new 'baby' in 1950. This Pacemaker was not much smaller than conventional styles, but seemed to be back then. It had the season's new look, which included a grille with four horizontal blades widening as they neared the bumper and twin struts forming a triangle with a company medallion at the top. Though only the grille was drastically changed, all the cars seemed lower. Basic equipment on all models included Durafab plastic interior trims; 18-inch steering wheel; twin, adjustable visors; full opening rear quarter windows for Club Coupes; new, two-piece curved Full-View windshield; front dome lamp; lockable parcel compartment; large trunk with mat and horizontal spare and a rearview mirror. Several Pacemaker features, including lighted grille/hood medallions; standard twin taillamps; latch-type front ventipanes; and a new streamlined hood ornament, were shared with Supers. Distinctive Pacemaker equipment included striped, Bedford Cord upholstery; front and rear rubber floor mats; Blue Spruce two-spoke steering wheel; fabric finish dash; seatback pockets in sedans only; ashtrays in front seatback and dash; trumpet horn; and parking lamps under the lower grille bar. Deluxe Pacemakers had a bit of extra trim and slightly richer appointments.

HUDSON I.D. NUMBERS: Serial numbers were on the right front door post. Engine numbers were the same and were found on the upper front right-hand side of six-cylinder blocks or between the first and second exhaust manifold flanges on eight-cylinder blocks. Serial numbers followed the same system. The first three symbols correspond with new model numbers. Pacemaker 500s were numbered 500-101 to 500-121481; Pacemaker Deluxes 50A-101 to 50A-121505; Super Sixes 501-101 to 501-121508; Commodore Sixes 502-101 to 502-121504; Super Eights 503-101 to 503-121491 and Commodore Eights 504-101 to 504-121500. Body/Style Numbers were not used through 1955. First columns in charts below show Pacemaker 500 or six-cylinder model numbers; second columns show Pacemaker Deluxe or eight-cylinder model numbers.

HUDSON PACEMAKER 500 (SERIES 500)/PACEMAKER DELUXE (SERIES 50A)

Model No.	Model No.	Body Type & Seating	Factory Price	Shipping Weight	Prod. Total
500	50A	4-dr Sed-6P	1933/1959	3510/3520	Note 1
500	50A	2-dr Brghm-6P	1912/1928	3475/3485	Note 1
500	50A	2-dr Clb Cpe-6P	1933/1959	3460/3470	Note 1
500	N/A	2-dr Cpe-3P	1807/—	3445/—	Note 1
500	50A	2-dr Conv Brghm-6P	2428/2444	3655/3665	Note 1

Note 1: Series production was 39,455 Pacemaker 500s and 22,297 Pacemaker Deluxes with no breakouts.

Note 2: Approximately 1,865 Pacemaker 500 convertibles were built.

Note 3: Approximately 660 Pacemaker Deluxe convertibles were built.

Note 4: The three-passenger coupe came only as a Pacemaker 500.

Note 5: Data slash for Pacemaker 500/below slash for Pacemaker Deluxe.

HUDSON SUPER —SERIES 501 SIX —SERIES 503 EIGHT —Supers were basically a 1949 carryover with the newly designed 1950 grille appearance. A small 'spear tip' ornament at the front of the body contour line, just above the wheel opening, served as a Super identifier. A broad sill panel molding was used as the only major bodyside trim. No fendertop ornaments were seen and the new, streamlined hood ornament matched that on Pacemakers. The Super equipment list comprised all basic features and items shared with Pacemakers plus striped Bedford cloth upholstery; two-tone woodgrain dash; windup clock; Cord robe hangers; light tan steering wheel; and door pillar assist straps. In addition, the following items were shared with Custom Commodores: ribbed carpet-like front mats; rear carpets; armrests at seat ends; sedan rear ventipanes; bright metal window and windshield reveal moldings; larger sedan and Brougham rear window; parking lamps in lower grille bar; license lamps in center rear bumper guards; fender skirts; twin air horns; ashtrays in seat ends; and dashboard and envelope-style seatback pockets in all models.

HUDSON SUPER SIX (SERIES 501)/SUPER EIGHT (SERIES 503)

Model No.	Model No.	Body Type & Seating	Factory Price	Shipping Weight	Prod. Total
501	503	4-dr Sed-6P	2105/2189	3590/3605	Note 1
501	503	2-dr Brghm-6P	2068/2152	3565/3575	Note 1
501	503	2-dr Clb Cpe-6P	2102/2186	3555/3560	Note 1
501	N/A	2-dr Conv Brghm-6P	2629/—	3750—	Note 1

Note 1: Series production included 17,246 Super Sixes and 1,074 Super Eights with no breakouts.

Note 2: Approximately 464 Super Six Convertible Broughams were built.

Note 3: Prices and shipping weights above slash for six/below slash for eight.

HUDSON CUSTOM COMMODORE —SERIES 502 SIX —SERIES 504 EIGHT —Commodores had upper level trim and enriched interiors. Four bumpers guards were seen, as were front fendertop ornaments. Side trim consisted of the broad body sill panel and a strip of molding that followed the body contour line several inches below it. At the front of this molding were model nameplates, while the rear portion widened and curved into the sill panel behind the enclosed rear wheelhousing. The Custom Commodore equipment list included all basic features and the additional items shared with Supers plus nylon Bedford Cord upholstery (in tan with brown stripes or blue-gray with blue stripes); foam rubber seat cushions; Durafab covered robe hangers; bright metal seatback hand grips; 16-inch rear seat center armrest; pop-out cigarette lighter; dash dimmer switch; leather grained dash and window garnish molding finish; three-spoke steering wheel; electric clock; crank-type ventipanes; two rear dome lights (in sedans and Club Coupes); and inner and outer bumper guards, front and rear. Basic items on Custom Commodores were slightly upgraded. For example, the rearview mirror was an extra large Deluxe type.

CUSTOM COMMODORE SIX (SERIES 502)/CUSTOM COMMODORE EIGHT (SERIES 504)

Model No.	Model No.	Body Type & Seating	Factory Price	Shipping Weight	Prod. Total
502	504	4-dr Sed-6P	2282/2366	3655/3675	Note 1
502	504	2-dr Clb Cpe-6P	2257/2341	3640/3575	Note 1
502	504	2-dr Conv Brghm-6P	2809/2893	3840/3885	Note 1

Note 1: Series production included 24,605 Custom Commodore Sixes and 16,731 Custom Commodore Eights with no breakouts.

Note 2: Approximately 700 Custom Commodore Six convertibles and 426 Custom Commodore Eight convertibles were built.

Note 3: Factory prices and shipping weights above slash for six/below slash for eight.

ENGINES:

(PACEMAKER SIX) Inline six. Flathead. Chrome alloy block. Displacement: 232 cid. Bore and stroke: 3-9/16 x 3-7/8 inches. Compression ratio: 6.7:1. Brake hp: 112 at 4000 rpm. Four main bearings. Solid valve lifters. Carburetor: Carter one-barrel WA-1 type Model 749S.

(SUPER/COMMODORE SIX) Inline six. Flathead. Chrome alloy block. Displacement: 262 cid. Bore and stroke: 3-9/16 x 4-3/8 inches. Compression ratio: 6.7:1. Brake hp: 123 at 4000 rpm. Four main bearings. Solid valve lifters. Carburetor: Type WGD Model 776S with L-shaped air horns.

(SUPER/COMMODORE EIGHT) Inline eight. Flathead. Chrome alloy block. Displacement: 254 cid. Bore and stroke: 3 x 3-1/2 inches. Compression ratio: 6.7:1. Brake hp: 128 at 4200 rpm. Five main bearings. Solid valve lifters. Carburetor: Carter Type WGD Model 773S with L-shaped air horns.

CHASSIS FEATURES: Wheelbase: (Pacemaker) 119 inches; (other models) 124 inches. Overall length: (Pacemaker) 201-1/2 inches; (other models) 208-3/32 inches. Front tread: 58-1/2 inches. Rear tread: 55-1/2 inches. Tires: (convertibles) 7.60 x 15; (all others) 7.10 x 15.

OPTIONS: Foam rubber Pacemaker seat cushions. Rear wheel covers (fender skirts) for Pacemaker. Mechanical or electric clock in Pacemaker. Pacemaker front bumper outer guards. White sidewall tires. Super front bumper outer guards. Foam rubber cushions in Supers. Super side ornamentation. Hydraulic window lifts for Super convertible. Radio. Heater. Overdrive manual transmission ($95). DriveMaster semi-automatic transmission ($105). Supermatic ($199). Aluminum cylinder head with 7.2:1 compression ratio. Rear axle ratios including 4.11:1 (standard); 4.55:1 (standard Supermatic) or 3.82:1 gears at no extra cost. Oil bath air cleaner. Vacuum booster pump.

HISTORICAL FOOTNOTES: The new Hudsons were introduced on Nov. 18, 1949. The firm slid to 13th rank in the American industry, with model year sales of 121,408 cars; calendar year output of 143,586 units. Prices were slightly reduced from the previous year and Hudson reported a $12 million profit on sales of $267 million. Canadian production, suspended during the war, was resumed at the Hudson factory in Tilbury, Ontario, April 1950. The Convertible Brougham, in both Commodore and Hornet series, came with hydraulic windows and leather trim. The same upholstery was featured on Super series convertibles, but hydraulic window lifts were optional. Convertible top colors were tan, black or maroon. A 'Fold Away' rear window was optional with all convertibles.

1951

PACEMAKER CUSTOM —SIX —SERIES 4A —The Hudson grille was changed again this year. It now had three horizontal blades. The top two were bowed to meet the bottom bar. A twin-strut triangle was seen near the center. Rectangular parking lights were housed outboard of the main grille bars on either side. The lamp housings were slightly rounded where they wrapped around the Pacemaker body corners, but looked squarer on other models. The sides of Pacemakers were trimmed only by 'spear tip' ornaments (without spears) and broad lower sill panels that stretched, from behind the front wheel opening, to the extreme rear of the car. Standard on Pacemakers were Hudson basics such as Twin-Contour wipers; gas gauge; Teleflash "idiot lights"; water temperature gauge; windshield/defroster vents; Cushion-Action door latches; theft-proof locks; push-button door handles; windshield and side window reveals; dash ashtray; rearview mirror; twin sun visors; full opening crank-out rear quarter windows in Club Coupes and Broughams; twin stop and taillamps; front dome light; lockable parcel compartment; twin air horns; and illuminated grille medallion. Pacemakers had the rear ashtray in the front seatback and door pillar assist straps in Brougham sedans. Upholstery was gray special-weave cord with red and brown stripes and Dura-fab plastic trim.

HUDSON I.D. NUMBERS: Serial numbers were on the right front door post. Engine numbers were the same and they were found on the upper front right-hand side of six-cylinder blocks or between the first and second exhaust manifold flanges on eight-cylinder blocks. Serial numbers followed the same system. The first two symbols correspond with new model designations and were a number and letter. Pacemaker Customs were numbered 4A-1001 to 4A-132072; Super Customs 5A-1001 to 5A-132246; Commodore Customs (Six) 6A-1001 to 6A-132586; Hornets 7A-1001 to 7A-132915 and Commodore Customs (Eight) 8A-1001 to 8A-132028. Body/Style Numbers were not used through 1955. First columns in charts below show Pacemaker 500 or six-cylinder model numbers; second columns show Pacemaker Deluxe or eight-cylinder model numbers.

PACEMAKER CUSTOM SIX (SERIES 4A)

Model No.	Model No.	Body Type & Seating	Factory Price	Shipping Weight	Prod. Total
4A	N/A	4-dr Sed-6P	2145	3460	Note 1
4A	N/A	2-dr Brghm-6P	2102	3430	Note 1
4A	N/A	2-dr Clb Cpe-6P	2145	3410	Note 1
4A	N/A	2-dr Cpe-3P	1964	3380	Note 1
4A	N/A	2-dr Conv Brghm-6P	2642	3600	Note 1

Note 1: Series production included 34,495 Pacemaker Customs with no breakouts.

Note 2: Approximately 425 Pacemaker convertibles were built.

SUPER CUSTOM —SIX —SERIES 5A —For 1951, Supers were given the new frontal treatment and basically the type of side trim used on 1950 Commodores, but without standard outer grille guards. Small hubcaps were seen. The regular assortment of equipment was identical to that listed for Pacemakers, with only a few exceptions. Variations included rear ashtrays housed in recess panels on the doors and inner rear quarter panels (instead of front seatback) and wing-type ventipanes for sedan rear quarter windows. Upholstery was in tan Bedford cloth with brown and maroon stripes. A new Hollywood model, with two-door pillarless hardtop styling, was introduced in September of 1951 as a late-year addition to the line. A new, rounded corner trapezoid-shaped front center grille guard was seen on all 'big' Hudsons, including the Supers.

SUPER CUSTOM SIX (SERIES 5A)

Model No.	Model No.	Body Type & Seating	Factory Price	Shipping Weight	Prod. Total
5A	N/A	4-dr Sed-6P	2287	3565	Note 1
5A	N/A	2-dr Brghm-6P	2238	3535	Note 1
5A	N/A	2-dr Clb Cpe-6P	2287	3525	Note 1
5A	N/A	2-dr Holly HT-6P	2605	3590	Note 1
5A	N/A	2-dr Conv Brghm-6P	2827	3720	Note 1

Note 1: Series production included 22,532 Super Custom Sixes with no breakouts.

Note 2: Approximately 1,100 Hollywood two-door hardtops and 282 convertibles were built in this series.

COMMODORE CUSTOM —SERIES 6A SIX —SERIES 8A EIGHT —No longer the flagship of the Hudson fleet, the Commodore Six was priced under a new Hudson Hornet line while Commodore Eights were marketed at equal-to-Hornet prices. Distinguishing Commodores from lower series were larger front fender nameplates; outer grille guards; front and rear metal hand grips on front seatbacks; rear window reveal moldings and three dimensional weave upholstery with stripes and Antique Crush Dura-fab trim. These features were also used in and on Hornets. The balance of equipment was the same found on Super Customs plus a 16-inch rear center armrest to provide a two-person seating arrangement. The Commodore convertible came in nine standard or four extra cost colors with dark red or blue genuine top grain leather upholstery and harmonizing leather grain trim. It again had hydraulic window lifts and a hydraulic roof with tan, black or maroon top material. A large, plastic rear window was optional.

CUSTOM COMMODORE SIX (SERIES 6A)/CUSTOM COMMODORE EIGHT (SERIES 8A)

Model No.	Model No.	Body Type & Seating	Factory Price	Shipping Weight	Prod. Total
6A	8A	4-dr Sed-6P	2480/2568	3600/3620	Note 1
6A	8A	2-dr Clb Cpe-6P	2455/2543	3585/3600	Note 1
6A	8A	2-dr Holly HT-6P	2780/2869	3640/3650	Note 1
6A	8A	2-dr Conv Brghm-6P	3011/3099	3785/3800	Note 1

Note 1: Series production included 16,979 Custom Commodore Sixes and 14,243 Custom Commodore Eights with no breakouts.

Note 2: In the Custom Commodore Six series, approximately 819 Hollywoods and 211 convertibles were built.

Note 3: In the Custom Commodore Eight series, approximately 669 Hollywoods and 181 convertibles were built.

Note 4: Factory prices and shipping weights above slash for six/below slash for eight.

HUDSON HORNET —SIX —SERIES 7A —The first of the famed Hudson Hornets was really a Commodore with a special high-performance six and a few distinctive identification and appointment details. Special features included a gold- and chrome-plated 'Skyliner Styling' hood mascot; pillar assist straps in coupes and sedans; Deluxe robe hanger hand grips and tailored pockets on back of the lounge-wide front seat; Hornet H-145 medallions in each front door valance panel; indirectly lighted precision instruments set into a polished chrome dash housing on a leather grained panel with non-glare Dura-fab top; and gleaming, rocketship-shaped Badges of Power in front of the bodyside rub moldings and on the trunk. These badges showed a rocket piercing two vertically angled bars, with Hornet lettering turning them into a letter 'H'. Upholstery was of the Commodore type and came in tan-brown with gold stripes or blue-gray with blue stripes. Antique Crush-type leather grained Dura-fab trim combinations were used. The high-compression, aluminum 'Power-Dome' cylinder head was standard on the Hornet engine, but the regular iron alloy head was a no-cost option.

HUDSON HORNET H-145 SIX (SERIES 7A)

Model No.	Model No.	Body Type & Seating	Factory Price	Shipping Weight	Prod. Total
7A	N/A	4-dr Sed-6P	2568	3600	Note 1
7A	N/A	2-dr Clb Cpe-6P	2543	3580	Note 1
7A	N/A	2-dr Holly HT-6P	2869	3630	Note 1
7A	N/A	2-dr Conv Brghm-6P	3099	3780	Note 1

Note 1: Series production included 43,666 Hudson Hornets with no breakouts.

Note 2: Approximately 2,101 Hollywood two-door hardtops and 551 convertibles were built in this series.

ENGINES:

(PACEMAKER SIX) Inline six. Flathead. Chrome alloy block. Displacement: 232 cid. Bore and stroke: 3-9/16 x 3-7/8 inches. Compression ratio: 6.7:1. Brake hp: 112 at 4000 rpm. Four main bearings. Solid valve lifters. Carburetor: Carter one-barrel WA-1 type Model 749S.

(SUPER/COMMODORE SIX) Inline six. Flathead. Chrome alloy block. Displacement: 262 cid. Bore and stroke: 3-9/16 x 4-3/8 inches. Compression ratio: 6.7:1. Brake hp: 123 at 4000 rpm. Four main bearings. Solid valve lifters. Carburetor: Type WGD Model 776S with L-shaped air horns.

(COMMODORE EIGHT) Inline eight. Flathead. Chrome alloy block. Displacement: 254 cid. Bore and stroke: 3 x 3-1/2 inches. Compression ratio: 6.7:1. Brake hp: 128 at 4200 rpm. Five main bearings. Solid valve lifters. Carburetor: Carter Type WGD Model 773S with L-shaped air horns.

(HORNET SIX) Inline six. L-head. Chrome alloy block. Displacement: 308 cid. Bore and stroke: 3-13/16 x 4-1/2 inches. Compression ratio: 7.2:1. Brake hp: 145 at 3800 rpm. Four main bearings. Solid valve lifters. Carburetor: Carter two-barrel type WGD Model 776S.

CHASSIS FEATURES: Wheelbase: (Pacemaker) 119-7/8 inches; (all others) 123-7/8 inches. Overall length: (Pacemaker) 201-1/2 inches; (all others) 208-1/2 inches. Front tread: 58-1/2 inches. Rear tread: 55-1/2 inches. Overall width: (Pacemaker and Super) 77-1/16 inches; (all others) 77-21/32 inches. Tires: (Super, Custom Commodore Six, Custom Commodore Eight, Hornet convertibles) 7.60 x 15; (Pacemaker convertible and all other models) 7.10 x 15.

OPTIONS: Foam rubber Pacemaker seat cushions. Rear wheel covers (fender skirts) for Pacemaker. Mechanical or electric clock in Pacemaker. Pacemaker front bumper outer guards. White sidewall tires. Super front bumper outer guards. Foam rubber cushions in Super. Super side ornamentation. Hydraulic window lifts for Super convertible. Radio. Heater. Overdrive manual transmission ($100). DriveMaster semi-automatic transmission for Pacemaker/Super only ($99). Supermatic, all except Hornet ($158). Hydra-Matic for Commodore or Hornet ($158). Available rear axles included units with 4.55:1, 4.11:1 and 3.58:1 gear ratios. The Power-Dome cylinder head was optional on lower series at extra cost. The standard cylinder head was optional on Hornets at no extra cost.

HISTORICAL FOOTNOTES: The new Hudson line was introduced in September 1950 and continued in extended production through January 1952. Hollywood hardtops were a late edition to the 1951 line. Model year deliveries hit 131,915 units. Calendar year sales dropped to 92,859 cars. Hudson was ranked 15th in the American industry. A loss of $1,125,210 was reported on sales volume of $186,050,832. Labor unrest and delays in getting government authorization to raise prices, during the Korean conflict, was responsible for the poor business year. The Hudson factory helped support stock car racing efforts with the new Hornets by providing special 'export' and 'severe usage' parts suitable for high-performance applications. Hudsons were able to win 12 of the 41 NASCAR Grand National contests held in 1951. Top Hudson Hornet drivers included Marshall Teague, Herb Thomas, Tim Flock and Dick Rathmann. A special dual carburetion package helped Herb Thomas take a checkered flag in the second Southern 500, at Darlington, S.C., with an 86.21 mph average speed. *Motor Trend* and *Mechanix Illustrated* determined the top speed of the stock 1951 Hudson Hornet at 97 mph. Herb Thomas captured Top Driver honors on the NASCAR circuit this season.

1952

PACEMAKER/WASP —SIX —SERIES 4B/5B —The Pacemaker was slightly downgraded for 1952 and had a plainer look. The twin-strut grille arrangement was deleted and fender skirts were optional. The 'spear tips' had a staggered look and a boomerang-shaped fin became the hood mascot. The rear end was spartan, having small oval taillamp lenses and only outer bumper guards. Standard specifications included fancy gray special-weave cord upholstery with red and brown stripes; ribbed rubber floor mats; dark brown painted dash; two-spoke light tan steering wheel; friction-type front ventipanes; two assist straps in sedans, one in Club Coupes; pop-out cigarette lighter; dash and seatback ashtrays; windshield and window reveal moldings; twin air horns; armrests at front seat end (plus rear seat end on sedans and Club Coupes); seatback pockets; woven trunk mat; and 232-cid engine. Prices were up about $165 over 1951. The new Wasp Six was built off the Pacemaker platform. Wasps were an inch longer, since they came with center rear bumper guards that protruded out that much further. In terms of price, the Wasp replaced the Super. In terms of character, it was to the Pacemaker what the Hornet was to the Commodore Eight: a slightly fancier and more powerful version of the same car. (This is borne out by name changes of 1953, when the Pacemaker was renamed Wasp and the term Super Wasp was applied if the bigger engine was used.) Standard 1952 Wasp specifications included tan special-weave cord upholstery with red and brown stripes; rear compartment carpeting; dark brown leather grained dash, door courtesy lamps; wind-up clock; three-spoke steering wheel with half-circle horn ring; armrests at seat ends, except convertible and Brougham rear seat; robe hanger and hand grips on front seatback; friction front ventipanes; windshield and window reveal moldings; rear center guard with license lamp; woven fabric trunk mat; fender skirts; pop-out lighter; dash ashtray (and front seatback type in sedans); distinctive Hudson triangle grille ornament; front fendertop ornaments; seatback pockets; side body rub rail moldings; and twin-strut front grille guard.

HUDSON I.D. NUMBERS: Serial numbers were on the right front door post. Engine numbers were the same and were found on the upper front right-hand side of six-cylinder blocks or between the first and second exhaust manifold flanges on eight-cylinder blocks. Serial numbers followed the same system. The first two symbols correspond with new model designations. The second symbol of the prefix changed to a letter 'B'. Pacemakers were numbered 132916 to 202512; Wasps 132916 to 202715; Commodore Sixes 132916 to 198220; Homets 132916 to 202916 and Commodore Eights 132916 to 200201. Body/Style Numbers were not used through 1955. First columns in charts below show Pacemaker or six-cylinder model numbers; second columns show Wasp or eight-cylinder model numbers.

PACEMAKER SIX (SERIES 4B)/WASP SIX (SERIES 5B)

Model No.	Model No.	Body Type & Seating	Factory Price	Shipping Weight	Prod. Total
4B	5B	4-dr Sed-6P	2311/2466	3390/3485	Note 1
4B	5B	2-dr Brghm-6P	2264/2413	3355/3470	Note 1
4B	5B	2-dr Clb Cpe-6P	2311/2466	3335/3435	Note 1
4B	N/A	2-dr Cpe-3P	2116/—	3305/—	Note 1
N/A	5B	2-dr Holly HT-6P	—/2812	—/3525	Note 1
N/A	5B	2-dr Conv Brghm-6P	—/3048	—/3635	Note 1

Note 1: Series 4B production included 7,486 Pacemakers with no breakouts.

Note 2: Series 5B production included 21,876 Wasps with no breakouts.

Note 3: Approximately 1,320 Hollywood two-door hardtops and 220 convertibles were built in Wasp series.

Note 4: Data above slash for Pacemaker/below slash for Wasp.

Note 5: The three-passenger coupe came only as a Pacemaker; the Hollywood and Convertible Brougham came only as a Wasp.

COMMODORE —SIX —SERIES 6B —The 1952 Commodore line featured new Hudson Aire identification and appointment items. They included double rub rail moldings that ran along the body contour line, from the front fenders to the rear fenders, with a downward sweep

1951 Hudson, Super Six Custom (Series 5A), sedan, OCW

1952 Hudson, Wasp (Series 5B), convertible brougham (with optional outer bumper guards), OCW

1953 Hudson, Hornet (Series 7C), sedan, OCW

1953 Hudson, Super Jet (Series 2C), sedan (with optional whitewall tires and rear wheel covers), OCW

1954 Hudson, Jet Liner (Series 3D), club sedan (with optional continental spare tire mount), OCW

towards the back bumper; twin-strut grille arrangement; front and rear center bumper guards; front fender nameplates; rocker sill beauty panels; large Deluxe hubcaps and taillights styled to form a continuous horizontal trim line. Standard equipment on sixes was markedly different than on eights. It included six-tone Bedford cord upholstery with tan and brown stripes; leather grained Dura-Fab trim; rear compartment carpets; dark brown leather grained dash; wind-up clock; three-spoke, half-ring steering wheel; armrests at ends of all seats (except convertible and Brougham); center rear seat armrest in sedan, Club Coupe and Hollywood; pop-out lighter; ashtrays at seat ends; dash ashtray; friction front ventipanes; leather grained window garnish moldings; reveal moldings; woven fabric trunk mat; fender skirts; Hudson triangle hood ornament; seatback pockets; front dome lamp (two side lamps in Hollywood); rear quarter dome lamps in sedan, Club Coupe and Hollywood; robe hanger and hand grips on seatback and front fendertop ornaments.

COMMODORE —EIGHT —SERIES 8B —The Commodore Eight had the following differences from the Commodore Six: nylon three-dimensional weave upholstery in tan-brown with gold stripes or blue-gray with blue stripes; foam rubber seat cushions; front and rear carpets; cord type, Dura-Fab covered robe hangers in all models; instrument lighting dimmer switch; Deluxe steering wheel; electric clock; crank-type front ventipanes; printed jute trunk mat and inline eight-cylinder engine. The front fender 'spear tips' on sixes were decorated with a number '6'; on eights with a number '8'. Front parking lenses for all Commodores were of the wraparound style seen on Wasps, but not on Pacemakers.

COMMODORE SIX (SERIES 6B)/COMMODORE EIGHT (SERIES 8B)

Model No.	Model No.	Body Type & Seating	Factory Price	Shipping Weight	Prod. Total
6B	8B	4-dr Sed-6P	2674/2769	3595/3630	Note 1
6B	8B	2-dr Clb Cpe-6P	2647/2742	3550/3580	Note 1
6B	8B	2-dr Holly HT-6P	3000/3095	3625/3660	Note 1
6B	8B	2-dr Conv Brghm-6P	3247/3342	3750/3770	Note 1

Note 1: Series 6B production included 1,592 Commodore Sixes with no breakouts.

Note 2: Series 8B production included 3,125 Commodore Eights with no breakouts.

Note 3: Approximately 100 Hollywood two-door hardtops and 20 convertibles were built in the Commodore Six series.

Note 4: Approximately 190 Hollywood two-door hardtops and 30 convertibles were built in the Commodore Eight series.

Note 5: Factory prices and shipping weights above slash for six/below slash for eight.

HUDSON HORNET —SIX —SERIES 7B —The Hornet for 1952 was based on the Commodore Eight. Special features seen on the Hornet included dark blue or brown leather grained window garnish moldings; Hornet 'Flying-H' identification on the side of front fenders and rear deck gold and chrome hood mascot; Hornet medallions on front door valance panels; and the high-compression H-145 six-cylinder engine. All other specifications matched those of the Commodore Eight. On a model-for-model basis the two series were again priced identically, with the 8A models weighing 30 pounds more than Hornets.

HUDSON HORNET SIX (SERIES 7B)

Model No.	Model No.	Body Type & Seating	Factory Price	Shipping Weight	Prod. Total
7B	N/A	4-dr Sed-6P	2749	3600	Note 1
7B	N/A	2-dr Clb Cpe-6P	2722	3550	Note 1
7B	N/A	2-dr Holly HT-6P	3071	3630	Note 1
7B	N/A	2-dr Conv Brghm-6P	3318	3750	Note 1

Note 1: Series production included 35,921 Hornets with no breakouts.

Note 2: Approximately 2,160 Hollywood two-door hardtops and 360 convertibles were built in the Hornet series.

ENGINES:

(PACEMAKER SIX) Inline six. L-head. Chrome alloy block. Displacement: 232 cid. Bore and stroke: 3-9/16 x 3-7/8 inches. Compression ratio: 6.7:1. Brake hp: 112 at 4000 rpm. Four main bearings. Solid valve lifters. Carburetor: Carter one-barrel type WA-1 Model 749S.

(WASP/COMMODORE SIX) Inline six. L-head. Chrome alloy block. Displacement: 262 cid. Bore and stroke: 3-9/16 x 4-3/8 inches. Compression ratio: 6.7:1. Brake hp: 127 at 4000 rpm. Four main bearings. Solid valve lifters. Carburetor: Carter one-barrel type WA-1 Model 776S.

(COMMODORE EIGHT) Inline eight. Flathead. Chrome alloy block. Displacement: 254 cid. Bore and stroke: 3 x 3-1/2 inches. Compression ratio: 6.7:1. Brake hp: 128 at 4200 rpm. Five main bearings. Solid valve lifters. Carburetor: Carter Type WGD Model 773S with L-shaped air horns.

(HORNET SIX) Inline six. L-head. Chrome alloy block. Displacement: 308 cid. Bore and stroke: 3-13/16 x 4-1/2 inches. Compression ratio: 7.2:1. Brake hp: 145 at 3800 rpm. Four main bearings. Solid valve lifters. Carburetor: Carter two-barrel type WGD Model 776S.

CHASSIS FEATURES: Wheelbase: (Pacemaker and Wasp) 119 inches; (all other models) 124 inches. Overall length: (Pacemaker) 201-1/2 inches; (Wasp) 202-1/2 inches; (all other models) 208-1/2 inches. Front tread: 58-1/2 inches. Rear tread: 55-1/2 inches. Tires: low-pressure, high volume Super-Cushion 7.10 x 15 tires were standard on all models except Hornet and Commodore convertibles, which were equipped with size 7.60 x 15 tires. Size 7.60 x 15 was optional on all other models at extra cost. White sidewall tires were optional at extra cost, with availability limited by Korean War production restrictions.

OPTIONS: Fender skirts for Pacemaker. Center bumper guards for Pacemaker. Large hubcaps for Pacemaker and Wasp. Front fender ornaments for Pacemaker. Radio. Radio antenna, roof mount type. Heater. Wind-up clock in Pacemaker. Electric clock in Wasp or Commodore Six. External windshield sun visor. Side window sun shields. Wheel trim rings. Oversize tires. Hydraulic window lifts in Wasp convertible (standard in other convertibles). Plastic rear window for convertible. Other standard factory and dealer installed accessories. Pacemaker models were available in five solid colors with six special hues optional at extra cost. All other Hudsons were available in 11 solid colors plus black, and 19 two-tones. Convertibles came only in solid colors. Hudson Motor Car Co. released a special 'High-Output' options catalog this year. It included the high compression Pacemaker Six with optional aluminum 7.2:1 compression cylinder head; the super high-output H-127 Wasp/Commodore Six with the same optional head and the high-output Super Eight engine with this 'Power Dome' cylinder head. Also, the 'Miracle H-Power' Hornet engine was available with both 7.2:1 aluminum head and 6.7:1 iron alloy head, plus a 7.2:1 iron alloy head. A dual-carburetor induction system with dual intake manifolds was released for the Hornet engine as the 'Twin-H' power package. Overdrive transmission was available for $111 extra. Hydra-Matic Drive could be ordered for $175.71 extra. Numerous types of special performance components were offered by the factory to professional stock car racers this year. Iron alloy 'Power Dome' cylinder heads were also available for Super Six and Super Eight engines.

HISTORICAL FOOTNOTES: The 1952 Hudson line was introduced during January 1952. Hudson Hornet stock cars won 27 of 34 NASCAR races held this year. Hudson drivers in NASCAR included Herb Thomas and Tim Flock. Marshall Teague began driving Hudsons in AAA competition, after taking the 1952 NASCAR Daytona stock car race in a Hornet. The car was torn down after the race and proved to be 100 percent stock. In AAA racing, Teague took 14 checkered flags for Hudson, while other drivers captured a total of five. For the year, the Hornets had captured 40 wins in 48 major stock car races. It was quite a feat. With model year sales of 70,000 cars and calendar year deliveries of 79,117 units, the company's sales rank moved up one notch to 14th position. In May 1952, Hudson announced that it was starting to tool-up for production of a new compact-sized line of 1953 models. This car became the Hudson Jet.

1953

SERIES 1C JET —SERIES 2C SUPER JET —SIX —A downsized Hudson flew on the scene in 1953. It was called the Jet. Marked by slab-sided styling with conventional notch back lines, the Jet looked different from other Hudsons. A fake air scoop decorated the front of the hood. The grille had a flat oval appearance with a chrome molding highlighting the upper opening. Super Jet script appeared on the fenders of the more highly trimmed line, which also had an air scoop ornament. Fender skirts were optional on both lines. Standard "custom car" equipment on the base model included Teleflash "idiot lights"; water temperature and gasoline gauges; Twin-Contour vacuum wipers; defroster vents; rotary door latches; theft-proof locks; push-button door handles; lock buttons; dash ashtray; wing-type front ventipanes; twin stop and taillamps; front parking lamps; manual dome light; lockable parcel compartment; twin horns and visors; and lighted ignition switch keyway. Upholstery was done in gray weave worsted striped red and brown. Super Jet extras included oversize tires; wing-type rear ventipanes; automatic dome lamps; and a host of features attached to the front seatback, such as pockets, coat hooks, cigarette lighter, robe hanger and ash receiver. Super Jets also had two-tone blue or green woven wool upholstery with Dura-fab leather grained trim.

HUDSON I.D. NUMBERS: Serial numbers were on the right front door post. Engine numbers were the same and were found on the upper front right-hand side of six-cylinder blocks or between the first and second exhaust manifold flanges on eight-cylinder blocks. Serial numbers followed the same system. The first two symbols were a prefix corresponding with model designations, with the second symbol changing to a 'C' in 1953. Jets were numbered 202917 to 268963; Super Jets 202917 to 269059; Wasps 202917 to 267518; Super Wasps 202917 to 267451 and Hornets 202917 to 267453. Body/Style

Numbers were not used through 1955. First columns in charts below show lower series; second columns show higher series; Hornet was offered only in one series coded in column one.

JET SIX (SERIES 1C)/SUPER JET SIX (SERIES 2C)

Model No.	Model No.	Body Type & Seating	Factory Price	Shipping Weight	Prod. Total
1C	2C	4-dr Sed-6P	1858/1954	2650/2700	Note 1
N/A	2C	2-dr Cpe Sed-6P	—/1933	—/2695	Note 1

Note 1: Series production included 21,143 Jets and Super Jets combined with no body style breakouts.

Note 2: The two-door Coupe Sedan came only as a Super Jet.

Note 3: Factory prices and shipping weights above slash for Jets/below slash for Super Jets.

WASP SERIES 4C —SUPER WASP SERIES 5C —SIX —The Wasp now became a midsize Hudson offering with traditional Step Down styling on the 119-inch wheelbase. Appearance changes included deletion of the twin-strut grille guard and the addition of an air scoop hood. Upholstery was in tan weave cord with red and brown stripes and Dura-fab trim. Power came from the former Pacemaker Six. A standard steering wheel, plain-top fenders and small hubcaps were identification features. Super Wasp models were comparable to the 1952 Wasp. They were upholstered in new nylon combinations with special check weave and Dura-fab trim. Two-tone green was standard with six solid exterior colors and 12 two-tone combinations. Two-tone blue was standard with four different solids and nine two-tones. However, both upholstery choices were optional with opposite colors at no extra cost. Leather upholstery was also a no-cost option on the Super Wasp convertible. Standard equipment on Super Wasps also included a special 127-hp six-cylinder engine; large hubcaps; front fendertop ornaments; combination fuel and vacuum pump; foam rubber front seat cushions; and Deluxe steering wheel.

WASP SIX (SERIES 4C)/SUPER WASP SIX (SERIES 5C)

Model No.	Model No.	Body Type & Seating	Factory Price	Shipping Weight	Prod. Total
4C	5C	4-dr Sed-6P	2311/2466	3380/3480	Note 1
4C	5C	2-dr Sed-6P	2264/2413	3350/3460	Note 1
4C	5C	2-dr Clb Cpe-6P	2311/2466	3340/3455	Note 1
N/A	5C	2-dr Holly HT-6P	—/2812	—/3525	Note 1
N/A	5C	2-dr Conv Brghm-6P	—/3048	—/3655	Note 1

Note 1: Series production included 17,792 Wasps and Super Wasps combined with no body style breakouts.

Note 2: Approximately 590 Hollywood two-door hardtops and 50 Convertible Broughams were built in the Super Wasp series.

Note 3: The Hollywood and the Convertible Brougham came only as Super Wasps.

Note 4: Factory prices and shipping weights above slash for Wasps/below slash for Super Wasps.

HUDSON HORNET —SIX —SERIES 7C —The 1953 Hudson Hornet was similar to the previous model bearing the same name, except that the strut bar look was eliminated from the grille and the air scoop hood look was used in its place. Hornets had most equipment used on Wasps plus front rectangular bumper guards; front outer bumper guards; electric clock; large hubcaps; front and rear foam seat cushions; and hydraulic window regulators for convertibles. The rocketship-shaped Hornet front fender and trunk ornaments were seen again. Special decorator check weave nylon upholstery was featured (in the same colors as Wasp interior) and a slim three-spoke steering wheel, with specially positioned horn button, was seen. Below the hood was the H-145 six-cylinder engine, with 'Power Dome' aluminum cylinder head standard.

HUDSON HORNET SIX (SERIES 7C)

Model No.	Model No.	Body Type & Seating	Factory Price	Shipping Weight	Prod. Total
7C	N/A	4-dr Sed-6P	2769	3570	Note 1
7C	N/A	2-dr Clb Cpe-6P	2742	3530	Note 1
7C	N/A	2-dr Holly HT-6P	3095	3610	Note 1
7C	N/A	2-dr Conv Brghm-6P	3342	3760	Note 1

Note 1: Series production included 27,208 Hornets with no breakouts.

Note 2: Approximately 910 Hornet Hollywood two-door hardtops were built.

ENGINES:

(JET/SUPER JET SIX) Inline six. L-head. Chrome alloy block. Displacement: 202 cid. Bore and stroke: 3 x 4-3/4 inches. Compression ratio: 7.5:1. Brake hp: 104 at 4000 rpm. Four main bearings. Solid valve lifters. Carburetor: Carter one-barrel type WA-1 Models 2009S or 2009SA.

(WASP SIX) Inline six. L-head. Chrome alloy block. Displacement: 232 cid. Bore and stroke: 3-9/16 x 3-7/8 inches. Compression ratio: 6.7:1. Brake hp: 112 at 4000 rpm. Four main bearings. Solid valve lifters. Carburetor: Carter one-barrel type WA-1 Model 749S.

(SUPER WASP SIX) Inline six. L-head. Chrome alloy block. Displacement: 262 cid. Bore and stroke: 3-9/16 x 4-3/8 inches. Compression ratio: 6.7:1. Brake hp: 127 at 4000 rpm. Four main bearings. Solid valve lifters. Carburetor: Carter one-barrel type WA-1 Model 776S.

(HORNET SIX) Inline six. L-head. Chrome alloy block. Displacement: 308 cid. Bore and stroke: 3-13/16 x 4-1/2 inches. Compression ratio: 7.2:1. Brake hp: 145 at 3800 rpm. Four main bearings. Solid valve lifters. Carburetor: Carter two-barrel type WGD Model 776S.

CHASSIS FEATURES: Wheelbase: (Jet) 105 inches; (Wasp) 119 inches; (Hornet) 124 inches. Overall length: (Jet) 180-11/16 inches; (Wasp) 201-1/2 inches; (Super Wasp) 202-1/2 inches; (Hornet) 208-1/2 inches. Front tread: (Jet) 54 inches; (all others) 58-1/2 inches. Rear tread: (Jet) 52 inches; (all others) 55-1/2 inches. Tires: (Jet) 5.90 x 15; (Super Jet) 6.40 x 15; (Hornet convertible) 7.60 x 15; (all others) 7.10 x 15.

OPTIONS: Two-door sedan rear seat armrests ($4). Front rectangular bumper guard ($24). Front outer bumper guards ($15). Electric clock, Jet ($22); Wasp ($19). Exhaust deflector ($2). Direction indicator, Jet ($21); Wasp ($24); Hornet ($24). Large hubcaps ($11). Cigar lighter ($4). Back-up lights, Super Jet ($18); Wasp and Hornet ($24). Glare-proof mirror ($5). Outside rearview mirror, Jet ($5); others ($6). Front fendertop ornaments ($7). Large plastic rear window for convertible ($10). Eight-tube push-button radio ($100). Six-tube manual radio ($82). Front foam seat cushions, Jet ($13); Wasp ($14). Rear foam seat cushions (same price per model). Heavy-duty shock absorbers ($14). Solex glass with sunshade windshield ($42). Deluxe steering wheel ($20). Wheel trim rings ($15). Orion convertible top ($134). Window and wing vent shades, except convertible and Hollywood hardtop ($18). Outside sun visor with traffic light viewer ($33). Remote control Weather Control heater, Jet ($73), others ($74). Rear fender skirts [Hudson called them "wheel covers"] ($15). Custom wheel discs, Jet and Wasp ($20); Super Wasp and Hornet ($18). Windshield washer ($11). Hydraulic window regulators for Super Wasp convertible ($67). Hand-buffed genuine leather trim ($132-$146 per body style). Note: leather trim not available on base Jet or blue combinations not available on base Wasp. Dura-fab trim ($53). Special solid paint colors on Jet ($27); other models ($28). Two-tone paint combinations on Super Jet only ($27); on Super Wasp or Hornet only ($31). Note: Special and two-tone colors were not available on base Jet or base Wasp. Tire options for Jet and Super Jet included whitewalls six-ply and Super Jet size on Jet at exchange prices from $6 to $50. Tire options on the Hornet convertible included whitewalls at $41 and six-ply blackwalls at $54 (exchange prices). Tire options on other Hornets, Wasps and Super Wasps included 7.60 x 15 size, whitewalls and special order six-ply choices at exchange prices from $22 to $72. Oil bath air cleaner ($8). Two oil bath air cleaners with 'Twin-H' power package ($16). Aluminum cylinder head, Wasp ($14); Jet ($12). Special 127-hp Super Wasp Six for Wasp ($37). Hydra-Matic Drive ($176). Oil filter ($14). Overdrive for Jet ($102); for other models ($111). Combination fuel and vacuum pump for base Wasp ($12); for Jet or Super Jet ($11). 'Twin-H' Power for all models, twin oil bath air cleaners mandatory on Wasp ($85.60). Available rear axles included units with 4.09:1, 4.10:1, 4.55:1, 4.27:1, 3.54:1, 3.31:1 and 3.07:1 gear ratios. Specific applications of axle ratios varied with models and transmissions, but options available were no extra cost. Cost of the high-performance 7-X engine from Hudson Dealer Parts Departments was $385.

HISTORICAL FOOTNOTES: The 1953 Hudson line was introduced in November 1952. Model year sales were 66,143 units. Calendar year production peaked at 67,089 cars. Hudson was the 15th ranked producer. A special 7-X engine package was released for "severe usage," such as stock car racing. An official power rating was not published, but 200 hp was estimated for cars with this option. Hudsons captured 22 (out of 37) major NASCAR races, with driver Herb Thomas winning championship honors for the season. In AAA competition 13 (out of 16) races went to Hudson. The Hornets took checkered flags in 35 of 53 contests. Rumors of an impending merger between Hudson and another independent manufacturer began circulating in Detroit.

1954

JET SIX —SERIES 1D —The 1954 Jet grille had four ribs on each side of the main blade and a center embossment. Standard equipment was the same as the previous year. Tan worsted weave upholstery with brown and red stripes was featured in combination with brown Plasti-hide trim. The base model lacked robe cords; courtesy lamps; front seatback pockets; wing-type rear ventipanes; coathooks; and a rear ashtray. Even a cigar lighter was extra. Two-tone paint was not available and the sole upholstery option was gray Plasti-hide with leather trim. On April 12,1954, a new Family Club Sedan was added

1954 Hudson, Hornet Special (Series 6D), club sedan, OCW

1954 Hudson, Italia GT sport coupe (27 custom built on Jet platform by Carrozzeria Touring of Milan, Italy), OCW

1955 Hudson, Wasp Custom (Series 40-2), sedan, HET

1956 Hudson, Hornet Custom (Series 60), sedan, HET

1956 Hudson, Wasp "Super" (Series 40), sedan (with optional two-tone paint scheme), HET

Above and below, 1954 Hudson, Hornet (Series 7D), sedan, OCW

1955 Hudson, Hollywood Custom (Series 60-2), hardtop, HET

1956 Hudson, Hornet Hollywood Custom (Series 80), hardtop, HET

1957 Hudson, Hornet Custom (Series 80), sedan (with optional two-tone paint scheme), HET

to the line as a stripped economy model. Priced $216 under the base sedan, this two-door had a non-scoop hood, plainer grille, black rubber windshield surround and even more spartan appointments.

HUDSON I.D. NUMBERS: Serial numbers were on the right front door post. Engine numbers were the same and were found on the upper front right-hand side of six-cylinder blocks or between the first and second exhaust manifold flanges on eight-cylinder blocks. The system of numbering Hudsons was changed. Each serial number had seven symbols. The first designated model, the others were the consecutive unit number. The starting number for all series was 269060 and they ran in mixed production. Engine numbers were the same. The serial number in Jet models was on the top right frame rail flange near the dash panel. Engine numbers were in the right front corner of the block near the top. Charts below list the lower series Model Number in first column and upper series Model Number in second column when two series are offered.

JET SIX (SERIES 1D)

Model No.	Model No.	Body Type & Seating	Factory Price	Shipping Weight	Prod. Total
1D	N/A	4-dr Sed-6P	1858	2675	Note 1
1D	N/A	2-dr Fam Clb Sed-6P	1621	2635	Note 1
1D	N/A	2-dr Utl Sed-6P	1837	2715	Note 1

Note 1: Mixed production with Super Jet/Jetliner series below.

SUPER JET SERIES 2D —JETLINER SERIES 3D —SIX —Block letters spelled out Super Jet on the front fenders of this one-step-up model. Features included hood air scoop ornamentation; horizontal front fender and door moldings; robe cords; wing-type rear door ventipanes; front seatback pockets; rear ashtray; courtesy door lights; coat hooks; and cigar lighter. Two-tone green or blue decorator selected worsted upholstery fabrics in a handsome check pattern with solid Plasti-hide trim were used. The Jetliner was a new top-level offering characterized by Jetliner fender block lettering; rear wheel covers (fender skirts); Custom wheel discs; rear fender horizontal rub moldings; body sill highlights; bright rear gravel shields; and chrome rear taillight trim. Most Super Jet appointments were included plus front and rear foam seat cushions and smartly pleated antique white Plasti-hide upholstery with headliner and bolsters of the same material in blue, green or red Worsted cloth. Super Jet combinations were optional at no extra cost

SUPER JET SIX (SERIES 2D)/JETLINER SIX (SERIES 3D)

Model No.	Model No.	Body Type & Seating	Factory Price	Shipping Weight	Prod. Total
2D	3D	4-dr Sed-6P	1954/2057	2725/2760	Note 1
2D	3D	2-dr Clb Sed-6P	1933/2046	2710/2740	Note 1

Note 1: Series production included 14,224 Jets, Super Jets and Jetliners combined with no body style breakouts.

Note 2: Data above slash for Super Jet/below slash for Jetliner.

WASP SERIES 4D —SUPER WASP SERIES 5D —SIX —New styling, resembling that of the Jets, was applied to regular Hudsons this year. The grille had a heavy, bowed molding tracing the upper radiator opening. There was a full-width, flat horizontal loop surrounding the wedge-shaped parking lights at each end. The main bar (top of the loop) was ribbed towards the middle and held a triangular Hudson medallion in a finned housing at its center. Behind this bar was an angled plate with four additional, wide-spaced ribs. Block letters spelled out Hudson below the scoop on the nose of the hood. Wasp or Super Wasp signature script was placed on the front fender tips above a full-length horizontal rub molding. Two-door hardtops had Hollywood script at the upper rear edge of front fenders. A panoramic one-piece windshield and protruding tip taillamps were new. Bright metal gravel shields with windsplit vents decorated the rear fendersides. Standard equipment on Wasps included fender skirts; cigar lighter; robe cord; front seatback pockets; rear ashtray; and special pattern cloth upholstery with blue or green Plasti-hide trim. Super Wasps had the same features plus the following additions or changes: large hubcaps; front foam seat cushions; Custom steering wheel; passenger assist handles; crank-type front ventipanes on Hollywoods and convertibles; courtesy door lights; combination fuel and vacuum pump; and two-tone blue or green check pattern tweed cloth upholstery with worsted bolster material and Plasti-hide trim. In Super Wasp convertibles blue, maroon or green leather cushions with Plasti-hide side trim was standard. The Super Wasp Hollywood hardtop had brown, blue or green nylon cord seats with snowflake design cloth upholstery and harmonizing Plasti-hide bolsters.

WASP SIX (SERIES 4D)/SUPER WASP SIX (SERIES 5D)

Model No.	Model No.	Body Type & Seating	Factory Price	Shipping Weight	Prod. Total
4D	5D	4-dr Sed-6P	2256/2466	3440/3525	Note 1
4D	5D	2-dr Clb Sed-6P	2209/2413	3375/3490	Note 1
4D	5D	2-dr Clb Cpe-6P	2256/2466	3360/3475	Note 1
N/A	5D	2-dr Holly HT-6P	—/2704	—/3570	Note 1
N/A	5D	2-dr Conv Brghm-6P	—/3004	—/3680	Note 1

Note 1: Series production included 11,603 Wasps and Super Wasps combined with no body style breakouts.

Note 2: Industry trade magazines indicate that, on a calendar year basis, Hudson built 2,654 Hollywoods and 222 convertibles with no series breakouts.

Note 3: Data above slash for Wasp/below slash for Super Wasp.

HORNET SPECIAL SERIES 6D —HORNET SERIES 7D —SIX — Hornets seemed a little more like Super Wasps this year, although the longer 124-inch wheelbase was still used. The appearance change to the Jet-like look brought an end to the front fender rocketship ornaments. Hudson signature script was seen on the fenders, but only the trunk lid had a special badge. As on Super Wasps, two-door hardtops also had Hollywood script at the high trailing edge of front fenders, above the full-length horizontal body rub moldings. Hornets had most Super Wasp equipment plus the following additions or changes: crank-type front ventipanes on all models; cast aluminum 'high-compression' head; electric clock; foam rubber rear seat cushions; Custom wheel discs; hydraulic window lifts (in convertibles); and special trims. Sedans and Club Coupes were upholstered in 15 percent nylon worsted Bedford cloth with broadcloth bolsters and Plasti-hide trim in different shades of the same colors: brown, blue or green. The Hornet Hollywood had similarly toned, snowflake design nylon cord seats with Plasti-hide bolsters. The convertible was done in blue, maroon or green genuine leather (with Plasti-hide side trim). Convertible tops were available in maroon, black or tan. Specific combinations of top colors with car finishes were recommended, but not considered mandatory. Also, the Hollywood hardtop could be had with tri-colored seat and headlining combinations of antique white Plasti-hide and red, blue and green bolsters, at no extra cost. The last models introduced by Hudson, in Detroit, were the Hornet Specials. They appeared March 19, 1954, at prices $115 to $140 lower than comparable Hornets. They had Hornet Special front fender script, Hornet engine and a subdued level of exterior brightwork, but Super Wasp interior trim.

HORNET SPECIAL SIX (SERIES 6D)/HORNET SIX (SERIES 7D)

Model No.	Model No.	Body Type & Seating	Factory Price	Shipping Weight	Prod. Total
6D	7D	4-dr Sed-6P	2619/2769	3560/3620	Note 1
6D	N/A	2-dr Clb Sed-6P	2571/—	3515/—	Note 1
6D	7D	2-dr Clb Cpe-6P	2619/2742	3505/3570	Note 1
N/A	7D	2-dr Holly HT-6P	—/2988	—/3655	Note 1
N/A	7D	2-dr Conv Brghm-6P	—/3288	—/3800	Note 1

Note 1: Series production included 24,833 Hornet Specials and Hornets combined with no body style breakouts.

Note 2: The Club Sedan came as a Hornet Special only; the Hollywood hardtop and Convertible Brougham came as Hornets only.

Note 3: Data above slash for Hornet Special/below slash for Hornet.

HUDSON ITALIA —CUSTOM SERIES —SIX —Twenty-six Hudson Italia coupes were built in 1954 on the Jet platform. The Italia body was styled and crafted by Carrozzeria Touring, of Milan, Italy, based on original sketches by Hudson's own Frank Spring. The sporty GT had aluminum coachwork; functional front fender scoops with brake cooling ducts; wraparound windshield; flow through ventilation; contoured leather bucket seats with three different densities of foam for proper support; deep-pile Italian floor carpeting; Borrani wire spoke wheels; white sidewall tires; radio; heater; back-up lights; and turn signals stacked in Jet-tube pipes tunneled into rear fenders. The Italia was announced, as a production model, on Jan. 14, 1954, the same day Hudson's merger with Nash Motors was approved. The 26 cars were actually designed and custom built as four-passenger Grand Touring 'image' cars to steal attention from Chevrolet Corvettes, Ford Thunderbirds and Ghia Chrysler show cars. Twenty-five were actually sold as production models, while a coupe prototype and four-door X-161 pilot model were also created. Twenty-one of these cars are known to still exist.

HUDSON ITALIA SIX (CUSTOM SERIES)

Model No.	Model No.	Body Type & Seating	Factory Price	Shipping Weight	Prod. Total
N/A	N/A	2-dr GT Spt Cpe-4P	4800	2710	27

HUDSON METROPOLITAN —(SERIES E) —FOUR —On May 1, 1954, Hudson Motor Car Co. became a division of American Motors Corp. Hudson dealers then undertook the sale of four-cylinder Metropolitans, previously marketed as a Nash offering in the United States. Hudson dealers were supplied with replacement grille center inserts having an 'H' instead of an "N". These were to be installed in Metropolitans sold as Hudsons. The cars were otherwise identical to Nash Metropolitans, which are mentioned elsewhere in this catalog. Even serial and engine numbers were the same. Hudson Metropolitans were marketed through 1956. Since these were early "captive imports," rather than a true domestic automobile, specifications are not listed in this catalog. They can be found in Krause Publications' *Standard Catalog Of Imported Cars 1946-1999* (second edition).

ENGINES:

(JET/SUPER JET SIX) Inline six. L-head. Chrome alloy block. Displacement: 202 cid. Bore and stroke: 3 x 4-3/4 inches. Compression ratio: 7.5:1. Brake hp: 104 at 4000 rpm. Four main bearings. Solid valve lifters. Carburetor: Carter one-barrel type WA-1 Models 2009S or 2009SA.

(WASP SIX) Inline six. L-head. Chrome alloy block. Displacement: 232 cid. Bore and stroke: 3-9/16 x 3-7/8 inches. Compression ratio: 7.0:1. Brake hp: 126 at 4400 rpm. Four main bearings. Solid valve lifters. Carburetor: Carter one-barrel type WA-1 Model 749S.

(SUPER WASP SIX) Inline six. L-head. Chrome alloy block. Displacement: 262 cid. Bore and stroke: 3-9/16 x 4-3/8 inches. Compression ratio: 7.0:1. Brake hp: 140 at 4000 rpm. Four main bearings. Solid valve lifters. Carburetor: Carter two-barrel type WGD Model 2115S.

(HORNET 'BIG' SIX) Inline six. L-head. Chrome alloy block. Displacement: 308 cid. Bore and stroke: 3-15/16 x 4-1/2 inches. Compression ratio: 7.5:1. Brake hp: 160 at 3800 rpm. Four main bearings. Solid valve lifters. Carburetor: Carter two-barrel type WGD Model 2115S.

(ITALIA SIX) Inline six. L-head. Chrome alloy block. Displacement: 201.5 cid (202). Bore and stroke: 3.00 x 4.75 inches. Compression ratio: 7.5:1. Brake hp: 114 at 4000 rpm. Four main bearings. Solid valve lifters. Induction system: Twin-H Power package with dual manifolding and carburetion (Carter carburetors).

CHASSIS FEATURES: Wheelbase: (Jet) 105 inches; (Wasp) 119 inches; (Hornet) 124 inches; (Italia) 105 inches. Overall length: (Jet) 180-11/16 inches; (Wasp) 201-1/2 inches; (Super Wasp) 202-15/32 inches; (Hornet) 268-7/8 inches. Front tread: (Jet/Italia) 54 inches; (other models) 58.5 inches. Rear tread: (Jet/Italia) 52 inches; (other models) 55.5 inches. Tires: (Jet) 5.90 x 15; (Super Jet/Jetliner) 6.40 x 15; (Hornet convertible) 7.60 x 15; (other models, except Italia) 7.10 x 15.

OPTIONS: Wasp two-door sedan rear armrest ($4). Power brakes except Jets ($43). Electric clock, in Jets ($22); in Wasps ($19). Exhaust deflector ($2). Direction indicators, in Jets ($16); in others ($20). Large hubcaps, Wasp only ($11). Jet cigar lighter ($4). Super Jet/Jetliner back-up lights ($18); same on Wasps and Hornets ($24). Glare-proof mirror ($5). Outside rearview mirror, in Jets ($5); all others ($6). Plastic convertible rear window ($10). Eight-tube push-button radio ($100). Six-tube manual radio, Jets only ($82). Front foam seats, in Jet/Super Jet ($13); in Wasp ($14). Rear foam seats, Jet/Super Jet ($13); in Wasp/Super Wasp ($14). Extra heavy-duty shock absorbers, in Jets ($5); other models ($14). Solex glass with sunshade windshield ($33). Heavy scale springs, front and rear or rear only, separate no cost option in Jets and other models. Power steering, Wasps and Hornets only ($177). Custom steering wheel, in Jet/Wasp ($20); in Super Jet/Jetliner ($19). Wheel trim rings, Jets and Wasps ($15). Orion convertible top ($134). Window and wing vent shades, except convertible and Hollywood hardtop ($18). Outside visor with traffic light viewer in Wasps and Hornets ($33). Weather Control heater with remote control, in Jets ($73); in others ($74). Rear wheel covers (fender skirts), in Jet/Super Jet only ($15). Custom wheel discs, on Jet/Super Jet and base Wasp ($20); on Super Hornet ($18). Wheels painted upper body color (no cost with two-tone paint). Windshield washer ($11). Hydraulic window regulators in Super Wasp convertible ($67). Safety Group including back-up lights; directionals; glare proof and outside rearview mirrors and windshield washer in Super Wasp and Hornet ($66). Safety Group with all the above items plus combination fuel/vacuum pump in Wasp ($78); in Super Jet/Jetliner ($66). Safety Group with all the above, less back-up lights in Jet ($49). Chrome-plated wire wheels, except Jets. Velchrome painted wire wheels (Special order in all models). The following equipment was available on models indicated, when sold as taxis or police cars: Extra-wide 2-1/4 inch brake (standard in Super Wasp, Hornet; special order in Wasp). Heavy-duty clutch (standard in Super Wasp, Hornet; special order in 1-2-3-4D). Heavy-duty battery (special order in 1-2-3D). Police/taxi special seat construction (special order in Jet, Super Jet, Jetliner). Color and Trim Options: Roman bronze or Pasture green special paint (no charge, except Jet/Wasp base models). Algerian blue, Coronation cream, St. Clair gray, or Lipstick red solid colors (extra cost). Jet gray Plasti-hide trim (extra cost). Super Jet blue or green Plasti-hide trim (extra cost). Jetliner worsted upholstery (no cost). Wasp Pioneer grain leather trim (extra cost). Super Wasp maroon Pioneer grain or green antique grain leather trim (extra cost). Super Wasp Hollywood Plasti-hide trim (no cost). Hornet sedan and Club Coupe blue, maroon or green antique grain leather trim (extra cost). Hornet Hollywood blue or maroon leather trim (extra cost). Tire options included white sidewalls, oversize or extra-ply construction types at a variety of exchange prices based on series, model and body style. A continental tire extension kit was offered as a dealer-installed accessory. Oil bath air cleaner ($8). Twin oil bath air cleaners for 'Twin-H' package, mandatory on base Wasp equipped with 'Twin H' ($16). Aluminum cylinder head optional on all, except Italia/Hornet, on Jets ($12); on others ($14). Super Wasp Six for base Wasp ($48) Hydra-Matic Drive ($178). Oil filter, no charge on Super Jet/Jetliner with Hydra-Matic (other models $14). Overdrive transmission on Jets ($102); on all others ($111). Combination fuel/vacuum pump, on Jets ($11); on all others ($12). 'Twin-H' power with dual carburetion and manifolding, 170 hp, dual air cleaners mandatory on base Wasp ($86).

HISTORICAL FOOTNOTES: Oct. 2, 1953, was the dealer introduction date for 1954 Hudson and Jet Utility Sedans. The Jetliner series was introduced 10 days later. Model year production totaled 51,314 cars. Calendar year production peaked at 32,287 cars, including 4,239 Ramblers. On Jan. 14, 1954, Hudson directors approved a merger with Nash-Kelvinator. On March 24, 1954, Hudson stockholders approved the merger. On April 12, 1954, the Jet Family Club Sedan was added to the line. On May 1, 1954, Hudson officially became part of American Motors Corp. Twenty-six days later, Hudson employees were notified that production was being switched to the Nash automobile factory in Kenosha, Wis. On Oct. 30, 1954, the 1954 Hudson model run ended in Detroit. Eleven days later the first Hornet/Rambler departed the Kenosha plant. On Dec. 28, 1954, the first 1955 Hudson Hornet V-8 was built at Kenosha. An era in Hudson's history had ended.

1955

HUDSON RAMBLER —SERIES 5500 —SIX —The year 1955 found 11 Nash Ramblers, thinly disguised with grille badge inserts and hubcaps with a letter 'H' in the center, at Hudson dealerships. Two 'Fleet Specials' were stripped, three-passenger economy models with painted lamp rims, rubber windshield surrounds and spartan appointments. Next in price came a Deluxe series with plated headlamp rims, Deluxe front fender script, plain air scoop, no hood ornament and slightly upmarket interior trim. A hood ornament and air scoop trim band were seen on the Super series, priced in the next higher bracket. At the top of the heap was a Custom series, with Custom front fender script, standard continental spare tire, enriched interior and all other Super features. These Hudson Ramblers were identical to the latest editions of the comparable Nash Rambler in features, trim and price.

HUDSON I.D. NUMBERS [HUDSON/RAMBLER] Serial numbers were located on a plate attached to the center cowl panel, below the hood. Cars built in Kenosha were numbered D-205001 to D-276099. Cars built at El Segundo, California, were numbered DC-15001 to DC-23325. Engine numbers were on the upper left corner of the block (with air conditioning at the left front side of the block) and ran H-45001 to H-131414. Nash and Hudson Ramblers were built in mixed production. Body type identification was possible, with (Body/Style) model numbers stamped on a plate located at the right side of dash, below hood. These numbers correspond to the Model Numbers in column two of charts below. [WASP/HORNET SUPER/HORNET CUSTOM] Wasps (built in Kenosha, Wis.) were numbered W-1001 to W-8026. Kenosha-built Hornet Sixes were numbered X-1001 to X-7523; V-8s Y-1001 to Y-7170. El Segundo-built Hornet Sixes were numbered XC-1001 to XC-1048; V-8s YC-1001 to YC-1048. Engine number locations were on a machined surface on the left-hand side of block (at side of second cylinder) for Series 40 (Wasp Six) and Series 60 (Hornet Six) and were on a machined surface on right-hand side of block (at side of cylinder number eight below exhaust manifold) for Series 80 (Hornet V-8). Engine numbers were M-1001 to M-8026 (Wasp Six); F-1001 to F-7523 (Hornet Six) and P-1001 to P-7170 (Hornet V-8). Body type identification was now possible with (Body/Style) model numbers stamped on a plate at the center of cowl panel, below hood. These numbers correspond to model numbers in column two of charts below.

HUDSON RAMBLER SIX (SERIES 2500/5500)

Series No.	Body Model No.	Body Type & Seating	Factory Price	Shipping Weight	Prod. Total
FLEET SPECIAL SERIES					
N/A	5504	2-dr Utl Wag-3P	1570	2500	21
N/A	5512	2-dr Del Bus Sed-3P	1457	2400	34
DELUXE SERIES					
N/A	5515	4-dr Sed-6P	1695	2567	Note 1
N/A	5516	2-dr Clb Sed-5P	1585	2432	0
N/A	5514	2-dr Sub-5P	1771	2528	0
SUPER SERIES					
N/A	5516-1	2-dr Clb Sed-5P	1683	2450	2,970
N/A	5514-1	2-dr Sub-5P	1869	2532	1,335
N/A	5515-1	4-dr Sed-6P	1798	2570	Note 1
N/A	5518-1	4-dr Cty Clb-6P	1975	2675	0
CUSTOM SERIES					
N/A	5515-2	4-dr Sed-6P	1989	2606	Note 1
N/A	5518-2	4-dr Cr Ctry-6P	2098	2685	12,023
N/A	5517-2	4-dr Cty Clb-5P	1995	2518	601

Note 1: Production of 7,210 Hudson Rambler four-door sedans was recorded with only the partial model breakouts shown here available.

WASP SUPER AND CUSTOM —SERIES 40 —SIX —The post-AMC merger Hudsons were introduced at the Chicago Auto Show, Feb. 23, 1955. Styling and engineering, though based on the Nash unit body and platform, were planned to give Hudsons a distinct character. For example, the former Jet engine was under the hood and the Hudson dual braking system was retained. Gone, however, was the traditional Hudson 'crab tread' stance. The Wasp front tread was three-sixteenths inch less than its rear tread. As far as the sheet metal went, the only panel interchangeable between Nashes and Hudsons was the rear deck lid. Overall styling was pleasant. A massive eggcrate grille filled the area below and between the single headlamps, with an inverted steer horn-shaped bar bordering the top. This upper border bar had a Hudson badge set into a housing at its center. Hudson block letters decorated the hood, which no longer had a simulated air scoop. It had a full-width cowl vent near the windshield base. Horizontal moldings stretched across the front fenders and doors. A higher molding swept rearwards from the wraparound windshield post towards the upper back fender region. A stand-up hood ornament and Wasp front fender nameplates were seen on Super models, which also had Super script on the sides of the cowl. Customs had a flatter hood ornament and Custom cowl side script and included a continental spare tire as standard. Wrapover rear roof pillars were seen on all models.

WASP SIX AND CUSTOM SIX (SERIES 40)

Series No.	Body Model No.	Body Type & Seating	Factory Price	Shipping Weight	Prod. Total
STANDARD SERIES					
N/A	35545-1	4-dr Sed-6P	2290	3254	Note 1
CUSTOM SERIES 40-2					
N/A	35545-2	4-dr Sed-6P	2460	3347	5,551
N/A	35547-2	2-dr Holly HT-6P	2570	3362	1,640

Note 1: Production of Super Wasp four-door sedans is included in Custom Wasp four-door sedan total.

HORNET SUPER AND CUSTOM —SERIES 60 SIX —SERIES 80 V-8 —The Hornet for 1955 had the same styling as the new Wasps on a longer wheelbase platform. Hornet nameplates were seen on the front fenders. Hardtops had Hollywood cowlside script as well. High quality interiors and standard continental spare tire carriers were regular equipment distinguishing Custom level cars. The Custom interior included 16-inch table-like rear seat armrests; transparent sun visors; roof package net; and padded dashboard. Hornet engine choices included the standard (160 hp) or 'Twin-H' (170 hp) versions of the big 308-cid six or a new V-8 built and supplied by Packard. Packard's new Twin Ultramatic transmission was both standard and mandatory in Hudsons equipped with a V-8.

HORNET SUPER AND CUSTOM SIX (SERIES 60)/V-8 (SERIES 80)

Series No.	Body Model No.	Body Type & Seating	Factory Price	Shipping Weight	Prod. Total
SUPER SIX SERIES 60-1					
N/A	35565-1	4-dr Sed-6P	2565	3495	Note 1
CUSTOM SIX SERIES 60-2					
N/A	35565-2	4-dr Sed-6P	2760	3562	5,357
N/A	35557-2	2-dr Holly HT-6P	2880	3587	1,554

Note 1: Production of Hornet Super Six four-door sedans is included in Hornet Custom Six four-door sedan total.

Series No.	Body Model No.	Body Type & Seating	Factory Price	Shipping Weight	Prod. Total
SUPER V-8 SERIES 80-1					
N/A	35585-1	4-dr Sed-6P	2825	3806	Note 1
CUSTOM V-8 SERIES 80-2					
N/A	35585-2	4-dr Sed-6P	3015	3846	4,449
N/A	35587-2	2-dr Holly HT-6P	3145	3876	1,770

Note 1: Production of Hornet Super V-8 four-door sedans is included in Hornet Custom V-8 four-door sedan total.

ENGINES:

(RAMBLER 'FLYING SCOT' SIX) Inline six. L-head. Cast iron block. Displacement: 195.6 cid. Bore and stroke: 3-1/8 x 4-1/4 inches. Compression ratio: 7.3:1. Brake hp: 90 at 3800 rpm. Four main bearings. Solid valve lifters. Carburetor: Carter one-barrel type YF Model 2014S.

(WASP SIX) Inline six. L-head. Cast iron block. Displacement: 202 cid. Bore and stroke: 3 x 4-3/4 inches. Compression ratio: 7.5:1. Brake hp: 120 at 4000 rpm. Four main bearings. Solid valve lifters. Carburetor: Carter one-barrel type WA-1 Model 2013S.

(HORNET 'BIG' SIX) Inline six. L-head. Chrome alloy block. Aluminum cylinder head. Displacement: 308 cid. Bore and stroke: 3-13/16 x 4-1/2 inches. Compression ratio: 7.5:1. Brake hp: 160 at 3800 rpm. Four main bearings. Solid valve lifters. Carburetor: Carter one-barrel type WA-1 Model 2113S.

(PACKARD EIGHT) V-8. Overhead valve. Cast iron block. Displacement: 320 cid. Bore and stroke: 3-13/16 x 3-1/2 inches. Compression ratio: 7.8:1. Five main bearings. Brake hp: 208 at 4200 rpm. Five main bearings. Non-adjustable hydraulic valve lifters. Carburetor: Carter two-barrel type WGD Model 2231SA.

CHASSIS FEATURES: Wheelbase: (Rambler four-door) 108 inches; (Rambler two-door) 100 inches; (Wasp) 114-1/4 inches; (Hornet) 121-1/4 inches. Overall length: (Rambler four-door) 186-1/4 inches or 193-3/8 inches with continental spare; (Rambler two-door) 178-1/4 inches or 185-3/8 inches with continental spare; (Wasp) 202-1/4 inches or 212-1/4 inches with continental spare; (Hornet) 209-1/4 inches or 219-1/4 inches with continental spare. Front tread: (Rambler) 54-5/8 inches; (all Hudson) 59-1/2 inches. Rear tread: (Rambler) 53 inches; (Wasp) 59-11/16 inches; (Hornet) 60-1/2 inches. Tires: (Rambler) 6.40 x 15; (Wasp) 6.70 x 15; (Hornet) 7.10 x 15.

OPTIONS: Rambler radio ($76). Rambler heater ($74). Rambler air conditioning ($345). Hudson air conditioning with heater ($395). Hudson twin speaker radio ($98). Hudson Weather Eye heater and defroster ($77). Power steering ($140). Power brakes ($39). Power windows ($128). Continental spare tire, except Customs. Reclining seats. Twin-Travel bed. Air mattress. Detachable window screens. Full wheel discs. Wasp 'Twin-H' six with two Carter one-barrel type WA-1 Model 2013S carburetors, 8.0:1 compression, aluminum cylinder head and 130 hp at 4000 rpm. Hornet 'Twin-H' six with two Carter one-barrel type WA-1 carburetors, 7.5:1 compression and 170 hp at 4000 rpm. Hornet Special V-8 with one Carter two-barrel type WGD Model 2352S carburetor, 8.25:1 compression and 215 hp at 4600 rpm. Hydra-Matic transmission ($179). Packard Twin Ultramatic transmission (mandatory on V-8 Hornets and included in factory price of these models). Overdrive manual transmission ($104). Available rear axle gear ratios: (Rambler) 3.77:1 and 4.40:1; (Hudson) 3.15:1, 3.54:1, 3.58:1, 4.10:1 and 4.40:1.

HISTORICAL FOOTNOTES: Model year production included 25,214 Ramblers, 7,191 Wasps, 6,911 Hornets, and 6,219 V-8s for a total of 45,535 Hudsons. Sales promotions such as a 'Dealer Volume Investment Fund' and 'Sun Valley Sweepstakes' (for salesmen) helped Hudson move upwards by seven percent in the sales volume ranking charts. A national contest offering new Hudsons and trips to Disneyland as prizes was open to public participation. Although Hudson's headquarters address was still 14250 Plymouth Road, Detroit 32, Mich., all production of 1955 models was quartered at the AMC factory, Kenosha, Wis.

1956

HUDSON RAMBLER —SERIES 5600 —SIX —The Hudson Jet was discontinued but Hudson dealers still had small cars to sell under the AMC 'family plan'. These were totally badge-engineered cars including the imported Metropolitan. "American" cars from American Motors included Hudson Ramblers built at Kenosha, Wis. They were, in fact, identical to 1956 Nash Ramblers, except for having hubcaps with an 'H' in the center and 'H' logo circular grille inserts.

HUDSON I.D. NUMBERS: The numbering system was the same as for previous models. Letter prefixes indicated model and place of origin. [HUDSON RAMBLER] Serial numbers were D-276101 for Kenosha-built cars; DKD-5601 for unassembled export and DT-5401 for Canadian models. [WASP] Serial numbers for Kenosha-built Wasps were W-8101 to W-10619. [HORNET] Serial numbers for Kenosha-built Hornet Sixes were X-7601 to X-10665. Serial numbers for Kenosha-built Hornet V-8s were Y-7201 to Y-10191. [HORNET SPECIAL] Serial numbers for Kenosha-built Hornet Special V-8s were Z-1001 to Z-2757. Hudson Rambler engine numbers started at B-1001 and up. Wasp and Hornet engine numbers were as follows: (Wasp Six) M-8701 and up (with M-10001 to M-10100 previously assigned to 1955 models); (Hornet Six) F-8601 and up; (Hornet V-8s) P-21001 to P-28804 and (Hornet Special V-8s) G-1001 to G-7288.

HUDSON RAMBLER SERIES

Model No.	Body/Style No.	Body Type & Seating	Factory Price	Shipping Weight	Prod. Total
DELUXE LINE					
N/A	5615	4-dr Sed-6P	1826	2891	Note 1
SUPER LINE					
N/A	5615-1	4-dr Sed-6P	1936	2906	Note 1
N/A	5618-1	4-dr Sta Wag-6P	2230	2992	Note 1
N/A	5613-2	4-dr HT Sta Wag-6P	2491	3095	Note 1
CUSTOM LINE					
N/A	5615-2	4-dr Sed-6P	2056	2929	Note 1
N/A	5619-2	4-dr HT Sed-6P	2221	2990	Note 1
N/A	5618-2	4-dr HT Sta Wag-6P	2326	3110	Note 1

Note 1: Production of 1956 Hudson Ramblers was 20,496 with no breakouts.

HUDSON WASP —SERIES 40 —SIX —A completely new V-shaped grille with a Hudson medallion set into another V-shaped dip in the center was a new styling trademark for 1956. Other changes included new hood ornaments and new rectangular front parking lamps set into wedge-shaped chrome moldings that accented the V-shape of the grille. There were air scoop fendertop ornaments and new bodyside rub rail moldings, which also had a V-shaped dip on the rear doors or fenders. In addition, the taillights were redesigned. The Wasp models could be identified by their Wasp nameplates inside the V-shaped dip in the rub rail molding. They could also be spotted by the chrome-enclosed panel on the rear fendersides, which was finished in lower body color. Popular features included Deep Coil ride; Triple-Safe hydraulic brakes (with a reserve mechanical system); positive action handbrake; Double-Safe single unit construction; tubeless tires; Select-O-Lift starter; drawer-type glove compartment; wraparound windshield and rear window; and double-acting airplane-type shock absorbers. The only model available in the 1956 Wasp lineup was the Super trim sedan. Twin-H power was optionally available.

HUDSON WASP SIX

Model No.	Body Style No.	Body Type & Seating	Factory Price	Shipping Weight	Prod. Total
SUPER LINE					
N/A	35645-1	4-dr Sed-6P	2416	3264	2,519

HUDSON HORNET —SERIES 60/80 —(SIX/V-8) —The 1956 Hornet had the same general styling changes as the new Wasp, but came with richer interior appointments and more standard equipment. All Hornet models had identification nameplates in the V-shaped dip in the side rub rail moldings. Custom trim level Hornets had a continental style spare tire and a chrome enclosed, gold-finished panel just to the rear of the V-shaped dip in the side molding. However, Super Hornets did not use either of these features having the chrome-enclosed rear fender panel painted lower body color. In 1956 Hornet V-8s, the Packard-built engine was used. Ultramatic transmission was again a mandatory option with this particular powerplant. Hornet Sixes came with the famous 308-cid Hudson 'Championship' six and could be had with three-speed manual, overdrive, or Hydra-Matic transmission. Hornet Sixes and Series 80 Hornet V-8s were on the longer 121-1/4-inch wheelbase. Super and Custom trim versions were offered as sixes and Customs only could be fitted with the V-8.

HUDSON HORNET SERIES

Model No.	Body/Style No.	Body Type & Seating	Factory Price	Shipping Weight	Prod. Total
SUPER LINE SIX					
60	35665-1	4-dr Sed-6P	2777	3545	Note 1
CUSTOM LINE SIX					
60	35665-2	4-dr Sed-6P	3019	3636	3,022
60	35667-2	2-dr Holly HT-6P	3136	3646	358
CUSTOM LINE V-8					
80	35685-2	4-dr Sed-6P	3286	3862	1,962
80	35687-2	2-dr Holly HT-6P	3429	3872	1,053

Note 1: Production Total of the Super Six included in total for Custom Six sedan.

HUDSON HORNET SPECIAL —SERIES 50 —V-8 —On March 5, 1956, the Hornet Special returned. It was a different type of car than the Hornet Special of 1954. The early Hornet Specials represented a cheaper version of the standard wheelbase Hornet. The 1956 Hornet Special had a cheaper price, but was actually something of a high-performance car. It came with a new AMC-built 250-cid overhead valve V-8 in the 114-1/4-inch wheelbase Wasp chassis. Exterior trim and interior appointments were comparable to Super Hornets. Three-speed manual transmission was standard and both overdrive or Hydra-Matic Drive were available at extra cost.

HUDSON HORNET SPECIAL SERIES 50

Model No.	Body/Style No.	Body Type & Seating	Factory Price	Shipping Weight	Prod. Total
SUPER LINE					
50	35655-1	4-dr Sed-6P	2626	3467	1,528
50	35657-1	2-dr Holly HT-6P	2741	3486	229

ENGINES:

(HUDSON RAMBLER SIX) Inline six. L-head. Cast iron block. Displacement: 195.6 cid. Bore and stroke: 3-1/8 x 4-1/4 inches. Compression ratio: 7.5:1. Brake hp: 120 at 4200 rpm. Four main bearings. Solid valve lifters. Carburetor: Carter type YF one-barrel Model 2014S.

(WASP SIX) Inline six. L-head. Cast iron block. Displacement: 202 cid. Bore and stroke: 3.00 x 4.75 inches. Compression ratio: 7.5:1. Brake hp: 120 at 4000 rpm. Four main bearings. Solid valve lifters. Carburetor: Carter type WA-1 one-barrel Model 2009S.

(WASP TWIN-H SIX) Inline six. L-head. Cast iron block. Displacement: 202 cid. Bore and stroke: 3.00 x 4.75 inches. Compression ratio: 8.0:1. Brake hp: 130 at 4000 rpm. Four main bearings. Solid valve lifters. Carburetor: Two Carter type WA-1 one-barrel Model 2013S.

(HORNET SIX) Inline six. L-head. Cast iron block. Displacement: 308 cid. Bore and stroke: 3-13/16 x 4-1/2 inches. Compression ratio: 7.5:1. Brake hp: 165 at 3800 rpm. Four main bearings. Hydraulic valve lifters. Carburetor: Carter type WGD two-barrel Model 2252S.

(HORNET TWIN-H SIX) Inline six. L-head. Cast iron block. Displacement: 308 cid. Bore and stroke: 3-13/16 x 4-1/2 inches. Compression ratio: 7.5:1. Brake hp: 175 at 4000 rpm. Four main bearings. Hydraulic valve lifters. Carburetor: Two Carter type WA-1 one-barrel Model 2113S.

(PACKARD EIGHT) V-8. Overhead valve. Cast iron block. Displacement: 352 cid. Bore and stroke: 4 x 3-1/2 inches. Compression ratio: 9.5:1. Brake hp: 220 at 4600 rpm. Five main bearings. Hydraulic valve lifters. Carburetor: Carter type WGD two-barrel Model 2231SA.

(HORNET SPECIAL EIGHT) V-8. Overhead valve. Cast iron block. Displacement: 250 cid. Bore and stroke: 3-1/2 x 3-1/4 inches. Compression ratio: 8.0:1. Brake hp: 190 at 4900 rpm. Five main bearings. Hydraulic valve lifters. Carburetor: Carter type WGD two-barrel Model 2352S.

CHASSIS FEATURES: Wheelbase: (Rambler) 108 inches; (Wasp/Hornet Special) 114.25 inches; (Hornet) 121.25 inches. Overall length: (Rambler) 191.14 inches; (Rambler with Continental tire) 198.89 inches; (Wasp/Hornet Special) 202.25 inches; (Hornet Special with Continental tire) 212.25 inches; (Hornet) 209.25 inches; (Hornet with Continental tire) 219.25 inches; (Rambler station wagon) 198.89 inches. Front tread: (Rambler) 57.75 inches; (Wasp/Hornet Special) 59.5 inches; (Hornet) 59.5 inches. Rear tread: (Rambler) 58 inches; (Wasp/Hornet Special) 59-11/16 inches; (Hornet) 60.5 inches. Tires: (Rambler) 6.40 x 15; (Wasp/Hornet Special) 6.70 x 15; (Hornet Six) 7.10 x 15; (Hornet V-8) 7.60 x 15.

OPTIONS: Power steering, in Rambler ($80). Air conditioning in Rambler ($345). Radio, in Rambler ($76). Heater, in Rambler ($74). All-Season air conditioning with heater, in Hudson ($395). Twin speaker radio, in Hudson ($98). Hudson Weather-Eye heater and defroster ($77). Power steering, in Hudson ($140). Power brakes, in Hudson ($39). Power windows, in Hudson ($128). Reclining seats and twin beds. Continental rear mount tire. Directional signals. White sidewall tires. Other standard options and accessories. Note: Power steering, power brakes and power windows were available on Hornets and Wasps only, Continental rear-mounted tires and reclining seats with twin beds were standard on all Custom models except station wagons, which were not available with the Continental tire. Three-speed manual transmission was standard. Ultramatic automatic transmission was a mandatory option in Hornets with the 352-cid V-8. Overdrive transmission ($107). Automatic transmission ($188). Twin-H carburetion. Heavy-duty air cleaner. Available rear axle gear ratios: 3.07:1; 3.15:1; 3.31:1; 3.58:1; 3.54:1; 4.00:1; 4.09:1; 4.40:1; 4.60:1.

HISTORICAL FOOTNOTES: Introduction date for the 1956 Hudson Wasp, Hornet Six and Hornet V-8 was Nov. 30, 1955. The 1956 Hudson Ramblers were then introduced on Dec. 15, 1955. It wasn't until March 5, 1956, that the Hornet Special V-8 appeared and thereafter began showing up in dealer showrooms. Calendar year output amounted to 10,671 units. Model year production hit its peak at 22,588 assemblies, excluding Hudson Ramblers. Seat belts were an option in 1956 and the 12-volt electrical system was introduced. Some 1956 Hudson factory literature included the weights of various options as follows: Hydra-Matic (105-125 pounds); overdrive (30-50 pounds); radio (13-18 pounds); Weather-Eye (18-22 pounds); air conditioning (120 pounds); power steering (42-50 pounds); power brakes (18 pounds); power windows (12 to 18 pounds); and Continental tire carrier (65 pounds).

1957

HUDSON HORNET —SERIES 80 —V-8 —Hudson trimmed its model lineup by an amazing figure of 11 cars in 1957, while its roofline was trimmed two inches. The Hudson Rambler, Wasp and Hornet Special series were dropped. Other new features included 14-inch wheels; a new Hydra-Matic with parking gear; standard 327-cid V-8 with dual exhaust; ball joint front suspension; interiors restyled along more modern lines (with new materials and colors) and standard padded dashboard in all lines. Styling changes included a new 'V' medallion in the center of the grille; dual-fin front fender ornaments; rear tailfin fenders with vertical lamps and a new side trim treatment with front fender and door accent panels. On Supers, the accent panel was painted. There were Hornet and Hollywood nameplates on the hardtops, as well as rear fender 'H' medallions. The Super Sedan had Hornet front door nameplates and no 'H' medallions. Hornet Customs could be identified by textured aluminum insert panels used on the front fenders, between the trim moldings. Nameplate and medallion placements were the same as on comparable Super styles.

HUDSON I.D. NUMBERS: The numbering system was the same as for previous models. Number plates were on a plate under the hood at the top center of dash on Hornets. Body/Style Numbers took the form 357( )( ) with the first symbol indicating Hudson; the second and third symbols indicating model year; the fourth symbol indicating the car-line or series and the fifth symbol indicating body type. Serial numbers Y-10501 to Y-14376 were used. Engine numbers were below the right rear exhaust port on V-8s. Engine numbers were N-1001 and up.

HUDSON HORNET

Model No.	Body/Style No.	Body Type & Seating	Factory Price	Shipping Weight	Prod. Total
SUPER V-8 LINE					
N/A	35785-1	4-dr Sed-6P	2821	3631	1,103
N/A	35787-1	2-dr HT Cpe-6P	2911	3655	266
CUSTOM V-8 LINE					
N/A	35785-2	4-dr Sed-6P	3011	3676	1,256
N/A	35787-2	2-dr HT Cpe-6P	3101	3693	483

Note 1: Total series production, including exports, was 4,108 units.

Note 2: An additional 72 Model 35660 Hudson Sixes were shipped overseas in 'knocked down' form.

ENGINE: V-8. Overhead valve. Cast iron block. Displacement: 327 cid. Bore and stroke: 4.00 x 3.25 inches. Compression ratio: 9.0:1. Brake hp: 255 at 4700 rpm. Five main bearings. Hydraulic valve lifters. Carburetor: four-barrel.

CHASSIS FEATURES: Wheelbase: 121.25 inches. Overall length: 209.25 inches. Front tread: 59-1/16 inches. Rear tread: 60-1/2 inches. Tires: 8.00 x 14.

POWERTRAIN OPTIONS: Three-speed manual transmission was standard. Overdrive transmission ($110). Automatic transmission ($232). Available rear axle gear ratios: 3.15:1, 4.10:1.

OPTIONS: Power brakes on Super ($40); on Custom (standard). Power steering ($100). Air conditioning ($415). Power windows ($109.50).

HISTORICAL FOOTNOTES: The last Hudsons were introduced on Oct. 25, 1957.

The gentleman sandwiched between the two ladies in the back of this 1916 Hudson Super Six phaeton doesn't appear to be too happy with the seating arrangements. Note the mansion's pristine concrete drive leading into the dirt street.

ESSEX

ESSEX — Detroit, Michigan — (1919-1932) — The Hudson was named for the Detroit department store magnate who had put up much of the money for the company; the Essex was named a decade later after Hudson officials let their fingers walk over a map of England in pursuit of a name with snob appeal. Initially, the car had its own sponsoring organization, the Essex Motor Company, which in October of 1917 leased the old No. 5 Studebaker plant on Franklin Avenue in Detroit for the manufacture of a lower-priced companion car to the Hudson. Ninety-two cars were built in 1918, but were designated as 1919 models. The first-generation Essex was a four-cylinder 55-hp four on a 108-1/2-inch wheelbase, with quite angular body lines and a robust performance. Tests conducted under AAA supervision at the Cincinnati Speedway in December 1919 resulted in 3,037.4 miles in 50 hours for a 60.75 mph average. Even more impressive was the transcontinental trek in August 1920 of four Essex automobiles (two starting from each coast) that resulted in a 4 day-21 hour-32 minute average for the quartet — and scads of publicity because a pouch of mail was carried in each car, with relief drivers sworn in as official letter carriers, and local newspaper headlines all across the country. But the most spectacular of the Essex achievements was in another area altogether: closed coachwork. The four-passenger coach introduced for 1922 at $1,495 was the lowest-priced closed car in America. "Only $300 More Than Touring Model," headlined an incredulous *Motor Age*. By 1925, the Essex coach was priced five dollars *less* than the touring model. This was unheard of in the industry. A "packing crate" the competition might deride, but the car sold like hotcakes. In 1922, the facade of a separate company for the Essex was dropped, and both Essex and Hudson were now produced by the Hudson Motor Car Company. For the 1924 model year, the Essex became a 28-hp L-head six, which though smoother than the four was not as robust. A perky boattail speedster was offered from 1927, four-wheel brakes became standard for 1928. In 1929, Essex sales contributed handsomely to the over 300,000 Hudson total, and the company was third in the industry. In 1932, the Essex had freewheeling, a vee radiator, a six-cylinder engine by now beefed up to 70 bhp — and a new model designation called Terraplane. In 1933, the Essex name was dropped, and the car thereafter became known simply as the Terraplane.

Essex Data Compilation by Robert C. Ackerson

1919

ESSEX — SERIES A — FOUR: "Everyone says nice things about the Essex," said one early ad for the Essex and few critics chose to dispute this assertion. The Essex was a conventional car in appearance but its angular body shape gave it a pleasing and easily identifiable style. But the real source of the Essex's appeal was its engine. Of F-head design, it turned out an impressive 55 hp and that was more than sufficient to make Essex synonymous with performance. Dealers nationwide capitalized on this big selling point by staging demonstrations of Essex performance to initially skeptical customers who soon became enthusiastic Essex owners. In December 1919, an Essex successfully completed a 50-hour endurance test in Cincinnati at an average speed of 60.75 mph. Initially the Essex was available only in touring car form but before the model year's end, roadster and sedan models were available.

I.D. DATA: Serial numbers on dash and right rear frame cross member. Starting: 5000. Ending: 75999. Engine numbers on left front motor mount.

Series A

Model No.	Body Type & Seating	Factory Price	Shipping Weight	Prod. Total
Series A	4-dr. Tr. Car-5P	1395	2450	NA
Series A	4-dr. Sed.-5P	2250	2955	NA
Series A	2-dr. Rds. 2P	1595	2625	NA

ENGINE: Inline Four. Cast iron block. B & S: 3-3/8 x 5 in. Disp.: 180 cu. in. Brake H.P.: 55 @ 2800 R.P.M. N.A.C.C. H.P.: 18.2. Main bearings: three. Valve lifters: mechanical. Carb.: Essex bronze piston type.

CHASSIS: [Series A] W.B.: 108.5 in. Front/Rear Tread: 56/56 in. Tires: 32 x 4.

TECHNICAL: Sliding gear transmission. Speeds: 3F/1R. Floor shift controls. Cork insert, wet clutch. Shaft drive. Hotchkiss rear axle. Overall ratio: 4.67:1. Mechanical brakes on rear wheels. Wooden spoke wheels. Rim size: 32 in.

OPTIONS: Houk wire wheels.

HISTORICAL: Introduced January 1919. Essex made 21,879 shipments to dealers during the 1919 calendar year. The president of Essex was William S. McAneeny. Essex Motors was formed in 1917, and while technically independent of Hudson, was Hudson financed and staffed. For example, McAneeny was Hudson's factory manager, and such Hudson executives as Roscoe B. Jackson and A.E. Barit held administrative positions at Essex. In addition, Hudson President Roy D. Chapin and other Hudson leaders served on the board of directors at Essex.

1920

ESSEX — SERIES 5-A, SERIES 6-A & SERIES 7-A — FOUR: No changes, except for a higher headlight position on later models, either in appearance or design were made in the Essex for 1920. However there were plenty of activities in which Essex cars were involved to keep the Essex name in the public's view. The most sensational was the transcontinental mail run of four stock Essex touring cars. Divided into two teams, leaving from San Francisco and New York, all four cars broke the old records for their respective directions, which had been set by the Hudson Super-Six in 1916. The fastest of the four Essex cars, traveling from San Francisco to New York City, completed its run in 4 days-14 hours-and 43 minutes.

I.D. DATA: Serial numbers on dash and right rear frame crossmember. Starting: 5000. Ending: 89999. Engine numbers on left front motor mount.

Series A

Model No.	Body Type & Seating	Factory Price	Shipping Weight	Prod. Total
NA	2-dr. Rds.-2P	1795	2545	NA
NA	4-dr. Tr. Car-5P	1795	2560	NA
NA	4-dr. Sed.-5P	2650	2900	NA
NA	2-dr. Cabr.-2P	2100	2675	NA

During 1920 Essex prices were reduced.

ENGINE: F-head. Inline Four. Cast iron block. B & S: 3-3/8 x 5 in. Disp.: 180 cu. in. Brake H.P.: 55 @ 2800 R.P.M. N.A.C.C. H.P.: 18.2. Main bearings: three. Valve lifters: mechanical. Carb.: Essex bronze piston type.

CHASSIS: [Series 5A] W.B.: 108.5 in. Frt/Rear Tread: 56/56 in. Tires: 32 x 4. [Series 6A] W.B.: 108.5 in. Front/Rear Tread: 56/56 in. Tires: 32 x 4. [Series 7A] W.B.: 108.5 in. Front/Rear Tread: 56/56 in. Tires: 32 x 4.

TECHNICAL: Sliding gear transmission. Speeds: 3F/1R. Floor shift controls. Multiple disc clutch, cork inserts, running in oil. Shaft drive. Semi floating, Hotchkiss rear axle. Overall ratio: 4.67:1. Mechanical brakes on two wheels. Wooden spoke wheels with detachable rims.

OPTIONS: Bumpers. Houk wire wheels. Spare tire.

HISTORICAL: Introduced December 1919. Essex made 23,669 shipments to dealers during the 1920 calendar year. The president of Essex was William S. McAneeny.

1921

ESSEX — NO SERIES I.D. — FOUR: Essex adopted Hudson's strategy of abandoning both series and serial number codes from 1921 through 1923. At the same time it also offered a second line of 1921 models identified as the "New, Improved Essex," in October 1921. In the main, these cars were changed only in minor mechanical and styling details. The four-door sedans received an ivory white panel on their rear door surfaces with the two-door cabriolet having the same feature on its doors. The open touring cars received new tops with improved weather protection.

I.D. DATA: Serial numbers on dash and right rear frame crossmember. Starting: 500000. Ending: 630411 (Serial number range for 1921-23 models). Engine number on left front motor mount.

Essex

Model No.	Body Type & Seating	Factory Price	Shipping Weight	Prod. Total
NA	2-dr. Rds.-2P	1595	2545	NA
NA	4-dr. Tr. Car.-5P	1595	2560	NA
NA	4-dr. Sed.-5P	2450	2900	NA
NA	2-dr. Cabr.-2P	2100	2675	NA

Essex prices were reduced during the 1921 model year.

ENGINE: F-head. Inline Four. Cast iron block. B & S: 3-3/8 x 5 in. Disp. 180 cu. in. Brake H.P.: 55 @ 2800 R.P.M. N.A.C.C. H.P.: 18.2. Main bearings: three. Valve lifters: mechanical. Carb.: Essex bronze piston type.

CHASSIS: No series identification 1921-23. W.B.: 108.5 in. Frt/Rear Tread: 56/56 in. Tires: 32 x 4.

TECHNICAL: Sliding gear transmission. Speeds: 3F/1R. Floor shift controls. Multiple disc clutch, cork inserts, running in oil. Shaft drive. Semi-floating rear axle. Overall ratio: 4.67:1. Mechanical brakes on two wheels. Wooden spoke wheels with detachable rims.

OPTIONS: Bumpers. Houk wire wheels. Spare tires.

HISTORICAL: Introduced December 1920 — first line, October 1921 — second version. Essex made 13,422 shipments to dealers during the 1921 calendar year. The president of Essex was William S. McAneeny.

1922

ESSEX — NO SERIES I.D. — FOUR: Hudson and Essex were merged into a single company in 1922 and shares in the new company were listed on the New York Stock Exchange. Essex, like Hudson, offered two versions of 1922 models with the first type phasing in the new drum-shaped fuel tank. A new wider body was adopted for the touring car with wider doors with front hinges. The Essex engine, in conjunction with the Super Six engine, adopted a Morse timing chain. Other engine refinements included a new cylinder head with a more efficient fuel intake and repositioned spark plugs now on the right side of the engine. New pistons with aluminum skirts were also used. However the Essex line for 1922 was best remembered for its new coach model that proved to be a key catalyst speeding up the demise of the open cars as the predominant body style among American automobiles. Alfred P. Sloan later wrote that the introduction of the Essex coach was "an event which was to profoundly influence the fortunes of Pontiac, Chevrolet, and the Model T." Although its styling was less than sensational, the low price of the coach, which, after being reduced from $1,492 to $1,245, was only $100 above a comparable closed car assured its success.

I.D. DATA: Serial numbers on dash and right rear frame crossmember. Starting: 500000. Ending: 630411 (Serial number range for 1921-1923 models). Engine numbers on left front motor mount.

Essex

Model No.	Body Type & Seating	Factory Price	Shipping Weight	Prod. Total
NA	4-dr. Tr. Car-5P	1045	2600	NA
NA	4-dr. Sed.-5P	1895	2900	NA
NA	2-dr. Cabr.-2P	1145	2575	NA
NA	2-dr. C'ch.-5P	1245	2685	NA

Note: The roadster model was initially listed as available for 1922. However, it appears none were produced during the model year. The cabriolet was produced in the second portion of the model year.

ENGINE: F-head. Inline Four. Cast iron block. B & S: 3-3/8 x 5 in. Disp.: 180 cu. in. Brake H.P.: 55 @ 2800 R.P.M. N.A.C.C. H.P.: 18.2. Main bearings: three. Valve lifters: mechanical. Carb.: Essex bronze piston type.

CHASSIS: No series identification used in 1921-23. W.B.: 108.5 in. Front/Rear Tread: 56/56 in. Tires: 32 x 4.

TECHNICAL: Sliding gear transmission. Speeds: 3F/1R. Floor shift. Multiple disc clutch, cork inserts, running in oil. Shaft drive. Semi-floating rear axle. Overall ratio: 4.67:1. Mechanical brakes on two wheels. Wooden spoke wheels with detachable rims.

OPTIONS: Bumpers. Houk wire wheels. Spare tire.

HISTORICAL: Introduced December 1921, second version — April 1922. Speed records: An Essex won the 183 cid and under engine size class at Pikes Peak with a run of 20 minutes-41 seconds. Essex made 36,222 shipments to dealers during the 1922 calendar year. The president of Essex was Roy D. Chapin.

1923

ESSEX — NO SERIES I.D. — FOUR: Changes in Essex were minor. During the model year the open touring car body adopted slightly narrower front doors and beginning in April a longer 28-inch gearshift was installed on all models.

I.D. DATA: Serial numbers on dash and right rear frame crossmember. Starting: 500000. Ending: 630411 (Serial number range for 1921-23 models). Engine numbers on left front motor mount.

Essex

Model No.	Body Type & Seating	Factory Price	Shipping Weight	Prod. Total
NA	4-dr. Tr. Car-5P	1045	2630	NA
NA	2-dr. Cabr.-2P*	1145	2575	NA
NA	2-dr. C'ch.-5P	1145	2685	NA

Note: * This model was dropped from the Essex line in August 1923.

ENGINE: F-head. Inline Four. Cast iron block. B & S: 3-3/8 x 5 in. Disp. 180 cu. in. Brake H.P.: 55 @ 2800 R.P.M. N.A.C.C. H.P.: 18.2. Main bearings: three. Valve lifters: mechanical. Carb.: Essex bronze piston type.

CHASSIS: No series identification for 1923. W.B.: 108.5 in. Front/Rear Tread: 56/56 in. Tires: 32 x 4.

TECHNICAL: Sliding gear transmission. Speeds: 3F/1R. Floor shift controls. Multiple disc clutch, cork inserts, running in oil. Shaft drive. Semi-floating rear axle. Overall ratio: 4.67:1. Mechanical brakes on two wheels. Wooden spoke wheels with detachable rims.

OPTIONS: Spare tire. Bumpers. Houk wire wheels.

HISTORICAL: Introduced December 1922. Essex made 42,577 shipments to dealers during the 1923 calendar year. The president of Essex was Roscoe B. Jackson. Essex not only won its class at the Pikes Peak Hill Climb but came away the overall victor of the Penrose trophy with a time of 18 minutes-47-3/4 seconds.

1924

ESSEX — NO SERIES I.D. — SIX: Beyond any doubt the most controversial feature of the 1924 Essex was its engine. Replacing the almost legendary F-head four was a six-cylinder of conventional L-head design. Its physical dimensions were decidedly on the small size, 2-5/8-inch bore and a 4-inch stroke that yielded 130 cubic inches. Hudson did not (and would not until 1929) report this engine's horsepower but a prominent Hudson-Essex-Terraplane historian once estimated it as 34. Later in the model year, Hudson increased the bore and stroke of this engine to 2-11/16 inches and 4-1/4 inches, respectively, which provided a displacement of 144.5 cubic inches and an estimated 40 horsepower. At the same time, deeper oil troughs were installed, which helped alleviate the tendency of its splash type lubrication to inadequately supply the rear bearings with oil on downgrades. As expected of a Hudson-built engine, the new Essex Six was fitted with a fully balanced, three-bearing crankshaft, aluminum pistons, roller valve lifters, a Morse timing chain, automatic spark advance and a cast enbloc intake manifold. The 1924 Essex's styling was less controversial although it was all new. The industry was moving towards a longer and lower look and new frame brackets allowing for a lower body mounting level plus a smooth hoodline and peaked fenders put the Essex in line with the times. Hudson offered two versions of the 1924 Essex and the latter featured 31 x 5.25 balloon tires in place of the older 31 x 3-3/4 tires.

I.D. DATA: Serial numbers on dash and right rear frame crossmember. Starting: 100001. Ending: 177750. Engine numbers on left side of cylinder block near water inlet elbow.

Essex

Model No.	Body Type & Seating	Factory Price	Shipping Weight	Prod. Total
NA	2-dr. C'ch.-5P	975	2305	NA
NA	4-dr. Tr. Car.-5P	900	2185	NA
NA	2-dr. C'ch.-5P (A)	945	2370	NA
NA	4-dr. Tr. Car.-5P (B)	850	2130	NA

Note 1: (A & B) These models replaced the initial Essex offerings in June 1924.

ENGINE: L-head. Inline Six. Cast iron block. B & S: 2-11/16 x 4-1/4 in. Disp.: 144.6 cu. in. Taxable H.P.: 17.32. Main bearings: three. Valve lifters: mechanical. Carb.: Stewart.

CHASSIS: No series identification for 1924. W.B.: 110.5 in. O.L.: 156.5 in. Front/Rear Tread: 56/56 in. Tires: 31 x 5.25.

TECHNICAL: Sliding gear transmission. Speeds: 3F/1R. Floor shift controls. Multiple disc clutch, cork inserts, running in oil. Shaft drive. Semi-floating rear axle. Mechanical (14-1/2 x 1-1/2 in.) brakes on rear wheels. Wooden spoke wheels with detachable rims.

OPTIONS: Front bumper. Rear bumper. Steel disc wheels.

HISTORICAL: Introduced December 1923, superseded by models introduced in June 1924. Essex made 74,523 shipments to dealers during the 1924 calendar year. The president of Essex was Roscoe B. Jackson. The Essex Six set a new record time for a climb up Mt. Wilson in California of 31 minutes-29 seconds.

1925

ESSEX — NO SERIES I.D. — FOUR: There were no changes of any consequence in the design of the Essex when the 1925 model year began. However during the year the size of the balloon tires fitted to the Essex were changed from 31 x 5.25 to 30 x 4.95 and minor engine modifications were made. Often criticized for its somewhat somber styling, the Essex coach was given a new, fresh appearance in March. The new body featured a curved windshield base, much thinner windshield and door posts and a reshaped windshield visor. As a step towards the adoption of a new Hudson built body with a steel framework, the Essex coach used more steel in its construction than had the older model. As was the case with Hudson, prices of Essex models were reduced significantly during the model year.

I.D. DATA: Serial numbers on dash and right rear frame crossmember. Starting: 177751. Ending: 337949. Engine numbers on left side of cylinder block near water inlet elbow.

Essex

Model No.	Body Type & Seating	Factory Price	Shipping Weight	Prod. Total
NA	4-dr. Tr. Car-4P	765 (B)	2185	NA
NA	2-dr. C'ch.-4P	895	2370	NA
NA	2-dr. C'ch.-4P (A)	765 (B)	2370	NA

Note 1: (A) This model replaced the older version in March 1925.

Note 2: (B) Initial price of the touring car and coach were, respectively, $900 and $895.

ENGINE: L-head. Inline Six. Cast iron block. B & S: 2-11/16 x 4-1/4 in. Disp.: 144.6 cu. in. N.A.C.C. H.P.: 17.32. Main bearings: three. Valve lifters: mechanical. Carb.: Stewart.

CHASSIS: No series designations for 1925. W.B.: 110.5 in. O.L.: 156.5 in. Front/Rear Tread: 56/56 in. Tires: 31 x 5.25 replaced by 30 x 4.95 in January 1925.

TECHNICAL: Sliding gear transmission. Speeds: 3F/1R. Floor shift controls. Multiple disc clutch, cork inserts, running in oil. Shaft drive. Semi-floating rear axle. Overall ratio: 5.6:1. Mechanical (14-1/2 x 1-1/2 in.) brakes on two (rear) wheels. Wooden spoke wheels with detachable rims.

OPTIONS: Front bumper. Rear bumper. Steel disc wheels.

HISTORICAL: Introduced December 1925. Essex made 159,634 shipments to dealers during the 1925 calendar year. The president of Essex was Roscoe B. Jackson. Profits of the Hudson Motor Car Company reached an all time high of $21,378,504 in 1925.

1926

ESSEX — NO SERIES I.D. — SIX: As was the case with Hudson, there were no changes in the appearance of the Essex until the Hudson-bodied versions of the sedan and coach appeared. The coach was two inches lower than its predecessor. Those cars built after July 24 featured a nickel-plated radiator shell. An addition to the Essex line was a four-door sedan.

I.D. DATA: Serial numbers on dash and right rear frame crossmember. Starting: 337845. Ending: 499999. Engine numbers on left side of cylinder block near water inlet elbow.

Essex

Model No.	Body Type & Seating	Factory Price	Shipping Weight	Prod. Total
NA	2-dr. C'ch.-4P	735	2455	NA
NA	4-dr. Tr. Car	795	2260	NA
NA	2-dr. C'ch.-4P(*)	695	2500	NA
NA	4-dr. Sed.-5P	795	2540	NA

Note 1: (*) Hudson-built body introduced in July 1926.

ENGINE: L-head. Inline Six. Cast iron block. B & S: 2-11/16 x 4-1/4 in. Disp.: 144.6 cu. in. N.A.C.C. H.P.: 17.32. Main bearings: three. Valve lifters: mechanical. Carb.: Stewart.

CHASSIS: No series designations. W.B.: 110.5 in. O.L.: 156.5 in. Front/Rear Tread: 56/56 in. Tires: 31 x 4.95.

TECHNICAL: Sliding gear transmission. Speeds: 3F/1R. Floor shift controls. Multiple disc clutch, cork inserts, running in oil. Shaft drive. Semi-floating rear axle. Overall ratio: 5.6:1. Mechanical (14-1/2 x 1-1/2 in.) brakes on two (rear) wheels. Wooden spoke wheels with detachable rims.

OPTIONS: Front bumpers. Rear bumpers.

HISTORICAL: Introduced December 1926. Essex made 157,247 shipments to dealers during the 1926 calendar year. The president of Essex was Roscoe B. Jackson. The new Hudson-built bodies for the Essex coach and sedan represented important steps towards the adoption of all-steel body construction.

1927

ESSEX SUPER SIX — NO SERIES I.D. — SIX: Essex moved much closer to Hudson in terms of both style and name in 1927. It was now labeled as the Essex Super Six and its appearance, highlighted by a Hudson-like hoodline, radiator plus a sensational boattailed speedabout model made it a standout among American automobiles for 1927. During the model year, the Essex engine received a longer, 4.5-inch stroke that increased its displacement to 153.2 cubic inches. Although no horsepower rating was released its output was significantly increased. In mid-summer, Hudson revised Essex styling by adding a full body length beltline molding, curving the rear body line and adopting smaller wheels and 30 x 5.00 tires.

I.D. DATA: Serial numbers on dash and right rear frame crossmember. Starting: 500001. Ending: 706270. Engine numbers on left side of cylinder block near water inlet elbow.

Super Six

Model No.	Body Type & Seating	Factory Price	Shipping Weight	Prod. Total
NA	2-dr. Spdbt.-2P	700	2150	NA
NA	4-dr. Spds.-4P	785	2230	NA
NA	2-dr. Cpe.-2P	735	2340	NA
NA	2-dr. Coach.-4P	735	2450	NA
NA	4-dr. Sed.-5P	785	2510	NA
NA	4-dr. Sed. DeL.-5P	895	2490	NA

ENGINE: L-head. Inline Six. Cast iron block. B & S: 2-11/16 x 4-1/4 in. (stroke later lengthened to 4-1/2 in. on June 25, 1927). Disp.: 144.7 cu. in; later model 153.2 cu. in. N.A.C.C. H.P.: 17.32. Main bearings: three. Valve lifters: mechanical. Carb.: Stewart downdraft.

CHASSIS: No series designation. W.B.: 110.5 in. O.L.: 156.5 in. Front/Rear Tread: 56/56 in. Tires: 31 x 5.00, later changed to 30 x 5.00 on June 25, 1927.

TECHNICAL: Sliding gear transmission. Speeds: 3F/1R. Floor shift controls. Single plate clutch, cork inserts, running in oil. Shaft drive. Semi-floating rear axle. Overall ratio: 5.6:1, later 5.4:1 installed except for speedabout. Mechanical brakes on two rear wheels. Wooden wheels. Rim size: 21 x 4 in.

OPTIONS: Front bumper. Rear bumper. Wire wheels. Spot lights. Leather upholstery ($15.00).

HISTORICAL: Introduced January 1927. Essex made 210,380 shipments to dealers during the 1927 calendar year. The president of Essex was Roscoe B. Jackson.

1928

ESSEX SUPER SIX — NO SERIES I.D. — SIX: The Essex for 1928 had an appearance that the *New York Times* described as "low hung." Its styling closely approximated, on a smaller scale, that of the Hudson. Thus it featured a trim, narrow radiator with vertical lines, and a winged man mascot in place of the old moto-meter. Other styling details included a bead line running from the radiator to the front windshield post, a shorter windshield visor, cowl mounted "saddle lights," and wider fenders. Although the boattailed speedabout Essex was not offered in 1928 the coupe models were given a more curved rear deck, which in conjunction with other styling changes gave them a contemporary appearance. The Essex was also fitted with Hudson's new black rubber steering wheel. A major technical advance for Essex was the adoption of four-wheel Bendix, three shoe mechanical brakes.

I.D. DATA: Serial numbers on dash and right rear frame crossmember. Starting: 706270, Ending: 928657. Engine numbers on left side of cylinder block near water inlet elbow.

Super Six

Model No.	Body Type & Seating	Factory Price	Shipping Weight	Prod. Total
NA	2-dr. Rds.-3P	850	2365	NA
NA	4-dr. Tr. Car-5P	750	2305	NA
NA	2-dr. Cpe.-2P	745	2475	NA
NA	2-dr. Cpe. R/S-3P	775	2535	NA
NA	2-dr. C'ch.-5P	735	2560	NA
NA	4-dr. Sed.-5P	795	2660	NA

ENGINE: Inline Six. Cast iron block. B & S: 2-11/16 x 4-1/2 in. Disp; 153.2 cu. in. N.A.C.C. H.P.: 17.32. Main bearings: three. Valve lifters: mechanical. Carb.: Stewart downdraft.

CHASSIS: No series designation. W.B.: 110-1/2 in. O.L.: 156.5 in. Front/Rear Tread: 56/56 in. Tires: 30 x 5.00.

TECHNICAL: Sliding gear transmission. Speeds: 3F/1R. Floor shift controls. Single plate clutch, cork inserts, running in oil. Shaft drive. Semi-floating rear axle. Overall ratio: 5.4:1. Mechanical brakes on four wheels. Wooden spoke wheels. Rim size: 20 x 4 in.

OPTIONS: Front bumper. Rear bumper. Leather upholstery.

HISTORICAL: Introduced January 1928. Essex made 229,887 shipments to dealers during the 1928 calendar year. The president of Essex was Roscoe B. Jackson. This was the greatest sales year for the Essex.

1929

ESSEX THE CHALLENGER — NO SERIES I.D. — SIX: Essex styling for 1929 continued the basic form introduced in 1928 but there were a number of minor revisions. The beltline now fully encircled the body and a slightly larger radiator shell was adopted. Hudson officially labeled the Essex for 1929 "Essex the Challenger" and not too surprisingly revived the old "National Challenge Week" promotion in early March. During that time Essex distributors and dealers staged various acceleration, braking, fuel consumption and general performance events. In one such demonstration an Essex sedan climbed Fort George Hill, then regarded as one of New York's steepest grades, from a standing start in high gear. In another run an Essex completed 30.5 miles through New York City on 1.5 gallons of gas. For the first time since the Essex F-head six had been introduced, Hudson officially released its horsepower rating, which turned out to equal the 55 hp of the old Essex four.

I.D. DATA: Serial numbers on dash and right rear frame crossmember. Starting: 928658. Ending: 1165673. Engine numbers on left side of cylinder block near water inlet elbow.

Challenger

Model No.	Body Type & Seating	Factory Price	Shipping Weight	Prod. Total
NA	2-dr. Spdbt.-4P	965	2500	NA
NA	4-dr. Phae.-5P	695	2490	NA
NA	2-dr. Rds.-4P	850	2460	NA
NA	2-dr. Cpe.-2P	695	2540	NA
NA	2-dr. Cpe. w/R/S-2P	725	2600	NA
NA	2-dr. Conv. Cpe.-4P	895	2570	NA
NA	2-dr. C'ch.-5P	695	2635	NA
NA	4-dr. Std. Sed.-5P	795	2745	NA
NA	4-dr. Twn. Sed.-5P	850	2795	NA

ENGINE: L-head. Inline Six. Cast iron block. B & S: 2-3/4 x 4-1/2 in. Disp.: 161.4 cu. in. C.R.: 5.8:1. Brake H.P.: 55 @ 3600 R.P.M. N.A.C.C. H.P.: 19.4. Main bearings: three. Valve lifters: mechanical. Carb.: Marvel 5 downdraft 1-1/8 in.

CHASSIS: No series designation. W.B.: 110.5 in. O.L.: 156.5 in. Front/Rear tread: 56/56 in. Tires: 30 x 5.00.

TECHNICAL: Sliding gear transmission. Speeds: 3F/1R (speedabout had three-speed plus overdrive). Floor shift controls. Single plate clutch, cork inserts, running in oil. Shaft drive. Semi-floating rear axle. Overall ratio: 5.6:1, speedabout 5.09:1. Bendix mechanical brakes on four wheels. 10 wooden spokes on wheels with detachable rims.

OPTIONS: Front bumper. Rear bumper. Single sidemount. Dual sidemount. Steel sidemount cover(s). Eight day automatic radio. Cigar lighter. Wire wheels. Rumble roof for rumbleseat. Utility trunk. Special trunk. Balljointed tire mount mirrors. Protect-a-hood. Lap robes. Spring covers. Window awnings. Spare tire locks.

HISTORICAL: Introduced January 1929. Essex made 227,653 shipments to dealers during the 1929 calendar year. The president of Essex was William J. McAneeny. Last year of phaeton until 1932. The 1929 Essex chassis was used for Hudson's first commercial offering, the Dover, which continued into 1931.

1930

ESSEX CHALLENGER — NO SERIES I.D. — SIX: Essex was a significantly changed automobile for 1930. It had a longer, 113-inch wheelbase, bodies that were on the average five inches wider than the 1929 versions along with a wider, by one inch, rear tread. Hudson said that "all Essex bodies are designed along modernistic lines" and this meant the Essex featured chrome plated hood hinges, a beaded body belt line and beaded runningboard aprons. The front doors now hinged at the windshield instead of the side pillars, which, in conjunction with wider doors, provided easier entrance and exit. Both Essex and Hudson featured rear fenders that were lengthened to cover the rear springs. The 1930 Essex was also equipped with a three-spoke rubber steering wheel. In response to critics who believed the older four-spoke, wood rimmed wheels were superior, Hudson retorted that "the new wheel has such a strength factor that repeated blows of a sledge hammer are necessary to demolish it." Additional interior features for 1930 included a new toggle handle windshield control and (on closed models) mohair and velour upholstery. Throttle and light controls were moved from the steering wheel to the dash. The Essex chassis was constructed of deeper, 7-1/16-inch (4-1/2-inch was used in 1925) side members and five crossmembers were fitted. Due to the double-drop design of the side members the center of gravity was lowered by 1-1/2 inches without any loss of road clearance. The Essex brake system was basically unchanged from 1929 but the shoes were redesigned to provide more uniform pressure over the drum contact area. The front suspension now was fitted forged cross ribs between the spring and king pin for additional axle strength. At the rear a new axle design provided both greater rigidity and improved gear contact. All four wheels' double-acting hydraulic shock absorbers replaced the single action strap types used previously. The Essex Challenger was also equipped with worm and sector steering that Hudson reported was a boon particularly to women drivers "who find little physical exertion necessary to operate the new Essex Challenger many miles a day." Hudson also redesigned the Essex engine for 1930. A larger, heavier crankshaft was adopted with a Lanchester torsional dampener, as well as a dual flow automatic lubrication system. This feature pumped oil alternately to the front and rear of the engine. The return to the crankcase was in the engine's center not the rear as previously.

I.D. DATA: Serial numbers on dash and right rear frame crossmember. Starting: 1070300. Ending: 1234266. Engine numbers on left side of cylinder block near water inlet elbow.

Challenger

Model No.	Body Type & Seating	Factory Price	Shipping Weight	Prod. Total
NA	2-dr. Rds. R/S-4P	695	2550	NA
NA	2-dr. Cpe.-2P	650	2660	NA
NA	2-dr. Coach.-5P	650	2730	NA
NA	2-dr. Cpe. R/S-4P	685	2700	NA
NA	4-dr. Std. Sed.-5P	715	2805	NA
NA	4-dr. Tr. Sed.-5P*	775	2850	NA
NA	4-dr. Brgm.-5P	795	2850	NA
NA	2-dr. Sun Sed.-5P*	695	2760	NA

* Composite steel and wood bodies built by Biddle & Smart, Amesbury, Massachusetts. Remaining model bodies of all steel construction by Hudson in Detroit.

ENGINE: L-head. Inline Six. Cast iron block. B & S: 2-3/4 x 4-1/2 in. Disp.: 161.4 cu. in. C.R.: 5.8:1. Brake H.P.: 58 @ 3300 R.P.M. N.A.C.C. H.P.: 19.8. Main bearings: three. Valve lifters: mechanical. Carb.: Marvel 1-1/4 in.

CHASSIS: No series designation. W.B.: 113 in. O.L.: 159 in. Front/Rear Tread: 56/57 in. Tires: 18 x 5.00.

TECHNICAL: Sliding gear transmission. Speeds: 3F/1R. Floor shift controls. Single plate clutch, cork inserts, running in oil. Shaft drive. Semi-floating rear axle. Overall ratio: 5.6:1. Bendix mechanical brakes on four wheels. Ten spoke wooden wheels with detachable rims. Rim size: 18 in.

OPTIONS: Front bumper. Rear bumper. Single sidemount. Dual sidemount. Steel sidemount cover(s). Radio. Cigar lighter. Wire wheels. Rumble roof for rumbleseat. Utility trunk. Special trunk. Tire mount mirrors. Protect-a-hood. Lap robes. Spring covers. Window awnings. Spare tire locks.

HISTORICAL: Introduced January 1930. Innovations: new automatic choke, adjustable heat riser, Marvel carburetor had a new accelerator pump, three-spoke rubber wheel, Lanchester torsional dampers, dual flow lubrication system. Essex made 76,158 shipments to dealers during the 1930 calendar year. The president of Essex was William J. McAneeny.

1931

ESSEX SUPER SIX — SERIES E — SIX: Essex styling changes for 1931 were highlighted by a bronze chromium plated grid for the radiator shell, a straight, instead of curved tie-bar for the headlights and fenders with a deeper flange that were designed to coincide symmetrically with the general flow of the body lines. The double row of hood louvers found on the 1930 models were replaced by a single set that were considerably larger. All models had new bumpers, hubcaps, runningboards and exterior hardware. The belt line moldings now extended the full length of the hood to the radiator shell. At the rear the body molding above the dust shield was higher and a larger rectangular rear window was featured. Essex interiors were available in Bedford cord, flat fabrics or velours and a new method of trimming significantly increased head room in all closed models. As much as five more inches of leg room was available in the Essex sedan models. A small but welcomed innovation was a new door lock mechanism that Hudson said maintained the outside handles in a rigid horizontal position, thus preventing the door rattle common to conventional designs. As was the case with all Hudson-built bodies those offered for the Essex had steel instead of wood roof rails. The Essex engine had the same 4-1/2-inch stroke as in 1930 but its bore was increased by 1/8 inch to 2-7/8 inches. Total displacement was 175.28 cubic inches. After many years of being extremely coy about the Essex engine's power Hudson became quite bold about its rating. In comparison to the 1930 Essex engine the new version developed three more horsepower at 20 mph and five more horsepower at 30 mph. Shared with Hudson was the Essex dual flow oil system and new duralumin clutch disc.

I.D. DATA: Serial numbers on dash and right rear frame crossmember. Starting: 1234267. Ending: 1281684. Engine numbers on left side of cylinder block near water inlet elbow.

Super Six Series E

Model No.	Body Type & Seating	Factory Price	Shipping Weight	Prod. Total
Series E	2-dr. Spt. Rds.-2P	725	2400	NA
Series E	2-dr. Cpe.-2P	595	2595	NA
Series E	2-dr. Cpe. R/S-4P	645	2645	NA
Series E	2-dr. Sp. Cpe. R/S-4P	725	2800	NA
Series E	2-dr. C'ch.-5P	595	2690	NA
Series E	4-dr. Std. Sed.-5P	695	2750	NA
Series E	4-dr. Tr. Sed.-5P	775	2815	NA
Series E	4-dr. Twn. Sed.-5P	735	2815	NA
Series E	4-dr. Sp. Sed.-5P	855	2950	NA
Series E	4-dr. Sed.-7P	895	2945	NA
Series E	Phaeton	725	—	NA

ENGINE: L-head. Inline six. Cast iron block. B & S: 2-7/8 x 4-1/2 in. Disp.: 175.28 cu. in. C.R.: 5.8:1. Brake H.P.: 60 @ 3300 R.P.M. N.A.C.C. H.P.: 19.8. Main bearings: three. Valve lifters: mechanical. Carb.: 1-1/4 in. Marvel 10-948.

CHASSIS: [Series E] W.B.: 113 in. Front/Rear Tread: 58/58 in. Tires: 19 x 5.00.

TECHNICAL: Sliding gear transmission. Speeds: 3F/1R. Floor shift controls. Single plate clutch, cork inserts, running in oil. Shaft drive. Semi-floating rear axle. Bendix mechanical brakes on four wheels. Ten spoke wooden wheels with detachable rims. Freewheeling ($35.00).

OPTIONS: Single sidemount. Heater. Wire wheels. Chrome windshield frames. Dual windshield wipers. Twin taillights. White sidewall tires. Spare tire cover.

HISTORICAL: Introduced December 1930. Essex made 40,338 shipments to dealers during the 1931 calendar year. The president of Essex was William J. McAneeny.

1932

ESSEX — SERIES E — SIX: The Essex had both all-new styling and numerous mechanical improvements for 1932. With their vee-shaped radiators, single piece bumpers and molded rear panels, the Essex models bore a close resemblance to the larger Hudsons. Making the 1931 appear extremely dated were the new models' curved windshield pillar, rounded rear body contour and deeper crowned fenders. The Essex's list of standard equipment included a "Quick-vision" instrument panel with tell-tale oil and generator signals, Startix, adjustable front and rear seats and twin "Neutraltone" muffler. During the year the name of the Series E Essex was altered from its original Greater Essex Super-Six to Essex Super-Six Pacemaker before ending up as just the Essex Pacemaker when the Essex Standard Series was introduced in May 1932.

ESSEX — SERIES EC — SIX: The four EC models lacked dual cowl lights and were available only in a Louise Blue finish. The radiator shell was not chrome-plated but painted to match the body. The EC Essex also lacked the chromed hood hinges and runningboard trim found on the Pacemaker Series.

I.D. DATA: Serial numbers on dash and right rear frame crossmember. Starting: 1281685. Ending: 1300384. Engine numbers on left side of cylinder block near water inlet elbow.

Series E

Model No.	Body Type & Seating	Factory Price	Shipping Weight	Prod. Total
Series E	4-dr. Phae.-5P	765	NA	NA
Series E	2-dr. Bus. Cpe.-2P	695	2775	NA
Series E	2-dr. Cpe.-4P	745	2840	NA
Series E	2-dr. C'ch.-5P	705	2860	NA
Series E	2-dr. Sp. Cpe. R/S-4P	795	2895	NA
Series E	4-dr. Twn. Sed.-5P	745	2950	NA
Series E	4-dr. Sp. Sed.-5P	845	3010	NA
Series E	2 dr. Conv. Cpe.	845	2760	NA
Series E	4-dr. St. Sed.-5P	775	2980	NA
Series EC				
Series EC	2-dr. C'ch.-5P	665	2785	NA
Series EC	4-dr. 3 Window Sed.-5P	735	2870	NA
Series EC	2-dr. Cpe.-2P	660	2680	NA
Series EC	2-dr. Cpe. R/S-4P	710	2750	NA

ENGINE: Inline six. Cast iron block. B & S: 2-15/16 x 4-3/4 in. Disp.: 193.1 cu. in. C.R.: 5.8:1. Brake H.P.: 70 @ 3200 R.P.M. Main bearings: three. Valve lifters: mechanical. Carb.: Marvel 10-997.

CHASSIS: [Series E] W.B.: 113 in. Front/Rear Tread: 58/58 in. Tires: 19 x 5.00. [Series EC] W.B.: 113 in. Front/Rear Tread: 58/58 in. Tires: 19 x 5.00 in.

TECHNICAL: Sliding gear transmission. Speeds: 3F/1R. Floor shift controls. Single plate clutch, cork inserts, running in oil. Shaft drive. Semi-floating rear axle. Overall ratio: 4.64:1, 5.0:1. Bendix mechanical brakes on four wheels. Choice of wire or wooden spoke wheels. Selective-control automatic clutch.

OPTIONS: Single sidemount. Dual sidemount. Fabric/metal sidemount cover(s). Clock. Cigar lighter. Interior visors. Passenger-side windshield wiper. Folding rear trunk rack. Shatterproof glass (windshield only or all around). Leather upholstery. Radio antenna. Glove compartment lock.

HISTORICAL: Introduced January 1932. An Essex Pacemaker set a new record for cross-country travel, from Los Angeles to New York City, of 60 hours-20 minutes. Essex made 17,425 shipments to dealers during the 1932 calendar year. The president of Essex was William J. McAneeny.

1926 Essex, coach, OCW

1927 Essex, Super Six, sedan, OCW

1928 Essex, Super Six, touring, OCW

1928 Essex, Super Six, coupe with rumbleseat, OCW

1932 Essex, Terraplane, phaeton, OCW

1930 Essex, Challenger, Sun sedan (with composite steel and wood body by Biddle & Smart), OCW

TERRAPLANE

TERRAPLANE — Detroit, Michigan — (1932-1938) — The Terraplane began in 1932 as a model of the Essex built by the Hudson Motor Car Company. Considerable fanfare was expended upon its introduction that July with Orville Wright receiving the first car built, Amelia Earhart seeing to the Terraplane's christening and receiving car number two. With a top speed of 80 mph and price range of $425-$590, the Terraplane managed to create a stir in the industry that year exceeded only by Henry Ford's new V-8, with the logical result that within a year the Essex-Terraplane had become simply the Terraplane. Its engine was a larger, more powerful version of the Essex six (193 cubic inches and 70 hp vis-à-vis 175 and 60) and, placed in a short wheelbase chassis, provided for a spirited performance, which the company called "land-flying." A 94-hp Terraplane eight (with Hudson engine) joined the line in 1933. As with the Super Six of 1916, Hudson sent its Terraplane racing and by the end of 1933, the company held no fewer than 50 AAA hill climb records in addition to a flying mile of 85.8 mph and a standing mile of 68 mph at Daytona Beach, Florida. In 1932, a Terraplane six had climbed Pikes Peak in record-breaking time, and in 1933, a Terraplane eight broke the Terraplane six's record there. Performances such as these naturally received a wide press, and resulted in the car being looked upon with favor by the British overseas and bootleggers and other nefarious fellows at home. Reid Railton used a Terraplane eight chassis for his first Railton sports cars in England (switching subsequently to a Hudson chassis). John Dillinger was a big fan of the Terraplane in the United States. Like the Hudson, the Terraplane was provided "Axle-Flex" semi-independent front suspension in 1934, the Bendix "Electric Hand" gearshift as an option in 1935, and "Duo-Automatic" hydraulic brakes in 1936. The industry's first all-steel turret top was introduced on the Terraplane in mid-November 1935, a month before Chevrolet and Pontiac. That the Terraplane was a popular car and contributing measurably to Hudson's financial well being during these mid-Depression years was undeniable. That Hudson believed the name might become even more popular than its own was among the reasons the car was referred to as the Hudson-Terraplane in sales literature and on its hubcaps in 1938. The Terraplane had come full circle. By 1939, the name was dropped altogether.

Terraplane Data Compilation by Robert C. Ackerson

1932

ESSEX-TERRAPLANE — SERIES K — SIX: Prior to the introduction of the Essex-Terraplane in July 1932 there was much consideration about what if any directions the automobile industry would take to reverse the downspiral of its sales charts. For Hudson's part, the mid-year introduction of the standard Essex series was seen as a step towards what was then described as the Model T market. Hudson denied that it had a new low-priced car in the works and just a few weeks before the Essex-Terraplane's arrival the biggest automotive news seemed to be the major price cuts made by Chevrolet, Ford, and Plymouth. The Essex-Terraplane changed all that in a hurry. Although its styling was decidedly conservative the Essex-Terraplane combined in one car the national preoccupation with economy via its low price with a much older interest in performance. With a $425 base price the least expensive Essex-Terraplane, the roadster was $35 less than the Ford V-8 and $20 less than an equivalent Chevrolet model. Compared to the older Essex version the new Essex-Terraplane coach was $190 less expensive and weighed 485 pounds less. This light weight was achieved by combining the body and frame into a single unit and utilizing virtually every part of the car as part of the body-chassis structure. For example, the pressing that formed the web of the frame also served as the bottom of the body. The Essex-Terraplane engine was basically that used in the 1932 Essex models. However it had a lower 5.5:1 compression ratio, a new three-point mounting arrangement and a new downdraft induction system. The new result, said Hudson, was that the Essex-Terraplane "has a higher propulsion effort per pound of car weight than any production car now on the market in this country or abroad."

I.D. DATA: Serial numbers on firewall, right side of frame, right front face of front axle and on rear axle housing. Starting: 350000. Ending: 364124. Engine numbers on left side of cylinder block near water inlet elbow. Starting: 5000.

Series K

Model No.	Body Type & Seating	Factory Price	Shipping Weight	Prod. Total
Series K	2-dr. Std. Rds.-2P	425	2010	NA
Series K	2-dr. Bus. Cpe.-2P	470	2135	NA
Series K	2-dr. C'ch.-5P	475	2205	NA
Series K	2-dr. Std. Cpe. R/S-4P	510	2490	NA
Series K	2-dr. Sp. Rds.-2P	525	2110	NA
Series K	4-dr. Std. Sed.-5P	550	2250	NA
Series K	Sp. C'ch.	515	2205	NA
Series K	4-dr. Sp. Sed.-5P	570	2250	NA
Series K	2-dr. Sp. Conv. Cpe.-2P	610	2145	NA
Series K	4-dr. Phae.-5P	495	2170	NA
Series K	2-dr. Sp. Bus. Cpe.-2P	510	2350	NA
Series K	2-dr. Sp. Cpe. R/S-4P	550	2190	NA

ENGINE: Inline. Six. Cast iron block. B & S: 2-15/16 x 4-3/4 in. Disp.: 193.1 cu. in. C.R.: 5.8:1. Brake H.P.: 70 @ 3200 R.P.M. Taxable H.P.: 20.7. Main bearings: three. Valve lifters: mechanical. Carb.: Carter 243S downdraft.

CHASSIS: [Series K] W.B.: 106 in. Frt/Rear Tread: 51-1/2/54-1/2 in. Tires: 17 x 5.25.

TECHNICAL: Sliding gear transmission. Speeds: 3F/1R. Floor shift controls. Single plate controls clutch, cork inserts, running in oil. Shaft drive. Semi-floating rear axle. Overall ratio: 4.55:1 (sedans), 4.11:1 (all others). Bendix mechanical brakes on four wheels. Wire spoke wheels (17 in.).

OPTIONS: Interior visors. Passenger-side windshield wiper.

HISTORICAL: Introduced July 1932. The Essex-Terraplane soon became renown as the "Hill Buster." In nationwide ads Hudson challenged every American marque to better Essex-Terraplane hill climbing or acceleration runs. At Pikes Peak an Essex-Terraplane won the Penrose Trophy. Innovations: Lightweight-body frame unit construction. Essex-Terraplane made 16,581 shipments to dealers during the 1932 calendar year. The president of Essex-Terraplane was William J. McAneeny.

1933

ESSEX-TERRAPLANE SIX — SERIES K — SIX: The Series K Terraplane retained the 106-inch wheelbase of 1932 but the elimination of the exterior windshield visor gave the car a fresh appearance. A revamped instrument panel placed all gauges directly in front of the driver.

TERRAPLANE DELUXE SIX — SERIES KU — SIX: In May the Terraplane Six line, which had consisted of both Standard and Special versions was revamped to make room for the 113-inch wheelbase Series KU Special Six models. The Special Six line was dropped and the Standard line was relabeled the Terraplane Standard Six. The Series KU line became the DeLuxe Six Terraplane in August. These were equipped with a walnut-finish dash panel, standard cigarette lighter and radio. External features included chrome grille bars, bright-finish dual horn, fender lights and twin taillamps.

ESSEX-TERRAPLANE EIGHT — SERIES KT — EIGHT: The eight-cylinder Essex-Terraplane was set apart from the six-cylinder models by its hood doors and front fender mounted auxiliary lights. Corresponding to the mid-year DeLuxe Six Essex-Terraplane were the DeLuxe Eight models identified by their chrome grille bars, twin horns mounted beneath the headlights.

I.D. DATA: Serial numbers on firewall, right side of frame, right front face on front axle and on rear axle housing. Starting: [Series K] 364125, [Series KU] 5001, [Series KU DeLuxe] 11865, [Series KT] 65001, [Series KT DeLuxe] 73463. Ending: [Series K] 372899, [Series KU] 11864, [Series KU DeLuxe] 21495, [Series KT] 73462, [Series KT DeLuxe] 78250. Engine numbers on left side of cylinder block near water inlet elbow. Starting [K/KU] 20501, [KT] 15001.

Standard Six Series K

Model No.	Body Type & Seating	Factory Price	Shipping Weight	Prod. Total
Series K	(Standard) 2-dr. Rds.-2P	425	2135	NA
Series K	4-dr. Phae.-5P	515	2220	NA
Series K	2-dr. Bus. Cpe.-2P	485	2220	NA
Series K	2-dr. Cpe.-4P	535	2260	NA

1933 Terraplane, Standard Six (Series K), business coupe, OCW

1933 Terraplane, Standard Eight (Series KT), coach, OCW

1934 Terraplane, Challenger Six (Series KS), coupe, OCW

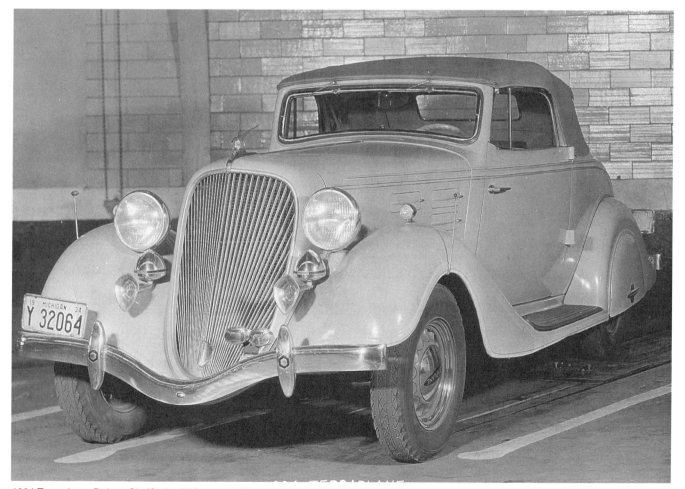

1934 Terraplane, Deluxe Six (Series KU), convertible coupe (with mid-year-change "three-door" hood shared with Hudson), OCW

Model No.	Body Type & Seating	Factory Price	Shipping Weight	Prod. Total
Series K	2-dr. C'ch.-5P	505	2275	NA
Series K	4-dr. Sed.-5P	555	2345	NA
Series K	(Special) 2-dr. Cpe.-4P	555	2310	NA
Series K	2-dr. Rds. R/S-4P	505	2220	NA
Series K	2-dr. C'ch.-5P	525	2335	NA
Series K	4-dr. Sed.-5P	575	2415	NA
Series K	2-dr. Conv. Cpe. R/S-4P	575	2275	NA
Series K	4-dr. Sed.-5P	575	2420	NA
Standard Six Series KU				
Series KU	2-dr. Cpe.-4P	555	2330	NA
Series KU	2-dr. Bus. Cpe.-2P	505	2320	NA
Series KU	2-dr. Spt. Rds. R/S-4P	505	2290	NA
Series KU	4-dr. Phae.-5P	535	—	NA
Series KU	2-dr. C'ch.-5P	525	2370	NA
Series KU	4-dr. Sed.-5P	575	2420	NA
Series KU	2-dr. Conv. Cpe.-2P	575	2315	NA
DeLuxe Six Series KU				
Series KU	4-dr. Sed.-5P	655	2500	NA
Series KU	2-dr. Bus. Cpe.-2P	585	2395	NA
Series KU	2-dr. Cpe. R/S-4P	635	2405	NA
Series KU	2-dr. Conv. Cpe. R/S-4P	655	2395	NA
Series KU	2-dr. C'ch.-5P	605	2450	NA
Series KU	2-dr. Spt. Rds. R/S-4P	585	2370	NA
Series KU	4-dr. Phae.-5P	615	—	NA
Standard Eight Series KT				
Series KT	2-dr. Bus. Cpe.-2P	615	2485	NA
Series KT	2-dr. Rds. R/S-4P	625	2455	NA
Series KT	2-dr. Rds.-2P	565	2410	NA
Series KT	2-dr. Cpe. R/S-4P	655	2545	NA
Series KT	2-dr. C'ch.-5P	615	2565	NA
Series KT	4-dr. Sed.-5P	675	2640	NA
Series KT	2-dr. Conv. Cpe.-4P	695	2495	NA
DeLuxe Eight Series KT				
Series KT	2-dr. Bus. Cpe.-2P	685	2540	NA
Series KT	2-dr. Rds. R/S-4P	895	2510	NA
Series KT	2-dr. Rds.-2P	635	2465	NA
Series KT	2-dr. Cpe. R/S-4P	725	2600	NA
Series KT	2-dr. C'ch.-5P	685	2625	NA
Series KT	4-dr. Sed.-5P	745	2700	NA
Series KT	2-dr. Conv. Cpe.-4P	765	2550	NA

ENGINE: [Series K, KU] Inline. Six. Cast iron block. B & S: 2-15/16 x 4-3/4 in. Disp.: 193.1 cu. in. C.R.: 5.8:1. Brake H.P.: 70 @ 3200 R.P.M. Taxable H.P.: 20.7. Main bearings: three. Valve lifters: mechanical. Carb.: Carter 267S. Optional Engine: Inline. Six. Cast iron block. B & S: 2-15/16 x 4-3/4 in. Disp.: 193.1 cu. in. C.R.: 7.0:1. Brake H.P.: 80 @ 3200 R.P.M. Main bearings: three. Valve lifters: mechanical. Carb.: Carter 267S. [Essex-Terraplane Eight] Inline. Cast iron block. B & S: 2.94 x 4.50 in. Disp.: 243.9 cu. in. C.R.: 5.8:1. Brake H.P.: 94 @ 3600 R.P.M. Taxable H.P.: 27.6. Main bearings: five. Valve lifters: mechanical. Carb.: Carter 261S one-barrel downdraft.

CHASSIS: [Series K] W.B.: 106 in. Frt/Rear Tread: 56/56 in. Tires: 17 x 5.25, 16 x 6.00 — Series K Special. [Series KU] W.B.: 113 in. Frt/Rear Tread: 56/56 in. Tires: 17 x 5.25, 16 x 6.00 — Series KU DeLuxe. [Series KT] W.B.: 113 in. Frt/Rear Tread: 56/56 in. Tires: 16 x 6.00.

TECHNICAL: Sliding gear transmission. Speeds: 3F/1R. Floor shift controls. Single plate clutch, cork inserts, running in oil. Shaft drive. Semi-floating rear axle. Overall ratio: 4.11:1 (4.56:1, 3.80:1 opt.). Bendix mechanical brakes on four wheels. Wire spoke wheels. Rim size: 17 in. — Series K, 16 in. — Series K Special, 17 in. — Series KU, 16 in. — Series KU DeLuxe, 16 in. — Series KT and KT DeLuxe. Automatic clutch.

OPTIONS: Single or dual sidemounts. [Series KU, KT only] automatic clutch, trunk rack, Majestic radio, dual taillights (non-DeLuxe models), fender lamps (non-DeLuxe models), 16 in. wheels [Series KU] two-tone paint.

HISTORICAL: Introduced January 1933. Under AAA supervision, stock Terraplanes set 72 hill climb and speed records in 1932 and 1933. Hudson touted the eight-cylinder model as the "only car that can beat the Terraplane 6" and at Daytona Beach a Terraplane 8 turned in an 85 mph top speed run and a 0-to-60 mph time of under 15 seconds. At Pikes Peak Al Miller broke the 1932 Terraplane-set record and once again won the Penrose Trophy with a run of 19 minutes-52.2 seconds. Second, third and fourth places in the stock class were also won by Terraplanes. Innovations: DeLuxe Six and Eight models had radios as standard equipment. Essex-Terraplane made 38,150 shipments to dealers during the 1933 calendar year. The president of Essex-Terraplane was William J. McAneeny (January-May); after May — Roy D. Chapin.

1934

TERRAPLANE — SERIES K — SIX: With the Essex name eliminated, Hudson's runningmate was known just as the Terraplane for 1934. Its styling was also completely new, highlighted by a broad grille with thin converging bars, flowing front and rear fender lines and seven tapered hood louvers. A built-in trunk was provided on coach and sedan models. Well equipped, the car had chrome windshield and vent window frames, chrome headlamps, front and rear ashtrays, robe rail, foot rest rail, door sill plates, full walnut-finish dash with indicator lights for oil pressure and generator, temperature gauge, ash receiver and rear armrests. Became known as the "Terraplane Standard" after introduction of the "Challenger."

TERRAPLANE DELUXE — SERIES KU — SIX: Riding on a 116-inch wheelbase, the DeLuxe added amenities such as twin chrome horns under the headlamps, twin taillamps, fender lamps, and dual windshield wipers. For a brief time a three-door hood was factory installed in place of the seven-louver style. Promoted as the "Terraplane Major" after introduction of the "Challenger."

TERRAPLANE CHALLENGER — SERIES KS — SIX: A mid-year introduction, the Challenger series offered a lower price but carried painted headlamps and windshield frame, painted dash, modest interiors and deleted amenities.

I.D. DATA: Serial numbers on firewall, right side of frame, right front face on front axle and on rear axle housing. Starting: [Series K] 373000, [Series KU] 21500, [Series KS] 396727. Ending: [Series KU] 28593, [Series K/KS] 416991. Engine numbers on left side of cylinder block opposite number one cylinder. Starting: 48000. Ending: 102999.

Challenger Six Series KS

Model No.	Body Type & Seating	Factory Price	Shipping Weight	Prod. Total
Series KS	2-dr. Cpe.-2P	565	2540	NA
Series KS	4-dr. Cpe. R/S-4P	610	2590	NA
Series KS	2-dr. C'ch.-5P	575	2600	NA
Series KS	4-dr. Sed.-5P	635	2670	NA
Series KS	4-dr. Sed. w/built-in trk.	635	NA	NA
Series KS	2-dr. C'ch. w/built-in trk.-5P	575	NA	NA
Standard Six Series K				
Series K	2-dr. Rds.-2P	NA	2465	NA
Series K	4-dr. Phae.-5P	NA	2615	NA
Series K	2-dr. Cpe.-2P	600	2600	NA
Series K	2-dr. Cpe.-4P	645	2605	NA
Series K	2-dr. Conv. Cpe. R/S-3P	695	2625	NA
Series K	2-dr. C'ch.-5P	615	2630	NA
Series K	2-dr. Compartment Vic.-5P	655	2655	NA
Series K	2-dr. C'ch. w/built-in trk.-5P	615	2655	NA
Series K	4-dr. Sed.-5P	875	2710	NA
Series K	4-dr. Compartment Sed.-5P	715	2735	NA
Series K	4-dr. Sed. w/built-in trk.	675	NA	NA
Deluxe Six Series KU				
Series KU	2-dr. Cpe.-4P	710	2700	NA
Series KU	2-dr. Cpe.-2P	665	NA	NA
Series KU	2-dr. Conv. Cpe. R/S-3P	750	2695	NA
Series KU	2-dr. C'ch.-5P	680	2730	NA
Series KU	2-dr. Compartment Vic.-5P	720	2755	NA
Series KU	4-dr. Sed.-5P	740	2780	NA
Series KU	4-dr. Compartment Sed.-5P	780	2805	NA
Series KU	4-dr. Sed. w/built-in trk.	740	NA	NA
Series KU	2-dr. C'ch. w/built-in trk.	680	NA	NA

ENGINE: [Series KS and K] L-head. Straight. Six. Chrome alloy block. B & S: 3 x 5 in. Disp.: 212 cu. in. C.R.: 5.75:1. Brake H.P.: 80 @ 3600 R.P.M. Taxable H.P.: 21.6. Main bearings: three. Valve lifters: mechanical. Carb.: Carter downdraft. Optional Engine: L-head. Straight. Six. Chrome alloy block. B & S: 3 x 5 in. Disp.: 212 cu. in. C.R.: 7.0:1. Brake H.P.: 89.5 @ 3600 R.P.M. Taxable H.P.: 21.6. Main bearings: three. Valve lifters: mechanical. Carb.: Carter downdraft. [Series KU] L-head. Straight. Six. Chrome alloy block. B & S: 3 x 5 in. Disp.: 212 cu. in. C.R.: 6.25:1. Brake H.P.: 85 @ 3600 R.P.M. Main bearings: three. Valve lifters: mechanical. Carb.: Carter downdraft. Optional Engine: L-head. Straight. Six. Chrome alloy block. B & S: 3 x 5 in. Disp.: 212 cu. in. C.R.: 7.0:1. Brake H.P.: 89.5 @ 3600 R.P.M. Taxable H.P.: 21.6. Main bearings: three. Valve lifters: mechanical. Carb.: Carter downdraft. Carter numbers for K and KU, 281S; for KS, 295S.

CHASSIS: [Series K, KS] W.B.: 112 in. O.L.: 190 in. Frt/Rear Tread: 56/56 in. Tires: 17 x 5.50. [Series KU] W.B.: 116 in. O.L.: 194 in. Frt/Rear Tread: 56/56 in. Tires: 16 x 6.00.

TECHNICAL: Sliding gear transmission. Speeds: 3F/1R. Floor shift controls. Single plate clutch, cork inserts, running in oil. Shaft drive. Semi-floating rear axle. Overall ratio: 4.11:1. Bendix mechanical brakes on four wheels. Pressed steel wheels (Series K, KU, rim size 16 in.). Wire spoke wheels (Series KS, rim size 17 in.).

OPTIONS: Single or dual sidemount. Sidemount covers. Radio. Heater. Dash, glovebox or rear view mirror-mounted clock. Cigar lighter. Bumper guards. Wheel trim rings. Turn signals. Wire spoke 16 in. wheels (Series K, KU). Fender skirts. Fender lamps (Series K). Twin taillamps (Series K). Axle-Flex. High compression two-piece alloy cylinder head. Startix. Luggage rack. Two-tone paint.

HISTORICAL: Introduced January 1934. Innovations: Axle-Flex front suspension — optional at no extra cost. Two parallel bars replaced the front axle's midsection to provide an independent front suspension system. Terraplane (and Hudson) first in industry to use pinned piston rings and direct-action (tube-type) shock absorbers this year. Terraplane made 56,804 shipments to dealers during the 1934 calendar year. The president of Terraplane was Roy D. Chapin.

1935

TERRAPLANE DELUXE — SERIES GU — SIX: The 1935 Terraplanes were fitted with all-steel bodies with styling that closely approximated that of Hudson. After receiving an all-new appearance the previous year, changes were minor. A new grille design of stamped steel featured 10 thin horizontal bars, stainless steel center spine and shell surround, and narrower vanes that angled outward from the grille base. The Terraplane's hood louvers were slightly tilted toward the rear of the car and were decorated with three horizontal stainless steel strips. Among the more significant changes to the Terraplane were new, wider by two and three inches, respectively, rear and front seats. In the Terraplane lineup only the DeLuxe Six models could be equipped with the Axle-Flex front suspension.

TERRAPLANE SPECIAL — SERIES G — SIX: The Special Six lacked the twin exterior horns that were mounted directly under the headlights on the GU models. In addition the Special Six was not fitted with the front window vent panes or two chrome taillamps that were standard on the DeLuxe Six.

I.D. DATA: Serial numbers on firewall, right side of frame. Starting: [Series GU] 52101, [Series G] 51101. Ending: [Series GU] 5213362, [Series G] 5137772. Engine numbers on left side of cylinder block opposite number one cylinder. Starting: 103000. Ending: 154813.

Special Six Series G

Model No.	Body Type & Seating	Factory Price	Shipping Weight	Prod. Total
Series G	2-dr. Tr. Brgh.-5P	625	2611	NA
Series G	2-dr. C'ch.-5P	595	2595	NA
Series G	4-dr. Sed.-5P	655	2655	NA
Series G	4-dr. Sub. Sed.-5P	685	2670	NA
Series G	2-dr. Bus. Cpe.-3P	585	2505	NA
Series G	2-dr. Cpe. R/S-4P	625	2555	NA
Deluxe Six Series GU				
Series GU	2-dr. Cpe. R/S-4P	675	2635	NA
Series GU	2-dr. Bus. Cpe.-3P	635	2565	NA
Series GU	2-dr. Conv. Cpe.-3P	725	2590	NA
Series GU	4-dr. Sed.-5P	705	2710	NA
Series GU	4-dr. Sub. Sed.-5P	735	2425	NA
Series GU	2-dr. C'ch.-5P	645	2665	NA
Series GU	2-dr. Tr. Brgm.-5P	675	2680	NA

ENGINE: L-head. Inline. Six. Chrome alloy block. B & S: 3 x 5 in. Disp. 212 cu. in. C.R.: 6.0:1. Brake H.P.: 88 @ 3800 R.P.M. Taxable H.P.: 21.6. Main bearings: three. Valve lifters: mechanical. Carb.: Carter downdraft. Optional Engine: L-head. Inline. Six. Chrome alloy block. B & S: 3 x 5 in. Disp. 212 cu. in. C.R.: 7.0:1. Brake H.P.: 100 @ 3800 R.P.M. Main bearings: three. Valve lifters: mechanical. Carb.: Carter downdraft. Carter carburetor numbers 311S for Series G, 209S for Series GU.

CHASSIS: [Series G] W.B.: 112 in. O.L.: 190 in. Frt/Rear tread: 56/56 in. Tires: 16 x 6. [Series GU] W.B.: 112 in. O.L.: 190 in. Frt/Rear tread: 56/56 in. Tires: 16 x 6.00.

TECHNICAL: Sliding gear transmission. Speeds: 3F/1R. Floor shift controls. Single plate clutch, cork inserts, running in oil. Shaft drive. Semi-floating rear axle. Overall ratio: 4.11:1. Bendix mechanical brakes on four wheels. Pressed steel wheels. Rim size: 16 in. Axle-Flex (DeLuxe Six only). Electric hand.

OPTIONS: Radio ($51.81). Seat covers (7.50). High compression cylinder head (18.50). Startix (8.50). Luggage carrier (10.00). Zenith radio (44.00). Twin air horns (11.50). Leather upholstery (18.81). Dual tail-stop lights. Single or dual sidemount. Sidemount covers. Heater. Dash- or glovebox-mounted clock. Cigar lighter. Bumper guard. Wheel trim rings. Turn signals. Fender skirts. Fender lamps (Series G). Twin taillamps (Series G). Two-tone paint not available.

HISTORICAL: Introduced December 1934. Terraplanes participated in numerous economy and performance trials. At Bonneville, Terraplanes averaged 24.24 mpg at a speed of 28 mph and 20.11 mpg at a speed of 50 mph. In an acceleration test the Terraplane needed 14.05 seconds to reach 50 mph from rest. In Brooklyn, New York, the New York City Police conducted stopping ability tests that demonstrated the Terraplane could stop in less than 61 feet from a 39 mph speed, which was approximately 30 percent better than the department's requirement. Terraplane made 70,323 shipments to dealers during the 1935 calendar year. The president of Terraplane was Roy D. Chapin.

1936

TERRAPLANE CUSTOM — SERIES 62 — SIX: Terraplane shared Hudson's new bodies for 1936. Its primary identification feature was a large vertical grille with a thin center divider bisecting a large chromed V. The center bar also served as the focus point for a series of nine slanted vee-lines that ran from the grille's top to bottom. Early in May deliveries of the Terraplane station wagon began, the first such model offered by Hudson.

TERRAPLANE DELUXE — SERIES 61 — SIX: The less costly DeLuxe Terraplanes lacked the externally mounted horns of the Custom models. In addition they were equipped with only a single taillight and their front door windows were not fitted with ventpanes. The wheelbase of all Terraplanes was increased to 115 inches.

I.D. DATA: Serial numbers on firewall, right side of frame right front door pillar post. Starting: [Series 61] 61101, [Series 62] 62101. Ending: [Series 61] 6169752, [Series 62] 6217041. Engine numbers on left side of cylinder block opposite number one cylinder. Starting: 157000. Ending: 246326.

Deluxe Six Series 61

Model No.	Body Type & Seating	Factory Price	Shipping Weight	Prod. Total
Series 61	2-dr. Cpe.-3P	640	2695	NA
Series 61	2-dr. Bus. Cpe.-3P	595	2615	NA
Series 61	2-dr. Brgm.-6P	615	2715	NA
Series 61	2-dr. Tr. Brgm.-6P	635	2715	NA
Series 61	2-dr. Conv. Cpe.-3/5P	715	2740	NA
Series 61	4-dr. Sed.-6P	670	2770	NA
Series 61	4-dr. Tr. Sed.-6P	690	2770	NA
Custom Six Series 62				
Series 62	2-dr. Tr. Brgm.-6P	685	2755	NA
Series 62	2-dr. Bus. Cpe.-3P	650	2665	NA
Series 62	2-dr. Cpe.-3/5P	690	2750	NA
Series 62	2-dr. Conv. Cpe.-3/5P	760	2975	NA
Series 62	2-dr. Brgm.-6P	665	2755	NA
Series 62	4-dr. Sed.-6P	720	2810	NA
Series 62	4-dr. Tr. Sed.-6P	740	2810	NA
Series 62	4-dr. Sta. Wag.-6P*	750	2925	NA

***Note:** The station wagon was officially listed in Terraplane's commercial line.

ENGINE: L-head. Inline. Six. Chrome alloy block. B & S: 3 x 5 in. Disp.: 212 cu. in. C.R.: 6.0:1. Brake H.P.: 88 @ 3800 R.P.M. Main bearings: three. Valve lifters: mechanical. Carb.: Carter 331S. Optional Engine: L-head. Inline. Six. Chrome alloy block. B & S: 3 x 5 in. Disp.: 212 cu. in. C.R.: 7.0:1. Brake H.P.: 100 @ 3800 R.P.M. Taxable H.P.: 21.6. Main bearings: three. Valve lifters: mechanical. Carb.: Carter 329S.

CHASSIS: [Series 61] W.B.: 115 in. Tires: 16 x 6.00. [Series 62] W.B.: 115 in. Tires: 16 x 6.00.

TECHNICAL: Sliding gear transmission. Speeds: 3F/1R. Floor shift controls. Single plate clutch, cork inserts, running in oil. Shaft drive. Semi-floating rear axle. Bendix hydraulic brakes on four wheels. Pressed steel wheels. Rim size: 16 in.

OPTIONS: Dual sidemounts. Fender skirts. Radio. Heater. Clock. Cigar lighter. Seat covers. Spotlight. Electric hand. Fog lights. Wheel trim rings. Sideview mirrors.

HISTORICAL: Introduced November 1935. Terraplane first to offer all-steel turret top. Terraplane (and Hudson) had Bendix hydraulic brakes on four wheels with backup system in which foot pedal picked up rear wheel mechanicals in case of hydraulic failure. Terraplane made 93,309 shipments to dealers during the 1936 calendar year. The president of Terraplane was Abraham Edward Barit.

1937

SUPER TERRAPLANE — SERIES 72 — SIX: With the exception of their hood length, wheelbase and grille design the 1937 Hudson and Terraplane were nearly identical. Key distinctions between the two makes included hubcaps, different shapes for the hood louver panel and domed taillight lenses for the Terraplane. Those used on the Hudson were cone shaped. The more costly Super Terraplanes carried front fender medallions, dual taillights and front window ventpanes.

TERRAPLANE DELUXE — SERIES 71 — SIX: The DeLuxe models had only a single taillight and did not have front window ventpanes.

I.D. DATA: Serial numbers on firewall, right side of frame right front door pillar post. Starting: [Series 71] 71101, [Series 72] 72101. Ending: [Series 71] 7170346, [Series 72] 7219907. Engine numbers on left side of cylinder block opposite number one cylinder. Starting: 250000. Ending: 351877.

Deluxe Six Series 71

Model No.	Body Type & Seating	Factory Price	Shipping Weight	Prod. Total
Series 71	2-dr. Bus. Cpe.-3P	595	2370	NA
Series 71	2-dr. Cpe.-3P	605	2715	NA
Series 71	2-dr. Vic. Cpe.-4P	850	2765	NA
Series 71	2-dr. Conv. Cpe.-3P	725	2765	NA
Series 71	2-dr. Conv. Brgm.-6P	800	2780	NA
Series 71	2-dr. Brgm.-6P	825	2830	NA
Series 71	4-dr. Sed.-6P	675	2865	NA
Series 71	4-dr. Tr. Sed.-6P	695	2865	NA
Series 71	2-dr. Tr. Brgm.-6P	645	2830	NA

Super Six Series 72

Model No.	Body Type & Seating	Factory Price	Shipping Weight	Prod. Total
Series 72	2-dr. Cpe.-3P	880	2755	NA
Series 72	2-dr. Vic. Cpe.-4P	700	2795	NA
Series 72	4-dr. Tr. Sed.-6P	745	2905	NA
Series 72	2-dr. Conv. Cpe.-4P	770	2825	NA
Series 72	2-dr. Conv. Brgm.-6P	845	2915	NA
Series 72	2-dr. Brgm.-6P	680	2875	NA
Series 72	2-dr. Tr. Brgm.-6P	700	2875	NA
Series 72	4-dr. Sed.-6P	725	2905	NA

ENGINE: L-head. Inline. Six. Alloy block. B & S: 3 x 5 in. Disp. 212 cu. in. C.R.: 6.25:1. Brake H.P.: 96 @ 3900 R.P.M. Taxable H.P.: 21.6. Main bearings: three. Valve lifters: mechanical. Carb.: Carter WI-348S. Optional Engine: L-head. Straight. Six. Chrome alloy block. B & S: 3 x 5 in. Disp. 212 cu. in. C.R.: 7.0:1. Brake H.P.: 107 @ 4000 R.P.M. Taxable H.P.: 21.6. Main bearings: three. Valve lifters: mechanical. Carb.: Carter 329S.

CHASSIS: [Series 71] W.B.: 117 in. O.L.: 194 in. Tires: 16 x 6.00, 15 x 7.00 opt. [Series 72] W.B.: 117 in. O.L.: 194 in. Tires: 16 x 6.00, 15 x 7.00 opt.

TECHNICAL: Sliding gear transmission. Speeds: 3F/1R. Floor shift controls. Single disc clutch, cork inserts, running in oil. Shaft drive. Semi-floating rear axle. Overall ratio: 4.11:1 (4.54:1 opt.). Bendix hydraulic brakes on four wheels. Steel artillery wheels — by Motor Wheel Corp. Rim size: 16 x 4.0 in. Hill-holder. Electric hand. 15-inch wheels. 15 x 7.00 tires.

OPTIONS: Radio. Heater. Clock. Cigar lighter. Radio antenna. Seat covers. Rear fender skirts. White sidewalls. Mohair fabric (closed models). Lacquer finish.

HISTORICAL: Introduced November 1936. Although it was soon broken by a Hudson 8, a Terraplane set a new 86.54 mph record for 24 hours at Bonneville in October 1936. For its share of the Hudson company's efforts at speed runs, the Terraplane contributed seven new Class C records. Terraplane (and Hudson) became first American automobile to have true three-passenger (a full 55 inches wide) front seat. Terraplane made 83,436 shipments to dealers during the 1937 calendar year. The president of Terraplane was Abraham Edward Barit.

1938

HUDSON TERRAPLANE DELUXE — SERIES 81 — SIX: Although there were two full series of Terraplanes offered, their days as a separate marque were limited. Sales literature and hubcaps indicated the cars as Hudson Terraplanes. The Hudson Terraplane had circular rather than oval-shaped headlights used on other Hudson series. The Terraplane grille featured a wide waterfall divider in addition to a horizontal bar pattern.

HUDSON SUPER TERRAPLANE — SERIES 82 — SIX: The Super Terraplane was powered by a 101 hp engine (compared to 91 hp in the DeLuxe versions). Both had identical exteriors without the front fender chevrons found on other Hudsons. Dual chrome exterior horns were fitted under the headlamps of the Series 82.

I.D. DATA: Hudson Terraplane DeLuxe: Car numbers on right front door post. Starting: 81119. Ending: 8156033. Hudson Super Terraplane: Car numbers on right front door post. Starting: 82153. Ending: 8256017. Engine numbers on top of cylinder block, right side, between numbers one and two exhaust flanges. Starting: 360000 all series. Engine number began matching serial number with car number 11630.

Hudson Terraplane DeLuxe — Series 81

Model No.	Body Type & Seating	Factory Price	Shipping Weight	Prod. Total
Series 81	2-dr. Cpe.-3P	789	2725	NA
Series 81	2-dr. Vic. Cpe.-5P	835	2775	NA
Series 81	2-dr. Conv. Cpe.-3P	926	2780	NA
Series 81	2-dr. Brgm.-6P	822	2820	NA
Series 81	2-dr. Tr. Brgm.-6P	843	2825	NA
Series 81	2-dr. Conv. Brgm.-6P	990	2860	NA
Series 81	4-dr. Sed.-6P	864	2885	NA
Series 81	4-dr. Tr. Sed.-6P	884	2890	NA

Hudson Super Terraplane — Series 82

Model No.	Body Type & Seating	Factory Price	Shipping Weight	Prod. Total
Series 82	2-dr. Cpe.-3P	845	2755	NA
Series 82	2-dr. Vic. Cpe.-5P	886	2805	NA
Series 82	2-dr. Conv. Cpe.-3P	971	2835	NA
Series 82	2-dr. Brgm.-6P	878	2865	NA
Series 82	2-dr. Tr. Brgm.-6P	899	2870	NA
Series 82	2-dr. Conv. Brgm.-6P	1034	2880	NA
Series 82	4-dr. Sed.-6P	915	2925	NA
Series 82	4-dr. Tr. Sed.-6P	935	2930	NA

ENGINE: L-head. Six. Chrome alloy block. B & S: 3 x 5 in. Disp.: 212 cu. in. C.R.: 6.25:1. Brake H.P.: 101 @ 4000 R.P.M. Taxable H.P.: 21.60. Main bearings: three. Valve lifters: mechanical. Carb.: Dual downdraft Carter WDO 397S.

CHASSIS: [Series 82] W.B.: 117 in. O.L.: 193-1/16 in. Frt/Rear tread: 56/59 in. Tires: 16 x 6.00 (15 x 7.00 opt.). [Series 81] W.B.: 117 in. O.L.: 193-1/16 in. Frt/Rear tread: 56/59 in. Tires: 16 x 6.00 (15 x 7.00 opt.).

TECHNICAL: Sliding gear, synchromesh transmission. Speeds: 3F/1R. Floor shift controls. Single disc clutch, cork inserts, running in oil. Shaft drive. Semi-floating rear axle. Overall ratio: 4.11:1. Bendix hydraulic brakes on four wheels. Steel disc wheels. Drivetrain options: Selective automatic shift. Automatic clutch.

OPTIONS: DeLuxe heater. Custom radio (seven tubes) Hudson-RCA Victor DB38. Custom hot water heater. Hydraulic hill-hold. Dual sidemounts (last year of availability). Fender skirts. Fog and spot lights. 15 x 7.00 tires.

1934 Terraplane, Challenger Six (Series KS), sedan, OCW

1937 Terraplane, station wagon (considered a commercial vehicle by the factory), OCW

1938 (Hudson) Terraplane, Super (Series 82), convertible brougham (with optional trumpet horns, bright wheel trim rings, whitewall tires and rear wheel shields), OCW

KAISER

Shipbuilder Henry J. Kaiser decided to make the automotive industry his port of call after the close of World War II. Teaming with Graham-Paige executive Joseph Frazer — in an association often shaken by personality conflicts — Kaiser moved quickly to beat the major makers into production of an all-new postwar car. The result was a novel-looking, straight-sided design with definite appeal to buyers of the day.

Data Compiled by G. Marshall Naul
Introduction by John A. Gunnell

Competing in a crowd of basically prewar cars that looked like the 'mothball fleet', Kaiser leaped to an encouraging start. Over 70,000 sales were achieved by the 1947 models and the future, indeed, looked bright. It wasn't long, however, before the more established brands threw off their prewar image and started to catch up. Being rather high-priced, the Kaisers (and companion Frazer models) simply could not compete. Sales began to decline in 1949 and financial problems ensued. But for a massive loan from the postwar Reconstruction Finance Corp., the firm may not have survived past this point.

After the loan was granted, Kaiser did survive for a time, although Frazer passed from the scene in 1951. To revitalize the remaining products, master craftsman Howard 'Dutch' Darrin was employed to restyle the line. Heavy emphasis was also placed on upgraded interior appointments, with major responsibility in this area falling to designer Carlton Spencer, who accomplished an outstanding job. To finish the task of remaking the cars, a powerful six from Continental Engines Co. — a Kaiser Industries subsidiary firm — was improved with new manifolding to produce more 'get-up-and-go'. The 115 hp produced by this 'Supersonic Six' made the 1951 Kaiser something less than a high-performance machine, but nevertheless it was a fine engine.

Another area in which Kaiser did some fine, if unappreciated work, was in the creation of unique body styles. One was a hatchback sedan called the Vagabond, in Deluxe trim, and Traveler, in standard form. The company also marketed a four-door convertible and a four-door Virginian hardtop sedan. The latter looked like a ragtop, but was actually a full-pillared automobile. None of these beautiful models sold well, nor did a Taxicab Special of 1949-1950.

Innovation with Kaiser did not stop with the above, since a number of unique products were also developed in the 1952-1954 period. One was the compact-size Henry J (also marketed through Sears, Roebuck and Co. as the Allstate).

A second innovation was the Kaiser-Darrin sports car. This spectacular-looking, fiberglass-bodied two-seater was developed and sold as a Kaiser product, as covered in this section. Later, it was revived, by Howard Darrin himself, between 1955 and 1958.

By 1952, Kaiser sales fell to the 32,000 unit level, which brought some interesting results. For example, in some years the company fell far short of selling the number of cars it had produced. In such cases, the leftovers were sometimes redecorated, given new serial numbers and re-introduced as the next line of cars. When all were sold, a new series would be introduced, without regard to the normal duration of the current model year. The 1952 Virginian (no longer a four-door hardtop) was such a car.

When the true 1952 Kaisers were introduced, in March of that calendar year, several new model names appeared. The Manhattan was the top-level series, while bottom-of-the-line cars were called Deluxe models. Added in 1953 was a fully equipped luxury model called the Dragon. It was named after the texture of its seating surface material, which was thought to be like the skin of the mythological beast. An option was a padded roof covered in special 'Bambu' vinyl.

If all of this sounds like a desperate attempt to reach out for new buyers, you've got a clear picture of the way things were in the company's last few years of domestic automobile production. On the other hand, you can imagine how modern collectors enjoy owning a car that was virtually the next thing to custom-built. Sales at this point were down to some 22,000 units per year and Kaiser was going broke.

Kaiser, of course, wasn't the only independent manufacturer having problems at this time and the trend was for the smaller companies to merge together, in order to survive against the 'Big Three'. In 1954, the same year that Nash and Hudson combined to form American Motors, Kaiser Motors bought Willys-Overland of Toledo, Ohio. The result became known as Kaiser-Willys, which thereafter operated as a subsidiary of Kaiser Industries. The Kaiser factory, in Willow Run, Mich., was sold to General Motors. Eventually, all production was transferred to Toledo.

For the 1954 model year, there were, again, two series of cars. The first consisted of 1953 leftovers that carried Body Number plates from Michigan and serial number plates from Ohio. However, all units of the later series were products constructed at the Willys plant. A new feature was a supercharged, 'Super-Power' six, which developed 140 bhp in Manhattan models. When sales for the calendar year peaked at only 17,000 units, Henry Kaiser could see the handwriting on the wall.

In 1955, Kaiser-Willys announced its intentions to pull out of the passenger car building business, at least in the United States. In the future, the company would concentrate solely on the domestic commercial vehicle market, where its Jeep product line was enjoying much stronger sales. Just over 1,000 Kaiser automobiles were turned out in 1955, with the majority shipped to South America to fill an order from Argentina. In the following months, the body dies and manufacturing equipment were also sent to Argentina, where the Kaiser would be marketed, as the Carabella, for another seven years.

While the Kaiser lasted for only 10 years in this country, marque enthusiasts are quick to point out the contributions made by these outstanding cars. In terms of styling, 1951 was the first year of the new second-generation Kaiser style. The 1952 models built upon the lead and can justly lay claim to helping to develop a new school of automotive design emphasizing sleek, low looks. Kaiser was also among the first to provide a full instrument panel crash pad as standard equipment. Kaiser is also given credit for being among the first to incorporate pop-out windshields. The company was one of the few automakers to offer seat belts at the time. In addition, Kaiser pioneered the use of dual purpose taillamps designed to serve as side safety markers, as well as stop and directional lights. Emphasis on the use of sound-deadening interior insulation, lavish upholstery trim options and supercharging as standard equipment are three other Kaiser milestones later accepted as industry standard.

1947

KAISER SPECIAL — (6-CYL) — K100 SERIES — The Kaiser was first conceived as a front-wheel-drive sedan designated the K-85 of which two working prototypes were built. Engineering difficulties and costs kept the K-85 from reaching production. The 1947 production models were introduced in August of 1946. They were based on the same body used for 1947 Frazers, which had been designed by Howard 'Dutch' Darrin. Both of these cars had the first true postwar sheet metal with envelope bodies and fenderlines that ran front to rear in an unbroken contour. Features included welded all-steel construction; between the wheel seating; exceptionally wide wheel rims; low center of gravity; low, luxurious seats; large luggage compartment; curved wraparound bumpers; dual horns; twin sun visors; dash mounted starter switch; two combination stop and taillights; automatic dome lights; and large hydraulic self-centering brakes. The Kaiser radiator grille was a strange mixture of vertical and horizontal blades with rectangular parking lamps placed outside the grillework, under the headlamps. A large hood badge bearing the letter 'K' above a buffalo shield was an obvious identification feature.

KAISER I.D. NUMBERS: Serial number was stamped on a tag on left front door post. Serial numbers consisted of a Model Number prefix and a six digit figure which is 001001 for the first car of the year. For 1947, prefix K-100=Special sedan; Prefix K-101=Custom sedan. Serial numbers for 1947 were K100-1001 to K100-66062 for Specials and K101-2000001 to K101-2005412 for Customs. Engine numbers were stamped on a pad on the left front upper corner of the engine block and on a plate on the left side of the block. Engine numbers for 1947 were K-100001 and up for both series. Kaisers also carried a numerical Body (Style) Number, which was identical to the Body numbers used on Frazers.

KAISER SPECIAL SERIES K100

Model No.	Body/Style No.	Body Type & Seating	Factory Price	Shipping Weight	Prod. Total
K100	1005	4-dr Sed-6P	1868	3305	65,062

NOTE 1: Prices and weights above are those in effect during April 1947.

NOTE 2: Prices changed to $1,967 and $2,104 later.

NOTE 3: Late-year factory weight was 3,295 pounds.

KAISER CUSTOM — (6-CYL) — SERIES K101 — The Custom was a more Deluxe version of the basic Kaiser sedan. This model was introduced on Sept. 25, 1947. Features included a special dashboard; window control knobs; custom styled back seats; robe holder; new ashtrays and package shelf; more interior trim; bright metal windshield frames; upholstered trunk compartment; passenger assist handles; chrome highlighted foot rests; courtesy lamps; bright finished handbrake lever; and lengthwise seamed headliner. Rocker panel moldings and Custom front fender script were seen as well as chrome wheel trim rings. Four front bumper guards were standard equipment. The

1947 Kaiser, Special (Series K100), sedan (prototype), OCW

1947 Kaiser, Custom (Series K101), sedan, OCW

1949 Kaiser, Custom Virginian (Series K492), hardtop sedan, OCW

1949 Kaiser, Special (Series K491), sedan, OCW

1950 Kaiser, Deluxe (Series K492), sedan, OCW

Custom interiors were carefully keyed to harmonize with special exterior shades such as Onyx; Linden Green; Clay Pipe Gray; Coral Sand; Horizon Blue and Hickory Brown Metallic.

KAISER CUSTOM SERIES K101

Model No.	Body/Style No.	Body Type & Seating	Factory Price	Shipping Weight	Prod. Total
K101	1015	4-dr Sed-6P	2301	3295	5,412

NOTE 1: The price for the 1947 Kaiser Custom sedan later increased to $2,456.

ENGINE: Inline six. L-head. Cast iron block. Displacement: 226.2 cid. Bore and stroke: 3-15/16 x 4-3/8 inches. Compression ratio: initially 6.8:1 changed to 7.3:1 near end of model year. Brake hp: 100 at 3600 rpm. Four main bearings. Solid valve lifters. Carburetor: Carter type W-1 or WA-1 one-barrel Models 574S, 622S or 622SA.

CHASSIS FEATURES: Wheelbase: 123.5 inches. Overall length: 203 inches. Front tread: 58 inches. Rear tread: 60 inches. Tires: 6.50 x 15.

CONVENIENCE OPTIONS: Defroster and heater ($48). Radio. Radio antenna. Stainless steel wheel trim rings. Tailpipe extension. Full wheel discs. Outside rearview mirror. External sun visor. Spotlights. Fog lamps. Plastic white sidewall discs. Front bumper guards. Rear bumper guards. White sidewall tires (when available). Clip-on vanity mirror. Locking gas cap. Three-speed manual transmission was standard. Automatic choke. Oil bath air cleaner. Vacuum booster fuel pump. Kaiser-Frazer Club Archives lists five available rear axle gear ratios.

HISTORICAL FOOTNOTES: The 1947 Kaiser Specials were introduced in August 1946 and the Kaiser Custom appeared in dealer showrooms after Sept. 25, 1946. Model year production peaked at 70,474 units. Calendar year sales of 144,490 cars including Frazers were recorded. Henry J. Kaiser was the chairman of the board for the company this year. Joseph W. Frazer was president and general manager. Frazer was also the chief executive officer of Graham-Paige Motors. On Feb. 1, 1947, the automotive assets of Graham-Paige were sold to the new Kaiser-Frazer company. Hood ornaments were not used on 1947 Kaiser-Frazer automobiles, although aftermarket mascots were available, which were custom designed for both cars. Kaiser-Frazer of Canada, Ltd. was formed in 1947.

1948

KAISER — (6-CYL) — SERIES K481 — There were minor changes in the Kaiser for 1948 and most were alterations adopted at some point in the 1947 model run. They included new bumper guards with a more angular, staggered look; a darker color field behind the large 'K' in the hood name badge; the elimination of two thin moldings at the outboard ends of the radiator grille opening; and removal of Special nameplates from the grille and rear deck (which appeared only on early 1947 cars anyway). Effective with car number 36446 the use of beige colored instrument faces, instead of green ones, was begun. Higher compression ratios were listed as a 1948 improvement, but use of this 7.3:1 ratio head began late in 1947 and was carried over for 1948 models. Apparently, only the earliest 1947s had a 6.8:1 ratio head design and this was actually a running production change. The horsepower rating was not affected. About 25 other technical changes, most of minor significance, were promoted by the company for the new year for both Kaisers and Frazers. The use of larger 7.10 x 15 tires was one of them.

KAISER I.D. NUMBERS: Serial number was stamped on a tag on left front door post. Serial numbers consisted of a Model Number prefix and a six digit figure which is 001001 for the first car of the year. The 1948 Body/Style number prefix changed to K481 for the lowest-priced line and K482 for Customs. The first symbol 'K' indicated Kaiser. The second and third symbols '48' indicated the 1948 model year. The fourth symbol was used for series designation. Serial numbers K481-1001 to K481-093587 were used on standard Kaiser models. Serial numbers K482-1001 to K482-002263 were used on Kaiser Customs. Engine numbers continued from 1947 or fell into a new range of numbers beginning at K100 and up.

KAISER SIX SERIES K481

Model No.	Body/Style No.	Body Type & Seating	Factory Price	Shipping Weight	Prod. Total
K481	K4811	4-dr Sed-6P	2244	3295	90,588

KAISER CUSTOM — (6-CYL) — SERIES K482 — The Custom continued as a more Deluxe version of the Kaiser Special with control knobs; clock; richer upholstery; custom styled back seats; robe holder; ashtrays; package shelf; bright metal windshield and window reveals; upholstered trunk compartment; passenger assist handles; chrome trimmed foot rests; courtesy lamps; bright metal handbrake lever; and headliner with seams running lengthwise. The exterior of Custom models was distinguished by identification script placed high on the trailing edge of the front fendersides (cowl side region) and bright rocker panel moldings. Front compartment carpeting was a new, running change.

KAISER CUSTOM SERIES K482

Model No.	Body/Style No.	Body Type & Seating	Factory Price	Shipping Weight	Prod. Total
K482	K4821	4-dr Sed-6P	2466	3295	1,263

ENGINES:

(BASE SIX) Inline six. L-head. Cast iron block. Displacement: 226.2 cid. Bore and stroke: 3-15/16 x 4-3/8 inches. Compression ratio: 7.3:1. Brake hp: 100 at 3600 rpm. Four main bearings. Solid valve lifters. Carburetor: Carter type W-1 or WA-1 one-barrel Models 574S, 622S or 622SA.

(DUAL MANIFOLD SIX) Inline six. L-head. Cast iron block. Displacement: 226.2 cid. Bore and stroke: 3-15/16 x 4-3/8 inches. Compression ratio: 7.3:1. Brake hp: 112 at 3600 rpm. Four main bearings. Solid valve lifters. Carburetor: Carter type WCD or WA-1. Dual manifold engine introduced at midyear.

CHASSIS FEATURES: Wheelbase: 123-1/2 inches. Overall length: 203 inches. Front tread: 58 inches. Rear tread: 60 inches. Tires: 7.10 x 15.

OPTIONS: Defroster and heater ($48). Radio. Radio antenna. Stainless steel wheel trim rings. Tailpipe extension. Round shaped outside rearview mirror. External sun visor. Clip-on vanity mirror. Locking gas cap. Spotlights. Fog lamps. Authentic white sidewall tires. Bumper guards. Accessory Group AG-1 including bumper guards front and rear; heavy-duty air cleaner; vacuum storage tank for wipers; spare tire and tube on wheel; license holder and guards; wheel trim rings; tailpipe extension; rear seat cigar lighter ($105). Three-speed manual transmission was standard. Automatic choke. Oil bath air cleaner. Vacuum booster fuel pump. Several available rear axle ratios.

HISTORICAL FOOTNOTES: Sales of 1948 Kaisers began in December 1947. Model year production peaked at 91,851 cars. Henry J. Kaiser was again chairman of the board this year. Joseph W. Frazer was president, Edgar F. Kaiser was general manager. A proud addition to the Harrah's Automobile Collection (now National Automobile Museum) in Reno, Nevada, for many years was a one-off 1948 Kaiser made for Edward Hunt's wife (Hunt was the director of the company's Detroit Engine Division). Hunt's wife was physically handicapped, so this car featured a styling and seating configuration not available in regular production cars. The rear doors were welded closed and had the seams filled in thereby making it a two-door sedan. A U-shaped, Davenport-style seat was found in the rear compartment. Called the Pinconning Special (Hunt's hometown in Michigan), the two-door sedan had a dark green roof and fenders, but was colored light green on the hood, rear deck and body above the belt. It is usually referred to as the "conference" car, although Pinconning Special script adorns both front fenders. Business disputes, revolving around corporate finances, erupted this season between Henry J. Kaiser and Cyrus Eaton of Otis & Co., a stock market firm. The overall effect was less than beneficial to Kaiser-Frazer's financial stability at the time.

1949

KAISER SPECIAL — (6-CYL) — SERIES K491 — With a styling program estimated to have cost $10 million, Kaiser-Frazer extensively revamped its 1949 models to make them look longer, lower and more modern. Actually, the height of the body was unchanged, but a full-width horizontal grille and fenders with 3-1/2 extra inches of overhang made for a lower appearance. The grille featured three wide, horizontal moldings that ran end-to-end and slightly around the front body corners. Rectangular parking lamps were set into the outboard ends of the center bar. On the nose of the car, right above the grille, was a rather large, wing-shaped chrome molding incorporating the company's large K-and-buffalo logo. The 'K' rose above the piece of plated pot metal, while the buffalo, against a black color field, was in the lower mid-section of the badge. Cloisonné finish was no longer used on the badge, as it was now strictly painted metal. Another obvious revision, among 42 styling changes claimed by designers, was larger taillights with more massive chrome housings. Rocker panel moldings were now used on all models. They were placed an inch or two above the edge of the lower body sill, between the front and rear wheelhousings. No hood ornaments were used and the low-priced Special had no exterior side nameplates. Interior treatments included a two-spoke steering wheel with a full horn-blowing ring that had a circular indentation at the top. There was a chrome-plated bottom support bar between the wheel's outer rim and the bright metal horn ring. In the center was a light-colored insert decorated with a large K-and-buffalo badge. The dash top was of painted metal; instrument panel trim was stainless steel; the emergency brake handle was chrome-plated and rubber floor mats were used. The circular housing on the glovebox door was filled with a plain insert, unless a clock (standard in Deluxe models) was ordered as optional equipment. A new model was the unique Traveler utility sedan. Priced less than $100 above the conventional sedan, the Traveler's standard equipment included heavy-duty springs; heavy-duty shock absorbers; a special license plate holder; fold-down rear seatback; plastic seat covers; and hatchback-style rear construction. The car was turned into a combination workhorse and carryall by welding the left rear door shut; moving the spare tire to a vertical mounting behind the driver's seat and horizontally splitting the rear deck sheet metal. Thus, the upper deck and window became a liftgate, while the lower deck was converted into a drop-down tailgate. It took a lot of braces, supports and structural re-engineering (plus repositioning of the bumper guards) to make things work just right, but the result was a combination passenger car and station wagon with a large cargo bed. For 1949-1950, Kaiser also built heavy-duty taxicabs in the low-trim line. They had a beefed-up suspension and more durable upholstery fabrics to suit the task at hand.

KAISER I.D. NUMBERS: Serial number was stamped on a tag on left front door post. Serial number consisted of a Model Number prefix and a six digit figure which is 001001 for the first car of the year. Serial numbers K491-1001 to K491-052740 were used on Special models. Serial numbers K-492-1001 to K492-045050 were used on Deluxe models. The first symbol 'K' designated Kaiser. The second and third symbols '49' designated the 1949 model year. The fourth symbol designated the trim level series, as follows: the lower number '1' indicated Special (low-trim) models and the higher number '2' indicated Deluxe (high-trim) models. A fifth symbol, shown in the Body/Style Number column of charts below, was added to code different body styles. Engine numbers for both series continued from 1948, with the range KM-1001 and up now specified for Deluxe models.

KAISER SPECIAL SERIES K491

Model No.	Body/Style No.	Body Type & Seating	Factory Price	Shipping Weight	Prod. Total
K491	K4911	4-dr Sed-6P	1995	3311	Note 2
K491	K4915	4-dr Utl Sed-6P	2088	3456	Note 2
K491	K4916	4-dr Taxi-6/8P	2216	3345	Note 2

NOTE 1: "Production Total" may actually be a sales total as serial number range ran through 53,996 instead of 52,740. Some cars were built and not sold.

NOTE 2: Kaiser's 1949-1950 production counted as a single total; see 1950.

NOTE 3: References list Traveler four-door, though left rear door was fixed.

KAISER DELUXE — (6-CYL) — SERIES K492 — The Deluxe series was characterized by richer interior and exterior appointments, the offering of a distinctive four-door hardtop called the Virginian and the late introduction of a four-door convertible. Sedans had paint color name listed in chrome script on the side of the cowl. Standard equipment on Deluxe sedans included all Special sedan features plus wheel trim rings; front compartment carpets; Deluxe two-spoke steering wheel with semi-circular horn-blowing ring; glovebox clock; padded dashboard; woodgrain front dash panel inserts; color-keyed interior parts (the brake controls, sun visors, headlining, rear ashtrays, pedal, pads and gearshift knob were all in harmonizing color tones); richer upholstery fabrics; and 112-hp six-cylinder engine. The Vagabond was the Deluxe trim version of the utility sedan. It had special front fender model script, standard fender skirts and wider rocker panel moldings. Genuine leather upholstery was optional in this style. The Virginian four-door hardtop sedan also had Deluxe dashboard trim; front carpets; wide rocker moldings; fender skirts with rocker panel extension moldings; suitable front fender identification script; chrome-plated lower window/belt reveal moldings; plated roof trim moldings; nylon top in black or tan with color-keyed inner liner; three-section rear window; and special, color-keyed interior trims. Released later in the run, as an option priced around $200, was the Custom Virginian package, including Custom script plates; Stockholm and Volta cloth upholstery; Imperial Crush floor coverings; extra brightwork and carpeted lower door panels. Few Custom Virginians were made and most of them served as company show cars. In January 1949, Kaiser added a four-door convertible (a true convertible sedan) to the Deluxe model lineup. It was styled and trimmed like the Virginian, except that it lacked front fender script and usually came with black top grain leather seating surfaces. Some sources classify all the convertibles as 1950 models, since November 1949 was considered the starting point for sales of '1950' Kaisers. However, the earliest Kaiser convertibles were coded as Body/Style K4922, which makes them true 1949 models (1950 convertibles were recoded K5022).

KAISER DELUXE SERIES K492

Model No.	Body/Style No.	Body Type & Seating	Factory Price	Shipping Weight	Prod. Total
DELUXE SERIES					
K492	K4921	4-dr Sed-6P	2195	3341	Note 1
K492	K4922	4-dr Conv-6P	3195	3725	Note 1
VIRGINIAN SERIES					
K492	K4923	4-dr HT Sed-6P	2995	3541	Note 1
VAGABOND SERIES					
K492	K4925	4-dr Utl Sed-6P	2288	3501	Note 1

NOTE 1: Kaiser's 1949-1950 production counted as a single total; see 1950.

ENGINES:

(BASE SIX) Inline six. L-head. Cast iron block. Displacement: 226.2 cid. Bore and stroke: 3-15/16 x 4-3/8 inches. Compression ratio: 7.3:1. Brake hp: 100 at 3600 rpm. Four main bearings. Solid valve lifters. Carburetor: Carter Model 622SB single downdraft carburetor on Specials.

(DUAL MANIFOLD SIX) Inline six. L-head. Cast iron block. Displacement: 226.2 cid. Bore and stroke: 3-15/16 x 4-3/8 inches. Compression ratio: 7.3:1. Brake hp: 112 at 3600 rpm. Four main bearings. Solid valve lifters. Carburetor: Carter type WCD or WA-1 with dual manifold (offered on Special taxicabs).

CHASSIS FEATURES: Wheelbase: 123-1/2 inches. Overall length: 203 inches. Front tread: 58 inches. Rear tread: 60 inches. Tires: 7.10 x 15.

OPTIONS: Defroster and heater ($48). Radio. Radio antenna. Stainless steel wheel trim rings. Tailpipe extension. Round shaped outside rearview mirror. External sun visor. Clip-on vanity mirror. Locking gas cap. Spotlights. Fog lamps. Authentic white sidewall tires. Bumper guards. Accessory Group AG-1 including bumper guards front and rear; heavy-duty air cleaner; vacuum storage tank for wipers; spare tire and tube on wheel; license holder and guards; wheel trim rings; tailpipe extension; rear seat cigar lighter ($105). Three-speed manual transmission was standard. Automatic choke. Oil bath air cleaner. Vacuum booster fuel pump. Several available rear axle ratios. Two-tone paint. Rear fender skirts. Option Accessory Groups: [Group AG-1] includes oil bath air cleaner and directional signal lights ($17.85). [Group AG-2] includes oil bath air cleaner; directional signal lights; rear cigar lighter; chrome wheel covers; and Deluxe bumper guards ($60). [Group AG-3] includes electric clock; chrome wheel discs; spare tire and tube on wheel; tailpipe extension; two front and three rear bumper guards; heavy-duty air cleaner; front cigar lighter; replaceable oil filter element; rear cigar lighter; and dual-action fuel pump ($105). [Group AG-8] includes heavy-duty grille and air cleaner; spare tire and tube on wheel; three rear bumper guards; front cigar lighter; replaceable oil filter element; and dual-action fuel pump in Vagabond ($40); in taxicab (standard). On Virginians and Vagabonds, rear fender skirts appear to have been what is called a 'standard option'. In other words, they are extra-cost items, but were probably installed on all cars unless specifically deleted.

HISTORICAL FOOTNOTES: The 1949 Kaiser sedan was publicly announced on Sept. 19, 1948. A handful of Kaiser convertibles have 1949 model coding. Kaiser-Frazer was America's 12th ranked automobile manufacturer that year. The new models were styled by a design team working under chief stylist Bob Cadwalloder. Color and trim combinations, which were most imaginative, were created by Carlton Spencer. An interesting point is that paint call-out nameplates were seen on the front fenders of Kaiser Deluxe models. They carried the name of the main body color, for example, 'Executive Green' or 'Caribbean Coral'.

1950

KAISER SPECIAL — (6-CYL) — SERIES K501 — Kaiser originally planned to market a face-lifted line of cars for the 1950 model year, but was unable to accomplish the changes on schedule, due to lack of money for development work. By October 1949, it was clear the revisions could not be ready in time. Therefore, the company decided to recode leftover 1949s as 1950 models and to save the new ideas for the following season. On Nov. 3, 1949, company dealers were sent a letter advising that, within four days, a factory representative would arrive with new serial number plates for installation on 1949 models remaining in stock. The sales agents were specifically told not to represent the cars as being different from the previous product. Technically speaking the 1950 Kaiser model year lasted only from the time that the serial number plates were switched (beginning Nov. 7, 1949) until March 15, 1950, when the all-new 1951 Kaiser line was introduced. Inspection of calendar year registration and production figures indicates that approximately 16 percent of the cars originally built to

1949 specifications were sold during this four month period. It has also been determined by automotive historians, that most of these were fancier and higher-priced models, such as Virginians and four-door convertibles. Important features promoted in all of these cars included All-Direction roominess; sway eliminator bar; coil front springs; Super-Cushion tires; double channel frame construction; ball-type midship bearings; two-piece propeller shaft; floating shoe brakes; Centrifuse brake drums; three-point engine mounting; vibration damper; direct-acting shock absorbers; spring leaf lifters; rubber cored spring shackles; hypoid rear axle; Clear-Vision steering wheel; external oil filter; ball bearing water pump; and automatic choke. The Kaiser Special could be identified by continued use of narrow chrome rocker panel strips below the doors and lack of front fender insignia.

KAISER I.D. NUMBERS: Serial number was stamped on a tag on left front door post. Serial numbers consisted of a Model Number prefix and a six digit figure which is 001001 for the first car of the year. The cars were recoded with a serial number plate having the prefix K501 for Specials and K502 for Deluxe models. The first symbol 'K' indicated Kaiser. The second and third symbols '50' indicated the 1950 model year. The fourth symbol indicated car-line. A fifth symbol indicating body type is listed in the Body/Style Number column of charts below. Sequential unit numbers for 1950 did not change from those used in 1949, although the ending number was arbitrarily raised to 600000 for Specials and 500000 for Deluxe models. Based on the 1949 sequences previously listed, car number K501-1052741 was the first 1950 Special; car number K502-045051 was the first 1950 Deluxe. Since the 1950 ending numbers are arbitrary, there is no way to pinpoint the exact model year output.

KAISER SPECIAL SERIES K501

Model No.	Body/Style No.	Body Type & Seating	Factory Price	Shipping Weight	Prod. Total
K501	K5011	4-dr Sed-6P	1995	3311	32,429
K501	K5015	4-dr Trav Utl Sed-6P	2088	3456	19,605
K501	K5016	4-dr Taxi-6/8P	N/A	N/A	2,641

NOTE 1: Kaiser's 1949-1950 production was counted as a single total.

NOTE 2: Approximately 16 percent of total was sold as 1950 models.

KAISER DELUXE — (6-CYL) — SERIES K502 — The Kaiser Deluxe models were also unchanged in specifications and received updated serial numbers sometime after Nov. 7, 1949. After the numbers were changed, they were sold as 1950 automobiles. In addition to the features listed for Specials, the Kaiser Deluxe utilized the 112-hp powerplant having a dual intake manifold and dual-throat carburetor as standard equipment. Deluxe sedans and utility sedans were identified by wider chrome rocker panels below the doors. There were Virginian or Vagabond front fender nameplates or script bearing main body colors, such as "Linden Green," on convertibles and sedans. The four-door convertible and Virginian had the same special equipment features as in 1949. Marque experts suggest that, due to their higher prices, most of these cars were sold as 1950 models.

KAISER DELUXE SERIES K502

Model No.	Body/Style No.	Body Type & Seating	Factory Price	Shipping Weight	Prod. Total
DELUXE SERIES					
K502	K5021	4-dr Sed-6P	2195	3341	37,756
K502	K5022	4-dr Conv-6P	3195	3726	42
VIRGINIAN SERIES					
K502	K5023	4-dr Vir HT Sed-6P	2995	3541	986
VAGABOND SERIES					
K502	K5025	4-dr Trav Utl Sed-6P	2288	3501	4,507

NOTE 1: Kaiser's 1949-1950 production was counted as a single total.

NOTE 2: Approximately 16 percent of total was sold as 1950 models.

ENGINES:

(BASE SIX) Inline six. L-head. Cast iron block. Displacement: 226.2 cid. Bore and stroke: 3-15/16 x 4-3/8 inches. Compression ratio: 7.3:1. Brake hp: 100 at 3600 rpm. Four main bearings. Solid valve lifters. Carburetor: Carter Model 622SB single downdraft carburetor on Specials.

(DUAL MANIFOLD SIX) Inline six. L-head. Cast iron block. Displacement: 226.2 cid. Bore and stroke: 3-15/16 x 4-3/8 inches. Compression ratio: 7.3:1. Brake hp: 112 at 3600 rpm. Four main bearings. Solid valve lifters. Carburetor: Carter type WCD or WA-1 with dual manifold (offered on Special taxicabs).

CHASSIS FEATURES: Wheelbase: 123-1/2 inches. Overall length: 203 inches. Front tread: 58 inches. Rear tread: 60 inches. Tires: 7.10 x 15.

OPTIONS: Defroster and heater ($48). Radio. Radio antenna. Stainless steel wheel trim rings. Tailpipe extension. Round shaped outside rearview mirror. External sun visor. Clip-on vanity mirror. Locking gas cap. Spotlights. Fog lamps. Authentic white sidewall tires. Bumper guards. Accessory Group AG-1 including bumper guards front and rear; heavy-duty air cleaner; vacuum storage tank for wipers; spare tire and tube on wheel; license holder and guards; wheel trim rings; tailpipe extension; rear seat cigar lighter ($105). Three-speed manual transmission was standard. Automatic choke. Oil bath air cleaner. Vacuum booster fuel pump. Several available rear axle ratios. Two-tone paint. Rear fender skirts. Option Accessory Groups: [Group AG-1] includes oil bath air cleaner and directional signal lights ($17.85). [Group AG-2] includes oil bath air cleaner; directional signal lights; rear cigar lighter; chrome wheel covers; and Deluxe bumper guards ($60). [Group AG-3] includes electric clock; chrome wheel discs; spare tire and tube on wheel; tailpipe extension; two front and three rear bumper guards; heavy-duty air cleaner; front cigar lighter; replaceable oil filter element; rear cigar lighter; and dual-action fuel pump ($105). [Group AG-8] includes heavy-duty grille and air cleaner; spare tire and tube on wheel; three rear bumper guards; front cigar lighter; replaceable oil filter element; and dual-action fuel pump in Vagabond ($40); in taxicab (standard). On Virginians and Vagabonds, rear fender skirts appear to have been what is called a 'standard option'. In other words, they are extra-cost items, but were probably installed on all cars unless specifically deleted.

HISTORICAL FOOTNOTES: The exact model year production of 1949-1950 Kaisers was 95,175 units. Some reference sources indicate the beginning of the 1950 model year as Jan. 9, 1950. However, the leftover 1949 cars were re-coded in November 1949. Possibly, the company waited until all cars were converted, before officially announcing the start of the new model year. Henry J. Kaiser was chairman of the board. Joseph W. Frazer was vice-chairman of the board.

1951

KAISER SPECIAL — (6-CYL) — SERIES K511 — The 1951 Kaiser was completely redesigned in a style that would remain essentially unchanged through the end of marque production in 1955. The new design was again the product of Howard 'Dutch' Darrin's skills. The general lines were less boxy than in the past, with greatly increased glass areas. There was a break in the fenderlines, at the rear doors, which eliminated the old pontoon shape. Gone also, was the bull-nosed frontal appearance, which was replaced with a more pleasing shape having a prominent center crease. The grille was formed by two horizontal bars, the main top number running the full width of the body and wrapping around the corners. The lower bar stretched only to the extremities of the radiator opening. A K-and-buffalo badge sat in front of the hood and a dart-like mascot enhanced its overall appearance. A unique 'Darrin Dip' was incorporated at the front of the roof. In this treatment, the upper windshield header had a gently curved contour on each side, with the curves dipping together, in a 'V' at the middle. The resulting 'sea gull's wing' shape would remain a Kaiser trademark until the end. The overall appearance was called "Anatomic Design," as it was claimed that the car fit the anatomy of the human body. It certainly allowed greater passenger comfort with substantial increases in headroom and legroom. Features included the largest windshield in the auto industry; safety locks on rear doors; scientifically achieved weight distribution; Direct-View instrumentation cluster; Tuck-Away spare tire well; rubber body mountings; steel covered rear springs; wraparound bumpers; insulated body; large diameter driveshaft; Hotchkiss drive air cooled clutch; and a 115-hp high-compression six with mushroom tappets, vibration damper, full-length water jacketing, fully-balanced crankshaft and external oil filter. Early 1951 Kaiser Specials were identifiable by the lack of chrome bodyside trim, although a narrow chrome side strip was added later in the run. It was of three-quarter length being mounted low on the body and running from behind the front wheelhousing to above the rear bumper wraparound.

KAISER I.D. NUMBERS: Serial number was stamped on a tag on left front door post. Serial numbers consisted of a Model Number prefix and a six digit figure which is 001001 for the first car of the year. Serial numbers K511-001001 to K511-067256 were used on Specials built at the Willow Run, Mich., factory. Cars built at three other assembly points carried a specific alphabetical serial number prefix, as follows: A=Long Beach, Calif.; B=Jackson, Mich.; and C=Portland, Ore. Engine numbers 100000 and up or 200000 and up were used on Kaisers and were continued into 1952. Body/Style codes show up as the fifth symbol in second column of charts below.

KAISER SPECIAL SERIES K511

Model No.	Body/Style No.	Body Type & Seating	Factory Price	Shipping Weight	Prod. Total
K511	K5111	4-dr Sed-6P	2212	3126	39,078
K511	K5110	2-dr Trav Utl Sed-6P	2265	3210	915
K511	K5113	2-dr Bus Cpe-3P	1992	3061	746
K511	K5114	2-dr Sed-6P	2160	3106	8,166
K511	K5115	4-dr Trav Utl Sed-6P	2317	3270	1,829

NOTE 1: Production Totals based on estimates by historians.

KAISER DELUXE — (6-CYL) — SERIES K512 — The Kaiser Deluxe models had the same new styling as Specials with additional trim features. They also had richer appointments and more standard equipment. They could be easily identified by a wide strip of chrome around the bottom of the body; foam rubber seat cushions; Deluxe dashboard treatments and rear seat ashtrays. Also included were bumper end wing guards; stainless steel belt moldings; bright window reveals; cotton headliner with wool facing; front compartment carpeting; padded vinyl dashboard; and Tenite plastic Deluxe steering wheel with horn-blowing ring. Deluxe interior combinations included Stockholm, Beaumont or Normandie cloths, genuine leather options and pleated, patterned vinyl in Travelers. A two-door Club Coupe with six-passenger seating replaced the three-passenger business coupe in the Deluxe line. Otherwise the high-trim bodystyles were a match for those in the Special series. Both 1951 lines were introduced in February 1950. This was due to Kaiser's carryover of 1949 models into model year 1950. The company now had the resources to make changes originally planned earlier. Thus, the company's 1951 model year lasted from the spring of 1950 through winter of 1951. In November 1950, the famous Kaiser Dragon trim option was initially marketed. Named for their heavy seat surfacing material — which was jokingly compared to the skin of a dragon — Kaisers sold with this option seem to have all come with certain other features, including Hydra-Matic transmission; white sidewall tires; and interior/exterior enrichments. The first series Dragons were sold through Feb. 6, 1951. They came with a choice of nine different exterior color combinations, each of which complemented a specific 'Dragon vinyl' trim combination, with seven selections cataloged. On these earliest Dragons the roof was painted, sometimes in a contrasting shade. Second series Dragons had padded tops. So did a third series offered after April 27, 1951. The second series models had three exterior color choices and were named after them. For example, Golden Dragons came with Arena yellow exteriors and black dinosaur vinyl trim; Silver Dragons came in Mariner gray with Scarlet dinosaur vinyl trim; and Emerald Dragons were painted Cape Verde green (metallic) with matching dinosaur vinyl fabrics. Third series cars came only as Tropical green 'Jade Dragons' with straw-colored interiors. Some Dragon features, such as a removable armrest in second series editions and padded 'Sport Topping' roof treatments, later became separate options for other Kaisers. Also, the armrest was not standard in third series Dragons to lower the price a bit. The GM-made Hydra-Matic four-speed automatic transmission was also available as an individual option for the first time in 1951.

KAISER DELUXE SERIES K512

Model No.	Body/Style No.	Body Type & Seating	Factory Price	Shipping Weight	Prod. Total
K512	K5121	4-dr Sed-6P	2328	3171	56,723
K512	K5120	2-dr Trav Utl Sed-6P	2380	3285	367
K512	K5124	2-dr Sed-6P	2275	3151	8,888
K512	K5125	4-drTrav Utl Sed-6P	2380	3285	984
K512	K5127	2-dr Clb Cpe-6P	2296	3111	4,606

NOTE 1: Production Totals based on estimates by historians.

ENGINE: Inline six. L-head. Cast iron block. Displacement: 226.2 cid. Bore and stroke: 3-15/16 x 4-3/8 inches. Compression ratio: 7.3:1. Brake hp: 115 at 3650 rpm. Four main bearings. Solid valve lifters. Carburetor: Carter type WGD two-barrel Model 781S.

CHASSIS FEATURES: Wheelbase: 118.5 inches. Overall length: (Special) 208.5 inches; (Deluxe) 210-3/8 inches. Front tread: 58 inches. Rear tread: 58.75 inches. Tires: 6.70 x 15.

OPTIONS: Defroster and heater ($48). Radio. Radio antenna. Stainless steel wheel trim rings. Tailpipe extension. Round shaped outside rearview mirror. External sun visor. Clip-on vanity mirror. Locking gas cap. Spotlights. Fog lamps. Authentic white sidewall tires. Bumper guards. Automatic choke. Oil bath air cleaner. Vacuum booster fuel pump. Several available rear axle ratios. Two-tone paint. Rear fender skirts. Conditioned air system. Accessory Groups: [Group AG-1] included directional signals and oil bath air cleaner ($17.85). [Group AG-2] included oil bath cleaner; directional signals; rear cigar lighter; chrome wheel covers; and Deluxe bumper guards ($60). [Group AG-3] included front cigar lighter; replaceable oil filter element; rear cigarette lighter; dual-action fuel pump; wheel discs; electric clock; spare and tube on wheel; tailpipe extension; two front and three rear bumper guards; and oil bath air cleaner ($105). [Group AG-21] included front cigar lighter; front vent wings; full wheel covers; chrome horn ring; dual horns; folding rear seat; Stockholm or Dragon vinyl upholstery; door trim moldings; armrest; right interior sun visor; four bumper guards; and dual rear ashtrays ($180.95). [Group AG-9] included oil bath air cleaner; directional signals; rear cigar lighter; tilt-type rearview mirror; Deluxe front and rear bumper guards; chrome wheel covers; tailpipe extension; electric clock; Tenite plastic Deluxe steering wheel; and electric windshield wipers ($113.59). Three-speed manual column-mounted transmission was standard equipment. Overdrive transmission ($98). Hydra-Matic four-speed automatic transmission ($162). Replaceable element oil filter.

HISTORICAL FOOTNOTES: The 1951 Kaiser line was publicly introduced on Feb. 16, 1950. The Allstate, built by Kaiser, but marketed by Sears, Roebuck and Co., was introduced Dec. 20, 1951, as a new model. The 1951 Henry J, being essentially the same car as the Allstate, was introduced in October 1950. Kaiser-Frazer started assembly plant operations in Israel, Canada and Japan during the 1951 model year; a facility in Rotterdam Netherlands began operations in 1949. Kaiser-Frazer's management stayed basically the same this year. The exact model year production of 1951 Kaisers was 145,031 units. Calendar year registrations peaked at 52,286 cars, but, of course, many 1951 models were registered in calendar year 1950. Hydra-Matic transmission was a popular new Kaiser option. In calendar year 1950, a total of 16,343 Kaisers built to 1951 specifications were equipped with this feature. In calendar year 1951, a total of 13,868 Kaisers and Frazers had Hydra-Matic transmissions installed while 15,898 Kaisers came with manual overdrive transmissions. On Nov. 1, 1951, the Office of Price Stabilization (a Korean War-era government agency) allowed Kaiser-Frazer to increase the price of its full-size models $42-$52.

1952

KAISER VIRGINIAN SPECIAL — (6-CYL) — SERIES K521 — There were two different series of 1952 Kaisers. The first series, called Virginians, was simply a carryover of 1951 offerings with new serial number codes. There were no essential changes in these cars, which hit the market on Dec. 15, 1951. Even the prices were the same as for comparable 1951 models, with slight adjustments in shipping weights being the main statistical change. The front grille was of the 1951 type. A Virginian script appeared on the front fenders. Continental tire kits were factory optional.

KAISER I.D. NUMBERS: Serial number was stamped on a tag on left front door post. Serial numbers consisted of a Model Number prefix and a six digit figure. This year only the starting serial number (proceeded by a factory code) was 1001001, instead of 001001. The third symbol was changed to a '2' to indicate the 1952 model year. Serial numbers K521-1001001 and up were used on Virginian Specials built at Willow Run. Serial numbers K522-1001001 and up were used on Virginian Deluxe models built at Willow Run. Serial number prefixes used at the Long Beach, Jackson and Portland assembly plants were the same as for 1951. Virginian engine numbers continued from 1951.

KAISER VIRGINIAN SPECIAL SERIES K521

Model No.	Body/Style No.	Body Type & Seating	Factory Price	Shipping Weight	Prod. Total
K521	K5211	4-dr Sed-6P	2212	3150	Note 1
K521	K5215	4-dr Trav Utl Sed-6P	2317	3260	Note 1
K521	K5214	2-dr Sed-6P	2160	3110	Note 1
K521	K5210	2-dr Trav Utl Sed-6P	2265	3210	Note 1
K521	K5213	2-dr Bus Cpe-3P	1992	3060	Note 1

NOTE 1: Total production of Special and Deluxe Virginians was 5,579 with no body style breakouts available.

KAISER VIRGINIAN DELUXE — (6-CYL) — SERIES K522 — The Virginian Deluxe was also a carryover of the 1951 Kaiser Deluxe. A Virginian front fender script was added. There were slightly revised shipping weights and new data plate coding. Virginians in both lines lasted only until March 14, 1952, at which point the true 1952 Kaisers were introduced. Today, Virginians are valued about the same as Deluxe 1951 Kaisers, although some collectors will pay a slight premium for a Virginian Club Coupe.

KAISER VIRGINIAN DELUXE SERIES 522

Model No.	Body/Style No.	Body Type & Seating	Factory Price	Shipping Weight	Prod. Total
K522	K5221	4-dr Sed-6P	2328	3180	Note 1
K522	K5225	4-dr Trav Utl Sed-6P	2433	3310	Note 1
K522	K5224	2-dr Sed-6P	2275	3145	Note 1
K522	K5220	2-dr Trav Utl Sed-6P	2380	3290	Note 1
K522	K5227	2-dr Clb Cpe-6P	2296	3125	Note 1

NOTE 1: Total production of Special and Deluxe Virginians was 5,578 with no body style breakouts available.

ENGINE: Inline six. L-head. Cast iron block. Displacement: 226.2 cid. Bore and stroke: 3-15/16 x 4-3/8 inches. Compression ratio: 7.3:1. Brake hp: 115 at 3650 rpm. Four main bearings. Solid valve lifters. Carburetor: Carter type WGD two-barrel Model 781S.

CHASSIS FEATURES: Wheelbase: 118.5 inches. Overall length: (Special) 208.5 inches; (Deluxe) 210-3/8 inches. Front tread: 58 inches. Rear tread: 58.75 inches. Tires: 6.70 x 15.

OPTIONS: Defroster and heater ($48). Radio. Radio antenna. Stainless steel wheel trim rings. Tailpipe extension. Round shaped outside rearview mirror. External sun visor. Clip-on vanity mirror. Locking gas cap. Spotlights. Fog lamps. Authentic white sidewall tires. Bumper guards. Automatic choke. Oil bath air cleaner. Vacuum booster fuel pump. Several available rear axle ratios. Two-tone paint. Rear fender skirts. Conditioned air system. Continental tire kit. Accessory Groups: [Group AG-1] included directional signals and oil bath air cleaner ($17.85). [Group AG-2] included oil bath cleaner; directional signals; rear cigar lighter; chrome wheel covers; and Deluxe bumper guards ($60). [Group AG-3] included front cigar lighter; replaceable oil filter element; rear cigarette lighter; dual-action fuel pump; wheel discs; electric clock; spare and tube on wheel; tailpipe extension; two front and three rear bumper guards; and oil bath air cleaner ($105). [Group AG-21] included front cigar lighter; front vent wings; full wheel covers; chrome horn ring; dual horns; folding rear seat; Stockholm or Dragon vinyl upholstery; door trim moldings; armrest; right interior sun visor; four bumper guards; and dual rear ashtrays ($180 95). [Group AG-9] included oil bath air cleaner; directional signals; rear cigar lighter; tilt-type rearview mirror; Deluxe front and rear bumper guards; chrome wheel covers; tailpipe extension; electric clock; Tenite plastic Deluxe steering wheel; and electric windshield wipers ($113.59). Three-speed manual column-mounted transmission was standard equipment. Overdrive transmission ($98). Hydra-Matic four-speed automatic transmission ($162). Replaceable element oil filter.

HISTORICAL FOOTNOTES: The Virginian was simply the 1951 Kaiser with a new name. This change was made at the time when most other manufacturers were introducing their new models. Kaiser made the change to stay competitive, without spending a lot of money.

KAISER DELUXE — (6-CYL) — SERIES K521 — The year 1952 was certainly a strange one for Kaiser. First the company brought out the Virginian models, which were really 1951 Kaisers with different fender badges and 1952 data plate codes. Then, on March 14, 1952, the company brought out an entirely new range of offerings, which were the real 1952 models, but used the same series codes as Virginians. These cars had new styling elements and higher prices. The grille had one, large full-width bar that ran horizontally across the front of the car. Below it was a more massive 'bridge' type grille guard that housed the license plate. Larger taillamps were seen at the rear, along with a more massive bumper having large, chrome pods at each end. The trunk lid was redone and seemed to be better integrated into the overall package. The Deluxe series was now the base trim level and could be identified by the words Kaiser Deluxe on the sides of the front fenders. A curved, one-piece windshleld was new, as was the lance-like hood ornament. A key-operated starter switch replaced the old button type. Standard features included airplane-type shock absorbers; mechanical handbrake; X-member frame construction; freeze-proof door locks; five-inch wide safety wheel rims; center point steering; and the 115-hp six with chrome piston rings, automatic warm-up feature, full pressure lubrication system and dual-throat carburetion.

KAISER I.D. NUMBERS: Serial number was stamped on a tag on left front door post. Serial numbers consisted of a Model Number prefix (shown in second column of charts below) and a six digit figure. The numbers at each factory were as follows: (Willow Run) K521-1200000 to K521-1218587; (Jackson) K521-B1001001 to K521-B1218587; (Portland) K521-C1001001 to K521-C1218587. Engine numbers 1165001 to 20530001 (Kaiser six with manual transmission); 2114001 (Kaiser six with Hydra-Matic); 165001 (Continental six with manual transmission) and 1218001 (Continental six with Hydra-Matic) were used. Manhattans used serial numbers K522-1200000 to K522-1207965, with the same factory prefixes and engine numbers.

KAISER DELUXE SERIES 521

Model No.	Body/Style No.	Body Type & Seating	Factory Price	Shipping Weight	Prod. Total
K521	K5211	4-dr Sed-6P	2537	3195	4,801
K521	K5215	4-dr Trav Utl Sed-6P	2643	3260	N/A
K521	K5214	2-dr Sed-6P	2484	3145	1,487
K521	K5210	2-dr Trav Utl Sed-6P	2590	3210	N/A
K521	K5213	2-dr Bus Cpe-3P	2296	3060	N/A

NOTE 1: Production Totals based on estimates by historians.

KAISER MANHATTAN SERIES — (6-CYL) — SERIES K522 — The Manhattan now represented the top trim level in the Kaiser model range. Manhattans could be identified by the words Kaiser Manhattan on the sides of front fenders and by the wide chrome trim around the bottom of the body. They had the same new styling features as 1952 Kaiser Deluxe models. There was also a wide dart-shaped beltline molding with embossed treatment; Deluxe instrument panel with padded crash pad; chrome horn-blowing ring and Deluxe steering wheel. Full carpeting and lavish upholstery trims were standard equipment. Many options were available, too. Technically, the Manhattan could be had in any of the nominally available styles, but experts seem to feel that no Manhattan Travelers were built outside of a few prototypes.

KAISER MANHATTAN SERIES 522

Model No.	Body/Style No.	Body Type & Seating	Factory Price	Shipping Weight	Prod. Total
K522	K5221	4-dr Sed-6P	2654	3220	15,839
K522	K5225	4-dr Trav Utl Sed-6P	2759	3310	N/A
K522	K5224	2-dr Sed-6P	2601	3185	1,315
K522	K5220	2-cr Trav Utl Sed-6P	2707	3290	N/A
K522	K5227	2-dr Clb Cpe-6P	2622	3185	263

NOTE 1: Production Totals based on estimates by historians.

ENGINE: Inline six. L-head. Cast iron block. Displacement: 226.2 cid. Bore and stroke: 3-5/16 x 4-3/8 inches. Compression ratio: 7.3:1. Brake hp: 115 at 3650 rpm. Five main bearings. Solid valve lifters. Carburetor: Carter type WGD two-barrel Model 999S.

CHASSIS FEATURES: Wheelbase: 118.5 inches. Overall length: (Special) 208.5 inches; (Deluxe) 210-3/8 inches. Front tread: 58 inches. Rear tread: 58.75 inches. Tires: 6.70 x 15.

OPTIONS: Conditioned air system. Chrome 'donut' style wheel discs. Tailpipe extension. Two-tone paint ($14). E-Z-Eye tinted glass ($15). White sidewall tires ($20). Defroster and heater ($48). Radio. Radio antenna. Stainless steel wheel trim rings. Round shaped outside rearview mirror. External sun visor. Clip-on vanity mirror. Locking gas cap. Spotlights. Fog lamps. Authentic white sidewall tires. Bumper guards. Automatic choke. Oil bath air cleaner. Vacuum booster fuel pump. Several available rear axle ratios. Rear fender skirts. Continental tire kit. Accessory Groups: [Group AG-1] included directional signals and oil bath air cleaner ($17.65). [Group AG-2] included oil bath air cleaner; directional signals; rear cigar lighter; chrome wheel covers; and Deluxe bumper guards ($60). [Group AG-3] included front cigar lighter; replaceable oil filter element; rear cigarette lighter; dual-action fuel pump; wheel discs; electric clock; spare and tube on wheel; tailpipe extension; two front and three rear bumper guards; and oil bath air cleaner ($105). [Group AG-21] included front cigar lighter; front vent wings; full wheel covers; chrome horn ring; dual horns; folding rear seat; Stockholm or Dragon vinyl upholstery; door trim moldings; armrest; right interior sun visor; four bumper guards; and dual rear ashtrays ($180.95). [Group AG-9] included oil bath air cleaner; directional signals; rear cigar lighter; tilt-type rearview mirror; Deluxe front and rear bumper guards; chrome wheel covers; tailpipe extension; electric clock; Tenite plastic Deluxe steering wheel; and electric windshield wipers ($113.59). Three-speed manual column-mounted transmission was standard equipment. Overdrive transmission ($98). Dual-Range Hydra-Matic four-speed automatic transmission ($179). Replaceable element oil filter.

HISTORICAL FOOTNOTES: The 1952 Kaiser Deluxe and Manhattan lines were introduced on March 14, 1952. The 1952 Allstate and 1952 Henry J were both introduced Dec. 20, 1951. Model year production (beginning February 1952) peaked at 32,131 units. Kaiser was involved in production of war materials including aircraft engines and C-119 Air Force cargo planes. On June 23, 1952, the company established a new electronics division. On Sept. 26, 1952, Kaiser Corp. announced its intention to market a plastic-bodied sports car designed by Howard 'Dutch' Darrin. The 700,000th Kaiser-Frazer automobile was built on Oct. 6, 1952. Henry J. Kaiser continued as chairman of the board, with Joe Frazer serving as vice-chairman and Edgar F. Kaiser as president. Chief engineer was G.C. Harbert and chief stylist was Herbert Weissinger. During calendar year 1952, Kaiser fitted 12,320 cars (excluding Henry Js) with overdrive transmissions, while 26,362 additional units featured Hydra-Matic Drive.

1953

KAISER DELUXE — (6-CYL) — SERIES K531 — Kaiser's passenger car business was on the decline in 1953 and economy measures were effected by reducing the number of body styles available. Still, some refreshing design changes were seen in this model year. They represented mainly detail refinements that could be accomplished at minimum cost. A chrome strip was added to the tops of rear fenders to create miniature tailfins. Concealed hinges on the rear deck made for a more modern appearance. Wider chrome caps were added to the headlights, patterned after the aftermarket chrome 'eyebrows' that were in vogue at this time. A new, bird-in-flight-type hood mascot was adopted. The Deluxe series was the base trim level and could be identified by Kaiser Deluxe front fender script; the lack of bumper end caps; the use of small hubcaps; unskirted rear fenders; untrimmed window sills; and side trim consisting of a narrow chrome spear running from behind the front wheel housing to the rear of the car on the lower body. Features being promoted included oversize, self-centering brakes; Safety-First lighting; wraparound bumpers and bin-type glove compartments.

KAISER I.D. NUMBERS: Serial number was stamped on a tag on left front door post. Serial numbers consisted of a Model Number prefix (shown in second column of charts below) and a six digit figure. Serial numbers for Kaiser Deluxe began at K531-001001 and up. Serial numbers for Kaiser Manhattans began at K532-001001 and up. The K530 series Kaiser Dragon 'hardtops' and K538 series Carolina models were added to the line. Their serial numbers followed the same basic pattern, with the series code as the prefix and same sequential number range. Engine numbers for all series were 2059001 and up (Kaiser six with stick shift); 2130001 and up (Kaiser six with Hydra-Matic); 1173001 and up (Continental six with manual transmission) and 1219001 and up (Continental six with Hydra-Matic). The body/style symbol for the new Dragon 'hardtop' was the digit '1', usually prefixed with the K530 series code.

KAISER DELUXE SERIES K531

Model No.	Body/Style No.	Body Type & Seating	Factory Price	Shipping Weight	Prod. Total
K531	K5311	4-dr Sed-6P	2513	3200	5,069
K531	K5314	2-dr Sed-6P	2459	3150	1,227
K531	K5315	4-dr Trav Utl Sed-6P	2619	3315	946

NOTE 1: Production Totals based on estimates by historians.

KAISER MANHATTAN — (6-CYL) — SERIES K532 — Manhattans featured the same styling refinements as Kaiser Deluxe models and, officially, came in the same three body styles. However, it's likely that no Manhattan Travelers were ever built. Identifying features of the higher trim level cars included dart-shaped window sill moldings; a wide chrome side spear running from front to rear fender; bumper wing caps; fender skirts with wide chrome moldings; full wheel discs; and a series nameplate high on the trailing edge of the front fendersides.

KAISER MANHATTAN SERIES K532

Model No.	Body/Style No.	Body Type & Seating	Factory Price	Shipping Weight	Prod. Total
K532	K5321	4-dr Sed-6P	2650	3265	18,603
K532	K5324	2-dr Clb Sed-6P	2597	3235	2,342
K532	K5325	4-dr Trav Utl Sed-6P	2755	3375	0

NOTE 1: Production Totals based on estimates by historians.

KAISER DRAGON — (6-CYL) — SERIES K530 — The new Kaiser Dragon was introduced, as an addition to the line, on Oct. 31, 1952, Halloween day. This model was certainly a treat, but was also quite "trick" as well. In fact, some buyers could have been tricked into thinking that it was a Packard or Cadillac. Standard equipment included all features normally listed as part of Kaiser's Group 100 options package, which carried a retail value of $1,273.98. The extras included all of the following: Hydra-Matic transmission; E-Z-Eye tinted glass; radio with antenna and rear speaker; white sidewall tires; Deluxe wheel covers; windshield washer; heater; defroster; air conditioning; shaded backlight; gold-plated hood and fender nameplates; door lock shields; personalized owners glovebox nameplate; and padded 'Bambu' vinyl top. This later material was also used for most of the interior appointments. As with the previous Dragons, three different series were released for the 1953 run, each having specific interior and exterior paint, fabric and trim combinations. An interesting point is that some Kaiser Deluxe models have been found with Dragon features. Also, the Dragons were not true pillarless hardtops, but sedans with the padded top applied in a manner resembling the style of hardtops (a border showing body color was left around the window openings). They were, however, beautiful and luxurious cars and are true collectors' items today.

KAISER DRAGON SERIES K530

Model No.	Body/Style No.	Body Type & Seating	Factory Price	Shipping Weight	Prod. Total
K530	K5301	4-dr Sed-6P	3924	3320	1,277

KAISER CAROLINA — (6-CYL) — SERIES K538 — The Kaiser Carolina sedan and club sedan were a running addition to the line on March 20, 1953. They were, conceptually, the opposite of the Dragon or, in other words, a stripped economy offering with less chrome, plainer upholstery and fewer standard equipment features. There were no sweep spears on the side of the Carolina bodies; no pads atop the dashboards; no chrome horn rings and inexpensive vinyl upholstery. Also, there were virtually no extra sales gained by marketing these low-budget cars. The Kaiser body simply didn't come off well when the chrome accents were removed.

KAISER CAROLINA SERIES K538

Model No.	Body/Style No.	Body Type & Seating	Factory Price	Shipping Weight	Prod. Total
K538	K5381	4-dr Sed-6P	2373	3185	1,136
K538	K5384	2-dr Clb Sed-6P	2313	3135	308

NOTE 1: Production Totals based on estimates by historians.

ENGINE: Inline six. L-head. Cast iron block. Displacement: 226.2 cid. Bore and stroke: 3-5/16 x 4-3/8 inches. Compression ratio: 7.3:1. Brake hp: 118 at 3650 rpm. Four main bearings. Solid valve lifters. Carburetor: Carter two-barrel.

CHASSIS FEATURES: Wheelbase: 118-1/2 inches. Overall length: 211-1/8 inches. Front tread: 58 inches. Rear tread: 58-3/4 inches. Tires: (Dragon) 7.10 x 15; (others) 6.70 x 15.

OPTIONS: Radio. Heater and defroster. Conditioned Air system. Power steering ($131). Spotlights. Fog lights. Wire wheels ($290). Two-tone paint. Wheel trim rings. Full wheel discs. Tailpipe extension. Front bumper guards. Rear bumper guards. Accessory Groups: [Group AG-31] includes chrome horn ring; narrow rub rail moldings; directional signals; and oil bath air cleaner, on Deluxe sedan and Traveler (standard); on Carolina and Deluxe Club Sedan ($33). [Group AG-32] includes tilt-type rearview mirror; rear cigar lighter; directional signals; oil bath air cleaner; bumper bridge caps; full wheel discs; exhaust deflector; Deluxe steering wheel; electric wipers; and electric clock, on Manhattan (standard); on others, except Dragon ($114). [Group AG-39] includes dual-action pump; front cigar lighter; right-hand visor; dual rear ashtrays; front vent wings; front and rear bumper guards; dual horns; full wheel covers; chrome horn rings and stationary rear seat and deck lid ($83). [Group 100] includes all items in Group AG-32 plus E-Z-Eye tinted glass and banded windshield; 7.10 x 15 white sidewall tires; dual range Hydra-Matic transmission; Laguna and Bambu upholstery; radio (eight-tube Deluxe) and antenna; rear seat speaker; Calpoint custom carpeting on floor and in trunk; heater and defroster; special sun visors; windshield washer; gold-finished glovebox door medallion; Bambu vinyl or Poplin 'Sport Topping'; special body finish in selected color; bright metal scalp and dart-shaped belt moldings; gold hood ornament and nose medallion; gold trunk handle with nameplate; gold trunk lock cover; gold front fender nameplates; chromed lower dash panel; chrome garnish moldings; upholstered trunk and glovebox walls; Bambu vinyl windlacing; and package shelf and interior quarter panels, on Dragon (standard); on other styles ($1,184). Dual-Range Hydra-Matic transmission was standard in Dragons. Three-speed manual transmission with column controls was standard in all other models. Hydra-Matic, as option ($179). Overdrive ($107).

HISTORICAL FOOTNOTES: Model year production was counted from September 1952 and hit only 31,272 units (excluding Henry J). A prototype Darrin sports car was exhibited by Kaiser on Feb. 22, 1953. On April 28, 1953, Kaiser Motors formally purchased Willys-Overland. Kaiser-Frazer Corp. got a name change to Kaiser Motors Corp. The acquisition of Willys created Willys Motors, Inc. and Kaiser Motors became part of Willys. Kaiser-Willys Sales Corp. marketed Kaiser vehicles. The first power steering unit was installed in a Kaiser on May 15, 1953. On Oct. 20, 1953, Kaiser reported a net operating loss of $10,796,754 in the first half of the year. Henry J. Kaiser was chairman of the board. Edgar F. Kaiser was company president. Joe Frazer's name no longer appeared on the list of Kaiser executives. Company headquarters were moved from Willow Run, Mich., to Toledo, Ohio.

1954

KAISER SPECIAL — (6-CYL) — SERIES K545 — General styling changes for 1954 Kaisers are said to have been inspired by Buick's famous XP-300 show car. They included a new "jet airscoop" grille. It had a bowed oval shape and multiple vertical louvers. There was a matching "air intake" chrome vent at the front of a simulated hood scoop. Massive, hooded headlamp units now enclosed the front parking lamps. The taillamp clusters were redesigned to be visible from the side as well as rear. The new front bumper had a vertical crease at its center and twin, vertical guards replaced the single unit 'bridge' type arrangement. A confusing situation was the offering of two distinctly different type Kaiser Specials for 1954. It seems that several thousand 1953 models were left over at the beginning of the year. It was decided to turn them into 1954 Specials. About 3,500 cars were converted this way by adding new grilles, taillights, trim and data plates. These cars had one-piece, non-wraparound rear windows; wide three-quarter-length lower body moldings; 1953-style interior and chassis features and Kaiser-Frazer (Willow Run) firewall code plates. A Kaiser script was on the left edge of the hood with Kaiser Special signatures on the front fenders. When all of the leftovers were sold a second series of Specials appeared. These later cars had much thinner, three-quarter-length lower bodyside moldings and somewhat less chrome on the roof gutters and around the windows. They also featured the trimmer new crash panel dashboard and three-piece wraparound rear window as introduced earlier on 1954 Manhattans. In addition, the firewall trim plates identified these units as products of Kaiser-Willys Corp., of Toledo, Ohio. They used cheaper interior appointments than the first series Specials, too. For example, rubber floor mats, all-cloth headliners and uninspired vinyl-patterned fabrics were seen. Regular equipment on all 1954 Kaiser Specials included wheel covers; bumper guards; chrome exhaust deflector; Deluxe steering wheel; electric wipers; electric clock; oil bath air cleaner; directional signals; rear cigarette lighter (except two-door Special sedan) and tilt-type rearview mirror. This was actually a case of clearing options off the shelf, rather than offering more fully equipped cars. Prices were increased accordingly.

KAISER I.D. NUMBERS: Serial number was stamped on a tag on left front door post. Serial numbers consisted of a Model Number prefix (shown in second column of charts below) and a six digit figure. The third symbol in the serial number was changed to a '4' to indicate the 1954 model year. All production was quartered at Toledo, Ohio. Serial numbers for Kaiser Specials were K545-001001 to K545-023114 and serial numbers for Kaiser Manhattans were K542-001001 to K542-005440. Engine numbers continued from 1953. Kaiser Darrin sports cars had serial numbers 161-001001 and up and engine numbers 3495001 and up.

KAISER SPECIAL

Model No.	Body/Style No.	Body Type & Seating	Factory Price	Shipping Weight	Prod. Total
FIRST SERIES (1953 TYPE)					
K545	K5451	4-dr Sed-6P	2192	3315	Note 1
K545	K5454	2-dr Clb Sed-6P	2141	3275	Note 1
SECOND SERIES (1954 TYPE)					
K545	K5451	4-dr Sed-6P	2192	3305	749
K545	K5454	2-dr Clb Sed-6P	2141	3265	180

NOTE 1: Production Totals based on estimates by historians.

NOTE 2: An estimated 3,500 1953 Kaisers were sold as 1954 Kaiser Specials.

SUPERCHARGED KAISER MANHATTAN — (6-CYL) — SERIES K542 — The 1954 Kaiser Manhattan had the same general styling changes outlined for Kaiser Specials plus the three section wraparound rear window (also used on second series 1954 Kaiser Specials). This window treatment featured curved glass, chrome division bars and curved outer glass panels that swept around the rear quarter region of the roof. The Manhattan interior was also redone with an aircraft-inspired treatment. It had a vertically pleated, full-width padded dashboard; inverted 'U' shaped speedometer and lever-type controls at the driver's left. Standard equipment (actually required options) used on Manhattans included bumper guards and wings; chrome wheel covers; tailpipe extension; oil bath air cleaner; directional signals; rear cigar lighter; tilt-type rearview mirror; windshield washer and 'donut' style chrome wheel trim rings. Kaiser lettering appeared, in script, on the left-hand tip of the hood and Kaiser Manhattan chrome signatures decorated the upper front fendersides. The big news, however, was under the hood. On Manhattans, a McCulloch centrifugal supercharger was standard. It turned the old 'Super Sonic Six' into the 140-hp 'Super Power Six' that had the same 226.2-cid engine.

SUPERCHARGED KAISER MANHATTAN SERIES K542

Model No.	Body/Style No.	Body Type & Seating	Factory Price	Shipping Weight	Prod. Total
K542	K5421	4-dr Sed-6P	2454	3375	4,107
K542	K5424	2-dr Clb Cpe-6P	2404	3335	218

NOTE 1: Production Totals based on estimates by historians.

KAISER DARRIN — (6-CYL) — SERIES 161 — Largely the brainchild of Howard Darrin (after whom it was named), the new Darrin sports car had first been announced on Sept. 26, 1952, with initial prototypes shown on Feb. 22, 1953. It appeared in limited numbers, mainly for testing and exhibition, during November 1953. That was about two months after production had actually commenced in Kaiser's Jackson, Mich., warehouse. The Willys merger and move to Toledo slowed the pace, but on Jan. 6, 1954, the car was finally released for public sale. Some sources indicate that actual deliveries began the same day. The fiberglass-bodied vehicle incorporated a number of radical ideas, including doors that slid forward, into the front fenders. 'Dutch' Darrin had first conceived of such an arrangement as early as 1922. Other features of the Kaiser Darrin included a three-position convertible top and a 161 cid/90 hp Willys F-head six with one-barrel carburetion. Early experimental versions used a special L-head six. Later units sold by Howard Darrin after Kaiser dropped the sports car (in mid-1954), could be had with McCulloch superchargers and 304-hp Cadillac V-8s.

KAISER DARRIN SERIES 161

Model No.	Body/Style No.	Body Type & Seating	Factory Price	Shipping Weight	Prod. Total
161	161	2-dr Spt Conv-2P	3655	2175	435

NOTE 1: Production total given is for production-type Kaiser Darrin.

NOTE 2: Between 12-62 pre-production experimental cars were built.

NOTE 3: Howard Darrin later sold some 50 leftover cars.

ENGINES:

(SPECIAL SIX) Inline six. L-head. Cast iron block. Displacement: 226.2 cid. Bore and stroke: 3-5/16 x 4-3/8 inches. Compression ratio: 7.3:1. Brake hp: 118 at 3650 rpm. Four main bearings. Solid valve lifters. Carburetor: Carter type WGD two-barrel Model 999S.

(SUPERCHARGED MANHATTAN SIX) Inline six. L-head. Cast iron block. Displacement: 226.2 cid. Bore and stroke: 3-5/16 x 4-3/8 inches. Compression ratio: 7.3:1. Brake hp: 140 at 3900 rpm. Four main bearings. Solid valve lifters. Carburetor: Carter type WCD two-barrel Model 2146S.

(PRODUCTION TYPE KAISER DARRIN SIX) Inline six. F-head. Cast iron block. Displacement: 161 cid. Bore and stroke: 3-1/8 x 3-1/2 inches. Compression ratio: 7.6:1. Brake hp: 90 at 4200 rpm. Four main bearings. Solid valve lifters. Carburetor: Carter type YF one-barrel.

(EXPERIMENTAL L-HEAD SIX) Inline six. L-head. Cast iron block. Aluminum Edmund's cylinder head. Displacement: 161 cid. Bore and stroke: 3.12 x 3.50 inches. Compression ratio: 8.0:1. Brake hp: 100 at 4200 rpm. Four main bearings. Solid valve lifters. Carburetor: Three Holley one-barrel with dual headers and exhaust. Special camshaft.

(EXPERIMENTAL SUPERCHARGED L-HEAD SIX) Inline six. L-head. Cast iron block. Displacement: 161 cid. Bore and stroke: 3.12 x 3.50 inches. Compression ratio: (N/A). Brake hp: (N/A). Four main bearings. Solid valve lifters. Induction: Carter type YF one-barrel carburetor and McCulloch centrifugal supercharger.

CHASSIS FEATURES: Wheelbase: (Special and Manhattan) 118.5 inches; (Darrin) 100 inches. Overall length: (Special and Manhattan) 211-1/8 inches; (Darrin) 183 inches. Front tread: (Special and Manhattan) 56 inches; (Darrin) 54 inches. Rear tread: (Special and Manhattan) 58.5 inches; (Darrin) 54 inches. Tires: (Special and Manhattan) 6.70 x 15; (Darrin) 5.90 x 15.

OPTIONS: Power brakes. Power steering ($131). Air conditioning. Eight-tube radio ($89). Heater ($68). White sidewall tires ($22). E-Z-Eye tinted glass ($16). Two-tone paint, Manhattan ($15). Leather upholstery, Manhattan ($250). Pin-crush vinyl trim, Manhattan ($125). Wire wheels ($290). Three-speed manual transmission was standard. Overdrive transmission ($107). Automatic transmission ($178). Available rear axle gear ratios: 3.91:1; 3.31:1; 4.55:1; 4.10:1.

HISTORICAL FOOTNOTES: The 1954 Kaiser Darrin sports car was introduced Jan. 6, 1954. The 1954 Kaiser Manhattan was introduced on Feb. 3, 1954, along with the first series-type Kaiser Special. The second series Kaiser Special was introduced on March 23, 1954. Production of cars built to 1954 specifications was halted on June 30, 1954. On July 19, some 400 workers were put on furlough and the car building assembly lines were utilized for manufacturing Willys commercial vehicles and Jeeps. Model year production of Kaisers was counted at only 5,818 units of which 435 were Kaiser Darrin sports cars. On Oct. 5, 1954, Board Chairman Henry J. Kaiser and Willys Motors President Edgar F. Kaiser signed a contract to produce cars, trucks and Jeeps in Argentina.

1955

KAISER MANHATTAN — (6-CYL) — SERIES K516 — The 1955 Kaiser Manhattan was the only model marketed for 1955. The Manhattan retained the basic styling of 1954, but the height of the center fin decorating the simulated hood scoop was increased. Also, two smaller side fins were added. This gave a total of five decorative fins surrounding the scoop. Model year output was exactly 1,231 cars of which 1,021 were built to fill an order from Argentina. Apparently, the remaining 210 cars were sold in the United States, along with another 270 leftover units retitled as 1955 models. All 1955 Manhattans were supercharged. The company ceased passenger car operations after shipping the final cars off to Argentina. The name Kaiser and the design did not, however, completely disappear. The tooling was sold to IKA, in Argentina, where the Kaiser was built from 1958 through 1962.

KAISER I.D. NUMBERS: The numbering system and code locations were the same as for previous models with the third and fourth symbols changed to '16' to indicate 1955 series. Serial numbers were 51367-10001 and up for sedans and 51467-1001 and up for club sedans.

KAISER MANHATTAN SERIES K516

Model No.	Body/Style No.	Body Type & Seating	Factory Price	Shipping Weight	Prod. Total
RETITLED 1954 SERIES					
516	51367	4-dr Sed-6P	2670	3375	226
516	51467	2-dr Clb Sed-6P	2617	3335	44
1955 SERIES (DOMESTIC)					
516	51367	4-dr Sed-6P	2670	3375	Note 1
516	51467	2-dr Clb Sed-6P	2617	3335	Note 1
1955 SERIES (ARGENTINA)					
516	51367	4-dr Sed-6P	2670	3375	Note 2
516	51467	2-dr Clb Sed-6P	2617	3335	Note 2

NOTE 1: Available statistics indicate 210 units made in 1955 for U.S. sale.

NOTE 2: Available statistics indicate 1,021 cars built for sale in Argentina.

ENGINES:

(SPECIAL SIX) Inline six. L-head. Cast iron block. Displacement: 226 2 cid. Bore and stroke: 3-5/16 x 4-3/8 inches. Compression ratio: 7.3:1. Brake hp: 118 at 3650 rpm. Four main bearings. Solid valve lifters. Carburetor: Carter type WGD two-barrel Model 999S.

(SUPERCHARGED MANHATTAN SIX) Inline six. L-head. Cast iron block. Displacement: 226.2 cid. Bore and stroke: 3-5/16 x 4-3/8 inches. Compression ratio: 7.3:1. Brake hp: 140 at 3900 rpm. Four main bearings. Solid valve lifters. Carburetor: Carter type WCD two-barrel Model 2146S.

CHASSIS FEATURES: Wheelbase: (Special and Manhattan) 118.5 inches; (Darrin) 100 inches. Overall length: (Special and Manhattan) 211-1/8 inches; (Darrin) 183 inches. Front tread: (Special and Manhattan) 56 inches; (Darrin) 54 inches. Rear tread: (Special and Manhattan) 58.5 inches; (Darrin) 54 inches. Tires: (Special and Manhattan) 6.70 x 15; (Darrin) 5.90 x 15.

OPTIONS: Power brakes. Power steering ($131). Air conditioning. Eight-tube radio ($89). Heater ($68). White sidewall tires ($22). E-Z-Eye tinted glass ($16). Two-tone paint, Manhattan ($15). Leather upholstery, Manhattan ($250). Pin-crush vinyl trim, Manhattan ($125). Wire wheels ($290). Three-speed manual transmission was standard. Overdrive transmission ($107). Automatic transmission ($178). Available rear axle gear ratios: 3.91:1, 3.31:1; 4.55:1; 4.10:1.

HISTORICAL FOOTNOTES: The 1955 Kaiser line was introduced Jan. 6, 1955. The last Kaisers built in the United States were shipped to Argentina in June 1955. Kaiser Motors was renamed Kaiser Industries, Inc. and was the platform for the actual creation of publicly held Kaiser business operations. Willys Motors, Inc. continued commercial vehicle operations as a subsidiary of Kaiser Industries Corp. Leftover Kaiser Darrin sports cars were marketed by some Kaiser dealers during the 1955 model year.

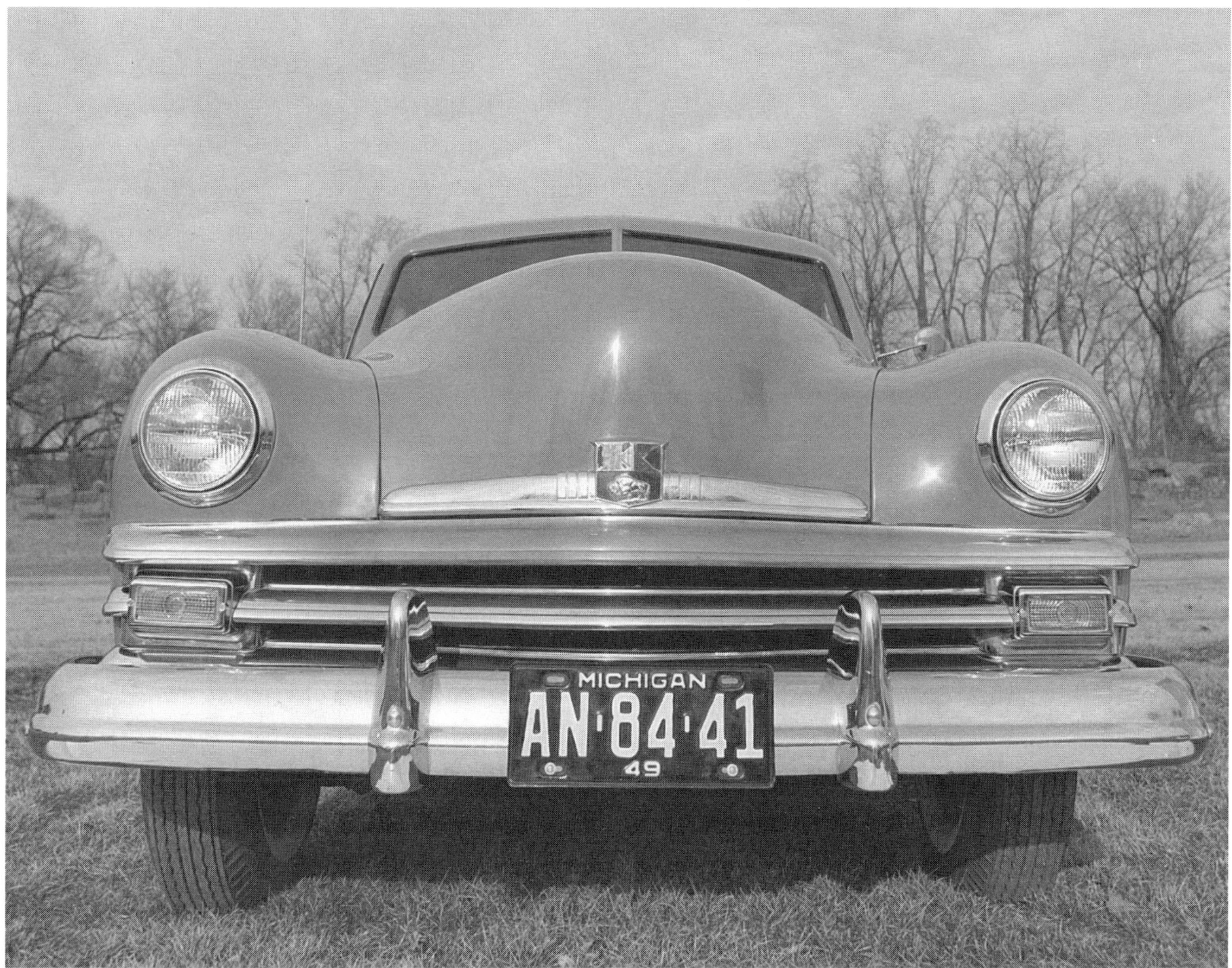

No mistaking the bison-badged snout of the 1949 Kaiser Special. The Kaiser line underwent a major design change that year to make the cars appear longer, lower and more modern.

1951 Kaiser, Deluxe (Series K512), club coupe, OCW

1951 Kaiser, Special (Series K511), sedan, OCW

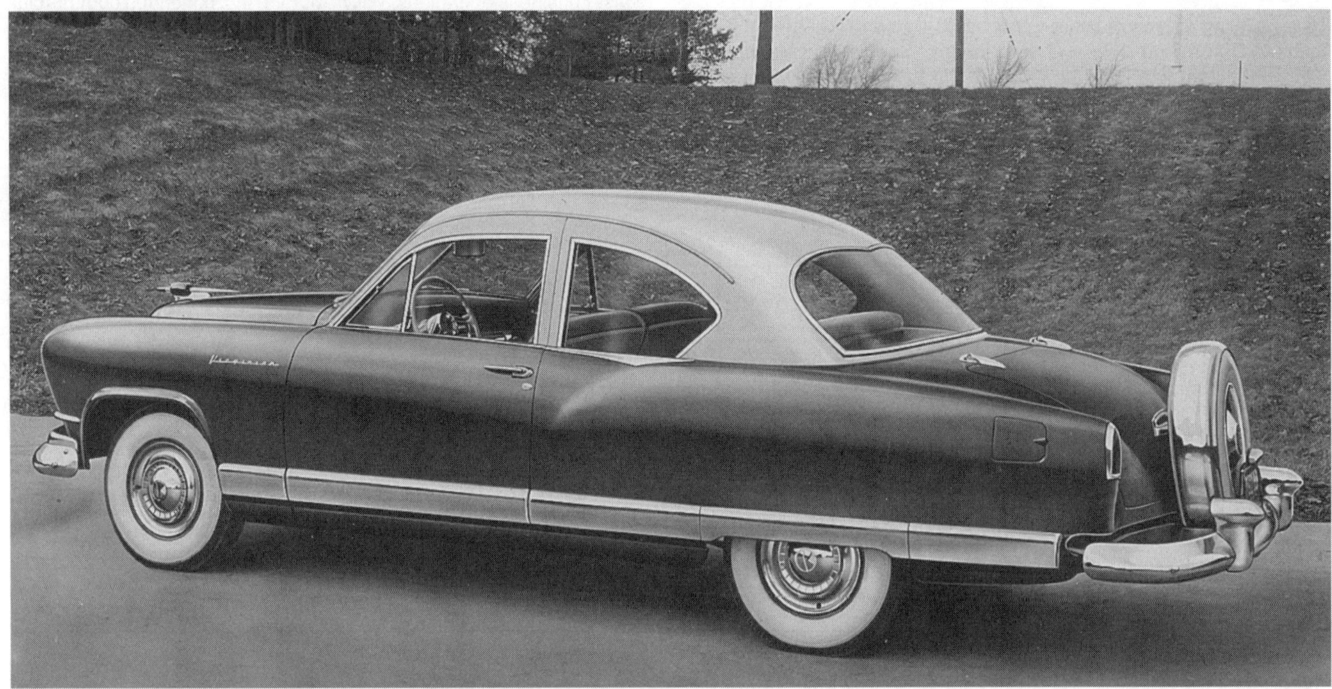

1952 Kaiser, Virginian Deluxe (First Series K522), club coupe, OCW

1952 Kaiser, Manhattan (Series K522), sedan, OCW

1954 Kaiser, Special (First Series K545), sedan (prototype with no fender script—in reality, a 1953 Manhattan with updated 1954 front body panels), OCW

above and below, 1954 Kaiser, Darrin (Series 161), sport convertible, OCW

FRAZER

The Frazer is considered the senior line of Kaiser-Frazer. This is because of the price differential, running $100 to $300 more than the equivalent Kaiser model. Frazer shared the same basic bodies with Kaiser from 1947 through 1950. It was designed by 'Dutch' Darrin, with some modifications by other stylists.

By G. Marshall Naul

The initial Frazer, for 1947, had a subdued grille. There was a Frazer crest, above block letters, indicating the make across the hood nose. The fenderlines ran from front through the rear wheels without a break in the line. The theme of horizontal lines was extended to the interior. There the instrument panel was arranged with instruments and controls in a straight line. In addition, there was a horizontal metal strip, over the glove compartment, with the name Frazer. The rear view was quite simple, with small taillights low on the rear fenders and an indentation in the trunk lid for the license plate. Although all Frazers used split windshield glass, the initial rear window was one-piece. The latter was rather shallow in height, giving less than ideal rear views. The bumpers for the 1947 Frazer were horizontally ribbed, where those of the Kaiser were not.

Early 1947 models were built late in May 1946. The Frazer line consisted of a standard sedan and a more expensive version called Manhattan, the latter costing nearly $400 more. The exact production figures for the 1949-1950 Frazers are not known, but have been estimated from registration figures.

Few changes were made for the 1948 model year. Of a minor nature, the changes were slightly higher compression, stiffer engine blocks, improvements to eliminate vapor lock and reduce vibration, wider tires (Goodyear Super-Cushion) and 28 new one- and two-tone color combinations. For 1948, Frazer accounted for only about 1.5 percent of the U.S. cars built.

Frazer's 1949-1950 models were face lifted. An unusual four-door convertible was added to the lineup. Among technical changes was the use of a previously optional dual downdraft carburetor as standard equipment. It helped increase horsepower on all Frazers from 100 to 112.

For 1951, the last year of production, Frazer added two models instead of cutting back its offerings. One new product was based on a utility sedan called the Vagabond, the name and design being adopted from the 1949 Kaiser. This body type combined the features of a sedan with the flexibility of a station wagon. It was the first hatchback automobile. Other cars of the era used similar themes, but Kaiser and Frazer used a unique design of dual rear hatches. In this system, one panel folded-down to form a tailgate, while the upper hatch opened upward to give nearly complete floor to ceiling interior access. The rear seat in the Vagabond folded flat, forward and backward, to give a level floor similar to a station wagon.

The second new model was a hardtop sedan, in the Manhattan line. This was similar to the Kaiser Virginian of the year before. Although padded tops were supposedly available, few were seen. Some were produced, though. These new body types, and indeed the entire 1951 Frazer production run, were built using leftover unsold 1949 and 1950 Kaiser and Frazer bodies.

Continued for 1951 was the convertible sedan. It was not a popular model, as it cost over $700 more than competitive convertibles. Only 131 were built. Today, marque collectors highly value the survivors.

The demise of the Frazer was in part due to Joseph Frazer's leaving the company in late 1949. Moreover, the sales of the Frazer were disappointingly small and the senior line was not considered to be profitable by Kaiser Motors.

1947

FRAZER STANDARD — (6-CYL) — SERIES F47 — The Frazer, along with its twin the Kaiser, was the first American car to exhibit true postwar styling. It hit the market in June 1946. Appearance features included sheet metal designed by the famous automotive craftsman 'Dutch' Darrin. This was the first envelope-type body, with fenderlines that ran from the front through the rear wheels without a break in contour. The theme of horizontal lines was extended to the interior where the instrument panel was arranged with instruments and controls in a straight line as well as a horizontal metal strip above the glove compartment with the name Frazer. The rear view was quite simple and featured small taillights low on the rear fenders and an indentation in the trunk lid to house the license plate. The one-piece radiator grille had five, full-length horizontal blades housed in a bright metal surround with solid parking lamp extensions at its outboard ends. Rectangular parking lights were set into these extensions, which nearly wrapped around the body corners. The entire grille curved smoothly in and out along its longitudinal axis. Frazer block lettering was seen above the grille, along with the corporate shield on the nose of the car. The bumpers had a unique, three-tier look and widely spaced vertical guards mounted almost in line with the headlamps.

FRAZER I.D. NUMBERS: The serial number was stamped on the left front door post. Frazer serial numbers consisted of a model prefix and a six digit figure which is 001001 for the first car of the year. In 1947, the model prefix F47 denoted a standard sedan; the prefix F47C a Manhattan sedan. Serial numbers for 1947 were F47-001001 to F47-037120. Frazer engine numbers were stamped on a pad on the left front corner of the engine block and on a plate on the left side of the block. Engine numbers for 1947 were GP or F-10001 and up; 50120 to 82999 and 210001 to 306999. The prefix 'GP' denoted Graham-Paige, a company which Frazer evolved from, while the prefix 'F' denoted Frazer vehicles built after the Graham-Paige tie-in was officially dropped. Effective with the car having serial number F47-9940 and engine number F-50120 the prefix 'GP' was changed to 'F' for the balance of production. Frazers also earned a Body/Style Number code on a large plate attached to the firewall. The code was as follows: 'F476' — standard 1947 four-door sedan; 'F47C5' — Manhattan 1947 four-door sedan; '4855' — standard 1948 four-door sedan; '4865' — Manhattan 1948 four-door sedan. (Commencing in 1949, these designations were revised and standardized on all K-F models, with '1' designating the four-door sedan and '2' the convertible; thus, for example, the 1949 standard Frazer carried body code '4951' while the Manhattan convertible carried body code '4962'.

FRAZER STANDARD SERIES F47

Model No.	Body/Style No.	Body Type & Seating	Factory Price	Shipping Weight	Prod. Total
F47	47-5	4-dr Sed-5P	2053	3365	36,120

NOTE 1: Above are 1947 prices.

NOTE 2: Some sources list prices $2,152 and $2,295; weight of 3,340 pounds.

FRAZER MANHATTAN — (6-CYL) — SERIES F47C — The Frazer Manhattan was based on the standard four-door sedan enriched with upgraded interior appointments designed by company stylist Carleton B. Spencer. It was introduced on March 23, 1947, as a running addition to the line. The Deluxe trimmings included broadcloth upholstery, carpeting, rear seat armrest, fancier steering wheel and four front bumper guards. Five exterior colors were provided: Teal blue, Gunmetal, Doeskin tan, Linden green and Turf green. They came in six harmonizing interior/exterior color combinations, or two-tone finishes. Wide chrome moldings were seen on the rocker panel trunk lid and window frames. Full chrome wheel discs; trim rings; concealed floor lamps; front seat assist handles; chrome instrument panel moldings and non-glare rearview mirrors were featured as well.

FRAZER MANHATTAN SERIES F47C

Model No.	Body/Style No.	Body Type & Seating	Factory Price	Shipping Weight	Prod. Total
F47C	47C5	4-dr Sed-5P	2550	3375	32,655

NOTE 1: Sources list a higher price of $2,712 for later Frazer Manhattans.

ENGINE: Inline. L-head six. Cast iron block. Displacement: 226.2 cid. Bore and stroke: 3-5/16 x 4-3/8 inches. Compression ratio: 6.9:1. Brake hp: 100 at 3600 rpm. Four main bearings. Solid valve lifters. Carburetor: Carter Type W-1 or WA-1 one-barrel Models 574S; 622S or 622SA.

CHASSIS FEATURES: Wheelbase: 123.5 inches. Overall length: 203 inches. Front tread: 58 inches. Rear tread: 60 inches. Tires: 6.50 x 15.

OPTIONS: Group AG1 includes front and rear bumper guards; heavy-duty (oil bath) air cleaner; storage tank for vacuum wipers; spare tire, tube and wheel and license plate holder guards ($66). Stainless steel wheel trim rings. Exhaust pipe extension. Full wheel discs. Outside rearview mirror. Heater. Radio. External sun shade. Spotlights. Fog lamps. Plastic white sidewall discs. Three-speed manual transmission was standard. Overdrive transmission ($80). Automatic choke, standard, not an option. Oil bath air cleaner. Vacuum booster fuel pump. Available rear axle gear ratios.

HISTORICAL FOOTNOTES: The 1947 Frazers were introduced June 29, 1946, and the Manhattan appeared in dealer showrooms March 23, 1947. Model year production peaked for both Kaisers and Frazers at 139,249 units. Calendar year production of 144,507 cars was recorded (these totals include Kaisers). Henry J. Kaiser was the chairman of the board of the company this year. Joseph W. Frazer was the president and general manager. Kaiser and Frazer automobiles were built off the same platform, with different decorative trims and upholstery appointments. The Kaiser-Frazer Corp. was incorporated August 9, 1945, in the state of Nevada. Production was planned partly to occur in a West Coast factory owned by Kaiser, but most was done in a refurbished factory at Willow Run, Mich., not far from Detroit. Production of a front-wheel-drive Kaiser, with similar styling, was anticipated at first. At least one prototype was built before this plan was scuttled. The first body drop took place May 29, 1946, and the first cars were shipped on June 22 of the same year. However, deliveries were slow until the fall of 1946. The Fashion Academy, of New York City, awarded the 1947 Frazer Manhattan its Gold Medal for design achievement.

1948

FRAZER STANDARD — (6-CYL) — SERIES F48 — There were no major changes in 1948 Frazers, although the company promoted 35 mechanical and styling improvements. They included such things as a higher compression ratio; relocated, dual action fuel pump; relocated exhaust system; new vibration damper; standard Goodyear super-cushion tires; heavier springs and shock absorbers; aluminum master cylinder; countersprung hood supports; lighter steel brake backing plates; and 15 other refinements. Appearance alterations included new colors; redesigned hubcaps; one-piece nameplate; front carpeting for Manhattans; leather upholstery options for Manhattans and five other minor styling revisions. Some of these were actually running changes first seen on late 1947 cars. Four bumper guards were employed at the front of both 1947 and 1948 models.

FRAZER I.D. NUMBERS: The serial number was stamped on the left front door post. Frazer serial numbers consisted of a model prefix and a six digit figure which is 001001 for the first car of the year. In 1948, the model prefix F485 denoted a standard sedan, the prefix F486 a Manhattan sedan. Serial numbers for 1948 were F485-1001 to F485-032480 on standard sedans; F486-1001 to F486-021591 for Manhattans. Frazer engine numbers were stamped on a pad on the left front corner of the engine block and on a plate on the left side of the block. Engine numbers for 1948 continued from 1947. Frazers also carried a Body/Style Number code on a large plate attached to the firewall with these codes corresponding to the data in the second column of charts below.

FRAZER STANDARD SERIES F48

Model No.	Body/Style No.	Body Type & Seating	Factory Price	Shipping Weight	Prod. Total
F48	F485	4-dr Sed-5P	2483	3340	29,480

FRAZER MANHATTAN — (6-CYL) — SERIES F48 — For 1948, the Frazer Manhattan received front compartment carpeting; leather upholstery options; a Manhattan script plate located on the front fenders, just forward of the door; and a chrome molding strip running between the front and rear wheel openings. A 112-hp six-cylinder engine with two-barrel carburetion, as in 1947, was available in the Manhattan only.

FRAZER MANHATTAN SERIES F48

Model No.	Body/Style No.	Body Type & Seating	Factory Price	Shipping Weight	Prod. Total
F48	F486	4-dr Sed-6P	2746	3375	18,591

ENGINE: Inline. L-head six. Cast iron block. Displacement: 226.2 cid. Bore and stroke: 3-5/16 x 4-3/8 inches. Compression ratio: 7.3:1. Brake hp: 100 at 3600 rpm. Four main bearings. Solid valve lifters. Carburetor: Carter Type WA-1 one-barrel Model 622SB.

CHASSIS FEATURES: Wheelbase: 123.5 inches. Overall length: 203 inches. Front tread: 58 inches. Rear tread: 60 inches. Tires: 7.10 x 15.

OPTIONS: Group AG1 includes same items as 1947 group plus stainless steel wheel trim rings; tailpipe extension and rear seat cigar lighter ($105). Full wheel discs. Outside rearview mirror. Heater. Radio and antenna. Twin fog lamps. Twin spotlights. Retractable radio antenna. External sun shade. White sidewall tires. Leather upholstery. Two-tone exterior finish. Three-speed manual transmission was standard. Overdrive transmission ($80). Manhattan six-cylinder 226.2 cid/112 hp two-barrel engine. Heavy-duty air cleaner. Available rear axle gear ratios: (standard) 4.09:1; (optional) 3.73:1; (overdrive) 4.27:1.

HISTORICAL FOOTNOTES: The 1948 Frazers were introduced in December 1947. The total Kaiser-Frazer production was 139,249 units. Calendar year production of 181,316 cars was recorded. Henry J. Kaiser was the chairman of the board of the company this year. Joseph W. Frazer was president and general manager. The 200,000th Kaiser-Frazer automobile was a 1948 Frazer Manhattan.

1949

FRAZER STANDARD — (6-CYL) — SERIES F49 — Several relatively minor changes were made in the Frazer for 1949, principally in the manner of trimming. The hood escutcheon or crest was lowered to a position just above the new grille and the name Frazer, in block letters, was on the grille. A wider chrome strip was lined under the doors and new taillights were surrounded by a chromed casting. The grille was made into a massive eggcrate-type with both horizontal and vertical bars. The previously optional 112-hp engine was standard equipment in both standard and Manhattan lines. For 1949, only about half as many Frazers were built and sold as there were in the previous year. By 1949, most other auto manufacturers also had new postwar body designs and Kaiser and Frazer sales fell sharply in the face of this new competition.

FRAZER I.D. NUMBERS: The serial number was stamped on the left front door post. Frazer serial numbers consisted of a model prefix and a six digit figure which is 001001 for the first car of the year. Body style prefixes changed to F4951 for standard Frazer sedan; F4961 for Frazer Manhattan sedan and F4962 for a new Frazer Manhattan four-door convertible. Serial numbers were F495-1001 to F495-030480 for standard Frazers and F496-1001 to F496-019591 for Manhattan models. Frazer engine numbers were stamped on a pad on the left front corner of the engine block and on a plate on the left side of the block. Engine numbers F-M1001 and up were used for both series. Frazers also carried a Body/Style Number code on a large plate attached to the firewall with these codes corresponding to the data in the second column of charts below.

FRAZER STANDARD SERIES F49

Model No.	Body/Style No.	Body Type & Seating	Factory Price	Shipping Weight	Prod. Total
F49	F4951	4-dr Sed-6P	2395	3386	14,700*

NOTE 1: *Production Total is an estimate; see 1950 notes.

FRAZER MANHATTAN — (6-CYL) — SERIES F49 — The Frazer Manhattan lineup now included a four-door sedan and a four-door convertible sedan. Both had distinctive, twin molding lower bodyside strips fashioned of bright metal. The bottom strip was narrower than the upper band, which decorated the bottoms of the doors (plus all body panels on the same level) between the front and rear wheel openings. There was also a strip of chrome at upper beltline level, which ran from just below the windshield post to the curved portion of the rear fenders. Fender skirts complete with dual trim moldings were standard on the new convertible sedan. Despite its attractive and unique body styling, the four-door convertible remained a rarity with just 62 examples being built.

FRAZER MANHATTAN SERIES F49

Model No.	Body/Style No.	Body Type & Seating	Factory Price	Shipping Weight	Prod. Total
F49	F4961	4-dr Sed-6P	2595	3391	9,950*
F49	F4962	4-dr Conv-6P	3295	3726	62

NOTE 1: Production Total is an estimate; see 1950 notes.

ENGINE: Inline. L-head six. Cast iron block. Displacement: 226.2 cid. Bore and stroke: 3-5/16 x 4-3/8 inches. Compression ratio: 7.3:1. Brake hp: 112 at 3600 rpm. Four main bearings. Solid valve lifters. Carburetor: Carter Type WCD two-barrel Models 685S; 685SA or 723S.

CHASSIS FEATURES: Wheelbase: 123.5 inches. Overall length: 207.5 inches. Front tread: 58 inches. Rear tread: 60 inches. Tires: 7.10 x 15.

CONVENIENCE OPTIONS: Group AG3 includes electric clock; chrome wheel discs; spare tire, tube and rim; tailpipe extension; two front bumper guards; front cigarette lighter; oil filter and vacuum booster fuel pump ($80). Radio. Antenna. Heater and defroster. Twin spotlights. Twin fog lamps. External sun visor. Fender skirts. Full wheel discs. Wheel trim rings. License plate frames. External sun visor. Leather upholstery trim. Bumper windguards. Two-tone finish. White sidewall tires. Hood ornament. Three-speed manual transmission was standard. Overdrive transmission ($96). Heavy-duty air cleaner. Available rear axle gear ratios: (standard) 3.73:1; 3.91:1 and 4.09:1; (optional with overdrive) 4.27:1 or 4.55:1.

HISTORICAL FOOTNOTES: The 1949 Frazers were introduced in September 1948 and the Manhattan convertible appeared in dealer showrooms in January 1949. Model year production peaked at 24,923 units. Calendar year production of 60,405 cars was recorded; including Kaisers. Henry J. Kaiser was the chairman of the board of the company this year. Joseph W. Frazer was vice-chairman of the board. Edgar Kaiser became the new president of Kaiser-Frazer Corp. A hood ornament was optional on Kaisers for the first time this year.

1950

FRAZER STANDARD — (6-CYL) — SERIES F50 — For 1950, Frazer claimed that its designers had "created a superb new Frazer that is the last word in luxury." In truth there was nothing new at all, since the 1950 models were identical to 1949s in virtually all respects. Standard models could be identified by a few trim distinctions. Many were leftover 1949 models. They had narrow chrome strips below the doors. All models had "Frazer" across the front radiator grille. Company literature highlighted welded steel body construction; Tru-line steering with triple control; Super-Cushion low pressure tires; and interior fabrics, produced by famous mills and looms, which were color styled to blend with exterior finishes. Other important features included centrifuge brake drums; floating shoe brakes; three-point engine mountings; ball-type mid ship bearings; double-channel box framing; hypoid rear axles; clear vision steering wheel; rubber cored spring brackets; spring leaf lifters; V-mounted shock absorbers; directional signals; automatic choke; external engine oil filter; oil bath air cleaner; ball bearing water pump; sway eliminator bar; wraparound bumpers; coil front springs; 27 cubic-foot luggage compartment; push-button door latches; and large ash receivers.

FRAZER I.D. NUMBERS: The serial number was stamped on the left front door post. Frazer serial numbers consisted of a model prefix and a six digit figure which is 001001 for the first car of the year. Body style prefixes changed to F5051 for standard Frazer sedan; F5061 for Frazer Manhattan sedan and F5062 for the Frazer Manhattan four-door convertible. Serial numbers were F505-1001 to F505-20000 for standard Frazers and F506-1001 to F506-11000 for Manhattan models. Frazer engine numbers were stamped on a pad on the left front corner of the engine block and on a plate on the left side of the block. Engine numbers were continued from 1949 in both series. Frazers also carried a Body/Style Number code on a large plate attached to the firewall with these codes corresponding to the data in the second column of charts below.

FRAZER STANDARD SERIES F50

Model No.	Body/Style No.	Body Type & Seating	Factory Price	Shipping Weight	Prod. Total
F50	F5051	4-dr Sed-6P	2395	3386	Note 1

NOTE 1: See 1949 Production Totals. Because 1950 Frazers were re-serial numbered, it is not possible to break out model year totals.

NOTE 2: Total 1949-1950 Frazer production was 24,923, estimated at 14,700 standards and 10,020 Manhattans.

NOTE 3: About 84 percent of the total were 1949 models and 16 percent were re-serial numbered as 1950 models.

FRAZER MANHATTAN SERIES — (6-CYL) — SERIES F50 — The Frazer Manhattan series continued with two four-door models, the sedan and convertible. They could be identified by the wide 'double-level' chrome strip below the doors and the Manhattan script plate attached to the trailing edge of the upper front fender sides. Fender skirts, with 'double-level' moldings on their lower edge were standard on the convertible sedan. Full chrome wheel discs; wheel trim rings; concealed floor lamps; front seat assist handles; chrome instrument panel moldings and non-glare rearview mirrors continued as standard equipment features.

FRAZER MANHATTAN SERIES F50

Model No.	Body/Style No.	Body Type & Seating	Factory Price	Shipping Weight	Prod. Total
F50	F5061	4-dr Sed-6P	2595	3391	Note 1
F50	F5062	4-dr Conv-6P	3295	3726	Note 1

NOTE 1: See Frazer Standard Note 2 above.

ENGINE: Inline. L-head six. Cast iron block. Displacement: 226.2 cid. Bore and stroke: 3-5/16 x 4-3/8 inches. Compression ratio: 7.3:1. Brake hp: 112 at 3600 rpm. Four main bearings. Solid valve lifters. Carburetor: Carter Type WCD two-barrel Models 685S; 685SA or 723S.

CHASSIS FEATURES: Wheelbase: 123.5 inches. Overall length: 207.5 inches. Front tread: 58 inches. Rear tread: 60 inches. Tires: 7.10 x 15.

OPTIONS: Group AG3 includes electric clock; chrome wheel discs; spare tire, tube and rim; tailpipe extension; two bumper guards front and three bumper guards rear; heavy-duty air cleaner; front cigarette lighter; replaceable element oil filter; rear cigarette lighter; and vacuum booster fuel pump ($105). Air conditioned comfort heater. Radio. Antenna. Spotlight. Twin spotlights. Fog lights. Twin fog lights. Fender skirts on sedans. Full wheel discs. Wheel trim rings. White sidewall tires. License plate frames. External sun visor. Traffic viewer. Leather upholstery trims. Two-tone finish. Hood ornament. Outside rearview mirror. Three-speed manual transmission was standard. Overdrive transmission ($96). Vacuum booster fuel pump available with Group AG1 accessory package or individually. Heavy-duty air cleaner optional on Frazer Standard series. Available rear axle gear ratios: (standard) 3.73:1, 3.91:1 and 4.09:1; (optional with overdrive) 4.27:1 or 4.55:1.

HISTORICAL FOOTNOTES: The 1950 Frazers were introduced in November 1949. The production of 1950 models was included with 1949 production totals. Industry statistics suggest that 16 percent of the cars had 1950 Frazer serial numbers. Cars of the two years were actually the same, all 1950 models having been leftover 1949s that were re-serial numbered. It is not possible to break out model year totals. Total 1949-'50 Frazer production was 24,923, estimated at 14,700 standards and 10,020 Manhattans, of which about 84 percent were 1949 models and 16 percent were re-serial numbered as 1950 models. On Nov. 7, 1949, all new and unused Frazers remaining in dealer stocks were re-coded as 1950 models. Many convertibles were sold as 1950 models, although total output of this style was only 68-72 units for both years combined. Kaiser-Frazer was America's 12th ranked automaker in 1950.

1951

FRAZER STANDARD — (6-CYL) — SERIES F51 — The Frazer was much face lifted for 1951, its last year of production. The new body design was based on styling proposals by Howard Darrin and executed by Herb Weissinger. The car featured crisp, highly defined body lines with rakish windstream curves and unbroken fender contours. Elements included large taillights set into high-crowned rear fenders; sculptured crease lines on front and rear fendersides and around the rear wheel opening plus a heavily chromed wind tunnel grille. The standard Frazer series comprised two body styles: the four-door sedan and the five-door Vagabond utility sedan. The latter body type combined the features of a conventional sedan with the flexibility of a station wagon. Other makes of the era used similar designs, but Frazer used a unique design of dual rear hatches. In this one panel folded down to form a tailgate while the upper hatch opened upward to give nearly complete floor to ceiling access to the interior. The rear seat folded flat forward to give a station wagon like flat cargo floor. The word Frazer appeared on the rear door of standard sedans, and Frazer Vagabond on the utility model.

FRAZER I.D. NUMBERS: The serial number was stamped on the left front door post. Frazer serial numbers consisted of a model prefix and a six digit figure which is 001001 for the first car of the year. Body style prefixes were changed as follows: F5151 = standard Frazer sedan; F5155 = standard Frazer Vagabond sedan; F5161 = Frazer Manhattan four-door hardtop sedan and F5162 = Frazer Manhattan four-door convertible. Serial numbers for standard Frazers were F515-1001 to F515-10931. Frazer engine numbers were stamped on a pad on the left front corner of the engine block and on a plate on the left side of the block. The engine numbers used on Manhattans were the same range used on the standard Frazers. Serial number prefixes for minor factories were 'A' for Long Beach; 'B' for Jackson and 'C' for Portland. Frazers also carried a Body/Style Number code on a large plate attached to the firewall with these codes corresponding to the data in the second column of charts below.

STANDARD FRAZER SERIES F51

Model No.	Body/Style No.	Body Type & Seating	Factory Price	Shipping Weight	Prod. Total
F51	F5151	4-dr Sed-6P	2359	3456	Note 1
F51	F5155	4-dr Utl Sed-6P	2399	3556	Note 1

NOTE 1: Actual F515 total: 9,931.

NOTE 2: Estimated breakdown: 6,900 sedans, 3,000 Vagabonds.

FRAZER MANHATTAN — (6-CYL) — SERIES F51 — The 1951 Frazer Manhattan line consisted of a four-door hardtop sedan and four-door convertible sedan. The new hardtop sedan was similar to the Kaiser Virginian of 1950. Both the Manhattan and the Virginian attempted to combine convertible lines with the convenience of a steel roof. They were not true pillarless hardtops in that fixed side window frames and small glass panels (located above the center of the body) were used for added structural support. Both of these reinforcements prevented unobstructed view out the sides of the car. The Virginian (Kaiser) had featured padded nylon top coverings to provide an even more convertible-like appearance. This feature, however, was seen on only a handful of the new Frazer Manhattan sedans and all may have been prototypes. According to marque experts, all but one known model have unpadded roofs. Manhattan identification features include the model name in script on the rear door and the distinct body styles. Deluxe equipment was supplied as standard. It included a carpeted luggage compartment; automatic trunk light; door armrests; chrome trimmed steering wheel; and bright metal interior moldings and trim. A Manhattan sedan was announced at 1951 model introduction, but apparently not produced.

FRAZER MANHATTAN SERIES F51

Model No.	Body/Style No.	Body Type & Seating	Factory Price	Shipping Weight	Prod. Total
F51	F5161	4-dr HT Sed-6P	3075	3771	152
F51	F5162	4-dr Conv-6P	3075	3941	131

ENGINE: Inline. L-head six. Cast iron block. Displacement: 226.2 cid. Bore and stroke: 3-5/16 x 4-3/8 inches. Compression ratio: 7.3:1. Brake hp: 115 at 3650 rpm. Four main bearings. Solid valve lifters. Carburetor: Carter Type WCD two-barrel Model 723S or Carter Type WGD two-barrel Models 781S or 813S.

CHASSIS FEATURES: Wheelbase: 123.5 inches. Overall length: (Standard Vagabond) 207-11/16 inches; (other models) 211-3/8 inches. Front tread: 58 inches. Rear tread: 60 inches. Tires: 7.10 x 15.

CONVENIENCE OPTIONS: Chrome wheel covers. Deluxe bumper guards. Directional signals. Rear cigarette lighter. Tailpipe extension. Tilt-type non-glare rearview mirror. Windshield washers. Chrome 'donut' wheel discs. Bumper guard ends. Electric clock. Chrome horn ring. Dual horns. Dual rear ashtrays. Tenite plastic steering wheel. Front vent wings. Four bumper guards. Air conditioned comfort heater. Radio. Radio antenna. Spotlights. Fog lights. Wheel trim rings. External sun visors. Traffic light viewer. White sidewall tires. Two-tone paint. Leather upholstery trims. Special paint colors. Outside rearview mirror. Padded top on Manhattan sedan. Three-speed manual transmission was standard equipment on F515 models. Automatic transmission was standard equipment on Manhattan F516 models. Overdrive transmission was available on F515 standard models only ($96). Automatic transmission was optional on F515 standard models only ($159). Heavy-duty air cleaner. Available rear axle gear ratios: (standard) 3.91:1; 4.55:1; (overdrive) 3.54:1; (Hydra-Matic) 4.09:1 or 4.27:1.

HISTORICAL FOOTNOTES: The 1951 Standard Frazer line went on sale during March 1950. The Frazer Manhattan models were introduced in August 1950. Model year sales totaled 10,214 units. Calendar year sales of all Kaiser-Frazer products was 99,343 cars. The company was America's 14th ranked manufacturer this season. Production of Frazers was discontinued at the close of the 1951 model run when the stock of leftover bodies was used up. An attractive 'charging knight' hood ornament was used on 1951 Frazers.

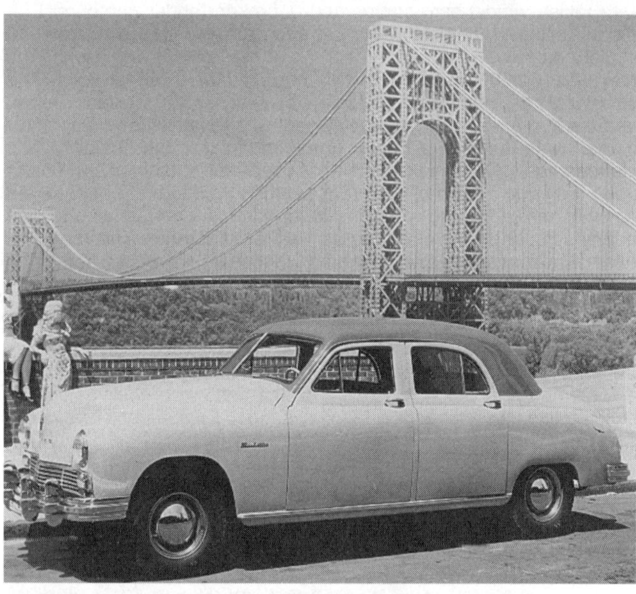

1947 Frazer, Manhattan (Series F47C), sedan, OCW

1950 Frazer, Standard (Series F50), sedan, OCW

1951 Frazer, Manhattan (Series F51), hardtop sedan, OCW

1951 Frazer, Standard (Series F51), sedan, OCW

1951 Frazer, Manhattan (Series F51), convertible sedan, OCW

RAMBLER 1902-1913

RAMBLER — Chicago, Illinois — (1897-1900)/Kenosha, Wisconsin — (1902-1913) — Rambler was the name of the bicycle produced in Chicago prior to the turn of the century by Thomas B. Jeffery and R. Philip Gormully, who operated the second largest bicycle factory in the United States, Colonel Albert Pope on the East Coast being first. The partners manufactured tires as well, as the G & J Tire Company, which ultimately became part of United States Rubber. Of the two men, it was Thomas Jeffery who was the most ardent about entering the automotive age, his young son Charles T. Jeffery enthusiastically urging him on. In 1897 Tom Jeffery built his first single-cylinder gasoline car, in 1898 Charles Jeffery built two more considerably more sophisticated machines. Aside from brief mentions in the press that Jeffery, along with E.C. Stearns and George N. Pierce, were "among the bicycle manufacturers who are experimenting with the motor vehicle," little attention was initially paid to these vehicles. In 1900, however, the cars were displayed at the automobile shows in Chicago in September and in New York City in November — and reporters recognized a good story when they saw it. The Jeffery-designed car was alternately referred to in the press as the G & J or the Rambler; it carried no plaque, so the confusion was understandable, though both Thomas and Charles Jeffery preferred the latter designation. However called, its features of a front-mounted engine and left-hand drive were advanced for an American car of the period, and press reaction was enthusiastic, though *The Motor Age* wondered about the marketability of the notion of steering from the left side of a car: "Whether this will become popular remains to be seen," the magazine commented. "It has many points in its favor, however." By now Thomas and Charles Jeffery had made two important decisions. The first was to sell their bicycle business — following the sudden death of Philip Gormully — to the American Bicycle Company, the conglomerate engineered by Colonel Pope, which was an attempt to monopolize bicycle manufacture in this country. The second was to buy a huge factory in Kenosha, Wisconsin, from which to launch themselves wholeheartedly into the automobile business. They retained rights to the Rambler name; the car left behind in their Chicago factory was produced for a while in 1901 by the American Bicycle people as the Hydro-Car. No doubt it was a variation of the earliest Thomas Jeffery car; the car taken to Kenosha was the son's more advanced design, which Charles advanced further by replacing the tiller with a steering wheel. Suddenly Thomas Jeffery had second thoughts, however, about the public acceptance of an automobile with front-mounted engine, left-hand drive and wheel steering. This delayed the onset of production, and when the new Rambler was introduced in February 1902 it had its engine mounted under the seat and was steered by tiller from the right side. Still, it was a honey of a car. "Its low price, $750, almost warrants some one in expecting something infinitely inferior . . ." *The Motor World* reported. "The vehicle is plainly a high class one . . . rare value for the money." Plainly, too, Tom Jeffery's conservatism paid off; a total of 1,500 cars were produced in 1902, a figure exceeded only by Ransom Olds with his curved dash runabout. Unlike Ransom Olds, Thomas Jeffery did not long remain content with a one-lunger. In 1904 Jeffery built 2,342 cars, some of them higher-powered two-cylinder versions with front-mounted engines — and all Ramblers had steering wheels now. The year following the company made an even more drastic change, discontinuing the single-cylinder midyear and focusing all effort on three larger two-cylinder cars priced from $1,200 to $3,000. Sales in 1905 increased to 3,807 cars. A Rambler four was introduced in 1906, and so was a certain *savoir faire* to Rambler advertising. From "The Right Car at the Right Price," Rambler promotion burst forth with "June Time Is Rambler Time" and other evocative phrases, all courtesy of new employee Edward S. Jordan, who would rise to become Jeffery's secretary and general manager before leaving to give the world the Jordan car and "Somewhere West of Laramie." By now the Jeffery company was an industry leader, and the Kenosha factory in which it turned out its Rambler cars was not only the largest in the country but was also widely reputed to be the best equipped. Thomas Jeffery was sitting on top of the world. Mass production, however, never interested him. Actually, the fortune he was making in the manufacture of medium-priced high-quality cars was a splendid one anyway. But on April 2, 1910, while vacationing in Italy, Thomas Jeffery died of a heart attack. His will stipulated that his business, which had previously traded under the name of Thomas B. Jeffery & Company, would now be incorporated as the Thomas B. Jeffery Company, though ownership remained entirely with the Jeffery family. His son Charles took over as president, and some changes followed, including the raising of production by about 500 cars a year from the 3,000-more-or-less that his father had preferred, and the attaching of such designations as Country Club, Knickerbocker and Valkyrie (Ned Jordan's idea, naturally) to various of the Rambler models. Not changed, however, was the Rambler's right-hand drive. The biggest change came in 1914. It was a new car altogether. The decision was a gutsy one, Rambler being among the oldest and most respected names in the industry. But now it was no more. The new car from the big Kenosha factory would be called the Jeffery.

1901

RAMBLER — MODEL A/B — ONE-CYLINDER: Models A and B, built in 1901, were experimental and were not offered for sale.

I.D. NUMBERS: [Both models] None.

Model No.	Body Type & Seating	Factory Price	Shipping Weight	Prod. Total
A/B	Runabout-2P	750	1200	2

ENGINE: Data unavailable.

TECHNICAL: Data unavailable.

CHASSIS: Data unavailable.

HISTORY: Experimental car designed by Charles Jeffery, son of Thomas B. Jeffery. Manufactured by Thomas B. Jeffery & Co., Kenosha, Wis.

1902

RAMBLER — MODEL C/D — ONE-CYLINDER: The Model D was identical to the Model C, except that it had a leather top, rubber side curtains and a storm apron.

I.D. NUMBERS: [Both models] 1-1500.

Model No.	Body Type & Seating	Factory Price	Shipping Weight	Prod. Total
C	Runabout-2P	750	1200	NA
D	Stanhope-2P	825	1250	NA

ENGINE: One-cylinder. Bore & Stroke: 4.5 x 6 in. NACC HP.: 8.1.

TECHNICAL: Data unavailable.

CHASSIS: Data unavailable.

HISTORY: First year of mass production for Thomas B. Jeffery & Co. Model year production (approx.): 1,500 cars.

1903

RAMBLER — MODEL E/F — ONE-CYLINDER: Basically a continuation of the 1902 Rambler line. The F had a leather top, rubber side curtains and a storm apron.

I.D. NUMBERS: [Model E] 1501-2850; [Model F] 2851-5192.

Model No.	Body Type & Seating	Factory Price	Shipping Weight	Prod. Total
E	Runabout-2P	750	1400	1350
F	Stanhope-2P	800	1400	2343

ENGINE: One-cylinder. Bore & Stroke: 5 x 6 in. NACC HP.: 8.1.

TECHNICAL: Data unavailable.

CHASSIS: Wheelbase: [Model E] 78 inches; [Model F] 78 inches.

HISTORY: Second year of mass production for Thomas B. Jeffery & Co. Model year production (approx.): 3,693 cars.

1904

RAMBLER — MODEL G/H — ONE-CYLINDER: Basically a continuation of the 1903 Rambler line. The Stanhope became a touring. A panel delivery truck was added.

RAMBLER — MODELS J/K/L — TWO-CYLINDER: The two-cylinder Rambler was over twice as powerful as the one-cylinder, for less than a 50 percent higher price. Typical standard equipment (Model L) included 30-inch wood artillery wheels: four full elliptic springs; 3-1/2 inch tires; two powerful brakes; tools and equipment (oilers, tire pump, tire repair kit); Solar triple-top brass oil sidelamps; No. 1 Solar brass headlamp; Solar brass taillight; brass tube horn; two willow baskets; canopy top with beveled plate glass swinging front and waterproof side curtains.

I.D. NUMBERS: [All models] 2850-5192.

Model No.	Body Type & Seating	Factory Price	Shipping Weight	Prod. Total
[ONE-CYL.]				
G	Roadster-2P	750	1500	NA
H	Roadster Touring-5P	850	1500	NA
D-1	Panel Delivery-2P	850	1500	NA
[TWO-CYL.]				
J	Roadster-2P	1100	1800	NA
J-2	Roadster-2P	1100	1800	NA
K	Touring-5P	1200	1800	NA
K-2	Touring-5P	1200	1800	NA
L	Touring-5P	1350	1725	NA
L-2	Touring-5P	1350	1725	NA

ENGINE: [One-cylinder]: Bore & Stroke: 5 x 6 in. NACC HP.: 7. [Two-cylinder] Bore & Stroke: 5 x 6 in. NACC HP.: 16.

TECHNICAL: Data unavailable.

CHASSIS: Wheelbase: [Models G/H] 81 inches; [Models J/K/L] 84 inches.

HISTORY: Two-cylinder series added. Calendar year production (approx.): 2,343. Prices given were for factory pickup sales. "An automobile that stands wear without constant repair," said a 1904 advertisement. Speed range of the Model L was six to 40 mph.

1905

RAMBLER — Type I/II — [18/20 HORSEPOWER] — TWO-CYLINDER: A larger new touring with a 90-inch wheelbase was designated the Surrey I. The Surrey II was the same basic car with a 10-inch longer wheelbase. A limousine was also marketed. Apparently, this was the first closed body Rambler.

I.D. NUMBERS: [All models] 5193-9000.

Model No.	Body Type & Seating	Factory Price	Shipping Weight	Prod. Total
[18/20 HP]				
Surrey I	Touring-5P	1200	2000	NA
Surrey II	Touring-5P	1650	2000	NA
Limo	Limousine-5P	3000	3000	NA

ENGINE: [Two-cylinder]: Bore & Stroke: 5 x 6 in. NACC HP.: 18/20.

TECHNICAL: Data unavailable.

CHASSIS: Wheelbase: [Type I] 90 inches; [Type II] 100 inches; [Limo] 112 inches.

HISTORY: Calendar year production (approx.): 3,807. First closed Rambler introduced. Rambler used the term "Surrey" to describe what was actually a Tonneau Touring car with cape cart top.

1906

RAMBLER — Type III/IV — 18/20 HORSEPOWER — TWO-CYLINDER: The 90-inch wheelbase and 100-inch wheelbase Tonneau Touring cars with cape cart tops comprised this carryover series.

RAMBLER — MODEL 14 — 20 HP — FOUR-CYLINDER: A five-passenger "Light Four" on a 106-inch wheelbase. Has a new four-cylinder engine.

RAMBLER — MODEL 15/16 — 40 HP — FOUR-CYLINDER: Rambler's first four-cylinder line was on a 112-inch wheelbase. A closed limousine was included, as well as a pair of touring cars. The 1906 Rambler Model 15 was advertised as a high-powered car with a four-cylinder engine, 35/40 horsepower, sliding gear transmission and all modern features, but simplified to the practical service of non-professional operators. "Our catalog will interest you and a personal examination will convince you that it is the car of the year," read the ad copy. The Model 15 was of open front entrance design, with doors fitted on its rear tonneau.

RAMBLER — MODEL 17 — 10/12 HP — TWO-CYLINDER: A short wheelbase runabout with light horsepower rating. Not shown in AMC specifications book.

RAMBLER — MODEL 19 — 18 HP — TWO-CYLINDER: Probably a renumbered version of the Type I or Type II.

RAMBLER — MODEL 147 — 20 HP — FOUR-CYLINDER: An improved version of the Model 14 with the new four-cylinder engine.

I.D. NUMBERS: [All 18 HP models and Model 15] 5193-9000; [Model 14/16/147] 9001-15300.

Model No.	Body Type & Seating	Factory Price	Shipping Weight	Prod. Total
[10/12 HP]				
17	Runabout-2P	800	NA	NA
[18/20 HP]				
Surrey III	Touring-5P	1350	2200	NA
Surrey IV	Touring-5P	1350	2200	NA
Model 19	Touring-2P	1250	2200	NA
[20/25 HP LIGHT FOURS]				
14	Touring-5P	1750	2300	NA
147	Touring-5P	1750	2400	NA
[35/40 HP FOURS]				
15	Touring-5P	2500	2600	NA
16	Limousine-5P	3000	3000	NA

ENGINES:

[Model 17] Two-cylinder. Bore & Stroke: 4-1/2 x 5 in. NACC HP.: 10/12.

[Type III/IV and Model 19] Two-cylinder. Bore & Stroke: 5 x 6 in. NACC HP.: 18/20.

[Model 14] Four-cylinder. Bore & Stroke: 4-1/2 x 4-1/2 in. NACC HP.: 20/25.

[Model 147] Four-cylinder. Bore & Stroke: 4 x 4-1/2 in. NACC HP.: 20.

[Model 15/16] Four-cylinder. Bore & Stroke: 5 x 5-1/2 in. NACC HP.: 35/40.

TECHNICAL: Data unavailable.

CHASSIS:

[Type III/IV] Wheelbase: 96 inches.

[Model 17] Wheelbase: 88 inches.

[Model 19] Wheelbase: 96 inches.

[Model 14/147] Wheelbase: 106 inches.

[Model 15/16] Wheelbase: 112 inches.

HISTORY: Calendar year production (approx.): 6,299. Offered by Thomas B. Jeffery & Co. with main office and factory in Kenosha, Wis., and sales branches in Boston, Mass.; Philadelphia, Pa.; Milwaukee, Wis.; Chicago. Ill.; San Francisco, Calif.; and New York City. The company's new Model 15 was also sold in 1907.

1907

RAMBLER — MODEL 27 — 16.2 HORSEPOWER — TWO-CYLINDER: A 90-inch wheelbase light two-cylinder roadster with an exclusive engine.

RAMBLER — MODEL 21/22 — 20 HP — TWO-CYLINDER: Technically, a continuation of the "Surrey" line of 1905-1906 using just the larger 100-inch wheelbase.

RAMBLER — MODEL 24/248 — LIGHT FOUR— 25/30 HP — FOUR-CYLINDER: Technically, a continuation of the Model 14 with two-inch longer wheelbase.

RAMBLER — MODEL 25/245 — 35/40 HP — FOUR-CYLINDER: Technically, a continuation of the Model 15/16 with largest Rambler engine and wheelbase.

I.D. NUMBERS: [All models] 9001-15300 continued from 1906.

Model No.	Body Type & Seating	Factory Price	Shipping Weight	Prod. Total
[16.2 HP]				
27	Roadster-2P	950	2000	NA
[18/20 HP]				
21	Touring-5P	1350	2000	NA
22	Roadster-2P	1250	2000	NA

[25/30 HP LIGHT FOURS]

Model No.	Body Type & Seating	Factory Price	Shipping Weight	Prod. Total
24	Touring-5P	2000	2600	NA
248	Touring-5P	1900	2600	NA
[35/40 HP FOURS]				
25	Touring-5P	2500	2600	NA
245	Touring-5P	2500	2600	NA

ENGINES:

[Model 27] Two-cylinder. Bore & Stroke: 4-1/2 x 5 in. NACC HP.: 16.2.

[Model 21/22] Two-cylinder. Bore & Stroke: 5 x 6 in. NACC HP.: 18/20.

[Model 24/248] Four-cylinder. Bore & Stroke: 4-1/2 x 4-1/2 in. NACC HP.: 25/30.

[Model 25/245] Four-cylinder. Bore & Stroke: 5 x 5-1/2 in. NACC HP.: 40.

[Model 15/16] Four-cylinder. Bore & Stroke: 5 x 5-1/2 in. NACC HP.: 35/40.

TECHNICAL: Selective sliding gear transmission.

CHASSIS:

[Model 27] Wheelbase: 90 inches.

[Model 21/22] Wheelbase: 100 inches.

[Model 24/248] Wheelbase: 108 inches.

[Model 25/245] Wheelbase: 112 inches.

HISTORY: Model 15 also built in 1907.

1908

RAMBLER — MODEL 31/37 — 22 HORSEPOWER — TWO-CYLINDER: The old 5 x 6-inch two-cylinder Rambler engine uprated to 22 NACC horsepower and installed in a larger 106-inch wheelbase. Quite large for a two-cylinder car.

RAMBLER — MODEL 34/34A/36 — LIGHT FOUR — 32 HP — FOUR-CYLINDER: Technically, a continuation of the Model 24/248 with four-inch longer wheelbase and slight horsepower rating boost. Heftier prices and weights apparent.

RAMBLER — MODEL 345 — 40 HP — FOUR-CYLINDER: A virtually unchanged carryover of the Model 245 with largest Rambler engine and wheelbase. Even has same price and weight.

I.D. NUMBERS: [Model 345] 9001-15300 continued from 1907; [All other models) 15603 to 17200.

[TWO-CYL.]

Model No.	Body Type & Seating	Factory Price	Shipping Weight	Prod. Total
31	Touring-5P	1400	2300	NA
37	Roadster-2P	1200	2300	NA
[LIGHT FOUR]				
34	Touring-5P	2250	2800	NA
34A	Roadster-3P	2250	2700	NA
36	Limousine-5P	3250	3000	NA
[40 HP FOUR]				
345	Touring-5P	2500	2600	NA

ENGINES:

[Model 31/37] Two-cylinder. Bore & Stroke: 5 x 6 in. NACC HP.: 22.

[Model 34/34A/36] Four-cylinder. Bore & Stroke: 4-1/2 x 4-1/2 in. NACC HP.: 32.4.

[Model 345] Four-cylinder. Bore & Stroke: 5 x 5-1/2 in. NACC HP.: 40.

TECHNICAL: Selective sliding gear transmission.

CHASSIS:

[Model 31/37] Wheelbase: 106 inches.

[Model 34/34A/36] Wheelbase: 112 inches.

[Model 345] Wheelbase: 112 inches.

HISTORY: New series production: 1,597 cars.

1909

RAMBLER — MODEL 41/47 — 22 HORSEPOWER — TWO-CYLINDER: The old 5 x 6-inch two-cylinder Rambler engine again in the large 106-inch wheelbase. A continuation of the 1908 two-cylinder with refinements only.

RAMBLER — MODEL 44/44A/44CC — LIGHT FOUR — 32 HP — FOUR-CYLINDER: Technically, a continuation of previous Light Four with one new Close-Coupled sedan model. Slightly heavier, but prices basically unchanged.

RAMBLER — MODEL 45 — 40 HP — FOUR-CYLINDER: The 245/345 drivetrain on a massive 123-inch wheelbase chassis. Much heavier, but no price hike. Touring becomes a seven-passenger model.

I.D. NUMBERS: [All models] 20001-21963.

[TWO-CYL.]

Model No.	Body Type & Seating	Factory Price	Shipping Weight	Prod. Total
41	Touring-5P	1350	2300	NA
47	Roadster-2P	1200	2300	NA
[LIGHT FOUR]				
44	Touring-5P	2250	2800	NA
44A	Roadster-3P	2250	2800	NA
44CC	C.C. Sedan-5P	2250	2800	NA
[40 HP FOUR]				
45	Touring-7P	2500	3400	NA
45CC	C.C. Sedan-4P	2500	3400	NA

ENGINES:

[Model 41/47] Two-cylinder. Bore & Stroke: 5 x 6 in. NACC HP.: 22.

[Model 44] Four-cylinder. Bore & Stroke: 4-1/2 x 4-1/2 in. NACC HP.: 32.4.

[Model 45] Four-cylinder. Bore & Stroke: 5 x 5-1/2 in. NACC HP.: 40.

TECHNICAL: Selective sliding gear transmission.

CHASSIS:

[Model 41/47] Wheelbase: 106 inches.

[Model 44] Wheelbase: 112 inches.

[Model 45] Wheelbase: 123 inches.

HISTORY: Calendar year production: 1,963 cars.

1910

RAMBLER — MODEL 53 — LIGHT FOUR — 32 HP — FOUR-CYLINDER: Technically, a continuation of previous Light Four on a three-inch larger wheelbase chassis. This is now the base series Rambler, with two-cylinder cars dropped.

RAMBLER — MODEL 54 — 40 HP — FOUR-CYLINDER: This car used the big Rambler engine in a 117-inch wheelbase chassis.

RAMBLER — MODEL 55 — 40 HP — FOUR-CYLINDER: This line used the big Rambler four in the biggest chassis and featured a new five-passenger limousine.

I.D. NUMBERS: [All models] 22501-24744.

[LIGHT FOUR]

Model No.	Body Type & Seating	Factory Price	Shipping Weight	Prod. Total
53	Touring-5P	1800	3200	NA
53RD	Roadster-2P	1800	3200	NA
[40 HP FOUR/117 in. wb]				
54	Touring-5P	2250	3400	NA
54CC	C.C. Sedan-4P	2250	3400	NA
[40 HP FOUR/123 in. wb]				
55	Touring-7P	2500	3400	NA
55CC	C.C. Sedan-4P	2350	3300	NA
55L	Limousine-5P	3750	3500	NA

ENGINES:

[Model 53] Four-cylinder. Bore & Stroke: 4-1/2 x 4-1/2 in. NACC HP.: 32.4.

[Model 54/55] Four-cylinder. Bore & Stroke: 5 x 5-1/2 in. NACC HP.: 40.

TECHNICAL: Selective sliding gear transmission.

CHASSIS:

[Model 53] Wheelbase: 109 inches.

[Model 54] Wheelbase: 117 inches.

[Model 55] Wheelbase: 123 inches.

HISTORY: Calendar year production: 2,243 cars.

1911

RAMBLER — MODEL 63 — LIGHT FOUR — 32 HP — FOUR-CYLINDER: Technically, a continuation of previous Light Four with another three-inch wheelbase stretch. New body styles included a coupe and a town car.

RAMBLER — MODEL 64 — 40 HP — FOUR-CYLINDER: This car, with the big Rambler engine, was the 54 with a three-inch longer wheelbase and new Toy Tonneau and Landaulet styles.

RAMBLER — MODEL 65 — 40 HP — FOUR-CYLINDER: The "Big Four" line got a bigger-by-five-inches stance for 1911 and a new Toy Tonneau model. In addition to the touring, the limousine was now a seven-passenger job.

I.D. NUMBERS: [All models] 25000-28000.

[LIGHT FOUR]

Model No.	Body Type & Seating	Factory Price	Shipping Weight	Prod. Total
63	Touring-5P	2175	3200	NA
63RD	Roadster-2P	2105	3200	NA
63C	Coupe-4P	2605	3500	NA
63TC	Town Car-7P	2880	3500	NA
[40 HP FOUR/120 in. wb]				
64	Touring-5P	2775	3400	NA
64TT	Toy Tonneau-4P	2775	3400	NA
64LAND	Landaulet-7P	3650	3500	NA
[40 HP FOUR/128 in. wb]				
65	Touring-7P	3050	3400	NA
65TT	Toy Tonneau-4P	3050	3400	NA
65LIM	Limousine-7P	4150	3500	NA

ENGINES:

[Model 63] Four-cylinder. Bore & Stroke: 4-1/2 x 4-1/2 in. NACC HP.: 32.4.

[Model 64/65] Four-cylinder. Bore & Stroke: 5 x 5-1/2 in. NACC HP.: 40.

TECHNICAL: Selective sliding gear transmission.

CHASSIS:

[Model 63] Wheelbase: 112 inches.

[Model 64] Wheelbase: 120 inches.

[Model 65] Wheelbase: 128 inches.

HISTORY: Calendar year production: 3,000 cars.

1912

RAMBLER — MODEL 73 — LIGHT FOUR — 32 HP — FOUR-CYLINDER: Technically, a continuation of previous Light Four with a massive eight-inch wheelbase stretch. New body styles included a limousine and close-coupled touring.

RAMBLER — MODEL 74 — 40/50 HP — FOUR-CYLINDER: This car, with the big Rambler engine, was based on the 64 with no change in wheelbase. New models included a close-coupled touring and the "Valkyrie" four-passenger Torpedo Touring. Standard equipment included a gas tank; lamps; horn; tools; and jack.

RAMBLER — MODEL 75/76 — 40/50 HP — FOUR-CYLINDER: The "Big Four" was technically similar to last year's Model 65. The models now had names such as Morain, Metropolitan and Cross-Country. Standard equipment included a gas tank; lamps; horn; and tools.

I.D. NUMBERS: [74/75] 25000-28000 continued from 1910; [All other models] 28001-31551.

[LIGHT FOUR]

Model No.	Body Type & Seating	Factory Price	Shipping Weight	Prod. Total
73-4CC	Country Club Touring-5P	1650	3600	NA
73RD4	Roadster-2P	1650	3600	NA
73S	Sub CC Torpedo Touring-4P	1650	3600	NA
73G	Gotham Limo.-7P	2750	3800	NA
73	Sedan-6P	2500	3800	NA
[40 HP FOUR/120 in. wb]				
74CC	Country Club Touring-5P	2250	3400	NA
74	Valkyrie Touring-4P	2250	3400	NA
[40 HP FOUR/128 in. wb]				
75-7M	Moraine Touring-7P	2500	3400	NA
76TOR	CC Torpedo Touring-6P	2850	3800	NA
76-7M	Metropolitan Touring-7P	2850	3800	NA
76L	Limousine-7P	4200	4000	NA

ENGINES:

[Model 73] Four-cylinder. Cast singly. Offset. Bore & Stroke: 4-1/2 x 4-1/2 in. NACC HP.: 32.4 (SAE). Holley carb.

[Model 74/75/76] Four-cylinder. Offset. Cast singly. Bore & Stroke: 5 x 5-1/2 in. NACC HP.: 40 (SAE). Four-cycle. Water-cooled. Holley carburetor. Force feed and splash lubrication system. Vertical tube radiator. Bosch ignition.

TECHNICAL: Selective sliding gear transmission. Speeds: 3F/1R. Band clutch. Shaft drive. Semi-floating rear axle. Right-hand steering and right-hand shifting and braking controls.

CHASSIS:

[Model 73] Wheelbase: 120 inches. 36 x 4 pneumatic tires front and rear. 16-gallon gas tank on touring and torpedo touring, 28-gallon on roadster.

[Model 74] Wheelbase: 120 inches. 36 x 4 pneumatic tires front and rear. 16-gallon gas tank on touring and torpedo touring.

[Model 75/76] Wheelbase: 128 inches. 40 x 4-1/2 pneumatic tires front and rear on 18-inch wheels. Semi-elliptic front springs. 3/4-elliptic rear springs. 26-gallon gas tank. Pressed steel frame.

HISTORY: Calendar year production: 3,550 cars.

1913

RAMBLER — MODEL 83 — LIGHT FOUR — 32 HP — FOUR-CYLINDER: The only Rambler left was the Model 83 with a Cross-Country Roadster, Cross-Country Touring (in four- or five-passenger configurations); Cross-Country sedan; and Gotham Limousine. All used the 32.4 (NACC) horsepower four and had a 120-inch wheelbase.

I.D. NUMBERS: [83] 31552-35987.

[LIGHT FOUR]

Model No.	Body Type & Seating	Factory Price	Shipping Weight	Prod. Total
83-4CC	Cross Country Touring-5P	1875	3600	NA
83CROSS	Cross Country Touring-4P	1875	3600	NA
83RD	Cross Country Roadster-2P	1815	3600	NA
83SEDAN	Cross Country Sedan-6P	2575	3800	NA
83G	Gotham Limousine-7P	2750	3800	NA

ENGINE: [Model 83] Four-cylinder. Cast singly. Offset. Bore & Stroke: 4-1/2 x 4-1/2 in. NACC HP.: 32.4 (SAE). Holley carb.

TECHNICAL: Selective sliding gear transmission. Speeds: 3F/1R. Band clutch. Shaft drive. Semi-floating rear axle. Right-hand steering and right-hand shifting and braking controls.

CHASSIS: [Model 83] Wheelbase: 120 inches. 36 x 4 pneumatic tires front and rear. 16-gallon gas tank on touring and torpedo touring; 28-gallon on roadster.

HISTORY: Calendar year production: 4,435 cars. Last year for Rambler name until revived by Nash for 1950 compact car. In 1914, the trade name Jeffery was adopted by Thomas B. Jeffery & Co. to identify the cars it manufactured.

1897 Rambler, runabout (with Thomas B. Jeffery), JAC

1900 Rambler, runabout, WLB

1902 Rambler, Model C, runabout, OCW

1904 Rambler, Model K, tonneau, OCW

1908 Rambler, Light Four (Model 36), limousine, OCW

1910 Rambler, Light Four (Model 53), roadster, OCW

1916 Jeffery, Four (Model 462), seven-passenger touring, OCW

1911 Rambler, Light Four (Model 63), coupe, OCW

JEFFERY 1914-1917

JEFFERY — Kenosha, Wisconsin — (1914-1917) — "To the end that his name may remain in the memories of men, we have named our new car the Jeffery." Charles Jeffery was speaking of his father, Thomas Jeffery, the man who had brought the Rambler to Wisconsin and who, as a local historian put it, changed Kenosha "from a prairie to a city." In the years since 1902, Thomas Jeffery had also constructed the largest automobile factory in the United States and had built the Rambler into one of the most respected and successful American automobiles. In 1910 he had died suddenly of a heart attack. Most likely, the principal motivating factor behind Charles Jeffery's decision to rename the car was sentiment; certainly discarding a name as revered as Rambler was a gutsy decision. The Jeffery was a new car, a 40 hp monobloc four on a 118-inch wheelbase and a 48 hp six on a 128-inch chassis. Both models featured left-hand drive, a feature of the first experimental cars built by Charles Jeffery at the turn of the century, but which Thomas Jeffery had decided against for all production Ramblers. New for the Thomas B. Jeffery Company, too, was a truck called the Quad. Production for 1914 totaled 10,417 Jeffery cars and 3,096 Jeffery Quads. In 1915 the four was refined, and the six was revised with worm drive — 60 days after being announced, dealers contracted for 6,000 of them. "Power A-Plenty and Parlor-Car Comfort," ads said. With the war in Europe, and the likelihood that America would be drawn into it, however, Charles Jeffery chose to concentrate his company's efforts on trucks, some 7,600 of them being produced, with only half that number of the Jeffery cars. In May that year Charles Jeffery embarked upon a trip that would forever change his life. The ship on which he set sail for what was expected to be yet another of his routine fact-finding treks on the Continent was the *Lusitania.* He was one of the 761 survivors of the torpedoes, but the memory of the four harrowing hours he spent in the icy water before being picked up by a trawler remained horrifically in his mind. Conceivably, too, the memory of his father's sudden death brought to him a vivid realization of his own mortality. During the summer of 1916, at the age of 40, he decided to retire, to spend the rest of his life in personal pursuits. Charles Jeffery sold his company to another Charles ... whose last name was Nash.

1913

1913 JEFFERY — MODEL 83 — FOUR: The 1913 Jeffery (a.k.a. Rambler 83) was a large car with a squarish cowl, large sidelights in the cowl and huge 9-1/4 in. drum style headlamps trimmed in black and nickel. It had a new radiator of distinctive curved-top design with seven curved horizontal moldings decorating it. The radiator had 12,000 square inches of cooling surface and was topped by a radiator cap of exclusive design. The touring model had what was called a 'straight line torpedo' body. It included a roomy tonneau seat four feet wide with 31 inches of legroom. It was 27 inches from the front seat to the dash. The name Cross-Country (which would appear on AMC/Rambler station wagons years later) was used to identify four open models and one sedan. Also available was the seven-passenger 'Gotham' limousine. Ad copywriters described the vehicle as a big car of exceeding beauty with fenders of sweeping grace and a radiator of new, distinctive design. It had doors that were 20 inches wide, which opened fully with no outside latches. The standard finish was English Purple Lake, referred to as 'a rare shade of deep maroon.' It was trimmed in nickel with the hood, fenders and filler panels in black enamel and nickel. Soft upholstery covered seats with eight inch deep cushions made of the finest selected long hair. Rear cushions had 45 double-acting steel coil springs. Traditional factory and aftermarket reference sources date the Jeffery marque from 1914 and list the Model 83 as a Rambler only. However, some period sources do exist that show this car as a Jeffery, separate from the Rambler. One is the Wisconsin *Motor Vehicle Weights Guidebook* (1924). Another is *Motor Age Passenger Car Serial Numbers* (1920). It is also a fact that the 1914 Jeffery C-4 was actually the Model 83, as both cars had identical specifications and used the same range of serial numbers. Since it is possible that some Model 83s got Jeffery nameplates, the car is listed here. Standard equipment on the Model 83 included Bosch Duplex ignition; fine large black and nickel headlamps; gas tank; black and nickel side and tail oil lamps; large toolbox with complete tool outfit; jack; tire pump; robe rail; and footrest.

I.D. NUMBERS: Serial numbers to left on front frame crossmember. Serial numbers for 1913 Rambler Model 83 to 1914 Jeffery C-4 were 31552 to 35987.

CROSS-COUNTRY

Model No.	Body Type & Seating	Factory Price	Shipping Weight	Prod. Total
83	4-dr Tr-5P	1875	3600	NA
83	4-dr Tr-4P	1875	3600	NA
83	2-dr Rdstr-2P	1815	3600	NA
83	4-dr Sed-6P	2575	3800	NA
GOTHAM				
83	4-dr Limo-7P	2825	3800	NA

NOTE 1: Apparently, this line was produced as a Rambler built by the Thomas B. Jeffery Co., with the five-passenger touring carded over as the 1914 Jeffery C-4 and serial numbers continued.

NOTE 2: The serial numbers suggest production of 4,435 units under both the Rambler and Jeffery names during the 1913-1914 period.

ENGINE: L-head. Four cylinder. Cast en bloc. Cast iron. B x S: 4-1/2 x 4-1/2 in. Disp.: (approximately 350 cid). NACC HP.: 32.4. Max. HP.: 42.

TECHNICAL: Electric starting. Cone clutch. Four-speed selective sliding gear transmission. Bevel gear final drive.

CHASSIS: I-beam front axle, forward-set. Drop frame and spring suspension. Front springs: 39 in. Rear springs: 52 in. Wheelbase: 120 in. Wheels: 36 in. 34 x 4 in. tires on demountable rims. Spare tire on demountable rim carried in rear. Braking surface: 400 sq. in.

HISTORICAL: An advertisement of 1912 promoted the Rambler Cross-Country as "The most comfortable car in America selling below $2,500." According to the maker, the car could creep along at four miles-per-hour in New York City's Fifth Ave. traffic or hit 50 mph on the open road. It took Abbey Hill, in New York, on high gear with five passengers, starting at 22 mph and going 30 mph at top. It took Viaduct Hill on high, starting at 25 mph, dropping to 12 mph at the crest, and going 18 mph at the top (passing two higher-priced cars while climbing.) In Philadelphia, the Model 83 challenged City Line Hill in high gear. At Kingston, New York, it climbed State St. Hill with six passengers aboard.

1914

JEFFERY — MODEL C-4 — FOUR: The 1914 Jeffery was the same large car that was the Rambler Model 83 a year earlier. Seen again were a squarish cowl, large sidelights in the cowl, huge 9-1/4 inch drum style headlamps trimmed in black and nickel and a radiator of curved-top design with seven curved horizontal moldings decorating it. The 'straight line torpedo' touring was the only model offered. It included a roomy tonneau seat four feet wide with 31 inches of legroom. Twenty inch wide doors opened fully on concealed latches. Finish was English Purple Lake (deep maroon) trimmed in nickel and black enamel. Soft leather upholstery covered seats with eight inch deep cushions made of the finest selected long hair. Rear cushions had 45 double-acting steel coil springs. Standard equipment on the Model C-4 included Bosch Duplex ignition; fine large black and nickel headlamps; gas tank; black and nickel side and tail oil lamps; large toolbox with complete tool outfit; jack; fire pump; robe rail; and footrest.

JEFFERY — MODEL 93 — FOUR: This was a line of five smaller wheelbased four-cylinder cars. They were characterized by a high and short hood, torpedo headlamps and beltline that met the windshield at a right angle. The Model 93 engine was smaller. It had 10 less NACC (National Automobile Chamber of Commerce) horsepower than the Model 83/C-4 engine.

JEFFERY — MODEL 96 — SIX: A larger car available to Jeffery buyers in 1914 was the Model 96. Judging from the engine bore and stroke specifications, the massive six-cylinder engine was basically the same as the Model 93's four-cylinder powerplant, with an extra 'jug' of two cylinders. There were six body styles, including a large seven-passenger limousine.

I.D. NUMBERS: Serial numbers to left on front frame crossmember. [Model C-4]: 31552 to 35987; [Model 93]: 40000 to 46200; [Model 96]: 38000 to 40000.

JEFFERY C-4 [CROSS-COUNTRY FOUR]

Model No.	Body Type & Seating	Factory Price	Shipping Weight	Prod. Total
C-4	4-dr Tr-5P	1875	3600	Note 1

JEFFERY MODEL 93 [FOUR]

Model No.	Body Type & Seating	Factory Price	Shipping Weight	Prod. Tota
93	4-dr Tr-5P	1550	2900	Note 2
93	2-dr Rdstr-2P	1550	3000	Note 2
93	All-Weather-4P	1950	2900	Note 2
93	4-dr Sed-4P	2350	3000	Note 2
(93 K)				
93	4-dr Limousine-7P	3000	3000	Note 2
JEFFERY MODEL 96 [SIX]				
96	2-dr Rdstr-2P	2250	3750	Note 3
96	4-dr Tr-5P	2250	3765	Note 3
96	4-dr Tr-6P	2300	3765	Note 3
96	4-dr Tr-7P	2350	3765	Note 3
96	4-dr Sed-5P	3250	3900	Note 3
96	4-dr Limo-7P	3700	4000	Note 3

NOTE 1: The Rambler Cross-Country Touring became the 1914 Jeffery C-4 and serial numbers suggest production of 4,435 units under both the Rambler and Jeffery names during the 1913-1914 period.

NOTE 2: Serial numbers indicate approximately 2,000 built.

NOTE 3: Serial numbers indicate approximately 6,200 built.

ENGINES

[C-4] L-head. Four-cylinder. Cast en bloc. Cast iron block. B x S.: 4-1/2 x 4-1/2 in. Disp.: (approximately 350 cid). NACC HP.: 32.4. Max. HP.: 42.

[93] L-head. Four-cylinder. Cast en bloc. Cast iron block. B x S.: 3-3/4 x 5-1/4 in. Disp.: 231.9 cid. NACC HP.: 22.5. Max. HP.: 38. Carb.: Rayfield. Pump cooling. Bosch ignition. U.S.L. electric starting/lighting.

[96] L-head. Six-cylinder. Cast in pairs. Cast iron block. B x S.: 3-3/4 x 5-1/4 in. Disp.: 347.9 cid. NACC HP.: 33.7. Max. HP.: 48. Carb.: Rayfield. Pump cooling. Bosch ignition. U.S.L. electric starting/lighting.

TECHNICAL

[C-4] Electric starting. Cone clutch. Four-speed selective sliding gear transmission. Bevel gear final drive.

[93] Electric starting. Cone clutch. Four-speed selective sliding transmission. Bevel gear final drive. Left-hand steering. Central controls. Bosch Duplex type ignition.

[96] Electric starting. Dry disc clutch. Four-speed selective sliding gear transmission. Spiral bevel gear final drive. Left-hand steering. Central controls for shifting and braking. Bosch ignition.

CHASSIS

[C-4] Wheelbase: 120 in. Tires: 34 x 4.

[93] Wheelbase: 116 in. Tires: 34 x 4 (front and rear). Rear springs: 3/4-elliptic.

[96] Wheelbase: 128 in. Tires: 37 x 4.5 (front and rear). Rear springs: 3/4-elliptic.

HISTORY: The Official Specifications 1902-1963 Rambler (and its predecessors) published by American Motors Corp. listed the 1914 model as the first Jeffery. In other sources indicated in the 1913 section above, 1914 is shown as the second year of the marque. Annual production was recorded as 10,417 automobiles and 3,096 Jeffery Quad trucks.

1915

JEFFERY — MODEL 93-2 — FOUR: This was a line of five smaller wheelbased four-cylinder cars. They were characterized by a high and short hood, torpedo headlamps and beltline that met the windshield post at a right angle. The backs of the touring car's front seat jutted up high above the beltline. This was the only four-cylinder Jeffery line this year. The factory specifications booklet cited above identities the 93-2 touring as a 'Chesterfield.' However, sources, such as *MoToR*, indicate that the Chesterfield was the touring car in the Model 104 six-cylinder line.

JEFFERY — MODEL 96-2 — SIX: The larger car available to Jeffery buyers in 1914, the Model 96-2, was carried over in just two body styles for 1915. They were the roadster and touring. These models were not shown in *MoToR's* annual show issue and were most likely discontinued after cars left in inventory were sold out.

JEFFERY — MODEL 106 — SIX: The 106 used the same engine as the Model 96 (which was the six-cylinder version of the Model 93 four). In fact, common serial numbers indicate that it was really just an extended version of the Model 96 chassis. It was not related to the new Model 104 six, which had an entirely different engine. One feature of this model that set it apart was a long wheelbase.

JEFFERY — MODEL 104 — SIX: This six-cylinder Jeffery series was the only really new product line for 1915. Some sources refer to it simply as the Jeffery Six. The touring car was called the 'Chesterfield Six.' It was characterized by a high hood, curved cowl top, low one-piece windshield and curved tonneau style front seat with lower seat-backs than those of the Model 93. The hoodsides were smooth on the Chesterfield. The line also included three other body types.

I.D. NUMBERS: Serial numbers to left on front frame crossmember. [93-2] 53000 to 60500; [96-2 and 106]: 52000 to 53000; [104]: 47000 to 48500.

JEFFERY MODEL93-2 [FOUR]

Model No.	Body Type & Seating	Factory Price	Shipping Weight	Prod. Total
93-2	4-dr Tr-5P	1500	2900	Note 1
93-2	2-dr Rdstr-2P	1500	2900	Note 1
JEFFERY MODEL 96-2 [SIX]				
96-2	4-dr Tr-5P	2300	3765	Note 2
96-2	2-dr Rdstr-2P	2350	3765	Note 2
JEFFERY MODEL 106 [SIX]				
106	4-dr Tr-7P	2400	3850	Note 2
JEFFERY MODEL 104 [SIX]				
104	4-dr Chesterfield Tr-5P	1650	2900	Note 3
104	2-dr Rdstr-2P	1650	2900	Note 3
104	All Weather-2P	1950	2900	Note 3
104	4-dr Sed-5P	2450	3000	Note 3

NOTE 1: Production: Approximately 7,500.

NOTE 2: Production: Approximately 1,000 (Model 96-2 and Model 106).

NOTE 3: Production: Approximately 1,500.

ENGINES

[93-2] L-head. Four-cylinder. Cast en bloc. Cast iron block. B x S.: 3-3/4 x 5-1/4 in. Disp.: 231.9 cid. NACC HP.: 22.5. Max. HP.: 38. Carb.: Rayfield. Pump cooling. Bosch ignition. U.S.L. electric starting/lighting.

[96-2/106] L-head. Six-cylinder. Cast in pairs. Cast iron block. B x S.: 3-3/4 x 5-1/4 in. Disp.: 347.9 cid. NACC HP.: 33.7. Max. HP.: 48. Carb.: Rayfield. Pump cooling. Bosch ignition. U.S.L. electric starting/lighting.

[104] L-head. Six-cylinder. Cast en bloc. Cast iron block. B x S.: 3 x 5 in. Disp.: 212.6 cid. NACC HP: 21.6. Max. HP: NA. Carb.: NA. Pump cooling. Bosch single ignition. Bijur electric starting/lighting.

TECHNICAL

[93-2] Electric starting. Cone clutch. Four-speed selective sliding transmission. Bevel gear final drive. Left-hand steering. Central controls. Bosch Duplex type ignition.

[96-2/106] Electric starting. Dry disc clutch. Four-speed selective sliding gear transmission. Spiral bevel gear final drive. Left-hand steering. Central controls for shifting and braking. Bosch ignition.

[104] Electric starting. Dry disc clutch. Four-speed selective sliding gear transmission. Worm gear final drive. Left-hand steering. Central controls for shifting and braking. Bosch ignition.

CHASSIS

[93-2] Wheelbase: 116 in. Tires: 34 x 4 (front and rear). Rear springs: 3/4-elliptic.

[96-2] Wheelbase: 128 in. Tires: 37 x 4.5 (front and rear). Rear springs: 3/4-elliptic.

[106] Wheelbase: 133-1/2 in. Tires: 34 x 4-1/2 in. (front and rear). Rear springs: 3/4-elliptic.

[104] Wheelbase: 122 in. Tires: 34 x 4 (front and rear). Rear springs: Cantilever.

HISTORY: Jeffery began to concentrate on the manufacture of four-wheel drive Quad trucks for military use in the Mexican War.

1916

JEFFERY — MODEL 462 — FOUR: At the beginning of 1916, Jeffery introduced the four-cylinder Model 462 for the New York Auto Show. It was obviously based on the 93/93-2 with identical bore and stroke, weight and wheelbase. The hood had vertical louvers on its lower side panels and retained a high feature line. The headlamps were again torpedo style. The cowl was curved. The front seatbacks stuck up high over the beltline.

JEFFERY — MODEL 661 — SIX: The 661 was an all-new six-cylinder model, apparently introduced after the start of the model year. A dry disc clutch replaced the cone type. The rear axle gear ratio was changed from 4.15:1 to 4.50:1.

I.D. NUMBERS: Serial number located to left of front frame crossmember. [462] 57000 to 60500. [661] 68000 to 69108.

JEFFERY MODEL 462 [FOUR]

Model No.	Body Type & Seating	Factory Price	Shipping Weight	Prod. Total
462Rdr	2-dr Rdstr-2P	1000	2800	Note 1
462-5	4-dr Tr-5P	1000	2800	Note 1
462-7	2-dr Tr-7P	1035	2825	Note 1
462Sedan	4-dr Sed-5P	1165	2850	Note 1
462S-7	4-dr Sed-7P	1200	2875	Note 1
462	4-dr Sed-5P	2450	3000	Note 1
JEFFERY MODEL 661 [SIX]				
661	4-dr Tr-5P	1435	3250	Note 2
661	2-dr Rdstr-2P	1465	3250	Note 2

NOTE 1: Production: Approximately 3,500.

NOTE 2: Production: Approximately 1,108.

ENGINES

[462] L-head. Four-cylinder. Cast en bloc. Cast iron block. B x S.: 3-3/4 x 5-1/4 in. Disp.: 231.9 cid. NACC HP.: 22.5. Max. HP.: 38. Carb.: Stromberg (gravity fed). Helical gear camshaft drive. Pump cooling. Bosch ignition. Bijur electric starting/lighting.

[661] L-head. Six-cylinder. Cast in pairs. Cast iron block. B x S.: 3-1/2 x 5-1/4 in. Disp.: 303 cid. NACC HP.: 29.4. Max. HP: 40. Carb.: Rayfield (vacuum fed). Pump cooling. Chain camshaft drive.

TECHNICAL

[462] Bijur electric starting. Cone clutch. Three-speed selective sliding gear transmission. Semi-floating rear axle with 4.15:1 ratio on high. Semi-elliptic front springs. Three-quarter elliptic rear springs. Force feed and splash lubrication. Pump cooling. Bosch single type ignition.

[661] Bijur electric starting. Dry disc clutch. Three-speed selective sliding gear transmission. Semi-floating rear axle with 4.50:1 ratio on high. Hotchkiss drive. Semi-elliptic rear springs. Force feed and splash engine lubrication. Pump cooling.

CHASSIS

[462] Wheelbase: 116 in. Tires: 34 x 4 (front and rear). Rear springs: 3/4-elliptic.

[661] Wheelbase: 125 in. Tires: 34 x 4 (front and rear). Rear springs: Semi-elliptic.

HISTORY: Jeffery continued to concentrate on the manufacture of four-wheel drive Quad trucks for military use. A primary customer for these units was the British government, as rumblings of war began to be heard in Europe.

1917

JEFFERY — MODEL 472 — FOUR: The Model 462 became the 472 for 1917. It now had a vacuum fuel system. A short, high hood with a slight slant to the front remained a design characteristic, but the beltline no longer met the windshield at a right angle. It now curved smoothly up to meet the base of the windshield stanchion. The front seatbacks no longer jutted high above the body; their tops could just be seen. Vacuum fed fuel delivery was a new four-cylinder feature.

JEFFERY — MODEL 671 — SIX: The 671 had a high hood that ran straight back to the cowl without a curve. The beltline met the windshield at about a 60-degree angle. It had torpedo headlights. The hood had vertical louvers. The engine had the same bore, but a smaller stroke, than the 661.

I.D. NUMBERS: Serial number located to left of front frame crossmember. [472]: 61000 to 62027; [472-2]: 76000 to 80000; [671 Touring]: 71800 to 86000; [671 Roadster]: 71796 to 71800; and [671 Sedan]: 86000 to 92999.

JEFFERY MODEL 472 [1st Series]

Model No.	Body Type & Seating	Factory Price	Shipping Weight	Prod. Total
472Rdr	2-dr Rdstr-2P	1065	2800	Note 1
472	4-dr Tr-7P	1095	2800	Note 1
JEFFERY MODEL 472 [2nd Series]				
472-2	2-dr Tr-7P	1095	2800	Note 2
472-2Sedan	4-dr Sed-7P	1260	2875	Note 2
JEFFERY MODEL 671 [SIX]				
671Rdr	2-dr Rdstr-2P	1335	3050	Note 3
671	4-dr Tr-7P	1365	3080	Note 3
671Sedan	4-dr Sed-7P	1530	3080	Note 3

NOTE 1: Production: Approximately 1,027.

NOTE 2: Production: Approximately 4,000.

NOTE 3: Production: Approximately 14,200 combined.

ENGINES

[472/472-2] L-head. Four-cylinder. Cast en bloc. Cast iron block. B x S.: 3-3/4 x 5-1/4 in. Disp.: 231.9 cid. NACC HP.: 22.5. Max. HP.: 38. Carb.: Stromberg V (vacuum fed). Helical gear camshaft drive.

[671] L-head. Six-cylinder. Cast in pairs. Cast iron block. B x S.: 3-1/2 x 4-5/8 in. Disp.: 267 cid. NACC HP.: 29.4. Max. HP.: 53. Carb.: Rayfield (vacuum fed). Pump cooling. Chain camshaft drive.

TECHNICAL

[472/472-2] Dry disc clutch. Three-speed selective sliding gear transmission. Bijur electrics. Semi-floating rear axle with 4.50:1 ratio on high. Semi-elliptic front springs. Three-quarter elliptic rear springs. Hotchkiss drive. Force feed and splash lubrication. Pump cooling.

[671] Bijur electric starting. Dry disc clutch. Three-speed selective sliding gear transmission. Semi-floating rear axle with 4.50:1 ratio on high. Hotchkiss drive. Semi-elliptic rear springs. Force feed and splash engine lubrication. Pump cooling.

CHASSIS

[462] Wheelbase: 116 in. Tires: 34 x 4 (front and rear). Rear springs: 3/4-elliptic.

[661] Wheelbase: 125 in. Tires: 34 x 4 (front and rear). Rear springs: Semi-elliptic.

HISTORY: *MoToR* magazine published a list of 149 pleasure car makers in 1918. Nash Motors Co., of Kenosha, Wis., was now listed as manufacturer of the Jeffery. The company was one of four Wisconsin automakers listed that year. There were others, but the list was of American Licensed Automobile Manufacturers (ALAM) member companies.

1918

JEFFERY — MODEL 671 — SIX: The 671 was carried over into early 1918, with no indications that any changes were made. The 1902-1963 specifications book published by AMC in 1962 listed serial numbers for 1918 Jefferys. However, the annual show issue of *MoToR* did not include Jeffery prices or specifications.

I.D. NUMBERS: Serial number located to left of front frame crossmember. [671] 86000 to 92999.

JEFFERY MODEL 671 [SIX]

Model No.	Body Type & Seating	Factory Price	Shipping Weight	Prod. Total
671Rdr	2-dr Rdstr-2P	1435	3050	Note 1
671	4-dr Tr-7P	1465	3080	Note 1
671 Sedan	4-dr Sed-7P	1630	3080	Note 1

NOTE 1: Production: Approximately 6,999.

ENGINE: [671] L-head. Six-cylinder. Cast in pairs. Cast iron block. B x S.: 3-1/2 x 4-5/8 in. Disp.: 267 cid. NACC HP.: 29.4. Max. HP.: 53. Carb.: Rayfield (vacuum fed). Pump cooling. Chain camshaft drive.

TECHNICAL: [671] Bijur electric starting. Dry disc clutch. Three-speed selective sliding gear transmission. Semi-floating rear axle with 4.50:1 ratio on high. Hotchkiss drive. Semi-elliptic rear springs. Force feed and splash engine lubrication. Pump cooling.

CHASSIS: [671] Wheelbase: 125 in. Tires: 34 x 4 (front and rear). Rear springs: Semi-elliptic.

HISTORY: The Jeffery 671 became the Nash 671 in 1918.

NASH 1920-1942

NASH — Kenosha, Wisconsin — (1917-1942 et seq.) — Born in 1864 in Illinois and abandoned by his parents at age six, Charles W. Nash was "bound out" by a district court to work for a Michigan farmer from whom he was to receive room, board and three months of schooling a year until age 21 when $100, a new suit of clothes and freedom would be his. But Charlie Nash ran away at age 12, got a paying job on another Michigan farm, learned the carpenter's trade, clerked in a grocery store in Flint, and by the early 1890s was the fastest cushion stuffer at the Flint Road Cart Company owned by William C. Durant and J. Dallas Dort. By 1895 he was managing the Durant-Dort Carriage Company, by 1910 he was heading the Buick Motor Car Company, by 1912 he was the president of General Motors. Rags to riches was a popular theme in novels of this period; Charlie Nash had managed to out-Alger Horatio. His career at General Motors ended in June 1916 like many did, in resignation following a policy dispute with Billy Durant. His next step was a logical one. He traveled to Kenosha and, with former GM man James Storrow, bought the Thomas B. Jeffery Company, former producers of the Rambler, the producers now of the Jeffery, and one of the oldest, best-known and largest automobile companies in the industry. The purchase price purportedly was $9 million. On July 29, 1916, Nash Motors Company was born. The Jeffery was continued awhile in production, with Nash nameplates appearing on the cars from the summer of 1917. Indeed, the first Nash introduced remained a badge-engineered Jeffery. The first "Nash" Nash arrived on April 18, 1918. It was a six designed by Erik Wahlberg, whom Nash had hired away from Oakland as his chief engineer; that the engine was overhead valve was no surprise given Nash's Buick experience, that both it and the Nash chassis (which featured Hotchkiss drive and semi-elliptic suspension all around) were formidably clean and tidy was commented upon with considerable favor in the trade press. Charlie Nash was a stickler for a conservative neatness, in car design and company management. Sales of 10,000+ cars in 1918 more than doubled to 27,000 in 1919. In its first 15 months of operation, Nash Motors netted over two million dollars. Prior to the Armistice, the four-wheel-drive truck begun as the Jeffery was continued as the Nash Quad, alongside a standard Nash truck, but Charlie Nash began phasing out commercial vehicle manufacture by the Twenties, as he launched a several-pronged attack in the production car field. Introduced in 1920 was a brand-new car in the $5,000 price range called the LaFayette, and built initially in Indianapolis, and that November in Kenosha, the Nash assembly line began humming with a new 35 hp four, in effect the 67 hp Nash six minus two cylinders and nine inches in wheelbase (or 112 inches), which Nash could sell for several hundred dollars less than his standard medium-priced product. For 1922 the four was provided rubber engine mounting and a "Carriole" sedan model at $1,350, which was five dollars more expensive and introduced a few weeks after the Essex coach, forever after allowing the Hudson company to legitimately claim honors in pioneering the closed car in the popular-price field. Still, a net profit of $7.6 million for 1922 had to make Charlie Nash feel good, as did sales for 1923, which passed the 50,000 mark for the first time, for a net profit of $9.3 million.

Nash Data Compilation by Arch Brown

The LaFayette venture, which had moved into a new factory in Milwaukee by January of 1923, had proved a commercial disaster, however, and after pouring two million dollars into it, Charlie Nash abandoned LaFayette manufacture early in 1924, moving the machinery from Milwaukee into the old Mitchell plant in Racine for which he had just managed to outbid Hupp. There from 1925 into 1926 he produced another new car at the opposite end of the scale from the LaFayette, the $865-$995 Ajax. He wasn't particularly thrilled with the fewer-than 25,000 Ajaxes sold during its first year, however, since more than 85,000 Nashes were delivered during the same period. But that was easily solved. The L-head Ajax six became the Nash Light Six during 1926, joining the Special and the Advanced ohv sixes, names having replaced the former numerical designations in 1925, the year Nash went six-cylinder across the board. In June of 1928 twin ignition arrived in Kenosha on the big Nashes, which increased horsepower measurably and made the Advanced a genuine 80 mph car, the Special good for 75 mph. The single-ignition Standard Six (former Light Six) shared its bigger brothers' invar-strutted aluminum pistons and compression ratio (5.0:1 from the former 4.5) for a car now capable of an easy 70 mph. These new Nashes were extremely fine cars with handsome Seaman bodies and price tags of $885-$2,190, which made for some of the greatest bargains in the industry that year. More than 138,000 Nashes were produced in 1928, and Nash Motors made over $20 million. Charlie Nash was 65 years old when the stock market crashed. Already he had introduced for the 1930 model year one of the most splendid Nashes of all — the Twin-Ignition Eight, an ohv straight eight with nine main bearings, 298.6 cubic inches, 100 hp at 2900 rpm: "80 Miles an Hour in 3 Blocks," the billboards would say, and the price range was just $1,675-$2,385. Because, unlike many manufacturers, Charlie Nash had not run wild during the Twenties, he was better prepared for the Thirties. His assets-to-liabilities ratio was by far the most exemplary in the automobile industry; in 1931 when most companies lost money, Nash Motors turned a profit of $4.8 million. For 1932 Wahlberg and crew came up with even nicer Nashes boasting ride control, freewheeling, five-point rubber-insulated engine suspension and "synchro-shift." Nineteen thirty-two was an awful year in America, with industry wide automobile production a mere 13 percent of the pre-Depression figure, but in Kenosha Charlie Nash's company made a million dollars. That year, in order to allow himself more time for long-range planning, he elevated associate Earl McCarty to Nash's presidency, retaining the chairmanship of the board that he had assumed after James Storrow's death in 1926. In 1933 he marked time with cars not noticeably different from 1932, and for the first time in history Nash Motors lost money, a situation repeated in 1934 though for a different reason; Charlie Nash had spent a fortune retooling for the new 1934 cars. The LaFayette name was revived for a car that now carried Nash into the low-priced ($595-$695) field. It used the L-head engine of the former Big Six, and although promoted under its own name until 1937, it was really a Nash model, just as the big Ambassador — and it was big, with wheelbases up to 142 inches — was at the opposite end of the Nash scale. In July of 1936 Charlie Nash purchased Seaman Body Corporation of Milwaukee (in which firm he had bought a half interest in 1919). In August Nash Motors was 20 years old, and Charlie Nash — now 72 — was growing tired. When Earl McCarty retired, Nash invited George W. Mason, the vice-president of Kelvinator Corporation, to become Nash president, to which Mason agreed so long as Nash bought Kelvinator. And so the deal was done. This provided comedians of the day with fodder for bad jokes: ice cube trays would now become standard equipment for Nash cars, Kelvinator refrigerators would get four-wheel brakes. But when the laughter died down, Nash had sold nearly 86,000 cars in 1937 (the best year of the decade) for a $3.5 million profit. The recession year of 1938 was bad for both cars and refrigerators, and the Nash-Kelvinator marriage had a $7.5 million loss. Under Mason's direction, Nash continued to build fine cars, however, with such interesting features from 1938 as the Weather-Eye controlled ventilation system and the option of overdrive first offered in 1936. Nineteen forty saw a 20-car production run of a nifty Ambassador Eight cabriolet styled by Alexis de Sakhnoffsky (who earlier had kibitzed with chief engineer Wahlberg on the 1934 Nash line) and the availability in England of a Perkins diesel-engined Nash. Since 1936 a Nash had been offered with a rear seat that converted into a bed. But it was 1941 that brought the biggest news from Nash; the Ambassador 600, which replaced the LaFayette and which boasted unitized body construction, torque tube drive, 75 bhp, 25-30 mpg and $750-$850 price tags. The public response was terrific; in 1941 sales topped 80,000 cars. Following Pearl Harbor, Nash cars ceased to be built in Kenosha, with Pratt & Whitney aviation engines manufactured instead for the duration of World War II. With the coming of peace, Nash was in a solid position as an independent. Nineteen forty-eight would mark the beginning of a new era for the company. In that year Charlie Nash died at age 84 on June 6th. Two months earlier, on April 1st, George Romney had arrived with a new idea of what a Nash should be.

1918

NASH — 680 — SIX: The 1918 Nash had a low hood line; short, vertical hood louvers; a painted radiator shell that was somewhat rounded on top; a slanted windshield on open models and shell headlamps.

I.D. DATA: Serial numbers on left front crossmember, just in back of radiator. Starting: 100101. Engine numbers on right front of flywheel housing just behind starting motor.

Series 680 — 6-cyl

Model No.	Body Type & Seating	Factory Price	Shipping Weight	Starting Serial #
681	4-dr. Tr.-5P	1295	2930	100101
682	4-dr. Tr.-7P	1545	3040	111601
683	2-dr. Rds.-4P	1295	2930	121001
684	2-dr. Sed.-5P	1985	3455	100108
685	2-dr. Cpe.-4P	2085	3225	94501

Note: Models 681 and 683 have a 121-in. wheelbase. Other models have a 127-in. wheelbase.

ENGINE: Inline. OHV. Cast enbloc. Six. Cast iron block. B & S: 3-1/4 x 5 in. Disp.: 248.9 cu. in. Brake H.P. 55 @ 2400 R.P.M. N.A.C.C. H.P.: 25.35. Main bearings: three. Valve lifters: solid. Carb.: Marvel.

CHASSIS: W.B.: 121 in.; 127 in. Frt/Rear Tread: 56/56 in. Tires: 34 x 4.

TECHNICAL: Selective, sliding gear transmission. Speeds: 3F/1R. Floor shift controls. Single dry plate clutch. Spiral bevel drive. Semi-floating rear axle. Overall ratio: 4.50:1. Two-wheel external mechanical brakes. Artillery wheels.

HISTORICAL: Introduced September 1, 1917. Enclosed overhead valve mechanism. Calendar year production: 10,283. The president of Nash was C.W. Nash. First Nash automobile. In its first full year of production, Nash accounted for one percent of all new car production in the U.S.

1919

NASH — 680 — SIX: The 1919 Nash was identical to the 1918 model.

I.D. DATA: Serial number on left front crossmember, just behind radiator. Starting: 106430. Engine numbers on right front of flywheel housing behind starting motor.

Series 680 — 6-cyl.

Model No.	Body Type & Seating	Factory Price	Shipping Weight	Starting Serial #
681	4-dr. Tr.-5P	1395	2930	106430
682	4-dr. Tr.-5P	1545	3040	111769
683	2-dr. Tr.-4P	1395	2930	121910
684	2-dr. Sed.-5P	2085	3455	120118
685	2-dr. Cpe.-4P	2085	3225	144035
686	2-dr. Rds.-2P	1490	2800	131851
687	4-dr. Spt. Tr.-4P	1595	2950	133351

Note 1: Models 681, 683, 686, and 687 have 121-in. wheelbase. Others have 127-in. wheelbase.

ENGINE: Inline. OHV. Cast enbloc. Six. Cast iron block. B & S: 3-1/4 x 5 in. Disp.: 248.9 cu. in. Brake H.P. 55 @ 2400 R.P.M. N.A.C.C. H.P.: 25.35. Main bearings: three. Valve lifters: solid. Carb.: Marvel.

CHASSIS: W.B.: 121 in. & 127 in. Frt/Rear Tread: 56/56 in. Tires: 33 x 4. (34 x 4-1/2 on 127-in. wheelbase models).

TECHNICAL: Selective, sliding gear transmission. Speeds: 3F/1R. Floor shift controls. Single dry plate clutch. Spiral bevel drive. Semi-floating rear axle. Overall ratio: 4.50:1. Two-wheel external mechanical brakes. Artillery wheels.

HISTORICAL: Introduced September 1, 1918. Calendar year production: 27,081. The president of Nash was C.W. Nash. Virtually unchanged from the previous year. Nash accounted for 1.6 percent of U.S. new car production for 1919. Nash also built 4,090 trucks during 1919, and during this year purchased a half-interest in the Seaman Body Corp., Milwaukee.

1920

NASH — 680 — SIX: The 1920 Nash was identical to the 1918-19 models.

I.D. DATA: Serial numbers on right rear engine girder at transmission base (effective July 11, 1920. Earlier cars, on left front crossmember, just back of radiator). Starting: 139330. Engine numbers on right front of flywheel housing just behind starting motor.

Series 680 — 6-cyl

Model No.	Body Type & Seating	Factory Price	Shipping Weight	Starting Serial #
681	4-dr. Tr.-5P	1490	2930	139330
682	4-dr. Tr.-7P	1640	3040	113661
684	4-dr. Sed.-7P	2575	3455	144334
685	2-dr. Cpe.-4P	2350	3225	144985
686	2-dr. Rds.-2P	1490	2800	132580
687	4-dr. Spt. Tr.-4P	1545	2950	134276

Note: Models 681, 686 and 687 had 121-in. wheelbase, other models have 127-in. wheelbase.

ENGINE: Inline. OHV. Cast enbloc. Six. Cast iron block. B & S: 3-1/4 x 5 in. Disp.: 248.9 cu. in. Brake H.P. 55 @ 2400 R.P.M. N.A.C.C. H.P.: 25.35. Main bearings: three. Valve lifters: solid. Carb.: Marvel.

CHASSIS: W.B. 121 in. and 127 in. Frt/Rear Tread: 56/56 in. Tires: 33 x 4 (34 x 4-1/2 on 127-in. wheelbase models).

TECHNICAL: Selective, sliding gear transmission. Speeds: 3F/1R. Floor shift controls. Single dry plate clutch. Spiral bevel drive. Semi-floating rear axle. Overall ratio: 4.50:1. Two-wheel external mechanical brakes. Artillery wheels.

HISTORICAL: Introduced September 1, 1920. Calendar year production was 35,084. The president of Nash was C.W. Nash. Nash Motors earned $7,007,471 during 1920. Nash accounted for 1.9 percent of U.S. auto production, 1920 essentially unchanged from 1918-1919 models. A new assembly plant was opened in Milwaukee.

1921

NASH — 680 — SIX: The 1921 Nash 680 was identical to 1918-1920 models.

I.D. DATA: Serial numbers on right rear engine girder at transmission base. Starting: 175874. Engine numbers on right front of flywheel housing just back of starting motor.

Series 680 — 6-cyl.

Model No.	Body Type & Seating	Factory Price	Shipping Weight	Starting Serial #
681	4-dr. Tr.-5P	1695	3068	175874
682	4-dr. Tr.-7P	1875	3198	167177
684	4-dr. Sed.-7P	2895	3708	178543
685	2-dr. Cpe.-4P	2650	3403	179003
686	2-dr. Rds.-2P	1695	2988	179551
687	4-dr. Spt. Tr.-4P	1850	3098	177655

Note: Models 681, 686 and 687 had a 121-in. wheelbase. Other models had a 127-in. wheelbase.

ENGINE: Inline. OHV. Cast enbloc. Six. Cast iron block. B & S: 3-1/4 x 5 in. Disp.: 248.9 cu. in. Brake H.P. 55 @ 2400 R.P.M. N.A.C.C. H.P.: 25.35. Main bearings: three. Valve lifters: solid. Carb.: Marvel.

CHASSIS: W.B.: 121 in.; 127 in. Frt/Rear Tread: 56/56 in. Tires: 33 x 4 (34 x 4-1/2 on 127-in. wheelbase models).

TECHNICAL: Selective, sliding gear transmission. Speeds: 3F/1R. Floor shift controls. Single dry plate clutch. Spiral bevel drive. Semi-floating rear axle. Overall ratio: 4.50:1. Two-wheel mechanical brakes. Wood artillery wheels.

NASH — 40 — FOUR: The new four-cylinder Nash models were similar in appearance to 680 series models except for their shorter, stubbier hoods.

I.D. DATA: Serial numbers on front frame crossmember just behind radiator on left side. Starting: 1000. Engine numbers on left side of crankcase just behind starting motor.

Series 40 — 4-cyl.

Model No.	Body Type & Seating	Factory Price	Shipping Weight	Starting Serial #
41	4-dr. Tr.-5P	1395	2502	1000
42	2-dr. Rds.-2P	1395	2432	1000
43	2-dr. Cpe.-3P	1985	2732	1000
44	4-dr. Sed.-4P	2185	2942	1000
45	2-dr. Cabr.-2P	1545	2676	1000

ENGINE: OHV. Inline. Four. Cast iron block. B & S: 3-1/4 x 5 in. Disp.: 165.9 cu. in. Brake H.P.: 35 @ 2200 R.P.M. N.A.C.C. H.P.: 16.9. Main bearings: two. Valve lifters: solid. Carb. Schebler.

CHASSIS: W.B. 112 in. Frt/Rear Tread: 56/56 in. Tires: 32 x 4.

TECHNICAL: Selective, sliding gear transmission. Speeds: 3F/1R. Floor shift controls. Single dry plate clutch. Spiral bevel drive. Semi-floating rear axle. Overall ratio: 4.50:1. Two-wheel mechanical brakes. Wood artillery wheels.

HISTORICAL: Introduced September 1, 1920 (Series 680); September 25, 1920 (Series 40). A new, four-cylinder series took Nash into a lower price range. Calendar year production: 20,850. The president of Nash was C.W. Nash. Severe postwar recession led to a sharp drop in production and sales. Nash accounted for 1.4 percent of U.S.

auto production in 1921. On February 14, 1921, the bore of the series "40" engine was increased to 3-3/8 in., raising the displacement to 178.9 cu. in. and the horsepower to 36.75 @ 2800 R.P.M. Starting serial number, cars with 178.9 cu. in. engine: 1782.

1922

"THE NASH SIX" — SERIES 690 — SIX: Styling similar to 680 series of 1918-21, except taller radiator, drum headlamps.

"THE NASH FOUR" — SERIES 40 — FOUR: Identical to 1921 Series 40.

I.D. DATA: [Series 690] Serial numbers on right rear engine girder at transmission base. Starting: 195754. Engine numbers on right front of flywheel housing just back of starting motor. [Series 40] Serial numbers on front frame crossmember just back of radiator, left side. Starting: 4511. Engine numbers on left side of crankcase just back of starting motor.

Series 690 — 6-cyl

Model No.	Body Type & Seating	Factory Price	Shipping Weight	Starting Serial #
691	4-dr. Tr.-5P	1545	2930	195754
692	4-dr. Tr.-7P	1695	2950	208441
693	4-dr. Sed.-5P	2040	3430	217938
694	4-dr. Sed.-7P	2695	3455	198240
695	2-dr. Vic.-4P	2395	3255	200013
696	2-dr. Rds.-2P	1525	2805	207559
697	4-dr. Spt. Tr.-4P	1695	3037	205729
Series 40 — 4-cyl.				
41	4-dr. Tr.-5P	1045	2502	4511
42	2-dr. Rds.-2P	1025	2432	4511
43	2-dr. Cpe.-3P	1645	2732	4511
44	4-dr. Sed.-5P	1835	2942	4511
45	2-dr. Cabr.-5P	1245	2676	4511
46	2-dr. Carriole-5P	1350	2824	4511

ENGINE: [Nash 690] Ohv. Inline. Six. Cast iron block. B & S: 3-1/4 x 5 in. Disp.: 248.9. C.R.: 4.2:1. Brake H.P.: 55 @ 2400 R.P.M. Taxable H.P.: 25.35. Main bearings: three. Valve lifters: solid. Carb.: Marvel. [Nash 40] Ohv. Inline. Four. Cast iron block. B & S: 3-3/8 x 5 in. Disp.: 178.9 cu. in. C.R.: 3.8:1. Brake H.P.: 36.75 @ 2800 R.P.M. Taxable H.P.: 18.23. Main bearings: two. Valve lifters: solid. Carb.: Schebler.

CHASSIS: [Series 690] W.B.: 121 in & 127 in. Frt/Rear Tread: 56/56 in. Tires: 33 x 4 (34 x 4-1/2 on 127-in. wheelbase models). [Series 40] W.B.: 112 in. Frt/Rear Tread: 56/56 in. Tires: 33 x 4.

TECHNICAL: Selective, sliding gear transmission. Speeds: 3F/1R. Floor shift controls. Single dry plate clutch. Spiral bevel. Semi-floating rear axle. Overall ratio: 4.50:1. Mechanical brakes on two wheels. Wood artillery wheels.

HISTORICAL: Introduced October 5, 1921. Innovations: First use of rubber engine mountings (Series 40). Two-door Carriole (Series 40) brought closed-car comfort to a lower-priced field. Calendar year production: 41,652. The president of Nash was C.W. Nash. Production doubled the 1921 figure; Nash accounted for 1.7 percent of U.S. automobile production and was eighth in U.S. auto sales. Nash claimed to manufacture a higher percentage of its components than any other automaker.

1923

"THE NASH SIX" — SERIES 690 — SIX: Identical to 1922 model, except disc wheels now optional, cowl ventilator used.

"THE NASH FOUR" — SERIES 40 — FOUR: Identical to 1921-22 Series 40.

I.D. DATA: Series 690 serial numbers on right rear engine girder at transmission base. Starting: 226409. Engine numbers on right front of flywheel housing just back of starting motor. Series 40 serial numbers on front frame crossmember just back of radiator, left side. Starting: 19436.

Series 690 — 6-cyl.

Model No.	Body Type & Seating	Factory Price	Shipping Weight	Starting Serial #
691	4-dr. Tr.-5P	1240	3030	226409
692	4-dr. Tr.-7P	1390	3150	226882
693	4-dr. Sed.-5P	2040	3430	218364
694	4-dr. Sed.-7P	2190	3580	232021
695	2-dr. Vic.-4P	1890	3330	232241
696	2-dr. Rds.-2P	1210	2930	232589
697	4-dr. Spt. Tr.-4P	1645	3530	227921
698	4-dr. Cpe.-5P	2090	3550	231401

Series 40 — 4-cyl.

Model No.	Body Type & Seating	Factory Price	Shipping Weight	Starting Serial #
41	4-dr. Tr.-5P	935	2720	19436
42	2-dr. Rds.-2P	915	2600	19436
46	2-dr. Carriole-5P	1275	2910	19436
47	4-dr. Sed. 5P	1445	3090	19436
48	4-dr. Spt. Tr.-5P	1195	2980	19436

ENGINE: Series 690 identical in all these respects to 1922 690 Series. Series 40 identical in all these respects to 1922 Series 40.

CHASSIS: Unchanged in these respects from 1922.

TECHNICAL: Identical to 1922 models except for overall drive ratio, Series 40, as noted below. Overall ratio: 4.50:1 (690); 4.89:1 (40). Wood artillery wheels (disc optional).

HISTORICAL: Introduced October 17, 1922. Calendar year registrations: 41,838. Calendar year production: 41,652. The president of Nash was C.W. Nash. Nash accounted for 1.6 percent of U.S. auto production during 1923.

1924

"THE NASH SIX" — SERIES 690 — SIX: Identical to 1922-23 690 Series.

"THE NASH FOUR" — SERIES 40 — FOUR: Identical to 1921-23 Series 40.

I.D. DATA: Series 690 serial numbers on right rear engine girder at transmission base. Starting: 256987. Engine numbers on right front of flywheel housing just back of starting motor. Series 40 serial numbers on front frame crossmember just back of radiator, left side. Starting: 34577.

Series 690 — 6-cyl

Model No.	Body Type & Seating	Factory Price	Shipping Weight	Starting Serial #
691	4-dr. Tr.-5P	1240	3120	256987
692	4-dr. Tr.-7P	1390	3230	248120
693	4-dr. Sed.-5P	2040	3550	248526
694	4-dr. Sed.-7P	2190	3700	240423
695	2-dr. Vic.-4P	1990	3440	240778
696	2-dr. Rds.-2P	1240	3030	254852
697	4-dr. Spt. Tr.-4P	1645	3530	251417
698	4-dr. Cpe-5P	2090	3550	259009
699	4-dr. Spt. Sed.-5P	1640	3400	269265
Series 40 — 4-cyl.				
41	4-dr. Tr.-5P	935	2720	34577
42	2-dr. Rds.-2P	915	2600	34577
46	2-dr. Carriole-5P	1275	2910	34577
47	4-dr. Sed.-5P	1445	3090	34577
48	4-dr. Spt. Tr.-5P	1145	2800	34577
49	2-dr. Cpe.-2P	1165	2750	34577

ENGINE: [Series 690] Identical in all these respects to 1922-23 Series 690. [Series 40] Identical in all these respects to 1922-23 Series 40.

CHASSIS: Unchanged in these respects from 1922-23.

TECHNICAL: Unchanged except for another increase in overall drive ratio. Overall ratio: 4.50:1 (690); 5.50:1 (40).

HISTORICAL: Introduced July 20, 1923. Innovations: Industry's first use of electric dashboard clock (optional). Calendar year registrations: 47,571. Calendar year production: 53,626. The president of Nash was C.W. Nash. Nash accounted for 1.7 percent of U.S. auto production in 1924. Last year for the Nash "Four." On February 27, 1924, Nash purchased the Racine plant of the bankrupt Mitchell Motors Co.

1925

NASH — ADVANCED "SIX" — SERIES 160 — SIX: Much updated from previous model: balloon tires, nickeled radiator shell; long, thin hood louvers; long visor, closed models; "boxy" configuration on closed models, particularly at the rear.

NASH — SPECIAL "SIX" — SERIES 130 — SIX: Similar in styling to 160 series, but smaller.

NASH — AJAX — SERIES 220 — SIX: "Vertical" styling similar to contemporary Nash models, but substantially smaller. Long visor on sedans, drum headlamps; low, flat hood.

I.D. DATA: Series 160 serial numbers on right side of front motor support. Starting: 288001. Engine numbers on engine block near starting motor. Series 130 serial numbers on top right side rear motor support or on left rear spring hanger. Starting: 51001. Engine numbers on engine block beside starting motor. Ajax serial numbers on right front spring hanger. Starting: 1001. Engine numbers on left side engine block, upper forward corner.

Series 160 — 6-cyl

Model No.	Body Type & Seating	Factory Price	Shipping Weight	Starting Serial #
161	4-dr. Tr.-5P	1375	3400	288001
162	4-dr. Tr.-7P	1525	3480	290351
163	2-dr. Sed.-5P	1485	3550	308325
164	4-dr. Sed.-7P	2290	3830	290601
165	2-dr. Vic.-4P	2090	3640	297901
166	2-dr. Rds.-2P	1375	3320	290791
168	4-dr. Cpe.-4P	2190	3750	291281
169	4-dr. Sed.-5P	1695	3860	291571
Series 130 — 6-cyl.				
131	4-dr. Tr.-5P	1095	2960	51001
132	2-dr. Rds.-2P	1095	2870	54573
133	2-dr. Sed.-5P	1225	3120	51001
134	4-dr. Sed.-5P	1545	3270	64990
Series 220 (formerly Ajax) — 6-cyl.				
21	4-dr. Sed.-5P	995	2410	—
51	4-dr. Tr.-5P	865	2210	—

ENGINE: [Series 160]: Ohv. Inline. Six. Cast iron block. B & S: 3-1/4 x 5 in. Disp.: 248.9 cu. in. Brake H.P.: 60 @ 2400 R.P.M. Taxable H.P.: 25.35. Main bearings: three. Valve lifters: solid. Carb.: Marvel U4S. [Series 130]: Ohv. Inline. Six. Cast iron block. B & S: 3-1/8 x 4-1/2 in. Disp.: 207.0 cu. in. Brake H.P.: 46 @ 2200 R.P.M. Taxable H.P.: 23.44. Main bearings: three. Valve lifters: solid. Carb.: Marvel U3S. [Series 220, formerly Ajax]: L-head. Inline. Six. Cast iron block. B & S: 3 x 4 in. Disp.: 169.6 cu. in. C.R.: 4.5:1. Brake H.P.: 40 @ 2400 R.P.M. Main bearings: seven. Valve lifters: solid. Carb.: Carter.

CHASSIS: [Series 160] W.B.: 121 in. and 127 in. Tires: 33 x 6.00. [Series 130] W.B.: 112-1/2 in. Tires: 31 x 5.25. [Series 220] W.B.: 108 in. Frt/Rear Tread: 56/56 in. Tires: 30 x 4.75.

TECHNICAL: Selective, sliding gear transmission. Speeds: 3F/1R. Floor shift controls. Single dry plate clutch. Spiral bevel drive. Semi-floating rear axle. Overall ratio: 4.50:1 (160); 4.88:1 (130). Mechanical brakes on four wheels. Steel disc wheels. Ajax: Selective, sliding gear transmission. Speeds: 3F/1R. Floor shift controls. Single dry plate clutch. Spiral bevel drive. Semi-floating rear axle. Overall ratio: 4.6:1. Mechanical brakes on four wheels. Steel disc wheels.

HISTORICAL: Introduced August 1, 1924. Innovations: Special "Six" replaced four-cylinder Nash. First use by Nash of four-wheel brakes. Calendar year registrations: 73,384. Calendar year production: 85,428. The president of Nash was C.W. Nash. Sales up 50 percent over 1924. Nash held 2.4 percent of new car registrations for the year. Ajax: Introduced May 1, 1925. Innovations: Nash's first entry in the "$1,000-market"; first L-head engine; first seven-bearing crankshaft. At time of introduction, the Ajax was the only car in its price class with four-wheel brakes. Calendar year production: 10,693 (1925 only). The president of Nash was C.W. Nash. About 20,000 Ajax cars sold before name was changed (May 1, 1926) to "Nash Light Six."

1926

NASH — ADVANCED "SIX" — SERIES 260 — SIX: Smoother, more rounded lines than 1925 models, particularly roof line at rear. Shorter visor than before.

NASH — SPECIAL "SIX" — SERIES 230 — SIX: Similar to 260 Series, but smaller.

NASH — LIGHT "SIX" — SERIES 220 — SIX: Identical but for name to 1925-26 Ajax.

I.D. DATA: Series 260 serial numbers on right side of front motor support. Starting: 330126. Engine numbers on engine block near starting motor. Series 230 serial numbers on top right side rear motor support or on left rear spring hanger. Starting: 75276. Engine numbers on engine block beside starting motor. Series 220 serial numbers on right frame member just ahead of rear spring rear bracket. Starting: 1001. Engine numbers on left side engine block, upper forward corner.

Series 260 — 6-cyl.

Model No.	Body Type & Seating	Factory Price	Shipping Weight	Starting Serial #
261	4-dr. Tr.-5P	1375	3400	330126
262	4-dr. Tr.-7P	1525	3480	330126
263	2-dr. Sed.-5P	1485	3550	330126
264	4-dr. Sed.-7P	2290	3830	336404
265	2-dr. Vic.-4P	2090	3640	336404
266	2-dr. Rds.-2P	1375	3320	337932
268	4-dr. Cpe.-4P	2190	3750	337932
269	4-dr. Sed.-5P	1525	3650	354114
Series 230 — 6-cyl.				
231	4-dr. Tr.-5P	1135	2960	75276
232	2-dr. Rds.-2P	1115	2870	81509
233	2-dr. Sed.-5P	1265	3120	75276
234	4-dr. Sp. Sed.-5P	1545	3300	75276
235	2-dr. Cpe.-2P	1165	3030	92070
236	2-dr. Rds.-2/4P	1225	2980	A20247
239	4-dr. Sed.-5P	1315	3170	98405
Series 220 — 6-cyl				
221	4-dr. Tr.-5P	865	2210	1001
224	4-dr. Sed.-5P	995	2410	1001
225	2-dr. Cpe.-2P	925	2310	1001

ENGINE: [Series 260] Ohv. Inline. Six. Cast iron block. B & S: 3-7/16 x 5 in. Disp.: 278.4 cu. in. Brake H.P.: 60 @ 2400 R.P.M. Taxable H.P.: 28.37. Main bearings: seven. Valve lifters: solid. Carb.: Marvel U4S. [Series 230] Ohv. Inline. Six. Cast iron block. B & S: 3-1/8 x 4-1/2 in. Disp.: 207.4 cu. in. Brake H.P.: 47 @ 2200 R.P.M. Taxable H.P.: 23.44. Main bearings: seven. Valve lifters: solid. Carb.: Marvel U38. [Series 220] L-head. Inline. Six. Cast iron block. B & S: 3 x 4 in. Disp.: 169.6 cu. in. C.R.: 4.5:1. Brake H.P.: 40 @ 2400 R.P.M. Taxable H.P.: 21.6. Main bearings: seven. Valve lifters: solid. Carb.: Carter.

CHASSIS: [Series 260] W.B.: 121 in., 127 in. Tires: 33 x 6.00. [Series 230] W.B.: 112-1/2 in. Tires: 31 x 5.25. [Series 220] W.B.: 108 in. Frt/Rear Tread: 56/56 in. Tires: 30 x 4.75.

TECHNICAL: Selective, sliding gear transmission. Speeds: 3F/1R. Floor shift controls. Single dry plate clutch. Spiral bevel drive. Semi-floating rear axle. Overall ratio: 4.5:1 (260); 4.9:1 (230); 4.6:1 (220). Mechanical brakes on four wheels. Steel disc wheels.

HISTORICAL: Introduced June 1, 1925 [260]; July 1, 1925 [230]; May 1, 1926 [220]. Innovations: First use of seven-bearing crankshafts in Nash's ohv engines [Series 260 and 230] as well as L-head [Series 220]. Calendar year registrations: 98,804. Calendar year production: 135,520. The president of Nash was C.W. Nash. Light "Six" [Series 220] represented a continuation of the Ajax under a new name. Evidently as the result of the name change, sales took a great leap forward. Sixty percent increase in Nash production for the year. Nash held 3.6 percent of new car registrations for the year.

1927

NASH — ADVANCED "SIX" — SERIES 260 — SIX: Little change in styling from 1926 model.

NASH — SPECIAL "SIX" SERIES 230 — SIX: Little change in styling from 1926 model.

NASH — LIGHT "SIX" SERIES 220 — SIX: Less boxy than 1926 model: Styling similar to 230 series, but smaller.

I.D. DATA: Series 260 serial numbers on right side of front motor support. Starting: 386972. Engine numbers on engine block near starting motor. Series 230 serial numbers on top right side rear motor support or on left rear spring hanger. Starting: A26276. Engine numbers on engine block beside starting motor. Series 220 serial numbers on right frame member just ahead of rear spring rear bracket. Starting: R28374. Engine numbers on left side engine block, upper forward corner.

Series 260 — 6-cyl

Model No.	Body Type & Seating	Factory Price	Shipping Weight	Starting Serial #
260	2-dr. Cpe.-2/4P	1775	3580	419570
261	4-dr. Tr.-5P	1340	3400	386972
262	4-dr. Tr.-7P	1490	3480	386972
263	2-dr. Sed.-5P	1425	3550	386972
264	4-dr. Sed.-7P	2090	3830	386972
265	2-dr. Vic.-4P	1790	3640	386972
266	2-dr. Rds.-2/4P	1475	3390	386972
267	4-dr. Amb. Sed.-5P	2090	3800	408304
268	4-dr. Cpe.-4P	1990	3750	386972
269	4-dr. Sed.-5P	1525	3650	386972
270	4-dr. Sp. Sed.-5P	1695	3650	410709
271	4-dr. Spt. Tr.-5P	1540	3500	415998
Series 230 — 6-cyl.				
231	4-dr. Tr.-5P	1135	2980	A26276
232	2-dr. Rds.-2P	1115	2900	A26276
233	2-dr. Sed.-5P	1215	3150	A26276
235	2-dr. Bus. Cpe.-2P	1165	3030	A26276
236	2-dr. Rds.-2/4P	1225	2980	A26276
237	4-dr. Cav. Sed.-5P	1695	3330	A42260
239	4-dr. Sed.-5P	1315	3170	A26276
240	4-dr. Sp. Sed.-5P	1485	3250	A44332
241	2-dr. Cabr.-2/4P	1290	3070	A46894

1918 Nash, Six (Model 681), five-passenger touring (with Charles Nash driving), OCW

1921 Nash, Six (Model 682), seven-passenger touring (with winter top designed by Seaman Body Corp.), OCW

1923 Nash, Six (Model 698), four-door coupe, OCW

1925 Nash, Special Six (Model 132), roadster, OCW

1927 Nash, Advanced Six (Model 267), Ambassador sedan (with Prince William of Sweden at wheel), OCW

1930 Nash, Twin-Ignition Eight (Model 498), phaeton, OCW

1932 Nash, Eight (Model 980), sedan, OCW

1933 Nash, Advanced Eight (Model 1181), convertible roadster, OCW

1933 Nash, Ambassador Eight (Model 1194), sedan, OCW

1938 Nash, Ambassador Eight (Model 3888), sedan, OCW

Series 220 — 6-cyl.

Model No.	Body Type & Seating	Factory Price	Shipping Weight	Starting Serial #
221	4-dr. Tr.-5P	865	2275	R28374
223	2-dr. Sed.-5P	925	2410	R46146
224	4-dr. Sed.-5P	995	2475	R28374
225	2-dr. Cpe.-2P	925	2310	R28374
227	4-dr. Del. Sed.-5P	1085	2550	R48852

ENGINE: [Series 260] Ohv. Inline. Six. Cast iron block. B & S: 3-7/16 x 5 in. Disp.: 278.4 cu. in. C.R.: 4.6:1. Brake H.P.: 69 @ 2500 R.P.M. Taxable H.P.: 28.4. Main bearings: seven. Valve lifters: solid. Carb.: Marvel U4S. [Series 230] Ohv. Inline. Six. Cast iron block. B & S: 3-1/4 x 4-1/2 in. Disp.: 224.0 cu. in. C.R.: 4.69:1. Brake H.P.: 52 @ 2600 R.P.M. Taxable H.P.: 25.3. Main bearings: seven. Valve lifters: solid. Carb.: Marvel U38. [Series 220] L-head. Inline. Six. Cast iron block. B & S: 3 x 4 in. Disp.: 169.6 cu. in. C.R.: 4.5:1. Brake H.P.: 40 @ 2400 R.P.M. Taxable H.P.: 21.6. Main bearings: seven. Valve lifters: solid. Carb.: one-inch Carter 82S/89S.

CHASSIS: [Series 260] W.B.: 121 in. and 127 in. Tires: 33 x 6.00. [Series 230] W.B.: 112-1/2 in. Tires: 31 x 5.25. [Series 220] W.B.: 108 in. Tires: 30 x 4.75.

TECHNICAL: Selective, sliding gear transmission. Speeds: 3F/1R. Floor shift controls. Single dry plate clutch. Spiral bevel drive. Semi-floating rear axle. Overall ratio: 4.50:1 [260]; 4.67:1 [230]; 4.77:1 [220]. Mechanical brakes on four wheels. Steel disc wheels.

HISTORICAL: Introduced June 1, 1926 [260]; July 6, 1926 [220]; August 1, 1926 [230]. Innovations: Larger bore, more power, Series 260 and 230. Calendar year registrations: 109,979. Calendar year production: 122,606. The president of Nash was C.W. Nash. Two new premium-level sedans, the Ambassador [Series 260] and Cavalier [Series 230] featured more rounded rear contours, a styling feature picked up by all advanced and special "Six" sedans for 1929. Nash held 4.2 percent of industry registrations for 1927.

1928

NASH — ADVANCED "SIX" — SERIES 360 — SIX: Similar in styling to 1927 model, but with taller radiator.

NASH — SPECIAL "SIX" — SERIES 330 — SIX: Similar in appearance to advanced (360) series, but smaller.

NASH — STANDARD "SIX" — SERIES 320 — SIX: Similar in styling to 360 and 330 series, but much smaller.

I.D. DATA: Series 360 serial numbers on right side of front motor support. Starting: 423612. Ending: 452099. Engine numbers on engine block near starting motor. Series 330 serial numbers on top right side rear motor support or on left rear spring hanger. Starting: A58246. Ending: A87449. Engine numbers on engine block beside starting motor. Series 320 serial numbers on right frame member just ahead of rear spring rear bracket. Starting: R71557. Ending: R119558. Engine numbers on left side engine block, upper forward corner.

Series 360 — 6-cyl.

Model No.	Body Type & Seating	Factory Price	Shipping Weight	Starting Serial #
360	2-dr. Cpe.-2/4P	1775	3650	423612
361	4-dr. Tr.-5P	1340	3400	423612
362	4-dr. Tr.-7P	1440	3500	423612
363	2-dr. Sed.-5P	1425	3620	423612
364	4-dr. Sed.-7P	1990	3830	423612
364-1	4-dr. Imp. Sed.-7P	2165	3900	440770
365	2-dr. Vic.-4P	1595	3640	423612
366	2-dr. Rds.-2/4P	1475	3400	423612
367	4-dr. Amb. Sed.-5P	1925	3820	422617
370	4-dr. Sed.-5P	1545	3650	423612
371	4-dr. Spt. Tr.-5P	1540	3500	423612
Series 330 — 6-cyl				
331	4-dr. Tr.-5P	1135	2980	A58246
333	2-dr. Sed.-5P	1215	3150	A58246
335	2-dr. Cpe.-2P	1165	3030	A58246
335R	2-dr. Cpe.-2/4P	1245	3030	A58246
336	2-dr. Rds.-2/4P	1225	2980	A58246
338	4-dr. Lan. Sed.-5P	1445	3380	A68271
340	4-dr. Sp. Sed.-5P	1335	3250	A58246
341	2-dr. Cabr.-2/4P	1290	3070	A58246
342	2-dr. Vic.-4P	1295	3170	A70804
Series 320 — 6-cyl.				
320	4-dr. Sed.-5P	995	2500	R71557
321	4-dr. Tr.-5P	865	2325	R71557
322	2-dr. Cabr.-2/4P	995	2505	R91928
323	2-dr. Sed.-5P	895	2450	R71557
325	2 dr. Cpe.-2P	875	2345	R71557
328	4-dr. Lan. Sed.-5P	1085	2610	R71557

ENGINE: [Series 360] Ohv. Inline. Six. Cast iron block. B & S: 3-7/16 x 5 in. Disp.: 279.0 cu. in. C.R.: 4.6:1. Brake H.P.: 70 @ 2400 R.P.M. Taxable H.P.: 28.35. Main bearings: seven. Valve lifters: solid. Carb.: Marvel U. [Series 330] Ohv. Inline. Six. Cast iron block. B & S: 3-1/4 x 4-1/2 in. Disp.: 224.0 cu. in. C.R.: 4.69:1. Brake H.P.: 52 @ 2600 R.P.M. Taxable H.P.: 25-35. Main bearings: seven. Valve lifters: solid. Carb.: Marvel. [Series 320] L-head. Inline. Six. Cast iron block. B & S: 3-1/8 x 4 in. Disp.: 184.1 cu. in. C.R.: 4.5:1. Brake H.P.: 45 @ 2600 R.P.M. Main bearings: seven. Valve lifters: solid. Carb.: Carter DRHO.

CHASSIS: [Series 360] W.B.: 121 in. and 127 in. Tires: 32 x 6.00. [Series 330] W.B.: 112-1/2 in. Tires: 30 x 5.25. [Series 320] W.B.: 108 in. Tires: 30 x 5.00.

TECHNICAL: Selective, sliding gear transmission. Speeds: 3F/1R. Floor shift controls. Single dry plate clutch. Spiral bevel drive. Semi-floating rear axle. Overall ratio: 4.50:1 (360); 4.88:1 (330); 4.77:1 (320). Mechanical brakes on four wheels. Steel disc wheels.

OPTIONS: Single sidemount. Dual sidemounts.

HISTORICAL: Introduced June 29, 1927. Calendar year registrations: 115,172. Calendar year production: 138,137. The president of Nash was C.W. Nash. Introduction in June 1928 of the stylish 1929 "400" series led to a sharp increase in sales for the calendar year. Nash's best year to date — not surpassed until 1949. (Nash held 3.67 percent of the 1928 automobile market.)

1929

NASH — ADVANCED "SIX" — SERIES 460 — SIX: Tall, narrow radiator; one-piece fenders; chromed, bowl-shaped headlamps with slight peak at top; tall, single row of vertical hood louvers; new "fish scale" radiator badge; double-bar bumpers.

NASH — SPECIAL "SIX" — SERIES 430 — SIX: Similar to advanced "six" except smaller; double row of vertical hood vents.

NASH — STANDARD "SIX" — SERIES 420 — SIX: Same general styling theme as advanced and special series, but considerably smaller. No "peak" on bowl-shaped headlamps; single row of vertical hood louvers.

I.D. DATA: [Series 460] Serial numbers on right side front motor support. Starting: 452100. Ending: 496399. Engine numbers on engine block near starting motor. [Series 430] Serial numbers on top right side rear motor support or of left rear spring hanger. Starting: A87450. Ending: B37581. Engine numbers on engine block beside starting motor. [Series 420] Serial numbers on right frame member just ahead of rear spring rear bracket. Starting: R119559. Engine numbers on left side engine block, upper forward corner.

Series 460 — 6-cyl

Model No.	Body Type & Seating	Factory Price	Shipping Weight	Starting Serial #
460	2-dr. Cpe.-2/4P	1775	3710	452100
461	2-dr. Cabr.-2/4P	1660	3675	452100
462	4-dr. Phae.-7P	1550	3700	452100
463	2-dr. Sed-5P	1480	3760	452100
464	4-dr. Sed.-7P	1990	3970	452100
465	4-dr. Limo.-7P	2190	4010	452100
467	4-dr. Amb. Sed.-5P	1925	3940	452100
470	4-dr. Sed.-5P	1550	3700	452100
Series 430 — 6-cyl				
431	4 dr. Phae.-5P	1250	3150	A87450
433	2-dr. Sed.-5P	1260	3400	A87450
434	2-dr. Cpe.-2/4P	1315	3250	A87450
435	2-dr. Cpe.-2P	1245	3250	A87450
436	2-dr. Rds.-2/4P	1345	3200	B18953
440	4-dr. Sed.-5P	1345	3400	A87450
441	2-dr. Cabr.-2/4P	1345	3260	A87450
442	2-dr. Vic.-4P	1345	3300	A87450
444	4-dr. Sed.-7P	1645	3530	B18339
Series 420 — 6-cyl				
420	4-dr. Sed.-5P	955	2725	R119559
421	4-dr. Phae.-5P	935	2500	R119559
422	2-dr. Cabr.-2/4P	955	2550	R119559
423	2-dr. Sed.-5P	885	2625	R119559
425	2-dr. Cpe.-2P	885	2500	R119559
428	4-dr. Lan. Sed.-5P	995	2725	R119559

ENGINE: [Series 460] Ohv. Inline. Six. Cast iron block. B & S: 3-7/16 x 5 in. Disp.: 278.4 cu. in. C.R.: 5.1:1. Brake H.P.: 78 @ 2900 R.P.M. Taxable H.P.: 28.4. Main bearings: seven. Valve lifters: solid. Carb.: Marvel U 1-1/4 in. updraft. [Series 430] Ohv. Inline. Six. Cast iron block. B & S: 3-1/4 x 4-1/2 in. Disp.: 224.0 cu. in. C.R.: 5.15:1. Brake H.P.: 65 @ 2900 R.P.M. Taxable H.P.: 25.3. Main bearings: seven. Valve lifters: solid. Carb.: Marvel U 1-1/4 in. updraft. [Series 420] L-head. Inline. Six. Cast iron block. B & S: 3-1/8 x 4 in. Disp.: 184.1 cu. in. C.R.: 5.0:1. Brake H.P.: 50 @ 2800 R.P.M. Taxable H.P.: 23.4. Main bearings: seven. Valve lifters: solid. Carb.: 1-1/8 in. Carter DRJH updraft.

CHASSIS: [Series 460] W.B.: 121 in. & 130 in. Tires: 32 x 6.00. [Series 430] W.B.: 116 in. & 122 in. Tires: 29 x 5.50. [Series 420] W.B.: 112-1/4 in. Tires: 30 x 5.00.

TECHNICAL: Selective, sliding gear transmission. Speeds: 3F/1R. Floor shift controls. Single dry plate clutch. Spiral bevel drive. Semi-floating rear axle. Overall ratio: 4.5:1 [460]; 4.8:1 [430]; 4.7:1 [420]. Mechanical brakes on four wheels. Wood artillery wheels: 20 in. [460, 420]; 19 in. [430].

OPTIONS: Single sidemount. Dual sidemounts (wires) ($125.00). Leather upholstery (25.00). Wire wheels (five) (40.00).

HISTORICAL: Introduced June 1, 1928. Innovations: First year for "Twin Ignition" (ohv models only) — two spark plugs firing each cylinder. First use by Nash of chromed brightwork. Calendar year registrations: 105,146. Calendar year production: 116,622. The president of Nash was C.W. Nash. Attractive new styling evidently inspired by LaSalle. Increased horsepower, all series. Longer wheelbases, standard and special series and most advanced models. Rumors were reported of a possible Nash-Packard merger. Nash held 2.7 percent of new car registrations.

1930

NASH — "TWIN-IGNITION EIGHT" — SERIES 490 — EIGHT: Similar in styling to 1929 Series 460, but larger, narrower chrome band at top of radiator shell as seen from front; figure "8" with inverted wings above Nash badge; automatic shutters covering radiator. (Largest, heaviest Nash built to date.)

NASH — "TWIN-IGNITION SIX" — SERIES 480 — SIX: Similar to Series 490, but smaller.

NASH — "SINGLE SIX" — SERIES 450 — SIX: Similar in styling to 1929 Series 420, except for narrow chrome band at top of radiator shell as seen from front.

I.D. DATA: [Series 490] Serial numbers on frame near starting motor. Starting: 496400. Ending: 509200. Engine numbers on engine block near starting motor. [Series 480] Serial numbers on top right side rear motor support or on left rear spring hanger. Starting: B37582. Ending: B54927. Engine numbers on engine block beside starter motor. [Series 450] Serial numbers on right frame member just ahead of rear spring rear bracket. Starting: R216590. Ending: R249707. Engine numbers on left side engine block, upper forward corner.

Series 490 — 8-cyl

Model No.	Body Type & Seating	Factory Price	Shipping Weight	Starting Serial #
490	4-dr. Sed.-5P	1695	4000	496400
491	2-dr. Cabr.-2/4P	1775	3840	496400
492	2-dr. Cpe.-2P	1775	3900	496400
492R	2-dr. Cpe.2/4P	1845	3950	496400
493	2-dr. Sed.-5P	1625	3950	496400
494	4-dr. Sed.-7P	2085	4170	496400
495	4-dr. Limo.-7P	2260	4210	496400
497	4-dr. Amb. Sed.-5P	1995	4050	496400
498	4-dr. Phae.-7P	1845	3770	505422
498S	4-dr. Spt. Phae.-5P	1975	3840	505965
499	2-dr. Vic.-5P	1945	3950	496400
Series 480 — 6-cyl				
480	4-dr. Sed.-5P	1385	3535	B37582
481	2-dr. Cabr.-2/4P	1355	3350	B37582
482	2-dr. Cpe.-2P	1295	3400	B37582
482R	2-dr. Cpe.-2/4P	1345	3450	B37582
483	2-dr. Sed.-5P	1295	3535	B37582
484	4-dr. Sed.-7P	1695	3750	B37582
485	4-dr. Limo.-7P	1920	3760	B47085
486	2-dr. Rds.-2/4P	1415	3250	B37582
488	4-dr. Phae.-7P	1425	3450	B37582
488S	4-dr. Spt. Phae.-5P	1545	3720	B37582
489	2-dr. Vic.-4P	1385	3400	B37582
Series 450 — 6-cyl				
450	4-dr. Sed.-5P	985	2850	R216590
451	2-dr. Cabr.-2/4P	985	2600	R216590
452	2-dr. Cpe.-2P	915	2650	R216590
452R	2-dr. Cpe.-2/4P	955	2700	R216590
453	2-dr. Sed.-5P	915	2750	R216590
455	4-dr. Land. Sed.-5P	1125	2900	R216590
456	2-dr. Rds.-2/4P	945	2550	R216590
457	4-dr. Del. Sed.-5P	1075	2900	R216590
458	4-dr. Phae.-5P	975	2650	R216590

ENGINE: [Series 490] Ohv. Straight eight. Cast iron block. B & S: 3-1/4 x 4-1/2 in. Disp.: 298.6 cu. in. C.R.: 5.25:1. Brake H.P.: 100 @ 3200 R.P.M. Taxable H.P.: 33.8. Main bearings: nine. Valve lifters: solid. Carb.: Marvel 2 in. [Series 480] Ohv. Inline. Six. Cast iron block. B & S: 3-3/8 x 4-1/2 in. Disp.: 242.0 cu. in. C.R.: 5.0:1. Brake H.P.: 74-1/2 @ 2800 R.P.M. Taxable H.P.: 27.3. Main bearings: seven. Valve lifters: solid. Carb.: Marvel 1-1/4 in. [Series 450] L-head. Inline. Six. Cast iron block. B & S: 3-1/8 x 4-3/8 in. Disp.: 201.3 cu. in. C.R.: 5.0:1. Brake H.P.: 60 @ 2800 R.P.M. Taxable H.P.: 23.4. Main bearings: seven. Valve lifters: solid. Carb.: Carter 1-5/16 in.

CHASSIS: [Series 490] W.B.: 124 in. and 133 in. Frt/Rear Tread: 56/58 in. Tires: 6.50 x 19. [Series 480] W.B.: 118 in. and 128-1/4 in. Frt/Rear Tread: 56-3/4/58-1/4 in. Tires: 5.50 x 19. [Series 450] W.B.: 114-1/4 in. Frt/Rear Tread: 56/57-1/4 in. Tires: 5.00 x 19.

TECHNICAL: Selective, sliding gear transmission. Speeds: 3F/1R. Floor shift controls. Single dry plate clutch. Spiral bevel drive. Semi-floating rear axle. Overall ratio: 4.5:1 (490, 480); 4.7:1 (450). Mechanical brakes on four wheels. Wood artillery wheels. Wheel size: 19 in.

OPTIONS: Single sidemount. Dual sidemounts (wire wheels) ($87.00). Five wire wheels (40.00).

HISTORICAL: Introduced October 1, 1929. Innovations: [Series 490] was first Nash "eight", and largest Nash built to date. Longer wheelbases than corresponding 1929 models. First use by Nash of radiator shutters. Calendar year registrations: 51,086. Calendar year production: 54,605. The president of Nash was C.W. Nash. Nash held 1.95 percent of new car registrations for 1930.

1931

NASH — SERIES 890 EIGHT: Nearly identical in styling to 480 series of 1930, but parking lamps mounted on fenders.

NASH — SERIES 880 — EIGHT: Similar in styling to six-cylinder 480 series of 1930, but with longer hood to accommodate straight-eight engine.

NASH — SERIES 870 — EIGHT: Similar in styling to 1930 "single six," series 450, but with longer hood to accommodate straight-eight engine. Figure "8" flanked by inverted wings above Nash radiator badge.

NASH — SERIES 660 — SIX: Identical in appearance except shorter hood, no "winged 8" radiator emblem.

I.D. DATA: [Series 890] Serial numbers on frame, adjacent to starting motor. Starting: 509201. Ending: 515399. Engine numbers on engine block right side, near starting motor. Starting: B70124. Ending: B74370. [Series 880] Serial numbers on frame adjacent to starting motor. Starting: B54928. Ending: B61757. Engine numbers on right side engine block near starting motor. Starting: B70124. Ending: B74370. [Series 870] Serial numbers on frame, adjacent to starting motor. Starting: X1001. Ending: X13116. Engine numbers on left side engine block next to generator. Starting: XE1000. Ending: XE13184. [Series 660] Serial numbers on frame, adjacent to starting motor. Starting: R249708. Ending: R261948. Engine numbers on left side engine block next to generator. Starting: E1000. Ending: E13290.

Series 890 — 8-cyl

Model No.	Body Type & Seating	Factory Price	Shipping Weight	Starting Serial #
890	4-dr. Sed.-5P	1565	4000	509201
891	2-dr. Cabr.-2/4P	1695	3840	509201
892	2-dr. Cpe.-2P	1695	3900	509201
892R	2-dr. Cpe.-2/4P	1745	3950	509201
894	4-dr. Sed.-7P	1925	4170	509201
895	4-dr. Limo.-7P	2025	4210	509201
897	4-dr. Amb. Sed.-7P	1825	4050	509201
898	4-dr. Phae.-7P	1595	3880	513589
899	2-dr. Vic.-5P	1765	3950	509201
Series 880 — 8-cyl				
880	4-dr. Sed.-5P	1295	3360	B54928
881	2-dr. Conv. Sed.-5P	1325	3275	B58597
882	2-dr. Cpe.-2P	1245	3200	B54928
882R	2-dr. Cpe.-2/4P	1285	3250	B54928
887	4-dr. Twn. Sed.-5P	1375	3400	B54928
Series 870 — 8-cyl				
870	4-dr. Sed.-5P	995	3000	X1001
871	2-dr. Conv. Sed.-5P	1075	2950	X8171
872	2-dr. Cpe.-2P	945	2870	X1001
872R	2-dr. Cpe.-2/4P	975	2920	X1001
877	4-dr. Sp. Sed.-5P	955	3000	X1001
Series 660 — 6-cyl				
660	4-dr. Sed.-5P	845	2800	R249708
662	2-dr. Cpe.-2P	795	2600	R249708
662R	2-dr. Cpe.-2/4P	825	2650	R249708
663	2-dr. Sed.-5P	795	2740	R249708
668	4-dr. Spt. Phae.-5P	895	2640	R249708

ENGINE: [Series 890] Ohv. Straight-eight. Cast iron block. B & S: 3-1/4 x 4-1/2 in. Disp.: 298.6 cu. in. C.R.: 5.25:1. Brake H.P.: 115 @ 3600 R.P.M. Taxable H.P.: 33.8. Main bearings: nine. Valve lifters: solid. Carb.: Stromberg UUR-2. [Series 880] Ohv. Straight-eight. Cast iron block. B & S: 3 x 4-1/4 in. Disp.: 240.0 cu. in. C.R.: 5.25:1. Brake H.P.: 88-1/2 @ 3400 R.P.M. Taxable H.P.: 28.8. Main bearings: nine. Valve lifters: solid. Carb.: Marvel. Torque: 100 lb.-ft. @ 200 R.P.M. [Series 870] L-head. Straight-eight. Cast iron block. B & S: 2-7/8 x 4-3/8 in. Disp.: 227.2 cu. in. C.R.: 5.0:1. Brake H.P.: 78 @ 3300 R.P.M. Taxable H.P.: 26.4. Main bearings: nine. Valve lifters: solid. Carb.: Stromberg E-2. Torque: 92 lb.-ft. @ 1600 R.P.M. [Series 660] L-head. Inline. Six. Cast iron block. B & S: 3-1/8 x 4-3/8 in. Disp.: 201.3 cu. in. C.R.: 5.0:1. Brake H.P.: 65 @ 3200 R.P.M. Taxable H.P.: 23.4. Main bearings: seven. Valve lifters: solid. Carb.: Carter DRT-08. Torque: 92 lb.-ft. @ 1600 R.P.M.

CHASSIS: [Series 890] W.B.: 124 in. and 133 in. Frt/Rear Tread: 56-1/4/58 in. Tires: 6.50 x 19. [Series 880] W.B.: 121 in. Frt/Rear Tread: 55-15/16/58-1/8 in. Tires: 5.50 x 18. [Series 870] W.B.: 116-1/4 in. Frt/Rear Tread: 56/58-3/8 in. Tires: 5.25 x 19. [Series 660] W.B.: 114-1/4 in. Frt/Rear Tread: 56/58-3/8 in. Tires: 5.00 x 19.

TECHNICAL: Selective, sliding gear transmission. Speeds: 3F/1R. Floor shift controls. Single dry plate clutch. Spiral bevel drive. Semi-floating rear axle. Overall ratio: 4.5:1 (890); 4.72:1 (880); 5.1:1 (870, 660). Mechanical brakes on four wheels. Artillery wheels (wire opt., extra cost). Rim size: 18 in. (880), 19 in. (all others).

OPTIONS: Single sidemount. Dual sidemounts.

HISTORICAL: Introduced October 1, 1930. Innovations: First Nash "Flathead Eight" (Series 870) downdraft carburetors, eight-cylinder models. Calendar year registrations: 39,366. Calendar year production: 38,616. The president of Nash was E.H. McCarty. Despite falling sales, Nash earned $4,808,000 during fiscal 1931. Nash held 2.06 percent of new car registrations for the year.

1932

NASH — SERIES 990 — EIGHT: Basically a carry-over of the 1931 890 series, but with a veed grille instead of the shuttered flat radiator. Headlamps bullet-shaped. Single-bar bumpers.

NASH — SERIES 980 — EIGHT: Similar in appearance to 990 series, but smaller.

NASH — SERIES 970 — EIGHT: Similar in styling to 870 series of 1931, but with slightly veed grille instead of flat radiator front.

NASH — SERIES 960 — SIX: Virtually identical in appearance to 970 series, but hood two inches shorter.

NASH — AMBASSADOR & ADVANCED "EIGHTS" — SERIES 1090 — EIGHT: Second series 1932 car. Slanted windshield, visor eliminated; more sweeping lines, especially fenders; semi-beavertail rear quarter. Ambassador models 1094-1099 were on the 142-in. wheelbase, longest ever offered by Nash. (These cars have been referred to by historian Dave Brownell as the "Kenosha Duesenbergs.") Advanced models similar, but shorter bodies on 133-in. wheelbase. Vertical, veed grille. Bullet-shaped, chrome-plated headlamps.

NASH — SPECIAL "EIGHT" — SERIES 1080 — EIGHT: Similar in appearance to 1090 series, but smaller; less brightwork on radiator shell.

NASH — STANDARD "EIGHT" — SERIES 1070 — EIGHT: Slanted windshield veed, vertical grille; sweeping fender lines; semi-beavertail rear section.

NASH — "BIG SIX" — SERIES 1060 — SIX: Similar in appearance to 1070 series, but shorter hood and front fenders.

I.D. DATA: [Series 990] Serial numbers on frame, adjacent to starting motor. Starting: 515400. Ending: 519299. Engine numbers on right side engine block near starting motor. Starting: 398700. Ending: 402599. [Series 980] Serial numbers on frame, adjacent to starting motor. Starting: B61758. Ending: B66800. Engine numbers on right side engine block near starting motor. Starting: B74371. Ending: B79449. [Series 970] Serial numbers on frame, adjacent to starting motor. Starting: X13117. Ending: X21317. Engine numbers on left side engine block next to generator. Starting: XE13185. Ending: XE21416. [Series 960] Serial numbers on frame, adjacent to starting motor. Starting: R261949. Ending: R267735. Engine numbers on left side engine block next to generator. Starting: R261949. Ending: R267735. [Series 1090] Serial numbers on frame, adjacent to starting motor. Starting: 519300. Ending: 521190. Engine numbers on right side engine block near starting motor. [Series 1080] Serial numbers on frame, adjacent to starting motor. Starting: B66800. Ending: B70020. Engine numbers on right side engine block near starting motor. [Series 1070] Serial numbers on frame, adjacent to starting motor. Starting: X21318. Ending: X25386. Engine numbers on left side engine block next to generator. [Series 1060] Serial numbers on frame, adjacent to starting motor. Starting: R267736. Ending: R274299. Engine numbers on left side engine block next to generator.

Series 990 — 8-cyl

Model No.	Body Type & Seating	Factory Price	Shipping Weight	Starting Serial #
990	4-dr. Sed.-5P	1565	4000	515400
991	2-dr. Cabr.-2/4P	1695	3840	515400
992	2-dr. Cpe.-2P	1695	3900	515400
992R	2-dr. Cpe.-2/4P	1745	3950	515400
994	4-dr. Sed.-7P	1925	4170	515400
995	4-dr. Limo.-7P	2025	4210	515400
996	4-dr. lwb. Sed.-5P	1825	4100	515400
997	4-dr. Amb. Sed.-5P	1825	4050	515400
998	4-dr. Phae.-7P	1595	3880	515400
999	2-dr. Vic.-5P	1765	3950	515400
Series 980 — 8-cyl				
980	4-dr. Sed.-5P	1295	3360	B61758
981	2-dr. Conv. Sed.-5P	1325	3275	B61758
982	2-dr. Cpe.-2P	1245	3200	B61758
982R	2-dr. Cpe.-2/4P	1285	3250	B61758
987	4-dr. Twn. Sed.-5P	1375	3400	B61758
Series 970 — 8-cyl				
970	4-dr. Sed.-5P	995	3000	X13117
971	2-dr. Conv. Sed.-5P	1075	2950	X13117
972	2-dr. Cpe.-2P	945	2870	X13117
972R	2-dr. Cpe.-2/4P	975	2920	X13117
977	4-dr. Sp. Sed.-5P	955	3000	X13117
Series 960 — 6-cyl.				
960	4-dr. Sed.-5P	845	2800	R261949
962	2-dr. Cpe.-2P	795	2600	R261949
962R	2-dr. Cpe.-2/4P	825	2650	R261949
963	2-dr. Sed.-5P	795	2740	R261949
968	4-dr. Spt. Phae.-5P	895	2640	R261949
Series 1090 — 8-cyl				
1090	4-dr. Sed.-5P	1595	4350	519300
1091	2-dr. Conv. Rds.-2/4P	1795	4270	519300
1092	2-dr. Cpe.-2P	1695	4210	519300
1092R	2-dr. Cpe.-2/4P	1695	4300	519300
1093	4-dr. Conv. Sed.-5P	1875	4470	519300
1094	4-dr. Sed.-7P	1955	4600	519300
1095	4-dr. Limo.-7P	2055	4650	519300
1096	4-dr. Sed.-5P	1855	4510	519300
1097	4-dr. Brgm.-5P	1855	4470	519300
1099	2-dr. Vic.-5P	1785	4300	519300
Series 1080 — 8-cyl				
1080	4-dr. Sed.-5P	1320	3870	B66800
1081	2-dr. Conv. Rds.-2/4P	1395	3750	B66800
1082	2-dr. Cpe.-2P	1270	3710	B66800
1082R	2-dr. Cpe.-2/4P	1320	3800	B66800
1083	4-dr. Conv. Sed.-5P	1475	4000	B66800
1089	2-dr. Vic.-5P	1395	3840	B66800
Series 1070 — 8-cyl				
1070	4-dr. Sed.-5P	1015	3400	X21318
1071	2-dr. Conv. Rds.-2/4P	1055	3270	X21318
1072	2-dr. Cpe.-2P	965	3250	X21318
1072R	2-dr. Cpe.-2/4P	1015	3300	X21318
1073	2-dr. Conv. Sed.-5P	1095	3275	X21318
1077	4-dr. Twn. Sed.-5P	975	3400	X21318
Series 1060 — 6-cyl.				
1060	4-dr. Sed.-5P	840	3200	R267736
1061	2-dr. Conv. Rds.-2/4P	895	3120	R267736
1062	2-dr. Cpe.-2P	777	3050	R267736
1062R	2-dr. Cpe.-2/4P	825	3100	R267736
1063	2-dr. Conv. Sed.-5P	935	3125	R267736
1067	4-dr. Twn. Sed.-5P	825	3150	R267736

ENGINE: [Series 990] Ohv. Straight-eight. Cast iron block. B & S: 3-1/4 x 4-1/2 in. Disp.: 298.6 cu. in. C.R.: 5.25:1. Brake H.P.: 115 @ 3600 R.P.M. Taxable H.P.: 33.8. Main bearings: nine. Valve lifters: solid. Carb.: Stromberg UUR-2. Torque: 100 lb.-ft. @ 1200 R.P.M. [Series 980] Ohv. Straight-eight. Cast iron block. B & S: 3 x 4-1/4 in. Disp.: 240.0 cu. in. C.R.: 5.25:1. Brake H.P.: 94 @ 3400 R.P.M. Taxable H.P.: 28.8. Main bearings: nine. Valve lifters: solid. Carb.: Stromberg UUR-2. Torque: 100 lb.-ft. @ 1200 R.P.M. [Series 970] L-head. Straight-eight. Cast iron block. B & S: 2-7/8 x 4-3/8 in. Disp.: 227.2 cu. in. C.R.: 5.00:1. Brake H.P.: 78 @ 3200 R.P.M. Taxable H.P.: 26.4. Main bearings: nine. Valve lifters: solid. Carb.: Stromberg EE-2. Torque: 92 lb.-ft. @ 1600 R.P.M. [Series 960] L-head. Inline. Six. Cast iron block. B & S: 3-1/8 x 4-3/8 in. Disp.: 201.3 cu. in. C.R.: 5.00:1. Brake H.P.: 65 @ 3200 R.P.M. Taxable H.P.: 23.4. Main bearings: seven. Valve lifters: solid. Carb.: Carter 1-5/16 in. Torque: 92 lb.-ft. @ 1600 R.P.M. [Series 1090] Ohv. Straight-eight. Cast iron block. B & S: 3-3/8 x 4-1/2 in. Disp.: 322.0 cu. in. C.R.: 5.25:1. Brake H.P.: 125 @ 3600 R.P.M. Taxable H.P.: 36.4. Main bearings: nine. Valve lifters: solid. Carb.: Stromberg UUR-2. [Series 1080] Ohv. Straight-eight. Cast iron block. B & S: 3-1/8 x 4-1/4 in.

Disp.: 260.8 cu. in. C.R.: 5.25:1. Brake H.P.: 100 @ 3400 R.P.M. Taxable H.P.: 31.2. Main bearings: nine. Valve lifters: solid. Carb.: Stromberg UUR-2. [Series 1070] L-head. Straight-eight. Cast iron block. B & S: 3 x 4-3/8 in. Disp.: 247.4 cu. in. C.R.: 5.1:1. Brake H.P.: 85 @ 3200 R.P.M. Taxable H.P.: 28.8. Main bearings: nine. Valve lifters: solid. Carb.: Stromberg EE-22. [Series 1060] L-head. Inline. Six. Cast iron block. B & S: 3-1/8 x 4-3/8 in. Disp.: 201.3 cu. in. C.R.: 5.1:1. Brake H.P.: 70 @ 3000 R.P.M. Taxable H.P.: 23.4. Main bearings: seven. Valve lifters: solid. Carb.: Stromberg E-2.

CHASSIS: [Series 990] W.B.: 124 in. and 133 in. Frt/Rear Tread: 56-1/4/58 in. Tires: 6.50 x 19. [Series 980] W.B.: 121 in. Frt/Rear Tread: 55-15/16/58-1/8 in. Tires: 6.00 x 18. [Series 970] W.B.: 116-1/4 in. Frt/Rear Tread: 56/58-3/8 in. Tires: 5.25 x 19. [Series 960] W.B.: 114-1/4 in. Frt/Rear Tread: 56/58-3/8 in. Tires: 5.00 x 19. [Series 1090] W.B.: 133 in. and 142 in. Frt/Rear Tread: 57-1/4/58 in. Tires: 7.00 x 18. [Series 1080] W.B.: 128 in. Frt/Rear Tread: 58-3/4/60-3/4 in. Tires: 6.50 x 17. [Series 1070] W.B.: 121 in. Frt/Rear Tread: 56-1/2/59-3/8. Tires: 5.50 x 18. [Series 1060] W.B.: 116 in. Frt/Rear Tread: 56-1/2/60 in. Tires: 5.25. x 18.

TECHNICAL: Selective, sliding gear transmission. Speeds: 3F/1R. Floor shift controls. Single dry plate clutch. Worm drive [1080, 1090]. Spiral bevel drive [all others]. Semi-floating rear axle. Overall ratio: 4.50:1 [990, 1090]; 4.46:1 [980]; 4.43:1 [1080]; 4.73:1 [970, 960]; 4.44:1 [1070]; 4.70:1 [1060]. Mechanical brakes on four wheels. Artillery or wire wheels. Wheel size: 19 in. [990, 970, 960]; 18 in. [980, 1090, 1070, 1060]; 17 in. [1080]. Drivetrain options: Freewheeling.

OPTIONS: Single sidemount. Dual sidemounts. Sidemounts cover(s).

HISTORICAL: Introduced June 1, 1931 [first series: 990 et al], March 1, 1932 [second series 1090 et al]. Innovations: Larger engines in all second series cars. Nash's first four-door convertible sedans [1090 and 1080 series]. Worm drive [1080, 1090 series]. Calendar year registrations: 20,233 [both series]. Calendar year production: 17,696 [both series]. The president of Nash was E.H. McCarty. First time Nash offered two series in one model year. A dismal year for sales, thanks to the Depression, but Nash made money in 1932 — the only auto manufacturer apart from General Motors to do so! (Profit for the fiscal year came to $1,029,552.) Nash held 1.85 percent of industry registrations for the year.

1933

NASH — AMBASSADOR "EIGHT" — SERIES 1190 — EIGHT: Identical in appearance to 1090 series of 1932, except for a medallion with the number "8" mounted on headlamp tie-bar. Models 1194-1199 were on the 142-in. chassis.

NASH — ADVANCED "EIGHT" — SERIES 1180 — EIGHT: Similar in appearance to 1190 series, but smaller; less brightwork on radiator shell than 1190.

NASH — SPECIAL "EIGHT" — SERIES 1170 — EIGHT: Identical in appearance to 1070 series standard "Eight" of 1932.

NASH — STANDARD "EIGHT" — SERIES 1130 — EIGHT: Identical in appearance to 1932 series 1060 "Big Six."

NASH — "BIG SIX" — SERIES 1120 — SIX: Identical in appearance to 1932 series 1060 "Big Six."

I.D. DATA: [Series 1190] Serial numbers on frame, opposite starting motor. Starting: 521191. Ending: 521800. Engine numbers on crankcase bell housing. Starting: 404491. Ending: 404992. [Series 1180] Serial numbers on frame, opposite starting motor. Starting: B70021. Ending: B70800. Engine numbers on crankcase bell housing. Starting: B82671. Ending: B83420. [Series 1170] Serial numbers on frame, right side. Starting: X25387. Ending: X26099. Engine numbers on left side near generator. Starting: XE25413. Ending: XE28189. [Series 1130] Serial numbers on frame, right side. Starting: X26100. Ending: X28100. Engine numbers on right side below valve cover. Starting: XE26000. Ending: XE28001. [Series 1120] Serial numbers on frame, right side. Starting: R274300. Ending: R278900. Engine numbers on right side below valve cover. Starting: E25700. Ending: E30211.

Series 1190 — 8-cyl

Model No.	Body Type & Seating	Factory Price	Shipping Weight	Starting Serial #
1190	4-dr. Sed.-5P	1575	4350	521191
1191	2-dr. Conv. Rds.-2/4P	1645	4270	521191
1192R	2-dr. Cpe.-2/4P	1545	4300	521191
1193	4-dr. Conv. Sed.-5P	1875	4470	521191
1194	4-dr. Sed.-7P	1955	4600	521191
1195	4-dr. Limo.-7P	2055	4650	521191
1196	4-dr. LWB Sed.-5P	1855	4510	521191
1197	4-dr. Brgm.-5P	1820	4470	521191
1199	2-dr. Vic.-5P	1785	4300	521191

Series 1180 — 8-cyl

Model No.	Body Type & Seating	Factory Price	Shipping Weight	Starting Serial #
1180	4-dr. Sed.-5P	1320	4000	B70021
1181	2-dr. Conv. Rds.-2/4P	1395	3750	B70021
1182	2-dr. Cpe.-2P	1255	3710	B70021
1182R	2-dr. Cpe.-2/4P	1275	3800	B70021
1183	4-dr. Conv. Sed.-5P	1575	3870	B70021
1189	2-dr. Vic.-5P	1395	3840	B70021

Series 1170 — 8-cyl

Model No.	Body Type & Seating	Factory Price	Shipping Weight	Starting Serial #
1170	4-dr. Sed.-5P	1015	3400	X25387
1171	2-dr. Conv. Rds.-2/4P	1055	3270	X25387
1172	2-dr. Cpe.-2P	965	3250	X25387
1172R	2-dr. Cpe.-2/4P	1015	3300	X25387
1173	2-dr. Conv. Sed.-5P	1095	3275	X25387
1177	4-dr. Twn. Sed.-5P	975	3400	X25387

Series 1130 — 8-cyl

Model No.	Body Type & Seating	Factory Price	Shipping Weight	Starting Serial #
1130	4-dr. Sed.-5P	845	3200	X26100
1131	2-dr. Conv. Rds.-2/4P	900	3050	X26100
1132	2-dr. Cpe.-2P	830	3050	X26100
1132R	2-dr. Cpe.-2/4P	845	3100	X26100
1133	2-dr. Conv. Sed.-5P	945	3150	X26100
1137	4-dr. Twn. Sed.-5P	830	3175	X26100

Series 1120 — 6-cyl.

Model No.	Body Type & Seating	Factory Price	Shipping Weight	Starting Serial #
1120	4-dr. Sed.-5P	745	3125	R274300
1121	2-dr. Conv. Rds.-2/4P	810	3000	R274300
1122	2-dr. Cpe.-2P	725	3000	R274300
1122R	2-dr. Cpe.-2/4P	745	3050	R274300
1123	2-dr. Conv. Sed.-5P	845	3100	R274300
1127	4-dr. Twn. Sed.-5P	695	3125	R274300

ENGINE: [Series 1190] Ohv. Straight-eight. Cast iron block. B & S: 3-3/8 x 4-1/2 in. Disp.: 322.0 cu. in. C.R.: 5.2:1. Brake H.P.: 125 @ 3600 R.P.M. Taxable H.P.: 36.4. Main bearings: nine. Valve lifters: solid. Carb.: Stromberg UUR-2. [Series 1180] Ohv. Straight-eight. Cast iron block. B & S: 3-1/8 x 4-1/4 in. Disp.: 260.8 cu. in. C.R.: 5.2:1. Brake H.P.: 100 @ 3200 R.P.M. Taxable H.P.: 31.2. Main bearings: nine. Valve lifters: solid. Carb.: Stromberg UUR-2. [Series 1170] L-head. Straight-eight. Cast iron block. B & S: 3 x 4-3/8 in. Disp.: 247.4 cu. in. C.R.: 5.1:1. Brake H.P.: 85 @ 3200 R.P.M. Taxable H.P.: 28.8. Main bearings: seven. Valve lifters: solid. Carb.: 1-7/16 in. Stromberg. [Series 1130] L-head. Straight-eight. Cast iron block. B & S: 3 x 4-3/8 in. Disp.: 247.4 cu. in. C.R.: 5.1:1. Brake H.P.: 80 @ 3200 R.P.M. Taxable H.P.: 28.8. Main bearings: nine. Valve lifters: solid. Carb.: Stromberg EX-2. Torque: 92 lb.-ft. @ 1600 R.P.M. [Series 1120] L-head. Inline. Six. Cast iron block. B & S: 3-1/4 x 4-3/8 in. Disp.: 217.8 cu. in. C.R.: 5.3:1. Brake H.P.: 75 @ 3200 R.P.M. Taxable H.P.: 25.3. Main bearings: seven. Valve lifters: solid. Carb.: Stromberg EX-2.

CHASSIS: [Series 1190] W.B.: 133 in. & 142 in. Tires: 7.00 x 18. [Series 1180] W.B.: 128 in. Tires: 6.50 x 17. [Series 1170] W.B.: 121 in. Tires: 5.50 x 18. [Series 1130] W.B.: 116 in. Tires: 5.50 x 17. [Series 1120] W.B.: 116 in. Tires: 5.50 x 17.

TECHNICAL: Selective, sliding gear transmission. Speeds: 3F/1R. Floor shift controls. Single dry plate clutch. Worm drive (1190, 1180), Spiral bevel (all others). Semi-floating rear axle. Overall ratio: 4.50:1 (1190), 4.71:1 (1180), 4.44:1 (1170, 1130), 4.70:1 (1120). Mechanical brakes on four wheels. Wire wheels. Wheel size: 18 in. (1190, 1170), 17 in. (all others).

OPTIONS: Single sidemount. Dual sidemounts. Sidemount cover(s).

HISTORICAL: Introduced December 1, 1932. Innovations: "Big Six" engine bored, horsepower raised from 70 to 75. Calendar year registrations: 11,353. Calendar year production: 14,973. The president of Nash was E.H. McCarty. Some "badge engineering," and a new "8" on the "Big Six" chassis. Otherwise the 1933 line was carried over from the 1932 second series. Nash production lowest since 1918, and for the first time in its history, the company lost money. (The loss came to $1,188,863.) Share of new car registrations: 0.76 percent.

1934

NASH — AMBASSADOR "EIGHT" — SERIES 1290 — EIGHT: High-styled body, designed by Count Alexis de Sakhnoffsky, featuring deep-skirted fender ribs running length of hood; horizontal door ventilators on hood sides; chromed, bullet-shaped headlamps, full beavertail rear section.

NASH — ADVANCED "EIGHT" — SERIES 1280 — EIGHT: Identical in appearance to Ambassador models (1290 series), but shorter.

NASH — "BIG SIX" — SERIES 1220 — SIX: Identical in appearance to 1280 series, but shorter hood and front fenders.

LA FAYETTE — SERIES 110 — SIX: Similar in design to Nash models, but smoother, less elaborate. (No embossing on hood and fenders, for instance.) Painted headlamp shells on standard models, chromed on others.

I.D. DATA: [Series 1290] Serial numbers on right side frame, under hood. Starting: 521801. Ending: 523253. Engine numbers on right side engine block. Starting: 405819. Ending: 406555. [Series 1280] Serial numbers on right side frame, under hood. Starting: B70801. Ending: B75001. Engine numbers on right side engine block. Starting: B85513. Ending: B87709. [Series 1220] Serial numbers on right side frame, under hood. Starting: R278901. Ending: R294724. Engine numbers on right side engine block. Starting: E35651. Ending: E46124. LaFayette serial numbers on right frame, under hood. Starting: L1001. Ending: L13700. Engine numbers on right front of engine block, just below valve cover. Starting: LE501. Ending: LE13200.

Series 1290 — 8-cyl

Model No.	Body Type & Seating	Factory Price	Shipping Weight	Starting Serial #
1290	4-dr. Sed.-5P	1575	4330	521801
1293	4-dr. Brgm.-5P	1625	4360	521801
1294	4-dr. Sed.-7P	1955	4590	521801
1295	4-dr. Limo.-7P	2055	4640	521801
1296	4-dr. Lwb. Sed.-5P	1955	4500	521801
1297	4-dr. Lwb. Brgm.-5P	1820	4460	521801
Series 1280 — 8-cyl				
1280	4-dr. Sed.-5P	1065	3540	B70801
1282	2-dr. Cpe.-2P	1045	3460	B70801
1282R	2-dr. Cpe.-2/4P	1065	3510	B70801
1283	4-dr. Brgm.-5P	1085	3570	B70801
1287	4-dr. Twn. Sed.-5P	1035	3540	B70801
1288	4-dr. Brgm. Sed.-5P	1145	3570	B70801
Series 1220 — 6-cyl.				
1220	4-dr. Sed.-5P	785	3370	R278901
1222	2-dr. Cpe.-2P	765	3290	R278901
1222R	2-dr. Cpe.-2/4P	785	3340	R278901
1223	4-dr. Brgm.-5P	795	3400	R278901
1227	4-dr. Twn. Sed.-5P	745	3370	R278901
1228	4-dr. Brgm. Sed.-5P	865	3400	R278901
Series 110 — 6-cyl.				
110	4-dr. Sed.-5P	695	3030	L1001
112	2-dr. Cpe.-2P	635	2925	L1001
112R	2-dr. Cpe.-2/4P	675	2970	L1001
113	4-dr. Brgm.-5P	745	3050	L10131
115	2-dr. Tr. Sed.-5P	685	3030	L1001
116	2-dr. Std. Sed.-5P	595	2970	L1001
117	4-dr. Std. Sed.-5P	645	3000	L4026
118	4-dr. Std. Brgm.-5P	695	3050	L10133

ENGINE: [Series 1290] Ohv. Straight-eight. Cast iron block. B & S: 3-3/8 x 4-1/2 in. Disp.: 322.0 cu. in. C.R.: 5.25:1. Brake H.P.: 125 @ 3600 R.P.M. Taxable H.P.: 36.4. Main bearings: nine. Valve lifters: solid. Carb.: Stromberg UUR-2. Torque: 115 lb.-ft. @ 4000 R.P.M. [Series 1280] Ohv. Straight-eight. Cast iron block. B & S: 3-1/8 x 4-1/4 in. Disp.: 260.8 cu. in. C.R.: 5.25:1. Brake H.P.: 100 @ 3400 R.P.M. Taxable H.P.: 31.2. Main bearings: nine. Valve lifters: solid. Carb.: Stromberg EE-22. Torque: 110 lb.-ft @ 3500 R.P.M. [Series 1220] Ohv. Inline. Six. Cast iron block. B & S: 3-3/8 x 4-3/8 in. Disp.: 234.8 cu. in. C.R.: 5.25:1. Brake H.P.: 88 @ 3200 R.P.M. Taxable H.P.: 27.3. Main bearings: seven. Valve lifters: solid. Carb.: Stromberg EX-32. Torque: 100 lb.-ft. @ 3500 R.P.M. [LaFayette] L-head. Inline. Six. Cast iron block. B & S: 3-1/4 x 4-3/8 in. Disp.: 217.8 cu. in. C.R.: 5.3:1. Brake H.P.: 75 @ 3200 R.P.M. Taxable H.P.: 25.3. Main bearings: seven. Valve lifters: solid. Carb.: Marvel "B".

CHASSIS: [Series 1290] W.B.: 133 in. and 142 in. O.L.: 214-1/4 in. Frt/Rear Tread: 57-1/4/60-1/4 in. Tires: 7.00 x 17. [Series 1280] W.B.: 121 in. O.L.: 198-3/16 in. Frt/Rear Tread: 57-7/8/60 in. Tires: 6.50 x 16. [Series 1220] W.B.: 116 in. O.L.: 194-1/2 in. Frt/Rear Tread: 57-7/8/60 in. Tires: 5.50 x 17 (6.25 x 16 opt.). [Series LaFayette (110)] W.B.: 113 in. Frt/Rear Tread: 56-1/2/59-11/16 in. Tires: 5.50 x 17 (6.25 x 16 opt.).

TECHNICAL: Selective, sliding gear transmission. Speeds: 3F/1R. Floor shift controls. Single dry plate clutch. Worm drive [Series 1290], spiral bevel drive [all others]. Semi-floating rear axle. Overall ratio: 4.72:1 [1290], 4.10:1 [1280], 4.44:1 [1220], 4.70:1 [LaFayette]. Mechanical brakes on four wheels. Steel artillery wheels. Wheel size: 17 in. [Series 1280 - 16 in.] Baker Axle-Flex independent front suspension.

OPTIONS: Single sidemount. Dual sidemount. Sidemount cover(s). Fender skirts. Radio. Heater. Clock. Cigar lighter. Radio antenna. Trunk. Trunk rack.

HISTORICAL: Introduced October 1, 1933 (Nash), January 10, 1934 (LaFayette). Innovations: First year for low-priced LaFayette. All Nash cars now using ohv engines. (L-head engine of previous "Big Six" now used in LaFayette). Draft-free ventilation system (all models). Calendar year registrations: 14,315 (Nash), 9,301 (LaFayette). Calendar year production: 28,664 (Nash and LaFayette). The president of Nash was E.H. McCarty. One millionth Nash car — a 1227 town sedan — was produced on April 27, 1934. A contest was held to find the oldest Nash automobile still in use by its original owner. Nash #1,000,000 was the prize. It went to Dr. E.O. Nash (no relation) of Pueblo, Colorado. His car, the 517th Nash to have been built, had traveled 215,580 miles. Loss for the fiscal year came to $1,625,078. Share of industry registrations: 1.25 percent (Nash and LaFayette combined.) Styled by Count Alexis de Sakhnoffsky.

1935

NASH — AMBASSADOR & ADVANCED "EIGHTS" — SERIES 3580 — EIGHT: Fastback "Aeroform" styling; streamlined fenders; sharply sloping pressed steel grille; recessed spare tire, behind flush door; teardrop headlamps. Ambassador name applied to top trim line.

NASH — ADVANCED "SIX" — SERIES 3520 — SIX: Identical in appearance to series 3580, except for shorter hood and front fenders.

LAFAYETTE — SERIES 3510 — SIX: Styling similar to 1934 LaFayette, with the following changes: horizontal louvers replaced vent doors in hood sides, extremely convex headlamp lenses.

I.D. DATA: [Series 3580] Serial numbers on right side frame, under hood. Starting: B75010. Ending: B77324. Engine numbers on right side engine block. Starting: B87710. Ending: B90024. [Series 3520] Serial numbers on right side frame, under hood. Starting: R294725. Ending: R303300. Engine numbers on right side engine block. Starting: E46125. Ending: E54700. LaFayette serial numbers on right frame, under hood. Starting: L13701. Ending: L23100. Engine numbers on right front of engine block, just below valve cover. Starting: LE13201. Ending: LE22600.

Series 3580 — 8-cyl

Model No.	Body Type & Seating	Factory Price	Shipping Weight	Starting Serial #
3580	4-dr. Sed.-6P	1165	3750	B75010
3585	2-dr. Vic.-6P	1115	3660	B75010
3588	4-dr. Amb. Sed.-6P	1290	3750	B75010
3589	2-dr. Amb. Vic.-6P	1240	3660	B75010
Series 3520 — 6-cyl.				
3520	4-dr. Sed.-6P	945	3630	R294725
3525	2-dr. Vic.-6P	895	3540	R294725
Series 3510 — 6-cyl.				
3510	4-dr. Std. Sed.-5P	670	3000	L13701
3512	2-dr. Std. Cpe.-2P	585	2925	L13701
3512R	2-dr. Sp. Cpe.-2/4P	700	2970	L13701
3513	4-dr. Std. Brgm.-5P	700	3050	L13701
3515	2-dr. Std. Tr. Sed.-5P	650	3030	L13701
3516	2-dr. Std. Sed.-5P	620	2970	L13701
3517	4-dr. Sp. Sed.-5P	720	3030	L13701
3518	4-dr. Sp. Brgm.-5P	750	3050	L13701

ENGINE: [Series 3580] Ohv. Straight-eight. Cast iron block. B & S: 3-1/8 x 4-1/4 in. Disp.: 260.8 cu. in. C.R.: 5.25:1. Brake H.P.: 100 @ 3400 R.P.M. Taxable H.P.: 31.25. Main bearings: nine. Valve lifters: solid. Carb.: Stromberg EE-22. Torque: 110 lb.-ft. @ 3500 R.P.M. [Series 3520] Ohv. Inline. Six. Cast iron block. B & S: 3-3/8 x 4-3/8 in. Disp.: 234.8 cu. in. C.R.: 5.25:1. Brake H.P.: 88 @ 3200 R.P.M. Taxable H.P.: 27.3. Main bearings: seven. Valve lifters: solid. Carb.: Stromberg EX-32. Torque: 100 lb.-ft. @ 3500 R.P.M. [LaFayette] L-head. Inline. Six. Cast iron block. B & S: 3-1/4 x 4-3/8 in. Disp.: 217.7 cu. in. C.R.: 5.54:1. Brake H.P.: 80 @ 3200 R.P.M. Taxable H.P.: 25.3. Main bearings: seven. Valve lifters: solid. Carb.: Marvel "B".

CHASSIS: [Series 3580] W.B.: 125 in. O.L.: 207 in. Frt/Rear Tread: 57-7/8/60 in. Tires: 6.50 x 16. [Series 3520] W.B.: 120 in. O.L.: 202 in. Frt/Rear Tread: 57-7/8/60 in. Tires: 6.25 x 16. [Series 3510 (LaFayette)] W.B.: 113 in. O.L.: 189-1/2 in. Frt/Rear Tread: 56-1/2/59-11/16. Tires: 5.50 x 17 (Std.), 6.00 x 16 (Opt.).

TECHNICAL: Selective, sliding gear transmission. Speeds: 3F/1R. Floor shift controls. Single dry plate clutch. Spiral bevel drive. Semi-floating rear axle. Overall ratio: 4.1:1 (3580), 4.4:1 (3520), 4.7:1 (LaFayette). Hydraulic brakes (Nash), Mechanical brakes (LaFayette) on four wheels. Steel artillery wheels. Wheel size: 16 in. (LaFayette std. models 17 in.). Overdrive (Nash models only).

OPTIONS: Single sidemount. Dual sidemounts (LaFayette only). Sidemount cover(s). Fender skirts. Radio. Heater. Clock. Cigar lighter. Radio antenna.

HISTORICAL: Introduced January 1, 1935. Innovations: Big 322 cu. in. "90" series gone from lineup. Number of body styles sharply reduced. First use of hydraulic brakes (Nash only; LaFayette still used mechanicals.) First year for all-steel body (Nash only). Calendar year registrations: 17,739 Nash, 17,445 LaFayette. Calendar year production: 44,637 (Nash and LaFayette). The president of Nash was E.H. McCarty. Loss for the year came to $610,227. Share of industry registrations: 1.29 percent.

1936

NASH — AMBASSADOR SUPER "EIGHT" — SERIES 3680 — EIGHT: Similar to 1935 model, but with steel top, die-cast chromed waterfall grille extending to top of hood; chromed, zeppelin-shaped die-cast vent grilles on hood sides; extruded trunk lid.

NASH — AMBASSADOR "SIX" — SERIES 3620 — SIX: Identical in appearance to series 3680 Ambassador Super "Eight."

NASH "400" — SERIES 3640 — SIX: Sharply sloping "alligator" hood with pressed steel grille; embossed steel disc wheels; fastback styling with no outside opening to luggage/spare tire compartment (sedan, victoria); extruded trunk lid (touring sedan and victoria); seamless steel top. The 400 was introduced May 20, 1935, with a 3540 series number indicating a 1935 model car. Following the LaFayette introduction on June 15th, however, Nash began advertising the 400 as a 1936 model.

NASH "400" DELUXE — SERIES 3640A — SIX: Similar to series 3640 with the following exceptions: chromed, die-cast waterfall grille extending to top of hood. Side-opening hood. Chromed, zeppelin-shaped die-cast vent grilles on hood sides. Steel artillery wheels.

LAFAYETTE — SERIES 3610 — SIX: First series: pressed steel grille, embossed disc wheels. Second series: die-cast, chromed waterfall grille, steel artillery wheels. Both series: styling similar to 3640 and 3640A series, except for different front end treatment, side-opening hood.

I.D. DATA: [Series 3680] Serial numbers on right side frame, under hood. Starting: B77325. Ending: B80026. Engine numbers on right side engine block. Starting: B90025. Ending: B92726. [Series 3620] Serial numbers on right side frame, under hood. Starting: R303301. Ending: R309300. Engine numbers on right side engine block. Starting: E54701. Ending: E60700. [Series 3640] Serial numbers on right side frame, under hood. Starting: C1001. Ending: C9500. Engine numbers on right side engine block. Starting: CE501. Ending: CE9000. [Series 3640A] Serial numbers on right side frame, under hood. Starting: C9501. Ending: C23000. Engine numbers on right side engine block. Starting: CE9001. Ending: CE22500. [LaFayette] Serial numbers on right frame, under hood. Starting: L23101. Ending: L50780. Engine numbers on right front of engine block, just below valve cover. Starting: LE22601. Ending: LE50277.

Series 3680 — 8-cyl

Model No.	Body Type & Seating	Factory Price	Shipping Weight	Starting Serial #
3680	4-dr. Sed.-6P	995	3820	B177325
3685*	2-dr. Vic.-6P*	945	3730	B177325
Series 3620 —6-cyl.				
3620	4-dr. Sed.-6P	885	3710	R303301
3625	2-dr. Vic.-6P	835	3620	R303301
Series 3640 —6-cyl.				
3640	4-dr. Sed.-6P	765	2970	C1001
3642	2-dr. Cpe.-3P	675	2900	C1001
3642R	2-dr. Cpe.-3/5P	725	2960	C1001
3643	2-dr. Tr. Vic.-6P	745	2970	C1001
3645	2-dr. Vic.-6P	715	2950	C1001
3648	4-dr. Tr. Sed.-6P	790	3000	C1001
Series 3640A — 6-cyl.				
3640A	4-dr. Sed.-6P	765	3020	C9501
3641A	2-dr. Cabr.-3/5P	800	3000	C9501
3642A	2-dr. Cpe.-3P	675	2950	C9501
3642AR	2-dr. Cpe.-3/5P	725	3010	C9501
3643A	2-dr. Tr. Vic.-6P	745	3020	C9501
3645A	2-dr. Vic.-6P	715	3000	C9501
3648A	4-dr. Tr. Sed.-6P	790	3050	C9501
Series 3610 —6-cyl.				
3610	4-dr. Sed.-6P	675	2950	L23101
3611	2-dr. Cabr.-3/5P	740	2930	L23101
3612	2-dr. 3W Cpe.-3P	595	2880	L23101
3612R	2-dr. 3W Cpe.-3/5P	650	2930	L23101
W3612	2-dr. 5W Cpe.-3P	610	2880	L23101
W3612R	2-dr. 5W Cpe-3/5P	665	2930	L23101
3613	2-dr. Tr. Vic.-6P	655	2950	L23101
3615	2-dr. Vic.-6P	625	2930	L23101
3618	4-dr. Tr. Sed.-6P	700	2980	L23101

* Questionable whether model 3685 was actually produced.

ENGINE: [Series 3680] Ohv. Straight-eight. Cast iron block. B & S: 3-1/8 x 4-1/4 in. Disp.: 260.8 cu. in. C.R.: 5.25:1. Brake H.P.: 102 @ 3400 R.P.M. Taxable H.P.: 31.25. Main bearings: nine. Valve lifters: solid. Carb.: Stromberg EE-1. Torque: 110 lb.-ft. at 3500 R.P.M. [Series 3620] Ohv. Inline. Six. Cast iron block. B & S: 3-3/8 x 4-3/8 in. Disp.: 234.8 cu. in. C.R.: 5.70:1. Brake H.P.: 93 @ 3400 R.P.M. Taxable H.P.: 27.3. Main bearings: seven. Valve lifters: solid. Carb.: Stromberg EX-2 or AX-2. Torque: 125 lb.-ft. @ 3500 R.P.M. [Series 3640] L-head. Inline. Six. Cast iron block. B & S: 3-3/8 x 4-3/8 in. Disp.: 234.8 cu. in. C.R.: 5.61:1. Brake H.P.: 90 @ 3400 R.P.M. Taxable H.P.: 27.3. Main bearings: seven. Valve lifters: solid. Carb.: Stromberg EX-22. Torque: 125 lb.-ft. @ 3500 R.P.M. [Series 3640A] (mechanically identical to Series 3640.) [LaFayette] L-head. Inline. Six. Cast iron block. B & S: 3-1/4 x 4-3/8 in. Disp.: 217.7 cu. in. C.R.: 5.61:1. Brake H.P.: 83 @ 3200 R.P.M. Taxable H.P.: 25.3. Main bearings: seven. Valve lifters: solid. Carb.: Marvel B2 (first series), Stromberg AX2 (second series).

CHASSIS: [Series 3680] W.B.: 125 in. O.L.: 207-1/8 in. Frt/Rear Tread: 58/60 in. Tires: 6.50 x 16. [Series 3620] W.B.: 125 in. O.L.: 207-1/8 in. Frt/Rear Tread: 58/60 in. Tires: 6.25 x 16. [Series 3640, 3640A] W.B.: 117 in. O.L.: 191-1/8 in. Frt/Rear Tread: 58/60-1/4 in. Tires: 6.00 x 16. [Series 3610] W.B.: 113 in. Frt/Rear Tread: 58/60-1/4 in. Tires: 6.00 x 16.

TECHNICAL: Selective, sliding gear transmission. Speeds: 3F/1R. Floor shift controls. Single dry plate clutch. Spiral bevel drive. Semi-floating rear axle. Overall ratio: 4.44:1 (Ambassador Super 8), 4.11:1 all others. Hydraulic brakes on four wheels. Steel artillery wheels (steel disc, series 3640 and first series LaFayette). Wheel size: 16 in.

OPTIONS: Fender skirts. Radio. Heater. Clock. Cigar lighter. Radio antenna.

HISTORICAL: Introduced November 15, 1935 [Ambassadors, 3680 and 3610]; May 20, 1935 [3640]; June 15, 1935 [LaFayette]; October 15, 1935 [3640A and second series LaFayette]. Innovations: 3640 "400" series; first to cast intake manifolds in engine block. "Double Bed" conversion offered in "400" and LaFayette sedans and victorias. Nash 400 first of its breed with one-piece steel top. Calendar year registrations: 43,070. Calendar year production: 53,038. The president of Nash was E.H. McCarty. Nash bought the remaining half interest in the Seaman Body Corp. during 1936. A profit of $1,020,708 was posted for the year. Share of industry registrations: 1.27 percent.

1937

NASH — AMBASSADOR "EIGHT" — SERIES 3780 — EIGHT: Veed die-cast grille, vertical bars. Highly ornate radiator ornament. Chrome spear on hood sides. Integral trunk, sedans and victorias. Split windshield.

NASH — AMBASSADOR "SIX" — SERIES 3720 — SIX: Identical to series 3780 except with less elaborate radiator ornament consisting of stylized wing; shorter hood and front fenders.

LAFAYETTE — SERIES 3710 — SIX: Identical in styling to senior Nashes with the following exceptions: radiator ornament with circular theme; horizontal bars in grille, chevrons on hood sides; shorter hood and front fenders than Ambassador series.

I.D. DATA: [Series 3780] Serial numbers on right side frame, under hood. Starting: B80031. Ending: B86030. Engine numbers on right side engine block. Starting: B92731. Ending: B98730. [Series 3720] Serial numbers on right side frame, under hood. Starting: R309311. Ending: R324310. Engine numbers on right side engine block. Starting: E60711. Ending: E75710. [LaFayette] Serial numbers on right side frame under hood. Starting: L50781 or H1001. Ending: L106280 or H10500. NOTE: Prefix "H" indicates car was assembled in Kenosha. "L" indicates assembled in Racine. Engine numbers located on right side of engine block. Starting: LE50281 or H1001 or HE501. Ending: LE105780 or H10500 or HE10000.

Series 3780 — 8-cyl

Model No.	Body Type & Seating	Factory Price	Shipping Weight	Starting Serial #
3781	2-dr. Cabr.-3/5P	960	3640	B80031
3782	2-dr. Cpe.-3P	855	3590	B80031
3782R	2-dr. Cpe.-3/5P	895	3640	B80031
3782A	2-dr. A.P. Cpe.-3/5P	910	3610	B80031
3783	2-dr. Vic.-6P	895	3690	B80031
3788	4-dr. Sed.-6P	945	3720	B80031
Series 3720 —6-cyl.				
3721	2-dr. Cabr.-3/5P	860	3320	R309311
3722	2-dr. Cpe.-3P	755	3290	R309311
3722R	2-dr. Cpe.-3/5P	795	3320	R309311
3722A	2-dr. A.P. Cpe.-3/5P	810	3310	R309311
3723	2-dr. Vic.-6P	795	3380	R309311
3728	4-dr. Sed.-6P	845	3400	R309311

Series 3710 —6-cyl.

Model No.	Body Type & Seating	Factory Price	Shipping Weight	Starting Serial #
3711	2-dr. Cabr.-3/5P	740	3180	L50781
3712	2-dr. Cpe.-3P	595	3140	L50781
3712R	2-dr. Cpe.-3/5P	650	3190	L50781
3712A	2-dr. A.P. Cpe.-3/5P	660	3160	L50781
3713	2-dr. Vic.-6P	650	3200	Note 1
3718	4 dr. Sed.-6P	700	3240	Note 1

Note 1: L50781 or H1001.

Note 2: The "All-Purpose" coupes (3712A, 3722A and 3782A) replaced the rumbleseat coupes (3712R et. al.) on April 1, 1937.

ENGINE: [Series 3780] Ohv. Straight-eight. Cast iron block. B & S: 3-1/8 x 4-1/4 in. Disp.: 260.8 cu. in. C.R.: 5.64:1. Brake H.P.: 105 @ 3400 R.P.M. Taxable H.P.: 31.25. Main bearings: nine. Valve lifters: solid. Carb.: Stromberg EE-1. Torque: 196 lb.-ft. @ 1800 R.P.M. [Series 3720] Ohv. Inline. Six. Cast iron block. B & S: 3-3/8 x 4-3/8 in. Disp.: 234.8 cu. in. C.R.: 5.67:1. Brake H.P.: 93 @ 3400 R.P.M. Taxable H.P.: 27.3. Main bearings: seven. Valve lifters: solid. Carb.: Stromberg EX-32. Torque: 174 lb.-ft. @ 1600 R.P.M. [LaFayette] L-head. Inline. Six. Cast iron block. B & S: 3-3/8 x 4-3/8 in. Disp.: 234.8 cu. in. C.R.: 5.6:1. Brake H.P.: 90 @ 3400 R.P.M. Taxable H.P.: 27.3. Main bearings: seven. Valve lifters: solid. Carb.: Stromberg AX-2. Torque: 171 lb.-ft. @ 1200 R.P.M.

CHASSIS: [Series 3780] W.B.: 125 in. O.L.: 204-7/16 in. Frt/Rear Tread: 58/60 in. Tires: 7.00 x 16. [Series 3720] W.B.: 121 in. O.L.: 200-7/16 in. Frt/Rear Tread: 58/60-1/4 in. Tires: 6.25 x 16. [Series 3710] W.B. 117 in. O.L.: 196-7/16 in. Frt/Rear Tread: 58/60-1/4 in. Tires: 6.00 x 16.

TECHNICAL: Selective, sliding gear transmission. Speeds: 3F/1R. Floor shift controls. Single dry plate clutch. Spiral bevel drive. Semi-floating rear axle. Overall ratio: 4.11:1. Hydraulic brakes on four wheels. Steel artillery wheels. Wheel size: 16 in. Overdrive.

OPTIONS: Fender skirts. Radio. Heater. Clock. Cigar lighter. Radio antenna. Bed conversion.

HISTORICAL: Introduced October 1, 1936. Calendar year registrations: 70,571. Calendar year production: 85,949. The president of Nash was George Mason. Merger of Nash Motors with Kelvinator Corp. to form Nash-Kelvinator Corp. effected this year. Nash "400" and LaFayette combined into a single series known (for 1937 only) as the "Nash-LaFayette 400." Profit for the year came to $3,640,747. Share of industry registrations: 2.03 percent.

1938

NASH — AMBASSADOR "EIGHT" — SERIES 3880 — EIGHT: Body styling similar to 1937 model, but with painted, bright-trimmed grille with horizontal bars. Series name on side of hood, wedge-shaped headlamps mounted on radiator sides. "Nash" in vertical letters at top of radiator grille.

NASH — AMBASSADOR "SIX" — SERIES 3820 — SIX: Identical in appearance to series 3880, except for shorter hood and front fenders.

NASH — LAFAYETTE — SERIES 3810 — SIX: Identical in appearance to senior Nashes, except for bullet-shaped headlamps and shorter hood/front fenders.

I.D. DATA: [Series 3880] Serial numbers on right front frame member. Starting: B86031. Ending: B88999. Engine numbers on right front side, engine block. Starting: B98731. Ending: B101699. [Series 3820] Serial numbers on right front frame member. Starting: R324311. Ending: R331399. Engine numbers on engine block, right front. Starting: E75711. Ending: E82799. [LaFayette] Serial numbers on right front frame member. Starting: L106281 or H10501. Ending: L128294 or H19449. Note: "L" indicates car assembled in Racine; "H" indicates assembly in Kenosha. Engine numbers on engine block, right front. Starting: LE105781 or HE10001. Ending: LE128424 or HE18949.

Series 3880 — 8-cyl

Model No.	Body Type & Seating	Factory Price	Shipping Weight	Starting Serial #
3881	2-dr. Cabr.-3/5P	1240	3620	B86031
3882	2-dr. A.P. Cpe.-3/5P	1165	3640	B86031
3883	2-dr. Vic.-6P	1150	3780	B86031
3885	2-dr. Cpe.-3P	1120	3580	B86031
3888	4-dr. Sed.-6P	1200	3790	B86031
Series 3820 —6-cyl.				
3821	2-dr. Cabr.-3/5P	1090	3340	R324311
3822	2-dr. A.P. Cpe.-3/5P	1015	3360	R324311
3823	2-dr. Vic.-6P	1000	3450	R324311
3825	2-dr. Cpe.-3P	970	3300	R324311
3828	4-dr. Sed.-6P	1050	3460	R324311

Series 3810 —6-cyl.

Model No.	Body Type & Seating	Factory Price	Shipping Weight	Starting Serial #
3811	2-dr. Del. Cabr.-3/5P	940	3240	Note 1
3812	2-dr. Del. Cpe.-3/5P	860	3230	Note 1
3813	2-dr. Del Vic.-6P	855	3290	Note 1
3814	2-dr. Del. Cpe.-3P	820	3160	Note 1
3815	2-dr. Cpe.-3P	770	3120	Note 1
3816	2-dr. Sed.-6P	805	3190	Note 1
3817	4-dr. Sed.-6P	850	3200	Note 1
3818	4-dr. Del. Sed.-6P	900	3300	Note 1

Note 1: L106281 or H10501

ENGINE: [Series 3880] Ohv. Straight-eight. Cast iron block. B & S: 3-1/8 x 4-1/4 in. Disp.: 260.8 cu. in. C.R.: 6.00:1. Brake H.P.: 115 @ 3400 R.P.M. Taxable H.P.: 31.2. Main bearings: nine. Valve lifters: solid. Carb.: Stromberg EE-7. Torque: 200 lb.-ft. @ 1200 R.P.M. [Series 3820] Ohv. Inline. Six. Cast iron block. B & S: 3-3/8 x 4-3/8 in. Disp.: 234.8 cu. in. C.R.: 6.00:1. Brake H.P.: 105 @ 3400 R.P.M. Taxable H.P.: 27.3. Main bearings: seven. Valve lifters: solid. Carb.: Stromberg EX-32. Torque: 190 lb.-ft. @ 1050 R.P.M. [LaFayette] L-head. Inline. Six. Cast iron block. B & S: 3-3/8 x 4-3/8 in. Disp.: 234.8 cu. in. C.R.: 5.83:1. Brake H.P.: 95 @ 3400 R.P.M. Taxable H.P.: 27.3. Main bearings: seven. Valve lifters: solid. Carb.: Stromberg EX-22 or AX-2. Torque: 175 lb.-ft. @ 1000 R.P.M.

CHASSIS: [Series 3880] W.B.: 125 in. O.L.: 204-11/16 in. Frt/Rear Tread: 58/61-3/8 in. Tires: 7.00 x 16. [Series 3820] W.B.: 121 in. O.L.: 200-11/16 in. Frt/Rear Tread: 58/60-1/4 in. Tires: 6.25 x 16. [Series 3810] W.B.: 117 in. O.L.: 196-11/16 in. Frt/Rear Tread: 58/60-1/4 in. Tires: 6.00 x 16.

TECHNICAL: Selective, sliding gear transmission. Speeds: 3F/1R. Floor shift controls. Single dry plate clutch. Spiral bevel drive. Semi-floating rear axle. Overall ratio: 4.11:1. Hydraulic brakes on four wheels. Steel disc wheels. Wheel size: 16 in. Drivetrain options: Hill-holder ($10.00). Overdrive (50.00). Dash-mounted, vacuum-operated shift (30.00).

OPTIONS: Fender skirts ($13.00). Radio (49.00). Heater (30.00). Clock. Cigar lighter. Radio antenna. White sidewall tires (3810) (20.00). White sidewall tires (3820) (22.50). White sidewall tires (3880) (27.50). Banjo steering wheel w/horn ring (11.00). Bed conversion.

HISTORICAL: Introduced October 15, 1937. Innovations: Optional dash-mounted, vacuum-controlled gearshift. Calendar year registrations: 31,814. Calendar year production: 32,017. The president of Nash was George Mason. Share of industry registrations: 1.68 percent. "400" designation dropped from LaFayette name. Essentially, the LaFayette had become the base Nash series, the radiator badge read simply "Nash."

1939

NASH — AMBASSADOR "EIGHT" — SERIES 3980 — EIGHT: Tall, narrow grille with wide-spaced horizontal bars, suggesting that Nash styling this year may have been inspired by the LaSalle. Rectangular headlamps inset in fenders. Vertical Nash emblem at center of trunk lid. Nash script on hubcaps.

NASH — AMBASSADOR "SIX" — SERIES 3920 — SIX: Identical in appearance to Series 3980 except for shorter hood and front fenders.

NASH — LAFAYETTE — SERIES 3910 — SIX: Identical in appearance to senior Nashes except for shorter hood and front fenders. Small LaFayette body plate behind front fender, just above runningboard.

I.D. DATA: [Series 3980] Serial numbers on right front frame member. Starting: R89000. Ending: R106299. Engine numbers on engine block, right front. Starting: B101700. Ending: B105551. [Series 3920] Serial numbers on right front frame member. Starting: R331400. Ending: R339999. Engine numbers on engine block, right front. Starting: E82800. Ending: E339399. [Series LaFayette] Serial numbers on right front frame member. Starting: H19450. Ending: H56999. Engine numbers on upper left front, engine block. Starting: HE18950. Ending: HE56499.

Series 3980 — 8-cyl

Model No.	Body Type & Seating	Factory Price	Shipping Weight	Starting Serial #
3980	4-dr. Tr. Sed.-6P	1235	3800	B89000
3981	2-dr. Cabr.-3/5P	1295	3740	B89000
3982	2-dr. A.P. Cpe.-3/5P	1210	3710	B89000
3983	2-dr. Vic.-6P	1205	3770	B89000
3985	2-dr. Cpe.-3P	1175	3720	B89000
3988	4-dr. Sed.-6P	1235	3800	B89000

Built to Forget ...that's why it will be long remembered

"Built for a pilot to forget!"

That, we believe, is the highest compliment that could be given an aircraft engine.

And that's the reputation the Packard-built Rolls-Royce engine has earned for itself—in famous planes like the Mustang, the Mosquito, and the Lancaster.

Behind the combat record of these Packard-built power-plants is Packard craftsmanship—the ability to turn out precision engines on a mass-production basis, at a rate the enemy never dreamed could be possible.

Packard takes pride in building an engine that pilots can "forget" while they're flying and fighting—but an engine whose role in this war will be long remembered.

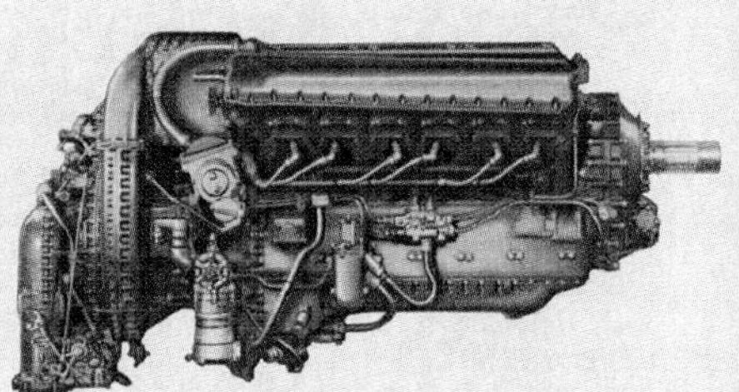

ASK THE MAN WHO ~~OWNS~~ FLIES ONE

Strafing at ground level or fighting in the stratosphere, pilots bet their lives on Packard-built engines—and win!

MUSTANG fighter
WARHAWK fighter
HURRICANE fighter
LANCASTER bomber

PACKARD
PRECISION-BUILT POWER

MOSQUITO fighter-bomber
NAVY PT boat
ARMY rescue boat

• When war progress permits, Packard cars will roll off assembly lines again. They will be cars worth waiting for—built by the same skills that have already produced more than 60,000 Rolls-Royce aircraft engines and Packard marine engines for PT boats.

Independent automakers were heavily involved in war materiel production as evidenced by these two ads promoting both Packard's and Studebaker's military contributions. Packard-built Rolls-Royce engines were used in several lines of fighter aircraft including Mustangs, Warhawks and Hurricanes. "Ask the man who flies one" lends a quality statement to the aircraft engines just as Packard touted the quality of its automobiles by stating "Ask the man who owns one." Studebaker supplied 2½-ton trucks to the Red (U.S.S.R.) Army as well as the armed forces of other United Nations allies per the lend-lease act. Studebaker was also involved in producing the Wright Cyclone engines that powered the Boeing Flying Fortress bombers as well as building "Weasel" personnel/cargo carriers.

©1945 The Studebaker Corp

Studebaker trucks "take to the air" in the service of the Red Army

THE realistic painting you see above was made from a photograph sent to Studebaker with the compliments of the General Automotive Division of the Red Army.

It shows how Studebaker trucks in the service of the Soviet Russian forces are swung, fully loaded, across unbridged ravines and streams.

The latest information obtainable indicates that a substantial portion of the powerful 2½-ton 6 x 6 trucks shipped to Russia from the United States have been Studebakers. These big Studebakers comprise approximately 40% of the hundreds of thousands of American trucks of all sizes made available to Marshal Stalin's fighting men under lend-lease.

Awarded To All Studebaker Plants

In recognition of this important help, Red Army authorities presented Studebaker with an album of hitherto unpublished photographs of the trucks in action—"as a token of appreciation of the excellent quality of your military-type truck."

Supplementing its huge production of heavy-duty trucks for the armed forces of the U.S.S.R. and other United Nations, Studebaker to date has built over 60,000 of the Wright Cyclone engines that power the world-famous Boeing Flying Fortress.

And now an amazing new vehicle, the sure-footed, versatile Studebaker Weasel personnel and cargo carrier, is reaching America's far-flung fighting fronts in impressive quantities.

Your War Bonds help America's fighters

Pictured is a convoy of Studebaker Weasels rollin[g] inland from a landing beach. Remember, wherev[er] they are—on land, at sea, or in the air—our valia[nt] fighting forces need the help that your War Bonds giv[e].

NASH

Leads the World in Motor Car Value

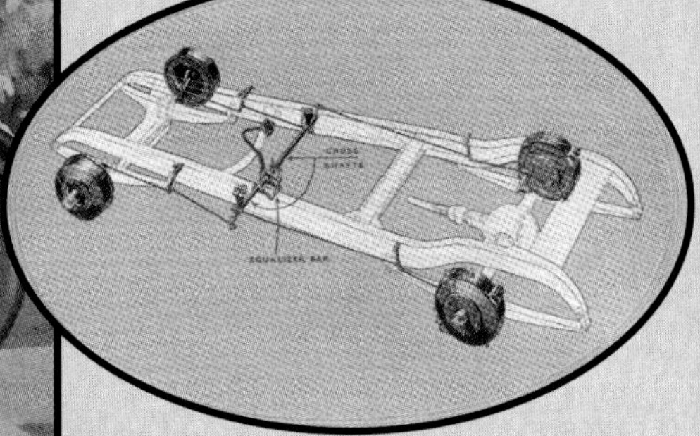

The 1927 Nash Ambassador four-door sedan offered several innovative features including an "enclosed" body design with French-type roof as well as (inset photos) the Advanced Six engine and four-wheel braking system. The Advanced Six featured a seven-bearing crankshaft, which allowed for exceptionally smooth operation. Nash offered four-wheel braking as standard equipment. The fully equalized system distributed 60 percent of the brake pressure to the rear wheels and 40 percent up front when the brakes were applied. This eliminated the dangerous swerving characteristics common to other brake systems of the time. The 127-inch wheelbase Ambassador sedan came equipped with Mohair Velvet upholstery and walnut window moldings and steering wheel.

The Nash Ambassador Airflyte, styled in the continental manner by Pinin Farina. Hood ornament by Petty, white sidewall tires extra.

To the Boy who wanted a Stutz Bearcat...

REMEMBER how you hungered for it? Remember how your pulse raced to its engine throb? That was it . . . that old Stutz Bearcat, Heaven-on-wheels to that boy you used to be!

Today we invite you to be young again—to thrill to the wonder and romance of travel again.

Come and take command of the proudest car ever styled by Pinin Farina of Europe—this new Nash Ambassador "Country Club"!

Come and wonder at *true* continental styling attuned to American standards of room and comfort . . . the luxury of custom interiors—with the widest seats, the greatest eye-level visibility ever built into an automobile. Relax in airliner reclining seats that ease dawn-to-sunset travel.

Then—feel the pounding of your pulse when the mighty "Le Mans" Dual-Jetfire engine lets loose. For this is the Nash custom power option that holds the top American record in the 24-hour road race at Le Mans, France!

Never have you known such performance . . . and never have you known such handling ease as you have with new Nash Power Steering.

And as the road unreels and new enchantments greet your eye you'll know why we even built sleeping beds in a Nash. For you're going to travel as you've never traveled before!

Let us put this great car in your hands. Discover why this brilliant Nash Ambassador is today's heaven-on-wheels for you!

Take the Key and See—
You'll Find None so New as **Nash** *Airflytes*

Nash Motors, Division Nash-Kelvinator Corporation, Detroit, Mich.

Recalling the brute speed and nimble handling characteristics of the legendary Stutz Bearcat, Nash used that speedster's imagery to promote its Ambassador Country Club hardtop in 1953. Touting the lure of the open road, Nash proclaimed, "...we invite you to be young again—to thrill to the wonder and romance of travel again." The Ambassador Country Club was styled by Pinin Farina of Europe and was powered by the LeMans Dual Jetfire six-cylinder engine.

After halting production of cars from 1933 to 1935, Errett Lobban Cord gave automobile manufacturing one final attempt beginning with the front-wheel-drive Cord 810 in 1936. The distinctive "coffin nose" styling was the creation of Gordon Buehrig, and the 810 was available in sedan, phaeton and convertible coupe body styles. Initial quality control problems and high price ($2,000 to $3,000) aside, the undoing of the Cord automobile in 1937 (then marketed as the 812) was E.L. Cord's decision to leave the automobile industry for other business pursuits. The Cord 810/812 was powered by the Lycoming V-8 rated at 125 hp. In 1937, a supercharged version of the 812 was offered, which boosted the Lycoming's horsepower to 170. In two years of production, fewer than 3,000 810/812 models were built. (Photo courtesy of Craig Ospedale)

During a production run that lasted almost 25 years (1946-1969), approximately 5,000 King Midget roadsters were built—the first two years available in kit form for around $270 while the later versions manufactured by Midget Motors Corp. of Athens, Ohio, sold for $1,095. What began as a single-seat, open vehicle developed by Claud Dry and Dale Orcuft to mimic the midget racers of the late-1940s evolved into a two-passenger, fendered vehicle with a cloth top in the 1950s. The third-generation (pictured) King Midget of the late-1950s remained mostly unchanged until its demise in 1969. This final version was a foot longer than its predecessor, had two functional doors and sported "fins" as was common to cars of that period. Through all of its transformations, the King Midget was always powered by a rear-mounted, air-cooled, single-cylinder engine. After initial production was underway, the three-speed manual transmission used gave way to an automatic (first, a unit having one-speed forward with no reverse and later a two-speed). An "economy" car, the King Midget was capable of 60 mpg.

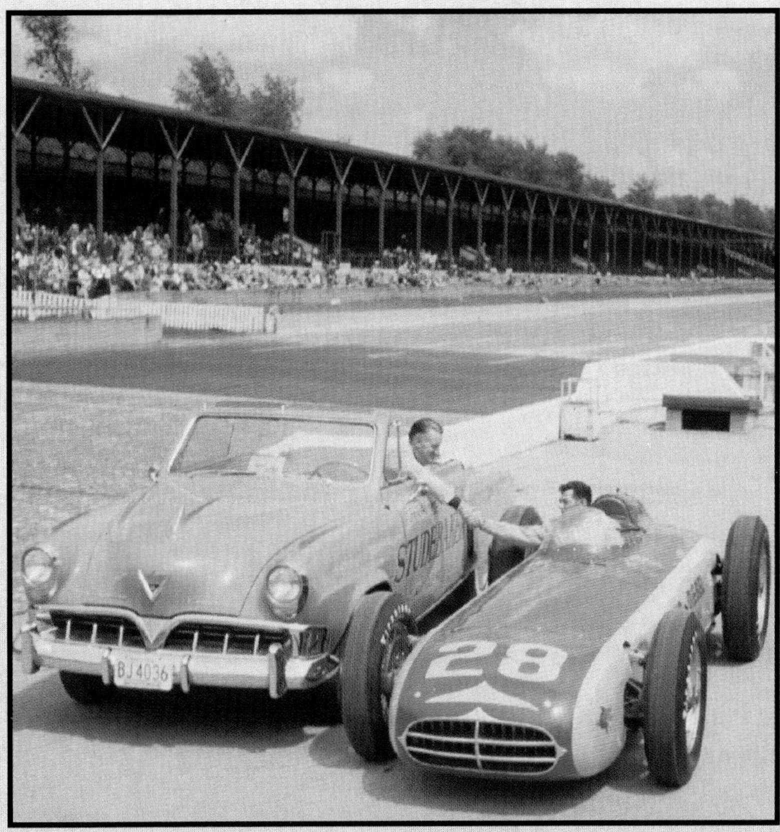

On May 30, 1952, a Studebaker Commander State convertible paced the Indianapolis 500 held at the "Brickyard." Studebaker Executive Vice-President P.O. Peterson drove the pace car, and is shown congratulating Freddie Agabashian, driver of the #28 Cummins Diesel Special. Agabashian started the race from the pole position, but finished twenty-seventh.

One of a long line of fine motorcars produced by Fred and August Duesenberg in Indiana, this 1931 Duesenberg SJ boattail speedster was custom bodied by Figoni of Italy. It was powered by a 420-cid/320-hp eight-cylinder engine equipped with a supercharger. When new, during the waning days of the Great Depression, the chassis alone for this speedster cost $8,500! (Photo courtesy of the Blackhawk Classic Auto Collection)

Not available as an Auburn model in 1930, the boattail speedster returned in 1931 as the Model 8-98 based on a 127-inch wheelbase. The two-passenger speedster was powered by the Lycoming straight-eight engine that was mounted at four points within the Auburn's revolutionary X-braced chassis (the first on a rear-drive automobile). While Auburn's sales fell in the immediate wake of the Great Depression, in 1931 they nearly tripled (34,228 vs. 12,985) the previous year's total. (Photo courtesy of Dave Lindsay)

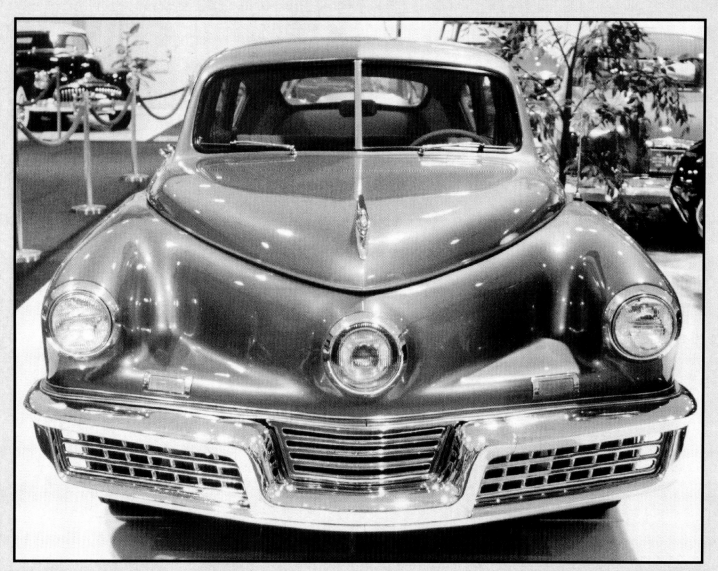

The popular subject of books and a major motion picture, Preston Tucker and the four-door sedan bearing his name epitomized the struggle of the independent automaker to gain solid footing in the American automotive industry. The 1948 Tucker—the only year the car was produced with just 51 cars assembled in that model year—was revolutionary in both design and in its safety features. Powered by a "pancake" six-cylinder engine derived from a helicopter powerplant, the air-cooled engine was located in the rear. Up front, a cyclops-like, centrally located third headlight pointed in the direction the car was being steered. The unique lines of the Tucker were the work of renowned automotive stylist Alex Tremulis. (Photo courtesy of Gast Classic Motorcars)

It was a turbulent year for Pierce-Arrow Motor Car Co. in 1934, with the automaker operating under receivership and seeking additional financing to remain afloat. Among the eight- and twelve-cylinder-powered automobiles offered in that model year was this two-door Brougham complete with Pierce-Arrow's symbolic Archer mascot poised over the radiator shell. Powered by a 385-cid eight-cylinder engine rated at 140 hp, maximum road speed of this Brougham was approximately 70 mph.

The Kaiser Darrin was the creation of famed automotive designer Howard "Dutch" Darrin. Being a fiberglass-bodied, two-seat sports car, the 1954 Darrin was a big departure from the other Kaiser offerings of that period. One of its many innovative features was forward sliding doors (into the front fenders). The Darrin was first announced late in 1952, with initial prototypes shown in early 1953. The sports car was made available to the public early in 1954, but the following year, Kaiser ceased all automobile production in the United States. "Dutch" Darrin then revived the sports car without the Kaiser name, and powered by a Cadillac V-8 in place of the six-cylinder engine that Kaiser had used. Approximately 50 Darrin sports cars were produced from 1955 until 1958 when production of the car ceased for good.

The 1965 Rambler Classic lineup, including this 770 series hardtop, was extensively restyled when compared to the previous year's model. Up front, new fenders and a veed-out grille accentuated the dual horizontal headlamps. In back, the rear was squared off and sported wraparound rectangular taillamps. Five different six-cylinder or V-8 engine options were available with the Rambler Classic 770 line.

This striking two-tone blue 1955 Hudson Hornet Custom four-door sedan was an eye-catcher as well as being all-new from tires to top. New features of the Hornet included a Packard-supplied V-8 engine, double strength single unit body construction, deep coil ride, all-season air conditioning and control tower visibility. Hornet Custom models also featured continental spare tire carriers as standard equipment.

In 1913, Hudson introduced its all-new six-cylinder engine in its Model 54 series automobiles. This mammoth Model 54 touring featured a wheelbase of 127 inches and weighed approximately 3,800 pounds. Its mighty 421-cid six-cylinder engine could propel the touring 0-to-60 mph in 30 seconds.

"Big Bad" AMX and "Mod" Javelin models offered by AMC midyear in 1969 were available in three unique colors named, respectively, Big Bad Blue, Big Bad Green and Big Bad Orange. Sales of the Big Bad AMX models totaled 284 in orange, 283 in green and 195 in blue. Many of the Mod Javelins ordered (total unknown) were also equipped with the Craig Breedlove option package that included a rooftop spoiler and simulated exhaust rocker mountings. Interestingly, some 30 years after these models were released, Breedlove is still making headlines chasing the World Land Speed Record.

For an additional $220, buyers of a 1975 AMC Gremlin could order the optional Levi's package to go along with the required, optional ($201) X package. Included in the Levi's package was a spun nylon version of denim—complete with orange stitching and copper rivets—for the seats, door inserts and map storage pockets as well as Levi's graphics for the sides of the car. The "hockey stick" striping was part of the X package. The Gremlin was available with either six-cylinder or V-8 power.

Series 3920 — 6-cyl.

Model No.	Body Type & Seating	Factory Price	Shipping Weight	Starting Serial #
3920	4-dr. Tr. Sed.-6P	985	3470	R331400
3921	2-dr. Cabr.-3/5P	1050	3430	R331400
3922	2-dr. A.P. Cpe.-3/5P	960	3360	R331400
3923	2-dr. Vic.-6P	955	3420	R331400
3925	2-dr. Cpe.-3P	925	3370	R331400
3928	4-dr. Sed.-6P	985	3450	R331400

Series 3910 — 6-cyl.

Model No.	Body Type & Seating	Factory Price	Shipping Weight	Starting Serial #
3910	4-dr. Del. Sed.-6P	885	3350	H19450
3911	2-dr. Del. Cabr.-3/5P	950	3340	H19450
3912	2-dr. Del. A.P. Cpe. -3/5P	860	3260	H19450
3913	2-dr. Del. Vic.-6P	855	3320	H19450
3914	2-dr. Del. Cpe.-3P	825	3270	H19450
3915	2-dr. Cpe.-3P	770	3200	H19450
3916	2-dr. Sed.-6P	810	3250	H19450
3917	4-dr. Sed.-6P	840	3290	H19450
3918	4-dr. Del. Tr. Sed.-6P	885	3350	H19450
3919	4-dr. Tr. Sed.-6P	840	3285	H19450

ENGINE: [Series 3980] Ohv. Straight-eight. Cast iron block. B & S: 3-1/8 x 4-1/4 in. Disp.: 260.8 cu. in. C.R.: 6.00:1. Brake H.P.: 115 @ 3400 R.P.M. Taxable H.P.: 31.2. Main bearings: nine. Valve lifters: solid. Carb.: Carter 436S. Torque: 200 lb.-ft. @ 1200 R.P.M. [Series 3920] Ohv. Inline. Six. Cast iron block. B & S: 3-3/8 x 4-3/8 in. Disp.: 234.8 cu. in. C.R.: 6.00:1. Brake H.P.: 105 @ 3400 R.P.M. Taxable H.P.: 27.3. Main bearings: seven. Valve lifters: solid. Carb.: Carter 435S. Torque: 190 lb.-ft. @ 1050 R.P.M. [Series LaFayette] L-head. Inline. Six. Cast iron block. B & S: 3-3/8 x 4-3/8 in. Disp.: 234.8 cu. in. C.R.: 6.30:1. Brake H.P.: 99 @ 3400 R.P.M. Taxable H.P.: 27.3. Main bearings: seven. Valve lifters: solid. Carb.: Stromberg EE-1. Torque: 179 lb.-ft. @ 1200 R.P.M.

CHASSIS: [Series 3980] W.B.: 125 in. O.L.: 208-1/4 in. Frt/Rear Tread: 55-3/4/61-3/8 in. Tires: 7.00 x 16. [Series 3920] W.B.: 121 in. O.L.: 204-1/4 in. Frt/Rear Tread: 58/60-1/4 in. Tires: 6.25 x 16. [Series 3910] W.B.: 117 in. O.L.: 200-1/4 in. Frt/Rear Tread: 58/60-1/4 in. Tires: 6.00 x 16.

TECHNICAL: Selective, sliding gear transmission. 3F/1R. Steering column controls. Single dry plate clutch. Hypoid drive. Semi-floating rear axle. Overall ratio: 4.10:1. Hydraulic brakes on four wheels. Steel disc wheels. Wheel size: 16 in. Drivetrain options: Hill-Holder. Overdrive.

OPTIONS: Fender skirts. Radio. Heater. Clock. Cigar lighter. Radio antenna. Fog lamps. Deluxe steering wheel. Bed conversion.

HISTORICAL: Introduced October 15, 1938. Calendar year registrations: 54,050. Calendar year production: 65,662. The president of Nash was George Mason. Share of industry registrations: 2.86 percent. Styled by George W. Walker.

1940

NASH — AMBASSADOR "8" — SERIES 4080 — EIGHT: Tall, narrow grille, similar to 1939 model except with thin, closely-spaced horizontal bars. Sealed beam headlamps. "Nash" script, lower right corner of trunk lid, and on hood sides just behind grille.

NASH — AMBASSADOR "SIX" — SERIES 4020 — SIX: Identical in appearance to 4080 Series except for shorter hood and front fenders.

NASH — LAFAYETTE — SERIES 4010 — SIX: Identical in appearance to Senior Nash Series except for shorter hood and front fenders. LaFayette body plate just above runningboard, behind front fender.

I.D. DATA: [Series 4080] Serial numbers on right front frame member. Starting: B106300. Ending: B110000. Engine numbers on engine block, right front. Starting: B105800. Ending: B109049. [Series 4020] Serial numbers on right front frame member. Starting: R340000. Ending: R353000. Engine numbers on engine block, right front. Starting: E339500. Ending: E352017. [Series LaFayette] Serial numbers on right front frame member. Starting: H57000. Ending: H76055. Engine numbers on upper left front, engine block. Starting: HE56500. Ending: H102862.

Series 4080 — 8-cyl

Model No.	Body Type & Seating	Factory Price	Shipping Weight	Starting Serial #
4080	4-dr. Tr. Sed.-6P	1195	3710	B106300
4081	2-dr. Cabr.-3/5P	1295	3640	B106300
4082	2-dr. A.P. Cpe.-3/5P	1170	3575	B106300
4083	2-dr. Sed.-6P	1165	3620	B106300
4085	2-dr. Cpe.-3P	1135	3555	B106300
4088	4-dr. Sed.-6P	1195	3705	B106300

Series 4020 — 6-cyl.

Model No.	Body Type & Seating	Factory Price	Shipping Weight	Starting Serial #
4020	4-dr. Tr. Sed.-6P	985	3385	R340000
4021	2-dr. Cabr.-3/5P	1085	3410	R340000
4022	2-dr. A.P. Cpe.-3/5P	960	3295	R340000
4023	2-dr. Sed.-6P	955	3350	R340000
4025	2-dr. Cpe.-3P	925	3290	R340000
4028	4-dr. Sed.-6P	985	3380	R340000

Series 4010 — 6-cyl.

Model No.	Body Type & Seating	Factory Price	Shipping Weight	Starting Serial #
4010	4-dr. Tr. Sed.-6P	875	3280	H57000
4011	2-dr. Cabr.-3/5P	975	3310	H57000
4012	2-dr. A.P. Cpe.-3/5P	850	3190	H57000
4013	2-dr. Sed.-6P	845	3235	H57000
4015	2-dr. Cpe.-3P	795	3190	H57000
4018	4-dr. Sed.-6P	875	3275	H57000

ENGINE: [Series 4080] Ohv. Straight-eight. Cast iron block. B & S: 3-1/8 x 4-1/4 in. Disp.: 260.8 cu. in. C.R.: 6.0:1. Brake H.P.: 115 @ 3400 R.P.M. Taxable H.P.: 31.2. Main bearings: nine. Valve lifters: solid. Carb.: Carter WDO-4655. Torque: 200 lb.-ft. @ 1200 R.P.M. [Series 4020] Ohv. Inline. Six. Cast iron block. B & S: 3-3/8 x 4-3/8 in. Disp.: 234.8 cu. in. C.R.: 6.00:1. Brake H.P.: 105 @ 3400 R.P.M. Taxable H.P.: 27.3. Main bearings: seven. Valve lifters: solid. Carb.: Carter 435S. Torque: 190 lb.-ft. @ 1050 R.P.M. [Series LaFayette] L-head. Inline. Six. Cast iron block. B & S: 3-3/8 x 4-3/8 in. Disp.: 234.8 cu. in. C.R.: 6.30:1. Brake H.P.: 99 @ 3400 R.P.M. Taxable H.P.: 27.3. Main bearings: seven. Valve lifters: solid. Carb.: Carter 458S. Torque: 179 lb.-ft. @ 1200 R.P.M.

CHASSIS: [Series 4080] W.B.: 125 in. O.L.: 207-3/16 in. Frt/Rear Tread: 57-11/16/61-3/8 in. Tires: 7.00 x 15. [Series 4020] W.B.: 121 in. O.L.: 203-3/16 in. Frt/Rear Tread: 56-7/8/60-1/4 in. Tires: 6.25 x 16. [Series 4010] W.B.: 117 in. O.L.: 199-3/16 in. Frt/Rear Tread: 56-7/8/60-1/4 in. Tires: 6.00 x 16.

TECHNICAL: Selective, sliding gear transmission. Speeds: 3F/1R. Steering column controls. Single dry plate clutch. Hypoid drive. Semi-floating rear axle. Overall ratio: 4.10:1. Hydraulic brakes on four wheels. Steel disc wheels. Wheel size: 4080: 15 in., 4020 and 4010: 16 in. Drivetrain options: Hill-Holder. Overdrive ($55.00).

OPTIONS: Fender skirts. Radio. Heater. Clock. Cigar lighter. Radio antenna. Bed conversion.

HISTORICAL: Introduced September 15, 1939. Calendar year registrations: 52,853. Calendar year production: 63,617. The president of Nash was George Mason. Share of industry registrations: 1.5 percent. A profitable year, but a disappointing one in terms of sales.

1941

NASH — AMBASSADOR "EIGHT" — SERIES 4180 — EIGHT: Pointed prow; split die-cast grilles on either side, featuring thin vertical ribs. Script on trunk reading "Nash 8."

NASH — AMBASSADOR "SIX" — SERIES 4160 — SIX: Identical to series 4180 except script on trunk reads "Nash 6."

NASH — AMBASSADOR "600" — SERIES 4140 — SIX: Identical to series 4180 except hood is substantially shorter; script on trunk reads "Nash 600"; shrouded rear fenders.

I.D. DATA: [Series 4180] Serial numbers on right front frame member. Starting: B110001. Ending: B113500. Engine numbers on engine block, right front. Starting: B110001. Ending: B113500. [Series 4160] Serial numbers on right front frame member. Starting: R353001. Ending: R383400. Engine numbers on engine block, right front. Starting: R353001. Ending: R383400. [Series 4140] Serial numbers on right frame member just ahead of dash. Starting: K5001. Ending: K55100. Engine numbers on right side of crankcase toward front. Starting: K5001. Ending: K55100.

Series 4180 — 8-cyl

Model No.	Body Type & Seating	Factory Price	Shipping Weight	Starting Serial #
4180	4-dr. Tr Sed.-6P	1151	3475	B110001
4181	2-dr. Cabr.-3/5P	1215	3580	B110001
4183	2-dr. Brgm.-5P	1081	3400	B110001
4187	4-dr. Sp. Sed.-6P	1051	3450	B110001
4188	4-dr. Sed.-6P	1101	3455	B110001

Series 4160 — 6-cyl.

Model No.	Body Type & Seating	Factory Price	Shipping Weight	Starting Serial #
4160	4-dr. Tr. Sed.-6P	1030	3300	R353001
4161	2-dr. Cabr.-3/5P	1095	3430	R353001
4162	2-dr. Cpe.-3P	905	3310	R353001
4163	2-dr. Brgm.-5P	974	3235	R353001
4165	2-dr. Sp. Cpe.-3P	855	3180	R353001
4167	4-dr. Sp. Sed.-6P	930	3300	R353001
4168	4-dr. Sed.-6P	985	3300	R353001
4169	2-dr. Sp. Sed.-6P	898	3320	R353001

1940 Nash, Ambassador Eight (Model 3981), cabriolet (with body by de Sakhnoffsky), OCW

1942 Nash, Ambassador 600 (Model 4248), sedan, OCW

1947 Nash, Ambassador (Series 60), Suburban, OCW

1948 Nash, 600 Deluxe (Series 40), business coupe, OCW

1949 Nash, Ambassador Custom (Series 60), sedan, OCW

1941 Nash, Ambassador Six (Model 4163), brougham, OCW

1946 Nash, 600 (Series 40), brougham sedan, OCW

1947 Nash, Ambassador (Series 60), sedan (official pace car for 1947 Indianapolis 500), OCW

above and below, 1950 Nash, Rambler Custom (Series 10), convertible landau, OCW

Series 4140 — 6-cyl.

Model No.	Body Type & Seating	Factory Price	Shipping Weight	Starting Serial #
4140	4-dr. Tr. Sed.-6P	860	2655	K5001
4142	2-dr. Cpe.-3P	783	2500	K5001
4143	2-dr. Brgm.-5P	810	2575	K5001
4145	2-dr. Sp. Cpe.-3P	731	2490	K5001
4146	2-dr. Sp. Sed.-6P	745	2630	K5001
4147	4-dr. Sp. Sed.-6P	780	2615	K5001
4148	4-dr. Sed.-6P	810	2630	K5001
4149	2-dr. Sed.-6P	777	2640	K5001

ENGINE: [Series 4180] Ohv. Straight-eight. Cast iron block. B & S: 3-1/8 x 4-1/4 in. Disp.: 260.8 cu. in. C.R.: 6.30:1. Brake H.P.: 115 @ 3400 R.P.M. Taxable H.P.: 31.2. Main bearings: nine. Valve lifters: solid. Carb.: Carter 511S. Torque: 200 lb.-ft. @ 1600 R.P.M. [Series 4160] Ohv. Inline. Six. Cast iron block. B & S: 3-3/8 x 4-3/8 in. Disp.: 234.8 cu. in. C.R.: 6.30:1. Brake H.P.: 105 @ 3400 R.P.M. Taxable H.P.: 27.3. Main bearings: seven. Valve lifters: solid. Carb.: Carter 435S. Torque: 195 lb.-ft. @ 1600 R.P.M. [Series 4140] L-head. Inline. Six. Cast iron block. B & S: 3-1/8 x 3-3/4 in. Disp.: 172.6 cu. in. C.R.: 6.87:1. Brake H.P.: 75 @ 3600 R.P.M. Taxable H.P.: 23.4. Main bearings: four. Valve lifters: solid. Carb.: Carter 513S. Torque: 136 lb.-ft. @ 1200 R.P.M.

CHASSIS: [Series 4180] W.B.: 121 in. O.L.: 200-3/4 in. Frt/Rear Tread: 57/61-1/4 in. Tires: 6.50 x 16. [Series 4160] W.B.: 121 in. O.L.: 200-3/4 in. Frt/Rear Tread: 57-1/2/60-1/2 in. Tires: 6.25 x 16. [Series 4140] W.B.: 112 in. O.L.: 194 in. Frt/Rear Tread: 56/59-3/4 in. Tires: 5.50 x 16.

TECHNICAL: Selective, sliding gear transmission. Speeds: 3F/1R. Steering column controls. Single dry plate clutch. Hypoid drive. Semi-floating rear axle. Overall ratio: 4.10:1. Hydraulic brakes on four wheels. Steel disc wheels. Wheel size: 16 in. Drivetrain options: Hill-holder ($13.00). Overdrive ($50.00: 4140) ($55.00: 4160, 4180).

OPTIONS: Fender skirts (except 4140). Radio (Deluxe $45.00) (Custom 65.00). Heater (Weather eye) (35.00). Clock. Cigar lighter. Radio antenna. Bed equipment, standard (17.50). Bed equipment, deluxe (24.50). Two-tone paint (10.50). Deluxe steering wheel (15.00).

HISTORICAL: Introduced October 1, 1940. Innovations: Ambassador "600" (4140) series pioneered unitized body/frame construction, first low-priced car with coil springs all around; sliding pillar type independent front suspension, similar to Lancia, up to 30 mpg claimed (hence the name: 20 gal. fuel tank x 30 mpg = 600 mile per tankful). Conventional construction and suspension used on 4160, 4180 series. Last year for "twin ignition." Calendar year registrations: 77,824. Calendar year production: 80,428. The president of Nash was George Mason. Share of industry registrations: 2.09 percent. Ambassador "600" marked Nash's re-entry into the low-priced field. Sales up sharply.

1942

NASH — AMBASSADOR "EIGHT" — SERIES 4280 — EIGHT: Similar to 1941 model, but with stainless steel grille at center, featuring short, horizontal blades. Parking lamps in fenders, above headlamps, chromed fender crowns and fender trim to match grille, deluxe-equipped cars only. Script on trunk reads "Nash 8."

NASH — AMBASSADOR "SIX" — SERIES 4260 — SIX: Identical in appearance to Series 4280, except script on trunk reads "Nash 6."

NASH — AMBASSADOR "600" — SERIES 4240 — SIX: Identical in appearance to Series 4280, except hood and front fenders are several inches shorter, script on trunk reads "Nash 600"; rear fenders shrouded.

I.D. DATA: [Series 4280] Serial numbers on right front frame member. Starting: B114001. Ending: B115000. Engine numbers on engine block, right front. Starting: B114001. Ending: B115000. [Series 4260] Serial numbers on right front frame member. Starting: R384001. Ending: R393090. Engine numbers on engine block, right front. Starting: R384001. Ending: R393090. [Series 4240] Serial numbers on right front frame member just ahead of dash. Starting: K56001. Ending: K77660. Engine numbers on right side of crankcase toward front. Starting: K56001. Ending: K77660.

Series 4280 — 8-cyl

Model No.	Body Type & Seating	Factory Price	Shipping Weight	Starting Serial #
4280	4-dr. Tr. Sed.-6P	1209	3465	B114001
4282	2-dr. Cpe.-3P	1134	3350	B114001
4283	2-dr. Brgm.-5P	1174	3385	B114001
4288	4-dr. Sed.-6P	1184	3465	B114001
4289	2-dr. Sed.-6P	1164	3485	B114001
Series 4260 — 6-cyl.				
4260	4-dr. Tr. Sed.-6P	1159	3335	R384001
4263	2-dr. Brgm.-5P	1124	3230	R384001
4268	4-dr. Sed.-6P	1134	3335	R384001
4269	2-dr. Sed.-6P	1114	3265	R384001
Series 4240 — 6-cyl.				
4240	4-dr. Tr. Sed.-6P	993	2655	K56001
4242	2-dr. Cpe.-3P	918	2540	K56001
4243	2-dr. Brgm.-5P	958	2580	K56001
4248	4-dr. Sed.-6P	968	2655	K56001
4249	2-dr. Sed.-6P	948	2605	K56001

ENGINE: [Series 4280] Ohv. Straight-eight. Cast iron block. B & S: 3-1/8 x 4-1/4 in. Disp.: 260.8 cu. in. C.R.: 6.60:1. Brake H.P.: 115 @ 3400 R.P.M. Taxable H.P.: 31.2. Main bearings: nine. Valve lifters: solid. Carb.: Carter WDO-538S. Torque: 200 lb.-ft. @ 1600 R.P.M. [Series 4260] Ohv. Inline. Six. Cast iron block. B & S: 3-3/8 x 4-3/8 in. Disp.: 234.8 cu. in. C.R.: 6.50:1. Brake H.P.: 105 @ 3400 R.P.M. Taxable H.P.: 27.3. Main bearings: seven. Valve lifters: solid. Carb.: Carter WAI-464S. Torque: 203 lb.-ft. @ 1600 R.P.M. [Series 4240] L-head. Inline. Six. Cast iron block. B & S: 3-1/8 x 3-3/4 in. Disp.: 172.6 cu. in. C.R.: 6.87:1. Brake H.P.: 75 @ 3600 R.P.M. Taxable H.P.: 23.4. Main bearings: four. Valve lifters: solid. Carb.: Carter WDO-513S. Torque: 138 lb.-ft. @ 1200 R.P.M.

CHASSIS: [Series 4280] W.B.: 121 in. O.L.: 205-1/2 in. Frt/Rear Tread: 57/60-1/4 in. Tires: 6.50 x 16. [Series 4260] W.B.: 121 in. O.L.: 205-1/2 in. Frt/Rear Tread: 57-1/2/60-1/2 in. Tires: 6.25 x 16. [Series 4240] W.B.: 112 in. O.L.: 196-1/2 in. Frt/Rear Tread: 56/59-3/4 in. Tires: 5.50 x 16.

TECHNICAL: Selective, sliding gear transmission. Speeds: 3F/1R. Steering column controls. Single dry plate clutch. Hypoid drive. Semi-floating rear axle. Overall ratio: 4.11:1. Hydraulic brakes on four wheels. Steel disc wheels. Wheel size: 16 in. Hill-Holder. Overdrive.

OPTIONS: Bumper front (std.). Rear bumper (std.). Single sidemount (N/A). Dual sidemounts (N/A). Sidemount cover(s) (N/A). Fender skirts (except 4240). Bumper guards (std.). Radio ($65.00). Heater (35.00). Clock (10.50). Cigar lighter (2.10). Radio antenna (incl. with radio). Seat covers. Spotlight (17.75). Cowl lamps (N/A). Bulb horn (N/A). Bed equipment (21.00). Oil filter (9.00). Outside mirror (right or left) (2.45). Foglights (12.00).

HISTORICAL: Introduced October 1, 1941. Calendar year production: 5,428. The 1942 "4280" series was Nash's last straight-eight. The president of Nash was George Mason. Short production year, due to U.S. entry into World War II. (Production ceased February 1, 1942.) Charles W. Nash and James Storrow purchased the Thomas B. Jeffery Co. of Kenosha, Wis., in 1916. Nash was a former vice-president of General Motors. Jeffery was best known for making the Rambler of the early 1900s.

NASH 1946-1957

Cars bearing the Nash name started to appear during 1917, although the first Nash-designed car was a 1918 model.

The firm's first post-World War II models were similar to the Nash 600, created in 1941 as a car that could travel 600 miles on one fill-up of its 20 gallon gasoline tank. George W. Mason, a former Chrysler works manager, became president in 1936 when Nash and Mason's Kelvinator Corp. merged to form Nash-Kelvinator.

The 1946 Nash 600 carried its prewar sheet metal on a 112-inch wheelbase chassis powered by an L-head six. It was marketed together with the fancier Ambassador, which used an overhead valve engine in a 121-inch wheelbase car. The Ambassador chassis was quite different from that of the 600. The smaller car had unitized construction, while the Ambassador retained the body-on-frame type. Also, the 600 had coil springs all around, while the Ambassador used semi-elliptic springs at the rear. Nash, unlike other independent automakers, avoided a major restyling in the earlier post-World War II years. The 600 became its bread-and-butter model. The Ambassador had richer appointments inside and out. These handsome looking cars were similar in style to contemporary Cadillacs, but Nash was headed in a new postwar direction and would continue building this type of vehicle only through 1948.

Strong sales were registered throughout the period, due primarily to America's dire need for cars from a period when manufacturing was artificially restricted. The ability to have some product on hand was helpful and probably played a role in having a unique honor bestowed upon Nash for the first and last time in 1947. The company was asked to supply the Official Pace Car for the Indianapolis 500-Mile Race. It was an Ambassador sedan.

Dramatically new for 1949, the Nash Airflyte series offered unit construction in a fastback body that looked like a baby Packard. These cars carried over features popular with buyers, such as an overhead valve six in the Ambassador series, full coil spring suspension, large 15-inch tires and the efficiency of an overdrive transmission. Styling features included fully enclosed front and rear wheelhousings, one-piece windshields, fold-down travel bed seats and the "Uniscope" dash instrument cluster that put all the gauges in one place.

Data compiled by Larry Daum

In his plans for the changing marketplace of the 1950s, George Mason saw that the early postwar seller's market would not last and he tried to merge all the independent automakers together. He was unable to do so, but did accomplish the introduction of the first compact car in 1950. Mason's small car interest was shared by George Romney, who joined Nash-Kelvinator in 1948 as Mason's administrative assistant.

Nash re-introduced the Rambler nameplate in 1950, affixing it to the midyear compact model built off a new platform. It first came only as an equipment-loaded convertible-landau. This was basically like a two-door hardtop with a soft top. When the roof was lowered on rails, the windows and frames remained in a fixed-upright position. The Rambler's engine was the original Nash 600 powerplant. It could go even further on a gallon of gas in the small Rambler.

A second model was soon added. This two-door station wagon was announced at the same price as the convertible. Mason's idea to make the compact marketable was to introduce fancier models first to gain respectability for the compact. This followed the old Nash advertising motto, "Built up to a standard, not down to a price" and it worked.

The year 1951 brought a two-door hardtop to the Rambler line. It was called the Country Club coupe. This was the first modern compact hardtop. It had loads of trim and a fashionable continental spare tire. The larger models were basically carried over in 1951, with a few detail changes.

Nash's Golden Anniversary was celebrated in 1952. There was new styling for the Ambassador and Statesman. A new notchback body created by Italy's Pininfarina was the fashion hit of the marque's 50th year. The fastback look was gone and eye appeal was greatly enhanced.

Shortly before George Mason's death in 1954, his dream of joining all the independent auto companies into one came partly true. Nash and Hudson merged, in May 1954, to form American Motors. Then, it fell to George Romney to lead the fledgling enterprise in its formative and perhaps most significant years. Also in 1954, a two-door sedan version of the Rambler American was finally introduced, along with a four-door sedan.

It took George Romney several years to fully integrate Nash and Hudson operations and fully develop AMC. During the interim, some of the autocracy of the two firms was retained. Both Nashes and Hudsons continued to appear in separate showrooms. Each kept some styling distinctions, although the basic Nash body was used for both. Hudson dealers were also supplied with a "badge-engineered" Rambler. It had Hudson nameplates, hubcaps and grille medallions. Both companies also sold badge-engineered versions of the first American-designed sub-compact. However, this pint-sized Metropolitan was built by Austin, in England. Like the hybrid Nash-Healey, also British-made, it falls beyond the scope of this catalog of "American" automobiles.

The Rambler and Ambassador were both restyled for 1955. Full front wheel openings were the major change for the smaller car, along with new exterior trim design. The Ambassador and Statesman received a new slab-cornered front end treatment. It had larger, but not full, front wheel cutouts along with a wraparound windshield and larger oval grille that incorporated the headlights. The Packard Clipper V-8 was made available in the full-size Nash Ambassador, along with Packard's Ultramatic transmission. Nash sixes continued to use General Motors' Hydra-Matic.

The big news for 1956 was a completely new type of Rambler, which debuted in the spring. They were based on the 1954 four-door model's 108-inch wheelbase. Cars in this series featured many Rambler firsts, including a new overhead valve six, two-tone exterior sweep panel treatments and optional Hydra-Matic. The fancier and larger economy class cars accounted for 82,000 of the 104,000 units sold during the year.

The grand finale came for both Nash and Hudson in 1957. By this stage of the merger program, Hudson production in Detroit had ceased completely and almost all AMC assemblies were done at the Nash facilities in Kenosha, Wis. The Ambassador was face lifted for the last time, with new emphasis placed on sportiness, luxury and V-8 power. In fact, AMC had its own V-8 since the middle of 1956.

No amount of effort was quite enough to turn the tide. In fact, just over 10,000 Nashes found buyers during the calendar year. The same basic product in Hudson trim sold just over 4,000.

When 1958 rolled around, both marques were relegated into the history books. The Nash and Hudson names were dropped at the last minute, just before the new models were introduced. Rambler became the name of the marque. The timing for the change was perfect. In 1958, rising auto prices and a general economic recession combined to boost buyer interest in small cars. The only such domestic product around at that time was the Rambler. For awhile, it would be a success.

1946

NASH 600 — SERIES 40 — (6-CYL) — Nash, like most manufacturers after World War II, brought out cars based on prewar models with minor modifications. A significant change in the 600 was the use of a conventional wishbone front suspension. It replaced the Lancia-inspired 1941-1942 "sliding-pillar" type. Other changes included a wider front grille, the repositioning of turn signals from atop the front fenders (in 1942) to a position inboard of the front headlights and a new hood crest showing the Nash coat of arms. This emblem was less stylized and ornate than in 1942. Like the 1941 original, the new "600" had unitized construction. The model name reflected the fact that Nash claimed the car would go 600 miles on a full 20-gallon tank of gas. Technical features included sealed-in manifolding; full-pressure lubrication; full-length water jackets; steel-strut aluminum alloy pistons; extra-hard cylinder blocks; double-automatic spark control; air-cooled voltage generator; radial balanced crankshaft; three-point rubber insulated engine mounting; crankshaft vibration dampener and 20-gallon fuel tank. Standard equipment varied by model as follows: [Deluxe] spare wheel and tire; no-draft ventilation; hi-test safety glass; Deluxe bumpers; twin bumper guards front and rear; dual horns, sun visors and windshield wipers; front door armrests; dome light; cigar lighter; instrument panel ashtray and center-rear compartment ashtray. [Four-door sedans] rear quarter compartment ashtray and robe cord. [Two- and four-door sedans) assist cords. [Custom] Wind-up-type clock; metal rear fender gravel pads; door locks; glove compartment locks; Deluxe steering wheel; rear quarter vent windows; combination plastic and lacquered radio; grille; rotary door locks; sealed beam headlights; stainless steel runningboard moldings; carpet insert in front floor mat and voltage control generator.

NASH I.D. NUMBERS: The Vehicle Identification Plate located on the right-hand side of the cowl below the hood contains engine serial number and number codes for model paint and trim. Engine serial number matches the serial number. Model number has four symbols. The first two symbols indicate model year: 46 = 1946. The third symbol indicates series: 4 = 600; 6 = Ambassador. The fourth symbol indicates body style. (All four numbers appear in Body/Style Number column of charts below). Engine numbers located on right-hand side of crankcase towards front and on front upper left-hand side of block. Engine serial numbers for 1946 were: [600] K-77701 to K-135801; [Ambassador] R-393101 to R-429001.

NASH 600 SERIES 40

Model No.	Body/Style No.	Body Type & Seating	Factory Price	Shipping Weight	Prod. Total
40	4640	4-dr Trk Sed-6P	1342	2740	7,300
40	4643	2-dr Brgm Sed-6P	1293	2685	8,500
40	4648	4-dr FsBk Sed-6P	1298	2780	42,300

NASH AMBASSADOR — SERIES 60 — (6-CYL) — The Ambassador shared the looks and detail changes seen on the 600, but had a nine inch longer wheelbase. Instead of unitized construction, it featured separate chassis/frame engineering. However, the sheet metal and body construction were the same as for 600s from the cowl back. The car's extra nine inches of sheet metal was originally planned for a Nash overhead valve straight eight. The inline eight engine was dropped from production after World War II. The Ambassador now used a slightly updated overhead valve six with 112 hp. Technical features included sealed-in manifolding; full-pressure lubrication; full-length water jackets; steel-strut aluminum alloy pistons with four rings; extra-hard cylinder block; double automatic spark control; air-cooled voltage generator; radial-balanced crankshaft with vibration dampener; four-point rubber insulated engine mounting; oil filter; six quart crankcase and 20-gallon fuel tank.

AMBASSADOR 60 SERIES

Model No.	Body/Style No.	Body Type & Seating	Factory Price	Shipping Weight	Prod. Total
60	4660	4-dr Trk Sed-6P	1511	3335	3,875
60	4663	2-dr Brgm Sed-6P	1453	3260	4,825
60	4664	4-dr Sub-6P	1929	3470	275
60	4668	4-dr FsBk Sed-6P	1469	3360	26,925

ENGINES:

(NASH 600 SIX) Inline. L-head. Cast iron block. Displacement: 172.6 cid. Bore and stroke: 3-1/8 x 3-3/4 inches. Compression ratio: 6.8:1. Brake hp: 82 at 3800 rpm. Four main bearings. Solid valve lifters. Carburetor: Carter one-barrel WAI-611S.

(AMBASSADOR SIX) Inline. Overhead valve. Cast iron block. Displacement: 234.8 inches. Bore and stroke: 3-3/8 x 4-3/8 inches. Compression ratio: 6.8:1. Brake hp: 112 at 3400 rpm. Seven main bearings. Solid valve lifters. Carburetor: Carter one-barrel Model YF.

CHASSIS FEATURES: Wheelbase: (600) 112 inches; (Ambassador) 121 inches. Overall length: (600) 199-9/16 inches; (Ambassador) 208-9/16 inches. Front tread: (600) 56-13/16 inches; (Ambassador) 57-1/2 inches. Rear tread: (600) 59-3/4 inches; (Ambassador) 60-1/2 inches. Tires: (600) 6.00 x 16; (Ambassador) 6.50 x 15.

OPTIONS: Foam rubber cushions. Conditioned air system. Vacuum booster pump. Radio and antenna. Directional signals. Oil bath air cleaner. Oil filter. There were no available engine options. The standard transmission was a three-speed manual type with overdrive offered as an option on the Ambassador only.

HISTORICAL FOOTNOTES: From 1946-1948, Nash produced a wood-bodied four-door sedan in the style of the Chrysler Town & Country. A total of 1,000 of these wood covered "Suburbans" were built in this three-year period. The fastback sedan was called the Slip Stream. Nash built 98,769 cars in calendar 1946 for eighth place in auto industry sales rankings.

1947

NASH 600 — SERIES 40 — (6-CYL) — The Nash 600 for 1947 received few changes from 1946. The front grilles were widened again and new raised center hubcaps were used.

NASH I.D. NUMBERS: The Vehicle Identification Plate located on the right-hand side of the cowl below the hood contains engine serial number and number codes for model, paint and trim. Engine serial number matches the serial number. Model number has four symbols. The first two symbols indicate model year: 47 = 1947. The third symbol indicates series: 4 = 600; 6 = Ambassador. The fourth symbol indicates body style. (All four numbers appear in Body/Style Number column of charts below). Engine numbers located on right-hand side of crankcase towards front and on front upper left-hand side of block. Engine serial numbers for 1947 were: [600] K-136001 to K-153244; [Ambassador] R-429201 to R-440922.

NASH 600 SERIES 40

Model No.	Body/Style No.	Body Type & Seating	Factory Price	Shipping Weight	Prod. Total
40	4740	4-dr Trk Sed-6P	1464	2786	21,500
40	4743	2-dr Brgm-6P	1415	2731	12,100
40	4748	4-dr FsBk Sed-6P	1420	2826	27,700

NASH AMBASSADOR — SERIES 60 — (6-CYL) — The only changes for the 1947 Ambassador was the addition of the same front grille as used on Nash 600s plus the same raised center hubcaps. The four-door Nash Suburban was distinguished by wooden side panels. The fastback sedan was called the Slip Stream.

AMBASSADOR 60 SERIES

Model No.	Body/Style No.	Body Type & Seating	Factory Price	Shipping Weight	Prod. Total
60	4760	4-dr Trk Sed-6P	1809	3387	15,927
60	4763	2-dr Brgm-6P	1751	3312	8,673
60	4764	4-dr Sub-6P	2227	3522	595
60	4768	4-dr FsBk Sed-6P	1767	3412	14,505

ENGINES:

(NASH 600 SIX) Inline. L-head. Cast iron block. Displacement: 172.6 cid. Bore and stroke: 3-1/8 x 3-3/4 inches. Compression ratio: 6.8:1. Brake hp: 82 at 3800 rpm. Four main bearings. Solid valve lifters. Carburetor: Carter one-barrel WAI-611S.

(AMBASSADOR SIX) Inline. Overhead valve. Cast iron block. Displacement: 234.8 inches. Bore and stroke: 3-3 8 x 4-3/8 inches. Compression ratio: 6.8:1. Brake hp: 112 at 3400 rpm. Seven main bearings. Solid valve lifters. Carburetor: Carter one-barrel Model YF.

CHASSIS FEATURES: Wheelbase: (600) 112 inches; (Ambassador) 121 inches. Overall length: (600) 199-9/16 inches; (Ambassador) 208-9/16 inches. Front tread: (600) 56-13/16 inches; (Ambassador) 57-1/2 inches. Rear tread: (600) 59-3/4 inches; (Ambassador) 60-1/2 inches. Tires: (600) 6.00 x 16; (Ambassador) 6.50 x 15.

OPTIONS: Foam rubber cushions. Cruising gear (Ambassador only). Conditioned air system. Vacuum booster pump. Radio and antenna. Directional signals. Oil bath air cleaner. Oil filter (600 only). There were no available optional engines. The standard transmission was a three-speed manual type with Warner Gear overdrive available at extra cost.

HISTORICAL FOOTNOTES: Production for calendar year 1947 increased to 113,315 cars and Nash came in 10th in sales. A one-of-a-kind 12-passenger Nash limousine was built to carry executives and VIPs around the plant. It had four doors on each side. A Nash Ambassador was the Official Pace Car for the Indianapolis 500-Mile Race. The five percent of total U.S. auto sales earned by Nash this season was a strong showing for an independent manufacturer. New assembly sites in El Segundo, Calif., and Toronto, Ontario, Canada, were acquired by Nash-Kelvinator Corp. this year. George W. Mason was chairman of the board and president of the company. Production of the 1947 line commenced in December 1946.

1948

NASH 600 — SERIES 40 — (6-CYL) — Changes to the 1948 Nash consisted of the removal of a chrome molding just below the beltline, giving the cars a clean-sided look. Hoodside moldings did not run as far forward and the hood badge design was changed. In addition, the model line was expanded to meet an anticipated upsurge in buyer demand. Included, for the first time since before World War II, was a three-passenger business coupe and upgraded Custom versions of the two-door Brougham and the four-door Slip Stream and Trunk Sedan.

NASH I.D. NUMBERS: The Vehicle Identification Plate located on the right-hand side of the cowl below the hood contains engine serial number and number codes for model paint and trim. Engine serial number matches the serial number. Model number has four symbols. The first two symbols indicate model year: 48 = 1948. The third symbol indicates series: 4 = 600 Super/Deluxe; 5 = 600 Custom; 6 = Ambassador Super; 7 = Ambassador Custom. The fourth symbol indicates body style. (All four numbers appear in Body/Style Number column of charts below). Engine numbers located on right-hand side of crankcase towards front and on front upper left-hand side of block. [600 SERIES] Serial numbers ran from K-196901 to K-259792. Engine numbers ran from KE-55001 to KE-120132 and no longer matched serial numbers. [AMBASSADOR SERIES] Serial numbers ran from R-468501 to R-514594. Engine serial numbers ran from RE-40001 to RE-82095.

NASH 600 SERIES 40

Model No.	Body/Style No.	Body Type & Seating	Factory Price	Shipping Weight	Prod. Total
SUPER LINE/DELUXE LINE					
40	4840	4-dr Trk Sed-6P	1587	2786	25,103
40	4843	2-dr Brgm-6P	1538	2731	11,530
40	4848	4-dr FsBk Sed-6P	1534	2826	25,044
40	4842	2-dr Bus Cpe-3P	1478	2635	925
CUSTOM LINE					
40	4850	4-dr Trk Sed-6P	1776	2786	346
40	4853	2-dr Brgm-6P	1727	2731	170
40	4858	4-dr FsBk Sed-6P	1732	2826	332

NASH AMBASSADOR — SERIES 60 — (6-CYL) — The 1948 Ambassador also had the chrome molding just below the beltline removed for a cleaner side appearance. In addition, the model line was also expanded to meet an anticipated surge in sales caused by the return to full postwar production after the settling of labor disputes and the relaxation of materials restrictions. Added were Custom versions of the two-door Brougham and the four-door Slip Stream (fastback) and Trunk Sedan. Also, for the first time since 1941, a convertible was added to the line, but only 1,000 were made. This was to be the last full-size Nash convertible ever made, although a 1950 Nash Rambler compact-size convertible would be produced. Not until 1965 would Nash Motor's successor, AMC, build a full-size convertible again.

AMBASSADOR 60 SERIES

Model No.	Body/Style No.	Body Type & Seating	Factory Price	Shipping Weight	Prod. Total
SUPER LINE					
60	4860	4-dr Trk Sed-6P	1916	3387	14,248
60	4863	2-dr Brgm-6P	1858	3312	7,221
60	4864	4-dr Sub-6P	2239	3522	130
60	4868	4-dr FsBk Sed-6P	1874	3412	14,777

CUSTOM LINE

Model No.	Body/Style No.	Body Type & Seating	Factory Price	Shipping Weight	Prod. Total
60	4870	4-dr Trk Sed-6P	2105	3387	4,102
60	4873	2-dr Brgm Sed-6P	2047	3312	929
60	4878	4-dr FsBk Sed-6P	2063	3412	4,143
60	4871	2-dr Conv-6P	2355	3465	1,000

ENGINES:

(NASH 600 SIX) Inline. L-head. Cast iron block. Displacement: 172.6 cid. Bore and stroke: 3-1/8 x 3-3/4 inches. Compression ratio: 6.8:1. Brake hp: 82 at 3800 rpm. Four main bearings. Solid valve lifters. Carburetor: Carter one-barrel WAI-662S.

(AMBASSADOR SIX) Inline. Overhead valve. Cast iron block. Displacement: 234.8 inches. Bore and stroke: 3-3/8 x 4-3/8 inches. Compression ratio: 6.8:1. Brake hp: 112 at 3400 rpm. Seven main bearings. Solid valve lifters. Carburetor: Carter one-barrel Model YF.

CHASSIS FEATURES: Wheelbase: (600) 112 inches; (Ambassador) 121 inches. Overall length: (600) 200 inches; (Ambassador) 209-3/16 inches. Front tread: (all) 57-1/2 inches. Rear tread: (600) 59-11/16 inches; (Ambassador) 60-1/2 inches. Tires: (600) 6.40 x 15 Super Cushion; (Ambassador) 6.50 x 15; 7.10 x 15 Super Cushion optional.

OPTIONS: Foam rubber cushions. Cruising gear (Ambassador only). Conditioned air system. Vacuum booster pump. Radio and antenna. Directional signals. Oil bath air cleaner. Oil filter (600 only). There were no available option1al engines. The standard transmission was a three-speed manual type with Warner Gear overdrive available at extra cost.

HISTORICAL FOOTNOTES: Charles Nash died on June 6, 1948, at the age of 84. The 1948 Ambassadors were the last Nashes to use separate frames. Production began at the El Segundo, Calif., factory this year. The starting month for production of Nash products built to 1948 specifications was November 1947. This would be the last year that Nash used the term "Brougham" to describe its club coupe. (Starting with the 1949 Nash Airflyte, the Brougham model became a two-door sedan featuring two individual "lounge-chair" style seats, angled towards the center of the car, with a permanent center armrest between them.) Calendar year production peaked at 118,621 units or 3.04 percent of total domestic sales for the entire industry. George W. Mason retained the top corporate posts and George Romney served as Nash-Kelvinator vice-president. The fastback sedan was again called a Slip Stream.

1949

NASH 600 — SERIES 40 — (6-CYL) — Nash introduced its first totally redesigned postwar car line in 1949. The Nash Airflyte series, as it was called, featured single-unit construction, one-piece curved windshield, "Uniscope" gauge cluster (a pod atop the steering column containing all instruments) and fully reclining front seatbacks. In 1949, Nash was the first U.S. manufacturer of mass produced automobiles to totally commit to unitized single-unit construction and one of the first in the world to do so. These "bathtub" Nashes (as they were known) were styled with an eye toward aerodynamics. At 60 mph in wind tunnel tests, the Airflyte had only 113 pounds of drag. (In comparison, a similar looking 1949 Packard had around 171 pounds of drag.)

NASH I.D. NUMBERS: The Vehicle Identification Plate located on the right-hand side of the cowl below the hood contains engine serial number and number codes for model, paint and trim. Engine serial number matches the serial number. Model number has four symbols. The first two symbols indicate model year: 49 = 1949. The third symbol indicates series: 2 = 600 Special; 4 = 600 Super; 5 = 600 Custom; 6 = Ambassador Super; 7 = Ambassador Custom; 9 = Ambassador Super Special. The fourth symbol indicates body style. (All four numbers appear In Body/Style Number column of charts below). Engine numbers located on right-hand side of crankcase towards front and on front upper left-hand side of block. [600 SERIES] The starting serial number for the Nash 600 of 1949 was K-260501 for cars assembled in Kenosha, Wis. Unassembled export serial numbers began at 4KD-1401. Starting serial number for El Segundo, Calif., was KC-1001. Starting engine serial number for all 1949 Nash 600s was S-1001. [AMBASSADOR SERIES] The starting serial number for the Ambassador six of 1949 was: R-515501 for Kenosha, Wis.; 6KD-1501 for unassembled export and RC-1001 for El Segundo. Starting engine serial numbers for all 1949 Ambassadors was A-1001.

NASH 600 SERIES 40

Model No.	Body/Style No.	Body Type & Seating	Factory Price	Shipping Weight	Prod. Total
SUPER SPECIAL LINE					
40	4923	2-dr Brgm-5P	1846	2960	2,564
40	4928	4-dr Sed-6P	1849	2960	23,606
40	4929	2-dr Sed-6P	1824	2935	9,605
SUPER LINE					
40	4943	2-dr Brgm-5P	1808	2960	2,954
40	4948	4-dr Sed-6P	1811	2950	31,194
40	4949	2-dr Sed-6P	1786	2935	17,006
CUSTOM LINE					
40	4953	2-dr Brgm-5P	1997	2970	17
40	4958	4-dr Sed-6P	2000	2985	199

NASH AMBASSADOR — SERIES 60 — (6-CYL) — The Nash Ambassador for 1949 shared all the styling changes of the 1949 Nash 600. The difference was largely that the Ambassador had a nine inch longer wheelbase due to its longer front end. Coil spring suspension and torque tube drive were featured on both the Ambassador and the Nash 600. The same three series or trim levels were available in the Ambassador: Super, Super Special and Custom.

NASH AMBASSADOR SERIES 60

Model No.	Body/Style No.	Body Type & Seating	Factory Price	Shipping Weight	Prod. Total
SUPER LINE					
60	4963	2-dr Brgm-5P	2191	3390	1,541
60	4968	4-dr Sed-6P	2195	3385	17,960
60	4969	2-dr Sed-6P	2170	3365	4,602
CUSTOM LINE					
60	4973	2-dr Brgm-5P	2359	3415	1,837
60	4978	4-dr Sed-6P	2363	3415	6,539
60	4979	2-dr Sed-6P	2338	3400	691
SUPER SPECIAL LINE					
60	4993	2-dr Brgm-5P	2239	3390	807
60	4998	4-dr Sed-6P	2243	3385	6,777
60	4999	2-dr Sed-6P	2218	3365	2,072

ENGINES:

(NASH 600 SIX) Inline. L-head. Cast iron block. Displacement: 172.6 cid. Bore and stroke: 3-1/8 x 3-3/4 inches. Compression ratio: 6.8:1. Brake hp: 82 at 3800 rpm. Four main bearings. Solid valve lifters. Carburetor: Carter one-barrel WAI-694S.

(AMBASSADOR SIX) Inline. Overhead valve. Cast iron block. Displacement: 234.8 inches. Bore and stroke: 3-3/8 x 4-3/8 inches. Compression ratio: 6.8:1. Brake hp: 112 at 3400 rpm. Seven main bearings. Solid valve lifters. Carburetor: Carter one-barrel WAI-683S.

CHASSIS FEATURES: Wheelbase: (600) 112 inches; (Ambassador) 121 inches. Overall length: (600) 201 inches; (Ambassador) 210 inches. Front tread: (all) 54-11/16 inches. Rear tread: (600) 59-11/16 inches; (Ambassador) 60-1/2 inches. Tires: (600) 6.40 x 15; (Ambassador) 7.10 x 15.

OPTIONS: Bed, single ($19); double ($39). Exhaust pipe extensions ($2). Fog lights, pair ($13). Spotlight, door mounted ($20). Back-O-Matic Lights, pair ($9). Fuel purifier ($2). License plate frames ($2). Electric snap-up gas cap ($5). Magnalite trouble light ($4). Nonglare mirror ($4). Rearview mirror, right and left ($3). Visor vanity mirror ($1). Deluxe fiber seat covers (interwoven pattern, blue color) in two-door sedan and four-door sedan ($25); in Broughams ($31). Deluxe fiber Sportster-type seat covers in all two-door and four-door sedans ($28); in Broughams ($35). Rayon twill seat covers with maroon, blue or brown color, in all sedans ($48); in Broughams ($51). Trim rings ($12). Wheel discs ($17). Tissue dispensers ($3). Hood ornaments ($9). Windshield washer ($7). Rear window wiper ($14). Front grille guard ($25). Rear grille guard ($20). Fender guard, pair ($10). Nash Karvisor ($26). Directional signals ($16). Radio ($82). Manual antenna ($7). Vacuum antenna ($14). Warner Gear overdrive.

HISTORICAL FOOTNOTES: The 1949 Nash line began production in October 1948. A total of 130,000 units was produced for the model year. Calendar year production was counted at 142,592 cars or 2.78 percent of the total domestic auto business. Nine Ambassadors were built by the engineering department (under the direction of M.F. Moore, vice-president of Nash Research) with automatic transmissions. Three-passenger models and the wood-veneered Suburban sedan were dropped this year. Nash was America's 10th ranked maker of the season.

1950

NASH STATESMAN — SERIES 40 — (6-CYL) — The Nash 600 was renamed Statesman for 1950 and its L-head six-cylinder engine had a one-quarter inch larger stroke. This increased displacement from 172.6 cid to 184 cid and increased horsepower from 82 to 85. One significant styling change made in this year was a much larger rear window, which was helpful to the driver considering that the fastback design made seeing the traffic behind difficult. The bumper guards grew slightly thicker and the cars had a Statesman script on their front fenders. Seat belts were available with the Statesman and the Ambassador in their first use on a U.S. built car. Both the Statesman and the Ambassador came in two basic trim levels, Super and Custom for 1950. The Statesman also had a low-priced "line leader" Deluxe Business Coupe. Custom models had rear seat armrests; carpets; courtesy lights; a Custom steering wheel; and full wheel discs. Some 1950 models were built in the new Canadian factory. Production figures for Canada are unavailable.

NASH I.D. NUMBERS: The Vehicle Identification Plate located on the right-hand side of the cowl below the hood contains engine serial number and number codes for model, paint and trim. Engine serial number matches the serial number. Model number has four symbols. The first two symbols indicate model year: 50 = 1950. The third symbol indicates series: 2 = Rambler; 3 = Statesman; 4 = Super Statesman; 5 = Custom Statesman; 6 = Ambassador Super; 7 = Ambassador Custom. The fourth symbol indicates body style. (All four numbers appear in Body/Style Number column of charts below). Engine numbers located on right-hand side of crankcase towards front and on front upper left-hand side of block. [STATESMAN]: Serial numbering for Statesman sixes built in Kenosha were K-340001 to K-436892; in El Segundo KC-9501 to KC-23007; in Canada KT-1001 and up; and for unassembled export units 4KD-2301 and up. Engine numbers for 1950 Statesman sixes were S-92001 to S-205947. [AMBASSADOR]: Serial numbering for Ambassador sixes built in Kenosha were R-556001 to R-599704; in El Segundo RC-3501 to RC-8488; and for unassembled export units RD-2101 and up. (No Ambassadors were assembled in Canada). Engine numbers for 1950 Ambassadors were A-46001 to A-96151. [RAMBLER]: The serial numbers were D-1001 to D-12263. Engine numbers were F-1001 to F-12574.

NASH STATESMAN SERIES 40

Model No.	Body/Style No.	Body Type & Seating	Factory Price	Shipping Weight	Prod. Total
NASH DELUXE					
40	5032	2-dr Bus Cpe-3P	1633	2830	1,198
SUPER LINE					
40	5043	2-dr Brgm-5P	1735	2940	1,489
40	5048	4-dr Sed-6P	1738	2965	60,090
40	5049	2-dr Sed-6P	1713	2930	34,196
CUSTOM LINE					
40	5053	2-dr Brgm-5P	1894	2965	132
40	5058	2-dr Sed-6P	1897	2990	11,500
40	5059	2-dr Sed-6P	1872	2950	2,693

NASH AMBASSADOR — SERIES 60 — (6-CYL) — The 1950 Nash Ambassador had a longer hood than the 1949 model, as well as the enlarged back window. Otherwise, there were not many significant changes. An Ambassador script appeared on the fenders for identification. The year's major innovation was the introduction of a GM-built Hydra-Matic transmission, available only on the 1950 Nash Ambassador. A new cylinder head design was also introduced for the 234.8 cid overhead valve Ambassador engine and raised the output to 115 hp. Custom models differed from the Supers by featuring a rear seat with a folding center armrest; front floor carpeting; courtesy lights; a Custom steering wheel; and large wheel discs.

NASH AMBASSADOR SERIES 60

Model No.	Body/Style No.	Body Type & Seating	Factory Price	Shipping Weight	Prod. Total
SUPER LINE					
60	5063	2-dr Brgm-5P	2060	3335	716
60	5068	4-dr Sed-6P	2064	3350	27,523
60	5069	2-dr Sed-6P	2039	3325	7,237
CUSTOM LINE					
60	5073	2-dr Brgm-5P	2219	3385	108
60	5078	4-dr Sed-6P	2223	3390	12,427
60	5079	2-dr Sed-6P	2198	3365	1,045

NASH RAMBLER — SERIES 10 — (6-CYL) — Nash introduced the compact Nash Rambler Convertible Landau in March 1950. The first cars built by Nash's predecessor, the Thomas B. Jeffery Co. of Kenosha, Wis., also used this name. The compact car had a 100-inch wheelbase and used the 82-hp six-cylinder engine from the Nash 600. The first model introduced was the two-door Convertible Landau. A two-door station wagon was introduced two months later on June 23. Both models came loaded with options such as radio and antenna; Custom steering wheel; turn signals; wheel discs; electric clock; courtesy lights; Custom upholstery; and foam seat cushions. On the convertible only, a sliding top (in black or tan fabric) could be raised over "bridge beam" side rails above the doors. The Rambler used Hotchkiss drive, unlike the torque tube drive of the conventional Nash.

NASH RAMBLER SERIES 10

Model No.	Body/Style No.	Body Type & Seating	Factory Price	Shipping Weight	Prod. Total
10	5021	2-dr Cus Conv-5P	1808	2430	9,330
10	5024	2-dr Cus Sta Wag-5P	1808	2515	1,712
10	5026	2-dr Cus Trk Sed	—	—	6
10	5114	2-dr Sup Sta Wag	—	—	1
10	5124	2-dr Cus Sta Wag	—	—	1
10	5121	2-dr Cus Conv-5P	1808	2430	378

NOTE 1: 378 convertibles built in California July/August 1950 possibly were prototypes.

ENGINES:

(STATESMAN SIX) Inline. L-head. Cast iron block. Displacement: 184 cid. Bore and stroke: 3-1/8 x 3-3/4 inches. Compression ratio: 7.0:1. Brake hp: 85 at 3800 rpm. Four main bearings. Solid valve lifters. Carburetor: Carter one-barrel WAI-694S.

(AMBASSADOR SIX) Inline. Overhead valve. Displacement: 234.8 cid. Bore and stroke: 3-3/8 x 4-3/8 inches. Compression ratio: 7.3:1. Brake hp: 115 at 3400 rpm. Seven main bearings. Solid valve lifters. Carburetor: Carter one-barrel WAI-746S.

(RAMBLER SIX) Inline. L-head. Cast iron block. Displacement: 172.6 cid. Bore and stroke: 3-1/8 x 3-3/4 inches. Compression ratio: 7.25:1. Brake hp: 82 at 3800 rpm. Four main bearings. Solid valve lifters. Carburetor: Carter one-barrel Model YF-757S.

CHASSIS FEATURES: Wheelbase: (Statesman) 112 inches; (Ambassador) 121 inches; (Rambler) 100 inches. Overall length: (Statesman) 201 inches; (Ambassador) 210 inches; (Rambler) 176 inches. Front tread: (Statesman and Ambassador) 54-11/16 inches; (Rambler) 53-1/4 inches. Rear tread: (Statesman) 59-11/16 inches; (Ambassador) 60-1/2 inches; (Rambler) 53 inches. Tires: (Statesman) 6.40 x 15; (Ambassador) 7.10 x 15; (Rambler) 5.90 x 15.

OPTIONS: Electric clock (standard on Custom models). Mechanical clock. Overdrive. Two-tone colors. Directional signals (standard on Custom models). Emergency brake alarm. Fender signal. Floor mat pads. Foam rubber seat cushion (standard on Custom). Fuel purifier. Locking gas cap. Electric locking gas cap. Fender guards. Grille guards. Trunk guards. Hood ornament. Hydra-Matic transmission (Ambassador). License frames. Back-O-Matic lights. Fog lights (pair). Spotlight (front door). Spotlight (with rearview mirror). Trouble light. Mattress. Zipper case for bed. Rearview mirror. Deluxe rearview outside mirror. Visor vanity mirror. Oil filter (Statesman and Ambassador). Heavy-duty oil bath air cleaner (Statesman and Ambassador). Optoshade inside sun shield. Custom radio with manual antenna. Custom radio with vacuum antenna. Deluxe radio with vacuum antenna. Rear speaker for Deluxe radio. Rear door safety locks. Front divided seatback for four-door sedan, with bed (standard on Custom models). Reclining front seat. Fiber Regal seat covers. Fiber Majestic seat covers. Top-Flyte Custom rayon seat covers in maroon, blue and green. Custom steering wheel (standard equipment in Custom models). White sidewall tires, size 6.40 x 14 four-ply. White sidewall tires, size 6.40 x 15 six-ply. White sidewall tires, size 7.10 x 15 four-ply. White sidewall tires, size 7.10 x 15 six-ply. Tissue dispenser packet. Tool pouch. Set of five stainless steel chrome trim rings. Leather upholstery. Outside window visors for two-door; four-door Visor shade. Weather-Eye conditioned air system. Five chrome stainless steel wheel discs (standard on Custom models). Window screen for two-door; four-door. Windshield washer. Rear window wiper.

HISTORICAL FOOTNOTES: Production of 1950 Nash products began in September 1949. A total of 160,354 Statesman and Ambassador models, along with 11,428 Ramblers, were produced for the model year. Sales were counted at 191,665 cars, putting Nash 10th in the auto sales race. This broke the all-time record for Nash production. The official model introduction date for the new Rambler convertible was April 14, 1950. Together, the two Rambler body styles helped Nash achieve the assembly of 71 percent of all convertibles and 3.6 percent of all station wagons built in the United States in calendar year 1950. The compact line was an immediate success. Nash calendar year production leaped to 189,543 cars or 2.84 percent of total auto industry sales. The three-passenger Nash was reintroduced this year, as a back seat-less business car intended strictly for commercial use. Several Nash models competed successfully in stock car races during 1950. Their greater fuel economy meant that fewer pit stops were required. Many Nash owners reported 25-30 mpg in normal operation, according to the company's advertisements.

1951

NASH STATESMAN — SERIES 40 — (6-CYL) — The 1951 Nash Statesman featured a new electric shaver-type grille and side marker lights along with new rear fenders and fender lights. Statesman script was on the front fender for identification. Super models had basic features. Customs also had foam seat cushions; front floor carpets; courtesy lights; a rear seat center armrest; Custom steering wheel; and full wheel discs. Hydra-Matic automatic transmission made its debut on the Statesman in 1951.

NASH I.D. NUMBERS: The Vehicle Identification Plate located on the right-hand side of the cowl below the hood contains engine serial number and number codes for model, paint and trim. Engine serial number matches the serial number. Model number has four symbols. The first two symbols indicate model year: 51 = 1951. The third symbol indicates series: 0 = Rambler Utility; 1 = Rambler Super; 2 = Rambler Custom; 3 = Statesman; 4 = Super/Deluxe Statesman; 5 = Custom Statesman; 6 = Ambassador Super; 7 = Ambassador Custom. The fourth symbol indicates body style. (All four numbers appear in Body/Style Number column of charts below). Engine numbers located on right-hand side of crankcase towards front and on front upper left-hand side of block. [NASH STATESMAN SERIES 40]: Serial numbers for 1951 Nash Statesman models built at Kenosha were K-438001 to K-518763; 4KD-3201 and up for unassembled export; KC-23501 and up for El Segundo and KT-22501 and up for cars made in the Toronto, Ontario, Canada, assembly plant. Engine numbers for the Statesman six were S-207001 to S-306795 for all assembly points. [NASH AMBASSADOR SERIES 60]: Serial numbers for the 1951 Nash Ambassador models built at Kenosha were R-600501 to R-655753; 6KD-2071 and up for unassembled exports and RC-8701 and up for El Segundo. Ambassadors were not manufactured at the Canadian plant. Engine numbers for all Ambassador six engines were A-97001 to A-160453. [NASH RAMBLER SERIES 10]: The serial numbers for 1951 Ramblers built in Kenosha were D-12501 to D-78917; DKD-1201 for unassembled export and DC-1501 for El Segundo. Engine numbers for 1951 Ramblers were F-1001 to F-83778. The Rambler Deliveryman utility wagon line had serial numbers D-66495 and up/engine numbers F-89802 and up.

NASH STATESMAN SERIES 40

Model No.	Body/Style No.	Body Type & Seating	Factory Price	Shipping Weight	Prod. Total
SUPER/DELUXE LINES					
40	5132	2-dr Del Bus Cpe-3P	1710	2835	52
40	5143	2-dr Brgm-5P	1812	2935	152
40	5148	4-dr Sed-6P	1815	2970	52,325
40	5149	2-dr Sed-6P	1790	2930	22,261
CUSTOM LINE					
40	5153	2-dr Brgm-5P	1971	2950	38
40	5158	4-dr Sed-6P	1974	2990	14,846
40	5159	2-dr Sed-6P	1949	2940	2,141

NASH AMBASSADOR — SERIES 60 — (6-CYL) — The 1951 Nash Ambassador received the same revised front grille and side marker lights and new rear fenders as the 1951 Statesman. The major difference from the Statesman was the Ambassador's nine inch longer front end. Supers had basic features. Customs had a rear seat with a folding center armrest; courtesy lamps; front carpeting; Custom steering wheel and large wheel discs.

NASH AMBASSADOR SERIES 60

Model No.	Body/Style No.	Body Type & Seating	Factory Price	Shipping Weight	Prod. Total
SUPER LINE					
60	5163	2-dr Brgm-5P	2158	3370	40
60	5168	4-dr Sed-6P	2162	3410	34,935
60	5169	2-dr Sed-6P	2137	3370	4,382
CUSTOM LINE					
60	5173	2-dr Brgm-5P	2317	3395	37
60	5178	4-dr Sed-6P	2321	3445	21,071
60	5179	2-dr Sed-6P	2296	3380	1,118

NASH RAMBLER — SERIES 10 — (6-CYL) — The major change for 1951 was the introduction of a new Rambler model called the Country Club hardtop. This was the first two-door compact hardtop to be introduced in the United States. This body style had been popularized by the introduction of two-door hardtops in several GM car-lines in 1949.

NASH RAMBLER SERIES 10

Model No.	Body/Style No.	Body Type & Seating	Factory Price	Shipping Weight	Prod. Total
10	2104	2-dr Utl Wag-3P	1673	2415	1,569
10	5114	2-dr Sta Wag-5P	1723	2515	5,568
10	5117	2-dr HT Cpe-5P	—	—	1
10	5121	2-dr Conv-5P	1837	2430	14,881
10	5124	2-dr Cus Sta Wag-5P	1837	2515	28,617
10	5126	2-dr Clb Sed-6P	—	—	50
10	5127	2-dr Cty Clb-5P	1968	2420	19,317

ENGINES:

(STATESMAN SIX) Inline. L-head. Cast iron block. Displacement: 184 cid. Bore and stroke: 3-1/8 x 3-3/4 inches. Compression ratio: 7.0:1. Brake hp: 85 at 3800 rpm. Four main bearings. Solid valve lifters. Carburetor: Carter one-barrel Model YF-824S.

(AMBASSADOR SIX) Inline. Overhead valve. Displacement: 234.8 cid. Bore and stroke: 3-3/8 x 4-3/8 inches. Compression ratio: 7.3:1. Brake hp: 115 at 3400 rpm. Seven main bearings. Solid valve lifters. Carburetor: Carter one-barrel WAI-746S.

(RAMBLER SIX) Inline. L-head. Cast iron block. Displacement: 172.6 cid. Bore and stroke: 3-1/8 x 3-3/4 inches. Compression ratio: 7.25:1. Brake hp: 82 at 3800 rpm. Four main bearings. Solid valve lifters. Carburetor: Carter one-barrel Model YF-757S.

CHASSIS FEATURES: Wheelbase: (Statesman) 112 inches; (Ambassador) 121 inches; (Rambler) 100 inches. Overall length: (Statesman) 201 inches; (Ambassador) 211 inches; (Rambler) 176 inches. Front tread: (Statesman and Ambassador) 54-11/16 inches; (Rambler) 53-1/4 inches. Rear tread: (Statesman) 59-11/16 inches; (Ambassador) 60-1/2 inches; (Rambler) 53 inches. Tires: (Statesman) 6.40 x 15; (Ambassador) 7.10 x 15; (Rambler) 5.90 x 15.

OPTIONS: Radio. Vacuum control antenna. Spotlight with mirror. Door-top outside mirror. Door mount outside mirror. Back-up lights. Fog lights. Nonglare rearview mirror. Visor vanity mirror. Curb-L-Arm. Custom seat covers. License plate frame. Exhaust extension. Protect-O-Mat for floor. Automatic windshield washer. Rear window wiper. Opto-shade for windshield. Vent shades. Outside windshield visor. Magnalite trouble light. Gas cap lock. Tissue dispenser. Bed mattress. Plastic screens.

HISTORICAL FOOTNOTES: In 1951, Nash introduced Rambler hardtop, Suburban and Deliveryman (utility wagon) models; suspended operations in Canada and received a defense contract to build Pratt & Whitney aero engines. Korean War allocations prevented introduction of the Rambler four-door sedan this season. Annual model introductions were held on Sept. 22, 1950. The Nash Rambler Country Club hardtop was introduced, as an addition to the line, on June 28, 1951. In November 1951, the company received permission from the Economic Stability Agency to increase prices. The subsequent jump was $64 in Rambler; $48-$55 in Statesman and $61-$66 in Ambassador retail prices. Model year production counted 125,203 standard size models and 80,000 compact Ramblers, with the production run beginning in September 1950. Calendar year production hit 161,209 units or 30.2 percent of total American industry output. Over 82,731 Nash products were assembled with optional overdrive transmission, while another 64,775 cars had automatic drives (GM Hydra-Matic). The new Deliveryman was a station wagon-type vehicle, with only one seat, intended strictly for commercial package carrying work. In most reference sources it was listed as a truck and described as a utility wagon, which is how it appears in the specifications charts above. During 1951, Nash made 6.9 percent of all convertibles, 3.9 percent of all hardtops and 15.2 percent of all station wagons produced in the United States. During the calendar year, 25,962 automatic transmission attachments were sold, while 82,731 cars had the optional Warner Gear overdrive.

1952

NASH STATESMAN — SERIES 40 — (6-CYL) — The year 1952 marked the 50th anniversary of Nash Motor Co. and its predecessor, the Thomas B. Jeffery Co. Nash used the occasion to introduce a totally redesigned line of big cars called Nash Golden Airflytes. These were partly styled by Italian designer Pinin Farina and had more conventional lines than the 1949-1951 models. The Statesman and the Ambassador again shared sheet metal from the cowl back. The 1952 Statesman had its wheelbase increased to 114-1/4 inches and the engine was stroked one-quarter inch to 195.6 cid. This increase in displacement boosted the Statesman engine's output to 88 hp at 3800 rpm.

NASH I.D. NUMBERS: The Vehicle Identification Plate located on the right-hand side of the cowl below the hood contains engine serial number and number codes for model, paint and trim. Engine serial number matches the serial number. Model number has four symbols. The first two symbols indicate model year: 52 = 1952. The third symbol indicates series: 0 = Rambler Utility; 1 = Rambler Super; 2 = Rambler Custom; 4 = Super Statesman; 5 = Custom Statesman; 6 = Ambassador Super; 7 = Ambassador Custom. The fourth symbol indicates body style. (All four numbers appear in Body/Style Number column of charts below). Engine numbers located on right-hand side of crankcase towards front and on front upper left-hand side of block. [NASH STATESMAN SERIES 40]: Serial numbers for 1952 Statesman models built at Kenosha were K-519001 to K-562291; for unassembled export KD-4301 and up; for El Segundo KC-37001 to KC-42976; and for Toronto KT-6101 and up. Engine numbers for the Statesman sixes were S-308001 to S-361836 for all assembly points. [NASH AMBASSADOR SERIES 60]: Serial numbers for 1952 Ambassador models built at Kenosha were R-656001 to R-691337; for unassembled export 6KD-3501 and up; for El Segundo RC-14501 to RC-18798. There was no Canadian production for this series. Engine numbers for the Ambassador sixes were A-165001 to A-205789 for all assembly points.

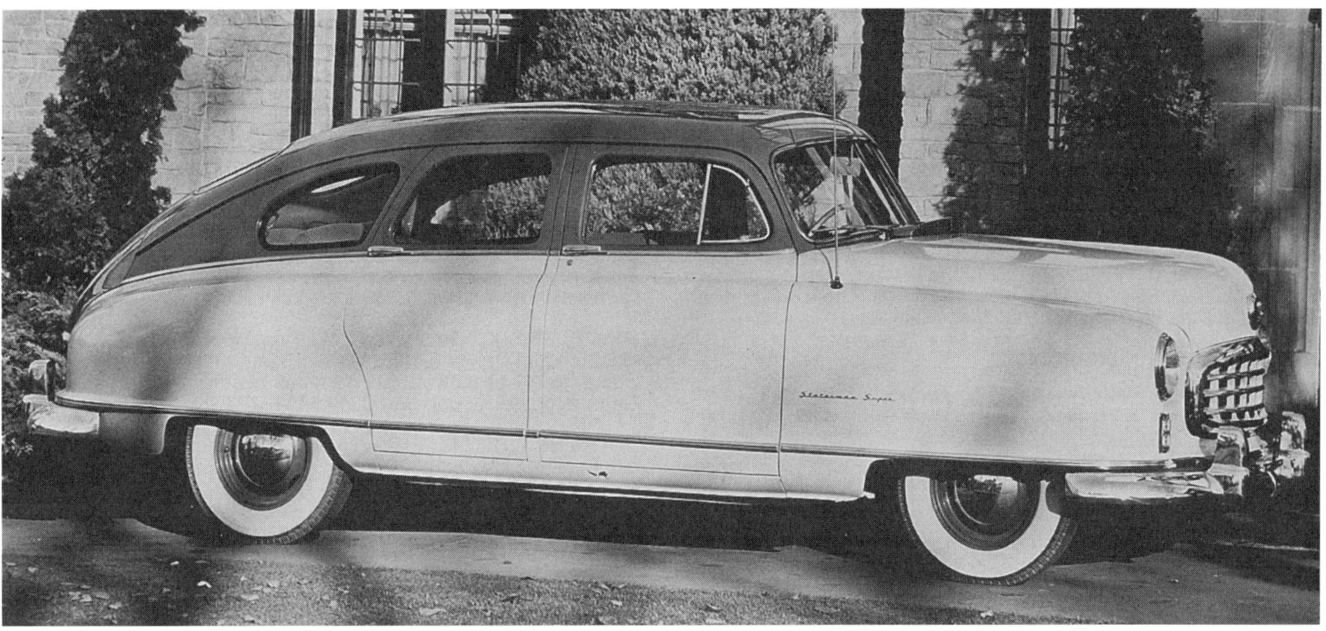

1950 Nash, Statesman Super (Series 40), sedan, OCW

1951 Nash, Ambassador Super (Series 60), sedan, OCW

1952 Nash, Rambler Country Club (Series 10), hardtop, OCW

1953 Nash, Rambler Custom (Series 10), convertible landau, OCW

1951 Nash, Ambassador Custom (Series 60), sedan, OCW

1953 Nash, Rambler Custom (Series 10), station wagon, OCW

1953 Nash, Ambassador Custom Country Club (Series 60), hardtop, OCW

[NASH RAMBLER SERIES 10]: Serial numbers for 1952 Rambler models built at Kenosha were D-79501 to D-127045; for unassembled export DKD-2301 and up; and for El Segundo DC-4101 to DC-8914. Engine numbers for all 1952 Nash Ramblers were F-85001 to F-139394. [NASH-HEALEY I.D. NUMBERS]: Serial numbers N-2001 to N-2109 were used on cars built at Warwick, England as 1951 models. Motor numbers were NHA-1001 and up. The beginning number for cars built at Warwick as 1952 models was N-2086. However, the beginning 1952 number was then followed by N-2103, N-2104, N-2106 and N-2200 with numbers following in sequence after N-2200. Engine numbers for 1952 were NHA-1088 and up, but did not necessarily follow each other in sequence. The model number for the Nash-Healey was 25162 (1951) and 25262 (1952). The first two symbols indicate the series. The third symbol indicates model year. The fourth and fifth symbols are the equivalent of a body/style number.

NASH STATESMAN SERIES 40

Model No.	Body/Style No.	Body Type & Seating	Factory Price	Shipping Weight	Prod. Total
SUPER LINE					
40	5245	4-dr Sed-6P	2178	3045	27,304
40	5246	2-dr Sed-6P	2144	3025	6,795
CUSTOM LINE					
40	5255	4-dr Sed-6P	2332	3070	13,660
40	5256	2-dr Sed-6P	2310	3050	1,872
40	5257	2-dr Cty Clb HT-6P	2433	3095	869

AMBASSADOR — SERIES 60 — (6-CYL) — The 1952 Nash Ambassador shared the same styling and design changes as the 1952 Nash Statesman, the major difference being the seven inch longer front end. The 1952 Nash Ambassador came in two series: Super and Custom. Supers had basic features. Customs added foam seat cushions; two-tone upholstery; electric clock; directional signals; chrome wheel discs; and front and rear courtesy lights. For 1952, the Ambassador engine was bored one-eighth inch, yielding 252.6 cid.

NASH AMBASSADOR SERIES 60

Model No.	Body/Style No.	Body Type & Seating	Factory Price	Shipping Weight	Prod. Total
SUPER LINE					
60	5265	4-dr Sed-6P	2557	3430	16,838
60	5266	2-dr Sed-6P	2521	3410	1,871
CUSTOM LINE					
60	5275	4-dr Sed-6P	2716	3480	19,585
60	5276	2-dr Sed-6P	2695	3450	1,178
60	5277	2-dr HT Cpe-6P	2829	3550	1,228

NASH RAMBLER — SERIES 10 — (6-CYL) — The 1952 Nash Rambler line received no major changes from 1951. Custom models came with the Nash "Weather-Eye" conditioned air system and a radio as standard equipment. The Greenbrier station wagon was an upgraded model with two-tone paint and richer trim.

NASH RAMBLER SERIES 10

Model No.	Body/Style No.	Body Type & Seating	Factory Price	Shipping Weight	Prod. Total
10	2204	2-dr Utl Wag-5P	1842	2415	1,248
10	5214	2-dr Sta Wag-5P	2003	2515	2,970
10	5221	2-dr Conv-5P	2119	2430	3,108
10	5224	2-dr Sta Wag-5P	2119	2515	19,889
10	5227	2-dr Cty Clb-5P	2094	2420	25,785

NOTE 1: Station wagon production included 4,425 Greenbriers.

NASH-HEALEY — SERIES 25 — (6-CYL) — The Nash-Healey sports car had a special two-passenger open body made of aluminum, an adjustable steering wheel and leather upholstery. The first Nash-Healey, model 25162, used the 234.8-cid Nash six and is sometimes called a "951" model. The second version, model 25262, switched to the 252.6-cid "LeMans" engine with dual carburetion. The English-built sports car's styling traits included a grille of outward curved vertical chrome bars entirely circled by a heavy chrome molding. There were model designations on the front fender and in back of the wheel opening. The full hood had a unique hatch cover (air scoop) at the center with a vertical grille at the opening. These cars were built at Warwick, England, and sold by Nash dealers. Styling by Pinin Farina was seen on 1952 models and late in the year, the more powerful LeMans engine was released. According to *Ward's Automotive Yearbook 1953* the official introduction date of the Nash-Healey, in the United States, was Feb. 16, 1951. Since the Nash-Healey was of foreign manufacture, it will not be covered fully in this catalog, beyond the data given below.

NASH-HEALEY SERIES N-25

Model No.	Body/Style No.	Body Type & Seating	Factory Price	Shipping Weight	Prod. Total
N-25	25162	2-dr Spts Conv-2P	4063	2690	104
N-25	25262	2-dr Spts Conv-2P	5909	2750	150

NOTE 1: Style 25162 is usually considered a 1951 model; 25262 is the 1952 model.

ENGINES:

(STATESMAN SIX): Inline. L-head. Cast iron block. Displacement: 195.6 cid. Bore and stroke: 3-1/8 x 4-1/4 inches. Compression ratio: 7.1:1. Brake hp: 88 at 3800 rpm. Four main bearings. Solid valve lifters. Carburetor: Carter one-barrel Model YF-824S.

(AMBASSADOR SIX) Inline. Overhead valve. Displacement: 252.6 cid. Bore and stroke: 3.50 x 4.375 inches. Compression ratio: 7.3:1. Brake hp: 120 at 3700 rpm. Seven main bearings. Solid valve lifters. Carburetor: Carter one-barrel Type WA (side-inlet).

(RAMBLER SIX) Inline. L-head. Cast iron block. Displacement: 172.6 cid. Bore and stroke: 3-1/8 x 3-3/4 inches. Compression ratio: 7.25:1. Brake hp: 82 at 3800 rpm. Four main bearings. Solid valve lifters. Carburetor: Carter one-barrel Model YF-757S.

(NASH-HEALEY SIX) Inline. Overhead valve. Displacement: 234.8 cid. Bore and stroke: 3.375 x 4.375 inches. Compression ratio: 8.0:1. Brake hp: 125 at 4000 rpm.

(LEMANS SIX) Inline. LeMans. Overhead valve. Displacement: 252.6 cid. Bore and stroke: 3.50 x 4.375 inches. Compression ratio: 8.0:1. Brake hp: 140 at 4000 rpm.

CHASSIS FEATURES: Wheelbase: (Statesman) 114-1/4 inches; (Ambassador) 121-1/4 inches; (Rambler) 100 inches. Overall length: (Statesman) 202-1/4 inches; (Ambassador) 209-1/4 inches; (Rambler) 176 inches. Front tread: (Statesman) 55-1/2 inches; (Ambassador) 55-5/8 inches; (Rambler) 55-3/8 inches. Rear tread: (Statesman) 59-11/16 inches; (Ambassador) 60-1/2 inches; (Rambler) 53 inches. Tires: (Statesman) 6.70 x 15; (Ambassador) 7.10 x 15; (Rambler Super) 5.90 x 15; (Rambler Custom) 6.40 x 15.

OPTIONS: Radio. Vacuum control antenna. Spotlight with mirror. Door-top outside mirror. Door mount outside mirror. Back-up lights. Fog lights. Nonglare rearview mirror. Visor vanity mirror. Curb-L-Arm. Custom seat covers. License plate frame. Exhaust extension. Protect-O-Mat for floor. Automatic windshield washer. Rear window wiper. Opto-shade for windshield. Vent shades. Outside windshield visor. Magnalite trouble light. Gas cap lock. Tissue dispenser. Bed mattress. Plastic screens. Rambler grille guard. Windshield washer. Rambler trunk guard. Trunk light. Rooftop carrier. Overdrive indicator. Visor pouch. Continental tire mount. Statesman 7.35:1 high-compression cylinder head. Ambassador 8.25:1 high-compression cylinder head. Rambler 7.6:1 high-compression cylinder head.

HISTORICAL FOOTNOTES: The 1952 Nash Ambassador and Statesman models were introduced March 14, 1952. The updated Rambler appeared on April 1, 1952. The Nash-Healey (sometimes considered a 1951 model) made its American debut as a 1952 Nash offering. Production hit a peak of 152,141 units or 3.51 percent of American auto sales. Model year production included 99,086 Statesman/Ambassador models and 55,055 Ramblers. Over 20 percent of all Nash products, or 28,950 cars, had Hydra-Matic Drive this year. The optional Warner Gear overdrive was installed in 74,535 units. The Nash-Healey took first place in its class in the French Grand Prix, at LeMans, plus a third place overall. These racing models used the LeMans "Dual-Jetfire" Ambassador engine, later released as a production car powerplant.

1953

NASH STATESMAN — SERIES 40 — (6-CYL) — The 1952 Golden Anniversary styling for the Statesman went almost unchanged for 1953. The only outward change was the addition of vertical chrome stripes in the fresh air intake just below the front windshield. Supers had basic features. Customs added foam seat cushions; two-tone upholstery; electric clock; directional signals; chrome wheel discs; and front and rear courtesy lights.

NASH I.D. NUMBERS: The Vehicle Identification Plate located on the right-hand side of the cowl below the hood contains engine serial number and number codes for model, paint and trim. Engine serial number matches the serial number. Model number has four symbols. The first two symbols indicate model year: 53 = 1953. The third symbol indicates series: 0 = Rambler Utility; 1 = Rambler Super; 2 = Rambler Custom; 3 = Statesman; 4 = Super Statesman; 5 = Custom Statesman; 6 = Ambassador Super; 7 = Ambassador Custom. The fourth symbol indicates body style. (All four numbers appear in Body/Style Number column of charts below). Engine numbers located on right-hand side of crankcase towards front and on front upper left-hand side of block. [NASH STATESMAN SERIES 40]: Serial numbers for the Statesman six were K-563501 to K-615291 for Kenosha; 4KD-4801 and up for unassembled export; KC-43001 to KC-47173 for El Segundo and KT-6901 and up for Toronto, Canada. Engine serial numbers were S-365001 to S-425053. [NASH AMBASSADOR SERIES 60]: Serial numbers for the Ambassador six were R-692101 to R-721686 for Kenosha; 6KD-3901 and up for unassembled export and RC-19001 to RC-21984 for El Segundo. Engine serial numbers were A-210001 to A-243959. (LeMans Dual-Jetfire engine numbers were prefixed by LMA. [NASH RAMBLER SERIES 10]: Serial numbers for 1953 were D-127501 to D-155727 for Kenosha-built cars; DKD-2701 and up for unassembled export and DC-9001 to DC-12299 for El Segundo. Engine serial numbers were F-140001 to F-166688 for cars without Hydra-Matic and H-1001 for cars with Hydra-Matic.

NASH STATESMAN SERIES 40

Model No.	Body/Style No.	Body Type & Seating	Factory Price	Shipping Weight	Prod. Total
SUPER LINE					
40	5345	4-dr Sed-6P	2178	3045	28,445
40	5346	2-dr Sed-6P	2144	3025	7,999
CUSTOM LINE					
40	5355	4-dr Sed-6P	2332	3070	11,476
40	5356	2-dr Sed-6P	2309	3050	1,305
40	5357	2-dr HT Cpe-6P	2433	3095	7,025

NOTE 1: Beginning in 1953, Nash often publicized FAP (factory-as-delivered prices) rather than ADP (advertised delivered prices) retail costs. FAP did not include federal tax and some preparation and handling charges, while ADP did. Earlier editions of this catalog reflected FAPs for 1953 and up models. This edition shows the ADPs based on March issues of industry trade journals through 1956.

AMBASSADOR — SERIES 60 — (6-CYL) — The 1952 Golden Anniversary styling from 1952 for the 1953 Ambassador went almost unchanged for 1953. The only outward change was the addition of vertical chrome strips in the fresh air intake just below the front windshield. The 1953 Nash Ambassador again came in two series: Super and Custom. Supers had basic features. Customs added foam seat cushions; two-tone upholstery; electric clock; directional signals; chrome wheel discs; and front and rear courtesy lights. In addition, a new dual carburetor LeMans Dual-Jetfire engine (similar to the engine used in the Nash-Healeys raced at LeMans and thusly named) was made optional on 1953 Ambassadors. This engine produced 140 hp at 4000 rpm.

NASH AMBASSADOR SERIES 60

Model No.	Body/Style No.	Body Type & Seating	Factory Price	Shipping Weight	Prod. Total
SUPER LINE					
60	5365	4-dr Sed-6P	2557	3430	12,489
60	5366	2-dr Sed-6P	2521	3410	1,273
CUSTOM LINE					
60	5375	4-dr Sed-6P	2716	3480	12,222
60	5376	2-dr Sed-6P	2695	3450	428
60	5377	2-dr HT Cpe-6P	2829	3550	6,438

NASH RAMBLER — SERIES 10 — (6-CYL) — The 1953 Nash Rambler was completely restyled for 1953 and distinguished by a lowered hood, single bar front grille and enclosed front and rear fenders. The new styling was credited to Pinin Farina and had many of the styling features of the 1952 and 1953 Golden Anniversary Ambassador and Statesman. Custom models came with the Nash "Weather-Eye" conditioned air system and a radio as standard equipment. Custom convertible and Country Club hardtop models included continental spare tire. Dual-Range Hydra-Matic became an option available for the first time on the 1953 Nash Rambler with Hydra-Matic-equipped cars receiving an engine with five more brake horsepower than manual transmission cars.

NASH RAMBLER SERIES 10

Model No.	Body/Style No.	Body Type & Seating	Factory Price	Shipping Weight	Prod. Total
10	2304	2-dr Deliveryman	—	—	9
10	5314	2-dr Sta Wag-5P	2003	2555	1,114
10	5321	2-dr Conv-5P	2150	2590	3,284
10	5324	2-dr Sta Wag-5P	2119	2570	10,598
10	5327	2-dr Cty Clb-5P	2125	2550	15,255

NOTE: Includes three Model 5306 — two-door sedan Deluxe.

NOTE: Includes 3,536 Greenbrier station wagon and 7,035 DiNoc station wagons.

ENGINES:

(STATESMAN SIX) Inline. L-head. Cast iron block. Displacement: 195.6 cid. Bore and stroke: 3-1/8 x 4-1/4 inches. Compression ratio: 7.45:1. Brake hp: 100 at 3800 rpm. Four main bearings. Solid valve lifters. Carburetor: Carter two-barrel WCD-2034S.

(AMBASSADOR SIX) Inline. Overhead valve. Displacement: 252.6 cid. Bore and stroke: 3.50 x 4.375 inches. Compression ratio: 7.3:1. Brake hp: 120 at 3700 rpm. Seven main bearings. Solid valve lifters. Carburetor: Carter one-barrel Type YH-895-S or YH-895-SA.

(AMBASSADOR "LEMANS" SIX) Inline. Overhead valve. Displacement: 252.6 cid. Bore and stroke: 3.50 x 4.375 inches. Compression ratio: 8.0:1. Brake hp: 140 at 4000 rpm. Carburetors: (front) Carter YH-973-S; (rear) Carter YH-974-S.

(RAMBLER SIX) Inline. L-head. Cast iron block. Displacement: 184.1 cid. Bore and stroke: 3-1/8 x 4 inches. Compression ratio: 7.25:1. Brake hp: 85 at 3800 rpm. Four main bearings. Solid valve lifters. Carburetor: Carter one-barrel Model YF-2014S.

(RAMBLER HYDRA-MATIC SIX) Inline. L-head. Cast iron block. Displacement: 195.6 inches. Compression ratio: 7.3:1. Four main bearings. Solid lifters. Brake hp: 90 at 3800 rpm. Carburetor: Carter one-barrel Model YF.

CHASSIS FEATURES: Wheelbase: (Statesman) 114-1/4 inches; (Ambassador) 121-1/4 inches; (Rambler) 100 inches. Overall length: (Statesman) 202-1/4 inches; (Ambassador) 209-1/4 inches; (Rambler Super) 176 inches; (Rambler Custom with continental tire extension) 185-3/8 inches. Front tread: (Statesman) 55-1/2 inches; (Ambassador) 55-5/8 inches; (Rambler) 55-3/8 inches. Rear tread: (Statesman) 59-11/16 inches; (Ambassador) 60-1/2 inches; (Rambler) 53 inches. Tires: (Statesman) 6.70 x 15; (Ambassador) 7.10 x 15; (Rambler Super) 5.90 x 15; (Rambler Custom) 6.40 x 15.

OPTIONS: Weather-Eye conditioned air system. Reclining seat and twin bed. Hydra-Matic automatic transmission. Automatic overdrive. Radio with twin speakers. Solex glass. White sidewall tires. Two-tone paint. Power steering (Ambassador only). Oil bath air cleaner. Rambler higher-compression engine with Hydra-Matic transmission.

HISTORICAL FOOTNOTES: Calendar year production amounted to 93,504 Nash models and 41,825 Ramblers. In calendar year 1953, Nash built 3,501 convertibles, 13,533 station wagons and 34,356 hardtops.

1954

NASH STATESMAN — SERIES 40 — (6-CYL) — The 1954 Nash Statesman carried over the 1952-1953 Golden Anniversary styling with a minor face lift of the body. Changes included a new front concave grille and new chrome headlight bezels. Continental rear tire carriers were added as standard on all Custom models. Also, new interiors and instrument panels on both the Statesman and Ambassador appeared for 1954.

NASH I.D. NUMBERS: The Vehicle Identification Plate located on the right-hand side of the cowl below the hood contains engine serial number and number codes for model, paint and trim. Engine serial number matches the serial number. Model number has four symbols. The first two symbols indicate model year: 54 = 1954. The third symbol indicates series: 0 = Rambler Deluxe; 1 = Rambler Super; 2 = Rambler Custom; 4 = Statesman Super; 5 = Statesman Custom; 6 = Ambassador Super; 7 = Ambassador Custom. The fourth symbol indicates body style. (All four numbers appear in Body/Style Number column of charts below). Engine numbers located on right-hand side of crankcase towards front. [NASH STATESMAN SERIES 40]: Starting serial numbers for the Nash Statesman were K-615501 for Kenosha; 4KD-5101 for unassembled export; KC-47201 for El Segundo and KT-9101 for Toronto, Canada. Starting engine serial numbers were J-1001 for 1954. [NASH AMBASSADOR SERIES 60]: Starting serial numbers for the Nash Ambassador were R-722501 for Kenosha; 6KD-4201 for unassembled export and RC-22001 for El Segundo. Starting engine serial numbers were A-246001 for 1954. [NASH RAMBLER SERIES 10]: Starting serial numbers for the 1954 Nash Rambler were D-171501 for Kenosha; DKD-3001 for unassembled export and DC-12301 for El Segundo. Starting engine serial numbers for the 1954 Nash Rambler were F-170001.

NASH STATESMAN SERIES 40

Model No.	Body/Style No.	Body Type & Seating	Factory Price	Shipping Weight	Prod. Total
SUPER LINE					
40	5445	4-dr Sed-6P	2178	3045	11,401
40	5446	2-dr Sed-6P	2130	3025	1,855
CUSTOM LINE					
40	5455	4-dr Sed-6P	2362	3095	4,219
40	5456	2-dr Sed-6P	2340	3050	24
40	5457	2-dr HT Cpe-6P	2468	3120	2,726

1953 Nash, Ambassador Custom (Series 60), sedan, OCW

1954 Nash, Statesman Custom (Series 40), sedan, OCW

1954 Nash, Statesman Super (Series 40), sedan, OCW

1954 Nash, Ambassador Custom (Series 60), sedan, OCW

1954 Nash, Rambler Custom (Series 10), sedan, OCW

1955 Nash, Ambassador Custom (Series 80), sedan, OCW

1955 Nash, Ambassador Custom Country Club (Series 80), hardtop, OCW

NASH AMBASSADOR — SERIES 60 — (6-CYL) — The 1954 Nash Ambassador, with a seven inch longer wheelbase than the Nash Statesman, shared the same changes as the Statesman for 1954. They included a new front concave grille and new chrome headlight bezels, new instrument panel and new interior. A continental rear tire carrier was standard on all Custom models.

NASH AMBASSADOR SERIES 60

Model No.	Body/Style No.	Body Type & Seating	Factory Price	Shipping Weight	Prod. Total
SUPER LINE					
60	5465	4-dr Sed-6P	2412	3430	7,433
60	5466	2-dr Sed-6P	2360	3025	283
CUSTOM LINE					
60	5475	4-dr Sed-6P	2595	3095	10,131
60	5477	2-dr HT Cpe-6P	2730	3120	3,581

NASH RAMBLER — SERIES 10 — (6-CYL) — The 1954 Nash Rambler received no major appearance changes for 1954. However, several new models were added to the lineup. New for 1954 were a four-door sedan and a four-door station wagon on a new, longer 108-inch wheelbase. Also added were a Deluxe and Super two-door sedan on the 100-inch wheelbase as low-line price leaders. To cut costs, radios and heaters were changed from standard equipment to options.

NASH RAMBLER SERIES 10

Model No.	Body/Style No.	Body Type & Seating	Factory Price	Shipping Weight	Prod. Total
10	2404	2-dr Utl Wag-5P	1444	2425	56
10	5406	2-dr Del Sed-5P	1550	2425	7,273
10	5414	2-dr Sub-5P	1945	2520	504
10	5415	4-dr Sup Sed-5P	1995	2570	4,313
10	5416	2-dr Sup Sed-5P	1865	2425	300
10	5417	2-dr Cty Clb-5P	1945	2465	1,071
10	5421	2-dr Conv-5P	2125	2555	221
10	5424	2-dr Sta Wag-5P	2095	2535	2,202
10	5425	4-dr Cus Sed-5P	2175	2630	7,640
10	5427	2-dr Cus HT Cpe-5P	2095	2515	3,612
10	5428	4-dr Cus Sta Wag-5P	2200	2715	9,039

ENGINES:

(STATESMAN SIX): Inline. L-head. Cast iron block. Displacement: 195.6 cid. Bore and stroke: 3-1/8 x 4-1/4 inches. Compression ratio: 8.5:1. Brake hp: 110 at 4000 rpm. Four main bearings. Solid valve lifters. Carburetor: Carter two-barrel WCD-2098S; or Carter YF-2137-S; or Carter YF-2137-SA.

(AMBASSADOR SIX) Inline. Overhead valve. Displacement: 252.6 cid. Bore and stroke: 3.50 x 4.375 inches. Compression ratio: 7.6:1. Brake hp: 130 at 3700 rpm. Seven main bearings. Solid valve lifters. Carburetor: Carter one-barrel Type YH-895-S or YH-895-SA.

(LEMANS "DUAL-JETFIRE" SIX) Inline. Overhead valve. Displacement: 252.6 cid. Bore and stroke: 3.50 x 4.375 inches. Compression ratio: 8.0:1. Brake hp: 140 at 4000 rpm. Carburetors: (front) Carter YH-973S; (rear) Carter YH-974S.

(RAMBLER SIX) Inline. L-head. Cast iron block. Displacement: 184.1 cid. Bore and stroke: 3-1/8 x 4 inches. Compression ratio: 7.25:1. Brake hp: 85 at 3800 rpm. Four main bearings. Solid valve lifters. Carburetor: Carter one-barrel Model YF-2014S.

(RAMBLER HYDRA-MATIC SIX) Inline. L-head. Cast iron block. Displacement: 195.6 inches. Compression ratio: 7.3:1. Four main bearings. Solid lifters. Brake hp: 90 at 3800 rpm. Carburetor: Carter one-barrel Model YF.

CHASSIS FEATURES: Wheelbase: (Statesman) 114.3 inches; (Ambassador) 121.3 inches; (Rambler 10) 100 inches; (Rambler four-door) 108 inches. Overall length: (Statesman) 202.3 inches; (Statesman with continental kit) 212.3 inches; (Ambassador) 209.3 inches; (Ambassador with continental kit) 219.3 inches; (Rambler 10 Super) 178.3 inches; (Rambler 10 Custom with continental tire extension) 185.4 inches; (Rambler four-door) 186.3 inches; (Rambler four-door with continental kit) 193.4 inches. Front tread: (Statesman) 55.5 inches; (Ambassador) 59.7 inches; (Rambler) 53.4 inches. Rear tread: (Statesman) 55.6 inches; (Ambassador) 60.5 inches; (Rambler) 53 inches. Tires: (Statesman) 6.70 x 15; (Ambassador) 7.10 x 15; (Rambler Super) 5.90 x 15; (Rambler Custom) 6.40 x 15.

OPTIONS: Rambler (general prices). Oil bath air cleaner ($7.50). Airliner reclining seats only ($111.45); and twin beds ($18). Air mattresses for twin bed ($15). Electric clock ($17). Two-tone color ($16). Directional signals ($16). LeMans Dual-Jetfire engine for Ambassador (N/A). Foam cushions front or rear ($10); both front and rear ($20). Solex glass ($19). Hydra-Matic transmission ($179). Overdrive ($104). Power brakes. Power steering. Radio and antenna standard. Rambler Custom steering wheel ($14); with overdrive power pass ($19.95). Heavy springs and shocks ($6). White sidewall tires, size 6.40 x 15 ($25). White sidewall tires, size 5.90 x 15 ($22). Upholstery options ($80). Electric window lifts (Ambassador only). Wheel discs, four ($21). Weather-Eye, standard Rambler; optional Statesman and Ambassador.

HISTORICAL FOOTNOTE: On April 22, 1954, Nash and Hudson merged to form American Motors Corp. The official date for the beginning of AMC was May 1. George Mason hoped to bring Studebaker and Packard into the new corporation as well, but he passed away before this could be accomplished. Nash, in 1954, was the first to introduce low-price air-conditioning systems to mass market automobiles. The system Nash invented for use then is the basis for all modern auto air conditioning systems. Previously, air conditioning was expensive and available only on expensive automobiles in limited quantities and filled half the trunk area. Nash's system was much more compact and easily serviced and integrated into the underhood area of the car. Calendar year production included 37,779 Ramblers and 29,371 Nashes. The total of 67,150 cars made Nash America's 13th largest automaker. Model year production was 62,911 units made to 1954 specifications. The LeMans "Dual-Jetfire" six was advertised as an engine "that has won many Grand Prix d'Endurance awards." In calendar year 1954, Nash was credited with building 6,065 hardtops, 11,800 station wagons and four convertibles.

1955

NASH STATESMAN — SERIES 40 — (6-CYL) — The 1955 Nash Statesman had a completely revised version of 1952's Golden Anniversary styling. A "Scena-Ramic" wraparound windshield appeared. Another new feature was a long character molding that ran from the front to the rear fender. The headlights were enclosed in a redesigned oval grille. The new concave grille had multiple chrome dividers. Custom models had the continental spare tire mount.

NASH I.D. NUMBERS: The Vehicle Identification Plate located on the right-hand side of the cowl below the hood contains engine serial number and number codes for model, paint and trim. Engine serial number matches the serial number. Model number has four symbols. The first two symbols indicate model year: 55 = 1955. The third symbol indicates series: 0 = Rambler Deluxe; 1 = Rambler Super; 2 = Rambler Custom; 4 = Statesman Super; 5 = Statesman Custom; 6 = Ambassador Super; 7 = Ambassador Custom. The fourth symbol indicates body style. (All four numbers appear in Body/Style Number column of charts below). Engine numbers located on right-hand side of crankcase towards front. [NASH STATESMAN SERIES 40]: Serial numbers for the Statesman six were K-635001 to K-649123 for Kenosha; 4KD-5401 and up for unassembled export; KC-48101 and up for El Segundo and KT-10501 and up for Toronto, Canada. Engine serial numbers were S-440001 to S-453100 for single-carburetor versions and J-30001 to J-33070 for dual-carburetor versions. [NASH AMBASSADOR SERIES 60]: Serial numbers for the Ambassador six were R-742901 to R-757866 for Kenosha; 6KD-4401 and up for unassembled export and RC-23001 and up for El Segundo, with no Canadian production of this series. Starting engine serial numbers were A-270001 to A-278691 for single carburetor Super Six and LMA-270001 to LMA-277002 for dual-carburetor versions. [NASH AMBASSADOR SERIES 80]: Serial numbers for the Ambassador V-8s were V-1001 to V-11444 for Kenosha; 8KD-1001 and up for unassembled export and VC-1001 and up for El Segundo. Starting engine serial number for all Ambassador Eights was P-1001 to P-11444. [NASH RAMBLER SERIES 10]: Serial numbers for Ramblers were D-205001 to D-276099 for Kenosha; DKD-3701 and up for unassembled export and DC-15001 to (Nash) DC-23326/(Hudson) DC-23325 for El Segundo. Engine serial numbers for all Ramblers were H-45001 to H-131414.

NASH STATESMAN SERIES 40

Model No.	Body/Style No.	Body Type & Seating	Factory Price	Shipping Weight	Prod. Total
SUPER LINE					
40	5545-1	4-dr Sup Sed-6P	2215	3134	12,877
CUSTOM LINE					
40	5547-2	2-dr HT Cpe-6P	2495	3220	1,395
40	5545-2	4-dr Cus Sed-6P	2385	3204	Note 1

NOTE 1: Custom four-door production included with Super four-door total, with no breakout available.

AMBASSADOR — SERIES 60 — (6-CYL) — The 1955 Nash Ambassador six received the same type of appearance changes as the 1955 Nash Statesman including: new wraparound windshield, new long character moldings from front to rear fenders; and headlights enclosed in a redesigned oval-concave grille.

NASH AMBASSADOR SERIES 60

Model No.	Body/Style No.	Body Type & Seating	Factory Price	Shipping Weight	Prod. Total
SUPER LINE					
60	5565-1	4-dr Sup Sed-6P	2480	3538	13,809
CUSTOM LINE					
60	5567-2	2-dr HT Cpe-6P	2795	3593	1,395
60	5565-2	4-dr Cus Sed-6P	2675	3576	Note 1

NOTE 1: Custom four-door production included with Super four-door total, with no breakout available.

NASH AMBASSADOR — SERIES 80 — (V-8) — The year 1955 marked the introduction of an overhead valve V-8 engine in the Ambassador line. The new powerplant was a 320-cid engine purchased from Packard. It was only available with Twin Ultramatic transmission. The 1955 Nash Ambassador V-8 was distinguished by V-8 emblems on its rear fenders and Ambassador (Custom or Super) V-8 emblems on front fenders. Styling was otherwise the same as on the Ambassador six.

NASH AMBASSADOR SERIES 80

Model No.	Body/Style No.	Body Type & Seating	Factory Price	Shipping Weight	Prod. Total
SUPER LINE					
80	5585-1	4-dr Sup Sed-6P	2775	3795	8,805
CUSTOM LINE					
80	5587-2	2-dr HT Cpe-6P	3095	3839	1,775
80	5585-2	4-dr Cus Sed-6P	2965	3827	Note 1

NOTE 1: Custom four-door production included with Super four-door total, with no breakout available.

NASH RAMBLER — SERIES 10 — (6-CYL) — The 1955 Nash Rambler received a minor face lift over 1954. New features included the addition of a new cellular grille and full wheel cutouts in the front fenders. Both Nash and Hudson marketed versions of the Rambler in 1955.

NASH RAMBLER SERIES 10

Model No.	Body/Style No.	Body Type & Seating	Factory Price	Shipping Weight	Prod. Total
FLEET (100" WHEELBASE)					
10	2504	2-dr Utl Wag-5P	—	2500	14
DELUXE (100" W.B. TWO-DOOR/108" W.B. FOUR-DOOR)					
10	5512	2-dr Del Bus Sed-3P	1328	2400	43
10	5516	2-dr Del Clb Sed-5P	1585	2432	Note 1
10	5515	4-dr Del Sed-6P	1695	2567	Note 1
SUPER (100" W.B. TWO-DOOR/108" W.B. FOUR-DOOR)					
10	5516-1	2-dr Sup Clb Sed-5P	1683	2450	8,979
10	5514-1	2-dr Sup Sub-5P	1869	2532	2,379
10	5515-1	4-dr Sup Sed-6P	1798	2570	15,998
10	5518-1	4-dr Sup Cr Cty-6P	1807	2675	Note 1
CUSTOM (100" W.B. TWO-DOOR/108" W.B. FOUR-DOOR)					
10	5517-2	2-dr Cus Cty Clb HT-5P	1995	2518	2,993
10	5515-2	4-dr Cus Sed-6P	1989	2606	Note 1
10	5518-2	4-dr Cus Sta Wag-5P	2098	2685	25,617

NOTE 1: Production included with same Style Number in other trim lines.

ENGINES:

(STATESMAN SIX): Inline. L-head. Cast iron block. Displacement: 195.6 cid. Bore and stroke: 3-1/8 x 4-1/4 inches. Compression ratio: 7.45:1. Brake hp: 100 at 3800 rpm. Four main bearings. Solid valve lifters. Carburetor: Carter one-barrel YF-22585.

(STATESMAN SIX DUAL CARB): Inline. L-head. Cast iron block. Displacement: 195.6 cid. Bore and stroke: 3-1/8 x 4-1/4 inches. Compression ratio: 8.0:1. Brake hp: 110 at 4000 rpm. Four main bearings. Solid valve lifters. Carburetor: Carter one-barrel, (front) YH-973S; (rear) YH-974S.

(AMBASSADOR SIX) Inline. Overhead valve. Displacement: 252.6 cid. Bore and stroke: 3.50 x 4.375 inches. Compression ratio: 7.6:1. Brake hp: 130 at 3700 rpm. Seven main bearings. Solid valve lifters. Carburetor: Carter one-barrel type YH-895-S.

(LEMANS "DUAL-JETFIRE" SIX) Inline. Overhead valve. Displacement: 252.6 cid. Bore and stroke: 3.50 x 4.375 inches. Compression ratio: 7.6:1. Brake hp: 140 at 4000 rpm. Carburetor: (front) Carter YH-973S; (rear) Carter YH-974S.

(RAMBLER SIX) Inline. L-head. Cast iron block. Displacement: 195.6 inches. Compression ratio: 7.3:1. Four main bearings. Solid valve lifters. Brake hp: 90 at 3800 rpm. Carburetor: Carter one-barrel Model YF.

(AMBASSADOR V-8) V-8. Overhead valve. Cast iron block. Displacement: 320 inches. Bore and stroke: 3-13/16 x 3-1/2 inches. Compression ratio: 7.8:1. Brake hp: 208 at 4200 rpm. Non-adjustable hydraulic valve lifters. Five main bearings. Carburetor: Carter two-barrel Model WGD.

CHASSIS FEATURES: Wheelbase: (Statesman) 114.3 inches; (Ambassador) 121.3 inches; (Rambler 10) 100 inches; (Rambler four-door) 108 inches. Overall length: (Statesman) 202.3 inches; (Statesman with continental kit) 212.3 inches; (Ambassador) 209.3 inches; (Ambassador with continental kit) 219.3 inches; (Rambler 10 Super) 178.3 inches; (Rambler 10 Custom with continental kit) 185.4 inches; (Rambler four-door) 186.3 inches; (Rambler four-door with continental kit) 193.4 inches. Front tread: (Statesman) 55.5 inches; (Ambassador) 59.7 inches; (Rambler) 53.4 inches. Rear tread: (Statesman) 55.6 inches; (Ambassador) 60.5 inches; (Rambler) 53 inches. Tires: (Statesman) 6.70 x 15; (Ambassador) 7.10 x 15; (Rambler Super) 5.90 x 15; (Rambler Custom) 6.40 x 15.

OPTIONS: [Rambler]: Rambler oil bath air cleaner ($8). Reclining seats ($11); with twin bed ($18). Air mattress for twin bed ($15). All season air conditioning ($345). Electric clock ($17). Two-tone color ($16). Directional signals ($16). Foam seat cushions, front or rear ($10). Foam seat cushions, front and rear ($20). Solex glass ($19). Hood ornament ($11). Hydra-Matic transmission ($179). Overdrive ($104). Radio and antenna ($76). Heavy-duty springs ($8). White sidewall tires, size 6.40 x 15 ($27). Black sidewall tires, size 6.40 x 15 ($37). White sidewall tires, size 6.40 x 15, six-ply tubeless construction ($70). Upholstery ($55). Vacuum booster pump ($3). Weather-Eye heater ($74). [Nash]: Radio. Electric antenna. Visor vanity mirror. Non-glare rearview mirror. Outside mirror. Spotlight and mirror. Wire wheel covers. Back-up lights. Windshield washer. Fog lights. Rear window wiper. Trunk light. Electric clock. Air mat. Hand spotlight. Plastic screens. Luggage carrier. Door top shades. Curb-L-Arms. Sola-cell cooling system. Dyna-Flyte dual plate distributor. Oil filter. Fuel filter. Gas filler guard. Hood ornament. Door edge guards. Exhaust extension. License plate frame.

HISTORICAL FOOTNOTES: Nash had a slow start in 1955, but, once started, moved along at a warm pace. The company wound up the model year with sales of 109,102 units. Calendar year output was 83,852 Ramblers and 51,315 Nashes for 10th place in the industry. Dealer contests and sales promotions were instrumental in stimulating deliveries. A total of 81,237 Nash/Hudson units were built, highest run for the line in history. An added feather in Rambler's cap was its consistent holding of number one spot in used car value, as reflected in *NADA* reports. Dealer introductions took place Nov. 23, 1954. Two new engines were introduced: the top-powered 220-hp Ambassador Jetfire V-8 with Twin Ultramatic and a Statesman six overhead valve powerplant. Model year production began October 1954 and included 40,133 Statesman/Ambassadors and 56,023 Ramblers. Calendar year production included 7,442 two-door hardtops and 28,163 station wagons.

1956

NASH STATESMAN — SERIES 40 — (6-CYL) — The 1956 Nash Statesman received a major face lift. The front and rear fenders were restyled. There were larger, more visible front running lights and, also, new taillights. A revised hood ornament and one-piece rear window were seen. Chrome side stripping revisions included a shallow "Z" shape on the side of the car and outline moldings on the hood and rear fender sides. The only Statesman model available for 1956 was the four-door Super sedan. Its engine was redesigned to an overhead valve configuration.

NASH I.D. NUMBERS: The Vehicle Identification Plate located on the right-hand side of the cowl below the hood contains engine serial number and number codes for model, paint and trim. Engine serial number matches the serial number. Model number has four symbols. The first two symbols indicate model year: 56 = 1956. The third symbol indicates series: 0 = Rambler Deluxe; 1 = Rambler Super; 2 = Rambler Custom; 4 = Statesman Super; 5 = Statesman Custom; 6 = Ambassador Super; 7 = Ambassador Custom. The fourth symbol indicates body style. (All four numbers appear in Body/Style Number column of charts below). Engine numbers located on right-hand side of crankcase towards front. [NASH STATESMAN SERIES 40]: Starting serial numbers for the Statesman six were K-649201 for Kenosha; 4KD-5701 for unassembled export and KT-11101 for Toronto, Canada. Starting engine serial number was DB-1001. [NASH AMBASSADOR SERIES 60]: Starting serial numbers for the Ambassador six were R-757901 for Kenosha and 6KD-4601 for unassembled export. Starting engine serial numbers were A-279001 for single carburetor versions and LMA-277001 for the dual-carburetor versions. [NASH AMBASSADOR SERIES 80]: Starting serial numbers for Ambassador Eights were V-11501 for Kenosha and 8KD-1101 for unassembled export. Starting engine serial number was P-21001 for Ambassador Eights. [NASH AMBASSADOR SPECIAL SERIES 50]: Starting serial numbers were U-1001 for Kenosha, UKD-1001 for unassembled export

1956 Nash, Ambassador Custom Country Club (Series 80), hardtop, OCW

1955 Nash, Rambler Custom Country Club (Series 10), hardtop, OCW

above and below, 1957 Nash, Ambassador Super Country Club (Series 80), hardtop, OCW

1957 (Nash), Rambler Custom (Series 20), hardtop station wagon, OCW

1957 Nash, Ambassador Super (Series 80), sedan, OCW

1957 Nash, Ambassador Custom (Series 80), sedan, OCW

and UT-1001 for cars built in Toronto, Canada. Starting engine serial number was G-1001 for all Series 50 Ambassador V-8s. [NASH RAMBLER SERIES 10]: Starting serial numbers for 1956 Ramblers were D-276101 for Kenosha, DKD-5601 for unassembled export and KT-5401 for Toronto, Canada. Starting engine serial number for all Ramblers was B-1001.

NASH STATESMAN SERIES 40

Model No.	Body/Style No.	Body Type & Seating	Factory Price	Shipping Weight	Prod. Total
40	5645-1	4-dr Sup Sed-6P	2385	3199	7,438

NASH AMBASSADOR — SERIES 60 — (6-CYL) — The 1956 Nash Ambassador six was available in only one body style, the four-door Super sedan. It shared all the styling changes of 1956 Statesman models on the seven inch longer wheelbase of the Ambassador platform. An Ambassador Super script appeared on front fenders.

NASH AMBASSADOR SERIES 60

Model No.	Body/Style No.	Body Type & Seating	Factory Price	Shipping Weight	Prod. Total
60	5665-1	4-dr Sup Sed-6P	2689	3555	5,999

NASH AMBASSADOR — SERIES 80 — (V-8) — The 1956 Nash Ambassador eight shared the same styling changes as the Ambassador six. The Super V-8 sedan was equipped and trimmed similar to the Super Six sedan. Customs had the name "Ambassador Custom" on the front fenders and "Ambassador Country Club" on the hardtops. On later production models, vertical chrome moldings are added to the front fenders of Customs. The V-8 was, again, a Packard-built engine, and a larger 352-cid displacement block was used. This engine was only available with Packard's Ultramatic transmission attached.

NASH AMBASSADOR SERIES 80

Model No.	Body/Style No.	Body Type & Seating	Factory Price	Shipping Weight	Prod. Total
80	5685-1	4-dr Sup Sed-6P	2956	3748	3,885
80	5685-2	4-dr Cus Sed-6P	3195	3846	Note 1
80	5687-2	2-dr Cus HT Cpe-6P	3338	3854	796

NOTE 1: Production of Super and Custom four-door sedans is counted as a single total with no breakout available.

NASH AMBASSADOR SPECIAL — SERIES 50 — (V-8) — The Nash Ambassador Special V-8 was introduced as a midyear 1956 model. It came out in April with a V-8 engine of AMC's own design and manufacture. The Ambassador Special was available in three models: a Super four-door sedan, a Custom four-door sedan and a two-door hardtop coupe. Supers had single side rub-rail moldings and chrome moldings across the front of the hood and fenders. Power brakes, an "Airliner" reclining seat and continental tire mounting were standard on Custom models. They also had double chrome side rub-rail moldings enclosing a separate color area and a chrome band across the front of the hood and fenders, down to the bumper wings. On later production models, vertical chrome moldings are added to the front fenders of Customs.

NASH AMBASSADOR SPECIAL SERIES 50

Model No.	Body/Style No.	Body Type & Seating	Factory Price	Shipping Weight	Prod. Total
50	5655-1	4-dr Sup Sed-6P	2355	3397	4,145
50	5655-2	4-dr Cus Sed-6P	2462	3418	Note 1
50	5657-1	2-dr Cus HT Cpe-6P	2541	3567	706

NOTE 1: Production of Super/Custom four-door sedans is counted as a single total with no breakout available.

NASH RAMBLER — SERIES 10 — (6-CYL) — The 1956 Nash Rambler received a major redesign of the long-wheelbase four-door sedan and station wagon. The short-wheelbase cars were dropped. (They would re-appear, with a few minor changes, as the 1958 American.) The 1956 models were totally redesigned on the outside, with a new oval-shaped grille housing the headlights located inside the grille. Running lights (front parking lights that stayed on even when the headlights were turned on) were set high in each front fender. They complemented the new rear fenders and revisions to the rear deck. Chrome trim and color treatments with three-tone color combinations were available and a wraparound rear window appeared. Also introduced was the first four-door hardtop station wagon. Nash production was discontinued at the El Segundo, Calif., plant.

NASH RAMBLER SERIES 10

Model No.	Body/Style No.	Body Type & Seating	Factory Price	Shipping Weight	Prod. Total
DELUXE (108" WHEELBASE)					
10	5615	4-dr Del Sed-6P	1829	2891	21,966
SUPER (108" WHEELBASE)					
10	5615-1	4-dr Sup Sed-6P	1939	2906	Note 1
10	5618-1	4-dr Sup Sta Wag-6P	2233	2992	21,554
CUSTOM (108" WHEELBASE)					
10	5613-2	4-dr Cty Clb Wag-6P	2491	3095	402
10	5615-2	4-dr Cus Sed-6P	2056	2990	Note 1
10	5618-2	4-dr Cus Crs Cty Wag-6P	2326	3110	Note 1
10	5619-2	4-dr Cus HT Sed-6P	2224	2990	2,155

NOTE 1: If two models have the same first four symbols in Body/Style Numbers the production of cars with different levels of trim is not separately broken out.

ENGINES:

(STATESMAN SIX) Inline. Overhead valve. Cast iron block. Displacement: 195.6 cid. Bore and stroke: 3-1/8 x 4-1/4 inches. Compression ratio: 7.47:1. Brake hp: 130 at 4500 rpm. Four main bearings. Solid valve lifters. Carburetor: Carter two-barrel WCD 2350S or Stromberg BVX-25 Model 380288. A 12-volt electrical system was used for the first time.

(AMBASSADOR SIX) Inline. Overhead valve. Displacement: 252.6 cid. Bore and stroke: 3.50 x 4.375 inches. Compression ratio: 7.6:1. Brake hp: 135 at 3700 rpm. Seven main bearings. Solid valve lifters. Carburetor: Carter one-barrel Type YH-2368S).

(LEMANS "DUAL-JETFIRE" SIX) Inline. Overhead valve. Displacement: 252.6 cid. Bore and stroke: 3.50 x 4.375 inches. Compression ratio: 7.6:1. Brake hp: 145 at 4000 rpm. Carburetor: (front/rear) Carter YH-2369S.

(AMBASSADOR/PACKARD V-8) Overhead valve. Displacement: 352 cid. Bore and stroke: 4 x 3-1/2 inches. Compression ratio: 9.55:1. Brake hp: 220 at 4600 rpm. Five main bearings. Hydraulic valve lifters. Carburetor: Carter two-barrel WGD-2231S.

(AMBASSADOR/AMC V-8) Overhead valve. Cast iron block. Displacement: 250 cid. Bore and stroke: 3-1/2 x 3-1/4 inches. Compression ratio: 8.0:1. Brake hp: 190 at 4900 rpm. Five main bearings. Nonadjustable hydraulic valve lifters. Carburetor: Carter two-barrel WGD.

(RAMBLER SIX) Inline. Overhead valve. Cast iron block. Displacement: 195.6 cid. Bore and stroke: 3-1/8 x 4-1/4 inches. Compression ratio: 7.47:1. Brake hp: 120 at 4200 rpm. Four main bearings. Solid valve lifters. Carburetor: Carter one-barrel Model AS-2349S.

CHASSIS FEATURES: Wheelbase: (Rambler) 108 inches; (Statesman) 114.3 inches; (Ambassador 50/60) 121.3 inches. Overall length: (Rambler) 191.1 inches; (Rambler Custom with continental kit) 198.9 inches; (Statesman) 202.3 inches; (Ambassador 50/60) 209.3 inches. Front tread: (Rambler) 57.8 inches; (Statesman/Ambassador 50 and 60) 56.6 inches. Rear tread: (Rambler) 58 inches; (Statesman) 59.7 inches; (Ambassador 50/60) 60.5 inches. Tires: (Rambler) four-ply tubeless, size 6.40 x 15; (Statesman) 6.70 x 15; (Ambassador 50) 7.60 x 15; (Ambassador 60) 7.10 x 15.

OPTIONS: (all models) Radio. Hood ornament. Outside mirror. Nonglare rearview mirror. Spotlight mirror. Back-up lights. Windshield washer. Air screens. Center pillar overlay (four-door sedan). Locking gas cap. Filler neck guard. Cross Country cargo straps. Power brakes. Exhaust extension. Curb indicators. Trunk light. Door top shades. Door edge guards. Rear window wiper (Statesman and Ambassador). Oil filter. Sola-cell. Seat belts. Rear door safety locks.

HISTORICAL FOOTNOTES: Dealer introductions of 1956 models took place on Nov. 22, 1955. Cars were sold by both Hudson and Nash dealers and the Series 10 models were known as American Motors Ramblers. The Hudson and Nash products were comparable, except for hood medallions and their "N" or "H" wheel cover insignias. The company's automotive division sustained a sizable loss while its appliance division enjoyed its most profitable year since 1950. During the year, the corporation completed the sale of idle plants and equipment (El Segundo, Calif., and the Hudson-Gratiot plant in Detroit) for a net amount of $5.3 million. Year 1956 saw production by American Motors of 104,190 cars (79,166 Ramblers, 17,842 Nashes, 7,182 Hudsons). American Motors Corp. produced its 2,000,000th single-unit construction car on March 27, 1956. Genuine leather trims were available in the following 1956 models: Ambassador Six and Ambassador V-8 sedans; Ambassador Country Club hardtop; Rambler sedan; Rambler four-door hardtop and Rambler Country Club station wagon.

1957

NASH AMBASSADOR — SERIES 80 — (V-8) — The Nash Ambassador for 1957 was available only with a 327-cid AMC V-8 engine in two-door hardtops and four-door sedans. Super and Custom trim levels were provided. The Nash Ambassador six and Statesman six were discontinued. The new Ambassador received a major face lift incorporating the first four-beam headlight system used on any U.S. car. Also seen was completely new front end styling, including a new cellular grille, front parking lights on top of the front fenders and new lightning streak side trim. The Ambassador Super had its name on the front fenders in script, small hubcaps and single lightning streak side trim with no upper beltline molding. Ambassador Customs had script with that name on the fenders, dual molding lightning streak trim and full wheel covers. This was the last year for Nash production.

NASH I.D. NUMBERS: The Vehicle Identification Plate located on the right-hand side of the cowl below the hood contains engine serial number and number codes for model, paint and trim. Engine serial number matches the serial number. Model number has four symbols. The first two symbols indicate model year: 57 = 1957. The third symbol indicates series: 1 = Rambler; 8 = Ambassador Super; 7 = Ambassador Custom. The fourth symbol indicates body style. (All four numbers appear in Body/Style Number column of charts below). Suffixes were added behind the four numbers on some models, as follows: 1 = Super; 2 = Custom. No suffix means Deluxe. Engine numbers located on right-hand side of crankcase towards front. [NASH AMBASSADOR SERIES 80]: Starting serial number for the Nash Ambassador was V-16501, with all Nash Ambassadors built in Kenosha. Starting engine serial number is N-1001. [RAMBLER SIX SERIES 10]: Starting serial number for the 1957 Rambler six was D-341001. Starting engine serial numbers were B-73001 for the standard engine and CB-2001 for the optional six-cylinder engine. [RAMBLER V-8 SERIES 20]: Starting serial number for the 1957 Rambler V-8 was A-1001. Starting engine number was G-7501. [RAMBLER REBEL SERIES 30]: Starting serial number for the Rambler Rebel was F-1001. Starting engine serial number was CN-1001.

NASH AMBASSADOR SERIES 80

Model No.	Body/Style No.	Body Type & Seating	Factory Price	Shipping Weight	Prod. Total
80	5785-1	4-dr Sup Sed-6P	2821	3639	3,098
80	5785-2	4-dr Cus Sed-6P	3011	3701	5,627
80	5787-1	2-dr Sup HT-6P	2910	3655	608
80	5787-2	2-dr Cus HT-6P	3101	3722	997

NOTE 1: Prices given for 1957 models are ADP figures from *Official Automobile Guide* (87th edition) effective Jan. 1, 1957.

RAMBLER SIX — SERIES 10 — (6-CYL) — The Rambler six for 1957 continued the 108-inch wheelbase with a few minor changes. Included were new vertical, front running lights, with horizontal bright metal dividers positioned below the headlights; a new wing-shaped ornament on top of the rectangular grille section and the elimination of side color accent trim running over the roof. Three series were again available. Deluxe models had the lowest level of trim and equipment and were essentially built for fleet customers. Super series models carried a single, full-length side molding with the word Super, in script, on the rear fenders. Deluxe models came with no series name or side moldings. The Custom series models came with Rambler Custom script on the front fenders and dual side moldings, with a round medallion at the forward end.

RAMBLER SIX SERIES 10

Model No.	Body/Style No.	Body Type & Seating	Factory Price	Shipping Weight	Prod. Total
DELUXE LINE					
10	5715	4-dr DeL Sed-6P	1961	1962	9,402
10	5718	4-dr DeL Sta Wag-6P	2291	3034	75
SUPER LINE					
10	5715-1	4-dr Sup Sed-6P	2123	2914	16,320
10	5718-1	4-dr Sup Sta Wag-6P	2410	3042	14,083
10	5719-1	4-dr Sup HT-6P	2208	2936	612
CUSTOM LINE					
10	5715-2	4-dr Cus Sed-6P	2213	2938	10,520
10	5718-2	4-dr Cus Sta Wag-6P	2500	3076	17,745

NOTE 1: The Deluxe station wagon, Style 5718, was for fleet use only.

RAMBLER V-8 — SERIES 20 — (V-8) — The Rambler, for 1957, was also available with a V-8 engine of 250 cid. The same four-door station wagon and sedan styles were offered with this brand new Rambler powerplant. Super and Custom trim levels were provided. Super series models carried a single, full-length side molding with the word Super, in script, on the rear fenders. Deluxe models came with no series name or side moldings. The Custom series models came with Rambler Custom script on the front fenders and dual side moldings, with a round medallion at the forward end.

RAMBLER V-8 SERIES 20

Model No.	Body/Style No.	Body Type & Seating	Factory Price	Shipping Weight	Prod. Total
SUPER LINE					
20	5725-1	4-dr Sup Sed-6P	2253	3223	3,555
20	5728-1	4-dr Sup Sta Wag-6P	2540	3359	2,461
CUSTOM LINE					
20	5723-2	4-dr Cus HT Sta Wag-6P	2715	3409	182
20	5725-2	4-dr Cus Sed-6P	2343	3259	3,199
20	5728-2	4-dr Cus Sta Wag-6P	2630	3392	4,560
20	5729-2	4-dr Cus HT Sed-6P	2428	3269	485

RAMBLER REBEL — SERIES 30 — (V-8) — The 1957 Rambler Rebel used the Ambassador 327-cid engine in a Rambler V-8 body. This limited-production car was available exclusively in light silver-gray metallic finish. It had black nylon and silver-gray vinyl upholstery. However, many of the cars were later repainted by dealers, due to excessive fading of the silver-gray paint. The 1957 Rebel featured a side molding of bronze/gold anodized aluminum, which ran the full length of the car. The four-door hardtop body style was the only one available. The Rebel was the first attempt by American Motors to build a high-performance car. In fact, this was the first time a large engine had been placed in a true intermediate-size chassis (an idea Pontiac would find great success with in the GTO) by any automaker. In an April 1957 *Motor Trend* test it was found that the only car capable of a faster 0-to-60 mph time than the Rebel was the fuel-injected Corvette. Fuel-injection had actually been planned for the 1957 Rebel with 288 hp possible. However, problems with the electric control unit prevented its production. Thus, a mildly re-worked 327-cid Ambassador engine was used.

RAMBLER REBEL SERIES 30

Model No.	Body/Style No.	Body Type & Seating	Factory Price	Shipping Weight	Prod. Total
30	5739-2	4-dr Cus HT Sed-6P	2786	3353	1,500

ENGINES:

(AMBASSADOR V-8) Overhead valve. Cast iron block. Displacement: 327 cid. Bore and stroke: 4 x 3-1/4 inches. Compression ratio: 9.0:1. Brake hp: 255 at 4700 rpm. Five main bearings. Hydraulic valve lifters. Carburetor: Carter four-barrel Model WCFB-2593SA. Equipped with dual exhaust and 12-volt electrical system.

(RAMBLER SIX) Inline. Overhead valve. Cast iron block. Displacement: 195.6 cid. Bore and stroke: 3-1/8 x 4-1/4 inches. Compression ratio: 8.25:1. Brake hp: 125 at 4200 rpm. Four main bearings. Solid valve lifters. Carburetor: Carter one-barrel Model AS-2580S.

(RAMBLER V-8) Overhead valve. Cast iron block. Displacement: 250.1 cid. Bore and stroke: 3-1/2 x 3-1/4 inches. Compression ratio: 8.0:1. Brake hp: 190 at 4900 rpm. Five main bearings. Non-adjustable hydraulic valve lifters. Carburetor: Carter two-barrel Model WGD-2352SA.

(RAMBLER REBEL V-8) Overhead valve. Cast iron block. Displacement: 326.7 cid. Bore and stroke: 4 x 3-1/4 inches. Compression ratio: 9.0:1. Brake hp: 255 at 4700 rpm. Five main bearings. Solid valve lifters. Carburetor: Carter four-barrel Model WCBF-2593SA.

CHASSIS FEATURES: [NASH AMBASSADOR] Wheelbase: 121.3 inches. Overall length: 209.3 inches (219.3 inches with continental tire mount). Front tread: 59.1 inches. Rear tread: 60.5 inches. Tires: 8.00 x 14. [RAMBLER] Wheelbase: 108 inches. Overall length: (station wagon) 193.6 inches; (four-door sedan) 191.14 inches; (four-door sedan with continental kit) 198.89 inches. Front tread: 57-3/4 inches. Rear tread: 58 inches. Tires: (six) 6.40 x 15; (V-8) 6.70 x 15.

OPTIONS: [AMBASSADOR] Power steering. Power brakes (standard on Custom). Powerlift windows. Weather-Eye heating and ventilating system. All-Season air conditioning. Airliner reclining seats (standard on Custom). Electric clock (standard on Custom). Oil filter. Oil bath air cleaner. Hydra-Matic automatic overdrive. Continental tire mount. Twin speaker radio. Whitewall tubeless tires. Solex glass. Back-O-Matic lights. Windshield washer. Special leather seat trim (Custom only). Two-tone paint. Three-tone paint (Custom only). Heavy-duty springs and shocks. Factory applied undercoating. Padded sun visors (standard on Custom). Dealer-installed seat belts. [RAMBLER] Six-cylinder engine with two-barrel carburetor and Power Pack (135 hp). Weather-Eye heating and ventilating system. All-Season air conditioning. Radio. Airliner reclining seats. Rear foam cushions (standard on all except Deluxe). Padded instrument panel and padded sun visors. Directional signals. Electric clock. Cigarette lighter (standard on all except Deluxe). Continental tire mount (not available on station wagon). Chrome wheel covers. Power steering. Power brakes. Automatic or overdrive transmission. Oil filter. Oil bath air cleaner on six-cylinder. Solex glass. Hood ornament. Special leather seat trim (Custom only). Back-O-Matic lights. Windshield washer. Size 6.70 x 15 tires. Heavy-duty springs and shocks. Seat belts. Travel rack leather straps. Child guard door locks.

HISTORICAL FOOTNOTES: Dealer introductions for the 1957 models were held Oct. 25, 1956. Calendar year production of 3,561 Nash automobiles gave the marque a .06 percent market share. The Rambler nameplate did somewhat better with calendar year production of 109,178 cars for a 1.78 percent slice of the pie.

RAMBLER 1958-1965

In many ways the 1958 and later models of the Rambler marked a second coming of the marque.
The history of the modern Rambler goes back to 1950, when it was offered as the first successful modern compact car. In 1954, American Motors Corp. (AMC) was formed when Nash-Kelvinator and Hudson merged. Just before the start of 1958, AMC decided to discontinue Nash and Hudson. Instead, it would concentrate on selling a revised series of cars, including a new version of the original Rambler compact.

By Larry Daum

Still affectionately known as the "Nash-Rambler" and heralded as such on the 1958 record "Beep Beep" by the Playmates, the little car enjoyed a fair amount of popularity in its new "American" identity (adopted because "Rambler" had become the name of a larger, fancier model line). Release of this "old-but-new" American was particularly well-timed. It came out immediately after a 1957 economic recession. As a result, high sales of the model increased AMC's industry market share substantially.
In 1958, AMC offerings included more than the just the American, though. The 1957 Rambler model was face lifted. It had a nine-inch stretch in wheelbase and overall length. The Ambassador was AMC's full-size car, continuing a model begun in 1932 by Nash. The Ambassador used the 327-cid V-8 formerly used in top-of-the-line Nashes, not to be confused with the unrelated Chevrolet 327-cid engine.
AMC was the only major U.S. automaker to increase sales in the recession year of 1958. Every other make was down substantially that year. The consumer trend was to smaller cars and the Rambler was the only U.S. compact car around. AMC was at the right place at the right time.
In 1959, the two-door station wagon was revived in the American line and slight styling changes were made to the Rambler, Rebel and Ambassador models. Rambler registrations doubled for 1959, as the introduction of the Studebaker Lark went virtually unnoticed at the AMC factory in Kenosha, Wisconsin.
Things got more competitive in 1960. New compacts were introduced by Ford, Plymouth and Chevrolet. AMC countered with a four-door American. All companies were emphasizing station wagons for 1960. AMC was right there too, with 14 of them, including three-seat models in all but the American series. As a result, AMC held its own for 1960 despite the threats from the "Big Three."
Even more competition came in 1961 as Pontiac, Oldsmobile, Buick and Dodge introduced new smaller cars. The intermediate-size models were called Rambler Classics for 1961. But the most exciting news from AMC was the completely face-lifted Rambler American series with a four-door station wagon and a convertible added. The American and Classic series came in three levels of trim: Deluxe, Super, and Custom. The Custom Classic had an overhead valve conversion of the Nash L-head six, plus a short-lived aluminum version of the same engine.
Two things disappeared from 1962 AMCs. One was an optional 250-cid V-8 in Classics. The other was the shrinking of the 117-inch Ambassador wheelbase. It now had the 108-inch span of the Classic, but trim and upholstery differences separated the two car lines. The Super line was discontinued as a middle-market designation and "400" identification was used for a new top-of-the-line model designation. Two-door sedans were added to the Classic and Ambassador series. It was the first time that Rambler offered the body style in this size car since 1957.
A two-door hardtop was added to the American Series for 1963. The Classic and Ambassador got completely new bodies. A restyling included all-new curved side glass. Wheelbases of the new models increased four inches, but overall length was shorter. Model names were revamped. Deluxe and Custom designations were replaced with numbers: American 220, 330 and 440; Classic 550, 660 and 770; and Ambassador 880 and 990.
In 1964, the Rambler American was completely restyled. It looked somewhat like Chrysler's famous turbine car. The wheelbase was increased to 106 inches. The Classic and Ambassador received a minor face lift, including new front grille and rear end designs. A special model of the Classic called the Typhoon was used to introduce AMC's new Torque-Command six-cylinder engine.
The 1965 American was little changed. Classics and Ambassadors got crisper lines in a major face lift. The Ambassador grew four inches in wheelbase and five inches overall. Convertibles were added to the Classic 770 and Ambassador 990 lines. Much publicity was devoted to the new Marlin, which was introduced as a midyear 1965 model and competitor to the Mustang and Barracuda. It was essentially the Classic with a fastback roof.
The Marlin and Ambassador continued in 1966, but the Rambler name was not applied to them. They were "AMC" models, now. Ads in magazines had blue and red stripes in the lower right-hand corner signifying the new brand name. The copy advised interested buyers to drive the car of their choice at their "American Motors/Rambler dealer."

1958

RAMBLER AMERICAN — (6-CYL) — SERIES 01 — The 1955 Nash Rambler was brought back into production as the 1958 American joining the model lineup in January. It had minor styling revisions. They included a small grille with a rounded-off rectangular shape and plain bodysides. A two-door sedan was the only model available and came in Super and Deluxe trim levels. The former featured bright metal windshield and beltline trim to distinguish it from Deluxe models. The 195.6-cid six was used, but had the water pump moved to the front.

RAMBLER I.D. DATA: Serial number under hood on firewall's right dash panel; right-hand wheelhouse panel. Six-cylinder engine number on upper left front corner of engine block. V-8 engine number on top at front of block; or front of block; or center, left side of block, above oil pan. [American] Starting serial number M-1001 for Kenosha, Wis. Starting engine number E1001. [Rambler Six] Starting serial number D-409001. Starting engine numbers B-145001 (standard engine); or CB9001 (power-pack engine). [Rebel] Starting serial number for the Rebel V-8 was A-16001. Starting engine number was G-24001. [Ambassador] Starting serial number for the Ambassador V-8 was V-27001. Starting engine number was N-17001.

RAMBLER AMERICAN SERIES 01

Model No.	Body/Style No.	Body Type & Seating	Factory Price	Shipping Weight	Prod. Total
DELUXE LINE					
01	5802	2-dr Bus Cpe-3P	1775	2439	184
01	5806	2-dr Sed-5P	1789	2463	15,765
SUPER LINE					
01	5806-1	2-dr Sed-5P	1874	2475	14,691

RAMBLER SIX — (6-CYL) — SERIES 10 — The Rambler Six received new front and rear fenders. It represented a major restyling of the 108-inch wheelbase Rambler body. The new front fenders featured quad headlights on all but Deluxe models, which had single headlights standard (dual optional). Several states still had laws against dual headlights. The Rambler's rear fenders featured small, restrained tailfins. This was a move towards conforming with current styling trends. The Rambler line was one of the last to add tailfins to its cars and one of the first to drop them. The Custom and Super models also featured new side trim moldings. All models had Rambler nameplates just above the grille. Custom models had Custom nameplates on the rear deck or tailgate, dual sidespear moldings on front fenders and both doors, with a single molding on the rear fenders. Sedans and hardtops had paint inside dual front moldings and wagons had simulated woodgrain trim. Super models had Super nameplates on front fenders and single full-length bodyside moldings. Deluxe models had no nameplates or side moldings. Deluxe models included directional signals, hood or fender ornaments, ashtray, baked enamel colors, fuel filter, bumper jack and wheel lug wrench and hubcaps. In addition, Supers had dual horns, step-on parking brake, cigar lighter and door armrests.

RAMBLER SIX SERIES 10

Model No.	Body/Style No.	Body Type & Seating	Factory Price	Shipping Weight	Prod. Total
DELUXE LINE					
10	5815	4-dr Sed-6P	2047	2947	12,723
10	5818	4-dr Crs Cty Wag-6P	2376	3056	78
SUPER LINE					
10	5815-1	4-dr Sed-6P	2212	2960	29,699
10	5819-1	4-dr Cty Clb HT-6P	2287	2983	983
10	5818-1	4-dr Crs Cty Wag-6P	2506	3069	26,452
CUSTOM LINE					
10	5815-2	4-dr Sed-6P	2327	2968	16,850
10	5818-2	4-dr Crs Cty Wag-6P	2621	3079	20,131

RAMBLER REBEL — (V-8) — SERIES 20 — The Rebel shared the styling of the Rambler six, with the biggest difference being the powertrain. Rebel Customs earned V-8 front fender emblems. New was a deep-dip rustproofing process. A wide side trim panel with a "half-speartip" front shape was used. It had a contrasting beauty insert step. Split fin hood ornaments were used on both Rebels and Rambler sixes, while side trim of the type described above appeared on Custom models up.

RAMBLER REBEL SERIES 20

Model No.	Body/Style No.	Body Type & Seating	Factory Price	Shipping Weight	Prod. Total
DELUXE LINE (FLEET)					
20	4825	4-dr Sed-6P	2177	3287	22
SUPER LINE					
20	5825-1	4-dr Sed-6P	2342	3300	2,146
20	5828-1	4-dr Crs Cty Wag-6P	2636	3410	1,782
CUSTOM LINE					
20	5825-2	4-dr Sed-6P	2457	3313	2,595
20	5828-2	4-dr Crs Cty Wag-6P	2751	3418	3,101
20	5829-2	4-dr Cty Clb HT-6P	2532	3328	410

AMBASSADOR — (V-8) — SERIES 80 — The 1958 Ambassador was built off of the 108-inch Rambler chassis by adding nine-inch longer front end sheet metal. The dropping of the Nash and Hudson names from the Ambassador was a last minute decision made by George Romney and American Motor's upper management. A number of cars were made with Nash and Hudson emblems ahead of the Ambassador nameplates on the sides of the front fenders. Factory photos exist that show the Nash Ambassador nameplates on these cars. Early factory literature also has noticeable airbrushing of the Nash emblems out of the catalogs. The 1958 Ambassador earned model identification just above the grille, on front fenders and on the rear deck lid. Side trim featured dual jet-stream side moldings, which were painted a contrasting color. The tone used for the insert harmonized with body colors used on Super models. Silver aluminum side trim was used inside the moldings on Custom models, which also featured model nameplates on the rear deck lid or tailgate. There were three bright metal windsplits on the rear window pillars of hardtops and sedans and on the wide pillars of station wagons. Super nameplates were on rear fenders of Super models.

AMBASSADOR SERIES 80

Model No.	Body/Style No.	Body Type & Seating	Factory Price	Shipping Weight	Prod. Total
SUPER LINE					
80	5885-1	4-dr Sed-6P	2587	3456	2,774
80	5888-1	4-dr Sta Wag-6P	2881	3544	1,051
CUSTOM LINE					
80	5885-2	4-dr Sed-6P	2732	3462	6,369
80	5889-2	4-dr HT Sed-6P	2822	3475	1,340
80	5888-2	4-dr Sta Wag-6P	3026	3568	2,742
80	5883-2	4-dr HT Wag-6P	3116	3586	294

BASE ENGINES

(RAMBLER AMERICAN) Inline, L-head Six: Cast iron block. Displacement: 195.6 cid. Bore and stroke: 3-1/8 x 4-1/4 inches. Compression ratio: 8.0:1. Brake hp: 90 at 3800 rpm. Four main bearings. Solid valve lifters. Carburetor: Carter Type YF-2014S one-barrel.

(AMBASSADOR) V-8: Overhead valve. Cast iron block. Displacement: 327 cid. Bore and stroke: 4 x 3-1/4 inches. Compression ratio: 9.7:1. Brake hp: 270 at 4700 rpm. Five main bearings. Hydraulic valve lifters. Carburetor: Holley four-barrel Model 4150C.

(RAMBLER SIX) Inline Six: Overhead valve. Cast iron block. Displacement: 195.6 cid. Bore and stroke: 3-1/8 x 4-1/4 inches. Compression ratio: 8.7:1. Brake hp: 127 at 4200 rpm. Four main bearings. Solid valve lifters. Carburetor: Carter Type YF one-barrel Model 2014S.

(REBEL V-8 ENGINE) V-8: Overhead valve. Cast iron block. Displacement: 250 cid. Bore and stroke: 3-1/2 x 3-1/4 inches. Compression ratio: 8.7:1. Brake hp: 215 at 4900 rpm. Five main bearings Solid valve lifters Carburetor: Holley four-barrel Model 4150C.

CHASSIS FEATURES: Wheelbase: (American) 100 inches; (Rambler and Rebel) 108 inches; (Ambassador) 117 inches. Overall length: (American) 178.32 inches; (Rambler and Rebel) 191.14 inches: (Ambassador) 200.14 inches. Add 7.75 inches to overall length for Rambler and Ambassador with continental tire carrier. Front tread: (American) 54.62 inches; (Rambler and Ambassador) 57.75 inches; (Rebel) 58.75 inches. Rear tread: (American) 55 inches; (Rambler) 58 inches; (Rebel and Ambassador) 59.13 inches. Tires: (American) 5.90 x 15; (Rambler six) 6.40 x 15; (Rambler Rebel) 7.50 x 14; (Ambassador) 8.00 x 14.

OPTIONS: Power brakes ($38). Power steering ($85). Air conditioning ($369). Weather-Eye heater ($72). Tinted glass ($27). Wheel discs ($16). Rearview mirror ($4). Two-tone paint ($16). Continental tire ($60). Undercoating ($15). Oil filter ($9). Reclining seat ($15). White-wall tires ($40). Manual radio ($58). Clock ($18). Deluxe push-button radio ($90). Rear foam cushion. Left outside rearview mirror. Custom steering wheel. Heavy-duty rear springs and shock absorbers. Windshield washer. Ambassador V-8 Power Saver fan. Power windows. Back-O-Matic lights. Inside anti-glare mirror. Padded instrument panel and sun visor. Dealer accessories: Seat belts. Travel rack straps. Child guard door locks. Three-speed manual transmission was standard. Overdrive transmission ($112.50). Flash-O-Matic transmission ($200). Push-button Flash-O-Matic transmission ($219.50). Rambler "Power-Pack" 195.6 cid/138 hp two-barrel engine. Dual exhaust ($18.50). Positive traction rear axle ($39.50). Oil bath air cleaner ($7.15). Heavy-duty radiator ($19.85). Available rear axle gear ratios (standard) 4.10:1; (optional) 4.44:1; 3.55:1 and 3.15:1. Size 6.40 x 15 tires for American.

HISTORICAL FOOTNOTES: The full-sized Ramblers were introduced Oct. 22, 1957, and the American appeared in dealer showrooms the same day. Model year production peaked at 162,182 units. Calendar year sales of 199,236 cars were recorded. George Romney was the chief executive officer of the company this year. R.D. Chapin was executive vice-president and general manager of the automotive division. The company made a $26 million profit after two straight years of losses. An expansion program was initiated by year's end.

1959

RAMBLER AMERICAN — (6-CYL) — SERIES 01 — The American continued as a compact model with the smooth, rounded styling that dated to 1954. Front fender namescripts revealed the American name only (as opposed to the previous year when Rambler American script appeared), but no side moldings were seen. The grille had a rectangular shape and was surrounded by a chrome housing with rounded corners. A fine, grid-type insert was used, the vertical members looking slightly more prominent. A round medallion was housed in the grille's center. Super models had bright metal trim around the windshield and rear window. A chrome molding decorated the upper beltline. Deluxe models had black rubber windshield and rear window trim and lacked belt moldings. A handful of panel deliveries were built off the station wagon platform. One style had glass rear side windows, the second had metal panels in the same location. The Super two-door sedan was rated for one more passenger than other noncommercial models.

RAMBLER I.D. DATA: Serial number under hood on firewall right dash panel; right-hand wheelhouse panel. Six-cylinder engine number on upper left front corner of engine block. V-8 engine number on top at front of block; or front of block; or center, left side of block, above oil pan. [American] Starting serial number M-32001 for Kenosha, Wis. Starting engine number E33001. [Rambler Six] Starting serial number D-516001. Starting engine numbers B-227001 (standard engine) or CB-36001 (power-pack engine). [Rebel] Starting serial number for the Rebel V-8 was A-26001. Starting engine number was G-34501. [Ambassador] Starting serial number for the Ambassador V-8 was V-41501. Starting engine number was N-32501.

RAMBLER AMERICAN SERIES 01

Model No.	Body/Style No.	Body Type & Seating	Factory Price	Shipping Weight	Prod. Total
PANEL DELIVERY LINE					
01	5904-7	2-dr Glass Dly	—	—	3
01	5904-8	2-dr Steel Dly	—	—	3
DELUXE LINE					
01	5902	2-dr Bus Sed-5P	1821	2435	443
01	5904	2-dr Sta Wag-5P	2060	2554	15,256
01	5906	2-dr Sed-5P	1835	2476	29,954
SUPER LINE					
01	5904-1	2-dr Sta Wag-5P	2145	2570	17,383
01	5906-1	2-dr Sed-6P	1920	2492	28,449

RAMBLER SIX — (6-CYL) — SERIES 10 — Rambler had new grilles, new arrangements of side trim and re-contoured rear tailfins. The new fender treatment blended the fins into the upper beltline in a smooth, down-curving line. On all models a horizontal gap ran above the upper grille bar and between the dual headlamps. Stand-up chrome letters spelling the word Rambler appeared in the gap. The manufacturer's name also decorated the deck lid tailgate. Custom models had Custom nameplates at the front of the rear missile-shaped side molding. A narrower, straight molding extended along the upper bodyside from just behind the headlamps to the missile-shaped molding. Super models had Super nameplates within the tip of the "missile." On these cars the straight front molding stopped just beyond the middle of the front door, without hitting the rear trim. Deluxe models had no series nameplates or side trim and dual headlamps were optional. The lower grille insert was of cellular-grid design.

RAMBLER SIX SERIES 10

Model No.	Body/Style No.	Body Type & Seating	Factory Price	Shipping Weight	Prod. Total
DELUXE LINE					
10	5915	4-dr Sed-6P	2098	2934	26,157
10	5918	4-dr Crs Cty Wag-6P	2427	3047	422
SUPER LINE					
10	5915-1	4-dr Sed-6P	2268	2951	72,577
10	5919-1	4-dr HT Sed-6P	2343	2961	2,683
10	5918-1	4-dr Crs Cty Wag-6P	2562	3082	66,739
CUSTOM LINE					
10	5915-2	4-dr Sed-6P	2383	2956	35,242
10	5918-2	4-dr Crs Cty Wag-6P	2677	3097	38,761

RAMBLER REBEL — (V-8) — SERIES 20 — The Rebel shared the same body styling features as the Rambler six. The major external difference was that the Custom models had Rebel V-8 emblems on the front fenders, ahead of the wheel openings. The scripts placed within the missile-shaped rear molding panel earned the name of the trim line, except on the plain-looking Deluxe models, which had no script.

RAMBLER REBEL V-8 SERIES 20

Model No.	Body/Style No.	Body Type & Seating	Factory Price	Shipping Weight	Prod. Total
DELUXE LINE					
20	5925	4-dr Sed-6P	2228	3283	113
SUPER LINE					
20	5925-1	4-dr Sed-6P	2398	3287	3,488
20	5928-1	4-dr Crs Cty Wag-6P	2692	3398	3,634
CUSTOM LINE					
20	5925-2	4-dr Sed-6P	2513	3295	4,046
20	5929-2	4-dr HT Sed-6P	2588	3338	691
20	5928-2	4-dr Crs Cty Wag-6P	2807	3407	4,427

AMBASSADOR EIGHT — (V-8) — SERIES 80 — The 1959 Ambassador retained the same basic styling seen in 1958, with changes being comparable to those seen on Rambler and Rambler Rebel. The wide gap above the upper grille bar had Ambassador spelled out in standup block letters. Similar lettering appeared on the deck lid or tailgate. Custom models had silver aluminum trim inside dual side moldings. ScotchLite reflecting sections were found on the rear face of the back fenders. The four-door hardtop had Custom Country Club written on the rear fender tips. Other cars, depending on trim line, read Custom or Super in the same spot. The front of the side trim spear had Ambassador lettering at its tip. The side trim, although similar to the Rambler type had more of a lightning bolt shape than a missile shape. The upper molding "zigged" (but the lower molding did not "zag") upwards, just below the rear side window. The Ambassador grille was distinctive in that it had a full-width horizontal central bar, instead of a cellular grid-type insert. The bar had a V-shaped dip at its center.

AMBASSADOR EIGHT SERIES 80

Model No.	Body/Style No.	Body Type & Seating	Factory Price	Shipping Weight	Prod. Total
DELUXE LINE					
80	5985	4-dr Sed-6P	—	3428	155
SUPER LINE					
80	5985-1	4-dr Sed-6P	2587	3428	4,675
80	5988-1	4-dr Crs Cty Wag-6P	2881	3546	1,762
CUSTOM LINE					
80	5985-2	4-dr Sed-6P	2732	3437	10,791
80	5989-2	4-dr Cty Clb HT-6P	2822	3483	1,447
80	5988-2	4-dr Cty Clb HT Wag-6P	3026	3562	4,341
80	5983-2	4-dr Crs Cty Wag-6P	3116	3591	578

BASE ENGINES

(RAMBLER AMERICAN) Inline, L-head Six: Cast iron block. Displacement: 195.6 cid. Bore and stroke: 3-1/8 x 4-1/4 inches. Compression ratio: 8.0:1. Brake hp: 90 at 3800 rpm. Four main bearings. Solid valve lifters. Carburetor: Carter Type YF-2014S one-barrel.

(RAMBLER SIX) Inline Six: Overhead valve. Cast iron block. Displacement: 195.6 cid. Bore and stroke: 3-1/8 x 4-1/4 inches. Compression ratio: 8.7:1. Brake hp: 127 at 4200 rpm. Four main bearings. Solid valve lifters. Carburetor: Carter Type YF-2014S one-barrel.

(REBEL V-8 ENGINE) V-8: Overhead valve. Cast iron block. Displacement: 250 cid. Bore and stroke: 3-1/2 x 3-1/4 inches. Compression ratio: 8.7:1. Brake hp: 215 at 4900 rpm. Five main bearings. Solid valve lifters. Carburetor: Holley four-barrel Model 4150C.

(AMBASSADOR) V-8: Overhead valve. Cast iron block. Displacement: 327 cid. Bore and stroke: 4 x 3-1/4 inches. Compression ratio: 9.7:1. Brake hp: 270 at 4700 rpm. Five main bearings. Hydraulic valve lifters. Carburetor: Holley four-barrel Model 4150C.

CHASSIS FEATURES: Wheelbase: (American) 100 inches; (Rambler/Rebel) 108 inches; (Ambassador) 117 inches. Overall length: (American) 178.32 inches; (Rambler/Rebel) 191.15 inches; (Ambassador) 200.15 inches. Front tread: (American) 54.62 inches; (Rambler/Ambassador) 57.75 inches; (Rebel) 58.75 inches. Tires: (American station wagon) 6.40 x 15; (American passenger car) 5.90 x 15; (Rambler six) 6.40 x 15; (Rebel V-8) 7.50 x 14; (Ambassador) 8.00 x 14.

OPTIONS

AMERICAN: Weather-Eye heater ($72). Oil-bath cleaner ($7.15). Oil filter ($9.30). Solex glass ($26.95). Front or rear foam seat cushions ($9.95). Reclining seat ($14.95). Manual radio and antenna with single speaker ($57.70). Size 5.90 x 15, four-ply rayon tires on sedans ($32.50); size 6.40 x 15 four-ply rayon tires on sedans ($52.80); size 6.40 x 15 four-ply rayon tires on station wagons ($36.05). Undercoating ($14.95). Windshield washer ($11). Wheel discs ($15.25). Electric clock ($15.25). Outside rearview mirror ($3.95). Inside tilt mirror ($4.95). Custom steering wheel ($7.70). Heavy-duty springs and shocks ($4.00). Two-tone paint on sedans ($15.95). Two-tone paint on station wagons ($17.95). Continental tire carrier ($59.50). Heavy-duty cooling system ($12.50). Three-speed manual transmission was standard. Overdrive transmission, in American ($102). Flash-O-Matic automatic transmission, in American ($179).

RAMBLER/REBEL: Flash-O-Matic push-button transmission with Rambler six ($199.50); with Rebel V-8 ($219.50). Overdrive ($112.50). Power steering with Rambler six ($69.50); with Rebel V-8 ($79.50). Power window lifts ($99.50). Power brakes ($37.95). Oil filter ($9.75). Oil bath air cleaner on Rambler six ($7.50). Radio with manual antenna and single speaker ($75.65); with dual speaker ($86.40). Weather-Eye heater and ventilator ($76). Size 6.40 x 15 four-ply tires on Rambler six ($35.90); size 6.70 x 15 four-ply tires on Rambler six ($48.30); size 7.50 x 14 four-ply tires on Rebel ($39.90). Wheel discs ($15.95). Two-tone paint on Deluxe sedans ($16.95); on Super sedans ($18.95); on Custom sedans ($22.95); on Super wagons ($18.95); on Custom wagons ($29.95) and on station wagon solid with Di-Noc ($49.95). Solex tinted glass ($33). Backup lights ($9.95). Continental tire carrier ($69.50). Front or rear foam cushion ($12.50). Reclining front seat ($25.50). Windshield washer ($11.50). Electric clock ($15.95). Padded instrument panel with visors ($19.95). Rambler six power pack ($19.50). Undercoating ($14.95). Left or right headrests ($12). Air conditioning ($369). Rambler Rebel V-8 Power-Lok differential ($39.50). Inside rearview mirror ($4.95). Outside rearview mirror ($5.25). Rebel dual exhaust ($15.50). Deluxe six-cylinder dual headlights ($23.50). Rear air coil suspension ($98.50). Self-adjusting brakes ($7.45). Three-speed manual transmission was standard. Overdrive transmission, in American ($102); all other models ($113). Flash-O-Matic automatic transmission, in American ($179), in Rambler six ($200); in Rebel V-8 ($220); in Ambassador ($230). Two-barrel carburetor, in Rambler six ($20). Power-Lok positive traction rear axle, in Rambler ($40); in Ambassador ($43). Heavy-duty air cleaner, in Rambler six ($8); in Ambassador (standard). Optional rear axle gear ratios available at no extra charge.

AMBASSADOR: Flash-O-Matic push-button transmission ($229.50). Overdrive ($114.50). Power steering ($89.50). Power window lifts ($99.50). Power brakes ($39.95). Radio and antenna with dual speakers ($91.90); on station wagons ($87.10). Weather-Eye heater and ventilator ($82.50). Size 8 x 15 four-ply rayon tires ($43.55); size 8 x 15 four-ply nylon tires ($67.30). Wheel discs ($16.95). Two-tone paint on Super and Custom ($22.95). Solid with Di-Noc on station wagons ($59.95). Solex tinted glass ($33). Backup lights ($9.95). Continental tire carrier ($76.50). Rear foam cushion ($14.35). Reclining front seat ($25.50). Windshield washer ($11.50). Electric clock ($17.95). Padded instrument panel and visors ($19.95). Undercoating ($14.95). Air conditioning ($398). Power-Lok differential ($42.50). Inside rearview mirror ($4.95). Outside rearview mirror ($5.25). Power-Saver fan ($19.50). Heavy-duty radiator ($8). Self-adjusting brakes ($7.45). Heavy-duty cooling system ($19.85). Dual exhaust ($18.50). Adjustable front seats ($20). Left and right headrests ($24). Three-speed

1958 Rambler, American Super (Series 01), sedan, OCW

1959 Rambler, Ambassador Custom Country Club (Series 80), hard-top sedan, OCW

1959 Rambler, American Super (Series 01), station wagon, OCW

1962 Rambler, Ambassador 400 (Series 6280), six-passenger station wagon, OCW

1965 Rambler, 990 Cross Country (Series 80), station wagon, OCW

1959 Rambler, Rebel Custom (Series 20), sedan, OCW

1961 Rambler, American Custom (Series 01), convertible, OCW

1965 Rambler, 660 Classic (Series 10), sedan, OCW

1965 Rambler, 880 (Series 80), sedan, OCW

manual transmission was standard. Power-Lok positive traction rear axle ($43). Heavy-duty air cleaner standard in Ambassador. Optional rear axle gear ratios available at no extra charge.

HISTORICAL FOOTNOTES: The full-sized Ramblers were introduced Oct. 8, 1958, and the Americans appeared in dealer showrooms the same day. Model year production peaked at 374,240 units. Calendar year sales of 401,446 cars were recorded. George Romney was the chief executive officer of the company this year. A record profit of $60,341,823 was earned. Rambler qualified as America's fourth-ranked maker. Resale value on Ramblers was considered high at this time, a point Rambler salesmen often stressed. America was in a recession and a small economy car trend had begun. Rambler benefited greatly, achieving net sales of $869,849,704.

1960

RAMBLER AMERICAN — (6-CYL) — SERIES 01 — Annual styling revisions included removal of upper beltline moldings from below the windows of all Americans. A new four-door sedan was introduced in this series. A rooftop luggage rack was standard on the station wagons. A minor change was an increase in the door opening angle, from 55- to 75-degrees. Supers had a horizontal front spear on the doors and fenders and American front fender scripts. Customs had a similar chrome spear and, like Supers, used chrome windshield and rear window surrounds. Deluxe models had no side trim or bright metal window surrounds. Custom, Super or Deluxe scripts appeared at the rear of all cars and all had either American or Rambler American scripts on the front fendersides.

RAMBLER I.D. DATA: VIN on plate on right wheelhouse panel below hood. First symbol identified series: A=Rebel V-8; B=American; C=Rambler; H=Ambassador. Second through fifth symbols were sequential production number. Starting serial numbers were: [American] B-100001; [American for knocked-down export] BK-10001; [Rambler] C-100001; [Rambler for knocked-down export] CK-10001; [Rebel V-8] A-100001; [Rebel V-8 for knocked-down export] AK-10001; [Ambassador V-8] H-100001; [Ambassador V-8 for knocked-down export] HK-10001. Body number plate riveted to left front door hinge pillar has additional data. First line indicates body production sequence number. Second line indicates "Model No." consisting of first two symbols indicating model year and additional symbols indicating body style and series. Complete "Model No." corresponds to column two of charts below. Third line gives trim data. Fourth line gives paint color data. Six-cylinder engine number on upper left front corner of engine block. V-8 engine number on top at front of block; or front of block; or center, left side of block, above oil pan. Starting in late 1959 for the 1960 model year AMC discontinued engine serial numbers. An "Engine Day Build Code" system gave all engines of a type the same six symbol code. The first symbol of the engine day build code is a single digit number code for the year of manufacture starting with 1=1959; 2=1960; 3=1961; 4=1962; 5=1963; 6=1964; 7=1965; etc. The second and third symbols indicated month of build: 01=Jan.; 02=Feb.; etc. The numbers differed in the fourth symbol, a letter code designating the engine displacement and carburetion. Letter codes were: A=195.6 cid/90 hp L-head six; B=195.6 cid/127 hp aluminum OHV six; C=195.6 cid/127 hp cast-iron OHV six; D=195.6 cid/138 hp six 2V; E=327 cid/250 hp V-8 2V; F=327 cid/270 hp V-8 4V; G="287" engine. The fifth and sixth symbols indicated day of manufacture as appropriate. In engine number 201A22: first symbol 2=1960; 01=Jan.; A=195.6 cid/90 hp six and 22=22nd day of month.

RAMBLER AMERICAN SERIES 01

Model No.	Body/Style No.	Body Type & Seating	Factory Price	Shipping Weight	Prod. Total
DELUXE LINE					
01	6005	4-dr Sed-5P	1844	2474	22,593
01	6006	2-dr Sed-5P	1795	2451	23,960
01	6004	2-dr Sta Wag-5P	2020	2527	12,290
01	6002	2-dr Bus Cpe-3P	1781	2428	630
SUPER LINE					
01	6005-1	4-dr Sed-6P	1929	2490	21,108
01	6006-1	2-dr Sed-5P	1880	2462	17,233
01	6004-1	2-dr Sta Wag-6P	2105	2549	15,093
CUSTOM LINE					
01	6005-2	4-dr Sed-6P	2059	2551	3,272
01	6006-2	2-dr Sed-5P	2010	2523	2,994
01	6004-2	2-dr Sta Wag-5P	2235	2606	1,430

RAMBLER SIX — (6-CYL) — SERIES 10 — The Rambler's tailfins were lowered and canted out slightly. A convex lower rear fender contour was new. The Rambler grille was redesigned. It had two rows of "cells" in its gridwork, instead of three. Stand-up chrome letters still spelled out Rambler in the horizontal space between the head lamps, above the grille. The word Rambler was also on the rear. Customs had a suitable script on the rear also, plus full-length trim moldings that widened into dual moldings between the wheel housings. Supers had different model identifying scripts at the rear and full-length side trim moldings. Deluxe models had suitable rear scripts, but no side trim. Dual headlamps were optional on Deluxe models. On all lines, the twin fin hood ornaments of the past were gone and were not replaced.

RAMBLER SIX SERIES 10

Model No.	Body/Style No.	Body Type & Seating	Factory Price	Shipping Weight	Prod. Total
DELUXE LINE					
10	6015	4-dr Sed-6P	2098	2912	37,666
10	6018	4-dr Sta Wag-6P	2427	3051	24,001
SUPER LINE					
10	6015-1	4-dr Sed-6P	2268	2930	88,004
10	6018-1	4-dr Sta Wag-6P	2562	3054	59,491
10	6018-3	4-dr Sta Wag-8P	2687	3117	8,456
CUSTOM LINE					
10	6015-2	4-dr Sed-6P	2883	2929	38,003
10	6910-2	4-dr HT Sed-6P	2458	2981	3,937
10	6018-2	4-dr Sta Wag-6P	2677	3057	32,092
10	6018-4	4-dr Sta Wag-8P	2802	3137	5,718

RAMBLER REBEL — (V-8) — SERIES 20 — Rebels had the same general styling changes as Rambler sixes. They included lower, canted fins; convex rear fenders; grille with two rows of cellular grids; side trim revisions; and deletion of hood ornaments. Rambler sales features for 1960 included single unit-body construction; deep-dip rustproofing; deep coil spring ride; self-adjusting brakes (optional); push-button automatic gear shift selection (optional), and "Air Liner" reclining seats (optional). Rebel V-8 emblems appeared on front fenders again this year. A new base powerplant was used. The former 215-hp four-barrel V-8 (with standard dual exhaust) became optional. A number of Ramblers were built for export this year. These cars were shipped overseas in completely knocked-down (CKD) form, or in other words, unassembled. This meant that the importing country was providing employment for workers who would assemble the cars there. Such cars had a two symbol alphabetical serial number prefix, with the second letter "K" indicating "CKD" sales.

RAMBLER REBEL V-8 SERIES 20

Model No.	Body/Style No.	Body Type & Seating	Factory Price	Shipping Weight	Prod. Total
DELUXE LINE					
20	6025	4-dr Flt Sed-6P	2217	3252	143
SUPER LINE					
20	6025-1	4-dr Sed-6P	2387	3270	3,826
20	6028-1	4-dr Sta Wag-6P	2681	3391	3,328
20	6028-3	4-dr Sta Wag-8P	2806	3446	718
CUSTOM LINE					
20	6025-2	4-dr Sed-6P	2502	3278	3,969
20	6029-2	4-dr HT Sed-6P	2577	3319	579
20	6028-2	4-dr Sta Wag-6P	2796	3395	3,613
20	6028-4	4-dr Sta Wag-8P	2921	3447	886

AMBASSADOR SERIES — (V-8) — SERIES 80 — On the top-line series the letters above the grille spelled Ambassador, a name that appeared on the deck lid or tailgate as well. This series featured the new compound wraparound windshield and a distinctive grille design. Fashioned of aluminum, the lower insert ran fully across the car with a pattern of medium-sized square openings stamped out of the metal. Bombsight style front fender ornaments were seen. Side trim consisted of dual moldings running in a tapering line from the middle of the extreme rear body corner and coming to a point just in back of the dual headlamps. On Customs an aluminum beauty panel insert was placed within the moldings and, on all models, the word Ambassador appeared at the tip. In addition, scripts placed on the deck lid of passenger models or tailgate of station wagons identified Supers or Customs. Foam rear seat cushions, full wheel discs, electric clock, padded dashboard and padded sun visors were standard on Customs. A low-cost Deluxe sedan was built in limited numbers for fleet use only and not cataloged with regular cars.

AMBASSADOR EIGHT SERIES 80

Model No.	Body/Style No.	Body Type & Seating	Factory Price	Shipping Weight	Prod. Total
DELUXE LINE					
80	6085	4-dr Flt Sed-6P	2395	3384	302
SUPER LINE					
80	6085-1	4-dr Sed-6P	2587	3395	3,990
80	6088-1	4-dr Sta Wag-6P	2881	3531	1,342
80	6088-3	4-dr Sta Wag-8P	3006	3581	637
CUSTOM LINE					
80	6085-2	4-dr Sed-6P	2732	3408	10,949
80	6089-2	4-dr Cty Clb HT-6P	2822	3465	1,141
80	6088-2	4-dr Sta Wag-6P	3026	3538	3,849
80	6083-2	4-dr Cty Clb HT Wag-6P	3116	3583	435
80	6088-4	4-dr Sta Wag-8P	3151	3592	1,153

BASE ENGINES

(RAMBLER AMERICAN) Inline, L-head Six: Cast iron block. Displacement: 195.6 cid. Bore and stroke: 3-1/8 x 4-1/4 inches. Compression ratio: 8.0:1. Brake hp: 90 at 3800 rpm. Four main bearings. Solid valve lifters. Carburetor: Carter Type YF-2014S one-barrel.

(RAMBLER SIX) Inline Six: Overhead valve. Cast iron block. Displacement: 195.6 cid. Bore and stroke: 3-1/8 x 4-1/4 inches. Compression ratio: 8.7:1. Brake hp: 127 at 4200 rpm. Four main bearings. Solid valve lifters. Carburetor: Holley model 1904-FC one-barrel.

(REBEL V-8) V-8: Overhead valve. Cast iron block. Displacement: 250 cid. Bore and stroke: 3-1/2 x 3-1/4 inches. Compression ratio: 8.7:1. Brake hp: 200 at 4900 rpm. Five main bearings. Hydraulic valve lifters. Carburetor: Holley model 2040 two-barrel.

(AMBASSADOR EIGHT) V-8: Overhead valve. Cast iron block. Displacement: 327 cid. Bore and stroke: 4 x 3-1/4 inches. Compression ratio: 8.7:1. Brake hp: 250 at 4700 rpm. Five main bearings. Hydraulic valve lifters. Carburetor: Holley model 2040 two-barrel.

CHASSIS FEATURES: Wheelbase: (American) 100 inches; (Rambler/Rebel) 108 inches; (Ambassador) 117 inches. Overall length: (American) 178.32 inches; (Rambler/Rebel) 189.5 inches; (Ambassador) 198.5 inches. Front tread: (American) 54.6 inches; (Rambler/Rebel) 58.75 inches; (Ambassador) 57.75 inches. Rear tread: (American) 55.0 inches; (Rambler/Rebel) 59.13 inches; (Ambassador) 59.13 inches. Tires: (American standard passenger car) 5.90 x 15, (American Custom and station wagon) 6.40 x 15; (Rambler six) 6.40 x 15; (Rambler/Rebel) 7.50 x 14; (Ambassador) 8.00 x 14.

OPTIONS

AMERICAN: Anti-freeze ($3.80). Two-tone color on sedans ($15.95), on station wagons ($17.95); special application (except Fleet) ($29.50). Overdrive transmission ($102). Lever control Flash-O-Matic transmission ($178.50). Weather-Eye ($72). Power steering ($69.50). Oil bath air cleaner ($7.15). Oil filter ($9.30). Solex glass ($26.95). Front and rear Deluxe foam rubber seat cushions ($19.90); front only ($9.95); rear only ($9.95). Reclining seat ($14.65). Manual radio and antenna ($57.70). Size 5.90 x 15 four-ply rayon white sidewall tires on sedans ($27.40); size 6.40 x 15 four-ply rayon white sidewall tires on sedans ($44.45); size 6.40 x 15 four-ply nylon white sidewall tires on sedans ($60.80); size 6.40 x 15 four-ply rayon white sidewall tires on sedans ($30.35); size 6.40 x 15 four-ply nylon white sidewall tires on wagons ($46.70). Undercoating ($14.95). Windshield washer ($11). Back-up lights ($9.95); Wheel discs ($15.25). Electric clock ($15.25). Continental tire carrier on sedans ($59.50). Self-adjusting brakes ($7.45). Inside "tilt" rearview mirror ($4.95). Outside left or right rearview mirror ($3.95); left and right ($7.90). Custom steering wheel ($7.70). Twin-Grip differential ($29.50). Pair of license plate frames ($4.05); rear only ($2.05). Heavy-duty front and rear shocks ($2.70). Heavy-duty front and rear shocks and rear springs ($4). Heavy-duty radiator ($3.00). Heavy-duty cooling system ($12.50). Three-speed manual transmission was standard. Overdrive transmission ($102). Automatic transmission ($179). Custom American six-cylinder 195.6 cid/125 hp two-barrel engine. Heavy-duty air cleaner. Available rear axle gear ratios.

RAMBLER/REBEL: Flash-O-Matic push-button transmission on Rambler six ($199.50), on Rebel V-8 ($219.50). Overdrive ($112.50). Power steering on Rambler six ($69.50); on Rebel V-8 ($79.50). Power window lifts ($99.50). Power brakes ($37.95). Oil filter ($9.75). Oil-bath air cleaner on Rambler six ($7.50). Radio with manual antenna and single speaker ($75.65); with dual speaker ($86.40). Weather-Eye heater and ventilator ($76). Solex tinted glass ($33). Back-up lights ($9.95). Continental tire carrier ($69.50). Front or rear foam cushion ($12.50); reclining front seat ($25.50). Windshield washer ($11.50). Electric clock ($15.95). Padded instrument panel and visors ($19.95). Undercoating ($14.95). Left or right headrests ($12). Air conditioning ($369). Inside rearview mirror ($4.95). Outside rearview mirror ($5.25). Deluxe six-cylinder dual headlights ($23.50). Rear air coil suspension ($98.50). Self-adjusting brakes ($7.45). Wheel discs ($15.95). Twin-Grip differential on six-cylinder ($34.50), on V-8 ($39.50). Parking brake warning light ($3.95). Light package including trunk or cargo, two courtesy, parking and brake warning lights ($9.95). Two-tone paint on sedans, except Custom ($19.95); two-tone paint on Custom ($24.95); two-tone paint on wagons except Custom ($21.95), two-tone paint on Custom wagons ($29.95) solid with Di-Noc ($59.95). Power Pak on six-cylinder ($19.50); on V-8 ($37.50). Size 6.40 x 15 rayon white sidewall four-ply tires on six-cylinder except three-seat wagon ($30.30), size 6.40 x 15 nylon ($46.70), size 6.70 x 15 rayon ($40.50). Size 7.50 x 14 white sidewall four-ply tires on V-8 except three-seat wagon ($32.10); size 7.50 x 14 nylon ($49.15). Size 6.40 x 15 nylon white sidewall four-ply Captive Air for three-seat wagons on six-cylinder ($28.10); size 7.50 x 14 nylon four-ply on V-8 ($29.50). Three-speed manual transmission was standard. Overdrive transmission ($113). Automatic transmission ($200). Rebel V-8 250 cid/215 hp four-barrel engine ($80). Positive traction rear axle available at extra cost. Heavy-duty air cleaner available on some as standard equipment, others as extra cost. Available rear axle gear ratios.

AMBASSADOR: Overdrive transmission ($114.50). Push-button Flash-O-Matic transmission ($229.50). Power Pack ($229.50). Weather-Eye ($37.50). Air conditioning and heavy-duty cooling system ($398.00). Power brakes ($39.95). Power steering ($89.50). Power window lifts ($99.50). Solex glass ($99.50). Front foam rubber seat cushions ($14.35). Rear foam rubber seat cushions ($14.35). Reclining seat ($25.50). Left and right headrests ($24). Left or right headrest ($12). Individually adjustable front seats ($20). Radio and antenna with front speakers for wagons ($75.65); for sedans ($91.90). Size 8.00 x 14 white sidewall rayon four-ply tires for station wagons (except three-seat wagon) ($35.25); size 8.00 x 14 white sidewall nylon four-ply ($54.15), Captive Air nylon tires, size 8.00 x 14 white sidewall (four tires) ($113.70); size 8.00 x 14 white sidewall (five tires) ($169.45); size 8.00 x 14 white sidewall for three-seat wagons ($32.40). Undercoating ($14.95). Windshield washer ($11.50). Back-up lights ($9.95). Wheel discs ($16.95). Electric clock ($16.95). Parking brake warning light ($3.95). Padded instrument panel and sun visors ($19.95). Self-adjusting brakes ($7.45). Inside "tilt" rearview mirror ($4.95). Left or right outside rearview mirror ($5.25); Left and right outside rearview mirrors ($10.50). Power-Saver fan ($19.50). Twin-Grip differential ($42.50). Pair of license plate frames ($4.05); rear only ($2.05). Light package ($9.95). Heavy-duty front and rear shocks ($3.80). Heavy-duty front and rear shocks and front springs with heavy-duty rear springs in sedans ($5.00). Extra heavy-duty springs in sedans ($7.25). Heavy-duty rear springs on station wagon ($6.50). Air-Coil ride rear suspension ($98 50). Heavy-duty radiator ($8.00). Heavy-duty cooling system ($19.85). Two-tone, Deluxe sedans ($22.95); two-tone Super and Custom sedans ($24.95), two-tone Super and Custom wagons ($29.95), solid paint with Di-Noc on wagons ($59.95). Three-speed manual transmission was standard. Overdrive transmission ($115). Automatic transmission ($200). Ambassador V-8 327 cid/270 hp four-barrel engine ($90). Positive traction rear axle available at extra cost. Heavy-duty air cleaner available on some as standard equipment; others as extra cost. Available rear axle gear ratios.

HISTORICAL FOOTNOTES: The 1960 Ramblers were introduced Oct. 14, 1959. Model year production peaked at 458,841 units. Calendar year sales of 485,745 cars were recorded. George Romney was the chief executive officer of the company this year. Annual sales topped the billion dollar mark for the first time in the company's six-year history. A new lakefront body plant was constructed for 1961 assemblies. Of all 1960 Ramblers built, 49.4 percent had automatic transmission; 8.9 percent had V-8 engines; 9.4 percent had power brakes, 0.4 percent had power windows; 7.5 percent had tinted glass; 3.8 percent had air-conditioning; 1.6 percent had dual exhaust; and 14.6 percent used overdrive transmissions.

1961

RAMBLER AMERICAN — (6-CYL) — SERIES 01 — America's recognized economy king was all new in style and beauty for 1961. The American was even more compact than ever and easier to park. Features included all welded, single unit construction, deep-dip rustproofing and a ceramic armored muffler and tailpipe guaranteed to the original owner for the life of the car. Styling features included a new trapezoidal grille insert. It was made of perforated aluminum lattice work. The hood earned a stand-up "R" ornament. The simple rear end design featured circular taillamps and optional round back-up lamps. A new body style was a two-door convertible. Standard equipment on Deluxe models included air cleaner; front armrests; front ashtray; cigar lighter; dual sun visors; turn signals; black floor mats; black rubber cargo mats in wagons; and black tubeless tires. Super models had all of the above, plus rear door armrests; rear ashtray; colored rubber mats in wagons; colored floor mats; automatic dome switches on front doors; station wagon travel rack; front foam cushion; and chrome horn ring. Custom models had all of the above plus oil-bath air cleaner; colored carpet in station wagons; dual horns; two-tone steering wheel; and wheel discs.

RAMBLER I.D. DATA: VIN on plate on right wheelhouse panel below hood. First symbol identified series: A=Rebel V-8; B=American; C=Rambler; H=Ambassador. Second through last symbols were sequential production number. Starting serial numbers were: [American] B-221001; [American for knocked-down export] CK-10701; [Rambler] C-400001; [Rambler for knocked-down export] CK-10401; [Rebel V-8] A-118001; [Rebel V-8 for knocked-down export] AK-10001; [Ambassador V-8] H-125001; [Ambassador V-8 for knocked-down export] HK-10001. Body number plate riveted to left front door hinge pillar has additional data. First line indicates body production sequence number. Second line indicates "Model No." consisting of first two symbols indicating model year and additional symbols indicating body style and series. Complete "Model No." corresponds to column two of charts below. Third line gives trim data. Fourth line gives paint color data. Six-cylinder engine number on upper left front corner of engine block. V-8 engine number on top at front of block; or front of block; or center, left side of block, above oil pan. Continuing in 1961, AMC employed an "Engine Day Build Code" system giving all engines of a type the same six symbol code. The first symbol of the engine day build code is a single digit number code for the year of manufacture starting with 3=1961. The second and third symbols indicated month of build: 01=Jan., 02=Feb., etc. The numbers differed in the fourth symbol, a letter code designating the engine displacement and carburetion. Letter codes were: A=195.6 cid/90 hp L-head six; B=195.6 cid/125 hp aluminum OHV six; C=195.6 cid/127 hp cast-iron OHV six; N/A=195.6 cid/138 hp six 2V; N/A=250 cid/200 hp V-8; N/A=250 cid/215 hp V-8, E=327 cid/250 hp V-8 2V, F=327 cid/270 hp V-8 4V, G="287" engine. The fifth and sixth symbols indicated day of manufacture as appropriate. In motor number 301A22: first symbol 3=1961; 01=Jan.; A=195.6 cid/90 hp six and 22=22nd day of month.

RAMBLER AMERICAN SERIES 01

Model No.	Body/Style No.	Body Type & Seating	Factory Price	Shipping Weight	Prod. Total
DELUXE LINE					
01	6102	2-dr Flt Bus Cpe-3P	1831	2454	355
01	6106	2-dr Sed-6P	1845	2480	28,555
01	6105	4-dr Sed-6P	1894	2513	17,811
01	6108	4-dr Sta Wag-6P	2129	2583	7,260
01	6104	2-dr Sta Wag-6P	2080	2539	5,666
SUPER LINE					
01	6105-1	4-dr Sed-6P	1979	2520	15,741
01	6106-1	2-dr Sed-6P	1930	2489	14,349
01	6108-1	4-dr Sta Wag-6P	2214	2590	10,071
01	6104-1	2-dr Sta Wag-6P	2165	2546	5,749
CUSTOM LINE					
01	6105-2	4-dr Sed-6P	2109	2578	5,920
01	6105-2	4-dr Cus Sed-5P	—	—	1,629
01	6106-2	2-dr Sed-6P	2060	2547	4,883
01	6107-2	2-dr Conv-6P	2369	2732	10,855
01	6107-2	2-dr Cus Conv-5P	—	2745	2,063
01	6108-2	4-dr Sta Wag-6P	2344	2648	3,679
01	6104-2	2-dr Sta Wag-6P	2295	2607	1,417

NOTE 1: Customs have five-passenger, bucket seating.

RAMBLER CLASSIC SIX — (6-CYL) — SERIES 10 — The Rambler six was renamed for 1961. It received a new front end featuring a one-piece rectangular, extruded aluminum grille with the letters Rambler underneath, just above the bumper. The park/turn lights were located just below the front bumper. New front and rear bumpers were also used along the new side trim. Deluxe Series standard equipment included: turn signals; twin panel ashtrays; air cleaner; front armrests; cigar lighter; dual headlamps; dual sun visors; station wagon travel rack; and five black tubeless tires. Super Series models were equipped the same as above, plus dual horns; rear door armrests; front foam cushions and rear ashtrays. Custom Series models were equipped with all the above, plus wheel discs; electric clock; glovebox light; two-tone steering wheel; carpets; and rear vent window. A major engineering change and a first for the industry was the introduction of a die-cast aluminum six-cylinder engine for Classic Custom models. The special die-cast block was made of an innovative aluminum-silicon alloy with centrifugal cast-iron cylinders bonded to the block. This was advertised as "America's first Die-Cast aluminum six" and was optional on Deluxe and Super models in the Classic Series. Other highlights for this line were freshly sculptured side styling and one-piece bumpers.

RAMBLER CLASSIC SIX SERIES 10

Model No.	Body/Style No.	Body Type & Seating	Factory Price	Shipping Weight	Prod. Total
DELUXE LINE					
10	6115	4-dr Sed-6P	2098	2905	40,398
10	6118	4-dr Sta Wag-6P	2437	3014	19,848
SUPER LINE					
10	6115-1	4-dr Sed-6P	2268	2923	62,563
10	6118-3	5-dr Sta Wag-8P	2697	3087	4,465
10	6118-1	4-dr Sta Wag-6P	2572	3047	38,370
CUSTOM LINE					
10	6115-2	4-dr Sed-6P	2413	2898	26,497
10	6115-2	4-dr Cus Sed-6P	—	2853	2,901
10	6118-2	4-dr Sta Wag-6P	2717	2984	16,394
10	6118-4	5-dr Sta Wag-8P	2842	3023	2,741

NOTE 1: Customs have five-passenger, bucket seating.

NOTE 2: AMC called wagon with side-hinged tailgate a five-door station wagon.

RAMBLER CLASSIC EIGHT — (V-8) — SERIES 20 — Like the Classic six, the Rambler Classic V-8 gave buyers the best of both worlds: big car room and comfort, compact car economy and handling ease. Styling for both lines was the same, as was the availability of three different levels of trim: Deluxe, Super and Custom. As on American and Classic six models, a chrome signature placed on the right-hand lower corner of the deck lid identified the line that each car was in. A Classic script was attached to the front fendersides, below the tapering dual side moldings. Cars with the V-8 had large badges attesting to that fact located under the namescript directly behind the front wheel opening. This engine was advertised as a "high-performance" option.

RAMBLER CLASSIC EIGHT SERIES 20

Model No.	Body/Style No.	Body Type & Seating	Factory Price	Shipping Weight	Prod. Total
DELUXE LINE					
20	6125	4-dr Sed-6P	2227	3237	121
SUPER LINE					
20	6125-1	4-dr Sed-6P	2397	3255	2,156
20	6128-1	4-dr Sta Wag-6P	—	—	1,964
20	6128-3	5-dr Sta Wag-8P	2826	3408	382
CUSTOM LINE					
20	6125-2	4-dr Sed-6P	2512	3252	2,071
20	6128-4	5-dr Sta Wag-8P	2941	3420	382
20	6128-2	4-dr Sta Wag-6P	2816	3378	1,777
CUSTOM 400 LINE					
20	6125-5	4-dr Sed-6P	2662	3283	109

NOTE 2: AMC called wagon with side-hinged tailgate a five-door station wagon.

AMBASSADOR EIGHT— (V-8)— SERIES 80 — The 1961 Ambassador was promoted as a high-performance luxury compact. The body styling was highly revised at the front end. Although based on Rambler Classic-type sheet metal, the front wheel panels were extended into a highly sculptured, bullet-shaped panel that blended into protruding and flat bullet-shaped fender ends. The entire front panel of the car was set back several inches from the fender tips and incorporated a new one-piece aluminum grille, one-piece front bumper and bold dual headlights. The grille was "veed" on its horizontal plane and angled backwards on its vertical axis. This gave the front of the car a "shovel nose" look. There were seven fine horizontal bars, a trapezoidal outer surround and a gold Ambassador script in the lower right corner. An identification shield also appeared at the center of the hood, above the grille. Side trim included series identification scripts (Super or Custom) ahead of the front wheel openings; a horizontal side spear that branched out into a dual molding on the rear doors and fenders; anodized aluminum insert on Customs; identification shields on the roof pillar; and fin-shaped front fender top ornaments with bright metal extensions towards the rear. The Ambassador Deluxe had all equipment that was standard on Classic Deluxe models, plus dual horns. The Ambassador Super series has, in addition to equipment listed for Classic Super, hood insulation, glovebox light and rear door vent window. Ambassador Custom models have all Classic Custom features plus Handi-Pak Carrier, padded dash and visors, rear foam cushion and hood insulation.

AMBASSADOR EIGHT SERIES 80

Model No.	Body/Style No.	Body Type & Seating	Factory Price	Shipping Weight	Prod. Total
DELUXE LINE					
80	6185	4-dr Flt Sed-6P	2395	3343	273
SUPER LINE					
80	6185-1	4-dr Sed-6P	2537	3361	3,299
80	6188-1	4-dr Sta Wag-6P	2841	3493	1,099
80	6188-3	5-dr Sta Wag-8P	2966	3560	277
CUSTOM LINE					
80	6185-2	4-dr Sed-6P	2682	3370	9,269
80	6188-2	4-dr Sta Wag-6P	2986	3495	3,010
80	6188-4	5-dr Sta Wag-8P	3111	3566	784
CUSTOM 400 LINE					
80	6185-5	4-dr Sed-6P	2812	3387	831

NOTE 1: Customs have five-passenger, bucket seating.

NOTE 2: AMC called wagon with side-hinged tailgate a five-door station wagon.

BASE ENGINES

(AMERICAN SIX) Inline, L-head Six: Cast iron block. Displacement: 195.6 cid. Bore and stroke: 3-1/8 x 4-1/4 inches. Compression ratio: 8.0:1. Brake hp: 90 at 3800 rpm. Four main bearings. Solid valve lifters. Carburetor: Carter Type YF-2014S one-barrel.

(DELUXE/SUPER SIX) Inline, L-head Six: Cast iron block. Displacement: 195.6 cid. Bore and stroke: 3-1/8 x 4-1/4 inches. Compression ratio: 8.0:1. Brake hp: 90 at 3800 rpm. Four main bearings. Solid valve lifters. Carburetor: Carter Type YF-2014S one-barrel.

(CUSTOM SIX) Inline Six: Overhead valve. Cast iron block. Displacement: 195.6 cid. Bore and stroke: 3-1/8 x 4-1/4 inches. Compression ratio: 8.7:1. Brake hp: 125 at 4200 rpm. Four main bearings. Solid valve lifters. Carburetor: Holley one-barrel Model 1908-FC.

(CLASSIC SIX) Inline Six: Overhead valve. Cast aluminum block. Displacement: 195.6 cid. Bore and stroke: 3.125 x 4.25 inches. Compression ratio: 8.7:1. Brake hp: 127 at 4200 rpm. Four main bearings. Solid valve lifters. Carburetor: Holley one-barrel Model 1908-FC.

(REBEL V-8) V-8: Overhead valve. Cast iron block. Displacement: 250 cid. Bore and stroke: 3-1/2 x 3-1/4 inches. Compression ratio: 8.7:1. Brake hp: 200 at 4900 rpm. Five main bearings. Hydraulic valve lifters. Carburetor: Holley two-barrel Model H-2040.

(AMBASSADOR EIGHT) V-8: Overhead valve. Cast iron block. Displacement: 326.7 cid. Bore and stroke: 4.00 x 3.25 inches. Compression ratio: 8.7:1. Brake hp: 250 at 4700 rpm. Five main bearings. Hydraulic valve lifters. Carburetor: Holley two-barrel Model H-2040.

CHASSIS FEATURES: Wheelbase: (American) 100 inches; (Classic) 106 inches; (Ambassador) 117 inches. Overall length: (American) 173.1 inches; (Classic) 189.8 inches; (Ambassador) 199 inches. Overall width: (American) 70.0 inches; (Classic) 72.4 inches; (Ambassador) 73.6 inches. Tires: (American) 6.00 x 15 inches: (Classic six) 6.50 x 15; (Classic Eight) 7.50 x 14; (Ambassador) 8.00 x 14.

OPTIONS

AMERICAN: Anti-freeze ($3.80). Two-tone paint on sedans ($15.95); on station wagons ($17.95); Special application ($29.50). Overdrive transmission ($102). Lever control Flash-O-Matic ($164.85). Weather-Eye ($74). Overhead valve engine ($59.50). Air conditioning with heavy-duty cooling system ($359). Power brakes ($37.95). Power steering ($72). Oil-bath air cleaner ($7.15). Oil filter ($9.30). Solex glass ($26.95). Front and rear Deluxe foam rubber seat cushion ($19.90); front only ($9.95); rear only ($9.95). Reclining seat ($25.50). Undercoating ($14.95). Windshield washer ($11). Back-up lights ($9.95). Wheel discs ($15.25). Electric clock ($15.25). Continental tire carrier on sedans ($59.50). Self-adjusting brakes ($7.45). Inside "tilt" rearview mirror ($4.95). Left- or right-hand outside rearview mirror ($3.95); Left- and right-hand outside rearview mirror ($7.90). Custom steering wheel ($7.70). Twin-Grip differential ($29.50). Pair of license plate frames ($4.05); rear only ($2.05). Heavy-duty front and rear shocks ($2.70). Heavy-duty front and rear shocks and rear springs ($4). Heavy-duty radiator ($3). Heavy-duty cooling system ($12.50). Push-button radio and antenna ($58.50), manual radio ($53.95). Individually adjusted front seats ($20). Crankcase ventilation system ($3.25). Padded instrument panel ($12.75). Size 6.00 x 15 four-ply rayon white sidewall tires ($28.35), size 6.50 x 15 four-ply rayon black sidewall tires ($14.65), size 6.50 x 15 four-ply rayon white sidewall tires ($46); size 6.50 x 15 four-ply nylon black sidewall tires ($28.40), size 6.50 x 15 four-ply nylon white sidewall tires ($62.90).

RAMBLER/REBEL: Flash-O-Matic push-button transmission for six-cylinder ($199.50); for V-8 ($219.50). Overdrive ($112.50). Power steering for six-cylinder ($74.00); for V-8 ($79.50). Power window lifts ($99.50). Power brakes ($39.95). Oil filter on Classic six Deluxe and Super ($9.75). Oil-bath air cleaner for six-cylinder models ($9.75). Radio with manual antenna and front speaker ($69.95); with front and rear speaker ($80.70). Weather-Eye heater and ventilator ($76). Solex tinted glass ($33). Back-up lights ($9.95). Continental tire carrier ($69.50). Front and rear foam cushions ($12.50). Reclining front seat ($25.50). Windshield washer ($11.50). Electric clock ($15.95). Padded instrument panel and visors ($21.50). Undercoating ($14.95). Left or right headrests ($12). Air conditioning ($369). Inside rearview mirror ($5.25). Self-adjusting brakes ($7.45). Wheel discs ($15.95). Twin-Grip differential for six-cylinder ($34.50); for V-8 models ($39.50). Parking brake warning light ($3.95). Light package ($3.95). Two-tone paint on sedans ($19.95); on Custom ($24.95); on wagons ($21.95); on Custom wagons ($29.95); on Special (except Fleet) ($29.50). Power Pack on two-barrel six-cylinder models ($12); on four-barrel and dual exhaust V-8 models ($47.50). Individually adjustable front seats ($20). Crankcase ventilation system ($3.25). Side hinged tailgate on two-seat wagons ($39.50). Lock-O-Matic door locks on four-doors ($29.85). Pair of license plate frames ($4.05). Front and rear heavy-duty shocks ($3.80); with heavy-duty front and rear springs on sedans ($5). Heavy-duty rear springs on wagons ($7.25). Heavy-duty radiator on six-cylinder ($5); on V-8 ($9.50). Heavy-duty cooling system on six-cylinder ($15.35); on V-8 ($19.85). Aluminum die-cast six-cylinder engine and oil filter on Classic six, Deluxe and Super ($30).

AMBASSADOR: Overdrive transmission ($114.50). Push-button Flash-O-Matic transmission ($229.50). Power Pack ($47.50). Weather-Eye ($92.50). Air conditioning and heavy-duty cooling system ($398). Power brakes ($41.95). Power steering ($89.50). Power window lifts ($99.50). Solex glass ($33). Front foam rubber seat cushions ($14.35). Rear foam rubber seat cushions ($14.35). Reclining seat ($25.50). Left and right headrests ($24), Left or right headrest ($12). Individually adjustable front seats ($20). Radio and antenna with front speaker in station wagons ($69.95). Radio and antenna with front and rear speakers in sedans ($86.20). Crankcase ventilation system ($3.25). Undercoating ($14.95). Windshield washer ($11.50). Back-up lights ($9.95). Wheel discs ($16.95). Electric clock ($17.95). Parking brake warning light ($3.95). Padded instrument panel and sun visors ($21.50). Side hinged tailgate for two-seat wagons ($39.50). Lock-O-Matic door locks in four-doors ($29.85). Self-adjusting brakes ($7.45). Inside "tilt" rearview mirror ($4.95). Left or right outside rearview mirror ($5.25). Left and right outside rearview mirror ($10.50). Power-saver fan ($19.50). Twin-Grip differential ($42.50). Pair of license plate frames ($4.05); rear only ($2.05). Light package ($9.95). Heavy-duty front and rear shocks ($3.80). Heavy-duty front and rear shocks and front springs with heavy-duty rear springs in sedans ($5.00). Extra heavy-duty rear springs on sedans ($7.25). Heavy-duty rear springs on wagons ($6.50). Heavy-duty radiator ($9.50). Heavy-duty cooling system ($19.85). Plus a variety of tire and paint options too numerous to list.

HISTORICAL FOOTNOTES: The full-size Ramblers were introduced Oct. 5, 1961. Model year production peaked at 377,900 units. Calendar year sales of 380,525 cars was recorded. R.E. Cross was the chief executive officer of the company this year. American Motors Corp. announced the introduction of the Custom 400 entries (bucket seat four-door sedans) in late April 1961.

1962

RAMBLER AMERICAN — (6-CYL) — SERIES 6200 — The 1962 Rambler American had no major styling changes. The Super models were dropped and replaced by a "400" that had the overhead valve engine standard. Bucket seats were optional only with the "400". A new Canadian assembly plant was opened in Brampton, Ontario, Canada, to build Americans and Classics. Standard equipment for Deluxe models included air cleaner, oil filter, front armrests, front ashtray, dual sun visors, turn signals, black rubber floor mats, black rubber cargo mats in wagons and five black tubeless tires, self-adjusting brakes and front foam cushion. Custom models featured all of the above, plus rear door armrests, rear ashtray, colored carpet in wagons, automatic dome switches on front doors, station wagon travel rack, chrome horn ring and cigar lighter. The 400 models had all the above plus dual horns, two-tone steering wheel, wheel discs, chrome front seat trim, vinyl pleated upholstery, padded instrument panel and visors, metallic door panel insert, door scuff plate, trim and vinyl, glovebox lock and overhead valve engine including 45-amp battery.

RAMBLER I.D. DATA: VIN on plate on right wheelhouse panel below hood. First symbol identified series: B=American; C=Rambler; 2=Super; 5=400; H=Ambassador. Second through last symbols were sequential production number. Starting serial numbers were: [American] B-375001; [American for knocked-down export] BK-13001; [Canadian-built Americans] BT-100201; [Rambler] C-625001 [Rambler for knocked-down export] CK-11501 [Canadian-built Rambler] CT-206001; [Ambassador V-8] H-160001; [Ambassador V-8 for knocked-down export] HK-10301. Body number plate riveted to left front door hinge pillar has additional data. First line indicates body production sequence number. Second line indicates "Model No." consisting of first two symbols indicating model year and additional symbols indicating body style and series. Complete "Model No." corresponds to column two of charts below. Third line gives trim data. Fourth line gives paint color data. Six-cylinder engine number on upper left front corner of engine block. V-8 engine number on top at front of block; or front of block; or center, left side of block, above oil pan. Continuing in 1962, AMC employed an "Engine Day Build Code" system giving all engines of a type the same six symbol code. The first symbol of the engine day build code is a single digit number code for the year of manufacture starting with 4=1962. The second and third symbols indicated month of build: 01=Jan.; 02=Feb.; etc. The numbers differed in the fourth symbol, a letter code designating the engine displacement and carburetion. Letter codes were: A=195.6 cid/90 hp L-head six; B=195.6 cid/125 hp aluminum OHV six; C=195.6 cid/127 hp cast-iron OHV six; N/A=195.6 cid/138 hp six 2V; E=327 cid/250 hp V-8 2V; F=327 cid/270 hp V-8 4V; G="287" engine. The fifth and sixth symbols indicated day of manufacture as appropriate. In engine number401A22: first symbol 4=1962; 01=Jan.; A=195.6 cid/90 hp six and 22=22nd day of month.

RAMBLER AMERICAN SERIES 6200

Model No.	Body/Style No.	Body Type & Seating	Factory Price	Shipping Weight	Prod. Total
Deluxe Line					
6200	6202	2-dr Bus Cpe-3P	1832	2454	281
6200	6205	4-dr Sed-6P	1895	2500	17,758
6200	6206	2-dr Sed-6P	1846	2480	29,665
6200	6208	4-dr Sta Wag-6P	2130	2573	6,304
6200	6204	2-dr Sta Wag-6P	2081	2555	4,434
Custom Line					
6200	6205-2	4-dr Sed-6P	1958	2512	13,884
6200	6206-2	2-dr Sed-6P	1909	2492	12,710
6200	6208-2	4-dr Sta Wag-6P	2190	2600	8,998
6200	6204-2	2-dr Sta Wag-6P	2141	2565	4,398
400 Line					
6200	6205-5	4-dr Sed-6P	2089	2585	5,773
6200	6206-5	2-dr Sed-6P	2040	2558	4,840
6200	6207-5	2-dr Conv-5P	2344	2735	13,497
6200	6208-5	4-dr Sta Wag-6P	2320	2692	3,134

RAMBLER CLASSIC — (6-CYL) — SERIES 6210 — The 1962 Rambler Classic Six had all but the smallest trace of tailfins removed from the rear end. There were new, round taillights, a new front grille and new side trim and moldings. The die-cast aluminum block was standard on all Classic Sixes and optional on the Custom and Deluxe lines. Other innovations for the year were a new brake system with tandem master cylinder and a hydraulic tilting front seat. Standard equipment for the Classic Six Deluxe series included turn signal, air cleaner, front armrests, cigar lighter, dual headlamps, dual sun visors, station wagon travel rack, front ashtrays, oil filter, front foam cushion, and five black tubeless tires. The Classic Six Custom series had all the above features plus electric clock, glovebox light, carpets, rear armrests, rear ashtrays, dual horns and automatic dome light switch. Three-seat station wagons have four black Captive Air nylon tires. Classic Six 400 series included all the above features plus padded dash and visors, rear door vent windows, two-tone steering wheel, wheel discs, wagon robe rail and aluminum engine. (Cast iron engine optional at no cost.)

RAMBLER CLASSIC SERIES 6210

Model No.	Body Style No.	Body Type & Seating	Factory Price	Shipping Weight	Prod. Total
Deluxe Line					
6210	6215	4-dr Sed-6P	2050	2888	38,082
6210	6216	2-dr Sed-6P	2000	2866	14,811
6210	6218	4-dr Sta Wag-6P	2380	3014	28,203
Custom Line					
6210	6215-2	4-dr Sed-6P	2200	2898	68,699
6210	6216-2	2-dr Sed-6P	2150	2876	12,652
6210	6218-2	4-dr Sta Wag-6P	2492	3024	53,671
6210	6218-4	5-dr Sta Wag-6P	2614	3094	6,322
400 Line					
6210	6215-5	4-dr Sed-6P	2349	2853	31,255
6210	6216-5	2-dr Sed-6P	2299	2841	5,521
6210	6218-5	4-dr Sta Wag-6P	2640	2985	21,281

RAMBLER AMBASSADOR — (V-8) — SERIES 6280 — The Rambler Ambassador, for 1962, used the Rambler Classic Six body and running gear with the same minimal styling changes. Both models now shared use of the 108-inch wheelbase. This was basically the 1962 Rambler Rebel V-8 with a new name. At the same time, the 117-inch wheelbase Ambassador was dropped. The Ambassador V-8 Deluxe came standard with an air cleaner, front armrests, front ashtrays, cigar lighter, dual headlamps, dual horns, oil filter and front foam cushion. The Ambassador V-8 Custom had all the features listed for Ambassador Deluxe, plus rear armrests, rear ashtrays, carpets, electric clock, glovebox light, hood insulation, automatic dome light switch, rear door vent windows and station wagon travel rack. The Ambassador V-8 400 had all the features listed for Ambassador Deluxe and Custom, plus Handi-Pak Carrier, padded dash and visors, station wagon robe rail, rear foam cushion, wheel discs and four black nylon Captive Air tires on three-seat station wagon.

RAMBLER AMBASSADOR SERIES 6280

Model No.	Body Style No.	Body Type & Seating	Factory Price	Shipping Weight	Prod. Total
Deluxe Line (Fleet Only)					
6280	6285	4-dr Sed-6P	2336	3249	421
6280	6286	2-dr Sed-6P	2282	3227	45
6280	6288	4-dr Sta Wag-6P	2648	3375	77
Custom Line					
6280	6285-2	4-dr Sed-6P	2464	3259	7,398
6280	6286-2	2-dr Sed-6P	2410	3237	659
6280	6288-2	4-dr Sta Wag-6P	2760	3385	4,302
400 Line					
6280	6285-5	4-dr Sed-6P	—	3283	15,120
6280	6286-5	2-dr Sed-6P	2551	3261	459
6280	6288-5	4-dr Sta Wag-6P	2901	3408	6,401
6280	6288-6	4-dr Sta Wag-8P	3023	3471	1,289

BASE ENGINES

(AMERICAN SIX) Inline, L-head Six: Cast iron block. Displacement: 195.6 cid. Bore and stroke: 3-1/8 x 4-1/4 inches. Compression ratio: 8.0:1. Brake hp: 90 at 3800 rpm. Four main bearings. Solid valve lifters. Carburetor: Carter Type YF-2014S one-barrel.

(DELUXE/SUPER SIX) Inline, L-head Six: Cast iron block. Displacement: 195.6 cid. Bore and stroke: 3-1/8 x 4-1/4 inches. Compression ratio: 8.0:1. Brake hp: 90 at 3800 rpm. Four main bearings. Solid valve lifters. Carburetor: Carter Type YF-2014S one-barrel.

(CUSTOM SIX) Inline Six: Overhead valve. Cast iron block. Displacement: 195.6 cid. Bore and stroke: 3-1/8 x 4-1/4 inches. Compression ratio: 8.7:1. Brake hp: 125 at 4200 rpm. Four main bearings. Solid valve lifters. Carburetor: Holley one-barrel Model 1908-FC.

(CLASSIC SIX) Inline Six: Overhead valve. Cast aluminum block. Displacement: 195.6 cid. Bore and stroke: 3.125 x 4.25 inches. Compression ratio: 8.7:1. Brake hp: 127 at 4200 rpm. Four main bearings. Solid valve lifters. Carburetor: Holley one-barrel Model 1908-FC.

(REBEL V-8) V-8: Overhead valve. Cast iron block. Displacement: 250 cid. Bore and stroke: 3-1/2 x 3-1/4 inches. Compression ratio: 8.7:1. Brake hp: 200 at 4900 rpm. Five main bearings. Hydraulic valve lifters. Carburetor: Holley two-barrel Model H-2040.

(AMBASSADOR EIGHT) V-8: Overhead valve. Cast iron block. Displacement: 326.7 cid. Bore and stroke: 4.00 x 3.25 inches. Compression ratio: 8.7:1. Brake hp: 250 at 4700 rpm. Five main bearings. Hydraulic valve lifters. Carburetor: Holley two-barrel Model H-2040.

CHASSIS FEATURES: Wheelbase: (American) 100 inches; (Classic/Ambassador) 108 inches. Overall length: (American) 173.1 inches; (Classic/Ambassador) 190 inches. Front tread: (American) 54.6 inches; (Classic/Ambassador) 57.8 inches. Rear tread: (American) 55 inches; (Classic/Ambassador) 58 inches. Tires: (American) 6:00 x 15 inches; (Classic) 6.50 x 15; (Ambassador) 7.50 x 14.

OPTIONS

AMERICAN: Anti-freeze ($4.25). Two-tone paint on sedans ($15.95); on station wagons ($17.95); special application [except fleet] ($29.50). Overdrive transmission ($102). Lever control Flash-O-Matic ($164.85). Weather-Eye ($74.20). Overhead valve engine. Oil-bath cleaner and 45-amp battery ($59.50). Air conditioning with heavy-duty cooling system ($360). Power brakes ($39.95) Power steering ($72 20). Oil-bath air cleaner ($7.15). Solex glass ($26.95); windshield only ($8.95). Seat cushion, foam rubber, rear ($9.95). Reclining seat ($25.50). Undercoating ($11.95). Windshield washer ($11). Back-up lights ($9.95). Wheel discs ($14.95). Electric clock ($15.30). Inside rearview "tilt" mirror ($4.95). Left or right outside rearview mirror ($3.95); Left and right outside rearview mirror ($7.90). Twin-Grip differential ($29.60). Pair of license plate frames ($3.50); rear only ($1.75). Heavy-duty front and rear shocks ($2.70). Heavy-duty front and rear shocks and rear springs ($4). Heavy-duty radiator ($3.05). Heavy-duty cooling system with radiator fan shroud ($12.50). Push-button radio and antenna ($58.50); manual ($52.50). Individually adjusted front seats ($20). Crankcase ventilation system, required on all California cars ($4.95). Padded instrument panel and visors ($17.60). 6.00 x 15 4-ply rayon whitewall tires ($28); 6.50 x 15 4-ply rayon blackwall tires ($8.10); 6.50 x 15 4-ply rayon whitewall tires ($37.45). Bucket seats ($59.50). Right lounge-tilt seat and headrest ($20.00). Left or right headrests ($12.00); Left and right ($24.00). Load levelers ($25); load levelers with heavy-duty front shocks ($27.10). Two front seat belts ($20.60); four belts, front and rear ($41.20). E-stick transmission (automatic clutch, only available with standard and overdrive transmissions) ($59.50). Light package [trunk, cargo or glovebox] with two courtesy lamps, parking brake warning lamp and automatic dome light on Deluxe models ($9.95). Parking brake warning light ($3.95).

CLASSIC/AMBASSADOR: Air conditioning, All-Season on Classic [tinted glass required] ($370); on Ambassador [tinted glass required] ($399). Back-up lights ($9.95). Bucket seats in 400 ($59.50). Electric clock on Classic Deluxe ($15.95). Two-tone paint for sedans ($19.95); for wagons ($21.95); special application ($29.50). Dowgard coolant for Classic ($4.25); for Ambassador ($6.25). Heavy-duty cooling system, on Classic ($15.35); on Ambassador ($19.85). Crankcase ventilation system ($4.95). Aluminum six-cylinder engine on Classic Deluxe and Custom ($30). Rear foam cushions [standard in Ambassador 400] ($9.95). Individually adjustable front seats ($20); reclining front seat ($25.50). Tinted glass ($37.65); windshield tinted glass ($11.50). Left or right headrest ($12.00). Two license plate frames ($3.50); rear license plate frame ($1.75). Light package ($9.95). Load levelers ($32.15); load levelers with heavy-duty front shocks ($36.00); same with heavy-duty front shocks and springs ($38.70). Inside tilt mirror ($4.95). Left or right outside mirror ($5.30). Padded instrument panel and visors ($21.60). Parking brake warning light ($3.95). Power brakes on Classic ($41.95); on Ambassador ($43.95). Two-door power door locks on Classic ($23.45). Four-door power door locks on Classic and Ambassador ($29.85). Power pack on Classic ($12); on Ambassador ($47.50). Power Saver fan on Classic ($47.50). Power Saver fan on Ambassador ($19.60). Power steering on Classic ($74.20); on Ambassador ($81.20). Power windows ($102.25). Heavy-duty radiator for Classic ($5.05); for Ambassador ($9.55). Single speaker radio and antenna for Classic, Ambassador wagon ($64.95); dual speakers for Classic and Ambassador sedans ($77.25). Two front seat belts ($20.60); four seat belts front and rear ($41.20). Seat lounge tilt with headrest ($20.75). Heavy-duty front and rear shocks ($3.85). Heavy-duty springs and shocks, except wagons ($5.05). Extra heavy-duty springs and shocks, rear, except wagons ($7.30); wagons ($6.55). Side hinge tailgate on Classic and Ambassador six-passenger wagons ($39.60). Tires: Classic: 6.50 x 15 4-ply whitewall rayon, except nine-passenger wagons ($29.60); 6.70 x 15 4-ply black rayon, except nine-passenger wagons ($8.70); 6.70 x 15 4-ply rayon whitewall, except nine-passenger wagons ($39.90); 6.50 x 15 4-ply whitewall nylon Captive Air (four) on nine-passenger wagon ($27.30); 6.70 x 15 4-ply black nylon Captive Air (four) on nine-passenger wagon ($7.50); 6.70 x 15 4-ply whitewall nylon Captive Air (four) on nine-passenger wagon ($36.30). Ambassador: 7.50 x 14 4-ply white sidewall rayon except nine-passenger wagon ($31.40); 7.50 x 14 4-ply white sidewall nylon Captive Air (four) on nine-passenger wagon ($28.95), 8.00 x 14 4-ply black rayon except nine-passenger wagon ($14.20); 8.00 x 14 4-ply white sidewall rayon except nine-passenger wagon ($48.35); 8.00 x 14 4-ply black nylon Captive Air (four) on nine-passenger wagon ($12.95); 8.00 x 14 4-ply white sidewall nylon Captive Air (four) on nine-passenger wagon ($44.50) plus a variety of tire options too numerous to list. Flash-O-Matic transmission on Classic ($186.50); on Ambassador ($219.50). Overdrive transmission on Classic ($108.50); on Ambassador ($114.95). Twin-Grip differential on Classic ($34.60); on Ambassador ($42.70). Undercoating ($14.95). Weather-Eye heater ($76). Wheel discs (standard on 400) ($14.95). Windshield washer ($11.95).

HISTORICAL FOOTNOTES: The full-sized Ramblers were introduced Oct. 6, 1961, and the compact Americans appeared in dealer showrooms the same day. Model year production peaked at 442,300 units. Calendar years sales of 434,788 cars were recorded. R.E. Cross was the chief executive officer of the company this year. The 2,000,000th Rambler built since 1902 was produced on Feb. 1, 1962, in Kenosha, Wis. In June of that same year, a strike by the supplier ended availability of aluminum engines for 1962. The next season four suppliers and four different versions of such engines were seen. Low installation rate options included V-8 engines (8.2 percent); power brakes (7.9 percent); bucket seats (13.4 percent); air conditioning (6.5 percent) and dual exhaust (1.5 percent).

1963

RAMBLER AMERICAN — (6-CYL) — SERIES 6301 — The addition of a pair of two-door hardtops to the 100-inch wheelbase American marked the return of this body style in a Rambler. American Motors' last pillarless coupe had been offered in 1960. New grilles and trim were evident. The grille was of the same trapezoidal shape as in 1962, but had an insert with a pattern of closely-spaced vertical bars. At the rear end several changes were noticeable. First, the license plate bracket was moved from the center of the rear deck lid panel to a position below the middle of the back bumper bar. Second, the Rambler lettering across the edge of the 1962 deck lid was replaced with a logo nameplate mounted where the license plate had been. A redesigned power convertible top; transistorized radio; dual-braking system improvements; new wheel discs; a self-adjusting clutch for the semi-automatic "E-Stick" transmission; and better heating and air conditioning units were other notable advances. Model designations were changed to American 220, American 330 and American 440 instead of Deluxe, Custom and 400, respectively. A new two-door hardtop called the 440-H was introduced. It had a special roof pillar badge; edged type roof; and contrast-finished side insert panel. Standard equipment on Americans included five 6.00 x 15 blackwall tires; front foam cushions; front armrests; sun visors; oil filter and roof luggage rack on station wagons. Custom models also had carpets; a cigarette lighter; and rear armrests; "400" models also had wheelcovers; two-tone steering wheel; glovebox lock; padded dash and sun visors, dual horns and front door dome light switches.

RAMBLER I.D. DATA: VIN on plate on right wheelhouse panel below hood. First symbol identified series: B=American G=Classic Six; Z=Classic Eight; H=Ambassador Eight. Second through last symbols were sequential production number. Starting serial numbers were: [American] B-515001; [American for knocked-down export] BK-15001; [Canadian-built American] BT-110001; [Classic Six] G-100001; [Classic Six for knocked-down export] GK-10001; [Canadian-built Classic Six] GT-220001; [Classic Eight] Z-100001; [Classic Eight knocked-down for export] ZK-1001; [Ambassador V-8] H-210001; [Ambassador V-8 for knocked-down export] HK-11001. Body Number plate riveted to left front door hinge pillar has additional data. First line indicates body production sequence number. Second line indicates "Model No." consisting of first two symbols indicating model year and additional symbols indicating body style and series. Complete "Model No." corresponds to column two of charts below. Third line gives trim data. Fourth line gives paint color data. Six-cylinder engine number on upper left front corner of engine block. V-8 engine number on top at front of block; or front of block; or center left side of block, above oil pan. Continuing in 1963, AMC employed an "Engine Day Build Code" system giving all engines of a type the same six symbol code. The first symbol of the engine day build code is a single digit number code for the year of manufacture starting with 5=1963. The second and third symbols indicated month of build: 01=Jan., 02=Feb., etc. The numbers differed in the fourth symbol, a letter code designating the engine displacement and carburetion. Letter codes were: A=195.6 cid/90 hp L-head six; B=195.6 cid/125 hp aluminum OHV six; C=195.6 cid/127 hp cast iron OHV six; N/A=195.6 cid/138 hp six 2V; E=327 cid/250 hp V-8 2V; F=327 cid/270 hp V-8 4V; G=287 cid/198 hp V-8 engine. The fifth and sixth symbols indicated day of manufacture as appropriate. In engine number 501A22: first symbol 5=1963; 01=Jan.; A=195.6 cid/90 hp six and 22=22nd day of month.

RAMBLER AMERICAN SERIES 6301

Model No.	Body/Style No.	Body Type & Seating	Factory Price	Shipping Weight	Prod. Total
AMERICAN 220 (DELUXE) LINE					
6301	6305	4-dr Sed-6P	1895	2485	14,419
6301	6306	2-dr Sed-6P	1846	2472	27,780
6301	6302	2-dr Bus Sed-3P	1832	2446	162
6301	6308	4-dr Sta Wag-6P	2130	2549	4,436
6301	6304	2-dr Sta Wag-6P	2081	2528	3,312
AMERICAN 330 (CUSTOM) LINE					
6301	6305-2	4-dr Sed-6P	1958	2500	9,666
6301	6308-2	4-dr Sta Wag-6P	2190	2561	6,848
6301	6304-2	2-dr Sta Wag-6P	2141	2539	3,204
AMERICAN 440 LINE					
6301	6305-5	4-dr Sed-6P	2089	2575	2,937
6301	6306-5	2-dr Sed-6P	2040	2556	1,486
6301	6309-5	2-dr HT-6P	2136	2550	5,101
6301	6309-7	2-dr 440H-4P	2281	2567	9,749
6301	6307-5	2-dr Conv-5P	2344	2743	4,750
6301	6308-5	4-dr Sta Wag-6P	2320	2638	1,874

NOTE 1: The 440H hardtop came with bucket seats and 138-hp "power pack" six.

RAMBLER CLASSIC SIX — (6-CYL) — SERIES 6310 — The Rambler Classic for 1963 was completely redesigned. It had a clean, lower and narrower box shape on a longer 112-inch wheelbase. The front grille consisted of a double convex surface of fine U-shaped vertical bars with Rambler across the front. It was a one-piece aluminum stamping. New curved glass side windows were used along with new push-button door handles. New series identification numbers were placed in the center of the trunk lid. There was also Rambler identification trim below the trunk lid. A new tri-pose engine mounting system was used. It replaced a four-point system used earlier. At the beginning of the 1963 model year, only a Classic Six was available and it came in Deluxe, Custom and 400 series. After the release of the Classic Eight series, in January, the series names were changed to 550, 660 and 770. The base Classic 550 models compared to Deluxe models and had no side trim. Standard equipment included directional signals; dual headlamps; air clearer; five 6.50 x 15 blackwall tires; front foam cushions; front armrests; sun visors and oil filter. The one-step-up Classic 660s compared to Custom models. They had a dual horizontal molding on the front fender and single molding from the front door back. In addition to base equipment, "660s" had front door dome light switches; rear armrests; rear ashtrays; glovebox lock; electric clock; carpet; dual horns and luggage rack on station wagons (blackwall Captive Air nylon tires on nine-passenger station wagons). The top-of-the-line Classic 770s compared to the "400" range cars and earned a full-length dual molding with contrasting insert. The Classic 770 had all of this, plus electric clock; padded dash and visors; rear door vent window; wheel discs; two-tone steering wheel; station wagon robe rail; foam cushions; and the die-cast aluminum six (with cast iron engine as a no-cost option).

RAMBLER CLASSIC SIX SERIES 6310

Model No.	Body/Style No.	Body Type & Seating	Factory Price	Shipping Weight	Prod. Total
CLASSIC SIX 550 LINE					
6310	6315	4-dr Sed-6P	2105	2729	43,315
6310	6316	2-dr Sed-6P	2055	2720	14,417
6310	6318	4-dr Sta Wag-6P	2435	2893	26,261

CLASSIC SIX 660 LINE

Model No.	Body Style No.	Body Type & Seating	Factory Price	Shipping Weight	Prod. Total
6310	6315-2	4-dr Sed-6P	2245	2740	71,646
6310	6316-2	2-dr Sed-6P	2195	2725	11,064
6310	6318-4	5-dr Sta Wag-8P	2609	2885	5,752
6310	6318-2	4-dr Sta Wag-6P	2537	2890	46,282

CLASSIC SIX 770 LINE

Model No.	Body Style No.	Body Type & Seating	Factory Price	Shipping Weight	Prod. Total
6310	6315-5	4-dr Sed-6P	2349	2686	35,281
6310	6316-5	2-dr Sed-6P	2299	2663	5,496
6310	6318-5	4-dr Sta Wag-6P	2640	2828	19,319

RAMBLER CLASSIC EIGHT — (V-8) — SERIES 6350 — The Rambler Classic V-8 shared the same all-new styling as the Rambler Classic Six. The main trim difference was the attachment of V-8 emblems on the front fenders, behind the wheel openings. As on the six-cylinder models, features included redesigned grilles, curved side glass, a sharper silhouette and an advanced type of unitized construction that reduced the number of parts and welds in the assembly by 30 percent. The Classic took on the semi-automatic "E-stick" transmission and it was in early February that the V-8 (287 cid) was introduced at the Chicago Automobile Show as a running addition to the 1963 line that created this new series. Numbering on either the center edge of the deck lid or center of tailgate identified each car as a 550, 660 or 770 Classic. Side molding treatments for each of the lines were the same ones described for the Classic Sixes of a comparable trim level. A "Twin Stick" five-speed (overdrive) floor-mounted transmission was offered in some models. The right-hand lever was for locking the overdrive function in or out, while the left-hand lever was the floor shifter. Standard equipment for each series was the same as installed in Classic Six series, except for the different engine.

RAMBLER CLASSIC V-8 SERIES 6350

Model No.	Body/Style No.	Body Type & Seating	Factory Price	Shipping Weight	Prod. Total
CLASSIC V-8 550 LINE					
6350	6355	4-dr Sed-6P	2210	3109	3,444
6350	6356	2-dr Sed-6P	2160	3100	992
6350	6358	4-dr Sta Wag-6P	2540	3273	2,318
CLASSIC V-8 660 LINE					
6350	6355-2	4-dr Sed-6P	2345	3120	11,067
6350	6356-2	2-dr Sed-6P	2300	3105	1,369
6350	6358-4	5-dr Sta Wag-9P	2714	3265	1,150
6350	6358-2	4-dr Sta Wag-6P	2642	3340	7,237
CLASSIC V-8 770 LINE					
6350	6355-5	4-dr Sed-6P	2454	3130	7,869
6350	6356-5	2-dr Sed-6P	2404	3113	1,341
6350	6358-5	4-dr Sta Wag-6P	2754	3208	4,399

AMBASSADOR — (V-8) — SERIES 6380 — The Ambassador was on the same platform as the Rambler Classic and varied mainly in terms of trim. The grille had a horizontal center blade that carried an Ambassador nameplate at its middle. A lower band of horizontal trim decorated the body, between the two wheel housings. Ambassador scripts were earned on the side of the back fenders and the rear treatment included a vertically ebbed, horizontal beauty panel. Rambler Classic-type taillamps with chrome division bars were added. There were center-mounted Ambassador nameplates and a logo badge on the top center edge of the trunk. At the beginning of the 1962 model year, Ambassadors were available in Custom and 400 series. After the rearrangement of the Rambler Classic series in January, the Ambassador also changed to three distinct levels of trim. The Ambassador 800 models were somewhat similar to previous low-rung Customs. Standard equipment was comprised of five 7.50 x 14 blackwall tires; sun visors; air cleaner; front armrests; front ashtray; cigar lighter; dual headlamps; dual horns; oil filter; front foam cushions and station wagon travel rack. Ambassador 880 was a new mid-range series, offering more trim and equipment than the base Ambassador, but not quite as many extras as the former 400. It had all the 800 features, plus front and rear armrests; ashtrays; carpets; hood insulation; automatic dome light switch and chrome horn ring. The top-of-the-line Ambassador 990 had everything found on the lower priced lines plus electric clock; padded dashboard; padded sun visors; station wagon robe rail; front and rear seat cushions; full wheel discs and Captive Air tires on nine-passenger station wagon.

AMBASSADOR SERIES 6380

Model No.	Body/Style No.	Body Type & Seating	Factory Price	Shipping Weight	Prod. Total
AMBASSADOR 800 LINE					
6380	6385	4-dr Sed-6P	2391	3140	437
6380	6386	2-dr Sed-6P	2337	3110	41
6380	6388	4-dr Sta Wag-6P	2703	3270	113
AMBASSADOR 880 LINE					
6380	6385-2	4-dr Sed-6P	2519	3145	7,667
6380	6386-2	2-dr Sed-6P	2465	3116	1,042
6380	6388-2	4-dr Sta Wag-6P	2815	3275	4,929

AMBASSADOR 990 LINE

Model No.	Body Style No.	Body Type & Seating	Factory Price	Shipping Weight	Prod. Total
6380	6385-5	4-dr Sed-6P	2660	3158	14,019
6380	6386-5	2-dr Sed-6P	2606	3132	1,764
6380	6388-6	5-dr Sta Wag-9P	3018	3305	1,687
6380	6388-5	4-dr Sta Wag-6P	2956	3298	6,112

BASE ENGINES

(AMERICAN 220/330) Inline Six: Cast iron block. Displacement: 195.6 cid. Bore and stroke: 3.125 x 4.25 inches. Compression ratio: 8.0:1. Brake hp: 90 at 3800 rpm. Four main bearings. Solid valve lifters. Carburetor: Carter Type RBS one-barrel Model 3487S.

(AMERICAN 440/RAMBLER CLASSIC SIX) Inline Six: Overhead valve. Cast iron block. Displacement; 195.6 cid. Bore and stroke: 3.125 x 4.25 inches. Compression ratio: 8.7:1. Brake hp: 126 at 4200 rpm. Four main bearings. Solid valve lifters. Carburetor: Holley one-barrel Model 1909-2555.

(AMERICAN 440H) Inline Six: Cast iron or aluminum block. Displacement: 195.6 cid. Bore and stroke: 3.125 x 4.25 inches. Compression ratio: 6.7:1. Brake hp: 138 at 4500 rpm. Four main bearings. Solid valve lifters. Carburetor: Carter Type WCD two-barrel Model 3434S.

(RAMBLER CLASSIC EIGHT) V-8: Overhead valve. Cast iron block. Displacement: 287 cid. Bore and stroke: 3-3/4 x 3-1/4 inches. Compression ratio: 8.7:1. Brake hp: 198 at 4700 rpm. Five main bearings. Hydraulic valve lifters. Carburetor: Holley two-barrel Model 2209-2699.

(AMBASSADOR EIGHT) V-8: Overhead valve. Cast iron block. Displacement: 326.7 cid. Bore and stroke: 4.00 x 3.25 inches. Compression ratio: 8.7:1. Brake hp: 250 at 4700 rpm. Five main bearings. Hydraulic valve lifters. Carburetor: Holley two-barrel Model H-2040.

CHASSIS FEATURES: Wheelbase: (American) 100 inches; (Classic/Ambassador) 112 inches. Overall length: (American) 173.1 inches; (Classic/Ambassador) 189.3 inches. Front tread: (American) 54.6 inches; (Classic) 58.2 inches; (Ambassador) 58.6 inches. Rear tread: (American) 55 inches; (Classic) 57.4 inches, (Ambassador) 57.5 inches. Tires: (American) 6.00 x 15 inches; (Classic eight-passenger wagon) 7.00 x 14; (other Classics) 6.50 x 15; (Ambassador) 7.50 x 14.

OPTIONS

AMERICAN: Anti-freeze ($4.25). Two-tone colors on sedans ($15.95); two-tone color on station wagons ($17.95), two-tone color on hardtops except 440H ($37.90), two-tone color on convertible ($21.95), special color application ($29.50). Overdrive transmission ($102). Lever control Flash-O-Matic ($164.85). Weather-Eye ($74.20). Overhead valve engine ($59.50). Air conditioning including heavy-duty cooling system ($360). Power brakes ($39.95). Power steering ($72.20). Oil-bath air cleaner ($7.15). Solex glass ($26.95). Solex windshield only ($8.95). Rear foam rubber seat cushion ($9.95). Reclining seat ($25.50). Undercoating ($14.95). Windshield washer ($11.95). Back-up lights ($10.70). Wheel discs ($14.95). Electric clock ($15.30). Inside "tilt" rearview mirror ($4.95). Left or right outside rearview mirror ($3.95); Left and right outside rearview mirror ($7.90). Twin-Grip differential ($29.60). Pair of license frames ($3.50); rear license frame only ($1.75). Front and rear heavy-duty shocks ($2.70). Heavy-duty front and rear shocks and rear springs ($4). Heavy-duty radiator ($3.55). Heavy-duty cooling system ($12.50). Push-button radio and antenna ($58.50); manual radio and antenna ($52.50). Individually adjusted front seats ($20). Padded instrument panel and visors ($17.60). Bucket seats on American 440 ($99.50); left and right bucket seats on American 440 ($24). Rear load levelers ($32.15). Load levelers with heavy-duty front shocks ($34.85). Two front seat belts ($17.85); four front and rear seat belts ($37). E-Stick transmission, automatic clutch available only with standard or overdrive gearboxes ($59.50). Visibility group A ($21.25). Light group ($19.60). Chrome horn ring ($7.70). Heavy-duty battery ($6.50). Air conditioning adapter group ($20.55). 33-amp alternator ($12). Vinyl seat upholstery ($15). Left- or right-hand lounge-tilt seat and headrest ($21). Left- and right-hand lounge-tilt seat and headrest ($42). Power-Pack, twin throat carburetor ($12). Twin-stick floor shift transmission and overdrive ($134.50).

CLASSIC/AMBASSADOR: All-Season air conditioning ($380-$399). Alternator ($12). Backup lights ($10.70). Heavy-duty battery ($6.50). Bucket seats ($99.50). Electric clock ($15.95). Two-tone color on sedans ($19.95); two-tone color on wagons ($21.95); special color applications ($29.60). Dowgard coolant ($4.25-$6.25). Heavy-duty cooling system ($17.20-$19.85). Six-cylinder aluminum engine ($30). Rear foam cushions ($9.95). Adjustable front seats ($20). Reclining front seat ($25.50). Front lounge-tilt seat with headrest ($21). Tinted glass ($39.50-$45.50). Tinted windshield ($15.95). Left or right headrest ($12). Chrome horn ring ($7.70). Light group ($19.60). Load levelers ($32.15). Load levelers with heavy-duty front shocks ($36). Load levelers with heavy-duty front shocks and springs ($38.70). Inside tilt mirror ($4.95). Outside left or right mirror ($5.30). Outside rearview remote control mirror ($11.95). Padded instrument panel and visors ($19.95). Power brakes ($42.95-$43.95). Power door locks on two-doors ($23.45); power door locks on four-doors ($29.85). Power Pack ($12.00-$23.75). Power Saver fan ($19.60). Power steering ($19.60-$81.20). Power windows ($102.25). Heavy-duty radiator ($5.55-$9.55). Single speaker radio and antenna ($64.95). Dual speaker radio and antenna ($77.25). Front seat belts ($17.85). Front and rear seat belts ($37). Heavy-duty springs and shocks ($5.05). Extra heavy-duty springs and rear shocks ($7.30). Heavy-duty springs and shocks ($6.55). Side hinge tailgate ($39.60). Twin stick transmission ($141.00-$147.50). Flash-O-Matic transmission ($186.50-$219.50). Overdrive transmission ($108.50-$114.95). Twin-Grip differential ($37.50-$42.70). Undercoating ($14.95). Visibility group A ($22.50). Visibility group B ($28.85). Weather-Eye Heater ($78). Wheel discs ($14.95). Windshield washer ($11.95). Numerous tire choices.

HISTORICAL FOOTNOTES: The 1963 Rambler line was introduced Oct. 5, 1962, and the Rambler Classic V-8 appeared in dealer showrooms during February. Model year production peaked at 464,000 units. Calendar year sales of 441,508 cars were recorded in the United States. R.E. Cross was the chief executive officer of the company this year. Options and accessories seeing low installation rates included: power windows (0.5 percent). V-8 engines (17 percent); power brakes (8.1 percent); bucket seats (9.6 percent) and air conditioning (8.2 percent). A Rambler took top honors in the Mobilgas Economy Run. The 1963 Rambler line was picked as "Car of the Year" by *Motor Trend* magazine.

1964

RAMBLER AMERICAN — (6-CYL) — SERIES 6401 — The Rambler American for 1964 was totally redesigned. Wheelbase was increased from 100 inches to 106 inches. The new styling was cleaner with the corners more rounded. The front fenders were rounded near the front headlights and styled similarly to Chrysler's famous experimental turbine car. Front foam seat cushions; a cigarette lighter (except 220); and five 6.45 x 14 blackwall tires were standard in all Americans. 220s and 330s had the 90-hp six-cylinder engine. American 440s featured the 125-hp six. In addition, the 440-H had wide reclining bucket seats, rear foam seat cushions; front seat belts; wheel discs; and, on station wagons, a roof luggage rack.

RAMBLER I.D. DATA: VIN on plate on right wheelhouse panel below hood. First symbol identified series: B=American; G=Classic Six; Z=Classic Eight; H=Ambassador Eight. Second through last symbols were sequential production number. Rambler American Series 6401 starting serial numbers were B-650001 for cars built in Kenosha, Wis., BK-16001 for unassembled export and BT-115401 for Brampton, Ontario, Canada. Rambler Classic Series 6410 starting serial numbers were G-500001 for cars built in Kenosha, Wis., and GK-14001 for unassembled export. Starting serial numbers for Rambler Classic V-8s were Z-155001 for cars built in Kenosha, Wis., and ZK-11001 for unassembled export. All Classics built in Brampton, Ontario, Canada had a starting serial number of GT-239001. Rambler Ambassador Series 6380 starting serial numbers were H-255001 for cars built in Kenosha, Wis., and HK-12001 for unassembled export. Starting serial numbers for all Rambler Ambassador V-8s built in Brampton, Ontario, Canada were HT-33301. Body Number plate riveted to left front door hinge pillar has additional data. First line indicates body production sequence number. Second line indicates "Model No." consisting of first two symbols indicating model year and additional symbols indicating body style and series. Complete "Model No." corresponds to column two of charts below. Third line gives trim data. Fourth line gives paint color data. Six-cylinder engine number on upper left front corner of engine block. V-8 engine number on top at front of block; or front of block; or center, left side of block, above oil pan. Continuing in 1964, AMC employed an "Engine Day Build Code" system giving all engines of a type the same six symbol code. The first symbol of the engine day build code is a single digit number code for the year of manufacture starting with 6=1964. The second and third symbols indicate month of build: 01=Jan., 02=Feb., etc. The numbers differed in the fourth symbol, a letter code designating the engine displacement and carburetion. Letter codes were: A=195.6 cid/90 hp L-head six; B=195.6 cid/125 hp aluminum OHV six; C=195.6 cid/127 hp cast iron OHV six; N/A=195.6 cid/138 hp six 2V; E=327 cid/250 hp V-8 2V; F=327 cid/270 hp V-8 4V; G=287 cid/198 hp V-8; L=232 cid/145 hp six. The fifth and sixth symbols indicate day of manufacture as appropriate. In engine number 601A22: first symbol 6=1964; 01=Jan.; A=195.6 cid/90 hp six and 22=22nd day of month.

RAMBLER AMERICAN SERIES 6401

Model No.	Body/Style No.	Body Type & Seating	Factory Price	Shipping Weight	Prod. Total
AMERICAN 220					
6401	6405	4-dr Sed-6P	1964	2527	18,225
6401	6406	2-dr Sed-6P	1907	2506	32,716
6401	6408	4-dr Sta Wag-6P	2240	2661	8,062
AMERICAN 330					
6401	6405-2	4-dr Sed-6P	2057	2526	19,379
6401	6406-2	2-dr Sed-6P	2000	2504	15,171
6401	6408-2	4-dr Sta Wag-6P	2324	2675	20,587
AMERICAN 440					
6401	6405-5	4-dr Sed-6P	2150	2572	6,590
6401	6409-5	2-dr HT-6P	2133	2596	19,495
6401	6409-7	2-dr 440-H HT-5P	2292	2617	14,527
6401	6407-5	2-dr Conv-6P	2346	2752	8,907

RAMBLER CLASSIC SIX — (6-CYL) — SERIES 6410 — The major styling change for the Classic line was a new grille. It had six stacks of short, bright metal "dashes" running between dual outboard headlamps. The headlights were horizontally positioned in rounded rectangular housings. The entire ensemble was surrounded by a barbell-shaped chrome grille shell with Rambler lettering stamped into the upper bar. Side trim varied by line. Classic 550 models had a bright rocker panel strip, but no lower beltline molding. Classic 660 models added a horizontal mid-bodyside step, of constant width, which ran from the headlights to the taillights. The Classic 770 models used the same basic trim, but had a "butter knife" shaped front tip on the molding. This tip was horizontally ebbed and carried "770" numbering. All three lines had a Classic script plate on the back edge of the rear fender. A 232-cid six-cylinder engine was introduced in a limited number of Classic two-door hardtops beginning in late April 1964. All of these special cars were painted Solar Yellow (with black roofs) and only 2,520 were built. They had distinctive "Typhoon" rear fender badges, in place of the regular Classic script. However, the Typhoon six-cylinder engine was also provided, as a $59.95 powertrain option, in Classic 770 models. It produced 145 brake hp at 4300 rpm. Standard equipment in all Rambler Classic 550s included front foam cushions; dual headlights; and five 6.95 x 14 blackwall tires. Classic 660s also had automatic dome lights; rear armrests; glovebox lock; carpets and dual horns. Classic 770s had extras such as an electric clock; padded dash and visors; two-tone steering wheel and full wheel discs.

RAMBLER CLASSIC SIX SERIES 6410

Model No.	Body/Style No.	Body Type & Seating	Factory Price	Shipping Weight	Prod. Total
CLASSIC 550					
6410	6415	4-dr Sed-6P	2116	2755	21,310
6410	6416	2-dr Sed-6P	2066	2732	6,454
6410	6418	4-dr Sta Wag-6P	2446	2915	13,164
CLASSIC 660					
6410	6415-2	4-dr Sed-6P	2256	2758	37,584*
6410	6416-2	2-dr Sed-6P	2206	2736	3,976
6410	6418-2	4-dr Sta Wag-6P	2548	2916	26,671
CLASSIC 770					
6410	6415-5	4-dr Sed-6P	2360	2763	14,337*
6410	6416-5	2-dr Sed-6P	2310	2740	1,278*
6410	6419-5	2-dr Typ HT-6P	2397	2789	8,996*
6410	6419-7	2-dr HT-5P	2509	2818	2,520
6410	6418-5	4-dr Sta Wag-6P	2651	2921	10,523*

NOTE 1: (*) indicates limited number of cars had optional Typhoon six.

NOTE 2: According to Body Style Number, the following number of Typhoon six attachments were recorded: 6415-2 (6); 6415-5 (2,025); 6416-5 (71); 6418-2 (4); 6418-5 (1,720) and 6419-5 (429).

RAMBLER CLASSIC EIGHT — (V-8) — SERIES 6410 — The styling and equipment features of the Rambler Classic, when equipped with V-8 power, were the same as for the Classic Six, except for the engine and engine identification badges. The optional V-8 was a 287.2 cid/198 hp engine. Cars with this engine installed received V-8 fender badges that were placed behind the front wheelhousing and under the lower beltline molding.

RAMBLER CLASSIC EIGHT SERIES 6410

Model No.	Body/Style No.	Body Type & Seating	Factory Price	Shipping Weight	Prod. Total
CLASSIC 550					
6410	6415	4-dr Sed-6P	2221	3115	2,760
6410	6416	2-dr Sed-6P	2171	3092	545
6410	6418	4-dr Sta Wag-6P	2551	3275	2,199
CLASSIC 660					
6410	6415-2	4-dr Sed-6P	2361	3118	11,374
6410	6416-2	2-dr Sed-6P	2311	3096	873
6410	6418-2	4-dr Sta Wag-6P	2653	3276	10,908
CLASSIC 770					
6410	6415-5	4-dr Sed-6P	2465	3123	9,451
6410	6416-5	2-dr Sed-6P	2415	3100	669
6410	6418-5	4-dr Sta Wag-6P	2756	3281	8,835
6410	6419-5	2-dr HT-6P	2502	3149	11,872

RAMBLER AMBASSADOR 990 — (V-8) — SERIES 6480 — The 1964 Ambassador 990 looked like a Rambler Classic with some of its teeth knocked out. At the center of each stack of chrome grille dashes, a few dashes were omitted. This left a gap that was filled with Ambassador lettering. Seen on the hood, above the center of the grille, was a winged medallion. Side trim consisted of rocker sill moldings; full-length horizontal lower beltline steps, horizontal chrome slashes on the rear roof pillar, and vertical louvers on the front fenders behind the wheel openings. The deck lid or tailgate was decorated with a horizontal beauty panel that matched the general texture of the front grille. A chrome extension panel appeared between the rear bumper and wheelhousing. Ambassador standard equipment included front foam seat cushions; dual headlights; five 7.35 x 14 blackwall tires; V-8 engine; electric clock; rear foam seat cushions and wheel discs. An optional feature on Ambassador 990 was a bucket seat combination with a special between-the-seat cushion permitting a third person to ride in front. Ambassador scripts were positioned at the lower rear side of the back fenders. The special Ambassador 990-H two-door hardtop came standard with front and rear armrests; front and rear seat cushions and wheel opening moldings. The 990 convertible had wheel opening moldings and a power top. Ambassador wagons had a rooftop luggage carrier.

RAMBLER AMBASSADOR 990 SERIES 6480

Model No.	Body/Style No.	Body Type & Seating	Factory Price	Shipping Weight	Prod. Total
6480	6485-5	4-dr Sed-6P	2671	3204	9,827
6480	6489-5	2-dr HT-6P	2736	3213	4,407
6480	6489-7	2-dr 990-H HT-6P	2917	3255	1,464
6480	6488-5	4-dr Sta Wag	2985	3350	2,995

BASE ENGINES

(AMERICAN 220/330) Inline Six: Cast iron block. Displacement: 195.6 cid. Bore and stroke: 3.125 x 4.25 inches. Compression ratio: 8.0:1. Brake hp: 90 at 3800 rpm. Four main bearings. Solid valve lifters. Carburetor: Carter Type RBS one-barrel Model 3708S.

(AMERICAN 440) Inline Six: Overhead valve. Cast iron block. Displacement: 195.6 cid. Bore and stroke: 3.125 x 4.25 inches. Compression ratio: 8.7:1. Brake hp: 125 at 4200 rpm. Four main bearings. Solid valve lifters. Carburetor: Holley one-barrel Model 1909-2555-3.

(AMERICAN 440-H) Inline Six: Cast iron or aluminum block. Displacement: 231.9 cid. Bore and stroke: 3.125 x 4.25 inches. Compression ratio: 8.7:1. Brake hp: 138 at 4600 rpm. Four main bearings. Solid valve lifters. Carburetor: Carter Type WCD two-barrel Model 3706S.

(CLASSIC 550/660/770) Inline Six: Cast iron block. Displacement: 195.6 cid. Bore and stroke: 3.125 x 4.25 inches. Compression ratio: 8.7:1. Brake hp: 127 at 4200 rpm. Four main bearings. Solid valve lifters. Carburetor: Carter RBS one-barrel Model 2727S.

(RAMBLER CLASSIC EIGHT) V-8: Overhead valve. Cast iron block. Displacement: 287.2 cid. Bore and stroke: 3-3/4 x 3-1/4 inches. Compression ratio: 8.7:1. Brake hp: 198 at 4700 rpm. Five main bearings. Hydraulic valve lifters. Carburetor: Holley 2209-3305 two-barrel.

(AMBASSADOR EIGHT) V-8: Overhead valve. Cast iron block. Displacement: 326.7 cid. Bore and stroke: 3.75 x 3.25 inches. Compression ratio: 8.7:1. Brake hp: 250 at 4700 rpm. Five main bearings. Hydraulic valve lifters. Carburetor: Holley 2300-2442-1 two-barrel.

(AMBASSADOR 990-H) V-8: Overhead valve. Cast iron block. Displacement: 326.7 cid. Bore and stroke: 4.00 x 3.25 inches. Compression ratio: 9.7:1. Brake hp: 270 at 4700 rpm. Five main bearings. Hydraulic valve lifters. Carburetor: Holley 4150-1957-1 four-barrel.

CHASSIS FEATURES: (American) 106 inches; (Classic/Ambassador) 112 inches. Overall length: (American) 177.3 inches (Classic station wagon) 190 inches; (Classic passenger car) 190.5 inches; (Ambassador station wagon) 190 inches; (Ambassador passenger car) 190.5 inches. Width: (American) 68.6 inches (all other models) 71.3 inches. Height: (American sedan) 54.5 inches; (Classic sedan) 54.6 inches; (Ambassador sedan) 55.3 inches. Tires: (Ambassador) 7.50 x 14 inches; (American) 6.00 x 14; (Classic) 6.50 x 14.

OPTIONS

AMERICAN: Anti-freeze ($4.25). Two-tone colors on sedans ($15.95); two-tone color on station wagons ($17.95); two-tone color on hardtops except 440-H ($37.90); two-tone color on convertible ($21.95); special color application ($29.50). Overdrive transmission ($102). Lever control Flash-O-Matic ($164.85). Weather-Eye ($74.20). Overhead valve engine ($59.50). Air conditioning including heavy-duty cooling system ($360). Power brakes ($39.95). Power steering ($72.20). Oil-bath air cleaner ($7.15). Solex glass ($26.95). Solex windshield only ($8.95). Rear foam rubber seat cushion ($9.95). Reclining seat ($25.50). Undercoating ($14.95). Windshield washer ($11.95). Back-up lights ($10.70). Wheel discs ($14.95). Electric clock ($15.30). Inside tilt rearview mirror ($4.95). Left or right outside rearview mirror ($3.95); left and right outside rearview mirror ($7.90). Twin-Grip differential ($29.60). Pair of license frames ($3.50); rear license frame only ($1.75). Front and rear heavy-duty shocks ($2.70). Heavy-duty front and rear shocks and rear springs ($4). Heavy-duty radiator ($3.55). Heavy-duty cooling system ($12.50). Push-button radio and antenna ($58.50); manual radio and antenna ($52.50). Individually adjusted front seats ($20). Padded instrument panel and sun visors ($17.60). Bucket seats on American 440 ($99.50); left and right bucket seats on American 440 ($24). Rear load levelers ($32.15). Load levelers with heavy-duty front shocks ($34.85). Two front seat belts ($17.85); four front and rear seat belts ($37). E-Stick transmission, automatic clutch available only with standard or overdrive gearboxes ($59.50). Visibility group A ($21.25). Light group ($19.60). Chrome horn ring ($7.70). Heavy-duty battery ($6.50). Air conditioning adapter group ($20.55). 33-amp alternator ($12). Vinyl seat upholstery ($15). Left- or right-hand lounge-tilt seat and headrest ($21). Left- and right-hand lounge-tilt seat and headrest ($42). Power-Pack, twin throat carburetor ($12). Twin-stick floor shift transmission and overdrive ($134.50).

CLASSIC/AMBASSADOR: All-Season air conditioning ($380-$399). Alternator ($12). Back-up lights ($10.70). Heavy-duty battery ($6.50). Bucket seats ($99.50). Electric clock ($15.95). Two-tone color on sedans ($19.95); two-tone color on wagons ($21.95); special color applications ($29.50). Dowgard coolant ($4.25-$6.25). Heavy-duty cooling system ($17.20-$19.85). Six-cylinder aluminum engine ($30). Rear foam seat cushions ($9.95). Adjustable front seats ($20). Reclining front seat ($25.50). Front lounge-tilt seat with headrest ($21). Tinted glass ($39.50-$45.50). Tinted windshield ($15.95). Left or right headrest ($12). Chrome horn ring ($7.70). Light group ($19.60). Load levelers ($32.15). Load levelers with heavy-duty front shocks ($36). Load levelers with heavy-duty front shocks and springs ($38.70). Inside tilt mirror ($4.95). Outside left or right mirror ($5.30). Outside rearview remote control mirror ($11.95). Padded instrument panel and visors ($19.95). Power brakes ($42.95-$43.95). Power door locks on two-doors ($23.45); power door locks on four-doors ($29.85). Power Pack ($12.00-$23.75). Power Saver fan ($19.60). Power steering ($19.60-$81.20) Power windows ($102.25). Heavy-duty radiator ($5.55-$9.55). Single speaker radio and antenna ($64.95). Dual speaker radio and antenna ($77.25). Front seat belts ($17.85). Front and rear seat belts ($37). Heavy-duty springs and shocks ($5.05). Extra heavy-duty springs and rear shocks ($7.30). Heavy-duty springs and shocks ($6.55). Side hinge tailgate ($39.60). Twin stick transmissions ($141.00-$147.50). Flash-O-Matic transmission ($186.50-$219.50). Overdrive transmission ($108.50-$114.95). Twin-Grip differential ($37.50-$42.70). Undercoating ($14.95). Visibility group A ($22.50). Visibility group B ($28.85). Weather-Eye Heater ($78). Wheel discs ($14.95). Windshield washer ($11.95). Numerous tire choices.

HISTORICAL FOOTNOTES: The 1964 Ramblers were introduced Oct. 15, 1963. Model year registrations peaked at 379,412 units. Calendar year production of 393,863 cars was recorded. R.E. Cross was the chief executive officer of the company this year. A new option was Adjust-O-Tilt steering.

1965

RAMBLER AMERICAN — (6-CYL) — SERIES 01 — The 1965 Rambler American retained the same basic styling as in 1964. The front horizontal bar grille now had indentations made in it. This gave the appearance that it was divided into three parts. Rocker panel moldings were added to all lines, except "220s". New chrome side trim was also used on all but "220" models, which did not have bodyside moldings. Standard equipment on "220" models included turn signals; heavy-duty lights; front armrests; dual sun visors; rubber floor mats; front foam seat cushions; front seat belts; one front ashtray; dome or pillar lamps; Fresh-Air ventilation; two coat hooks; 60-amp battery and blue/green panel illumination. The "330" models had all of these items, plus rear armrests; cigarette lighter; rear ashtrays; carpets and station wagon luggage rack. The "440" models added richer appointments and trim, plus a lockable glovebox. Standard or base technical features of all 1965 Ramblers included column-mounted three-speed manual transmission; self-adjusting Double-Safety brakes; oil, gas and fuel pump filters; power booster fuel pump; Anti-Smog system and ceramic armored exhaust system. A new "232" engine was available and the E-Stick transmission was dropped.

RAMBLER I.D. DATA: VIN on plate on right wheelhouse panel below hood. First symbol identified series: B=American; G=Classic Six; Z=Classic Eight; H=Ambassador Eight. Second through last symbols were sequential production number. [American] Starting serial numbers were P-100001 for cars with the "196" six; PK-100001 for export models with the "196" six; W-100001 for cars with the "232" six; WK-100001 for export models with the "232" six. The starting serial numbers for Canadian production were as follows: PT-500001 for "196" six; QT-500001 for "199" six, VT-500001 for "232" six. [Classic] Starting serial numbers were J-100001 for cars with the "199" six; JK-100001 for export models with the "199" six; L-1500001 for cars with the "232" six, LK-100001 for export models with the "232" six Z-275001 for cars with the "287" V-8; ZK-12001 for export models with the "287"; U-100001 for cars with the "327" V-8; UK-100001 for export models with the "327 V-8. The starting serial numbers for Canadian production were as follows: JT-500001 for cars with the "199" six; LT-500001 for cars with "232" six, ZT-500001 for cars with the "287" V-8. [Marlin] Starting serial numbers were 2K-100001 for cars with the "232" six; 4-100001 for cars with the "327" V-8; 4K-10001 for export models with the "327" V-8. [Ambassador] Starting serial numbers were S-100001 for cars with the "232" six and SK-10001 for export models with the same engine; E-100001 for cars with the "287" V-8 and EK-10001 for export models with the same engine; H-100001 for cars with the "327" V-8 and HK-13001 for export cars with the same engine. The starting serial numbers for Canadian built cars were as follows: ST-500001 for cars with the "232"; ET-500001 for cars with the "287" V-8; and HT-500001 for cars with the "327" V-8. Body Number plate riveted to left front door hinge pillar has additional data. First line indicates body production sequence number. Second line indicates "Model No." consisting of first two symbols indicating model year and additional symbols indicating body style and series. Complete "Model No." corresponds to column two of charts below. Third line gives trim data. Fourth line gives paint color data. Six-cylinder engine number on upper left front corner of engine block. V-8 engine number on top at front of block; or front of block; or center, left side of block, above oil pan. Continuing in 1965, AMC employed an "Engine Day Build Code" system giving all engines of a type the same six symbol code. The first symbol of the engine day build code is a single digit number code for the year of manufacture starting with 7=1965. The second and third symbols indicate month of build: 01=Jan.; 02=Feb.; etc. The numbers differed in the fourth symbol, a letter code designating the engine displacement and carburetion. Letter codes were: A=195.6 cid/90 hp L-head six; B=195.6 cid/125 hp six; N/A=195.6 cid/138 hp OHV six; F=327 cid/270 hp V-8 4V; G=287 cid/198 hp V-8; L=232 cid/145 hp six; L=232 cid/155 hp six; J=199 cid/128 hp six. The fifth and sixth symbols indicated day of manufacture as appropriate. In engine number 701A22: first symbol 7=1965; 01=Jan.; A=195.6 cid/90 hp six and 22=22nd day of month.

RAMBLER AMERICAN SERIES 01

Series No.	Body/Style No.	Body Type & Seating	Factory Price	Shipping Weight	Prod. Total
220 SERIES					
01	6505	4-dr Sed-6P	2036	2518	13,700
01	6506	2-dr Sed-6P	1979	2495	26,409
01	6508	2-dr Sta Wag-6P	2312	2684	5,224
330 SERIES					
01	6505-2	4-dr Sed-6P	2129	2522	15,148
01	6506-2	2-dr Sed-6P	2072	2490	9,065
01	6508-2	2-dr Sta Wag-6P	2396	2682	12,313
440 SERIES					
01	6505-5	4-dr Sed-6P	2222	2580	5,194
01	6507-5	2-dr Conv-5P	2418	2747	3,882
01	6509-5	2-dr HT Cpe-6P	2205	2596	13,784
01	6509-7	2-dr 440-H HT-4P	2327	2622	8,164

RAMBLER CLASSIC — (6-CYL) — SERIES 10 — Rambler Classics received a completely restyled front end for 1965, plus new rear end sheet metal. The front featured new fenders and a grille having "veed-out" horizontal bars, with three vertical division bars that created four sections. Dual horizontal headlamps flanked the grille on either side. The rear was squared-off and had wraparound, rectangular taillamps. Three trim levels were provided: "550", "660" and "770". Five body styles were offered, including a new convertible. Standard equipment on "550" models included front armrests; dual visors; cigar lighter; one front ashtray; rubber floor covering (and trunk mat); front foam seat cushions; dome or pillar lights; front seat belts; Fresh Air ventilation; station wagon luggage rack; two coat hooks; 60-amp battery; and blue/green panel lighting. The "660" models had all of the above, plus rear armrests; two front ashtrays; rear ashtrays; carpets and locking glovebox. The "770" had all the above features, except no coat hooks on convertibles. Trim bars were seen on the rear roof pillar and "770" trim and appointments were richer. A 199-cid six was standard in the "550". A 232-cid six was the base powerplant for the other lines. A 287-cid V-8 was extra in "550s', a 327-cid V-8 in other lines.

RAMBLER CLASSIC SERIES 10

Series No.	Body/Style No.	Body Type & Seating	Factory Price	Shipping Weight	Prod. Total
550 SERIES					
10	6515	4-dr Sed-6P	2192	2987	30,869
10	6516	2-dr Sed-6P	2142	2963	7,082
10	6518	4-dr Sta Wag-6P	2522	3134	13,759
660 SERIES					
10	6515-2	4-dr Sed-6P	2287	2882	50,638
10	6516-2	2-dr Sed-6P	2282	2991	4,561
10	6518-2	4-dr Sta Wag-6P	2624	3155	32,444
770 SERIES					
10	6515-5	4-dr Sed-6P	2436	3029	23,603
10	6519-5	2-dr HT Cpe-6P	2436	3063	14,778
10	6519-7	2-dr 770-H HT-5P	2548	3089	5,706
10	6517-5	2-dr Conv-6P	2696	3169	4,953
10	6518-5	4-dr Sta Wag-6P	2727	3180	15,623

MARLIN — (6-CYL/V-8) — SERIES 50 — The 1965 Marlin was introduced in February 1965 as a midyear addition to the line. It was basically a Rambler Classic with special fastback roof styling. Different taillights were used, but the grille was of the Classic type with the vertical division bars removed. A special Marlin hood ornament was used. The Marlin was American Motors Corp.'s answer to the Ford Mustang, but could accommodate six passengers, as opposed to only four in the Mustang.

MARLIN SERIES 50

Series No.	Body/Style No.	Body Type & Seating	Factory Price	Shipping Weight	Prod. Total
50	6559-7	2-dr HT FsBk-6P	2638/2724	3100/3231	10,327

NOTE: Marlin factory price and shipping weight to left of slash denote 6-cyl./V-8 to right. Approximate breakout of Marlins equipped with 6-cyl. vs. V-8 is 2,000 vs. 8,300, respectively.

RAMBLER AMBASSADOR — (6-CYL) — SERIES 80 — The 1965 Ambassador had a totally new front end with a four-inch longer wheelbase than Classics. The front featured vertical, quad headlamps and a grille of numerous horizontal bars that "veed" slightly outwards along the horizontal plane. Bright metal side trim ran from the rear along the top edge of the body and around the front of the car (crossing the grille). The taillamps wrapped around the body corners and could be seen from both the rear and the side. A convertible, four-door sedans, station wagons, two-door sedans and hardtops were offered in specific lines. A new Ambassador Six marked the first time since 1956 that a six-cylinder engine had been offered in Ambassadors.

RAMBLER AMBASSADOR SERIES 80

Series No.	Body/Style No.	Body Type & Seating	Factory Price	Shipping Weight	Prod. Total
AMBASSADOR 880 SERIES					
80	6585-2	4-dr Sed-6P	2565	3120	10,564
80	6586-2	2-dr Sed-6P	2512	3087	1,301
80	6588-2	4-dr Sta Wag-6P	2879	3247	3,812
AMBASSADOR 990 SERIES					
80	6585-5	4-dr Sed-6P	2656	3151	24,852
80	6587-5	2-dr Conv-6P	2955	3265	3,499
80	6588-5	4-dr Sta Wag-6P	2970	3268	8,701
80	6589-5	2-dr HT Cpe-6P	2669	3168	5,034
80	6589-7	2-dr 990-H HT-5P	2837	3198	6,382

BASE ENGINES

(AMERICAN 220/330) Inline Six: Cast iron block. Displacement: 195.6 cid. Bore and stroke: 3.125 x 4.25 inches. Compression ratio: 8.0:1. Brake hp: 90 at 3800 rpm. Four main bearings. Solid valve lifters. Carburetor: Carter Type RBS one-barrel Model 3708S.

(AMERICAN 440/440-H) Inline Six: Overhead valve. Cast iron block. Displacement: 195.6 cid. Bore and stroke: 3.125 x 4.25 inches. Compression ratio: 8.7:1. Brake hp: 125 at 4200 rpm. Four main bearings. Solid valve lifters. Carburetor: Holley one-barrel Model 1909-2555-3.

(CLASSIC 550) Inline Six: Cast iron block. Displacement: 198.8 cid. Bore and stroke: 3.75 x 3.25 inches. Compression ratio: 8.5:1. Brake horsepower: 128 at 4400 rpm. Four main bearings. Solid valve lifters. Carburetor: Holley one-barrel Model 1909-2555-3.

(CLASSIC 660/700/MARLIN SIX) Inline Six: Cast iron block. Displacement: 231.9 cid. Bore and stroke: 3.75 x 3.50 inches. Compression ratio: 8.5:1. Brake horsepower: 145 at 4300 rpm. Carburetor: Carter WCD-3882 two-barrel.

(CLASSIC 660/770/MARLIN EIGHT) V-8: Overhead valve. Cast iron block. Displacement: 287 cid. Bore and stroke: 3-3/4 x 3-1/4 inches. Compression ratio: 8.7:1. Brake hp: 198 at 4700 rpm. Five main bearings. Hydraulic valve lifters. Carburetor: Holley Model 2209-2699.

(AMBASSADOR 990 SIX) Inline Six: Cast iron block. Displacement: 231.9 cid. Bore and stroke: 3.75 x 3.50 inches. Compression ratio: 8.5:1. Brake horsepower: 155 at 4400 rpm. Carburetor: Carter WCD-3888S two-barrel.

(AMBASSADOR EIGHT) V-8: Overhead valve. Cast iron block. Displacement: 326.7 cid. Bore and stroke: 3.75 x 3.25 inches. Compression ratio: 8.7:1. Brake hp: 250 at 4700 rpm. Five main bearings. Hydraulic valve lifters. Carburetor: Holley four-barrel.

CHASSIS FEATURES: Wheelbase: (American) 106 inches; (Classic/Marlin) 112 inches; (Ambassador) 116 inches. Overall length: (American) 177.25 inches; (Classic station wagon) 193 inches; (other Classic/Marlin) 195 inches; (Ambassador station wagon) 197 inches. Front tread: (Ambassador/Marlin) 58.6 inches; (American) 56 inches; (Classic) 58.2 inches. Rear tread: (Ambassador/Marlin) 57.6 inches; (American) 55 inches; (Classic) 57.4 inches. Tires: (Ambassador/Marlin) 7.35 x 14 inches; (American) 6.45 x 14; (Classic) 6.95 x 14.

OPTIONS: Air conditioner adapter group with heavy-duty radiator and seven-amp battery ($19). All-Season air conditioner, in American ($295.85), in Classic ($312.05), in Ambassador with power-saver fan required with V-8 ($321). 40-amp alternator ($8.95). Appearance Group A for Americans except 440-H and wagons, includes rocker panel molding, deck molding, rear fender moldings and spinner wheel discs ($55.54); same on 440-H ($39.75). Appearance Group A for Classics except not available on 770-H, includes rocker panel moldings, wheel opening moldings and spinner wheel discs ($58.05); same for Classic 880 ($60.30). Appearance Group B. includes same as above except wire wheelcovers for Americans, except 440-H and wagon ($92.65); for 440-H ($76.95); for Classic, except 770-H ($92.65); and for Classic 880 ($94.90). Back-up lights ($10.70). Heavy-duty battery ($6.50). Front disc brakes for Classic/Ambassador, includes power assist ($79.95). Slim bucket seats with console, 440 and 770 ($99.50), 440-H and 770-H with reclining bucket seats required ($40). Slim bucket seats with front armrest and cushion in Ambassador, with reclining seats required ($99.50). Wide bucket seats without console, 440/770 reclining seats required [standard in 440-H/770-H] ($59.50). Slim front bucket seats with armrest and console in Ambassador 990, requires reclining seats ($119.50); same in 990-H ($20). Front bumper guards ($11.50). Front and rear bumper guards, except wagons ($23). Two-barrel carburetor with 232-cid engine ($11.55). Electric clock ($15.95). Two-tone paint on American sedans and hardtops ($16.95); on American wagons ($18.95); on Classic/Ambassador hardtops and sedans ($19.95). on Classic/Ambassador wagons ($21.95). Special paint color application, except fleet cars ($29.50). Simulated Ambassador wagon woodgrain trim ($22.20). Dowgard coolant ($5). Heavy-duty cooling system, six ($10.95); V-8 ($14.95). California crankcase ventilation ($5.05). L-head 196-cid engine in 220/330 ($38.55). 232-cid two-barrel engine in 220/330 with automatic required ($84.95); in 440/440-H with automatic required ($49.95); in 550 only ($39.95). 327-cid V-8 four-barrel engine in Classic and Ambassador small V-8s ($81.95). Rear foam seat cushion ($9.95). Individually adjustable front seats ($20). Reclining front seat ($25.50). Tinted glass, in American ($27.95), in Classic/Ambassador cars ($45.50), in Classic/Ambassador wagon ($39.50). Tinted windshield only, in American ($12.95); in Classic and Ambassador ($19.95). Headrest ($12). Light Group ($19.60). Inside tilt mirror ($4.95). Outside mirror; either side ($5.30). Outside rearview mirror with remote-control ($11.95). Oil-bath air cleaner with L-head ($7.15). Padded panel and visors ($19.95). Padded dash panel, convertible ($17.50). Padded visors ($4.50). Power brakes, in American/Classic ($42.95), in Ambassador ($43.95). Power Saver fan ($19.60). Power steering, in American/Classic ($85.95) in Ambassador ($96.90). Power tailgate window ($31.95). American convertible power top ($49.95). Front power windows, except Americans and convertibles and hardtops ($59.50). Station wagon power front windows and power tailgate window, except Americans ($91.45). Power front and rear windows, except Americans, not available on two-door sedans or convertibles ($102.25). Wagons, except Americans, power front, rear and tailgate windows ($134.20). Radio and manual antenna in Americans ($49.50). Push-button radio and antenna in Americans ($56.50). Push-button AM radio in Classic/Ambassador ($58.50). Push-button AM/FM radio in Classic/Ambassador ($129.30). DuoCoustic rear speaker in Classic/Ambassador sedans and hardtops ($12.60). VibraTone rear speaker in Classic/Ambassador sedans and hardtops ($40.50). Heavy-duty radiator in American ($3.35). Heavy-duty radiator in Classic/Ambassador ($5.35). Airliner reclining seats in American, standard 440-H, others ($25.50). Adjustable front seat in Americans, requires reclining seats ($20). Front seat belt deletion ($11 credit). Retractable front seat belts ($7.50). Retractable front and non-retractable rear seat belts ($26.70). Retractable seat belts front and rear ($45.80). Front and rear shocks in American ($2.70). Front and rear shocks in Classic/Ambassador ($3.85). Heavy-duty front and rear springs, in American ($5.15 cars/$6.55 wagons). Heavy-duty front and rear shocks and rear springs in Classic/Ambassador cars ($5.05). Heavy-duty front and rear extended springs, in Classic/Ambassador ($7.30 cars/$6.55 wagons). Adjustable steering wheel in Classic/Ambassador, requires automatic transmission ($43). Custom steering wheel in 220/550 ($7.70). Side hinge tailgate, except Americans ($39.60, but standard with third seat). Station wagon third seat, except American and 550 ($85). Flash-O-Matic transmission, in American ($171.25); in Classic Six ($186.50); in Classic Eight ($193.65); in Ambassador Six ($212.35); in Ambassador Eight ($219.50). Overdrive transmission, in Americans without 232-cid engine ($105.50); in Classic Six ($108.50); in Classic Eight or Classic with 232-cid engine ($11.35); in Ambassador ($114.95). Flash-O-Matic Shift Command transmission, in American with 232-cid engine and slim bucket seats ($186.25); in Classic with 232-cid two-barrel engine, requires slim bucket seats ($201.50); in Classic V-8, requires slim bucket seats ($208.65); in Ambassador Six, requires bucket seats and console ($227.30). In Ambassador V-8, requires bucket seats and console ($234.50). Twin Stick transmission ($134.50-$147.50). Twin-Grip differential (($37.55-$42.70). Undercoating ($17.20). Wheel discs ($20.55). Wheel discs with spinners ($14.05-$34.55). Wire wheelcovers with spinners ($48.70-$69.15). Windshield washer ($11.95). Electric wipers ($8.95 American/$10.95 others). Vinyl upholstery ($15.00-$24.50). Credit for Weather-Eye heater deletion ($72-$79). Various tire options.

HISTORICAL FOOTNOTES: The full-sized Ramblers were introduced in September 1964 and the Americans appeared in dealer showrooms at the same time. Calendar year registrations of 324,669 cars were recorded. Calendar year sales were counted at 346,367 units. American Motors was the country's ninth largest automaker this season. The "Rambulance", a station wagon conversion for the economy class emergency vehicle market, was available again this year. A total of 246 such vehicles were sold between 1960 and 1965 to police and fire departments in small towns.

AMC 1966-1975

In February 1962, George Romney resigned as president and chairman of American Motors Corp. (AMC) to campaign successfully for Governor of Michigan. The board of directors elected him vice-chairman and granted him a leave of absence. Richard E. Cross was named board chairman, and Roy Abernathy became president.

Data Compiled by Larry Daum

During the next few years, AMC invested $300 million in new advanced-designed engines, bodies and plant facilities. Romney had been the primary driving force behind AMC's small car program. When he left, Abernathy, a former Packard sales manager, began going into direct competition with the "big three" automakers.

An entirely new line of larger cars was introduced in the 1967 model year, with the Classic series becoming the Rebel. New luxury models, including convertibles, were introduced. Roy D. Chapin, Jr., son of a founder of Hudson Motor Car Co., was made chairman and chief executive officer on Jan. 9, 1967, with William V. Luneburg as president and chief operating officer. Chapin staked out a new and bold direction for American Motors. Among the many forward steps taken to strengthen confidence in the company was a sharp reduction in delivered prices of the low-priced Rambler American models to make them more competitive with imports, which again were on the rise. Chapin pledged to introduce six new models in the next 18 months. The first was the Javelin, bowing on Sept. 26, 1967, as a 1968 model. A two-passenger sports car, the AMX, bowed in February 1968. Both cars were designed to change AMC's image from a company that had once advertised, "The only race we are interested in is the human race." Now the ads read, "We just haven't been the same since we discovered racing."

In July 1968, AMC sold its Kelvinator appliance business to White Consolidated Industries of Cleveland, Ohio. The company could now devote its full and complete energy to the automotive business. The Hornet replaced the Rambler American in the fall of 1969, as a 1970 model. The Rambler name was discontinued. A new sub-compact, the Gremlin, bowed in April 1970, as the first American sub-compact. On Feb. 5, 1970, AMC acquired Kaiser-Jeep Corp. in a transaction involving cash debentures and American Motors' stock. The deal was part of a planned expansion and acquisition program. Kaiser-Jeep became the Jeep Division of AMC and was the leading worldwide manufacturer of four-wheel-drive vehicles.

In March 1971, a wholly owned subsidiary, AM General Corp., was created by AMC. The company assumed the assets of both AMC's former U.S. government contracts and that of Kaiser-Jeep's General Products Division, whose plants were in Mishawaka, Indianapolis, and South Bend, Ind. Cruse W. Moss was named president of AM General, which made tactical wheeled vehicles for the military and delivery vehicles for the U.S. Postal Service in Studebaker's old Chippewa Ave. plant in South Bend.

In 1971, AM General announced that it planned to enter the urban transit bus field, with production in the AM General plant in Mishawaka. A deal had been arranged to manufacture a bus originally designed by Canadian Flyer. In 1973, AM General began bidding successfully on contracts, including one to build buses for the Washington, D.C. Mass Transit District.

Nineteen seventy-one also marked the redesign of the Javelin and a major face lift and name change for the intermediates from Rebel to Matador. Also new was a station wagon version of the Hornet, called the Sportabout. It sold extremely well. A sport model of the Hornet, the SC360, which did not sell well, was also introduced.

The year 1972 brought little change to AMC's model lineup, but a gasoline crisis in 1972 and 1973 brought on by an Arab oil embargo increased AMC's sales of its smaller, more economical models. A special model in an AMC "designer series" of cars, was the Pierre Cardin Javelin. Inspired by fashion designer Pierre Cardin, it was available in 1972 and 1973. Another designer car, for 1972 only, was the Gucci Sportabout in the Hornet series.

In 1973, the Hornet series received a new body style. Its hatchback body style had many imitators after 1973.

The two-door Matador received a major face lift in 1974, making it into a sleek new body style aimed at NASCAR racing. With its fastback body style, it came in two special models. The Matador X was a special sporty model and the Cassini Matador, inspired by fashion designer Oleg Cassini, was a luxury model. Four-door station wagon versions of the Matador received few changes and remained basically the same as the year before. The Ambassador made its last appearance in 1974. Then it was discontinued.

The big news at AMC for 1975 was the introduction of the Pacer in March at the Chicago Auto Show. The Pacer was AMC's first new-from-the-ground-up car to come along in a long time. It featured a unique hatchback body with a larger passenger's side door than driver's side door, a high glass area and a sloping hood. It had originally been intended as a front-wheel drive, rotary-engined car, but General Motors' discontinuance of its rotary engine program forced a return to a conventional drivetrain layout. Also for 1975, a special "Touring" package was offered on the Sportabout, including special interior and exterior trim.

1966

RAMBLER AMERICAN — (SIX) — SERIES 01 — The 1966 American was redesigned. It had a squared-off front end. The 330 models and the old 196.5-cid overhead valve six were dropped. A new top-of-the-line model, called the Rambler Rogue, was introduced. Rear taillamps were larger. At the Chicago Automobile Show, in mid-season, a new 290-cid overhead valve V-8 was announced and a four-speed manual transmission was introduced.

VEHICLE IDENTIFICATION NUMBERS: Stamped on plate welded to right fender below hood. First symbol A = AMC. Second symbol 6 = 1966. Third symbol identifies assembly plant: K = Kenosha, Wis.; B = Brampton, Ont. (Canada). Fourth symbol identifies transmission. Fifth symbol identifies body type (corresponds to fourth digit in Body/Style Number column of charts in this catalog). Sixth symbol identifies car-line (corresponds to Model Number suffix in charts). Seventh symbol identifies series and engine. Last six symbols are sequential production number starting at 100001.

RAMBLER AMERICAN SERIES 01

Series No.	Body/Style No.	Body Type & Seating	Factory Price	Shipping Weight	Prod. Total
220 LINE					
01	6605-0	4-dr Sed-6P	2086	2574	15,940
01	6606-0	2-dr Sed-6P	2017	2554	24,440
01	6608-0	4-dr Sta Wag-6P	2369	2740	5,809
440 LINE					
01	6605-5	4-dr Sed-6P	2203	2582	14,543
01	6606-5	2-dr Sed-6P	2134	2562	5,252
01	6607-5	2-dr Conv-6P	2486	2782	2,092
01	6608-5	4-dr Sta Wag-6P	2477	2745	6,603
01	6609-5	2-dr HT Cpe-6P	2227	2610	10,255
01	6609-7	2-dr Rogue HT-5P	2370	2630	8,718

RAMBLER CLASSIC — (SIX)— SERIES 10 — The 1966 Classic received a new grille, new roof and larger taillights on the same basic 1965 body. The top-level model was a two-door hardtop called the Rebel. The 660 Series designation was dropped. During the last three months of production the 290-cid V-8 took the place of the 287-cid V-8, as the smallest optional eight-cylinder engine.

RAMBLER CLASSIC SERIES 10

Series No.	Body/Style No.	Body Type & Seating	Factory Price	Shipping Weight	Prod. Total
550 LINE					
10	6615-0	4-dr Sed-6P	2238	2885	22,485
10	6616-0	2-dr Sed-6P	2189	2860	5,505
10	6618-0	4-dr Sta Wag-6P	2542	3070	9,390
770 LINE					
10	6615-5	4-dr Sed-6P	2337	2905	46,044
10	6619-5	2-dr HT Cpe-6P	2363	2935	8,736
10	6617-5	2-dr Conv-5P	2616	3070	1,806
10	6618-5	4-dr Sta Wag-6P	2629	3071	24,528
REBEL LINE					
10	6619-7	2-dr HT Cpe-5P	2523	2950	7,512

MARLIN — (SIX/V-8) — SERIES 50 — The 1966 Marlin received few changes. A new grille was used and many features, formerly standard, were now optional. This included power steering and brakes. The price dropped by nearly $500. And the Rambler nameplate was deleted from the rear of the car.

MARLIN SERIES 50

Series No.	Body/Style No.	Body Type & Seating	Factory Price	Shipping Weight	Prod. Total
50	6659-7	2-dr HT FsBk-6P	2423/2523	3100/3231	4,547

NOTE: Marlin factory price and shipping weight to left of slash denote 6-cyl./V-8 to right. Approximate breakout of Marlins equipped with 6-cyl. vs. V-8 is 1,200 and 3,400, respectively.

AMBASSADOR — (SIX) — SERIES 80 — The 1966 Ambassadors had a new roof, larger and more visible taillamps and new chrome trim pieces alongside the car, on the tip of the front fenders. They took the form of a small ribbed rectangle. The top-level Ambassador was now called the Ambassador DPL, which would soon become "Diplomat."

AMBASSADOR SERIES 80

Series No.	Body/Style No.	Body Type & Seating	Factory Price	Shipping Weight	Prod. Total
880 LINE					
80	6685-2	4-dr Sed-6P	2455	3006	Note 1
80	6686-2	2-dr Sed-6P	2404	2970	Note 1
80	6688-2	4-dr Sta Wag-6P	2759	3160	Note 1
990 LINE					
80	6685-5	4-dr Sed-6P	2574	3034	Note 1
80	6689-5	2-dr HT Cpe-6P	2600	3056	Note 1
80	6687-5	2-dr Conv-5P	2968	3432	1,798
80	6688-5	4-dr Sta Wag-6P	2880	3180	Note 1
DPL LINE					
80	6689-7	2-dr HT Cpe-5P	2756	3090	Note 1

NOTE 1: Total 1966 Rambler Ambassador Series production exceeded 71,000 units. No breakout per body style (except for convertible) is currently available.

BASE ENGINES: Inline Six. Overhead valve. Cast iron block. Displacement: 198.8 cid. Bore and stroke: 3.75 x 3.00 inches. Compression ratio: 8.5:1. Brake hp: 128 at 4400 rpm. Seven main bearings. Hydraulic valve lifters. Carburetor: Holley one-barrel.

CHASSIS FEATURES: Wheelbase: (American) 106 inches; (Classic/Rebel/Marlin) 112 inches; (Ambassador) 116 inches. Overall length: (American) 181 inches; (Classic/Rebel/Marlin) 195 inches; (Ambassador station wagon) 200 inches; (other Ambassadors/DPL) 199 inches. Tires: (American) 6.45 x 14 inches; (other station wagons) 7.35 x 14; (all other models) 6.95 x 14.

OPTIONS: Power brakes ($42). Power steering ($84). Air conditioning, American ($303); Classic ($319); Ambassador ($328). Power steering, Ambassador ($95). Front disc brakes ($91). Two-tone paint. Wheel disc, standard on Rogue/Rebel/DPL and Marlin. Turbo-cast wheelcovers. Wire wheelcovers with spinners. Slim band whitewall tires. Bumper guards with rubber facings. Black vinyl-covered hardtop roof. Reclining seats, bucket-type standard on Rogue/Rebel/DPL. Safety headrests. Tachometer. Vinyl upholstery in station wagons. Side-hinged tailgate, Classic/Ambassador wagons only. Simulated woodgrain wagon paneling, Ambassadors only. Appearance group with wheel discs, rocker and wheelhouse moldings, standard on "990" and DPL. Rear seat foam cushions, standard on 770/Rebel/990/DPL/Marlin. Electric clock, standard in Rebel/990/DPL/Marlin. Cruise Command speed control, automatic transmission mandatory. Special black two-tone paint, for Rogue with vinyl roof. AM all-transistor radio, in Americans. Air-Guard, exhaust emissions control system. Four-Way hazard warning signals. Custom steering wheel, standard on all except "220" models. Remote control left-hand outside rearview mirror. AM/FM all transistor radio, for all except Americans. Three-speed manual transmission was standard. Au-

1966 AMC, Rambler American 440 (Series 01), station wagon, OCW

1966 AMC, Rambler Classic 770 (Series 10), convertible, OCW

1966 AMC, Marlin (Series 50), fastback hardtop, OCW

1967 AMC, Rambler Rebel Westerner (Series 10), station wagon, OCW

1967 AMC, Marlin (Series 50), fastback hardtop, OCW

1966 AMC, Rambler American 440 Rogue (Series 01), hardtop, OCW

1966 AMC, Rambler Classic Rebel (Series 10), hardtop, OCW

1966 AMC, Ambassador DPL (Series 80), hardtop, OCW

1967 AMC, Rambler Rebel SST (Series 10), hardtop, OCW

1967 AMC, Ambassador 990 (Series 80), sedan, OCW

tomatic transmission ($187). Four-speed manual floor shift transmission was optional. American six-cylinder 232 cid/155 hp two-barrel engine ($51). All Series V-8 287 cid/198 hp two-barrel engine ($106). V-8 327 cid/250 hp two-barrel engine ($32). V-8 327 cid/270 hp four-barrel engine ($65). Positive traction rear axle was optional.

HISTORICAL FOOTNOTES: The 1966 Ramblers were introduced Oct. 7, 1965, and the Marlin appeared in dealer showrooms at midyear. Model year production peaked at 295,897 units. Calendar year sales of 346,367 cars were recorded. R.D. Chapman, Jr., was the chief executive officer of the company this year. A total of 45,235 AMC models were made with 327-cid V-8s. Only 623 cars were built with 290-cid V-8s during the 1966 model year. The 287-cid V-8 was used in 44,300 additional units. AMC held a 3.71 percent share of the total market this year. Bucket seats were installed in 11.5 percent of all 1966 Ramblers: 27.6 percent had V-8s; 4.3 percent had disc brakes; 3.4 percent had movable steering columns; 10.9 percent had limited-slip differentials; 12.1 percent had air conditioning and only one percent had power windows.

1967

RAMBLER AMERICAN — (SIX) — SERIES 01 — The 1967 Rambler American used the same body styling as the previous year's models, with only minor changes. New taillamps were of the same, rectangular shape, but were shorter and higher. A new side molding was used on the 440 and Rogue models. It was positioned lower on the beltline. A 343-cid V-8 with four-barrel carburetion was available as optional equipment. This was also the last season for the Rambler American convertible. Only seven convertibles were assembled with the 343-cid engine. All 1967 Ramblers and Ambassadors were marketed in six-cylinder series, with V-8 engines as options.

VEHICLE IDENTIFICATION NUMBERS: Starting in 1967 (but also found on some 1966 models), American Motors used a new vehicle identification system. There were 13 symbols in the Vehicle Identification Number, which was located below the hood, on the top right-hand inner fender panel. The first symbol designated the manufacturer: A = American Motors. The second symbol designated the model year: 7 = 1967. The third symbol designated the assembly plant: B = Brampton, Ontario, Canada, K = Kenosha, Wis. The fourth symbol designated the type of transmission, as follows: S = three-speed manual on column; 0 = three-speed manual with overdrive; A = automatic transmission on column, C = three-speed manual with floor shift; F = four-speed manual with console and floor shift and M = four-speed manual with floor shift and no center console. The fifth symbol designated Body Style: 5 = four-door sedan; 7 = two-door sedan; 8 = four-door station wagon and 9 = two-door hardtop. The sixth symbol designated class of body: 0 = 220/550; 2 = 880; 5 = 440/770/990 and 7 = Rogue/SST/DPL/Marlin. The seventh symbol designated series and engine type, as follows: (American 01 Series) A = 199-cid six with one-barrel carburetor; B = 232-cid six with two-barrel carburetor; C = 290-cid V-8 with two-barrel carburetor; D = 290-cid V-8 with four-barrel carburetor; E = 232-cid six with one-barrel carburetor and X = 343-cid V-8 with four-barrel carburetor. (Ambassador 80 Series) M = 232-cid six with two-barrel carburetor; N = 290-cid V-8 with two-barrel carburetor; P = 232-cid six with one-barrel carburetor; Q = 343-cid V-8 with four-barrel carburetor and R = 343-cid V-8 with two-barrel carburetor. (Rebel Series 10) F = 232-cid six with one-barrel carburetor; G = 232-cid six with two-barrel carburetor; H = 290-cid V-8 with two-barrel carburetor; J = 343-cid V-8 with two-barrel carburetor and K = 343-cid V-8 with four-barrel carburetor. (Marlin Series 50) S = 232-cid six with one-barrel carburetor, T = 232-cid six with two-barrel carburetor; U = 290-cid V-8 with two-barrel carburetor; V = 343-cid V-8 with two-barrel carburetor and W = 343-cid V-8 with four-barrel carburetor. The remaining symbols were six digits representing the sequential serial number and starting with 100001 for domestic cars; 700001 for Canadian cars and 10001 for export cars.

RAMBLER AMERICAN SERIES 01

Series No.	Body/Style No.	Body Type & Seating	Factory Price	Shipping Weight	Prod. Total
AMERICAN 220 LINE					
01	6705	4-dr Sed-6P	2142	2621	10,362
01	6706	2-dr Sed-6P	2073	2591	24,834
01	6708	4-dr Sta Wag-6P	2425	2767	2,489
AMERICAN 440 LINE					
01	6705-5	4-dr Sed-6P	2259	2613	7,523
01	6706-5	2-dr Sed-6P	2191	2586	3,317
01	6709-5	2-dr HT Cpe-6P	2283	2643	4,970
01	6708-5	4-dr Sta Wag-6P	2533	2769	4,135
AMERICAN ROGUE LINE					
01	6709-7	2-dr HT Cpe-5P	2426	2663	4,129
01	6707-7	2-dr Conv-6P	2611	2821	921

RAMBLER REBEL — (SIX) — SERIES 10 — Rebel nameplates now adorned the cars that used to be called Classics, as the series name was changed this year. The Rambler Rebel was also a totally redesigned automobile poised on a longer, 114-inch wheelbase. The top-of-the-line entry was known as the SST, which stood for Super Sport Touring (not Super Sonic Transport). New body styling featured slightly rounded body contours with a semi-fastback roof on two-door styles. In February 1967, AMC introduced three special, limited-production station wagons. The first was called the Briarcliff and 400 examples were sold only in the Eastern portion of the United States. The second was the Mariner, marketed to just 600 buyers in coastal areas. Finally, there was the Westerner, which found 500 customers in the Midwest. A new venturi-styled grille was one appearance highlight. The 550 models had the lowest level of trim and Rebel signatures low on the sides of the cowl, behind the front wheel opening. On 770 models a lower body molding traversed the entire length of the body, arching over both front and rear wheelhousings. The SST was adorned with simulated air intake scoops ahead of the rear wheel openings and upper beltline accent trim, but had no lower body moldings. A five-year/50,000-mile warranty covered the 1967 engines and drivetrains.

RAMBLER REBEL SERIES 10

Series No.	Body/Style No.	Body Type & Seating	Factory Price	Shipping Weight	Prod. Total
REBEL 550 LINE					
10	6715	4-dr Sed-6P	2319	3055	10,249
10	6716	2-dr Sed-6P	2294	3089	9,121
10	6718	4-dr Sta Wag-6P	2623	3287	6,845
REBEL 770 LINE					
10	6715-5	4-dr Sed-6P	2418	3053	24,057
10	6719-5	2-dr HT Cpe-6P	2443	3092	9,685
10	6718-5	4-dr Sta Wag-6P	2710	3288	18,240
REBEL SST LINE					
10	6719-7	2-dr HT Cpe-5P	2604	3109	15,287
10	6717-7	2-dr Conv-5P	2872	3180	1,686

MARLIN — (SIX/V-8) — SERIES 50 — The 1967 Marlin was longer, lower and wider and had a two-inch increase in wheelbase. The sporty AMC entry retained its distinctive fastback roof styling and semi-elliptical side window openings. It was basically an Ambassador with a fastback roof, instead of being a streamlined Rambler Classic. American Motors hoped to increase Marlin sales by upgrading the car in this manner. It was also quite a distinctive product: a large, six-passenger sports car aimed at the family man with a "Walter Mitty" complex. There were smoother bodysides, a new rectangular gas filler door and Rally lights incorporated into the grille. Side marker lights could be seen on the trailing edge of the rear fenders, just ahead of the wraparound rear bumper ends. A full-length lower body molding helped create a slim appearance and followed the pattern seen on Rebels, arching over both wheelhousings. The rear deck area was cleaned-up a bit by removal of the large, round medallion. Marlins (as well as Ramblers) with V-8 power had V-shaped emblems at the forward edge of the front fenders. Unfortunately, the Marlin again had problems in the marketplace, as sales dropped to even lower levels than the previous year's drop-off.

MARLIN SERIES 50

Series No.	Body/Style No.	Body Type & Seating	Factory Price	Shipping Weight	Prod. Total
50	6759-7	2-dr HT FsBk-6P	2668/2766	3282/—	2,545

NOTE: Marlin factory price and shipping weight to left of slash denote 6-cyl./V-8 to right. Approximate breakout of Marlins equipped with 6-cyl. vs. V-8 is 400 and 2,200, respectively.

AMBASSADOR — (SIX) — SERIES 80 — The 1967 Ambassador was the top American Motors' model, but it actually shared the basic body of the new Rebel. The major difference was that the front end stretched four inches longer. It had vertically stacked quad headlights flanking a horizontal bar grille. Ambassador scripts were placed on the sides of the front fenders (behind the wheel opening) and on the left-hand edge of the hood. There was also a new stand-up hood ornament and segmented vertical taillamps. The basic 880 had low level trim and appointments with almost bare bodysides. The 770 models had a full-length lower side molding similar to that described for other lines. The starring role went to the DPL, which carried a horizontal center grille divider and integral Rally lights up front. This was the final season before the curtain dropped on the Ambassador convertible.

AMBASSADOR SERIES 80

Series No.	Body/Style No.	Body Type & Seating	Factory Price	Shipping Weight	Prod. Total
AMBASSADOR 880 LINE					
80	6785-2	4-dr Sed-6P	2657	3279	9,772
80	6786-2	2-dr Sed-6P	2619	3310	3,623
80	6788-2	4-dr Sta Wag-6P	2962	3486	3,540

AMBASSADOR 990 LINE

Series No.	Body/Style No.	Body Type & Seating	Factory Price	Shipping Weight	Prod. Total
80	6785-5	4-dr Sed-6P	2776	3324	17,809
80	6789-5	2-dr HT Cpe-6P	2803	3376	6,140
80	6788-5	4-dr Sta Wag-6P	3083	3545	7,919
AMBASSADOR DPL LINE					
80	6789-7	2-dr HT Cpe-5P	2958	3394	12,552
80	6787-7	2-dr Conv-5P	3143	3434	1,260

BASE ENGINES

INLINE SIX: Overhead valve. Cast iron block. Displacement: 199 cid. Bore and stroke: 3-3/4 x 3 inches. Compression ratio: 8.5:1. Brake hp: 128 at 4400 rpm. Seven main bearings. Hydraulic valve lifters. Carburetors: Carter Type RBS one-barrel or Holley one-barrel Model 1931C-3705.

INLINE SIX: Overhead valve. Cast iron block. Displacement: 232 cid. Bore and stroke: 3.75 x 3.50 inches. Compression ratio: 8.5:1. Brake hp: 145 at 4400 rpm. Seven main bearings. Hydraulic valve lifters. Carburetor: Carter Type RBS one-barrel or Holley one-barrel Model 1931C-3705.

V-8: Overhead valve. Cast iron block. Displacement: 287.2 cid. Bore and stroke: 3.75 x 3.25 inches. Compression ratio: 8.7:1. Brake hp: 198 at 4700 rpm. Five main bearings. Hydraulic valve lifters. Carburetor: Carter WCD or Holley two-barrel.

CHASSIS FEATURES: Wheelbase: (American) 106 inches; (Rebel) 114 inches; (Ambassador/Marlin) 118 inches. Overall length: (American station wagon) 181 inches; (American passenger car) 181 inches; (Rebel station wagon) 198 inches; (Rebel passenger car) 197 inches; (Marlin) 201.45 inches; (Ambassador station wagon) 203 inches; (Ambassador passenger car) 202.5 inches. Front tread: (American) 56 inches; (Rebel Six) 58.2 inches; (all other models) 58.6 inches. Rear tread: (American) 55 inches; (all other models) 58.5 inches. Tires: (American passenger car) 6.45 x 14 inches; (American station wagon) 6.95 x 14; (all other passenger models) 7.35 x 14; (all other station wagons) 7.75 x 14.

RAMBLER AMERICAN OPTIONS: All-transistor manual radio ($49). All-transistor push-button radio ($57). Tachometer. All-Season air conditioning ($311). Twin-Grip differential ($37). Electric washer/wipers, electric wipers mandatory with V-8 ($18). Power steering ($34). Power brakes ($42). Power tailgate window ($31). All-vinyl upholstery, standard equipment in Rogue ($24). Exterior appearance group, includes rocker moldings and wheelcovers ($77). Full wheel discs, standard on Rogue ($21). Turbo-cast wheelcovers ($61). Reclining seats for 220/440 models ($25). Reclining bucket seats with center armrest and cushion, for Rogue convertible, standard on Rogue hardtop ($96). Safety headrests ($15). Custom steering wheel for American 220, standard on other models ($8). V-8 handling package. Sports steering wheel, 440 and Rogue only ($11). Black or white vinyl roof for hardtops ($75).

AMBASSADOR/MARLIN OPTIONS: Adjust-O-Tilt steering wheel ($42). Cruise-Command automatic speed control ($44). Power disc brakes ($91). All-Season air conditioning ($350). Stereo system with 8-track tape ($133). Custom Trim package for DPL hardtop, includes: Morocco Brocade fabric in five colors for seats and door panels; two matching pillows and Custom nameplates ($49). Black or white vinyl roof, for hardtops and 990 sedan ($75). Two-tone paint ($19). Station wagon woodgrained exterior paneling ($100). Reclining bucket seats, standard in DPL hardtop ($142). Individually adjustable reclining seats, standard in DPL convertible ($45). Center console, with bucket seats and console shift options only ($113). Electric clock ($16). Tachometer ($48). Passenger third seat for station wagons ($112). Sports steering wheel, standard in DPL models ($16). Safety headrests ($45). AM/FM all-transistor radio ($134). Vinyl upholstery, standard in DPL convertible ($25). Full wheel discs, standard on Marlin and DPL ($21). Turbo-cast wheelcovers ($40). Light Group, standard in DPL ($16).

REBEL OPTIONS: All-Season air conditioning ($350). Adjust-O-Tilt steering wheel ($42). Cruise-Command automatic speed control ($44). Eye-level 6,000 rpm. tachometer $48). New 8-track stereo tape player, in sedans and hardtops with rear speaker ($134). Black or white vinyl roof, on hardtops and 770 sedan ($75). Two-tone paint ($26). Simulated woodgrain station wagon trim ($100). Vibra-Tone rear seat speaker for all-transistor radios ($52). Power steering ($84). Power brakes ($42). Power disc brakes for V-8 models ($91). Power tailgate window ($32). Station wagon third passenger seat ($112). Reclining, individually adjustable seats, standard in SST convertible ($45). Reclining bucket seats, standard in SST hardtop and not available in 550 model ($78). Vinyl upholstery, standard in SST convertible ($25). Solex glass, all window ($34); windshield only ($21). Sports steering wheel, in 770 and SST only ($16). Electric clock ($16). Rear foam seat cushion, standard in 770 and SST models and on third station wagon seat ($11). Wheel discs, standard on SST ($21). Turbo-cast wheelcovers ($61).

POWERTRAIN OPTIONS: Three-speed manual transmission was standard. Three-speed manual transmission with overdrive, in American Six ($109); others ($115). Automatic transmission, in American ($174); in Rebel ($186); in Ambassador/Marlin ($217). Four-speed manual transmission, with V-8 engines only ($184). Shift-Command automatic transmission with thumb-button operated floor shift, in Rogue with buckets and console ($192); in 770 and SST ($205); in Ambassador 880/Marlin ($217). Six-cylinder 232 cid/145 hp engine, in American ($39). Six-cylinder 232 cid/155 hp two-barrel engine, in American ($51); in other models ($12). V-8 290 cid/200 hp two-barrel engine, in American ($119). V-8 290 cid/225 hp four-barrel engine, in American ($32). V-8 343 cid/235 hp two-barrel engine, in Marlin/Rebel/Ambassador ($58). V-8 343 cid/280 hp four-barrel engine, in Marlin/Rebel/Ambassador ($91). Air Guard exhaust emissions control system for V-8s ($45). Engine Mod system for sixes, mandatory smog-control option for California ($11). Closed crankcase ventilation system, mandatory in California ($50). Heavy-duty clutch for V-8 with manual transmission ($5). Dual exhaust ($26).

HISTORICAL FOOTNOTES: The full-sized models were introduced Oct. 6, 1966, and the American appeared in dealer showrooms the same day. Model year production peaked at 235,522 units. Calendar year sales of 229,058 cars were recorded. R.D. Chapin, Jr., was the chief executive officer of the company this year. American Motors financial branch, called Redisco, Inc., was sold to Chrysler this year. A new advertising agency, Wells, Rich, Greene, Inc., of New York City, was engaged by AMC's brand new management team and came up with a series of humorous, but effective ad campaigns that focused on product advantages. A total of 1.2 percent of all AMC products had four-speed manual transmissions; 16.3 percent had bucket seats, 45 percent V-8 powerplants and 11.2 percent vinyl tops.

1968

RAMBLER AMERICAN — (SIX) — SERIES 01 — The 1968 Rambler American used the same body styling as the 1966 and 1967 models. There were several changes in decorative trim. A new grille featured a single horizontal strip of chrome across the insert with a Rambler nameplate at the left-hand side. Signature scripts on the sides of front fenders were moved, from in back of the headlights, to a point behind the wheel opening. Rectangular side markers were seen on both front and rear fenders. Squarish taillamps were set into the rear panel and a Rambler badge was placed near the right taillight lens. The base American 220 came as a four-door sedan or the year's only two-door sedan. This car had no side body moldings and equipment consisted of a Weather-Eye heater; front armrests; front seat foam cushions and dome or side pillar lights. The American 440 had a single, wide strip of ribbed chrome molding positioned high on the bodysides. It connected the front and rear side markers. There was also a bright metal horizontal strip between the taillamps; carpeting; rear armrests; cigarette lighter; glovebox lock; dual horns and Custom steering wheel. The station wagon came with all-vinyl upholstery and larger tires. The top model was the Rogue two-door hardtop that had all American 440 features, plus a larger base six-cylinder engine, special Rogue identification scripts (in place of American signatures) and higher level interior appointments. All Americans were marketed as sixes, with V-8s available as optional equipment.

VEHICLE IDENTIFICATION NUMBERS: The 1968 serial numbers were located on top of the right front wheelhouse panel. The unit body data plate was riveted to the left front door, below the latch mechanism. In 1968, American Motors refined the 13 symbol identification code system introduced the previous year. The third symbol was now a letter designating transmission type, instead of a number designating the assembly plant. (The transmission codes themselves were unchanged.) The fourth symbol was a number designating car-line, as follows: 0 = American; 1 = Rebel; 3 = AMX; 7 = Javelin and 8 = Ambassador. The fifth symbol designated body type using the 1967 number codes. The sixth symbol designated the series or class of body, as follows: 0 = American 220/Rebel 550; 2 = Ambassador; 5 = American 440/Rebel 770/Ambassador DPL and 7 = AMX/Rogue/SST Ambassador. The seventh symbol was a letter designating engine type (without regard to car-line), as follows: A = 199-cid six one-barrel; B = 232-cid six one-barrel; C = 232-cid six two-barrel; M = 290-cid V-8 two-barrel; N = 290-cid V-8 four-barrel; S = 343-cid V-8 two-barrel; T = 343-cid V-8 four-barrel; W = 390-cid V-8 two-barrel and X = 390-cid V-8 four-barrel. The following group of symbols was the sequential serial number and began with 100001 for cars built in Kenosha, Wis., and 700001 for cars built in Brampton, Ontario, Canada.

RAMBLER AMERICAN SERIES 01

Series No.	Body/Style No.	Body Type & Seating	Factory Price	Shipping Weight	Prod. Total
AMERICAN 220 LINE					
01	6805	4-dr Sed-6P	2024	2638	16,595
01	6806	2-dr Sed-6P	1946	2604	53,824
AMERICAN 440 LINE					
01	6805-5	4-dr Sed-6P	2166	2643	11,116
01	6808-5	4-dr Sta Wag-6P	2426	2800	8,285
AMERICAN ROGUE LINE					
01	6809-7	2-dr HT Cpe-6P	2244	2678	4,549

NOTE: Prices on many American Motors' cars were increased around May 1, 1968. The above prices are those in effect at the end of the model year.

RAMBLER REBEL — (SIX/V-8) — SERIES 10 — Offering the only convertible left in the AMC stable, the Rebel was modestly restyled for 1968. The Rambler name was removed from the hood and the taillamps now took the form of three horizontal, curved rectangles, instead of the two large rectangles seen the year before. Square, recessed door handles were another new feature and bodyside moldings were eliminated. The base Rebel 550 models earned this designation below the signature scripts on the sides of front fenders and on the right-hand corner of the trunk lid's rear face. More than a dozen safety changes, enacted to satisfy government regulations, included new front side marker lamps and a preset door locking system. Regular equipment on 550s included all standard safety features; heater; front armrests (on four-doors); cigar lighter; dual headlamps; front seat foam cushions and dome or side pillar lamps. Station wagons came with a rooftop travel rack and all-vinyl upholstery and convertibles featured power operated tops. Rebel 770 models had all the above items, plus rear ashtrays; rear armrests; Custom steering wheel; glovebox lock; dual horns and cloth and vinyl or all-vinyl seats. The 770 station wagons also had a hidden storage compartment and vertical tailgate with power window on three-seat options. Model identification numbers were seen in the usual places and read 770. The Rebel SST came only with V-8 power, exclusively in sport body styles, and represented the top-of-the-line. Trim and equipment distinctions included SST lettering (below front fenderside scripts); wheelhouse trim moldings; simulated chrome air vents ahead of rear wheel opening; individually adjustable reclining seats and special interior appointments. Wheel discs were standard on the SST, as was underhood insulation. This was the final season for Rambler convertibles and the two low-production Rebel ragtops were the last that American Motors would offer, at least for several years until merging with Renault and offering the 1985 Alliance ragtop.

RAMBLER REBEL SERIES 10

Series No.	Body/Style No.	Body Type & Seating	Factory Price	Shipping Weight	Prod. Total
REBEL 550 LINE					
10	6815	4-dr Sed-6P	2443	3062	14,712
10	6817	2-dr Conv-6P	2736	3195	377
10	6818	4-dr Sta Wag-6P	2729	3301	7,427
10	6819	2-dr HT Cpe-6P	2454	3117	7,377
REBEL 770 LINE					
10	6815-5	4-dr Sed-6P	2542	3074	22,938
10	6818-5	4-dr Sta Wag-6P	2854	3306	11,375
10	6819-5	2-dr HT Cpe-6P	2556	3116	4,420
REBEL SST LINE (V-8)					
10	6817-7	2-dr Conv-6P	2999	3427	823
10	6819-7	2-dr HT Cpe-6P	2775	3348	9,876

NOTE 1: The Rebel SST came only with the Typhoon 290-cid V-8 as base powerplant.

NOTE 2: See 1968 American Series note. The above prices are those in effect at the end of the model year.

AMBASSADOR — (SIX/V-8) — SERIES 80 — The 1968 Ambassador had a grille with squarer corner extensions, a grid-style insert with black-out finish and a wider horizontal center divider that gave a twin slot look. Side molding treatments remained basically unchanged and consisted of a full-length chrome strip, mounted low on the body, which arched over the wheel openings. The stand-up hood ornament was eliminated. Taillights were now divided horizontally instead of vertically. Cars with Typhoon power had V-shaped rear fender ornaments. The new paddle type AMC door handles were used. In a move that was heavily promoted, air conditioning became standard Ambassador equipment. The base model was no longer called the 880 (although these numbers still appeared as the last three symbols in the series designation) and was simply referred to as the Ambassador. It came with All-Season air conditioning; all standard safety features; 60-amp battery; heater; front and rear armrests; cigarette lighter; front and rear ashtrays; carpets; front foam seat cushions; dome or side pillar lights; glovebox lock; dual horns and headlights (still vertically stacked) and a Custom steering wheel. Ambassador wagons had a roof rack and lockable storage compartment, plus power tailgate window on three-seat types. The Ambassador DPL earned these three letters on a nameplate located below the side fender scripts and featured full wheel discs and upgraded appointments. Both the Ambassador and Ambassador DPL models were marketed as six-cylinder cars, with V-8 options. The flagship of the fleet was the Ambassador SST, which had all DPL items plus custom interior and exterior trim; individually adjustable reclining seats; woodgrain-look paneling on dashboard; electric clock; headlights-on warning buzzer; rear foam seat cushions and a 200-hp two-barrel V-8 engine. The Ambassador SST hardtop featured a special grille treatment, with integral Rally lights, and interior courtesy lamps.

AMBASSADOR SERIES 80

Model No.	Body/Style No.	Body Type & Seating	Factory Price	Shipping Weight	Prod. Total
AMBASSADOR LINE					
80	6885-2	4-dr Sed-6P	2820	3193	8,788
80	6889-2	2-dr HT Cpe-6P	2842	3258	3,360
AMBASSADOR DPL LINE					
80	6885-5	4-dr Sed-6P	2920	3265	13,265
80	6889-5	2-dr HT Cpe-6P	2941	3321	3,696
80	6888-5	4-dr Sta Wag-6P	3207	3475	10,690
AMBASSADOR SST LINE (V-8)					
80	6885-7	4-dr Sed-6P	3151	3476	13,387
80	6889-7	2-dr HT-6P	3172	3530	7,686

NOTE 1: The Ambassador SST came only with the 290-cid V-8 as base powerplant.

NOTE 2: See 1968 American Series note. The above prices are those in effect at the end of the model year.

JAVELIN — (SIX/V-8)— SERIES 70 — The new Javelin filled the slot vacated by the unsuccessful Marlin. It was American Motors Corp.'s entry into the pony car market that Ford created with the Mustang in 1964. The car was 189 inches long and on a 109-inch wheelbase platform. Power came from either the 232-cid six or the 343-cid V-8 in standard form. Styling characteristics included a split grille with black-out treatment and form-fitting bumper; single, square headlamp housings integrated into fenders; round parking lamps integrated into the bumper (below headlights); clean-lined body with smooth-flowing lines and a semi-fastback roofline with wide, flat sail panels. The profile exhibited a "venturi" silhouette. A full-width rear bumper; horizontal rectangular taillights and a black-out rear panel treatment characterized the rear. Javelin chrome signature scripts were seen in the left-hand grille insert; on the front fenders behind the wheel opening and in the center of the deck latch panel. Standard equipment included all regulation safety features; Custom steering wheel; heater; Flo-Thru ventilation; dual paint stripes along upper beltline; front armrests; cigarette lighter; front ashtray; carpeting; bucket seats with front foam cushions; compartment lights; glovebox lock; dual horns; wide profile tires and, for V-8s, a performance suspension with sway bar. There was also a Javelin SST, with all the above, plus reclining front bucket seats; wood-look Sports steering wheel and door panel trim; full wheel discs and moldings for the rocker panels, side windows and hood scoop. The Javelin went on sale Sept. 26, 1967, and by January a total of 12,390 had been sold. The company took the Javelin to Daytona Beach and other racetracks to show that it could really go. Later, the car showed promise in the new Trans-American racing series and, with full factory backing, narrowly missed unseating the championship Ford Mustang factory team. The Javelin was the last American pony car introduced and many enthusiasts thought it to be the best.

JAVELIN SERIES 70

Series No.	Body/Style No.	Body Type & Seating	Factory Price	Shipping Weight	Prod. Total
JAVELIN					
70	6879-5	2-dr FsBk-4P	2482	2826	29,097
JAVELIN SST					
70	6879-7	2-dr FsBk-4P	2587	2836	26,027

NOTE 1: The Javelin was introduced as a six-cylinder series, with optional V-8s available at extra cost. Prices above are those in effect at the end of the model year.

AMX — (V-8) — SERIES 30 — Round number two in the AMC revitalization program officially kicked off on Feb. 24, 1968, with the mid-year introduction of the AMX two-seater sports car at the Chicago Automobile Show. Actually, the car had made its initial public appearance about a week earlier, when it was press previewed at Daytona International Speedway in Daytona Beach, Fla. The model designation stood for "American Motors Experimental" and it was the first American two-passenger, steel-bodied production type sports car to be seen since the 1955-1957 Ford Thunderbird. A kid brother to the Javelin, the AMX was built off a 97-inch wheelbase version of the same platform. Features included thin shell reclining bucket seats; carpeted interior; woodgrained steering wheel and door panel trim;

the 290 cid/225 hp V-8; four-speed manual transmission; special suspension; glass-belted Goodyear tires and four-barrel carburetor. Power options included the 343-cid V-8 and a 390-cid engine with 315 hp that turned the little sportster into a real speed demon. It looked like a short Javelin with louvered hood bulges and a non-divided grille treatment. It carried special model identification within a large ring of chrome on the sail panels. Craig Breedlove established 106 world speed records with a 1968 AMX at Goodyear's Texas test track in February 1968. The following month, the AMX was seen in dealer showrooms, hoping to go half as fast in the race for sales. It was, however, primarily an image car designed to exhibit AMC's new approach to design, engineering, styling and marketing. A number of replica Craig Breedlove model AMXs with red, white and blue paint jobs and the 290-cid V-8 and four-speed transmission were sold. The number of Craig Breedlove Special AMXs made is believed to have been 50 cars.

AMX SERIES 30

Model No.	Body/Style No.	Body Type & Seating	Factory Price	Shipping Weight	Prod. Total
30	6839-7	2-dr FsBk-2P	3245	3097	6,725

NOTE: Prices above are introductory prices. The AMX was a midyear model and its retail pricing did not change when retails for other lines increased in the spring.

BASE ENGINES

INLINE SIX: Overhead valve. Cast iron block. Displacement: 199 cid. Bore and stroke: 3-3/4 x 3 inches. Compression ratio: 8.5:1. Brake hp: 128 at 4400 rpm. Seven main bearings. Hydraulic valve lifters. Carburetors: Carter Type RBS one-barrel or Holley one-barrel Model 1931C-3705.

INLINE SIX: Overhead valve. Cast iron block. Displacement: 232 cid. Bore and stroke: 3.75 x 3.50 inches. Compression ratio: 8.5:1. Brake hp: 145 at 4400 rpm. Seven main bearings. Hydraulic valve lifters. Carburetor: Carter Type RBS one-barrel or Holley one-barrel Model 1931C-3705.

V-8: Overhead valve. Cast iron block. Displacement: 290 cid. Bore and stroke: 3.75 x 3.25 inches. Compression ratio: 9.0:1. Brake hp: 200 at 4600 rpm. Five main bearings. Hydraulic valve lifters. Carburetor: AMC two-barrel Model 8HM2.

AMX V-8: Overhead valve. Cast iron block. Displacement: 290 cid. Bore and stroke: 3.75 x 3.25 inches. Compression ratio: 10.0:1. Brake hp: 225 at 4700 rpm. Five main bearings. Carburetor: Carter Type AFB four-barrel 4660S.

CHASSIS FEATURES: Wheelbase: (American) 106 inches; (Javelin) 109 inches; (Rebel) 114 inches; (Ambassador) 118 inches; (AMX) 97 inches. Overall length: (American) 181 inches; (Javelin) 189.2 inches; (Rebel wagon) 198 inches; (Rebel) 197 inches; (Ambassador wagon) 203 inches; (Ambassador) 202.5 inches; (AMX) 177.2 inches. Front tread: (Javelin) 57.9 inches; (AMX) 58.4 inches; (other models) See 1967 specifications. Rear tread: (Javelin and AMX) 57 inches; (other models) See 1967 specifications. Tires: (American) 6.45 x 14 inches; (American wagon) 6.95 x 14; (Javelin Six) 6.95 x 14; (Rebel and Ambassador Six) 7.35 x 14; (Rebel/Ambassador Six wagon) 7.75 x 14; (Rebel V-8) 7.35 x 14; (Ambassador V-8) 7.75 x 14; (AMX) E70-14.

AMERICAN OPTIONS: Power brakes ($42). Power steering ($84). Air conditioning ($311). Power disc brakes, V-8 only ($97). Solex glass, all windows ($29), windshield only ($16). Front and rear bumper guards ($23); front bumper guards only ($12). Vinyl top, hardtops only ($79). Individually reclining seats ($49). Sports steering wheel ($21). Custom steering wheel in 220 models ($9). Tachometer, with V-8 only ($48). Column shift automatic transmission ($174). Four-speed manual transmission, with V-8 ($184). Vinyl seat upholstery, standard on wagon ($24). Turbo-cast wheelcovers ($61). Wire wheelcovers ($66). Full wheel discs, all ($21). Electric windshield wipers ($12). Wide profile high-performance tires, exchange ($64). Push-button radio and antenna ($61). Rooftop station wagon travel rack ($39). Pair of headrests ($35). Special application paint colors ($28). Three-speed manual transmission was standard. Overdrive transmission was available for American. Automatic transmission was optional on all with floor control on specific models. Four-speed manual floor shift transmission, standard AMX; optional, with V-8 only, on other models. American six-cylinder 232 cid/145 hp one-barrel engine ($45). American V-8 290 cid/200 hp two-barrel engine ($119). American V-8 290 cid/225 hp four-barrel engine ($45).

REBEL OPTIONS: Power brakes ($42). Power steering ($34). Air conditioning ($356). Power disc brakes, V-8 only ($97). Solex glass, all windows ($34); windshield only ($21). Front and rear bumper guards ($23). Pair of headrests, bench seat ($35); bucket seats ($49). Two-tone paint ($32). Station wagon exterior woodgrained, 770 only ($100). SST exterior paint stripe ($14). AM push-button radio, all ($58). AM/FM push-button radio, all ($134). Black, blue or off-white vinyl roof, hardtop or sedan ($79). SST reclining bucket seats with center armrest ($91). Station wagon third rear-facing seat, includes power tailgate window ($112). Stereo 8-track player with two rear speakers ($134). Adjust-O-Tilt steering, with automatic only ($42). Speed control system, with automatic only ($44). Tachometer, with V-8 only ($48). SST Shift-Command console, with V-8 only ($249). Four-speed manual floor shift ($184). SST undercoating ($17). Vinyl seats, standard in convertible and wagon ($24). Sports steering wheel ($21). Turbo-cast wheelcovers, SST ($40); others ($51). Wire wheelcovers, SST ($45); other models ($66). Wheel discs, standard on SST ($45). Power windows, SST only ($100). Three-speed manual transmission was standard. Overdrive transmission was available for Rebel. Automatic transmission was optional on all with floor control on specific models. Four-speed manual floor shift transmission optional, with V-8 only. Rebel V-8 290 cid/200 hp two-barrel engine ($106). Rebel V-8 343 cid/235 hp two-barrel engine ($45). Rebel V-8 343 cid/280 hp four-barrel engine ($76).

AMBASSADOR OPTIONS: Power brakes ($43). Power steering ($95). Power disc brakes ($97). Twin-Grip differential ($42). Engine block heater ($18). Two-tone paint standard color ($32). DPL Special paint with painted side panel and accent trim ($45). Simulated woodgrain side paneling, DPL only ($100). Exterior paint stripe, SST only ($14). AM/FM push-button radio ($58). Vinyl top, hardtop or sedan only, three colors ($79). Reclining bucket seat with center armrest cushion ($91). Adjust-O-Tilt steering wheel ($42). Sports steering wheel ($21). Stereo 8-track with twin rear speakers ($134). Shift-Command console for V-8, SST only ($250). Four-speed manual transmission ($184). Turbo-cast wheelcovers SST/DPL ($40), others ($61). Wire wheelcovers, SST/DPL ($45), others ($66). Station wagon power side and tailgate windows, DPL only ($134). Power side windows, except base models ($100). Station wagon power tailgate window only ($33). Station wagon rear-facing third seat with power tailgate window ($95). Tachometer, V-8 only ($48). Visibility option package ($41). Light Group option package ($22). Engine cooling option package ($16). Handling option package ($10). Two front shoulder belts, all ($23). Three-speed manual transmission was standard. Overdrive transmission was available for Ambassador. Automatic transmission was optional on all with floor control on specific models. Four-speed manual floor shift transmission, standard AMX; optional, with V-8 only, on other models. Ambassador V-8 290 cid/200 hp two-barrel engine ($16). Ambassador V-8 343 cid/235 hp two-barrel engine ($58). Ambassador V-8 343 cid/280 hp four-barrel engine ($91). Four-barrel carburetor. Positive traction rear axle. Heavy-duty clutch.

NOTE: Prices for V-8s other than base 200 hp engine are in addition to basic cost of V-8 attachment.

JAVELIN OPTIONS: Power brakes ($42). Power steering ($85). Air conditioning ($356). Dual exhaust V-8 ($21). Solex glass, all windows ($31); windshield only ($21). Headrest, with bench seat ($35); with buckets ($49). Power disc brakes, V-8 ($97). Power steering ($84). Stereo 8-track player ($195). Individually adjusting seat ($49). White vinyl seat upholstery ($20). Adjust-O-Tilt steering ($42). Shift-Command automatic transmission with floor shift and console ($269). Twin-Grip differential ($42). Vinyl roof ($85). Turbo-cast wheelcovers, SST ($51); base model ($65). Handling package ($17). GO Pack performance package includes: 343-cid V-8; dual exhaust; power disc brakes; E-70 wide profile tires; Handling Package and Rally stripes ($266). Visibility Group package ($27). FM push-button radio and antenna ($61). AM/FM push-button radio and antenna ($134). Quick-ratio manual steering ($16). Four-speed manual transmission with floor shift ($184). Wire wheelcovers, SST ($51); base Javelin ($75). Three-speed manual transmission was standard, except AMX. Overdrive transmission was available for American/Ambassador/Rebel. Automatic transmission was optional on all with floor control on specific models. Four-speed manual floor shift transmission, standard AMX; optional, with V-8 only, on other models. Four-barrel carburetor. Positive traction rear axle. Heavy-duty clutch.

NOTE: Prices for V-8s other than base 200 hp engine are in addition to basic cost of V-8 attachment.

AMX OPTIONS: Specific prices for AMX options are not available. The options list was about the same as for Javelin (at about the same prices) plus, over-the-top striping; chrome steel mag wheels and dealer accessory Rally Pak gauge cluster. Automatic transmission was optional on all with floor control on specific models. Four-speed manual floor shift transmission standard AMX; optional, with V-8 only, on other models. Four-barrel carburetor. Positive traction rear axle. Heavy-duty clutch.

NOTE: Prices for V-8s other than base 200 hp engine are in addition to basic cost of V-8 attachment.

HISTORICAL FOOTNOTES: The AMC models were introduced Sept. 26, 1967, and the AMX appeared in dealer showrooms during March 1968. Model year production peaked at 272,726 units. Calendar year sales of 269,334 cars were recorded. R.D. Chapin, Jr. was the chief executive officer of the company this year. For the first time since 1965, American Motors Corp. operated in the black for 1968 (although no dividends were paid). This compared to a loss of 75.8 million in 1967. The company sold its Kelvinator division to White Consolidated Industries. Each AMC built in 1968 earned a metal dashboard plate bearing a special number (numbers 000001 to 006175 were used). This was intended to designate its rather special nature. However, the first 550 units, assembled in calendar year 1967, did not have this feature.

1969

RAMBLER — (SIX/V-8) — SERIES 01 — Formerly the Rambler American, the 1969 base model got a shortened name. It retained its compact dimensions and overall styling in line with AMC's new policy of maintaining design continuity from year to year for its low-priced models. American nameplates were gone from the grille and a new chrome side molding was used. Some of the mechanical improvements earmarked for the more expensive AMC products were incorporated in the Rambler. They included a new accelerator cable linkage, suspended accelerator pedal; Clear Power 24 battery and parking lamps that remained on with headlamps. Regular equipment included all regulation safety features; front armrests; front ashtrays; heater and defroster; head restraints; front foam seat cushions; a 199-cid six and 6.45 x 14 blackwall tires. The Rambler 440 models also had rear armrests and ashtrays; cigarette lighter; glovebox lock; and dual horns. The Rogue featured carpeting; Air Guard system and 232-cid six. Rambler wagons had 6.95 x 14 blackwall tires. With the help of Hurst Products Corp., a special Rogue offering was built exclusively during 1969. It was called the Hurst SC/Rambler and came only with the AMX type 390 cid/315 hp V-8 engine, four-speed manual floor shift transmission; and a host of other performance items as standard equipment. The retail price was $2,988. Original programming called for a limited run of just 500 units, but supply was far outstripped by demand. Ultimately, three runs of this model were made and the total output hit 1,512 units. The first batch, or A Group, had the major portion of the bodysides painted red, with a blue racing stripe traveling down the middle of the body and across the roof and deck. There was also a large blue arrow, pointing towards the hood scoop. The paint code for such cars was 00. The second, or B Group of Hurst SC/Ramblers were finished more conservatively. They had a largely white exterior, with narrow red and blue stripes. These cars had either a special (SPEC) or regular P-72 white paint code. The third group reverted to the original or A style, so of the three groups, the A style is predominant.

VEHICLE IDENTIFICATION NUMBERS: The numbering system and code locations were the same as on previous models. The second symbol was changed to a 9 to indicate the 1969 model year. The code F (four-speed manual transmission with floor shift and console) was no longer used as a third symbol. The code 7 (convertible) was also deleted. Otherwise, no changes were seen over previous nomenclature.

RAMBLER SERIES 01

Series No.	Body/Style No.	Body Type & Seating	Factory Price	Shipping Weight	Prod. Total
RAMBLER					
01	6905	4-dr Sed-6P	2076	2638	16,234
01	6906	2-dr Sed-6P	1998	2604	51,062
RAMBLER 440					
01	6905-5	4-dr Sed-6P	2218	2643	11,957
01	6908-5	2-dr Sed-6P	2478	2800	13,233
RAMBLER ROGUE					
01	6909-7	2-dr HT Cpe-6P	2296	2296	3,543
HURST SC/RAMBLER (V-8)					
01	6909-7	2-dr HT Cpe-6P	2998	2988	1,512

NOTE 1: The SC/Rambler came only with V-8 power. A total of 1,012 A-Group editions were built. A total of 500 B-Group editions were built.

REBEL — (SIX) — SERIES 10 — The Rebel's track was increased to 60 inches for 1969. There were styling revisions including a new grille deck lid and taillights. The outboard headlamps were housed separately in square surrounds while the inner lamps were part of the main grille. A horizontal bar pattern insert was used in both the main opening and the outboard headlamp surrounds. The taillamps wrapped around the rear body corners. On SST models the fake air scoops ahead of the rear wheel opening were replaced by four chrome side steps. Rebels were offered in six models: sedan, hardtop and wagon in the base series and the same three styles with SST equipment and trim. Basic equipment included standard safety features; head restraints; front armrests in two-doors; front and rear armrests in four-doors; front ashtray; cigar lighter; dual headlights; heater and defroster; front foam seat cushions; 7.35 x 14 blackwall tires; and the 232 cid/145 hp six. For all Rebels, V-8 engines were classed as optional equipment. The Rebel SST came with all the above items plus carpets; rear armrests in two-door styles; rear ashtray; Custom steering wheel; glovebox light; and dual horns. Wagons also featured a secret lockable rear storage compartment; roof luggage rack; dual hinged tailgate; and 7.75 x 14 blackwall tires.

REBEL SERIES 10

Series No.	Body Style No.	Body Type & Seating	Factory Price	Shipping Weight	Prod. Total
REBEL					
10	6915	4-dr Sed-6P	2484	3062	10,885
10	6919	2-dr HT Cpe-6P	2496	3117	5,396
10	6918	4-dr Sta Wag-6P	2817	3301	8,569
REBEL SST					
10	6915-7	4-dr Sed-6P	2584	3074	20,595
10	6919-7	2-dr HT Cpe-6P	2598	3140	5,405
10	6918-7	4-dr Sta Wag-6P	2947	3306	9,256

AMX — (V-8) — SERIES 30 — The 1969 AMC was described as being "more racy looking than ever," but was really little changed. Its introduction as a late-1968 entry precluded major revisions for its second year. There was a new 140 mph speedometer and tachometer with a larger face. Many minor running changes evolved as the year progressed, the most obvious being the addition of a hooded dash panel cover in most 1969s. New convenience items included a passenger grab handle above the glovebox and a between-the-seats package tray. Leather upholstery trims were a new option. The 290-cid four-barrel V-8 engine was the base powerplant and engines with displacements of 343 and 390 cid were available. Standard equipment included all safety items; front and rear ashtrays and armrests; cigarette lighter; collapsible spare tire; Sports steering wheel; courtesy lights; dual exhaust; carpets; Flo-Thru ventilation; glovebox lock; dual horns; instrument panel gauge cluster with tachometer; rear traction bars; front head restraints; reclining bucket seats; front foam seat cushions; wheel discs; heavy-duty suspension; E70 x 14 fiberglass-belted blackwall tires; four-speed manual transmission with floor shift; and 225-hp four-barrel V-8. Introduced as a midyear entry was the Big Bad AMX. This option-created-model came in three colors and had the bumpers painted the same shade as the body. A total of 284 orange-colored Big Bad AMXs were built as well as 195 similar models finished in blue and 283 additional cars done in green. A limited number of 52 or 53 Super Stock AMXs were made by the Hurst Corp. for AMC as special turn-key NHRA drag racing cars.

AMX SERIES 30

Series No.	Body/Style No.	Body Type & Seating	Factory Price	Shipping Weight	Prod. Total
AMX (V-8)					
30	6939-7	2-dr FsBk Cpe-2P	3297	3097	8,293

JAVELIN — (SIX) — SERIES 70 — The 1969 Javelin had a new twin venturi grille with a round, bull's-eye emblem on the left-hand side. Otherwise, it was largely unchanged. The side stripes were redesigned. There had formerly been two narrow parallel stripes running full-length along the beltline. Now there was a larger C stripe traveling down the mid-side of the car and turning downward at the trailing edge of the front wheelhousing. This change was put into effect on Jan. 9, 1969, so both designs appeared on 1969 models. Another Javelin revision was a new trim treatment for the instrument panel in standard-level cars and extensive use of woodgrained paneling in the Javelin SST interior. Introduced as a midyear addition was the Mod Javelin, which came in the same colors as the Big Bad AMX. Many Mod Javelins were marketed with the Craig Breedlove options package. It included a rooftop spoiler and simulated exhaust rocker mountings. A limited number of Javelins and some Rambler 440s were built in Germany, by Karmann Standard equipment included the safety group; carpets; head restraints; front ashtray and armrests; cigarette lighter; Custom steering wheel; compartment lights; Air Guard system; Flo-Thru ventilation; glovebox lock; heater and defroster; dual horns; front bucket seats; foam front seat cushions; 6.95 x 14 blackwall tires; three-speed manual transmission with floor-mounted control and the 232 cid/145 hp six. Optional V-8s were available. The Javelin SST had all base items plus a Sports steering wheel; reclining bucket seats; full wheelcovers; twin colored side stripes; and mag-style wheels.

JAVELIN SERIES 70

Series No.	Body/Style No.	Body Type & Seating	Factory Price	Shipping Weight	Prod. Total
JAVELIN					
70	6879-5	2-dr FsBk-4P	2512	2826	17,389
JAVELIN SST					
70	6879-7	2-dr FsBk-4P	2633	2836	23,286

AMBASSADOR — (SIX/V-8) — SERIES 80 — The Ambassador received a major face lift for 1969, with an all-new frontal treatment featuring horizontal, quad headlamps. The wheelbase was increased

1968 AMC, Rambler American 440 (Series 01), station wagon, OCW

1968 AMC, Javelin SST (Series 70), fastback hardtop, OCW

1969 AMC, Rambler Rogue (Series 01), hardtop, OCW

1969 AMC, Javelin SST (Series 70), fastback hardtop, OCW

1970 AMC, Gremlin (Series 40), sedan, OCW

above and below, 1968 AMC, AMX (Series 30), fastback hardtop, OCW

1969 AMC, Hurst SC/Rambler (A Group version), hardtop, OCW

1969 AMC, Ambassador SST (Series 80), sedan, OCW

1970 AMC, Hornet (Series 01), sedan, OCW

to 122 inches, a four-inch gain. The track was widened to 60 inches. The new front end had a sculptured hood and a new plastic grille with twin, oblong-shaped inserts finished in black-out style. An Ambassador signature was placed at the left-hand side of the upper insert. Horizontal taillamps were set into a rear deck beauty panel. There were also notch style taillight lenses integral with the rear fender extension caps and viewable from the side of the car. They served as side marker lamps and, directly ahead of them, there was another bright metal Ambassador script. The Ambassador had the same equipment as the Rebel SST, plus standard air conditioning; front sway bar; 8.25 x 14 blackwall tires; and a 155-hp two-barrel version of the 232-cid six. The Ambassador DPL also had wheel discs; DPL interior trim; and special, lower body exterior moldings with vinyl inserts. The Ambassador SST came standard with a clock; individually adjustable reclining seats; column-controlled Shift-Command automatic transmission; and a 200-hp two-barrel V-8, plus all DPL equipment. There was also an SST station wagon with simulated woodgrain exterior paneling on the sides and rear of the body. New custom velour seats and stainless steel side trim were among package options for the SST. All Ambassadors had a higher capacity air conditioning system, too. In most ads of the year, an SST Ambassador was shown with a uniformed chauffeur. "To make an appointment for a test ride," read the copy. "Visit your American Motors dealer. A number of them have chauffeurs available."

AMBASSADOR SERIES 80

Model No.	Body/Style No.	Body Type & Seating	Factory Price	Shipping Weight	Prod. Total
AMBASSADOR					
80	6885-2	4-dr Sed-6P	2914	3276	14,617
AMBASSADOR DPL					
80	6885-5	4-dr Sed-6P	3265	3358	12,665
80	6888-5	4-dr Sta Wag-6P	3504	3561	8,866
80	6889-5	2-dr HT Cpe-6P	3182	3403	4,504
AMBASSADOR SST (V-8)					
80	6885-7	4-dr Sed-6P	3605	3508	18,719
80	6888-7	4-dr Sta Wag-6P	3998	3732	7,825
80	6889-7	2-dr HT-6P	3622	3566	8,998

BASE ENGINES

RAMBLER: Inline six. Overhead valve. Cast iron block. Displacement: 198.8 cid. Bore and stroke: 3.75 x 3.00 inches. Compression ratio: 8.5:1. Brake hp: 128 at 4400 rpm. Seven main bearings. Hydraulic valve lifters. Carburetor: Carter Type RBS-4633S one-barrel.

ROGUE/JAVELIN: Inline six. Overhead valve. Cast iron block. Displacement: 231.9 (232) cid. Bore and stroke: 3.75 x 3.50 inches. Compression ratio: 8.5:1. Brake hp: 145 at 4300 rpm. Seven main bearings. Hydraulic valve lifters. Carburetor: Carter Type RBS-4631S one-barrel.

AMBASSADOR SIX: Inline six. Overhead valve. Cast iron block. Displacement: 231.9 (232) cid. Bore and stroke: 3.75 x 3.50 inches. Compression ratio: 8.5:1. Brake hp: 155 at 4400 rpm. Seven main bearings. Hydraulic valve lifters. Carburetor: Carter Type WCD two-barrel Model 4667S.

BASE V-8: Overhead valve. Cast iron block. Displacement: 289.8 (290) cid. Bore and stroke: 3.75 x 3.28 inches. Compression ratio: 10.0:1. Brake hp: 225 at 4700 rpm. Five main bearings. Hydraulic valve lifters. Carburetor: Carter Type AFB four-barrel Model 4660S.

OPTIONAL V-8: Overhead valve. Cast iron block. Displacement: 343.1 cid. Bore and stroke: 4.08 x 3.28 inches. Compression ratio: 10.0:1. Brake hp: 280 at 4800 rpm. Five main bearings. Hydraulic valve lifters. Carburetor: Carter Type AFB four-barrel Model 4662S.

HIGH-PERFORMANCE V-8: Overhead valve. Cast iron block. Displacement: 390 cid. Bore and stroke: 4.17 x 3.57 inches. Compression ratio: 10.2:1. Brake hp: 315 at 4600 rpm. Five main bearings. Hydraulic valve lifters. Carburetor: Carter Type AFB four-barrel Model 4665S.

CHASSIS FEATURES: Wheelbase: (Rambler/Rogue) 106 inches; (Rebel) 114 inches; (Javelin) 109 inches; (AMX) 97 inches; (Ambassador) 122 inches. Overall length: (Rambler/ Rogue) 181 inches; (Rebel wagon) 198 inches; (Rebel) 197 inches; (Javelin) 182.2 inches; (AMX) 177.2 inches; (Ambassador wagon) 207 inches; (Ambassador) 206.5 inches. Front tread: (Rebel/Ambassador) 60 inches; (other models) See 1968 specifications. Rear tread: (Rebel/Ambassador) 60 inches; (other models) See 1968 specifications. Tires: (all models) See text.

POWERTRAIN OPTIONS: Three-speed manual transmission was standard in most models. Automatic transmission was standard in Ambassador SST with base engine. Overdrive transmission, optional in Rambler and Rebel six ($116). Automatic transmission, optional in all ($171-$223); in Ambassador SST with 343-cid or 390-cid V-8 ($22-$32). Four-speed manual floor shift transmission, in Rogue with 225-hp V-8 ($193). Javelin close-ratio four-speed manual transmission with floor shift ($205). Rambler six-cylinder 223 cid/145 hp one-barrel engine ($45). Rebel six-cylinder 223 cid/155 hp two-barrel engine ($16). Rogue-Javelin V-8 290 cid/225 hp four-barrel engine ($45). Rebel-Ambassador V-8 343 cid/280 hp four-barrel engine ($80). Rebel-Ambassador V-8 309 cid/235 hp two-barrel engine ($52). Javelin V-8 343 cid/280 hp four-barrel engine ($91). AMX V-8 343 cid/280 hp four-barrel engine ($45). AMX V-8 390 cid/315 hp four-barrel engine ($123). Javelin SST/Ambassador SST V-8 390 cid/315 hp four-barrel engine ($168). Heavy-duty 70-amp battery ($8). Heavy-duty battery and 55-amp generator ($26). Heavy-duty cooling system ($53). Dual exhaust as separate V-8 option ($31). Positive traction rear axle ($42). Heavy-duty clutch, in Rambler with three-speed ($5); in Javelin with 200-hp V-8 ($11). Available rear axle gear ratios ($5).

RAMBLER CONVENIENCE OPTIONS: Power brakes ($42). Power steering ($90). Air conditioning ($324). Front and rear bumper guards, except wagon ($25). Special paint color application ($39). Two-tone paint in standard colors ($24). Tinted glass, (Javelin same price), all windows ($32); windshield ($23). push-button radio and antenna, same price all AMC models ($61). Station wagon rooftop travel rack ($39). Individually adjusting reclining bench seats ($52). Custom steering wheel, standard in Rambler 440 and Rogue ($12). Sports steering wheel, available Rambler Rogue only ($30). Automatic transmission oil cooler ($18). Column-shift Shift-Command automatic transmission in Rambler six ($171). Column-shift Shift-Command automatic transmission in 440 with V-8 ($190). Four-speed manual floor shift in Rogue with 225-hp V-8 ($193). Undercoating and underhood insulation pad ($21). Black or white vinyl roof, Rogue only ($79). Full wheel discs ($21). Electric windshield wipers, required in V-8 Ramblers ($15). Air conditioning package includes Solex glass ($387). Code 56-4 Appearance Group with sill moldings and wheel discs ($39). Code 70-1 Handling Package with heavy-duty sway bar, shocks and springs ($17). Light Group, includes door switches, trunk, courtesy, glovebox and other lamps ($23). Visibility Group with outside rearview remote control mirror, electric window/washer etc. ($29). Rambler sedan/hardtop, Size 6.45 x 14 two-ply whitewalls, exchange ($32). Rambler station wagon, six 6.95 x 14 two-ply whitewalls, exchange ($32). Rambler V-8, Size 6.95 x 14 two-ply whitewalls, exchange ($32).

HURST SC/RAMBLER OPTION PACKAGE: Standard equipment on the Group A SC/Rambler included: AMX 390-cid V-8 four-speed all-synchromesh close-ratio transmission; special Hurst shift linkage with T-handle; Sun tach mounted on steering column; dual exhaust system with special mufflers and chrome extensions; functional hood scoop for cold-air induction; Twin-Grip differential; 10-1/2 inch diameter clutch; 3.54:1 axle ratio; front power disc brakes, rear axle torque links; handling package with heavy-duty sway bar, springs and shocks; heavy-duty radiator and cooling system; 20.0:1 manual steering ratio; special application red, white and blue exterior finish; hood lock pins; dual racing mirrors; black-out grille; special emblems on front fenders/rear panel; 14x6-inch color-keyed mag-style wheels; five E70-14 Goodyear Polyglas wide-tread tires; Sports steering wheel; red, white and blue headrests; all-vinyl charcoal trim; full carpeting; individually adjustable reclining seats and more.

AMX/JAVELIN CONVENIENCE OPTIONS: Power brakes ($42). Power steering ($95). Air conditioning ($369). Rear bumper guards only ($13). Special application paint colors ($39). Console all Javelin with Shift-Command/column shift ($53). Javelin, instrument cluster with tachometer and 140 mph speedometer ($50). Automatic transmission oil cooler ($18). Javelin, Rally Side paint stripes, replacing pin stripes ($27). Stereo 8-track tape player, with manual radio ($195). All except Ramblers; AM/FM push-button radio and antenna ($134). Center armrest seat with cushion, bucket seats mandatory, in AMX, with four-speed ($35). Leather, upholstery trim AMX only ($79). Quick ratio manual steering ($16). Shift-Command, column control, in Javelins except SST with 343 V-8 ($223). Shift-Command, floor control, in Javelins with 200/280 hp V-8s ($287). Four-speed close-ratio manual floor shift, except with 200 hp V-8 ($205). Twin-Grip differential ($42). Air-Command ventilation, not available with air conditioning ($41). Wire wheelcovers, 14-inch, base Javelin ($72); Javelin SST and AMX ($51). Black, white or blue vinyl roof, all Javelins/not AMX ($100). Turbo-cast wheelcovers, base Javelin ($67); Javelin SST and AMX ($46). Mag-style wheelcovers, base Javelin only ($94). Six-inch extra-wide wheel rims ($72). Full wheel discs, all Javelins; not AMX ($21). Handling Package group ($19). AMX, higher-rate front and rear springs. Heavy-duty shocks ($19). Light Group, AMX ($20) all Javelins ($23). Electric clock plus, visibility package group ($43). Javelin E70-14 redline tires ($75); same AMX ($34). Go Package (Code 39-1), which retailed for $233.15 on cars with the 343-cid V-8 and $310.85 on cars with the 390-cid engine. It included power disc brakes; E70 redline tires; six-inch wide wheel rims; handling package, Twin-Grip heavy-duty cooling system and black white, red, blue or silver over-the-top racing stripe. The Javelin Go Package (code39-1/2); retailed for $265.50 when the 343-cid V-8 was ordered and $343.25 when the

390-cid engine was specified. It included the V-8; dual exhaust; power disc brakes; E70 wide profile redline tires; six-inch wide wheel rims; handling package; and black fiberglass hood scoops.

REBEL/AMBASSADOR CONVENIENCE OPTIONS: Power brakes, Rebel ($42); Ambassador ($43). Power steering ($100). Rebel air conditioning ($376). Front and rear bumper guards, except wagons ($32). Automatic speed control V-8/automatic ($52). SST Rebel station wagon, simulated woodgrain exterior paneling ($113). All tinted windows, in Ambassador ($39), in Rebel ($36). Automatic transmission oil cooler (standard Ambassador SST) ($18). Exterior paint stripe except SST models and DPL ($14). Power side windows, Ambassador SST/DPL cars ($105), wagons ($140). Duo-coustic rear speakers ($13). Stereo 8-track tape with manual radio, sedans/hardtops only ($134). Individually adjustable reclining seats ($58). Reclining bucket seats with front armrest and center cushion, SST only ($111). Station wagon third seat, includes power tailgate window ($118). Custom velour trim, Ambassador SST sedan, includes stainless trim insert ($68). All-vinyl seat upholstery, bench or individual cushion, standard in wagon ($24). Adjust-O-Tilt steering, automatic required ($45). Rebel Custom steering wheel, standard in SST ($13). Rebel SST and all Ambassadors, Sport-type steering wheel ($30). Shift-Command with column control (standard Ambassador SST) ($201). Shift-Command with column control, Rebel/Ambassador (except SST) with 343-cid V-8 ($223). Shift-Command, Ambassador SST with 343-cid V-8 ($22); with 390-cid V-8 ($37). Shift-Command with floor control, Ambassador (except SST) and Rebel SST ($280). Shift-Command with floor control, Ambassador SST with 343-cid V-8 ($69); with 390-cid V-8 ($79). Black, white or blue vinyl roof, Rebel SST except wagon ($90), Ambassador SST/DPL ($100). Wire wheelcovers, SST and DPL ($51); other models ($72). Turbo-cast wheelcovers, SST and DPL ($46); other models ($67). Full wheel discs, standard SST and DPL ($21). Visibility Group with electric clock, Ambassador SST ($29); others ($43).

HISTORICAL FOOTNOTES: The full-sized Ramblers were introduced Oct. 1, 1968, and the compact lines appeared in dealer showrooms the same day. Model year production peaked at 275,350 units. Calendar year production of 242,898 cars was recorded. R.D. Chapin was the chief executive officer of the company this year. This was the final season that the Rambler nameplate would appear. A total of 4,204,925 Ramblers were sold 1950-1969. Operations were profitable for the second year in-a-row, although AMC's net earnings were only $4.9 million, compared to $11.8 million one year earlier. Retail sales totaled 239,548 cars, an 11.1 percent decrease from 1968 levels. A total of 17,147 cars were made with 390-cid engines during the model year. Four-and-one-half percent had four-speed manual transmissions; 8.2 percent had disc brakes; 22.2 percent had bucket seats; 15.8 percent had vinyl roofs and five percent had styled steel wheels.

1970

HORNET — (SIX) — SERIES 01 — In 1970, the Rambler (American) was replaced with a new car that revived an old name. This was the Hornet, which reminded some people of the days when an AMC family member — Hudson Motors — had championed in stock car racing. The Hornet however, was not a performance car in its basic form. It was a compact, economy model with a modern, but conventional styling theme. It was basically the Rambler/American with a major face lift and more rounded body contours. The new Hornet was offered in two body styles, two- and four-door sedan, and in base or SST trim levels. Standard equipment, in addition to all regulation safety features, included front armrests and ashtrays, 6.45 x 14 blackwall tires and a 199 cid/128 hp six. The Hornet SST also had rear armrests; cigarette lighter; Custom steering wheel; colored carpets; rubber trunk mat; glovebox light; package tray; front foam seat cushions; and a larger, 232-cid six rated at 145 hp.

VEHICLE IDENTIFICATION NUMBERS: The numbering system and code locations were the same as on previous models. The second symbol was changed to 0 to indicate the 1970 model year. The third symbol 0 (indicating overdrive transmission) was no longer used. A new range of seventh symbols (indicating engine types) was adopted, as follows: A = 199-cid six; B = low-compression 199-cid six; E = 232-cid six with one-barrel carburetor; F = low-compression 232-cid six with one-barrel carburetor; G = 232-cid six with two-barrel carburetor; Q = low-compression 232-cid six with two-barrel carburetor; H = 304-cid V-8 with two-barrel carburetor; 1 = low-compression 304-cid V-8 with two-barrel carburetor; M = low-compression 304-cid V-8 with four-barrel carburetor; N = 360-cid V-8 with two-barrel carburetor; P = 360-cid V-8 with four-barrel carburetor; S = 390-cid V-8 with four-barrel carburetor and X = Rebel Machine 390-cid V-8 with four-barrel carburetor. The new Hornet adopted the Rambler/American Series 01 nomenclature. The midyear Gremlin had new Series 40 nomenclature. Other coding and nomenclature was unchanged from the past.

HORNET SERIES 01

Series No.	Body/Style No.	Body Type & Seating	Factory Price	Shipping Weight	Prod. Total
HORNET					
01	7005-0	4-dr Sed-6P	2072	2748	17,948
01	7006-0	2-dr Sed-6P	1994	2677	43,610
HORNET SST					
01	7005-7	4-dr Sed-6P	2221	2765	19,786
01	7006-7	2-dr Sed-6P	2144	2705	19,748

REBEL — (SIX/V-8) — SERIES 10 — The 1970 Rebel received new rear quarter panel styling and a more massive rear bumper. There were two large, horizontal-rectangular taillights with Rebel spelled out between them. There was a new vertically split and horizontally segmented grille. The Rebel SST had a bright metal molding on the front fenders, between the door handle and side marker lights. Model identification lettering was placed behind the front wheel opening and, on SST, below the rear roof pillar. There was similar Rebel lettering on the left lip of the hood. Standard Rebel features began with the regulation safety equipment (used in all 1970 AMC models), plus front and rear armrests (except two-door); front ashtray; cigarette lighter; dome or side lights; rubber trunk mat; dual headlights; front foam seat cushions; E78-14 fiberglass-belted blackwall tires; and 232 cid/145 hp six. The Rebel SST also had rear ashtrays; glovebox lock; dual horns and Custom steering wheel. Another special Rebel-based model was developed, for AMC, by the Hurst Products Co. The Rebel Machine was introduced at the National Hot Rod Association's World Championship Drag Race, in Dallas, Texas, during October 1969. Standard on this model were all Rebel SST features (except rear armrests and ashtrays); high-back bucket seats; Space-Saver spare tire; power front disc brakes; Ram-Air hood scoop; Handling Package; heavy-duty cooling system with Power-Flex fan; carpeting; 15 x 7-inch styled steel wheel; E60-15 fiberglass-belted tires with raised white letters; four-speed manual floor shift transmission and a 390 cid/340 hp four-barrel V-8 with dual exhaust. The Machine had the highest output engine ever used in an American Motors product offered for public sale. Of a total of 2,326 cars run, approximately the first 1,000 units were finished in white, with the lower beltline and hood done in blue. A red stripe traveled down the front fender and along the car to the deckside region. From there, the stripe crossed over the trunk and came back along the opposite bodyside. There were also blue and white stripes over the trunk, behind the red one and integrated into it. Later editions of the model were finished in a choice of solid colors and featured a black-out hood treatment with silver pin striping, plus optional red, white and blue graphics that could be added on the grille and body.

REBEL SERIES 10

Series No.	Body/Style No.	Body Type & Seating	Factory Price	Shipping Weight	Prod. Total
REBEL					
10	7015-0	4-dr Sed-6P	2626	3129	11,725
10	7019-0	2-dr HT Cpe-6P	2660	3148	1,791
10	7018-0	4-dr Sta Wag-6P	2766	3356	8,183
REBEL SST					
10	7015-7	4-dr Sed-6P	2684	3155	13,092
10	7019-7	2-dr HT Cpe-6P	2718	3206	6,573
10	7018-7	4-dr Sta Wag-6P	3072	3375	6,846
REBEL MACHINE (V-8)					
10	7019-7	2-dr HT Cpe-6P	3475	3650	1,936

AMX — (V-8) — SERIES 30 — The 1970 AMX got new rear lamps and a completely restyled front end and that was shared with Javelin performance models. The frontal treatment featured a grille that was flush with the hood and redesigned bumper housing squarish parking lamps. A horizontally divided, cross-hatched grille insert, with prominent bright vertical moldings, was used and also incorporated circular rally lights. The restyled hood had a large Ram-Air induction scoop that took in cold air for the engine. Height was reduced about one inch, while overall length grew about two inches. Standard equipment included all items used with Javelin SST models, plus a heavy-duty 60-amp battery; courtesy lights; rear traction bar; Space-Saver spare tire; tachometer; 140 mph speedometer; 14 x 6-inch styled steel wheels; E78-14 blackwall tires; four-speed manual floor shift transmission and 360 cid/290 hp four-barrel V-8 with dual exhaust system. The metal dashboard plates affixed to 1970 models were numbered 14469 to 18584. This was the final year for the original type AMX, although the nameplate would be used again on performance image Javelin and Hornet-based models.

AMX SERIES 30

Series No.	Body/Style No.	Body Type & Seating	Factory Price	Shipping Weight	Prod. Total
AMX					
30	7039-7	2-dr FsBk Cpe-2P	3395	3126	4,116

GREMLIN — (SIX) — SERIES 40 — Introduced April 1, 1970, the AMC Gremlin was hailed as the first modern U.S.-built sub-compact car. This unique entry was basically a Hornet from the trailing edge of the door forward. The rear styling had a slanted, Kammback theme. It angled from a foot, or so, behind the rear wheel opening (at the bottom) to a point on the roof that was nearly plumb with the rear wheel centerline. Model identification came from a front fender cartoon badge and model name script on the sail panel (between two angular windsplit depressions). The rear was decorated with a circular medallion set into a rectangular depression panel that arched over it. Recessed, rectangular taillamps were seen. A hatch-style rear window was featured on a four-passenger version. The two available models were a two-passenger commuter and the four-passenger version with a fold-down rear seat. Standard features included front armrests; front ashtray; 35-amp alternator (55-amp with air conditioner); dome light; exhaust emissions control system; rubber floor and trunk mats; heater and defroster; split-back front foam seat cushion; wheel trim hubcaps; dual pin stripes; B-rated 6.00 x 13 blackwall Polyester tires; three-speed manual transmission with column-mounted shift controls and 199 cid/128 hp six. The four-passenger model used the rear window liftgate feature and had a foam cushioned rear seat (with folding backrest). Gremlins optionally equipped with the 232-cid six came standard with floor shift transmission controls. A selection of 30 factory-installed options or accessories, plus seven packages, was provided.

GREMLIN SERIES 40

Series No.	Body/Style No.	Body Type & Seating	Factory Price	Shipping Weight	Prod. Total
40	7046-0	2-dr Sed-2P	1879	2497	872
40	7046-5	2-dr Sed-4P	1959	2557	27,688

JAVELIN — (SIX/V-8) — SERIES 70 — The new Javelin shared its basic styling features with AMX, but retained its own twin venturi-type grille without the previous bull's-eye badge. The headlights were better integrated into the nose, sharing a common upper border molding with the main grille. It had the same front bumper, front parking lights and hood as the AMX and, like the two-seat mini-mite, was an inch lower and two inches longer. Standard equipment began with all items (except package tray) that were found on the Hornet SST. Additional features included compartment lights; dual horns; high-back bucket seats; C78-14 tires (D78-14 with V-8) and three-speed manual gearbox with shift control on the floor. The Javelin SST also had a Sports steering wheel with horn-blow rim and full wheel discs. Two limited production Javelin SSTs were offered. The Javelin Trans Am had all SST equipment (minus sill moldings and paint stripes), plus front lower and rear deck spoilers; black vinyl interior; "390" Go-Package; F70-14 glass-belted tires with raised white letters; 14 x 6-inch mag-style wheels; Space-Saver tire with regular spare wheel; AM push-button radio; tachometer and 140 mph speedometer; Visibility Group; Light Group; power steering; Twin-Grip differential; 3.91:1 axle ratio; four-speed gearbox with Hurst floor shift and 390-cid four-barrel V-8 with heavy-duty cooling system. These cars were replicas of the Ronnie Kaplan Trans-Am Racing Team's competition machines and were finished in a three-segment red, white and blue paint scheme created by industrial designer Brooks Stevens. Only 100 cars were built, the amount necessary to make this model eligible for the Sports Car Club of America's popular Trans-Am races under 1969 "formulas." In early 1970, the SCCA formulas were changed and so were the AMC drivers. The new rules demanded 2,500 replicas built to certain specifications. This led to the production of the Mark Donohue Javelin SST. The majority of these cars had a special, thick-walled, 360-cid V-8 and all featured a unique ducktail rear spoiler with Mark Donohue signature script on the right-hand side.

JAVELIN SERIES 70

Series No.	Body/Style No.	Body Type & Seating	Factory Price	Shipping Weight	Prod. Total
JAVELIN					
70	7079-5	2-dr FsBk Cpe-4P	2720	2845	8,496
JAVELIN SST					
70	7070-7	2-dr FsBk Cpe-4P	2848	2863	19,714
JAVELIN/SST "TRANS AM" (V-8)					
70	7079-7	2-dr FsBk Cpe-4P	3995	3340	(100)*
MARK DONOHUEJAVELIN SST (V-8)					
70	7079-7	2-dr FsBk Cpe-4P	—	—	(2,501)*

NOTE 1: *The total of 19,714 Javelin SSTs includes both the Trans-Am and Mark Donohue Javelin models, as these were package models based on the Javelin SST.

AMBASSADOR — (SIX/V-8) — SERIES 80 — A new cross-hatched grille insert pattern characterized the 1970 Ambassador line. The rear quarter panels and bumper were also restyled. A large, rectangular taillamp crossed the back of the car. Trim distinctions between the various models followed the 1969 pattern. Standard equipment for the base Ambassador was the same as for the Rebel SST plus 55-amp alternator; air conditioning; F78-14 blackwall tires and 232 cid/155 hp six. The Ambassador DPL also had full wheel discs; Shift-Command automatic transmission (with base V-8) and a 304 cid/210 hp two-barrel V-8 engine. A standard extra Ambassador SST was individually adjustable reclining front seats. Ambassador DPL station wagons had all the regular DPL features plus cargo area carpets; rooftop travel rack and Dual-Swing tailgate. The Ambassador SST station wagon also had individually adjustable reclining front seats; woodgrained inside door panels; and woodgrained side and rear exterior paneling.

AMBASSADOR SERIES 80

Series No.	Body/Style No.	Body Type & Seating	Factory Price	Shipping Weight	Prod. Total
AMBASSADOR					
80	7085-2	4-dr Sed-6P	3020	3328	9,565
AMBASSADOR DPL (V-8)					
80	7085-5	4-dr Sed-6P	3588	3523	6,414
80	7089-5	2-dr HT Cpe-6P	3605	3555	2,036
80	7088-5	4-dr Sta Wag-6P	3946	3817	8,270
AMBASSADOR SST (V-8)					
80	7085-7	4-dr Sed-6P	3722	3557	19,687
80	7089-7	2-dr HT Cpe-6P	3739	3606	8,255
80	7088-7	4-dr Sta Wag-6P	4122	3852	5,714

NOTE 1: The exact model year output of 1970 Ambassadors was 59,941 cars.

NOTE 2: In figures rounded off to the nearest hundred, the model year output included the following: 3,500 base Ambassador sixes, 6,100 base Ambassador V-8s; 8,400 Ambassador DPLs (V-8 only); 27,900 Ambassador SSTs (V-8 only); 1,000 Ambassador station wagons with six-cylinder power and 13,000 Ambassador station wagons with V-8s.

ENGINES

(BASE SIX) Inline Six: Overhead valve. Cast iron block. Displacement: 199 cid. Bore and stroke: 3.75 x 3.00 inches. Compression ratio: 8.5:1. Brake hp: 128 at 4400 rpm. Seven main bearings. Hydraulic valve lifters. Carburetor: Carter Type YF one-barrel.

(BASE SIX) Inline Six: Overhead valve. Cast iron block. Displacement: 232 cid. Bore and stroke: 3.75 x 3.50 inches. Compression ratio: 8.5:1. Brake hp: 155 at 4400 rpm. Seven main bearings. Hydraulic valve lifters. Carburetor: Carter Type WCD two-barrel.

(BASE V-8) V-8. Overhead valve. Cast iron block. Displacement: 304 cid. Bore and stroke: 3.75 x 3.44 inches. Compression ratio: 9.0:1. Brake hp: 210 at 4400 rpm. Five main bearings. Hydraulic valve lifters. Carburetor: Autolite two-barrel Model 2100.

(REBEL "MACHINE" V-8) V-8. Overhead valve. Cast iron block. Displacement: 390 cid. Bore and stroke: 4.17 x 3.57 inches. Compression ratio: 10.0:1. Brake hp: 340 at 3600 rpm. Five main bearings. Hydraulic valve lifters. Carburetor: Autolite four-barrel Model 4300.

(AMX V-8) V-8. Overhead valve. Cast iron block. Displacement: 360 cid. Bore and stroke: 4.08 x 3.44 inches. Compression ratio: 10.0:1. Brake hp: 290 at 4800 rpm. Five main bearings. Hydraulic valve lifters. Carburetor: Autolite four-barrel Model 4300.

(JAVELIN/SST "TRANS AM" V-8) V-8. Overhead valve. Cast iron block. Displacement: 390 cid. Bore and stroke: 4.17 x 3.57 inches. Compression ratio: 10.0:1. Brake hp: 325 at 5000 rpm. Five main bearings. Hydraulic valve lifters. Carburetor: Autolite four-barrel Model 4300.

("MARK DONOHUE" JAVELIN V-8) V-8. Overhead valve. Cast iron thick-wall block. Displacement: 360 cid. Bore and stroke: 4.08 x 3.44 inches. Compression ratio: 10.0:1. Brake hp: 290 at 4800 rpm. Five main bearings. Hydraulic valve lifters. Carburetor: Autolite four-barrel Model 4300.

CHASSIS FEATURES: Wheelbase: (Gremlin) 96 inches; (AMX) 97 inches; (Javelin) 109.9 inches; (Hornet) 108 inches; (Rebel) 114 inches; (Ambassador) 122 inches. Overall length: (Gremlin) 161-1/4 inches; (AMX) 179 inches; (Javelin) 191 inches; (Hornet) 179.3 inches; (Rebel) 199 inches; (wagon) 198 inches; (Ambassador) 208 inches; (wagon) 207 inches. Front tread: (Gremlin) 57.5 inches; (AMX and Javelin) 59.1 inches; (Hornet) 57.2 inches; (Rebel and Ambassador) 59.7 inches. Rear tread: (Gremlin) 57 inches; (AMX, Javelin and Hornet) 56.6 inches; (Rebel and Ambassador) 60 inches. Tires: See text.

POWERTRAIN OPTIONS: Three-speed manual transmission was standard in most AMC models. Automatic transmission was standard in Ambassador DPL and SST. Shift-Command automatic transmission was optional on all models at various prices. Four-speed manual floor shift transmission in Javelin "360" and "390" V-8s. Close-ratio four-speed manual transmission with floor shift standard in Rebel "Machine" and AMX. Hornet/Gremlin six-cylinder 232 cid/145 hp one-barrel engine ($45). Base Hornet six-cylinder 232 cid/155 hp two-barrel engine ($65). Hornet SST/Rebel six-cylinder 232 cid/155 hp two-barrel engine ($19). Javelin/Ambassador/Rebel (except "Machine") V-8 360 cid/245 hp two-barrel engine ($41). Javelin/Ambassador/Rebel (except "Machine") V-8 360 cid/290 hp four-barrel engine ($86). Ambassador DPL/SST/Rebel SST/Javelin V-8 390 cid/325 hp four-barrel engine ($168). AMX V-8 390 cid/325 hp four-barrel engine ($11). Heavy-duty 70-amp battery ($13). Axle ratios, all optional ($10). Heavy-duty cooling, standard with air ($16). Dual exhaust, as separate option ($31). Twin-Grip positive traction rear axle ($43).

NOTE: Overdrive was no longer available. Three-speed manual floor shift with Gremlin V-8s only (as standard equipment).

GREMLIN/HORNET OPTIONS: Power brakes ($43). Power steering ($96). Air conditioning ($381). Front and rear bumper guards ($25). Locking gas cap ($6). Engine block heater ($16). Gremlin rooftop luggage rack ($39). Special application paint ($39). AM push-button radio ($62). Gremlin white, black or red Rally side stripes ($25). Custom steering wheel, Gremlin ($12). Gremlin Shift-Command with column controls ($195). Wheel disc covers ($25). Electric washer/wipers, Gremlin and Hornet ($20). Tinted glass, Gremlin, all windows ($34); windshield only ($26). Electric clock, in base Hornet only ($16). Air Command ventilation system, Hornet Group only ($41). Tinted glass, Hornet all windows ($34); windshield only ($26). Vinyl insert scuff side molding, Hornet Group ($27). Hornet SST two-tone paint ($24). Hornet Group exterior body striping ($19). Front disc brakes, Hornet Group, except base series ($84). Hornet SST caranaby plaid interior trim ($78). Hornet SST, individual seats fabric trim ($52); vinyl trim ($71). Hornet SST, bench seat, vinyl trim/standard base model ($20). Hornet base models, bench seat, cloth trim/standard SST ($13). Handling Package, Hornet Group ($23). Hornet Group Decor Package, with air ($34); without air ($58). Hornet Light Group Package ($25). Hornet SST, vinyl roof ($84).

REBEL/AMBASSADOR OPTIONS: Power brakes ($43). Power steering ($105). Air conditioning, Rebel Group ($380). Cruise Control, Rebel and Ambassador, with automatic ($60). Front and rear bumper guards, except station wagons ($32). Tinted glass, all windows, Ambassador ($42); Rebel ($37). Tinted windshield, Ambassador ($32); Rebel ($30). Two-tone paint, Rebel/Ambassador sedans and hardtops ($27). Bodyside accent panels and moldings, wagons except Style 7088-7 ($65). Special paint, other than standard ($39). Power side windows, Ambassador DPL/SST passenger cars ($105). Power side and tailgate window, Ambassador DPL/SST wagons ($140). Power tailgate window, standard with third wagon seat ($35). AM push-button radio ($62). AM/FM push-button radio, all AMC except Hornets ($134). Eight-track stereo tape, all Ambassador, except wagons ($134). Third seat Rebel SST and Ambassador DPL/SST wagons, with extras ($118). Vinyl bench seat, Ambassador Style 7085-2 and base Rebel ($24). Individual seat, fabric, Ambassador (standard SST) and Rebels, except "Machine" ($64). Velour individual cushion interior, Ambassador SST sedan ($68). Bucket seats fabric or vinyl Rebel/Ambassador SST hardtop ($123). Sports steering wheel with horn-blow, Ambassador, Rebel SST ($37). Tilt-O-Just steering wheel, Rebel/Ambassador with automatic ($45). Shift-Command, with floor shift, Rebel "Machine" with "390" V-8 ($188). Black, white or blue vinyl roof, Ambassador DPL/SST, except wagons ($106). Black, white or blue vinyl roof, Rebel SST hardtop and sedan ($95). Turbo-cast wheelcovers, Rebel (except "Machine"); Ambassador 7085-2 ($74). Wire wheelcovers, Rebel (except "Machine"), Ambassador Style 7085-2 ($74). Turbo-cast or wire wheelcovers, Ambassador SST or DPL ($49).

JAVELIN/AMX OPTIONS: Power brakes ($43). Power steering ($102). Air conditioning ($380). Rear bumper guards ($13). Command Air ventilation system, without air ($41). Center console, Javelin Group with column automatic shift only ($53). Tinted glass Javelin/AMX prices same as Hornet. Simulated exhaust-type rocker panel moldings, Javelin SST ($32). Simulated exhaust-type rocker panel moldings, base Javelin ($50). AMX two-tone finish with "black shadow" treatment ($52). Rally side stripes, solid color Javelin/AMX ($32). Power front disc brakes, V-8 engine required ($84). Eight-track stereo tape with manual radio/twin rear speakers ($195). Corduroy fabric bucket seats, Javelin SST only ($50). Leather trimmed bucket seats, AMX only ($34). Leather trimmed bucket seats, Javelin SST only ($127). Quick-ratio manual steering, for racing ($16). Javelin Code 533 spoiler roof, not available with vinyl top ($33). Tachometer and 140 mph speedometer with V-8 ($50). Shift-Command, column control, Javelin with "304" V-8 ($200). Shift-Command, column control, Javelin with "360" V-8 ($233). Shift-Command, column control Javelin six ($195). Shift-Command floor control Javelin with "304" V-8 ($264). Shift-Command, floor control, Javelin with "360" V-8 ($287). Shift-Command, floor control AMX with "390" V-8 ($118). Four-speed floor shift, Javelins with 290/325 hp V-8 ($205). Black, white or blue vinyl roof, Javelin only ($84). Turbo-cast wheelcovers, base Javelin ($74) Javelin SST ($49). Wire wheelcovers, base Javelin ($74) Javelin SST ($49). Styled steel wheels, 14 x 6 inch, base Javelin ($98); Javelin SST ($72). The Code 391/2 "Go-Package" retailed for $298.85 on the "360" AMX and $383.90 on the "390" AMX. It included one of these engines; power front disc brakes; F70-14 blackwall tires with raised white letters; Handling Package; heavy-duty cooling system; and functional Ram-Air induction scoop. The Code 391/2 "Go Package" retailed for $321.65 on the "360" Javelin and $409.75 on the "390" Javelin. Features included one of these engines; power front disc brakes; E70-14 redline tires; six-inch wheel rims; Handling Package; AMX Ram-Air hood and dual exhaust.

HISTORICAL FOOTNOTES: The AMC line was introduced Sept. 25, 1969, and the 1970 Gremlin appeared in dealer showrooms April 1, 1970. Model year production peaked at 242,664 units. Calendar year production of 276,110 cars was recorded. R.D. Chapin, Jr., was the chief executive officer of the company this year. A total of 11,125 AMC products, built in the 1970 model year, were equipped with 390-cid V-8 engines. Twenty percent of all AMC cars had bucket seats; 14.9 percent had vinyl roofs; styled wheels were ordered by 4.6 percent of 1970 buyers and four-speed transmission installations were made in 2.6 percent of all cars. The company referred to itself as "the new American Motors" in advertisements and presented buyers with the catch line: "If you had to compete with GM, Ford and Chrysler, what would you do?"

1971

HORNET — (SIX/V-8)— SERIES 01 — The Hornet received no major styling changes for 1971. Two new models were added, however, along with some springtime equipment packages. The new styles were a SST four-door Sportabout station wagon and a Hornet V-8 performance car called the SC/360 two-door sports sedan. Standard equipment on base Hornets was the same as that found on 1971 Gremlins, plus color-keyed rubber floor mats and larger, 6.45 x 14 blackwall tires. The Hornet SST models also had color-keyed carpets; cigarette lighter; Command-Air ventilation; glovebox; full width package tray; Custom steering wheel; and movable rear quarter windows. The Sportabout added a carpeted cargo area; rear liftgate; cargo compartment lock; and Space-Saver spare tire. The SC/360 sports sedan had the same equipment as Hornet SST passenger models plus front sway bar; slot style wheels; Space-Saver spare tire; D70-14 raised white letter tires; and a 360 cid/245 hp two-barrel V-8. Springtime changes included price increases for all Hornet SST V-8s and a Sportabout D/L package including color-keyed woodgrain side and rear panels; roof rack with integral air deflector; Custom wheelcovers; individual reclining seats; woodgrained instrument cluster trim; Sports rim-blow steering wheel; and D/L decals. In addition, free sun roofs were provided as part of several Hornet packages. The SC/360 was designed as a low-priced performance car that could pass as a compact and, thus, side-step rising insurance rates affecting the owners and buyers of such vehicles. Its trim included special around-the-beltline decals with SC/360 call-outs at the trailing edge of rear fenders. Optional, at $199, was a Go-Package that consisted of four-barrel carburetor; Ram-Air induction system; dual exhaust; Handling Package; tachometer; and Polyglas white letter tires. It included a wide hood scoop with black-out paint treatment. American Motors had programmed the model for 10,000 sales, but only 784 buyers were interested. Many expressed hope that the new 401-cid V-8 be offered in this car but insurance and marketing considerations precluded this. The Hornet SC/360 was sold only in 1971.

VEHICLE IDENTIFICATION NUMBERS: The numbering system and code locations were the same as on previous models. The second symbol was changed to a 1 to indicate the 1971 model year. A new third symbol was F (indicating three-speed manual transmission with floor shift). New sixth symbols, designating class of body, were as follows: 0 = Hornet and base Gremlin; 1 = Hornet SC/360. New seventh symbols (indicating engine types) were as follows: A = 258-cid six with one-barrel carburetor; B = 258-cid six, low-compression, with one-barrel carburetor; Z = 401-cid V-8 with four-barrel carburetor.

HORNET SERIES 01

Series No.	Body/Style No.	Body Type & Seating	Factory Price	Shipping Weight	Prod. Total
HORNET					
01	7106-0	2-dr Sed-6P	2174	2654	19,395
01	7105-0	4-dr Sed-6P	2234	2731	10,403
HORNET SST					
01	7106-7	2-dr Sed-6P	2324	2732	8,600
01	7105-7	4-dr Sed-6P	2274	2691	10,651
01	7108-7	4-dr Sta Wag-6P	2594	2827	73,471
HORNET SST SC/360 (V-8)					
01	7106-1	2-dr Spt Sed-6P	2663	3300	784

1970 AMC, Hornet SST (Series 01), sedan, OCW

1970 AMC, Rebel "The Machine" (Series 10), hardtop, OCW

1971 AMC, Matador (Series 10), station wagon, OCW

1971 AMC, Ambassador Brougham (Series 80), hardtop, OCW

1972 AMC, Hornet SST (Series 01), sedan, OCW

1970 AMC, AMX (Series 30), fastback hardtop, OCW

1971 AMC, Hornet Sportabout (Series 01), hatchback sedan, OCW

1971 AMC, Javelin AMX (Series 70), fastback hardtop, OCW

above and below, 1972 AMC, Gremlin (Series 40), sedan (with X option package), OCW

MATADOR — (SIX)—SERIES 10 — The former AMC Rebel became the Matador for 1971. The renamed product was significantly restyled with changes to taillamps; hood; grille; front fenders; bumper and valance panel. Wheelbase was increased to 118 inches. The Matador's appearance was characterized by an integrated bumper/grille; horizontal double-venturi grille insert and triple-rectangular taillight lenses integrated into a horizontal rear beauty panel. Body style offerings were limited to a two-door hardtop, four-door sedan, and four-door station wagon marketed in a single level of trim, but with many available options packages including the high-performance Go Machine group. Standard equipment was the same as for base Javelins plus rear armrests; rear ashtray; full-back bench seat cushion in sedans and wagon/split-back in hardtop; hardtop pillar lights; color-keyed cargo area carpets in wagon (and Dual-Swing tailgate) and three-speed transmission with column shift. The Matador was marketed as a six, with V-8 options. Additional equipment, installed when a V-8 with automatic transmission was ordered, included a transmission oil cooler.

MATADOR SERIES 10

Series No.	Body/Style No.	Body Type &Seating	Factory Price	Shipping Weight	Prod. Total
10	7118-0	4-dr Sed-6P	2770	3165	5
10	7119-0	2-dr HT Cpe-6P	2799	3201	1
MATADOR					
10	7115-7	4-dr Sed-6P	3163	3437	24,918
10	7119-7	2-dr HT-6P	3129	3360	7,661
10	7118-7	4-dr Sta Wag-6P	3493	3596	10,740

GREMLIN — (SIX) — SERIES 40 — Introduced as a midyear 1970 model, the Gremlin was unchanged for 1971 in terms of appearance. A technical revision was seen in the use of the 232-cid six as base engine as the smaller 199-cid six went out of production. There was also an attractive new Gremlin X option package. It was provided only for the four-passenger model at a price of $300 with blackwall tires or $334.35 with raised white letter tires. Included were spear side stripes; black-painted grille; 14 x 6-inch slot style wheels; Space-Saver spare; Custom interior appointments; front bucket seats; special X decals and D70-14 size tires (with raised white letter style considered as an option-within-option). Standard equipment on all Gremlins included 35-amp alternator; front armrests and ashtray; 50-amp battery; dome light; exhaust emissions control; rubber floor mats; bench seats; split-back front foam seat cushion; exterior paint stripes; and 6.00 x 13 black sidewall Polyester tires. The four-passenger model also featured a glovebox door; liftgate type rear window; and rear foam seat cushion with fold-down back. The 232 cid/135 hp six was base engine, with a bigger six optional.

GREMLIN SERIES 40

Series No.	Body/Style No.	Body Type & Seating	Factory Price	Shipping Weight	Prod. Total
40	7146-0	2-dr Sed-2P	1899	2503	2,145
40	7146-5	2-dr Sed-4P	1999	2552	74,763

JAVELIN—(SIX/V-8)—SERIES 70 — The 1971 Javelin was completely restyled. There were highly sculptured raised fenders, a twin-canopy roof with air spoiler-type rear window lip, and new full-width taillamps. The interior was completely redesigned and upgraded. It featured a curved cockpit-type instrument panel inspired by aircraft motifs. Three levels of trim were provided in one two-door hardtop style: base Javelin; Javelin SST and Javelin AMX. This new AMX was a four-place automobile, replacing the former two-seater. A rear-facing cowl induction hood, flush wire mesh grille and optional front and rear spoilers were claimed as the design work of race driver Mark Donohue, who raced Javelins successfully in SCCA Trans-Am competition. Standard equipment on the Javelin was the same as for Hornets plus Custom steering wheel; color-keyed carpets; glovebox lock; dual horns: high-back bucket seats; three-speed manual transmission with floor shift; C78-14 glass-belted tires; cigar lighter; and automatic transmission oil cooler with V-8s. The Javelin SST also had rear ashtray; rim-blow Sports steering wheel; rubber trunk mat; and wheelcovers. The AMX featured all this equipment plus electric clock; center console (without armrest); rear deck mounted spoiler; slot style wheels; E70-14 glass-belted tires; and 360 cid/245 hp two-barrel V-8.

JAVELIN SERIES 70

Series No.	Body/Style No.	Body Type & Seating	Factory Price	Shipping Weight	Prod. Total
JAVELIN					
70	7179-5	2-dr FsBk Cpe-6P	2879	2887	7,105
JAVELIN SST					
70	7179-7	2-dr FsBk Cpe-6P	2999	2890	17,707
JAVELIN/AMX (V-8)					
70	7179-8	2-dr FsBk Cpe-4P	3432	3244	2,054

AMBASSADOR—(SIX/V-8)—SERIES 80—The 1971 Ambassador received a new, die-cast rectangular grille. There were also new front end caps incorporating side marker lights visible in face or profile view. Car-line nameplates were downgraded one notch to make it seem that each line was one level higher. The Ambassador six sedan became the DPL. Offered in SST and top-level Brougham trims were the two-door hardtop and four-door sedans and station wagon. Along with air conditioning (as before) the standard equipment list was expanded to include automatic transmission. The Ambassador six came with all Matador features plus 55-amp alternator; front bumper guards; All-Season air conditioning; Shift-Command transmission; and a 258-cid six. Ambassador SSTs had, in addition, full wheelcovers and a 304 cid/210 hp V-8. Ambassador Broughams also had individually adjustable reclining seats and, for wagons, woodgrained exterior panels on the sides and rear.

AMBASSADOR SERIES 80

Series No.	Body/Style No.	Body Type & Seating	Factory Price	Shipping Weight	Prod. Total
AMBASSADOR DPL SIX					
80	7185-2	4-dr Sed-6P	3616	3315	6,675
AMBASSADOR SST (V-8)					
80	7185-5	4-dr Sed-6P	3852	3520	5,933
80	7189-5	2-dr HT Cpe-6P	3870	3561	1,428
80	7188-5	4-dr Sta Wag-6P	4253	3815	4,465
AMBASSADOR BROUGHAM (V-8)					
80	7185-7	4-dr Sed-6P	3983	3541	13,115
80	7189-7	2-dr HT Cpe-6P	3999	3580	4,579
80	7188-7	4-dr Sta Wag-6P	4430	3862	5,479

BASE ENGINES

(SIX) Inline Six: Overhead valve. Cast iron block. Displacement: 232 cid. Bore and stroke: 3.75 x 3.50 inches. Compression ratio: 8.0:1. Brake hp: 135 at 4400 rpm. Seven main bearings. Hydraulic valve lifters. Carburetor: Carter Type YF one-barrel.

(SC/360 V-8) V-8. Overhead valve. Cast iron block. Displacement: 360 cid. Bore and stroke: 4.08 x 3.44 inches. Compression ratio: 8.5:1. Brake hp: 245 at 4400 rpm. Five main bearings. Hydraulic valve lifters. Carburetor: Autolite two-barrel Model 2100.

(DPL SIX) Inline Six: Overhead valve. Cast iron block. Displacement: 258 cid. Bore and stroke: 3.75 x 3.90 inches. Compression ratio: 8.0:1. Brake hp: 150 at 3800 rpm. Seven main bearings. Hydraulic valve lifters. Carburetor: Carter Type YF one-barrel.

(BASE V-8) V-8. Overhead valve. Cast iron block. Displacement: 304 cid. Bore and stroke: 3.75 x 3.44 inches. Compression ratio: 8.4:1. Brake hp: 210 at 4400 rpm. Five main bearings. Hydraulic valve lifters. Carburetor: Autolite Model 2100 two-barrel.

POWERTRAIN OPTIONS: Automatic transmission was standard in Ambassador SST and Ambassador Brougham. Three-speed manual transmission with floor shift was standard in the Javelin Group. Three-speed manual transmission with column shift was standard in other models. Shift-Command with column shift, in Gremlin ($200); in Hornet six ($210); in Hornet "304" V-8 ($216); in Hornet SC/360 ($238); in Javelin/Matador six ($217); in Javelin/Matador with "304" V-8 ($223); in Ambassador SST/Brougham with "304" V-8 ($6); in Matador/Javelin with "360" V-8, except AMX ($246); in DPL with "360" V-8 ($29); in other Ambassadors with "360" V-8 ($23); in Matador with "401" V-8 ($256) and in non-DPL Ambassadors with "401" V-8 ($33). Shift-Command with floor shift and console, in Matador/Javelin with "304" V-8 and bucket seats ($279); in Brougham with "304" V-8 ($56); in non-AMX Javelin and Matador with "360" V-8 ($302); in AMX with "360" V-8 ($246); in Brougham with "360" V-8 ($79); in non-AMX Javelin and Matador with "401"V-8 ($312); in AMX with "401" V-8 ($256) and in "401" Ambassador Brougham ($89). Four-speed manual transmission with floor shift, available only in Matador with "Go-Machine" package and Javelin Group with 285/330 hp V-8s ($209). (**NOTE:** Some transmission attachment prices increased $4-$7 at midyear). Six-cylinder 360 cid/150 hp engine, in Gremlin and Hornet, except SC/360 ($54); in Javelin and Matador, except AMX ($50). Two-barrel 360 cid/245 hp V-8 in all, except Gremlin/Hornet and except standard in AMX ($48). Four-barrel 360 cid/285 hp V-8 in Javelin AMX ($49); in Matadors, Ambassadors and other Javelins ($97). Four-barrel 401 cid/330 hp V-8 in Javelin AMX ($137); in Matadors, Ambassadors and other Javelins ($137). Optional axle ratios ($12-$14). Heavy-duty 70-amp battery ($14-$15). Twin-Grip differential in Gremlin and Hornet ($43); in all other models ($47). Dual exhaust, in all with "360" four-barrel V-8 ($31). Dual exhaust were standard with the "401" V-8. Engine block heater ($12). Cooling system including heavy-duty radiator, Power flex fan and fan shroud ($16). Cold Start package ($18-$19).

CONVENIENCE OPTIONS: Power brakes ($45-$49). Power steering ($100-$111). Air conditioning ($399). Speed control, Matador/Ambassador ($63). Front and rear bumper guards, Gremlin/Hornet ($20); Javelin/Matador ($32). Locking-type gas cap, Gremlin ($6). Electric clock, in base Hornet only ($17). Electric rear defogger, Javelin/Matador/Ambassador passenger ($52). Front manual disc brakes, Javelin V-8 ($40). Engine block heater, all ($12). Heavy-duty cooling system, all ($16-$18). Tinted glass, all windows; Gremlin ($37); Hornet ($40); Matador/Javelin ($44); Ambassador ($47); Tinted windshield, Gremlin/Hornet ($30); Javelin ($32); Matador ($36); Ambassador ($38); Headlight delay system ($23). Roof luggage rack, Gremlin ($40); Matador wagon ($58). Deck luggage rack, Javelin ($35); Hornet sedan ($32); Sportabout ($47). Bodyside scuff molding, Gremlin/Hornet ($27); Javelin/Ambassador ($31). Two-tone paint, Hornet SST ($28); Matador/Ambassador sedan ($31); wagon ($71); Rally stripe, Javelins except AMX ($37); Gremlin ($30); Hornet (standard). Exterior paint stripe, basic Hornet -- standard Hornet SST -- ($10). Power front disc brakes, SC/360 and Hornet SST V-8 ($84); other V-8 ($89). Power side windows, Ambassador cars ($120); wagons with tailgate ($157). AM push-button radio, Gremlin/Hornet ($67); all others ($72). AM/FM Multiplex stereo, Javelin Group including AMX ($224). AM/FM push-button radio, Matador/Ambassador ($143). AM/radio with 8-track and two speakers, Javelin Group ($207). AM radio with 8-track and two speakers, Matador/Ambassador ($140). Leather bucket seats, Javelin SST/AMX ($84). Corduroy fabric bucket seats, Javelin SST/AMX ($52). Serape fabric reclinable seats, Matador hardtop ($71). Center console, Javelin Group, except standard AMX ($58). Vinyl center armrest bucket seats, Ambassador Style 7189-7 and Matador Style 7119-7 ($136). Fabric reclinable seats, Ambassador SST wagon ($96). "Harem" fabric reclinable seats, Ambassador Brougham passenger models ($75). Third station wagon seat with power tailgate and extras ($118). Custom steering wheel, Gremlin/Hornet ($14). Rim-blow Sports steering wheel, Gremlin/Hornet ($37); Matador/Ambassador ($40). Adjust-O-Tilt steering, Javelin/Matador/Ambassador ($49). Tachometer, Hornet SC/360 only ($50). Station wagon tailgate air deflector, Gremlin ($49); others ($22). Air adjustable rear suspension, Matador/Ambassador ($42). Undercoating, Hornet SC/360 ($18). Undercoating and hood insulation, Gremlin/Hornet ($22). Black, white, blue or green vinyl top, Matador ($97); Ambassador ($108). Standard wheelcovers ($27-$30). Custom wheelcovers ($25-$54). Turbo-cast or wire wheelcovers ($52-$75). Styled steel wheels, Gremlin "X"/AMX with "Go-Package" ($34-$37). Styled steel wheels, most other models ($99-$108); SC/360 ($46). Rear quarter vent windows, basic Hornet ($30). Electric wiper/washers, Gremlin/Hornet, except SC/360 ($21). Electric wiper/washers, Javelin/Matador/Ambassador ($22). Matador station wagon, woodgrained side panels ($117). Black, white, blue or green vinyl roof, Hornet, except SC/360 ($88); Javelin ($89). Calvary Twill recliner seat, Matador wagon ($96). Center armrest and cushion, Javelin without console ($51).

OPTION PACKAGES: (Matador "Go-Machine") $373 on Matador hardtops with "360" V-8/$461.10 on Matador hardtops with "401" V-8, includes selected engine; four-barrel carburetor; dual exhaust; Handling Package; power disc brakes; E60-15 Polyglas raised white letter tires; 15 x 7-inch styled steel wheels and Space-Saver spare tire. (Javelin/AMX "Go-Package") $410.90 on Javelin/AMX with "360" V-8/$498.95 on Javelin/AMX with "401" V-8 includes specified engine; four-barrel carburetor; dual exhaust; hood "T" stripe decal; Rally-Pac instrumentation; Handling Package; Cowl-Air carburetor induction system; heavy-duty cooling components; Twin-Grip differential; power disc brakes; E60-15 Polyglas raised white letter tires; 15 x 7-inch styled steel wheels and Space-Saver spare.

HISTORICAL FOOTNOTES: The full-sized AMC models were introduced Oct. 6, 1970, and the Gremlin appeared in dealer showrooms the same date. Model year production peaked at 244,758 units. Calendar year sales of 256,963 cars were recorded. R.D. Chapin, Jr., was the chief executive officer of the company this year.

1972

HORNET SST—(SIX/V-8)—SERIES 01 — All Hornets were SST models this year. In addition, all were marketed in six and V-8 series for the first time. Physical changes were minor, consisting mainly of trim and ornamentation revisions. One was a "silver line" treatment for the molded plastic radiator grille. There were also new taillights and an aluminum overlay panel below the trunk lid. Two model-creating options packages were available and served to upgrade the level of trim in specific attachments. For example, there was the Sportabout D/L (Deluxe) package that included color-keyed, woodgrained side and rear paneling; roof rack with air deflector; Custom wheelcovers; individually reclining seats; and "D/L" decals. It could be had, on the station wagon only, two different ways. With vinyl upholstery, the price tag was $236.25 and with "Scorpio" fabric upholstery the retail price was $283.55. A sporty "X" package priced at $118.55 included Sports steering wheel; Rally stripes; wide rocker panel moldings; slot-styled wheels; C78-14 tires; and special "X" emblems. The two-door sedan "X" package included the same equipment, less wide rocker panel moldings, at the same price. A designer series Hornet Sportabout was created by famed Italian fashion genius Dr. Aldo Gucci. It featured beige seats and door panels trimmed with red and green stripes. The Gucci crest appeared on the inside door panel, front fenders and headliners. Available in just four exterior colors -- Snow white; Hunter green; Grasshopper green and Yuca tan -- the Gucci Sportabout registered sales of 2,583 units. Standard Hornet equipment features began with all items found in Gremlins plus rear armrest; rear ashtray; cigarette lighter; two coat hooks; color-keyed carpets; cargo mat; 16-gallon gas tank; glovebox; full-width package tray; Custom steering wheel; and three-speed manual transmission with column shift. The Hornet Sportabout also had carpeting in the rear cargo area; rear liftgate; cargo compartment lock and Space-Saver spare tire. A Space-Saver spare was also standard on any Hornet with optional styled steel wheels. The 232-cid six-cylinder engine was the base powerplant and tire sizes varied with each different engine. Size 6.45 x 14 blackwall tires came as regular equipment with sixes. However, 6.95 x 14 tires were used with sixes having an air conditioner and were standard with V-8-powered sedans and Sportabouts. An improved type of Torque-Command automatic transmission was optionally available this year. A special Hornet Rallye model trim package was available in 1972 only with a special Hornet Rallye stripe treatment along the lines of the 1972 SC/360 stripe treatment, on two-door Hornets. It consisted of pleated vinyl bucket seats; manual disc brakes; handling package; 20:1 quick-ratio manual steering; fully-synchromesh three-speed manual transmission; three-spoke Sports steering wheel (15 inch); and "Rallye" emblems on rear fenders.

VEHICLE IDENTIFICATION NUMBERS: The numbering and code locations were the same as on previous models. The second digit was changed to a 2 to indicate the 1972 model year. A new third symbol was the Code E (indicating fully synchronized three-speed manual floor shift). There were also several new possibilities for the sixth symbol, (indicating class of body) as follows: 5 = Gremlin or Ambassador SST; 7 = Hornet SST, Sportabout, Matador, Javelin SST or Ambassador Brougham; 8 = Javelin AMX. New seventh symbols (indicating engine type) were as follows: M = 304-cid V-8 with low-compression and two-barrel carburetor (instead of "I"). Other codes were carried over from earlier years without change.

HORNET SST SERIES 01

Series No.	Body/Style No.	Body Type & Seating	Factory Price	Shipping Weight	Prod. Total
01	7206-7	2-dr Sed-6P	2199/2337	2627/2861	27,122
01	7205-7	4-dr Sed-6P	2265/2403	2691/2925	24,254
01	7208-7	4-dr Sta Wag-6P	2587/2725	2769/2998	34,065

NOTE 1: Data above slash for six/below slash for V-8.

MATADOR — (SIX/V-8) — SERIES 10 — The Matador was also marketed as a six/V-8 series for the first time this year. The 1972 Matador was fighting an identity crisis and was sometimes promoted as "A car you probably never heard of." In attempting to give it an image, AMC redesigned the grille. Ads highlighted the Matador's use by the Los Angeles Police Department. A horizontally lined, segmented pattern grille insert with three color-keyed bars amounted to the major frontal change. The rear also had new lamps and center panel trim, while the side of the car had a dual length pin stripe treatment. Old-fashioned cable controls in the heating system were switched to a vacuum operated type. Standard equipment was the same as used on 1972 Javelins, plus a front sway bar and 19.5-gallon fuel tank. The hardtop came with two side pillar lights and split-back bench seat. Station wagons had four plastic coat hooks; cargo compartment lock; Dual-Swing tailgate; and a larger, 258-cid base six. Tires were E78-14 blackwalls on passenger car models; G78-14 on station wagons. The base V-8 was the same as the Hornet SST's base V-8.

MATADOR SERIES 10

Series No.	Body/Style No.	Body Type & Seating	Factory Price	Shipping Weight	Prod. Total
10	7215-7	4-dr Sed-6P	2784/2883	3171/3355	36,899
10	7219-7	2-dr HT Cpe-6P	2818/2917	3210/3394	7,306
10	7218-7	4-dr Sta Wag-6P	3140/3239	3480/3653	10,448

NOTE 1: Data above slash for six/below slash for V-8.

GREMLIN — (SIX/V-8) — SERIES 40 — Since it was essentially a chopped-off Hornet, it made sense to market the Gremlin the same way: as a six or V-8. The two-seater was dropped, though. Stuffing the 304-cid V-8 engine into such a small package did require some engineering modifications. Special drivetrain and suspension components were used. Standard equipment included front armrests and ashtrays; 50-amp battery; dome light; rubber floor mats and trunk mat; glovebox door; heater and defroster; foam seat cushions; split-back front seat; fold down rear seat; 21-gallon fuel tank; opening-type tailgate; three-speed manual gearbox (with choice of column or floor controls); hubcaps; 37-amp alternator; exhaust emissions controls; exterior paint stripe; and blackwall tires. Size 6.00 x 13 rubber was used with the basic six; size 6.45 x 14 with air-conditioning or V-8s.

Also found on V-8-equipped models were a front sway bar and rear deck "5-Litre V-8" badge. A few new pieces of safety equipment used on all AMC products this year were three-point seat belts linked to a seat belt warning buzzer. The Gremlin, though small, was well-built and well-equipped. *Popular Mechanics* magazine wrote, "The best put-together cars out of Detroit this year may come out of Wisconsin...where American Motors makes them."

GREMLIN SERIES 40

Series No.	Body/Style No.	Body Type & Seating	Factory Price	Shipping Weight	Prod. Total
40	7246-5	2-dr Sed-4P	1999/2153	2494/2746	94,808

NOTE 1: Data above slash for six/below slash for V-8.

NOTE 2: Exactly 10,949 Gremlin V-8s were built in the model year.

JAVELIN SST — (SIX/V-8) — SERIES 70 — Small styling changes were the order of the year on Javelin SST. A new taillight treatment and grille were seen. The grille was a gridwork formed by three long, horizontal bright moldings and 11 shorter vertical bars. At the rear, there was full-width cross-hatch type decorative patterning in two rows on both Javelin and Javelin AMX. The Javelin AMX, however, used a different radiator grille design, which matched the center-bulge horizontal blade pattern of 1971. For the 1972 Javelin SST, French fashion designer Pierre Cardin created the Cardin-Javelin option. It featured an interior of multi-colored pleated stripes in Chinese red, plum, white and silver on a black background. Five exterior color choices were: Snow white; Stardust silver; Diamond blue; Trans-Am red; and Wild plum. Experts say that a few Cardin-Javelins left the factory with midnight black finish. The crest of the House of Cardin was applied to door panels and front fenders. Production amounted to 4,152 units for the designer special. Performance, too, was part of 1972 Javelin history, as George Follmer won a second SCCA Trans-Am title for AMC this year. The standard equipment list for the Javelin SST was the same as for Hornets, with several deletions or additions. For example, no rear armrest was used. There were, however, such items as a glovebox lock; dual horns; high-back bucket seats with front foam cushions; three-speed manual (full-synchromesh) transmission with floor control; Custom steering wheel; and C78-14 blackwall tires on sixes (D78-14s on V-8s). The Javelin AMX also had a Sports steering wheel; deck mounted spoiler; slot-style wheels with E70-14 blackwall tires; and standard 304-cid V-8.

JAVELIN SERIES 70

Series No.	Body/Style No.	Body Type & Seating	Factory Price	Shipping Weight	Prod. Total
JAVELIN SST					
70	7279-7	2-dr FsBk Cpe-4P	3807/2901	2875/3118	22,964*
JAVELIN AMX (V-8)					
70	7279-8	2-dr FsBk Cpe-4P	3109	3149	3,220

NOTE 1: Prices and weights above slash are for six/below slash for V-8.

***NOTE 2:** Totals include 100 Javelin 401 Alabama State Police Interceptors.

AMBASSADOR — (V-8) — SERIES 80 — The 1972 Ambassador received just a few changes, the most noticeable one being a new radiator grille. It incorporated three heavy horizontal bright blades that, together with thinner vertical blades, formed a grid of large, square openings. There was an Ambassador chrome signature script at the left-hand side. The rearview also reflected two changes: new taillights and an attractive center trim panel. Six styles were provided in two levels of trim: SST or Brougham. A six was not available. Standard equipment began with all items found in or on Matadors plus a big 55-amp alternator (to provide a strong electrical system with standard air conditioning); rear armrests; front and rear bumper guards on hardtops and sedans; inside hood release; power brakes; Torque Command gearbox; and the 304-cid V-8. The Brougham also had wheelcovers. All models, except station wagons, used E78-14 blackwall tires. Wagons came without the rear bumper guards, but had carpeted cargo spaces; rooftop luggage racks; and H78-14 tires. Brougham wagons had a tailgate air deflector and woodgrained exterior paneling. With prices beginning under $4,000, the Ambassador Eight was a bargain.

AMBASSADOR EIGHT SERIES 80

Series No.	Body/Style No.	Body Type & Seating	Factory Price	Shipping Weight	Prod. Total
AMBASSADOR SST					
80	7285-5	4-dr Sed-6P	3885	3537	11,929
80	7289-5	2-dr HT Cpe-6P	3902	3579	986
80	7288-5	4-dr Sta Wag-6P	4270	3833	5,256
AMBASSADOR BROUGHAM					
80	7285-7	4-dr Sed-6P	4002	3551	16,432
80	7289-7	2-dr HT Cpe-6P	4018	3581	4,137
80	7288-7	4-dr Sta Wag-6P	4437	3857	5,624

BASE ENGINES

NOTE: SAE net horsepower (nhp) ratings measuring output at the rear of the transmission with all accessories installed and operating are now used.

(BASE SIX) Inline Six. Overhead valve. Cast iron block. Displacement: 232 cid. Bore and stroke: 3.75 x 3.50 inches. Compression ratio: 8.0:1. SAE nhp: 100 at 3600 rpm. Seven main bearings. Hydraulic valve lifters. Carburetor: Carter Type YF one-barrel.

(BASE STATION WAGON SIX) Inline Six. Overhead valve. Cast iron block. Displacement: 258 cid. Bore and stroke: 3.75 x 3.90 inches. Compression ratio: 8.0:1. SAE nhp: 110 at 3500 rpm. Seven main bearings. Hydraulic valve lifters. Carburetor: Carter Type YF one-barrel.

(BASE V-8) V-8. Overhead valve. Cast iron block. Displacement: 304 cid. Bore and stroke: 3.75 x 3.44 inches. Compression ratio: 8.4:1. SAE nhp: 150 at 4400 rpm. Five main bearings. Hydraulic valve lifters. Carburetor: Autolite two-barrel Model 2100.

CHASSIS FEATURES: Wheelbase: (Gremlin) 96 inches; (Hornet) 108 inches; (Javelin) 110 inches; (Matador) 118 inches; (Ambassador) 122 inches. Overall length: (Gremlin) 161.3 inches; (Hornet) 179.3 inches; (Javelin) 191.8 inches; (Matador) 206 inches; (Ambassador) 210.8 inches. Front tread: (Gremlin and Hornet) 57.5 inches; (Javelin) 59.3 inches; (Matador and Ambassador) 59.9 inches. Rear tread: (Gremlin and Hornet) 57 inches; (Javelin, Matador and Ambassador) 60 inches.

POWERTRAIN OPTIONS: Torque-Command transmission was standard in Ambassador Series models with the base V-8 and was optional in other models at 15 different prices determined by series and engine attachment. The prices ranged from $200 for Gremlin/Hornet sixes to $257 for Matadors with the "401" V-8. In addition, Torque-Command was a $23 option for Ambassadors with the "360" V-8 and $35 extra in those with the big "401" V-8. Three-speed manual transmission with floor shift was available, as an option in Gremlin/Hornet models ($32). Torque-Command with floor shift was optional in Javelins, with the "304" V-8 ($282); with the "360" V-8 ($293) and with the "401" V-8 ($305). Four-speed manual was optional in Javelins only in combination with the four-barrel "360" V-8 or "401" V-8 ($188). The big 258-cid six was optional, in Gremlin/Hornet Group ($51), in Javelin SST ($43) in Matador passenger cars ($46). The 360-cid two-barrel V-8 was optional in Hornet/Javelin Group ($42). The 360-cid four-barrel V-8 was optional in Javelin ($85); in Matador/Ambassador ($89). The 401-cid four-barrel V-8 was optional in Javelin Group ($162) and in Matador/Ambassador Group models only when F78-14 tires were also used ($170). Optional axle ratios, all models ($12-$14). Heavy-duty 70-amp battery ($14-$15). Twin-Grip differential ($43-$46). Dual exhaust with "360" V-8 and four-barrel, standard with "401" V-8 ($28-$31). Heavy-duty cooling system ($16). A cowl-air induction system was included in "Go-Package" option groups.

CONVENIENCE OPTIONS: All-Season air conditioning, all models except Ambassador ($377). Gremlin/Hornet air conditioning package ($473). Front and rear bumper guards, Gremlin/Hornet ($21); Javelin ($29); Matador/Ambassador ($31). Center armrest cushion, Javelin without console ($54). Rear window defogger, Javelin ($45); Matador/Ambassador ($48). Front manual disc brakes, Gremlin/Hornet with 14-inch wheels ($47); Javelin ($47); Matador/Ambassador ($50). Engine block heater, Matador/Ambassador ($16); all others ($14). Tinted glass, all windows; Gremlin ($37); Hornet/Javelin ($40); Matador ($42); Ambassador ($49). Tinted windshield only, Gremlin/Hornet/Javelin ($30); Matador ($35). Tinted glass standard with air conditioned Ambassador. Headlights-off delay ($21). Gremlin, locking gas cap ($6). Station wagon rooftop luggage rack, Matador ($56); Sportabout, including air deflector ($61). Rear deck luggage rack, Hornet sedan ($32); Javelin SST ($32). Rally side stripes, Gremlin/Javelin SST ($33-$39). Hood "T" Stripe, AMX ($39). Color-keyed woodgrain panels, Sportabout ($95); Matador wagon ($113). Power brakes, Gremlin/Hornet/Javelin ($44) and Matador ($47). Power front disc brakes, Hornet with Rallye package ($32), Hornet/Gremlin ($79), Javelin ($77), Matador ($81), and Ambassador ($50). Power steering, Gremlin/Hornet, with 14-inch wheels only ($99); Javelin ($106) and Matador/Ambassador ($111). Power side window lifts, Matador Ambassador only ($123). Power tailgate window, in Matador/Ambassador wagons without third seat ($35). All power windows package, Ambassador wagon only ($158). AM push-button radio Gremlin/Hornet/Javelin ($66). AM/FM Multiplex stereo with two rear speakers, Javelin ($196), Matador/Ambassador ($230). Stereo tape player in Javelin with manual radio ($190). Gremlin bench seat with Custom trim ($79). Gremlin bucket seats with Custom trim ($117). Hornet Group "Scorpio" fabric trim with reclining seats ($109). "Harem" fabric trim in Ambassador Brougham ($69); in Ambassador Brougham wagon ($96). Matador/Ambassador wagon third seat, includes two safety belts, cargo mat and power tailgate window ($108). Adjustable rear air shocks, Matador/Ambassador ($40). Functional lower front spoiler, Javelin AMX with disc brakes ($31). Quick-ratio manual steering, 20:1 ratio with Gremlin/Hornet ($11); Javelin Group, 16:1 ratio ($15). Adjust-O-Tilt steering wheel, Gremlin/Hornet with Torque-Command and Javelin ($43); Matador/Ambassador ($46). Three-spoke Sports steering wheel, Gremlin ($33); Hornet/Javelin, standard AMX ($19); Matador/Ambassador ($20). Sun roof, Hornet two-door sedan without vinyl top, Sportabout and Gremlin ($142). Black; white; blue; green or brown vinyl roof, on Hornet/Javelin ($88); on Matador passenger models ($91);

and Ambassador passenger models ($109). Full wheelcovers ($72-$79). Custom wheelcovers ($50-$53). Turbo-Disc wheelcovers, Hornet D/L ($25); most other models ($75-$78) and Ambassador Brougham ($50). Spoke-style wheels (including Space-Saver spare on all except Matador/Ambassador), for cars with options packages that include special spoke wheel prices ($34-$50); on others ($99-$104).

OPTION PACKAGES: Gucci Sportabout package featured beige seats and door panels trimmed with red and green stripes. The Gucci crest appeared on the inside door panel, front fenders and headliners. Available in special exterior colors. Javelin Cardin bucket seats and Cardin trim for Javelin SST only ($85). Individual reclining seat with Hornet Sportabout Gucci trim ($142). Code 391 Javelin AMX "360 Go-Package", includes: specified engine; dual exhaust; hood "T" stripe decal; black-out rear panel; Rally-Pack instrumentation; Handling Package; Cowl-Air induction; heavy-duty cooling; Twin-Grip differential; power disc brakes; E60-15 Polyglas raised white letter tires; 15 x 7-inch styled steel wheels; and Space-Saver spare with regular 14-inch wheels ($428). Code 392 Javelin AMX "401 Go-Package", includes all above with 401-cid V-8 ($505). Code 633 Hornet sedan Rally-Package, includes vinyl bucket seats; manual front disc brakes; Handling Package; quick 20:1 ratio manual steering; three-speed floor shift transmission; Sports steering wheel; and "Rallye" emblems ($119). Gremlin "X" package, includes full-length spear decal; painted grille; 14 x 6-inch slotted wheels; D70-14 tires; Space-Saver spare; Custom bucket seat interior; cargo region insulation; 15-inch Sports steering wheel; and interior appointments package with special decals ($285.10 with regular tires; $319.55 with raised white letter tires).

HISTORICAL FOOTNOTES: The 1972 AMC models were introduced Sept. 22, 1971. Calendar year production peaked at 279,132 units. AMC set a record dollar sales total of $1.4 billion and pulled down a $30.2 million profit. The AMC Buyer Protection Plan was used as a 1972 sales motivation tool.

1973

HORNET—(SIX/V-8) — American Motors' popular compact was offered in 1973 with a new hatchback model. This brought to four the number of Hornet body styles. The third "door" combined the functions of window and trunk lid. It was top hinged and fully counter-balanced for easy opening and closing. The Hornet had new front fenders, a recessed hood with raised center crease line, and a new full-length grille. *CAR and DRIVER* magazine called the 1973 Hornet hatchback "the styling coup of '73" and this was used by AMC in one of its advertisements. An interesting Levi's Jean-style interior was added as a new option on June 20, 1973. The Hornet offered plenty of interior room, good economy, and a high degree of mechanical reliability. Standard equipment and trim continued in the pattern of earlier years.

VEHICLE IDENTIFICATION NUMBERS: The numbering system and code locations were the same as on previous models. The first symbol was changed to a "3" to indicate the 1973 model year. The third symbol "F" was no longer used. It had previously designated three-speed manual transmission with non-synchromesh first gear. A new fifth symbol was "3", used to designate the new three-door hatchback body. There were several variations in sixth symbols, as follows: "5" = Gremlin, "7" = Hornet hatchback, Hornet Sportabout, Matador, Javelin, Ambassador Brougham, and "8" = Javelin AMX. The coding system was otherwise unchanged.

HORNET SERIES 01

Series No.	Body/Style No.	Body Type & Seating	Factory Price	Shipping Weight	Prod. Total
01	7306-7	2-dr Sed-6P	2298/2436	2777/2990	23,187
01	7305-7	4-dr Sed-6P	2343/2481	2854/3067	25,452
01	7303-7	2-dr Hatch-5P	2449/2587	2818/3031	40,110
01	7308-7	4-dr Sta Wag-6P	2675/2813	2921/3134	44,719

NOTE 1: Data above slash for six/below slash for V-8.

MATADOR—(SIX/V-8)—SERIES 10 — The Matador received a new grille. It consisted of four groups of slim rectangles stacked triple high. In the center of each rectangle was a short horizontal molding. There were new interior colors and fabrics, too. It was marketed with carry-over sixes and V-8s. The Matador was again a hit with the Los Angeles Police Department, which added more Matadors to its fleet.

MATADOR SERIES 10

Series No.	Body/Style No.	Body Type & Seating	Factory Price	Shipping Weight	Prod. Total
10	7315-7	4-dr Sed-6P	2814/2853	3289/3502	33,822
10	7318-7	4-dr Sta Wag-6P	3197/3278	3627/3815	11,643
10	7319-7	2-dr HT Cpe-6P	2887/2986	3314/3527	7,067

NOTE 1: Data above slash for six/below slash for V-8.

GREMLIN — (SIX/V-8) — The basic Gremlin remained the same as last year's model. About the only significant changes were new safety bumpers and 6.45 x 17 standard sized tires. Equipped with the base 258-cid six, the Gremlin had lots of "guts" and averaged about 20 mpg of gas...excellent for 1973. The Gremlin was a lot heavier than other early subcompacts and better-suited to sustained high-speed touring. It was, however, plagued by ills such as carburetion; cooling; squeaking; and rattles. It was also quite prone to rust. New for 1973 were several optional equipment changes. A new bodyside trim design had the stripe "hopping up" behind the rear wheel opening and continuing to the rear of the fender at the higher level. It was used on the Gremlin "X", which also had special decals; painted grille; Custom interior appointments; bucket seats; slotted-style wheels; Space-Saver spare tire; and added cargo area sound insulation. A Levi's Gremlin package was also available, reproducing an authentic "blue jeans" look in a spun nylon version of denim for seats, door inserts and map storage pockets. There was also the orange stitching and copper rivets as found on real jeans. Standard equipment features for 1973 were essentially unchanged.

GREMLIN SERIES 40

Series No.	Body/Style No.	Body Type & Seating	Factory Price	Shipping Weight	Prod. Total
40	7346-5	2-dr Sed-4P	2098/2252	2642/2867	122,844

NOTE 1: 11,672 V-8 Gremlins were made in calendar 1973.

NOTE 2: Prices and weights above slash are for six/below slash for V-8.

GREMLIN SERIES 40 ENGINES: See 1972 Gremlin Series engines.

JAVELIN — (SIX/V-8) — SERIES 70 — The Javelin and Javelin AMX sports hardtops featured a new, smooth roofline. A new taillight treatment, with twin-pod lamps at each side of the car, was adopted. The Javelin AMX was unchanged otherwise, but the Javelin base models had a recessed plastic grille that was distinctive from the past. It was flush with the front of the car and incorporated rectangular Rallye lights. Bucket seats were standard in both Javelin and Javelin AMX lines, along with interior packaging of the aircraft cockpit-type. Both cars featured spoiler lips over the rear window, with a rear spoiler optional on AMX. Standard equipment was similar to that offered in 1972. A special model called the "Trans-Am Victory Javelin" was offered in 1973. It had a decal on the rear of the front fenders stating that the Javelin had won the SCCA Trans-Am championship for 1971 and 1972. Besides the decal, 14-inch slotted-style wheels with E70-14 raised white letter tires and Space-Saver spare were included at no extra charge. An advertisement featured George Follmer and Roy Woods, who had won the championship for AMC in 1972.

JAVELIN SERIES 70

Series No.	Body/Style No.	Body Type & Seating	Factory Price	Shipping Weight	Prod. Total
JAVELIN					
70	7379-7	2-dr FsBk Cpe-4P	2889/2983	2868/3104	25,195
JAVELIN AMX (V-8)					
70	7379-8	2-dr FsBk Cpe-4P	3191	3170	5,707

NOTE 1: Data above slash for six/below slash for V-8.

AMBASSADOR — (V-8) — SERIES 80 — Luxury was a key word in describing the 1973 Ambassador line of hardtop, sedan and station wagon. The SST Series was discontinued and Broughams were exclusively retained. A 304-cid V-8; automatic transmission; power steering; power front disc brakes; white sidewall tires; tinted glass; and AM radio were all standard Ambassador Brougham features. Guard-rail steel door beams, for side impact protection, were part of the construction after Jan. 1, 1973. In addition, a quieter type of seat belt warning buzzer was used. Styling features included a slightly redesigned grille with heavier vertical and horizontal moldings. The Ambassador signature was gone from the left side. On the front bumper, a black rubber impact strip appeared. There was a hood insulation pad; left outside rearview remote-control mirror; visor vanity mirror; electric clock; and electric, variable-speed windshield wipers on every 1973 Ambassador sold. All cars were also undercoated, for protection against rust. Three optional V-8s were offered.

AMBASSADOR SERIES 80

Series No.	Body/Style No.	Body Type & Seating	Factory Price	Shipping Weight	Prod. Total
80	7385-7	4-dr Sed-6P	4461	3763	31,490
80	7389-7	2-dr HT Cpe-6P	4477	3774	5,534
80	7388-7	4-dr Sta Wag-6P	4861	4054	12,270

NOTE 1: Data above slash for six/below slash for V-8.

BASE ENGINES

NOTE: SAE net horsepower (nhp) ratings measuring output at the rear of the transmission with all accessories installed and operating are now used.

1972 AMC, Javelin SST (Series 70), fastback hardtop, OCW

1973 AMC, Hornet X (Series 01), hatchback coupe, OCW

1973 AMC, Matador (Series 10), sedan, OCW

above and below, 1975 AMC, Matador (Series 10), coupe (with X option package), OCW

1972 AMC, Ambassador Brougham (Series 80), station wagon, OCW

1973 AMC, Hornet Sportabout D/L (Series 01), station wagon, OCW

1974 AMC, Gremlin (Series 40), sedan, OCW

1975 AMC, Hornet D/L (Series 01), sedan, OCW

1976 AMC, Pacer (Series 60), hatchback coupe (with D/L option package), OCW

(BASE SIX) Inline Six. Overhead valve. Cast iron block. Displacement: 232 cid. Bore and stroke: 3.75 x 3.50 inches. Compression ratio: 8.0:1. SAE nhp: 100 at 3800 rpm. Seven main bearings. Hydraulic valve lifters. Carburetor: Carter Type YF one-barrel.

(BASE STATION WAGON SIX) Inline Six. Overhead valve. Cast iron block. Displacement: 258 cid. Bore and stroke: 3.75 x 3.90 inches. Compression ratio: 8.0:1. SAE nhp: 110 at 3500 rpm. Seven main bearings. Hydraulic valve lifters. Carburetor: Carter Type YF one-barrel.

(BASE V-8) V-8. Overhead valve. Cast iron block. Displacement: 304 cid. Bore and stroke: 3.75 x 3.44 inches. Compression ratio: 8.4:1. SAE nhp: 150 at 4400 rpm. Five main bearings. Hydraulic valve lifters. Carburetor: Autolite two-barrel Model 2100.

CHASSIS FEATURES: Wheelbase: (Gremlin) 96 inches; (Hornet) 108 inches; (Javelin) 110 inches; (Matador) 118 inches; (Ambassador) 122 inches. Overall length: (Gremlin) 165.5 inches; (Javelin) 192.3 inches; (Ambassador) 212.9 inches; (Matador) 208.5 inches; (Hornet) 184.9 inches. Front tread: (Gremlin) 57.5 inches; (Hornet) 56.4 inches; (Javelin) 59.3 inches. Rear tread: (Gremlin/Hornet) 57 inches; (Javelin/Ambassador/Matador) 60 inches. Tires: (Hornet) 6.95 x 14; (Matador) E78-14; (Ambassador) F78-14; (Javelin) D78-14 and (Gremlin) 6.45 x 14.

POWERTRAIN OPTIONS: Torque-Command automatic transmission with column control was standard in Ambassador Broughams. Three-speed manual transmission with full synchromesh first gear and floor shift was standard in Gremlins -- optional in all other models, except Ambassadors. Other available transmissions for AMC cars included Torque-Command with column control; Torque-Command with floor shift; three-speed manual with column control (standard in all except Gremlin/Javelin/Ambassador) and, in select applications, four-speed manual with floor-mounted Hurst heavy-duty shifter. Engine choices for Gremlins were the 232 cid/100 hp six; 258 cid/110 hp six and 304 cid/150 hp V-8. These engines, plus a 360 cid/175 hp two-barrel V-8, were available in Hornets. Specific Matador models could also be ordered with a 360 cid/195 hp four-barrel V-8 or a 401 cid/255 hp four-barrel V-8. These same choices were also available for Javelin and Javelin AMX. Available in the Ambassador Brougham were the 150, 175, 195 and 255 hp engines (all V-8) with similar specifications. Optional rear axle ratios: 2.73:1; 2.87:1 and 3.54:1.

CONVENIENCE OPTIONS: Gremlin "X" package ($285). Sportabout D/L package ($284). "Gucci" vinyl interior, in Hornet ($142). Javelin AMX "360" Go-Package ($428). Javelin AMX "401" Go-Package ($476). Power brakes, standard in Ambassador ($44). Power disc brakes, standard in Ambassador ($79). Manual disc brakes ($47). Sun roof ($142). Station wagon third seat, includes two safety belts and power tailgate window ($108). Reclining seats average price ($80). Bucket seats, in selected models ($131). Power steering, Gremlin ($99). Factory air conditioning, Gremlin ($377). Vinyl roof, on Hornet ($88). Factory air conditioning, Javelin/Javelin AMX ($377). AM/FM stereo, Javelin/Javelin AMX ($196). Vinyl covered top, Javelin AMX ($88). AM/FM stereo, in Matador ($230). Vinyl covered top, on Matador except station wagon ($91). Power windows ($123). AM/FM stereo, in Ambassador ($61). Vinyl covered top, on Ambassador ($109).

HISTORICAL FOOTNOTES: Model year output for 1973 American Motors' models was registered at exactly 320,786 cars. The company held only a 3.3 percent share of the total car business. R.D. Chapin, Jr., continued as the firm's chief executive officer this year. Introduced on the American Motors' Jeep Wagoneer line this year was the innovative "Quadra-Trac" full four-wheel-drive system.

1974

HORNET — (SIX/V-8) — SERIES 01 — The styling seen on 1974 AMC Hornets was slightly revised. A new energy-absorbing front bumper looked much the same as before, but the full-width vinyl impact strip was replaced by rubber-faced bumper guards spaced widely apart, just inboard d the grille-mounted Rallye lights. The grille itself still consisted of many fine, vertical louvers, but the horizontal center bar that integrated the lamps was now finished in black. A new side trim treatment featured a thin, straight upper beltline molding that ran from the taillamps to the front fender tip and, then, down around the side marker light, with a shape paralleling the front fender edge contour. A second full-length molding ran from below the taillamp (and above the rear bumper end) to a point under the front side marker light. This molding was also straight, except in those places where it curved over the front and rear wheel openings. The Hornet nameplate was removed from the lip of the hood. Model nameplates seen alongside the car were moved from their 1973 position (on the upper cowlsides) to a point just behind the front side marker lights. Standard equipment for the basic Hornet began with all items found on Gremlins plus rear ashtray; color-keyed carpets; 16-gallon fuel tank; full-width package tray; Custom steering wheel; foam front bench seat; full-flow oil filter; three-speed manual column shifted transmission; 6.95 x 14 blackwall tires and, on all models except the hatchback, rear armrests. The Sportabout wagon and hatchback models also had cargo area carpeting, fold-down rear seats and a rear liftgate. Standard equipment on Hornet V-8s was a front sway bar. On cars with the optional 360-cid two-barrel V-8, a 60-amp battery was used in place of the regular 50-amp type.

VEHICLE IDENTIFICATION NUMBERS: The numbering system and code locations were the same as on previous models. The second symbol was changed to a "4" to indicate the 1974 model year. There were several possible changes in other symbols. The range of sixth symbols, indicating model, was modified as follows: "5" = Gremlin; "7" = Hornet; Javelin; Matador or Ambassador Brougham; "8" = Javelin AMX or Matador X; "9" = Matador Brougham; "P" = police car and "T" = taxicab. The range of seventh symbols, indicating type of engine, was modified as follows: "A" = 258-cid one-barrel six; "E" = 232-cid one-barrel six; "H" = 304-cid two-barrel V-8; "N" = 360-cid two-barrel V-8; "P" = 360-cid four-barrel V-8 and "A" = 401-cid four-barrel V-8. The range of eighth symbols was modified as follows: Cars coded 1-6 were built in Kenosha, Wis., and those coded 7-9 were built in Brampton, Ontario, Canada. Other coding was as in the past.

HORNET SERIES 01

Series No.	Body/Style No.	Body Type & Seating	Factory Price	Shipping Weight	Prod. Total
01	7403-7	2-dr Hatch-5P	2849/2987	2815/3042	55,158
01	7406-7	2-dr Sed-6P	2774/2912	2774/3001	29,950
01	7405-7	4-dr Sed-6P	2824/2962	2841/3068	29,754
01	7408-7	4-dr Sta Wag-6P	2987/3049	2908/3135	71,413

NOTE 1: Data above slash for six/below slash for V-8.

MATADOR — (SIX/V-8) — SERIES 10 — AMC drastically restyled the Matador two-door coupe. Sedans and wagons had modest changes with new grilles and front/rear bumpers. A big difference in appearance was the dropping of the integrated bumper/grille for a centrally divided unit with vertical louvers, square headlamp surrounds with Argent silver finish; round parking lamps mounted in grille (inboard of headlights) and Matador lettering on the left-hand hood lip. The front bumper was a shelf-like affair with center license plate indent flanked by rubber-faced bumper guards. Side trim on the sedans and wagons consisted of a thin, straight, three-quarter length molding. It ran from behind the front wheel opening to above the rear side marker light. There were model nameplates on the front fender, behind the wheel cutout. Standard equipment was the same as on base Javelins plus front sway bar; full insulation package including undercoating; 19.5-gallon fuel tank; side molding vinyl inserts; Custom steering wheel; full-back bench seats; and base six or V-8 engine. The 232-cid one-barrel six or 304-cid two-barrel V-8 were standard in sedans along with E78-14 blackwall tires. The base station wagon also included a rubber cargo area mat; lockable hidden storage compartment, Dual-Swing tailgate, H78-14 tires and bigger 258-cid one-barrel base six. Vinyl inserts were not used on side moldings on woodgrained wagons. The two-door Matador coupe was unique with its long, low, fast-looking silhouette. AMC enthusiasts compared it to the Jensen Interceptor. Major styling features were a long fast-sloping hood and a short rear deck. It was conceived with stock car racing in mind. After Mark Donohue captured the SCCA's Trans-Am Series championship in 1971, AMC created a factory racing team with Donohue as driver and Roger Penske as team manager. By the time the car hit the production stage, the Energy Crunch had negated the effect of performance on sales. But, 6,165 coupes with a fancy "Cassini" package were produced in 1974 and 1,817 more the following season. Matador coupes had a shorter wheelbase than sedans and wagons. They also had some equipment differences over these models, including split-back front seats and front door light switches. There was also a special Matador X. It was a full-fledged sub-model (not an option such as the Gremlin X), with extras including a three-spoke Sports steering wheel; with bodyside stripes; hood stripes; slotted-style wheels; blacked-out grille; Matador X cowl nameplates; automatic transmission; and two-barrel 304-cid V-8. Finally, for the low-buck luxury buyer, there was the Matador Brougham coupe with all base equipment, plus black vinyl bumper nerfing strips and full wheelcovers.

MATADOR SERIES 10

Series No.	Body/Style No.	Body Type & Seating	Factory Price	Shipping Weight	Prod. Total
MATADOR					
10	7415-7	4-dr Sed-6P	3052/3151	3444/3659	27,608
10	7416-7	2-dr Cpe-6P	3096/3195	3459/3674	31,169
10	7416-9	2-dr Brgm Cpe-6P	3249/3348	3486/3701	21,026
10	7418-7	4-dr Sta Wag-6P	3378/3477	3769/3957	9,709
MATADOR X (V-8)					
10	7416-8	2-dr Cpe-6P	3699	3674	10,074

NOTE 1: Data above the slash for six/below slash for V-8.

GREMLIN — (SIX/V-8) — SERIES 40 — There was a new grille for the 1974 Gremlin, but it didn't look totally fresh and new. A multitude of thin, horizontal blades filled a slightly taller opening. The molding around the entire insert was different. The side pieces had a bend instead of being straight. To complement the grille pattern, there were horizontal grooves on the headlight door/fender extension panels. They began just outside the grille surround and swept around the front body corners, with the upper grooves being interrupted by the headlamp lenses. A new bumper, of the energy-absorbing type, was used. It had a shelf-like appearance and black, rubber-faced guards. A Gremlin script was again placed on the left front face of the scoop-like hood bulge. Several new trim variations could be seen on the side of the Gremlin. The thin moldings, formerly used around the windsplits on the rear sail panels, were removed. In addition, the bodyside stripes were entirely redone. The overall effect was somewhat like that of a hockey stick with a pointed handle lying on its bottom edge. Changes in the rear included a thinner bumper; an AMC letter badge on the left side of the indentation panel; new, rubber-faced guards; and chrome bullet-shaped lamps surrounding the license plate (which was in a new location at the center). Standard equipment on the basic Gremlin included all regulation safety features; front armrests and ashtrays; 50-amp battery; dome light; rubber floor and trunk mats; glovebox door; heater and defroster; foam-cushioned split-back front seat; rear seat with fold-down back; 21-gallon fuel tank; opening-type rear liftgate; three-speed manual transmission with floor shift; hubcaps; 35-amp alternator; exterior paint stripes; and either the base 232-cid six or 304-cid V-8. Standard tires were 6.45 x 14 blackwalls and V-8s also had a front suspension sway bar.

GREMLIN SERIES 40

Series No.	Body/Style No.	Body Type & Seating	Factory Price	Shipping Weight	Prod. Total
40	7446-5	2-dr Sed-4P	2481/2635	2855/3094	171,128

NOTE 1: Data above slash for six/below slash for V-8.

NOTE 2: A total of 14,137 Gremlin V-8s were produced in model year 1974.

JAVELIN — (SIX/V-8) — SERIES 70 — Few cars see major changes in their last season. The Javelin, which was about to bite the dust, followed this long tradition for 1974. About the best way to tell 1973 and 1974 base models apart is to drive them. In the 1974 version, you will immediately notice the new three-point lap/shoulder harness with ignition interlock. In addition, the latter cars may go faster due to emission control advances. There were federally mandated bumper design changes, to ensure the cars could meet five mph impacts. This was done with the addition of shock-absorber mountings and black rubber bumper guards. The molding around the grille insert had an inverted trapezoid shape. On the AMX, red, white and blue letters were placed in the center of the grille. Circular rallye-style parking lamps were set into larger circles creating a bombsight appearance. Standard equipment included all items found on base Hornets (except rear armrests), plus dual horns; foam-cushioned high-back front bucket seats; front and rear bumper guards; manual front disc brakes; rubber trunk mat; D78-14 blackwall tires, three-speed manual floor shift transmission; a 232-cid six or 304-cid V-8 engine; and a front sway bar. Extra standard equipment for the AMX included a Sports steering wheel; deck mounted rear spoiler; and slotted-style wheels. Javelin AMX Go-Packages were supplied, with the price depending on what kind of tires the customer ordered and which engine was installed.

JAVELIN SERIES 70

Series No.	Body/Style No.	Body Type & Seating	Factory Price	Shipping Weight	Prod. Total
JAVELIN					
70	7479-7	2-dr FsBk Cpe-4P	2999/3093	2875/3117	22,556
JAVELIN AMX (V-8)					
70	7479-8	2-dr FsBk Cpe-4P	3299	3184	4,980

NOTE 1: Data above slash for six/below slash for V-8.

NOTE 2: Javelins and AMXs were never assembled in Canada, though some were assembled in foreign plants from U.S. made parts.

AMBASSADOR BROUGHAM—(V-8)—SERIES 80—The 1974 Ambassador received a completely new frontal treatment, which was more squared-off and designed to meet a new federal five mph barrier crash test. The grille surround was completely straight (though not flat) on top and bottom and outlined the entire grille including the dual headlights. These units had round lenses mounted in square bezels. A fine-grid pattern insert was divided, horizontally by two thicker bright moldings forming three levels of background gridwork. There was a stand-up hood ornament and Ambassador lettering on the left-hand hood lip. The new bumper, which no longer housed the park/turn lamps, was slightly thicker at the center and had an overall shelf-like look. There was a license plate indentation at the middle, flanked by a chrome and rubber guard on each side. Vinyl nerfing strips appeared at each end, wrapping around the corners. Side trim consisted of a straight, three-quarter length strip of chrome running from behind the front wheel opening to the rear of the car; rocker panel moldings; Ambassador nameplates in back of the front wheels; and, on station wagons, redesigned woodgrained paneling positioned higher on the bodysides. Two-door Ambassadors were dropped due to the Matador coupe's restyling. The two previously shared sheet metal from the cowl back. It was felt the new coupe was not suitable for the Ambassador market. Remaining were sedans and wagons, available in only Brougham level trim. Standard equipment included all items found on base Hornets plus a 62-amp generator; front and rear bumper guards; inside hood release; air conditioning; full insulation package; light group; visibility group; undercoating and hood insulation; power front disc brakes; power steering; push-button AM radio; tinted glass in all windows; dual headlights; wheel opening moldings; bright metal rocker panel accents; and the 304-cid two-barrel V-8. Ambassador Brougham station wagons came with an in-the-floor lockable cargo compartment; Dual-Swing tailgate; durable color-keyed carpeting for cargo area; exterior woodgrained trim; rooftop travel rack; and tailgate air deflector. It was the last season that the Ambassador would be offered.

AMBASSADOR BROUGHAM SERIES 80

Series No.	Body/Style No.	Body Type & Seating	Factory Price	Shipping Weight	Prod. Total
80	7485-7	4-dr Sed-6P	4559	3872	17,901
80	7488-7	4-dr Sta Wag-6P	4960	4115	7,070

BASE ENGINES

NOTE: SAE net horsepower (nhp) ratings measuring output at the rear of the transmission with all accessories installed and operating are now used.

(BASE SIX) Inline Six. Overhead valve. Cast iron block. Displacement: 232 cid. Bore and stroke: 3.75 x 3.50 inches. Compression ratio: 8.0:1. SAE nhp: 100 at 3600 rpm. Seven main bearings. Hydraulic valve lifters. Carburetor: Carter Type YF one-barrel.

(BASE STATION WAGON SIX) Inline Six. Overhead valve. Cast iron block. Displacement: 258 cid. Bore and stroke: 3.75 x 3.90 inches. Compression ratio: 8.0:1. SAE nhp: 110 at 3500 rpm. Seven main bearings. Hydraulic valve lifters. Carburetor: Carter Type YF one-barrel.

(BASE V-8) V-8. Overhead valve. Cast iron block. Displacement: 304 cid. Bore and stroke: 3.75 x 3.44 inches. Compression ratio: 8.4:1. SAE nhp: 150 at 4400 rpm. Five main bearings. Hydraulic valve lifters. Carburetor: Autolite two-barrel Model 2100.

CHASSIS FEATURES: Wheelbase: (Hornet) 108 inches; (Matador coupe) 114 inches; (other Matadors) 118 inches; (Gremlin) 96 inches; (Javelin) 110 inches; (Ambassador) 122 inches. Overall length: (Hornet) 187 inches; (Matador coupe) 209 inches; (other Matadors) 215.5 inches; (Matador "X") 209.4 inches; (Gremlin) 170.3 inches; (Javelin) 195.3 inches; (Ambassador) 219.3 inches. Front tread: (Gremlin) 57.5 inches; (Hornet) 56.4 inches; (Javelin) 59.3 inches. Rear tread: (Gremlin/Hornet) 57 inches; (Javelin/Ambassador/Matador) 60 inches. Tires: (Hornet) 6.95 x 14; (Matador) E78-14; (Ambassador) F78-14; (Javelin) D78-14 and (Gremlin) 6.45 x 14.

POWERTRAIN OPTIONS: Torque-Command automatic transmission with column control was standard in Ambassador Broughams with the base 304-cid V-8. Torque-Command was also standard in the Matador "X" with the base 304-cid V-8. Three-speed all-synchromesh manual transmission with floor control standard in Gremlin/Javelin groups. Three-speed all-synchromesh manual transmission with column control was standard in all other models. Torque-Command was optional in Ambassador Broughams and Matador "X" with 360-cid or 401-cid V-8s ($13-$35). Torque-Command was optional in all other models, with prices and attachments governed by series and type of engine ($200-$257). Torque-Command with floor shift control was optional in Hornet/Gremlin groups with prices and attachments governed by model and type of engine ($220-$251). Torque-Command with floor shift control and center console was optional in Javelins ($280-$305); in Matadors ($291-$316) and in Matador "X" ($59-$84) with price depending on choice of the 304, 360 or 401 V-8s; not available in sixes. Four-speed manual transmission with floor shift control was optional in Javelins with the 232-cid one-barrel six or 304-cid two-barrel V-8 ($188). Four-speed manual transmission with Hurst floor shifter was available in the Javelin AMX only as part of the "Go-Package" option. A 51-amp alternator was optional in Hornet/Gremlin/Matador groups ($13) and with air conditioning. A 62-amp generator was optional in the Matador group ($48). An 80-amp heavy-duty battery was optional in Ambassador/Matador groups ($21). A 10-inch heavy-duty clutch was optional in Gremlin/Hornet/Matador six ($12). A coolant recovery system was optional in Matador/Ambassador ($19). Heavy-duty cooling system, in Matador/Ambassador ($17). Dayco "DS-7" fan belt ($5). Heavy-duty "360" and "401" V-8, in Matador/Ambassador with heavy-duty Torque-Command only ($32). Manual low gear lock-out, with Matador V-8 and automatic transmission only (no charge). Dual exhaust were available as a separate option for the 360 V-8 and were standard with the 401 V-8. Engine option choices for the year included: 304-cid V-8 two-barrel with 150 nhp at 4200 rpm, 360-cid V-8 two-barrel with 175 nhp at 4000 rpm; 360-cid V-8 four-barrel with 195 nhp at 4400 rpm (single exhaust) and 220 nhp at 4400 rpm (dual exhaust); and 401-cid V-8 four-barrel with 235 nhp at 4600 rpm (single exhaust) and 315 nhp at 3100 rpm (dual exhaust). The 360-cid two-barrel engine was the minimum required engine size for cars sold in California. Prices for powertrain options now based on engine/transmission package (i.e.: Matador X/360 V-8/Torque-Command with floor shift and console package was $71.35 above Matador base price, which included regular Torque-Command and a 304-cid V-8).

POPULAR CONVENIENCE OPTIONS: Air conditioning, except Ambassador ($400). Air conditioning package, in Gremlin/Hornet ($490). Matador wagon vinyl roof ($100). Gremlin "X" hatchback package ($227). Gremlin "X" hatchback package with Levi's trim ($298). Hornet Sportabout D/L package, with vinyl trim ($284); with Custom fabric trim ($333). Hornet Sportabout "X" package ($139). Rooftop travel rack on Matador wagon ($56). Scuff side molding, except specific models ($38). Two-tone paint, on Hornets, except Sportabout ($30); on Matador/Ambassador, except wagons ($37). Special paint application, including painted bodyside panels and accent moldings, on Matador wagon ($69). Rally side stripes, on Gremlins ($33); on base Javelin ($38). Hood "T" stripes on Javelin AMX without "Go Package" -- standard with ($39). Color-keyed woodgrained exterior paneling, on Sportabout ($95); on Matador wagon, including rear panel ($113). Power brakes, except Matador/Javelin/Ambassador groups ($44). Front power disc brakes ($32-$81). Power steering ($99-$111). Power side windows, Ambassador only ($123). Power tailgate window, Matador/Ambassador two-seat wagons ($35); three-seat wagons (no charge). AM push-button radio ($66-$70). AM/FM push-button radio ($179); AM/FM Multiplex radio with four speakers, in Javelin/Matador/Ambassador ($161-$230). Stereo tape player, Javelin/Ambassador ($196-$200). Domino fabric trim in Hornet hatchback ($99); in Javelin ($47); in Hornet hatchback "X" ($50). Individual reclining seats with Venetian fabric special interior in Hornets ($109). Third seat with belts and power windows, Matador/Ambassador wagons ($108). Adjust-O-Tilt steering wheel ($43-$46). Sports steering wheel, in Gremlin ($33). Aluminum trim rings and hubcaps, Gremlin/Javelin ($33). Black, white, blue, green, brown or cinnamon vinyl roof, on Matadors ($91); on Ambassadors ($109); on Hornet/Javelin coupes ($88). Full wheelcovers ($27-$29). Custom wheelcovers ($23-$50). Javelin 14 x 7-inch slotted wheels ($205). Spoke-style 14 x 6-inch wheels on cars with "D/L", "X" or "Go" packages ($34-$49); as a separate option ($74-$104). Vent rear quarter windows in Gremlin/Hornet coupe ($28). Deluxe, intermittent electric windshield wipers ($23-$24).

OPTION PACKAGES: Gremlin Custom trim, includes: Custom door and seat trim in pleated vinyl; carpeting; extra insulation; Custom steering wheel; wheel opening and drip moldings; and cargo insulation, with bench seat ($109), with bucket seat ($147). Gremlin "X" package, includes: spear side decal; 14 x 6-inch slot wheels; Space-Saver spare with base D70-14 tires; Custom trim with bucket seats: cargo insulation; carpeting; 15-inch steering wheel; special interior appointments; and decals, with base tires ($314), with raised white letter tires ($349), with whitewall radial tires ($298), and with raised white letter radials ($410). Handling package ($23-$30). Hornet hatchback "X", includes: Sports steering wheel; rally stripes; slot wheels; "X" emblems, insulation; vinyl bucket seats; Space-Saver spare; and hidden compartment ($207). Levi's Custom trim package, includes: bucket seats with blue denim trim and Levi's buttons; special door trim; sun visors; insulation; denim litter container; blue headliner; front fender Levi's emblem; and, in Gremlin, carpets; cargo insulation and Custom steering wheel, in Gremlin ($165), in Hornet hatchback ($150), in Hornet hatchback "X" ($101). Levi's Custom trim package, in Gremlin "X" ($50). Rally-Pac instrumentation, in Javelin ($77). Gremlin/Hornet hatchback Rally "X" package, includes: three-speed floor shift or automatic; power steering; manual front disc brakes; gauges; black dash cluster; and leather Sports steering wheel, "X" models only, with air conditioning ($100); without ($199). Sportabout D/L package, includes: Sports steering wheel; rally stripes; slot wheels; and "X" emblems, with vinyl trim ($264), with Custom fabric trim ($313). Designer series Cassini Matador Brougham included Custom wheelcovers with copper-colored inserts; scuff moldings; a copper-colored vinyl roof; copper grille and headlamp bezels; black-carpeted trunk compartment and tire cover; special black seat and door trim with copper buttons; black headliner; black instrument panel with copper dials and overlays; black steering wheel with copper inserts in horn rim; and copper-colored floor carpeting ($299). The upholstery in this model was quite lavish, with the individually reclining seats covered in a rich, black nylon knit fabric having a tufted look. The "Oleg Cassini of Paris, France" crest was embroidered on each front headrest and also appeared, in medallion form, on the trailing edge of front fenders below the "dipping" feature line molding. Javelin AMX Go-Package included: (with 360-cid V-8) hood "T" stripe decal; black-finished rear panel; Rally-Pac instrumentation; Handling Package; heavy-duty cooling system; Twin-Grip differential; power disc brakes; slot-style wheels; Space-Saver spare; and FR78-14 raised white letter tires on 14-inch wheels ($372.30). Same with E60-15 tires and 15-inch slot-style wheels ($413.35). "401 Go-Package" includes the same features, but larger V-8 ($420.50 or $461.55, respectively). AMC also offered specially priced, factory-installed fleet options and fleet option packages.

HISTORICAL FOOTNOTES: Model year production introductions were scheduled for Sept. 15, 1973. Model year production was an all-time high of 509,496 units. Calendar year production peaked at 351,338 cars. Only 3,734 AMC models had 401-cid V-8 engines installed this year. Calendar year sales by dealer franchises in the United States totaled 355,093. Model year ended in November 1974 instead of June 1974, to take advantage of easier 1974 emission laws. This partly accounts for the large model year production figures. R.D. Chapin, Jr., was chairman and chief executive officer of AMC. A net profit of $28.6 million was made in a season that saw an energy conscious public shun the purchase of all new cars and, especially those reputed to be gas guzzlers. Luckily, AMC's traditional image did not place it deeply into this group. All 1974 AMC engines were designed to run on regular leaded, low lead or no lead fuels.

1975

HORNET — (SIX/V-8) — SERIES 01 — Four models made up the compact Hornet Series for 1975: hatchback; Sportabout sedan/station wagon and two-door sedan. A new grille featured a bold, six segment motif and had five bright vertical division bars against blacked-out vertical louvers within each segment. The outboard divisions contained new rectangular parking lamps. There was also a slightly different look to the front bumper, which was smoother and rounder in general appearance. Six trim packages were available; the sedan offering a new D/L group with individually reclining front seats and cut-pile carpets. It also included a bodyside molding (between the wheelwells at mid-body height), wheelcovers and special emblems. Then, there was the Hornet "X" group with such items as slot-style wheels; "X" emblems and full-length Rallye striping along the upper feature line. The hatchback and Sportabout could be had with the all-new "Touring" option. Cars with extra-cost decor trim had a different side molding treatment than described in the 1974 section. Basically, the full-length lower molding was gone. Standard equipment for the base Hornet followed the same pattern described in detail for 1974 models, plus electronic ignition. Identification came from Hornet nameplates right behind the front side marker lamps and on the right rear panel. There were also AMC badges on the left-hand side of the rear panel.

VEHICLE IDENTIFICATION NUMBERS: The numbering system and code locations were the same as for previous models with the second symbol changed to a "5" to indicate the 1975 model year. There were several possible changes in other symbols. The range of third symbols was modified as follows: the symbol "M" (for four-speed manual transmission) was dropped; the symbol "D" (three-speed manual floor shift with overdrive) and "O" (three-speed manual column shift with overdrive) were added. The range of fourth symbols now included "6" (for Series 60, Pacer). The fifth symbol "9" (two-door hardtop) was no longer used. Sixth symbols were now as follows: "5" = Gremlin; "7" = Hornet/Matador/Pacer; "P" = Police and "T" = Taxi. All other coding was the same used previously.

HORNET SERIES 01

Series No.	Body/Style No.	Body Type & Seating	Factory Price	Shipping Weight	Prod. Total
01	7503-7	2-dr Hatch-5P	3174/3312	2839/3085	13,441
01	7505-7	4-dr Sed-6P	3124/3262	2881/3147	20,565
01	7506-7	2-dr Sed-6P	3074/3212	2815/3061	12,392
01	7508-7	4-dr Sta Wag-6P	3374/3512	3844/3878	39,563

NOTE 1: Model year output totaled 85,961 units. Of these cars 77,886 were sixes and 8,075 were V-8s.

NOTE 2: Prices and weights above slash are for six/below slash for V-8.

MATADOR (COUPE) — (SIX/V-8) — SERIES 10 — After 1974, the Matador coupe was distinct from the four-door styles. This year, American Motors emphasized the difference by placing the two types into different series. The sedan and wagon were moved into the 80 Series slot, vacated by the Ambassador Brougham. That left the Matador coupe, by itself, in Series 10. Newly styled road wheels; front disc brakes and radial tires were standard equipment in the Matador "X" coupe. Styling changes included a new grille with full-length horizontal bars forming a rectangular pattern. The standard engine was the 258-cid six, with three V-8s optional. Eighty-nine cars left the factory with 401-cid V-8 engines though that engine was not on the normal equipment list. Factory records indicate four 401s were Matador coupes. The other 84 were used in Series 80 four-door sedans and wagons, probably law enforcement models. The electronic ignition system was now standard. Other regular features were the same as 1974. The

Matador "X" coupe was, technically, an option package, with a $199 price tag. Also remaining available was the Cassini Coupe of which 1,817 found buyers this season.

MATADOR (COUPE) SERIES 10

Series No.	Body/Style No.	Body Type & Seating	Factory Price	Shipping Weight	Prod. Total
10	7516-7	2-dr Cpe-6P	3446/3545	3562/3734	22,368

NOTE 1: Prices and weights above slash are for six/below slash for V-8.

GREMLIN — (SIX/V-8) — SERIES 40 — The Gremlin was basically unchanged for 1975. Standard equipment was the same as the previous year, plus electronic ignition system. Mechanical detail changes included a sturdier manual transmission and the optional availability of overdrive combined with six-cylinder attachments only. Also provided again, at extra cost, were the Levi's, Rally and Gremlin "X" packages. The "hockey stick" striping pattern was carried over on cars so-equipped. New body colors and radial-ply tires could be added. A slightly cleaner looking front bumper was used. Its upper edge had a single-bevel appearance, compared to the triple-bevel 1974 type. Also, the sail panel windsplit indentations were now in a slanted, vertical position and the flared wheel treatment was more subdued. Close inspection would also reveal that the bumper guards had a more wedge-shaped contour. Even with such refinements, no one had trouble spotting the Gremlin in a crowd. An interesting fact is that the price of the V-8 now came in at a dollar per pound.

GREMLIN SERIES 40

Series No.	Body/Style No.	Body Type & Seating	Factory Price	Shipping Weight	Prod. Total
40	7546-5	2-dr Sed-4P	2798/2952	2694/2952	56,011

NOTE 1: Model year output totaled 56,011 units. Of these 52,601 were sixes and 3,410 were V-8s.

NOTE 2: Prices and weights above slash are for the six/below slash for V-8.

PACER — (SIX) — SERIES 60 — The AMC Pacer was introduced on March 1, 1975, as a midyear model. It was billed as the first wide, small car, as it was 77 inches wide but had a short 100-inch wheelbase. The Pacer had many unique features including a passenger side door that was larger than the driver's door and one of the first rack and pinion steering systems available on a U.S. built car. The car was available, for 1975, only as a two-door hatchback. It had a short, fast-sloping hood, since it was originally designed to use General Motors' front-wheel drive Wankle rotary power unit. The cancellation of that program, by GM, forced AMC to re-engineer the car on short notice. It was transformed into a rear-wheel drive, piston-engine configuration. The only powerplant provided was the 232-cid six. Although its overall length was a compact-sized 171.5 inches, the Pacer's interior roominess matched or exceeded that of its full-sized contemporaries. It had a low beltline and large expanses of glass, giving extremely good visibility (and excellent motivation for air conditioning sales). The unconventional body featured a large rear window liftgate with dual, gas-filled cylinders for easy opening. With the rear seat folded, the cargo area expanded to nearly 30 cubic feet. Classified as a two-door sedan, buyers could order the "bubbly" vehicle as a base trim model, a sporty Pacer "X", or a lavish little Pacer "D/L".

PACER SERIES 60

Series No.	Body/Style No.	Body Type & Seating	Factory Price	Shipping Weight	Prod. Total
BASE PACER					
60	7566-7	2-dr Sed-6P	3299	2995	72,158
PACER "X" OPTION					
60	7566-7	2-dr Spt Sed-5P	3638	N/A	N/A
PACER "D/L" OPTION					
60	7566-7	2-dr DeL Sed-6P	3588	N/A	(19,050)

NOTE 1: Factory literature indicates that the optional reclining seats were available only as part of the Pacer D/L package. Industry records show that 26 percent of all 1975 Pacers had these seats. Based on these facts, it can be estimated that 19,050 Pacer D/L models were built during the 1975 model year.

MATADOR — (SIX/V-8) — SERIES 80 — Moved to a higher-numbered series, the Matador four-door styles featured new hoods, grilles and bumpers. The hood was flatter and the center crease ran into the upper grille surround molding. The redesigned grille featured full-width, horizontal blades with eight bright vertical divider moldings positioned along the protruding center section only. The horizontal blades extended right to the round headlamp lenses, making them seem better integrated into the overall appearance. The front bumper was smoother and rounder looking, eliminating the triple-bevel look of 1974. Another change was to rectangular parking lamps. Identification came from name badges on the front fendersides, behind the wheel openings. Side trim consisted of a three-quarter length belt molding, running from a point above the name badge to the rear. Standard equipment features matched those of the previous season, plus electronic ignition. A Brougham options package was available on both models, but at two different prices. The sedan was the basis of specially-assembled taxicab and police car models. The latter group earned 84 of the 89 401-cid V-8s installed in AMC products in the 1975 model year.

MATADOR SERIES 80

Series No.	Body/Style No.	Body Type & Seating	Factory Price	Shipping Weight	Prod. Total
80	7585-7	4-dr Sed-6P	3452/3551	3586/3746	27,522
80	7588-7	4-dr Sta Wag-6P	3844/3943	3878/4038	9,692

NOTE 1: Data above slash for six/below slash for V-8.

NOTE 2: Model year output totaled 59,582 units built in Kenosha, Wis. Of these cars, 10,965 were sixes and 48,617 were V-8s.

NOTE 3: The six-cylinder total includes 9,390 passenger cars and 1,575 station wagons. The V-8 total includes 40,500 passenger cars and 8,117 station wagons.

BASE ENGINES

(BASE SIX) Inline Six. Overhead valve. Cast iron block. Displacement: 232 cid. Bore and stroke: 3.75 x 3.50 inches. Compression ratio: 8.0:1. SAE nhp: 90 at 3050 rpm. Seven main bearings. Hydraulic valve lifters. Carburetor: one-barrel.

(BIG SIX) Inline Six. Overhead valve. Cast iron block. Displacement: 258 cid. Bore and stroke: 3.75 x 3.90 inches. Compression ratio: 8.0:1. SAE nhp: 95 at 3050 rpm. Seven main bearings. Hydraulic valve lifters. Carburetor: one-barrel.

(BASE V-8) Overhead Valve. Cast iron block. Displacement: 304 cid. Bore and stroke: 3.75 x 3.44 inches. Compression ratio: 8.0:1. SAE nhp: 120 at 3200 rpm. Five main bearings. Hydraulic valve lifters. Carburetor: two-barrel.

CHASSIS FEATURES: Wheelbase: (Gremlin) 96 inches; (Pacer) 100 inches; (Hornet) 108 inches; (Matador Series 10) 114 inches; (Matador Series 80) 118 inches. Overall length: (Gremlin) 170.3 inches; (Pacer) 171.5 inches; (Hornet) 187 inches; (Matador coupe) 209.3 inches; (Matador sedan) 216 inches; (Matador wagon) 215.5 inches. Front tread: (Pacer) 61.2 inches; (other models) See 1972 Chassis Features. Rear tread: (Pacer) 60.2 inches, (other models) See 1972 Chassis Features. Tires: (Gremlin) 6.45 x 14; (Pacer/Hornet) 6.95 x 14; (Matador coupe) ER78-14; (Matador sedan) FR78-14; (Matador wagon) HR78-14.

POWERTRAIN OPTIONS: Three-speed manual transmission was standard. Overdrive transmission, for sixes. Three-speed manual floor shift transmission. Hornet/Gremlin six-cylinder 258 cid/95 hp one-barrel engine. Pacer six-cylinder 258 cid/95 hp one-barrel engine. Hornet/Gremlin 304 cid/120 hp two-barrel engine. Matador coupe 304 cid/120 hp two-barrel V-8 (no charge). Matador coupe 360 cid/140 hp two-barrel V-8. Matador coupe 360 cid/180 hp four-barrel V-8. Matador sedan 304 cid/120 hp one-barrel V-8. Matador sedan 360 cid/140 hp two-barrel V-8. Matador sedan 360 cid/180 hp four-barrel V-8. Matador wagon 304 cid/120 hp two-barrel V-8. Matador wagon 360 cid/140 hp two-barrel V-8. Matador wagon 360 cid/180 hp four-barrel V-8. Positive traction rear axle. Heavy-duty clutch, for sixes.

HORNET/GREMLIN/MATADOR OPTIONS: Power steering, in Gremlin/Hornet ($119). Air conditioning, in Gremlin/Hornet group ($400). Gremlin "X" package ($201). Gremlin Levi's Custom trim package ($220). Gremlin Rallye option package ($133). AM/FM stereo, all except Matador Group ($179). Styled road wheels, Gremlin/Hornet group ($115). Hornet D/L package, on sedan ($299); on Sportabout ($293). Hornet Levi's Custom trim package ($125). Hornet "X" hatchback option package ($227). Hornet Sportabout "X" package ($139). Sportabout rooftop travel rack ($75). Hornet Rallye option package ($125). Matador air conditioning ($450). Matador AM/FM stereo system ($230). Matador AM/FM stereo with 8-track tape player ($300). Matador station wagon, third seat equipment ($121). Matador station wagon. Rooftop travel rack ($59). Matador "X" package ($199). Oleg Cassini coupe trim package ($299). Styled road wheels, on Matador group ($121). Matador Brougham package, wagon ($145); others ($105). Gremlin/Hornet group Econo-Miser package ($225). Gremlin, Custom trim package ($135). Reclining seats, as option ($75).

PACER OPTIONS: "X" package ($339). "D/L" package ($289). Decor package ($49). 232-cid six, one-barrel carburetor engine (standard). 258-cid six, one-barrel carburetor engine ($69). Torque-Command, column shift ($239.95). Torque-Command with floor shift available only with bucket or reclining seats ($259.95). Three-speed manual, column shift (standard). Three-speed manual floor shift ($19.95). Three-speed manual with overdrive column shift ($149). Twin-Grip differential ($46). Power steering ($119). Power front disc brakes ($79.35). Manual front disc brakes ($47.45). AM push-button radio ($69). AM/FM stereo radio, with four speakers ($179). Entertainment center with AM/FM stereo and tape player ($299). Hidden compartment ($29). Bucket seats ($99). Individual reclining seats, "D/L" only. Air conditioning system ($399.95). Tinted glass, all windows ($49). Rear window defogger ($59.95). Rear window washer and wiper ($49.95). Roof rack ($49.95). Cruise-command speed control with automatic transmission only ($65). Adjust-O-Tilt steering column with automatic transmission, column shift only ($49). Visibility group ($49.95). Deluxe electric windshield wipers with intermittent action ($24.95). Light group ($34.95). Door vent windows ($29.95). Sports steering wheel ($18.90). Wheel discs ($29.95). Styled road wheels ($115); with "X" package ($50); with "D/L" package ($85.05). Aluminum styled wheels ($200); with "X" package ($135); with "D/L" package ($170.05). Slot-style wheels ("X" only). Extra quiet insulation ($29.95). Protection group ($34,95). Bumper nerfing strips ($19). Handling package includes: heavy-duty springs, shocks and front sway bar ($29.95). Handling package with "X" or "D/L" package ($15). Front sway bar ($14.95). Vinyl roof ($99.95). Two-tone paint ($49). Whitewall tires ($34.45).

HISTORICAL FOOTNOTES: The AMC models made their debut Nov. 15, 1974, and the Pacer was introduced Feb. 28, 1975. The unique "bubble car" went on sale March 1, 1975. American Motors Corp.'s model year output hit 244,941 units. Calendar year production was recorded as 323,704 cars. Sales by U.S. dealers, for 1975 models only, were reported as 268,526 vehicles. R.D. Chapin, Jr., remained at the head of the company. Richard A. Teague, vice-president of styling gets the credit for the Pacer's unique and attractive appearance.

AMC 1976-1986

Best known through the 1950s and '60s for its compact economy cars, Wisconsin-based American Motors Corp., by 1976 appeared to be ready to abandon its largest models. The full-sized Ambassador disappeared after 1974. It was a victim of the U.S. gasoline crisis. So did the sporty Javelin coupe, leaving Matador as the largest AMC model. In 1970, the Gremlin—known for its "sawed-off" rear-end look—had arrived as the first domestic-built subcompact, just as Rambler had pioneered the compact trend two decades earlier. Another 1970 arrival was the compact Hornet, soon to become one of AMC's best sellers. Of even greater ultimate importance that year, however, was AMC's acquisition of Kaiser-Jeep's Toledo plant. Ordinary passenger cars did not always fare well through the 1970s and early '80s, but the company stayed afloat largely as a result of four-wheel-drive Jeep production.

Gremlin wasn't the only curious looking AMC model. At the Chicago Auto Show in 1975, the hatchback Pacer appeared, wearing an unusually large amount of glass and a passenger door larger than its mate, among other design features. Promoted as the "first wide small car," Pacer was designed from the ground up as a receptacle for a new front-drive Wankel (rotary) engine expected from GM. When that engine failed to materialize, Pacer had to turn to conventional powerplants, including the familiar AMC inline six and, later, a V-8. It was one of the first American cars with rack-and-pinion steering.

Not much changed for 1976. Matadors could get a choice of 360 cu. in. V-8s under the hood, and a stylish Barcelona package for the coupe. Gremlin offered a pair of packages to enhance its appeal: a sporty 'X' appearance option, and a more curious "Levi's" trim package. That one put simulated blue denim (actually nylon) and fake "buttons" on the seats and interior panels, and attracted quite a lot of attention. Though popular at first, Pacer sales flagged this year. People didn't seem so interested in smaller cars as the gas crunch eased.

Only Gremlin got any noticeable restyling for 1977—along with a new four-cylinder powerplant, supplied by Volkswagen. Pacer added a station wagon to the original hatchback sedan. The AMX name, abandoned a couple of years earlier, appeared again on a limited-edition Hornet model with front air dam, blackout grille, back-window louvers, and body graphics. Styling touches of that sort soon would become common on sporty models from just about every domestic manufacturer. High-performance 360 cu. in. V-8s were no longer offered under Matador hoods, and the 401 V-8 wasn't even available to police agencies, as it had been before. Following a $46 million loss in fiscal year 1976, AMC switched to black ink on the 1977 ledger book—but as a result of strong Jeep sales, not conventional passenger cars. Even price cuts and rebates didn't help. Other companies were planning compact models, and imports gained strength each year, but AMC couldn't seem to take hold of a major niche of the market. The agreement to purchase engines from VW/Audi was something new, and foretold the European connection that would eventually "save" AMC (temporarily) in the 1980s.

AMC took a stronger stab at the youth market in 1978, making AMX a separate model—again heavy on black accents—instead of a Hornet option. Hornet, in fact, was gone, replaced by a new and posher (but similar) Concord. Even Gremlin turned a bit toward performance with a new GT option package that used fiberglass body components. Pacers now came with a 304 cu. in. V-8 as well as two six-cylinder choices. Matador again offered a Barcelona package for the coupe, but this would be the mid-size's final season. Corporate net earnings reached their highest peak since 1973, but again due to Jeep popularity. Negotiations with Renault were already underway. They culminated in an agreement whereby AMC would distribute the French-built Le Car (and Renault might do likewise with Jeeps). More important for the future was the announcement that the two corporations planned a joint-venture passenger car to be built in the United States. In another agreement, AMC contracted to buy "Iron Duke" four-cylinder engines from Pontiac.

Gremlin bit the dust in 1979, replaced by a more stylish (but not dramatically different) Spirit subcompact. The performance-minded AMX switched to the shorter Spirit platform. AMC profits reached a record level as Renault bought an interest in the company for $200 million. Plans were made to begin assembly of Renault-designed cars in Kenosha as early as the 1982 model year—a target date that proved slightly premature.

V-8 engines disappeared for good the next year, as Pacer and AMX entered their final years. Eagle was the big news: the first major four-wheel-drive passenger car produced in America in modern times. Riding a Concord platform, the Eagle sat three inches higher off the ground to allow for the 4WD structure. It was also the first 4WD model to be built in volume with independent front suspension, and gave AMC something to offer that no other domestic automaker had. Unfortunately, not enough customers seemed to care. In December 1980, stockholders agreed to give Renault a 46 percent share of the company.

For 1981, AMC's selection shrunk to only three models: Spirit, Concord and Eagle, with Pontiac's 151 cu. in. four cylinder engine under their hoods. The Eagle was now offered on two platforms: the original Concord size, and an SX/4 coupe (and Kammback wagon) on the smaller Spirit chassis. Both Eagles sported dark Krayton lower body treatments. Sales slipped over 8 percent, but AMC's market share hung almost steady.

Neither the compact Concord nor subcompact Spirit was doing well as 1982 began, and their days were numbered. Spirit's new five-speed overdrive manual gearbox didn't help. Switchable two-/four-wheel drive was standard on Eagles, which attracted a moderate—but hardly overwhelming—following. The company's market share sunk below 2 percent, but late in the model year, production of the new Renault Alliance began in Kenosha. Early Alliance sales even helped AMC to recapture fourth place in domestic sales for the first time since 1978, beating out Volkswagen of America. Late in September, production of Spirits and the smaller Eagles moved to Canada, while big Eagles continued to be built in Wisconsin.

Only Eagles retained the Pontiac four-cylinder base engine for 1983. All final Spirits and Concords carried sixes. The new subcompact Alliance, designed in France, was revised to suit American tastes. That included electronic controls, Bendix fuel injection, and power steering and brakes. The 1.4-liter powerplants came from France. New Alliance notwithstanding, AMC managed to lose over $146 million in 1983, nearly as disastrous a figure as the 1982 loss. Early Alliances sold well, but the good news didn't last, especially as mechanical problems became evident.

A Renault-styled hatchback Encore joined the notchback Alliance for 1984, as Spirit and Concord departed. Only the big 4WD Eagle remained, powered by an AMC-built four or six. Eagle sales had looked promising at first, but sagged badly. For a change, AMC enjoyed a bit of profit this year, and could be forgiven a taste of optimism in what would prove to be a temporary respite.

The Renault-based models got bigger engine choices for 1985, as a convertible Alliance arrived—the first AMC soft-top since the '68 Rambler Rebel. Eagle added "shift-on-the-fly" 4WD but dropped the four-cylinder engine. The modest profit for 1984 indeed proved to be temporary, as AMC lost over $125 million this time around. Low-rate financing was tried for the first time, but couldn't attract enough customers. Production was slashed several times, with workers laid off. The United Auto Workers agreed to a pay cut only after AMC threatened to cease production entirely.

Jose Dedeurwaerder, AMC's president, predicted that "the worst is over," and the loss of $91 million in 1986 wasn't as bad as previous totals. But the company's share of sales dwindled to just one percent, even after low-rate financing of "zero" was offered. Even American Honda earned a bigger share. Eagle sales slipped below 10,000, amid AMC's insistence that the tough 4WD would remain in production in Canada—and despite rising interest in 4WD models. Chrysler's agreement to build its M-body cars at AMC's Kenosha facility helped pave the way for the Chrysler takeover (for $1 billion) a year later, in August 1987.

1976

Following the introduction of the Pacer in mid-1975, changes for the 1976 AMC model year were modest. Speedometers now reached only 90 mph. Some models had a new lockable, padded console. After January 1, brakes were enlarged to meet Federal standards. Six-cylinder engines had reshaped carburetor air passages a new thermostat, and an electric choke on some models. Since the full size Ambassador had been dropped for 1975, AMC stressed economy. Three-fourths of the company's vehicles rated over 20 MPG in EPA highway mileage estimates. Engines carried electronic ignition. 'Safe-Command' features on all models included: energy-absorbing bumpers and steering column; front head restraints; 4-way hazard warnings; lane-changer turn signals; backup and marker lights; padded sun visors and instrument panel; double-safety brake system with warning light. All models were painted in 'Luster-Guard' acrylic baked enamel. Standard body colors were Black; Sienna or Alpine Orange; Seaspray Green; Sand Tan; Firecracker Red; Brilliant Blue; Sunshine Yellow; plus Nautical Blue, Medium Blue, Dark Cocoa, Autumn Red, Evergreen, Burnished Bronze, Silver Frost or Limefire metallic.

GREMLIN — SERIES 40 — SIX/V-8 — Introduced with considerable sales success during 1970 as the first American-made subcompact, the sawed-off Gremlin entered 1976 wearing a new grille. A horizontal crossbar stood between (and surrounded) round amber parking lights. Originally created by chopping 17 inches off the Hornet design, it remained the only domestic subcompact without a four-cylinder engine. Standard engine was a 232 cubic-inch six with three-speed column shift; a 258 six and 304 V-8 were optional. More distinctive than most small cars, with a design not universally loved, Gremlin gained refinements through its early years but few major changes in its single two-door body style. From the 'B' pillar forward, it's essentially a Hornet, but with a flat hatchback that almost looks like a real hatch. Standard equipment included 6.45 x 14 blackwall tires, foam-cushioned seats, front ashtray, folding rear seat, Weather Eye heater/defroster, two-speed electric wipers/washers, dome light, rear lift window, front sway bar (V-8 only), rear bumper guards, front bumper nerfing strips, a 50-amp battery, and aluminum hubcaps. The sporty 'X' package, available only on Custom models, added a full-length body stripe with 'X' decal, painted lower back panel, engine-turned finish instrument cluster overlay, glove box decal, D70 x 14 tires on slot-style wheels, and a 'Space Saver' spare tire. Available again was the unique "Levi's" trim package, with sporty bucket seats, stowage/litter pouches and door trim in simulated blue denim (actually spun nylon) complete with "buttons;" plus blue headlining and sun visors and "Levi's" front fender decals. Rally stripes continued their unusual "hockey stick" design.

PACER — SERIES 60 — SIX — Great expectations greeted the wide, glassy 'bubble' Pacer when it appeared as a mid-1975 model. Riding a 100 inch wheelbase, it stood 77 inches wide, billed as "the first wide small car." *Business Week* called it the "hottest car of 1975." Unique features included a passenger door nearly four inches wider than that of the driver. A surprisingly roomy four-passenger interior belies the car's compact 170-inch length. The entire rear section tied into the massive B-pillar structure, cutting both length and weight. Aerodynamic styling helped improve fuel economy. A short sharply-sloped hood and enormous glass area give impressive visibility. But that hood was actually the result of having designed the car for a front-drive Wankel rotary engine, which never materialized from General Motors. Pacer was one of the first American cars to offer rack and pinion steering. Major change for 1976 was the availability of an optional 258 cu. in. six, with one- or two-barrel carburetor, in addition to the economy 232 six. Air conditioning was a most desirable extra, due to the large glass area. Twin gas-filled cylinders assisted opening of the large rear lift window. X package included vinyl bucket seats with manual floor shift, woodgrain dash overlay, sports steering wheel, extra-quiet insulation, 'X' ornamentation, color-keyed bodyside scuff moldings, bumper nerfing strips, front sway bar, and D78 x 14 blackwall tires. The luxurious D/L package consisted of basketry fabric interior, padded steering wheel, carpeted cargo area, woodgrain-overlay dash, wheel covers, color-keyed scuff moldings, bright license molding, nerfing strips, front sway bar, and special emblems. D/L models could also have Hyde Park fabric seat trim. Standard equipment included three-speed column shift; 6.95 x 14 tires; foam-cushioned bench seat; color-keyed carpeting and rubber cargo mat; folding second seat; bodyside scuff molding; Weather Eye heater/defroster; concealed two-speed wipers/washers; dome light; 50-amp battery; aluminum hubcaps; ashtray and lighter. Body colors were identical to other models, but not including Black, Sienna/Alpine Orange, Dark Cocoa, Limefire, or Nautical Blue. Alpine White, Golden Jade metallic, Aztec Copper metallic, Brandywine metallic, and Marine Aqua colors were unique to Pacer.

HORNET — SERIES 01 — SIX/V-8 — Introduced in 1970 at a cost of $40 million, the compact Hornet, new from the ground up, became one of AMC's best sellers. As in 1975, the Hornet lineup consisted of four models: a two-door hatchback (added for 1973), two- and four-door sedans and a four-door Sportabout wagon. Appearance changed little this year, apart from thin rubber strips placed at lower bumper ends. Hornet nameplates sat behind the front side marker lamps, and on the right rear panel. A 232 cu. in. six with three-speed column shift was standard, 258 six and 304 V-8 optional. Three option packages were available. Sportabouts and hatchbacks could have a 'Touring Interior' with individual reclining seats in tan vinyl, matching headliner, visors and door pull straps, sports steering wheel, woodgrain dash overlay and carpeted lower door panels. The sporty 'X' package, also for Sportabouts and hatchbacks, consisted of full-length rally striping, slot wheels with D70 x 14 blackwall tires, 'X' ornamentation on dash and lower back panel, plus black grille accents. Sedans with the luxury D/L package had reclining front seats and trim in tan 'Kasmir Knit' fabric; D/L Sportabouts came with 'Potomac Stripe' fabric (or vinyl) plus woodgrain body paneling, custom wheel covers, roof rack, and air deflector. Standard Hornet equipment included rear bumper guards, front bumper nerfing strips, Weather Eye heater/defroster, lighter, color-keyed carpeting and mats, locking glovebox, two-speed wipers/washers, front sway bar (V-8s), 50-amp battery, 6.95 x 14 blackwalls, and aluminum hubcaps. Hatchbacks and Sportabouts had a fold-down rear seat and rear lift window.

MATADOR (COUPE) — SERIES 10 — SIX/V-8 — Starting in 1975, the stylish mid-size Matador coupe stood apart from the four-door sedan and wagon with a different wheelbase and series number. For 1976, the coupe gained a new full-width, two-section grille that extended out to the fender tips, below the huge headlamp openings. Amber parking lights were rectangular. The Brougham package included individual reclining seats in "Hunter's Plaid" fabric, custom door trim panels, woodgrain dash overlay, full carpeting, wheel discs, hood paint stripes, bumper nerfing strips, rocker moldings, roll-down quarter windows, full length bodyside scuff moldings, wheel lip and grille moldings. Going a step further, a new Barcelona luxury package (only on the Brougham) added plush, crumpled-look velvety upholstery in tan or black Knap knit to the reclining front seats, plus special wheel covers and medallions. Barcelona buyers also got color-keyed cut pile carpeting, door pull straps and headlining, plus (with tan interior) tan grille, headlamp bezel and rear license accents. Distinctive red/yellow side striping, a unique hood ornament, hood and deck nameplates and fender and glovebox medallions identified the Barcelona. Base engine was the 258 cu. in six, with three V-8 options: a 304, 360 with two-barrel carburetor, and 360 with four-barrel carb and dual exhausts. Standard equipment was similar to Matador sedan, including front disc brakes.

MATADOR (SEDAN AND WAGON) — SERIES 80 — SIX/V-8 — AMC's intermediate model, little changed from 1975 when it gained a new hood, grille and bumpers, came in standard or Brougham trim. The grille has full-width horizontal blades, plus eight bright vertical divider bars along the protruding center section. Nameplates are behind the front wheel openings, just below the front of the three-quarter length belt moldings. Base engine was the 258 cu. in. six in sedans, a 304 V-8 in wagons (and all California Matadors). Two 360 cu. in. V-8s were optional. Only 20 Matadors held a 401 V-8, available only to law enforcement agencies. Standard equipment included a three-speed column shift transmission (automatic on wagons), foam-cushioned seats, color-keyed carpeting, front and rear ashtrays (front lighter), extra-quiet insulation package, Weather Eye heater/defroster, day/night mirror, two-speed wipers/washers, dome light, dual-swing wagon tailgate, front sway bar bumper guards (front only on wagon), plus manual front disc brakes on sedan (power discs on wagon). Sedans wore standard E78 x 14 blackwall tires (F78 x 14 with V-8); wagons H78 x 14. The Brougham package gave individual reclining seats in Custom Hyde Park fabric (Sof-Touch vinyl in wagons), woodgrain dash overlay, full carpeting, wheel covers, 'Brougham' script on 'C' pillars, roof rack and tailgate air deflector (wagon), hood paint stripes, a back panel overlay (sedan), and rocker panel moldings (except two-tone or woodgrain-panel wagon).

I.D. DATA: The 13-symbol Vehicle Identification Number (VIN) was embossed on a metal plate riveted to the top left surface of the instrument panel, visible through the windshield. The first letter (A) indicated the manufacturer, American Motors. The second digit denoted the model year ('6' 1976). Third was a letter identifying transmission type: 'S' three-speed manual, column shift; 'O' three-speed column shift with overdrive; 'E' three-speed floor shift; 'D' three-speed floor shift with overdrive; 'A' column-shift automatic; 'C' floor-shift automatic. The fourth digit denoted the car line (series): '0' Hornet; '1' Matador coupe; '4' Gremlin; '6' Pacer; '8' Matador sedan/wagon. Fifth digit identified body style: '3' two-door hatchback; '5' four-door sedan; '6' two-door sedan; '8' four-door station wagon. Digit six showed the model/group (body class): '3' Gremlin standard; '5' Gremlin Custom; '7' Pacer/Hornet/Matador; 'P' Police. The seventh letter indicated engine type: 'E' 232-6 1Bbl.; 'A' 258-6 1Bbl.; 'C' 258-6 2Bbl.; 'H' 304 V-8 2Bbl.; 'N' 360

V-8 2Bbl.; 'P' 360 V-8 4Bbl.; 'Z' 401 V-8 4Bbl. (police only). Digits 8 through 13 made up the sequential number, starting with 100001 for vehicles made at Kenosha, Wisconsin, and 700001 for those manufactured at Brampton, Ontario.

Note: Digits 4-6 are identical to the model number. A safety sticker attached to edge of left front door shows the month and year built, plus the VIN. A unit body identification plate riveted to the edge of the left front door displays the body number, model number, trim number, paint code number, and build sequence number. A six-symbol Build Code was engraved on a machined surface of the cylinder block of six-cylinder engines, between cylinders 2 and 3: or stamped on a metal tag attached to right bank valve cover on V-8 engines. The first digit indicates model year, second and third digits, the month of manufacture (1 January). The fourth letter indicates engine type, and is identical to the seventh letter of the VIN. Digits five and six denote the day of manufacture. V-8 engines also have cubic-inch displacement cast into the side of the block, between the second and third freeze plugs, usually under the motor mount.

GREMLIN SERIES 40

Series No.	Body/Style No.	Body Type & Seating	Factory Price	Shipping Weight	Prod. Total
40	7646-3	2-dr Sed-4P	2889/3051	2771/3020	Note 1
40	7646-5	2-dr Cust Sed-4P	2998/3160	2774/3023	Note 1

Note 1: Total model year production, 52,941 Gremlins (only 826 with V-8 engine).

PACER SERIES 60

60 7666-7		2-dr Sed-4P	3499	3114	117,244

HORNET SERIES 01

01	7603-7	2-dr Hatch-5P	3199/3344	2920/3169	Note 2
01	7605-7	4-dr Sed-6P	3199/3344	2971/3220	Note 2
01	7606-7	2-dr Sed-6P	3199/3344	2909/3158	Note 2
01	7608-7	4-dr Sta Wag-6P	3549/3694	3040/3289	29,763

Note 2; Total model year production: Hornet sedans and hatchbacks, 41,814 units (41,025 with six-cylinder engine, 789 with V-8). Of the 29,763 Sportabout wagons, 26,787 had a six, 2,976 a V-8 engine.

MATADOR (COUPE) SERIES 10

10	7616-7	2-dr Cpe-6P	3621/3725	3562/3811	Note 3

MATADOR (SEDAN AND WAGON) SERIES 80

80	7685-7	4-dr Sed-6P	3627/3731	3589/3838	Note 3
80	7688-7	4-dr Sta Wag-6P	—/4373	—/4015	11,049

Note 3: Model year production of coupe and sedan totaled 30,464 units (4,993 sixes and 25,471 V-8s).

FACTORY PRICE AND WEIGHT NOTE: Figure before the slash is for six-cylinder engine, after slash for V-8 engine.

ENGINES: BASE SIX (Gremlin, Hornet, Pacer): Inline. OHV. Six-cylinder. Cast iron block. Displacement: 232 cu. in. (3.8 liters). Bore & stroke: 3.75 x 3.50 in. Compression ratio: 8.0:1. Brake horsepower: 90 (SAE net) at 3050 R.P.M. Torque: 170 lb.-ft. at 2000 R.P.M. Seven main bearings. Hydraulic valve lifters. Carburetor: 1Bbl. Carter YF. BASE SIX (Matador coupe/sedan); OPTIONAL (Gremlin, Hornet, Pacer): Inline. OHV. Six-cylinder. Cast iron block. Displacement: 258 cu. in. (4.2 liters). Bore & stroke: 3.75 x 3.90 in. Compression ratio: 8.0:1. Brake horsepower: 95 at 3050 R.P.M. Torque: 180 lb.-ft. at 2100 R.P.M. (Matador, 2000 R.P.M.). Seven main bearings. Hydraulic valve lifters. Carburetor: 1Bbl. Carter YF. OPTIONAL SIX (Pacer only): Same as 258 cu. in. six above, but with Carter BBD 2Bbl. carburetor. Horsepower: 120 at 3400 R.P.M. Torque: 200 lb.-ft. at 2000 R.P.M. BASE V-8 (Matador station wagon); OPTIONAL (Gremlin, Hornet, other Matadors): 90-degree, overhead valve V-8. Cast iron block. Displacement: 304 cu. in. (5.0 liters). Bore & stroke: 3.75 x 3.44 in. Compression ratio: 8.4:1. Brake horsepower: 120 at 3200 R.P.M. Torque: 220 lb.-ft. at 2200 R.P.M. Five main bearings. Hydraulic valve lifters. Carburetor: 2Bbl. Motorcraft 2100. OPTIONAL V-8 (Matador): 90-degree, overhead valve V-8. Cast iron block. Displacement: 360 cu. in. (5.9 liters). Bore & stroke: 4.08 x 3.44 in. Compression ratio: 8.25:1. Brake horsepower: 140 at 3200 R.P.M. Torque: 260 lb.-ft. at 1600 R.P.M. Five main bearings. Hydraulic valve lifters. Carburetor: 2Bbl Motorcraft 2100. OPTIONAL HIGH-PERFORMANCE V-8 (Matador): Same as 360 cu. in. V-8 above, but with 4Bbl. Motorcraft 4350 carburetor and dual exhaust. Brake horsepower: 180 at 3600 R.P.M. Torque: 280 lb.-ft. at 2800 R.P.M. POLICE V-8 (Matador): 90-degree, overhead valve V-8. Cast iron block. Displacement: 401 cu. in. Bore & stroke: 4.165 x 3.68 in. Compression ratio: 8.25:1. Brake horsepower: 215 at 4200 R.P.M. Torque: 320 lb.-ft. at 2800 R.P.M. Five main bearings. Hydraulic valve lifters.

CHASSIS DATA: Wheelbase: (Gremlin) 96 in.; (Pacer) 100 in.; (Hornet) 108 in.; (Matador coupe) 114 in.; (Matador sedan/wagon) 118 in. Overall length: (Gremlin) 169.4 in.; (Pacer) 170 in.; (Hornet) 186 in.; (Matador coupe) 209.4 in.; (Matador sedan) 216 in.; (Matador wagon) 215.5 in. Height: (Gremlin) 52.3 in.; (Pacer) 52.7 in.; (Hornet) 52.2 in. except 4-dr sedan: 51.7 in.; (Matador coupe) 51.8 in.; (Matador sedan) 54.7 in.; (Matador wagon) 56.8 in. Front Tread: (Gremlin/Hornet) 57.5 in.; (Pacer) 61.2 in.; (Matador coupe) 59.7 in.; (Matador) 59.8 in. Rear Tread: (Gremlin/Hornet) 57.1 in.; (Pacer) 60.2 in.; (Matador) 60.0 in. Standard Tires: (Gremlin six) 6.45 x 14; (Gremlin V-8, Pacer, Hornet) 6.95 x 14; (Hornet V-8 sedan or wagon) D78 x 14; (Matador coupe/sedan, six) E78 x 14; (Matador coupe/sedan, V-8) F78 x 14; (Matador wagon) FR78 x 14 steel radial, or H78 x 14.

TECHNICAL: Three-speed manual transmission was standard: floor shift on Gremlin and Hornet hatchbacks, column shift on other models. Overdrive standard on Pacer with 258 cu. in. six (2Bbl.); optional with other Pacers and Gremlin/Hornet six. Manual transmission gear ratios: (1st) 2.99:1; (2nd) 1.75:1; (3rd) 1.00:1; (Rev) 3.17:1. Torque-Command three-speed automatic transmission optional on all models; column or floor shift selector. Standard axle ratio: (Gremlin) 2.73:1 except 304 V-8 with three-speed manual, 3.15:1 and 304 V-8 with automatic, 2.87:1; (Pacer) 2.73:1 except automatic shift and all with 258 six and 2Bbl. carb, 3.08:1; (Hornet) 2.73:1 except 304 V-8 with automatic, 2.87:1, and hatchback with floor shift, 3.15:1; (Matador) 2.87:1 except base six with manual shift, 3.54:1, and base six with automatic, 3.15:1. Hotchkiss drive. Steering: (Pacer) rack and pinion; (others) recirculating ball. Suspension: independent front coil springs (Pacer springs mounted between the two control arms); semi-elliptic rear leaf springs except (Matador) coil springs. Brakes: drum; front discs optional (standard on Matador). Breakerless Inductive Discharge electronic ignition. Fuel tank: (Gremlin/Matador wagon) 21 gal.; (Pacer/Hornet) 22 gal.; (Matador coupe/sedan) 24.5 gal. Unleaded fuel only.

DRIVETRAIN OPTIONS: 258 cu. in. six-cylinder engine, 1Bbl. carb: Gremlin/Pacer/Hornet ($69) 258 cu. in. six, 2Bbl.: Pacer ($99): Pacer with air conditioning ($69). 304 cu. in. V-8, 2Bbl.: Gremlin ($162); Hornet ($145); Matador ($104) but standard on wagon. 360 cu. in. V-8, 2Bbl.: Matador sedan/coupe ($150); wagon ($46). 360 cu. in. V-8, 4Bbl., dual exhaust: Matador sedan/coupe ($266); wagon ($162). Three-speed floor shift: Pacer with bucket or individual reclining seats ($21). Three-speed column shift with overdrive: Pacer, Hornet Sportabout with 232 six ($157). Three-speed floor shift with overdrive: Grem. or Hornet hatchback six ($157); Torque Command automatic transmission, column shift: Grem./Hornet six, Pacer ($252); Grem. V-8 ($281); Hornet V-8 ($262); Matador six ($261); Mat. 304 cu. in. V-8 ($268); Mat. 360 V-8 ($281); Mat. wagon ($13). Torque Command with floor shift lever: Grem. six, Pacer with bucket or reclining seats, and Hornet hatchback/Sportabout six ($273); Grem., Hornet hatchback/Sportabout V-8 ($283); Matador coupe with 304 V-8 and bucket seats ($330); Mat. coupe with 360 V-8 ($343). Optional axle ratio: Grem./Pacer/Hornet ($13); Mat. ($14). Twin Grip differential: Grem./Hornet ($49); Pacer ($49); Mat. ($53). Heavy-duty engine cooling system: Matador coupe ($18); others ($25); but standard with air conditioning. Heavy-duty suspension: Grem./Hornet ($27) including front sway bar for six-cylinder; Pacer/Matador ($32) with front sway bar on Pacer, rear on Matador. Front sway bar: Pacer ($18) but included with 'X' package. Rear sway bar: Matador ($16). 70-amp battery: Grem./Pacer/Hornet ($15); Mat. ($16). California emission system ($50). Trailer towing package; Matador V-8 ($116); with air conditioning ($91). Highway cruising package (cruise control and 2.53:1 axle ratio with six, 2.87:1 with V-8): Gremlin with auto. trans. ($59).

GREMLIN/HORNET/MATADOR CONVENIENCE/APPEARANCE OPTIONS: 'X' package: Gremlin ($189); Hornet ($179). Hornet sedan D/L package with 'Kasmir Knit' fabric ($169). Sportabout D/L package with 'Potomac Stripe' fabric ($350); with vinyl ($309); with touring interior ($214). Touring interior in "Sof-Touch" vinyl: Hornet hatchback/Sportabout ($169). Brougham package: Matador sedan ($179); Matador wagon ($199); Matador coupe ($249). Barcelona package: Matador coupe with Brougham package only ($149). "Levi's" custom fabric trim package: Gremlin ($89). Opera windows and padded vinyl roof package: Matador coupe ($524). Interior appointment package (parcel shelf, glovebox lock, lighter): Grem. ($21). Interior decor package (appointment pkg., carpeted cargo area, extra quiet insulation): Grem. ($49). Decor package (wheel covers and moldings): Grem/Hornet ($45); Grem. 'X' ($13); Hornet X or D/L ($14); Mat. coupe without Brougham pkg. ($59). Extra quiet insulation pkg.: Grem. ($32); Hornet ($31). Protection group: Grem./Hornet ($59); Mat. coupe ($69), or ($20) with Brougham pkg.; Mat. sedan/wagon ($21). Convenience group (dome/reading light, electric clock, stowage containers, dual horns): Grem./Hornet ($49); Matador ($52). Visibility group (remote control left mirror, visor mirror, 12" day/night mirror, deluxe wipers): Grem./Hornet ($45). Matador ($49). Remote control right mirror: Matador ($27), available with visibility group only. Power steering: Grem./Hornet ($125); Matador coupe ($136); Mat. sedan/wagon ($137). Power front disc brakes: Grem./Hornet ($84); Mat. ($60). Manual front disc brakes: Grem./Hornet ($50). Cruise control: Grem./Hornet ($69). Mat. ($72). All Season air conditioning: Grem./Hornet ($425); Mat. ($473). Air conditioning pkg. (incl. tinted glass and power steering): Grem./Hornet ($579). AM radio: Grem./Hornet ($75); Matador ($76). AM/FM/Stereo four-speaker radio ($199). Rear speaker for AM radio: Grem./Hornet ($20); Mat. ($21). 8-track tape player and AM/FM/Stereo radio: Matador

($299). Power windows: Matador Brougham sedan/wagon ($138). Power side and tailgate windows: Matador Brougham wagon ($179). Power tailgate window: Matador Brougham wagon ($41). Console: Grem./Hornet hatchback ($25). Hidden compartment: Grem. ($20); Hornet hatchback ($41). Individual fabric reclining seats: Hornet ($104); Matador Brougham wagon ($31); no charge on Matador Brougham coupe. Individual vinyl reclining seats: Hornet sedan ($84); Sportabout ($63); Matador Brougham coupe/sedan ($31). Bucket seats: Hornet hatchback ($49); Matador coupe ($96) but no charge with Brougham pkg. Fabric cushion trim, bench seat: Grem. ($29); no charge on Hornet sedan/hatchback, Matador. Vinyl cushion trim, bucket seats: Grem. ($49); Hornet sedan/hatchback ($21); no charge on Sportabout. Vinyl cushion trim, bench seat: Matador coupe ($31). Third seat: Matador wagon ($127). Carpeted cargo area: Grem. Custom ($15). Deluxe wipers: Grem./Hornet ($26); Mat. ($28). Rear defogger: Grem Hornet hatchback/Sportabout ($63); Matador coupe/sedan ($73). Rear defogger blower-type: Hornet sedan ($41). Light group: Grem. ($26); Hornet ($30); Matador ($29). Fuel economy gauge: Grem./Hornet ($26); Mat. ($28) but no charge with convenience group. Custom steering wheel: Grem. ($15). Sports steering wheel (3-spoke): Gremlin ($35); Grem. Custom, Hornet ($20); Mat. ($21). Leather-wrapped steering wheel: Gremlin ($49); Grem. Custom, Hornet ($34); Hornet hatchback/Sportabout with touring interior ($14); Matador ($35). Tilt steering wheel: Grem./Hornet ($52); Mat. ($54). Tinted glass: Grem. ($44); Hornet ($47); Matador ($51). Tinted windshield: Hornet ($36); Matador sedan/wagon ($42). Two-tone paint: Hornet except Sportabout ($36); Matador ($42) except wagon ($79). Special color combinations ($21) except Matador ($22). Vinyl roof: Grem. ($74); Hornet ($93); Mat. coupe/sedan ($105). Rally side stripes: Grem. ($39); Matador coupe except Barcelona ($41). Woodgrain panels: Hornet Sportabout ($99); included with Sportabout D/L pkg.; Matador wagon ($118). Roof rack: Grem. ($53); Sportabout ($75); Matador wagon ($62); Locking gas cap ($6). Tailgate air deflector: Gremlin ($22); Matador wagon ($24). Inside hood release: Grem./Hornet ($14). Front bumper guards: Grem./Hornet ($15); Engine block heater: Grem./Hornet ($17); Mat. ($18). Wheel covers (set of four): Gremlin ($32); Hornet ($31); Matador ($34). Custom wheel covers: Mat. ($55) or ($22) with Brougham pkg. Styled wheels with trim rings for D-size tires: Grem./Hornet ($121); with Grem. Custom 'X' or Hornet hatch/Sportabout 'X' pkg. ($56); Sportabout D/L ($68); Matador ($127) but ($93) with Brougham or Decor pkg. Aluminum styled wheels for D-size tires: Grem./Hornet ($210); Grem. Custom X or Hornet hatch/Sportabout 'X' pkg. ($145); Sportabout D/L pkg. ($157); Matador ($221) but ($187) with Brougham or Decor pkg. Space-Saver spare tire: Gremlin or Sportabout with regular wheels ($16); no charge with special wheels/tires. Tires: 6.45 x 14 whitewall: Gremlin ($36). 6.95 x 14: Grem. V-8 ($16). 6.95 x 14 whitewall: Grem. V-8 ($52); Hornet ($36). D78 x 14: Hornet ($16). D78 x 14 whitewall: Grem. with styled wheels ($68); Hornet ($52). D70 x 14 with white letters: Grem. Custom 'X', Hornet 'X' ($48). DR78 x 14 steel radial: Grem. ($140); Hornet ($124); Grem. Custom 'X' or Hornet 'X' ($66). DR78 x 14 whitewall: Grem. ($176); Hornet ($160); Grem. Custom 'X' or Hornet 'X' ($102). DR70 x 14 radial with white letters: Grem. ($212); Hornet ($196); Grem. Custom 'X' or Hornet 'X' ($139). E78 x 14 whitewall: Mat. ($38). E78 x 14 MSR: Matador V-8 coupe ($20). F78 x 14 whitewall: Matador ($58). F78 x 14 MSR: Mat. sedan with V-8 ($20). FR78 x 14 steel radial: Matador ($134). FR78 x 14 whitewall: Matador ($172). H78 x 14 whitewall: Matador wagon ($38). HR78 x 14: Matador ($154); wagon ($114). HR78 x 14 whitewall: Matador ($192); wagon ($152).

PACER CONVENIENCE/APPEARANCE OPTIONS: 'X' package ($339). D/L package ($199): not available with 'X' pkg. Rally package: front console, leather-wrapped steering wheel tachometer electric clocks, gauges ($139). Decor package: wheel covers and exterior moldings ($89); with D/L ($57). Extra quiet insulation package ($35). Protection group: floor mats, rocker panel moldings, scuff panel extensions ($37). Convenience group: dome/reading light, electric clock, stowage containers, dual horns ($49); with Rally pkg. ($34). Visibility group: remote left mirror, visor 12" day/night mirror, deluxe wipers ($55). Rear visibility package: rear wiper washer, defogger ($99). Power steering ($125). Power front disc brakes ($84). Manual front disc brakes ($50). Cruise control ($69). All Season air conditioning ($425). AM radio ($75). AM/FM/Stereo four-speaker radio ($199). Rear speaker ($20). 8-track tape player and AM/FM/Stereo radio ($299). Console ($25). Hidden compartment ($31). Individual reclining seats, D/L pkg.: 'Basketry' fabric ($63); 'Hyde Park' fabric ($84). Bucket seats, 'Sof-Touch' vinyl ($99); with D/L ($70). Vinyl bench cushion trim ($21). Deluxe wipers ($26). Rear defogger ($63). Rear wiper/washer ($52). Light group ($28). Fuel economy light ($18). Sports steering wheel ($20). Leather-wrapped steering wheel ($34); with 'X' package ($14). Tilt steering wheel ($52). Tinted glass ($52). Door vent windows ($30). Two-tone color ($52). Special color combinations ($21). Vinyl roof ($105). Roof rack ($52). Locking gas cap ($6). Bumper guards and nerfing strips ($53); with D/L or 'X' ($34). Engine block heater ($17). Wheel covers: set of four ($32). Styled wheels with trim rings for D-size tires: ($121); with 'X' package ($56); with D/L or Decor pkg. ($89). Aluminum styled wheels for D-size tires: ($210); with 'X' ($145); with D/L or Decor pkg. ($178). Tires: 6.95 x 14 whitewall ($36); D78 x 14 ($16); D78 x 14 WSW ($52); DR78 x 14 steel radial ($124); DR78 x 14 WSW ($160); DR70 x 14 radial with white letters ($196). Tires with 'X' package: D78 x 14 whitewall ($36); DR78 x 14 steel radial ($108); DR78 x 14 WSW ($145); DR70 x 14 radial with white letters ($181).

HISTORY: All 1976 AMC models debuted Sept. 24, 1975. Model year production totaled 283,275 (242,164 sixes and 41,111 V-8s). That came to 3.5 percent of the industry total, down from 3.74 percent the previous year and a healthy 5.3 percent in 1973. Calendar year production amounted to 213,606 units, well below the 323,704 total for 1975. Production halted on June 25, 1976. Calendar year sales came to 247,640, again down markedly from the previous year's 322,272. Hornets sold the best, while Matadors declined the most.

HISTORICAL FOOTNOTES: While other U.S. automakers recovered from the disastrous sales slump of 1975, AMC fell short of optimistic expectations. Pacer sales, in particular, slackened after an early surge, largely the result of a weakening market for small cars. Production rose from an initial 480 Pacers per day to 800 by late 1975; but a few months later, dealers were glutted. "We were too aggressive," admitted AMC President William V. Luneberg, due to early enthusiasm. Production was slashed, and 2,700 workers laid off. As the model year opened, AMC announced the acquisition of a new plant at Richmond, Indiana, to build a two-liter four-cylinder engine, whose design and tooling had been purchased from Audi for $60 million.

1977

AMC entered the 1977 model year with the same four models as before, ranging from the subcompact Gremlin to the mid-size Matador. Only the Gremlin received significant restyling, plus a new four-cylinder engine later in the model year. All six-cylinder engines now had a 'quench-head' design. Reshaped combustion chambers brought the compressed mixture closer to the spark plug. More models had a catalytic converter or Air Guard system for emission control. Coolant overflow systems were more common. Most sixes had a two-barrel carburetor. Front disc brakes became standard. Manual transmissions were fully synchronized, but the column shifter was gone; both standard three-speed and optional four-speed gearboxes had floor shifters. Standard AMC colors were Classic Black, Alpine White, Sand Tan, Firecracker Red, Brilliant Blue, Powder Blue, Sunshine Yellow, Lime Green, Tawny Orange and Sun Orange; plus nine metallics: Brandywine, Silver Frost, Misty Jade, Mocha Brown, Autumn Red, Midnight Blue, Loden Green, Golden Ginger, and Captain Blue. Vinyl roofs came in six 'Bravado Grain' colors.

GREMLIN — SERIES 40 — FOUR/SIX — Gremlin entered the 1977 model year wearing a new grille, bumper and front end sheet metal, enlarged taillights, plus a bigger all-glass rear lift window—the first body restyle since the subcompact's 1970 debut. Though four inches shorter than before, with increased rear glass area, Gremlin's basic (and distinctive) appearance was essentially unchanged. The length loss came from reducing the car's front overhang. Rectangular parking lights were inset within the new slanted, four-row eggcrate grille. Optional front bumper guards sat farther apart than before, while horizontal amber markers stood at the forward end of the front fenders. The 'Gremlin' nameplate no longer stood on the front of the hood bulge. But the biggest change didn't come until February 1977, when the four-cylinder 121 cu. in. engine, recently acquired from Volkswagen, was offered under Gremlin hoods. Rated 80 horsepower, the VW/Audi four had a belt-driven overhead cam, aluminum cross-flow head, and aluminum intake manifold. The 232 cu. in. six remained standard, but the V-8 was gone, enhancing Gremlin's image (and gas mileage ranking) in the economy car sweepstakes. Also appearing this year was a new Borg-Warner four-speed manual transmission with floor shifter. Industry sources show that 17.6 percent of Gremlins carried a four-speed. Foam-cushioned seats were upholstered in Rallye perforated vinyl. Standard equipment now included front disc brakes and three-speed floor shift, plus Weather Eye heater/defroster, front ashtray and lighter, locking glovebox, two-speed wiper/washers, dome light, color-keyed carpeting, body paint stripes, folding rear seat, rear bumper guards, and bright moldings for drip rails, wheel lips and rocker panels. Standard tires again were 6.95 x 14 blackwalls. Gremlin's sporty 'X' package used a new striping treatment, flowing at the rear in a slight curve rather than the familiar "hockey stick" shape. That package included bucket seats trimmed in Hot-Scotch plaid fabric, sports steering wheel, instrument panel overlay, 'X' decals on body stripes and glovebox door, a lower back panel stripe decal, D70 x 14 tires on slot-styled wheels, and extra quiet insulation. The unique "Levi's" trim package was available again this year.

PACER — SERIES 60 — SIX — Biggest news for the year-and-a-half old Pacer was the addition of a station wagon to the existing hatchback sedan. Adding cargo space to the already roomy design it was meant to challenge Chrysler's new compact wagons. Overly optimistic production plans had to be cut back, however, since domestic small cars weren't selling well. With rear seat folded, the wide wagon—just four inches longer than the sedan—held 47.8 cubic feet of cargo. Styling

1976 AMC, Matador Barcelona Brougham (Series 10), coupe, OCW

1977 AMC, Gremlin (Series 40), liftback sedan (with X option package), OCW

1977 AMC, Pacer (Series 60), station wagon (with D/L option package), OCW

1978 AMC, Concord (Series 01), hatchback coupe (with Sport option package), OCW

1978 AMC, Matador Barcelona Brougham (Series 80), sedan, OCW

1976 AMC, Matador Brougham (Series 80), station wagon, OCW

above and below, 1977 AMC, Hornet AMX (Series 01), hatchback coupe, OCW

1978 AMC, Matador Barcelona Brougham (Series 10), coupe, OCW

1979 AMC, Spirit Limited (Series 40), sedan, OCW

was identical to the hatchback sedan from the doors forward, but wagons had vertically-oriented three-section taillamps, unlike the sedan's horizontal units. The wagon's wide lift-up hatch reached down nearly to the bumper, for easy loading. Large side windows included 'flipper' vents for improved ventilation. Despite its short wheelbase, the wide (77 inches) Pacer ranked as a compact. Standard engine was again the 232 cu. in. six, with a 258 optional. Foam-cushioned bench seats were trimmed in Rallye perforated vinyl on wagons, in Basketry Print fabric on hatchback sedans. Standard equipment included a three-speed floor shift, front disc brakes, 6.95 x 14 blackwall tires (D78 x 14 on the wagon), heater/defroster, two-speed wiper/washers, dome light, ashtray and lighter, built-in assist on the rear hatch, color-keyed carpeting, folding second seat, and bodyside scuff moldings. Wagons had a locking stowage compartment in the rear quarter panel. Pacer's 'X' sedan package included perforated vinyl bucket seats, woodgrain dash overlay, sports steering wheel, custom door trim with vinyl inserts and door pull straps, upper door moldings, DR78 x 14 tires on slot-styled wheels, plus high level ventilation and extra quiet insulation packages. The D/L package contained individual reclining seats, custom door panels with assist straps, woodgrain dash overlay, custom steering wheel, light group, dual horns, day/night mirror, high level ventilation, wheel lip and rocker panel moldings, rear wheelhouse pads, bumper nerfing strips, extra quiet insulation, and D78 x 14 whitewalls on styled wheels. D/L wagon bodies had woodgrain side/rear overlays.

HORNET AND AMX — SERIES 01 — SIX/V-8 — For its final year, the Hornet line was highlighted by a limited edition AMX hatchback package, bringing back a nameplate that many remembered for sporty performance a few years earlier. In addition to 'AMX' graphics between door and rear wheelhouse, and at the rear, the package included a front air dam, color-coordinated bumpers, blacked-out grille, body-color rear window louvers, Euro-style brushed aluminum large roof band, twin flat black mirrors, floor console, gauges (including tachometer), soft-feel steering wheel, and brushed aluminum instrument panel overlay. Flared fenders topped DR78 x 14 tires. Base Hornet engine remained the 232 six coupled to three-speed floor shift, with a 258 six or 304 V-8 optional. Sixes could get the new four-speed manual shift. AMX hatchbacks required the 258 with four-speed, or V-8 with automatic. Standard Hornet equipment included rear bumper guards, corner nerfing strips on front bumpers, color-keyed carpeting and mats, Weather Eye heater/defroster, locking glovebox, and two-speed wiper/washers. Four-door V-8 sedans and wagons wore standard D78 x 14 tires; other models, 6.95 x 14 blackwalls. All trim packages and options were upgraded. Such luxuries as vinyl bucket seats, sports steering wheel and a carpeted cargo area were standard on hatchback Hornets. Foam-cushioned bench seats were trimmed in Veracruz fabric on sedans, Rallye perforated vinyl on wagons. Both 'X' and D/L packages were offered again. D/L models now included reclining front seats in Veracruz fabric on sedans (Rallye perforated vinyl on wagons) plus dual horns, light group, woodgrain dash overlay, 12-inch day/night mirror, D78 x 14 whitewalls, and dual bodyside stripes (sedans) or woodgrain body panel overlays (wagons).

MATADOR (COUPE) — SERIES 10 — SIX/V-8 — Unchanged externally, the new Matadors contained interior packages that had formerly been offered only in the luxury Brougham model (which was dropped this year). Engine choices remained as in 1976, but the high-performance 360 cu. in. V-8 was gone, as was the police 401. Standard equipment now included a 258 cu. in. six, Torque Command automatic transmission, power steering and front disc brakes, individual reclining seats in Brampton Plaid fabric, heater/defroster, color-keyed carpeting, front/rear ashtrays, front lighter, extra quiet insulation, two-speed wiper/washers, light group, protective bodyside scuff moldings, wheel covers, bumper guards, front sway bar, day/night mirror and custom steering wheel. F78 x 14 blackwall tires were standard. The luxury Barcelona package added tan Knap Knit fabric seats, color-keyed door trim panels and headlining, tan grille surround and headlight bezels, tan license plate depression and wheel covers, plus a special hood ornament, insignias and nameplates.

MATADOR (SEDAN AND WAGON) — SERIES 80 — SIX/V-8 — As in 1976, the coupe was officially a different series than the Matador sedan and wagon. Base engine remained a 258 cu. in. six with one-barrel carb, with 304 or 360 cu. in. V-8 optional. (The 304 V-8 was standard in wagons and California Matadors). Standard equipment was similar to the coupe, but wagons wore H78 x 14 blackwall tires and their seats were covered in Crush-Grain vinyl.

I.D. DATA: As before, the 13-symbol Vehicle Identification Number (VIN) was embossed on a metal plate riveted to the upper left surface of the instrument panel. Coding was the same as 1976, with the following changes. Model year code (second symbol) changed to '7' for 1977. Codes 'D', 'O' and 'S' for column-shift manual and overdrive transmissions (third symbol) were dropped; code 'M' for four-speed floor shift was added. Only two digits were now used for model/group (sixth symbol): '5' Gremlin; '7' Pacer/Hornet/Matador. Engine letters (seventh symbol) changed to: 'G' 121-4 2Bbl.; 'E' 232-6 1Bbl.; 'A' 258-6 1Bbl.; 'B' 258-6 2Bbl.; 'H' 304-8 2Bbl.; 'N' 360-8 2Bbl. In addition to month and year built, plus the VIN, the safety sticker attached to left front door now showed a safety compliance statement and consumer information (vehicle class, acceleration/passing figures, tire reserve load, and stopping distance). A federal emission control information label in the engine compartment identified the engine type and gave basic tune-up specs. The unit body identification plate was the same as 1976.

GREMLIN SERIES 40 (SIX-CYLINDER)

Series No.	Body/Style No.	Body Type & Seating	Factory Price	Shipping Weight	Prod. Total
40	7746-5	2-dr Sed-4P	2995	2811	Note 1
40	7746-7	2-dr CustSed-4P	3248	2824	Note 1

GREMLIN SERIES 40 (FOUR-CYLINDER)

40	7746-4	2-dr Sed-4P	3248	2564	7558

Note 1: Total model year production: 46,171 Gremlins (38,613 six-cylinder).

PACER SERIES 60

60	7766-7	2-dr Sed-4P	3649	3156	20,265
60	7768-7	2-dr Sta Wag-4P	3799	3202	37,999

HORNET SERIES 01

01	7703-7	2-dr Hatch-5P	3499/3662	3012/3245	11,545
01	7705-7	4-dr Sed-6P	3449/3613	3035/3268	31,331
01	7706-7	2-dr Sed-6P	3399/3563	2971/3204	6076
01	7708-7	4-dr Sta Wag-6P	3699/3863	3100/3333	28,891

Note 2: Total model year production: 77,843 Hornets (73,752 with six-cylinder, 4,091 with V-8).

MATADOR (COUPE) SERIES 10

10	7716-7	2-dr Cpe-5P	4499/4619	3704/3872	6825

MATADOR (SEDAN AND WAGON) SERIES 80

80	7785-7	4-dr Sed-6P	4549/4669	3713/3876	12,944
80	7788-7	4-dr Sta Wag-6P	—/4899	—/4104	11,078

Note 3: Model year production of Matador coupe and sedan totaled 19,769 units (2,447 sixes and 17,322 V-8s).

FACTORY PRICE NOTE: Figure before the slash in Hornet and Matador price columns is for six-cylinder engine, after slash for V-8 engine.

ENGINES: BASE FOUR (Gremlin): Inline. Overhead cam. Four-cylinder. Cast iron block; cast aluminum alloy head. Displacement: 121 cu. in. (2.0 liters). Bore & stroke: 3.41 x 3.32 in. Compression ratio: 8.1:1. Brake horsepower: 80 at 5000 R.P.M. Torque: 105 lb.-ft. at 2800 R.P.M. Five main bearings. Solid valve lifters. Carburetor: 2Bbl. Holley 5210. BASE SIX (Gremlin, Hornet, Pacer): Inline. OHV. Six-cylinder. Cast iron block. Displacement: 232 cu. in. (3.8 liters). Bore & stroke: 3.75 x 3.50 in. Compression ratio: 8.0:1. Brake horsepower: 88 at 3400 R.P.M. Torque: 164 lb.-ft. at 1600 R.P.M. Taxable H.P.: 33.75. Seven main bearings. Hydraulic valve lifters. Carburetor: 1Bbl. Carter YF. BASE SIX (Matador coupe/sedan): Inline. OHV. Six-cylinder. Cast iron block. Displacement: 258 cu. in. (4.2 liters). Bore & stroke: 3.75 x 3.90 in. Compression ratio: 8.0:1. Brake horsepower: 98 at 3200 R.P.M. Torque: 193 lb.-ft. at 1600 R.P.M. Seven main bearings. Hydraulic valve lifters. Carburetor: 1Bbl. Carter YF. OPTIONAL SIX (Gremlin, Hornet, Pacer): Same as 258 cu. in. six above but with Carter BBD 2Bbl. carburetor. Brake horsepower: 114 at 3600 R.P.M. Torque: 192 lb.-ft. at 2000 R.P.M. BASE V-8 (Matador station wagon); OPTIONAL (Hornet, other Matadors): 90-degree, overhead valve V-8. Cast iron block. Displacement: 304 cu. in. (5.0 liters). Bore & stroke: 3.75 x 3.44 in. Compression ratio: 8.4:1. Brake horsepower: 121 at 3450 R.P.M. (Matador, 126 at 3600). Torque: 219 lb.-ft. at 2000 R.P.M. Taxable H.P.: 45. Five main bearings. Hydraulic valve lifters. Carburetor: 2Bbl. Motorcraft 2100. OPTIONAL V-8 (Matador): 90-degree overhead valve V-8. Cast iron block. Displacement: 360 cu. in. (5.9 liters). Bore & stroke: 4.08 x 3.44 in. Compression ratio: 8.25:1. Brake horsepower: 129 at 3700 R.P.M. Torque: 245 lb.-ft. at 1600 R.P.M. Taxable H.P.: 53.3. Five main bearings. Hydraulic valve lifters. Carburetor: 2Bbl. Motorcraft 2100.

CHASSIS DATA: Wheelbase: (Gremlin) 96 in.; (Pacer) 100 in.; (Hornet) 108 in.; (Matador coupe) 114 in.; (Matador sedan/wagon) 118 in. Overall length: (Gremlin) 166.4 in.; (Pacer sedan) 170 in.; (Pacer wagon) 174 in.; (Hornet) 186 in.; (Matador coupe) 209.4 in.; (Matador sedan) 216 in.; (Matador wagon) 215.5 in. Height: (Gremlin) 52.3 in.; (Pacer sedan) 52.7 in.; (Pacer wagon) 53.0 in.; (Hornet) 52.2 in. except 4-dr sedan, 52.7 in.; (Matador coupe) 51.8 in.; (Matador sedan) 54.7 in.; (Matador wagon) 56.8 in. Front Tread: (Gremlin/Hornet) 57.5 in.; (Pacer) 61.2 in.; (Matador coupe) 59.7 in.; (Matador) 59.8 in. Rear Tread: (Gremlin/Hornet) 57.1 in.; (Pacer) 60.2 in.; (Matador) 60.0 in. Standard Tires: (Gremlin) 6.45 x 14; (Pacer sedan, Hornet) 6.95 x 14; (Pacer wagon, Hornet V-8 sedan/wagon) D78 x 14; (Matador coupe/sedan) F78 x 14; (Matador wagon) H78 x 14.

TECHNICAL: Three-speed, fully synchronized manual floor-shift transmission was standard on all except Matadors, which had standard automatic transmission. Four-speed floor shift optional. Three-speed manual gear ratios: (1st) 2.99:1; (2nd) 1.75:1; (Rev) 3.17:1. Four-speed ratios: (1st) 3.50:1; (2nd) 2.21:1; (3rd) 1.43:1; (Rev)

3.39:1. Torque-Command three-speed automatic transmission optional on Gremlin, Hornet and Pacer; column or floor shift selector. Three element torque converter. Automatic gear ratios: (Low) 2.45:1; (Intermediate) 1.45:1; (High) 1.00:1; (Rev) 2.20:1. Standard axle ratios: (Gremlin/Pacer/Hornet six) 2.73:1; 2.53:1 and 3.08:1 optional. (Hornet V-8) 2.87:1; 3.15:1 optional. (Matador six) 3.15:1. (Matador V-8) 2.87:1; 3.15:1 and 3.54:1 available. Steering: (Pacer) rack and pinion (others) recirculating ball. Suspension: independent front coil springs (Pacer springs mounted between the two control arms); semi-elliptic rear leaf springs except (Matador) coil springs. Brakes: front disc; rear drum. Breakerless Inductive Discharge electronic ignition. Fuel tank: (Gremlin and Matador wagon) 21 gal.; (Pacer/Hornet) 22 gal.; (Matador coupe/sedan) 24.5 gal. Unleaded fuel only.

DRIVETRAIN OPTIONS: 258 cu. in. six-cylinder engine, 2Bbl carb: Gremlin/Pacer/Hornet ($79). 304 cu. in. V-8, 2Bbl.: Hornet ($164); Matador ($179) but standard on wagon. 360 cu. in. V-8, 2Bbl.: Matador sedan/coupe ($179); wagon ($59). Four-speed manual floor shift: Gremlin, Pacer, Hornet hatchback ($105). Torque-Command automatic transmission, column shift: Gremlin, Hornet except hatchback, Pacer ($267). Torque-Command with floor shift lever: Gremlin, Pacer, Hornet hatchback/Sportabout ($289); Matador coupe with V-8 and bucket seats ($66). Twin Grip differential: Grem./Hornet/Pacer ($52); Matador ($56). Heavy-duty engine cooling system: Gremlin ($49); others ($27) but standard with air conditioning. Maximum cooling system: Matador V-8 ($45); Mat. V-8 with air ($18). Auxiliary automatic transmission oil cooler: Matador ($32). Heavy-duty suspension: Grem./Hornet ($29); Pacer/Matador ($34) with front sway bar on Pacer, rear on Matador. Front sway bar: Grem./Hornet/Pacer ($17) but included with radial tires. Rear sway bar: Matador ($17). Air-adjustable shock absorbers: Matador ($45), with H.D. suspension ($41). 70-amp battery: Grem./Pacer/Hornet ($16); Mat. ($18). California emission system ($53). High altitude package ($15). Gremlin performance package: 258 engine, four-speed, sports steering wheel, heavy-duty suspension ($259); with floor-shift automatic ($443). Pacer performance package: Same as Gremlin but including tach, clock and gauges ($349); with floor shift automatic ($533). Hornet hatchback performance package: 258 engine, four-speed, soft-feel steering wheel, heavy-duty suspension ($239); with floor shift automatic transmission ($423).

GREMLIN/HORNET/MATADOR CONVENIENCE/APPEARANCE OPTIONS: AMX package: Hornet hatchback ($799). 'X' package: Gremlin ($299); Hornet hatchback/wagon ($199). Hornet D/L package: sedan ($299); wagon ($399). Barcelona package: Matador coupe ($158). "Levi's" custom fabric trim package: Gremlin ($99); Gremlin 'X' ($50); Hornet hatchback ($49). Extra quiet insulation package: Grem./Hornet ($34); included with Gremlin 'X' pkg. Protection group: Grem./Hornet ($62). Interior decor/convenience group (vanity mirror, dome/reading light, clock, stowage containers, rubber mats): Gremlin ($65); Hornet ($71); Matador ($86). Visibility group (remote control left mirror, manual right mirror, day/night mirror, deluxe wipers): Grem./Hornet ($67). Visibility group (dual remote mirrors, deluxe wipers): Matador ($76). Deluxe visibility group (adds rear defogger): Gremlin, Hornet hatch/wagon ($134); Hornet sedan ($111); Mat. coupe ($154). Remote control left mirror: Grem./Hornet ($15); Matador ($16). Power steering: Grem./Hornet ($133). Power front disc brakes: Grem./Hornet ($60). Cruise control: Hornet ($60); Matador ($77). All Season air conditioning: Grem./Hornet ($451). Air conditioning package (incl. tinted glass and power steering): Grem./Hornet ($619); Matador ($557). AM radio: Grem./Hornet ($80), Matador ($81). AM/FM/Stereo four speaker radio ($211). Rear speaker for AM radio ($21-$22). Eight-track tape player and AM/FM/Stereo radio: Matador ($317). Power windows: Matador sedan/wagon ($146). Power side and tailgate windows: Matador wagon ($190). Power tailgate window: Matador wagon ($44); standard in three-seat. Console: Gremlin/Hornet hatchback ($27). Hidden compartment: Hornet hatchback ($44). Individual reclining seats: Hornet sedan/wagon ($67). Bucket seats: Matador coupe ($102). Custom vinyl door panel/bucket seat trim: Gremlin ($49); NC with bench seats or 'X' pkg. Third seat: Matador wagon ($135). Rear defogger: Gremlin, Hornet hatch/wagon ($67); Matador coupe/sedan ($78). Rear defogger, blower-type: Hornet sedan ($44). Dual horns: Grem./Hornet ($11). Light group: Grem. ($28); Hornet ($33). Sports steering wheel: Grem./Hornet hatchback ($21); Matador ($22). Soft-feel sports steering wheel: Gremlin, Hornet sedan/wagon ($36); Hornet hatchback or with 'X' pkg. ($11); Mat. ($37). Tilt steering wheel: Hornet sedan/wagon ($55); Matador ($57). Tinted glass: Gremlin ($47); Hornet ($50); Matador ($55). Two-tone paint: Hornet except Sportabout ($38); Matador ($45) except wagon ($84). Special color combinations ($23). Vinyl roof: Hornet ($99); Mat. coupe/sedan ($111). Rally side stripes: Gremlin ($41); Matador coupe ($43). Woodgrain paneling: Hornet Sportabout except 'X' ($105); incl. w/Sportabout D/L pkg.; Matador wagon ($125). Roof rack: Matador wagon ($66). Roof rack and air deflector: Hornet wagon ($80). Tailgate air deflector: Matador wagon ($25). Inside hood release: Gremlin ($15); Hornet ($25). Front bumper guards: Grem./Hornet ($16). Bumper nerfing strips: Matador coupe ($25). Door edge guards: Matador ($10). Engine block heater ($18-$19). Wheel covers (set of four): Gremlin, Hornet sedan/wagon ($34). Custom wheel covers: Gremlin, Hornet sedan/wagon ($56); Hornet hatchback, Matador ($22). Styled wheels with trim rings for D-size tires: Gremlin, Hornet sedan/wagon ($128); Hornet hatchback ($94); with 'X' or D/L pkg. ($63). Aluminum styled wheels for D-size tires: Gremlin, Hornet sedan/wagon ($223); Hornet hatchback ($189); with D/L ($158). Aluminum styled wheels: Matador ($198). Space-Saver spare tire: Gremlin or Sportabout with regular wheels ($17), no charge with special wheels/tires. Tires: 6.45 x 14 whitewall: Gremlin ($38). 6.95 x 14: Grem. ($17). 6.95 x 14 whitewall: Gremlin ($55); Hornet ($38). D78 x 14: Grem. ($34); Hornet ($17). D78 x 14 WSW: Grem. ($72); Hornet ($55); incl. with Hornet D/L. D70 x 14 with white letters: Gremlin, Hornet hatchback/wagon 'X' ($51). DR78 x 14 steel radial: Gremlin ($148); Hornet ($131); with Hornet D/L ($76); with 'X' pkg. ($71). DR78 x 14 whitewall: Gremlin ($186); Hornet ($169); with Hornet sedan/wagon D/L ($114), with 'X' ($109). DR78 x 14 white-letter radial: Hornet ($208); with D/L ($153). DR70 x 14 radial with white letters: Gremlin ($225), Gremlin or Hornet hatch/wagon with 'X' ($148). F78 x 14 whitewall: Matador coupe/sedan ($40). FR78 x 14 WSW steel radial: Matador ($160). H78 x 14 WSW: Matador wagon ($40). HR78 x 14 WSW steel radial: Matador ($182); wagon ($160).

PACER CONVENIENCE/APPEARANCE OPTIONS: 'X' package: sedan ($379). D/L package: sedan ($349); wagon ($379). Decor package: body moldings ($77); included with D/L pkg. Extra quiet insulation package ($37); incl. with 'X' and D/L pkgs. Interior decor/convenience group; lighted vanity mirror, dome/reading light, clock, stowage containers, rubber mats ($82). Visibility group: remote left mirror, right mirror, day/night mirror, deluxe wipers ($67). Deluxe visibility group: same, plus rear defogger ($134). Power steering ($133). Power disc brakes ($60). Cruise control ($73). All Season air conditioning ($451). AM radio ($80). AM/FM/Stereo four-speaker radio ($211). Rear speaker ($20). 8-track tape player and AM/FM/Stereo radio ($317). Console ($27). Hidden compartment: sedan ($33). Individual reclining seats ($69); included with D/L pkg. Vinyl bucket seats ($69); standard with 'X' pkg.; no charge with D/L. "Levi's" custom fabric trim ($99); with 'X' or D/L ($30). Rear defogger with tinted glass ($67). Rear wiper/washer ($56). Light group ($30). Sports steering wheel ($21); incl. with 'X' pkg. Soft-feel sports steering wheel ($36); with 'X' pkg. ($15). Tilt steering wheel ($55). Tinted glass ($20). Door vent windows ($32). Two-tone color: sedan ($55). Special color combinations ($23). Vinyl roof ($111). Roof rack ($56). Bumper guards and nerfing strips ($56). Bumper nerfing strips ($24); incl. with D/L pkg. Bumper guards ($32). Engine block heater ($18). Wheel covers: set of four ($34). Styled wheels for D-size tires: ($128); with sedan 'X' pkg. ($63); incl. in D/L pkg. Aluminum styled wheels for D-size tires: ($223); with 'X' sedan ($158); with D/L wagon ($95). Tires: 6.95 x 14 whitewall, sedan ($38); D78 x 14, sedan ($17); D78 x 14 whitewall: sedan ($55); wagon ($38); no charge with D/L. DR78 x 14 radial: sedan ($131); wagon ($114); with D/L ($76). DR78 x 14 whitewall radial: sedan ($169); wagon ($152); with D/L ($114). DR70 x 14 radial with white letters: sedan ($208); wagon ($191); with D/L ($153). Tires with sedan 'X' package; DR78 x 14 whitewall steel radial ($38); DR70 x 14 white-letter radial ($77).

HISTORY: All 1977 AMC models were introduced Oct. 5, 1976. Model year production: 213,125 (173,076 sixes, 32,491 V-8s and 7,558 Gremlin fours); production in U.S. only, 182,005. For calendar year 1977, U.S. production amounted to 156,994 units. Calendar year sales: 184,361 (2.0 percent of the industry total), down from 247,640 the year before. Model year sales (worldwide) amounted to 246,640, a 23 percent drop from 1976. The 1977 models began production at Kenosha on August 2.

HISTORICAL FOOTNOTES: Although the Jeep business remained strong (and profitable), boosting AMC's fiscal status, passenger cars weren't selling as the 1977 model year ended. After a $46.3 million loss in fiscal 1976, the company ended 1977 in the black to the tune of almost $8.3 million, with $2.2 billion in sales. AMC raised prices almost five percent (average) for 1977 and experienced inventory troubles as dealers had too many '77 models on hand. This led to price cuts and rebates at the end of 1976, in an attempt to sell off the bloated stocks of Gremlins and Pacers. The intensive marketing campaign, which included such extras as free air conditioning didn't help enough. The restyled Gremlin slipped 12 percent, Pacer sales slid 23 percent, while the Matador, nearing its last days, fell 37 percent. The production line closed periodically, for a week at a time. AMC was feeling pressured to strengthen its role as a producer of small cars, as other automakers had been introducing compact models—and many more were to come in the next few years. Although the Gremlin had been the first domestic vehicle to go head-to-head against the imports, neither it nor other AMC models were now selling well as the downsizing era began. Analysts remained puzzled as to the reason. Though common in Europe the agreement to purchase completed four-cylinder engines from VW/Audi was new to the U.S. Those engines were delivered intact to AMC's new plant at Richmond, Indiana, for hot testing. As of January 1977, there were 1,690 AMC dealer franchises. AMC's Buyer Protection Plan II now included a 24-month/24,000-mile engine/drivetrain warranty. Management received an ample shakeup. AMC President and CEO William V. Luneberg retired in May 1977, succeeded by Gerald C. Meyers. R.D. Chapin Jr. remained as chairman, but turned over much of the responsibility to Meyers and his team.

1978

Three of the four 1977 models carried over into the 1978 model year. The Hornet name disappeared replaced by a similar Concord compact. Instead of an option package for the Hornet, the AMX became a full-fledged model. This would be the final year for both the subcompact Gremlin and mid-size Matador. The Solid State Ignition (SSI) system introduced on some 1977 Canadian models was now standard. A new antimony battery never needed extra water. An AM/FM/stereo radio with Citizens Band and four speakers joined the option list (except on Gremlins). So did a digital clock. Standard colors were Classic Black, Alpine White, Powder Blue, Captain Blue metallic, Midnight Blue metallic, Sunshine Yellow, Sand Tan, Golden Ginger metallic, Mocha Brown metallic, Sun Orange, Khaki, British Bronze metallic, Loden green metallic, Quick Silver metallic, Firecracker Red, Autumn Red metallic, and Claret metallic.

GREMLIN — SERIES 40 — FOUR/SIX — Following its 1977 restyle, Gremlin turned to interior refinements for the '78 model year. These included color-keyed carpeting, a custom steering wheel, and a new instrument panel with standard AM radio. Engineering improvements cut down on engine noise and exhaust manifold rattles. Thirteen colors were available on Gremlins. Air conditioning was available with the four-cylinder engine. Custom Gremlins now sported standard whitewall B78 x 14 tires with wheel covers plus scuff moldings. Standard equipment also included a 232 cu. in. six-cylinder engine (or 2.0-liter four) with electronic ignition, three-speed floor shift, manual front disc brakes, heater/defroster, vinyl seat upholstery, rear bumper guards, body paint stripes, locking glovebox, and rocker panel moldings. Custom models also had wheel lip moldings and a parcel shelf, plus vinyl bucket seats up front; base Gremlins had bench seats front and rear. Six-cylinder Customs could come equipped with four-speed manual floor shift. Gremlin's 'X' package, offered only on Custom models, included bucket seats and interior trim in "Levi's" fabric; sports steering wheel; lower body decal stripes with contrasting pin stripes and "GREMLIN X" insignia on front door portion; "Levi's" decal; brushed aluminum instrument panel overlays; extra quiet insulation; decals on back panel and 'C' pillar; black wiper arms, 'B' pillars and side window frames. A front sway bar and DR78 x 14 blackwall radial tires on slot styled 14 x 6-inch wheels completed the 'X' package. Early in 1978, a performance-oriented Gremlin GT hit the market, wearing fiberglass body components. Actually a $649 option package, the GT's external features included a body-colored front air dam with striping, front and rear fender flares matched to body color, black side stripes with color-keyed pin striping, color-keyed front/rear bumper guards and nerfing strips, black grille insert, black mirrors (left one remote controlled), hood striping, black door and quarter-window frames, and black wiper arms. GT Gremlins rode on DR70 x 14 white-letter radials on spoke-style wheels with trim rings, and had a front sway bar. Bucket seats were soft-feel vinyl, with 'Levi's' upholstery optional. Motoring niceties also included a sports steering wheel, gauge package, brushed aluminum instrument panel overlay, extra quiet insulation package, and day/night mirror.

PACER — SERIES 60 — SIX/V-8 — Performance-minded Pacer buyers could now choose an optional 304 cu. in. V-8 rather than the 232 or 258 six. Again offered in hatchback sedan and wagon body styles, the panoramic Pacer also gained a new hood and grille, a longer station wagon liftgate, plus improved seat and leg room up front. The new, upward-bulging eggcrate grille, dominated by horizontal bars, had two lower rows extending full-width between the headlights; two narrower upper bars protruded up into the hood area. Huge parking lights wrapped around, from headlights well into fender sides. Some of that new front end restyling was done to squeeze in the V-8 engine. Various items that had formerly been optional now became standard including individual reclining front seats, rear armrests, a day/night rearview mirror, electric clock, custom steering wheel, woodgrain instrument panel and color-keyed wheel covers. Also standard were a light group, cigarette lighter, extra quiet insulation package, dual horns, inside hood release, locking glovebox, rocker panel and wheel lip moldings, hood and fender moldings, heater/defroster, carpeting, and bumper nerfing strips. Base engine was the 232 six with three-speed floor shift and D78 x 14 whitewall tires. As before, Pacers featured rack-and-pinion steering and an isolated suspension design, plus an oversized passenger door. Fifteen body colors were offered, including new Quick Silver, Khaki, British Bronze, and Claret. Pacer's Sport package, available on the hatchback sedan with 258 six or 304 V-8, included soft-feel vinyl bucket seats, a sports steering wheel, DR78 x 14 blackwall tires on slot style wheels with trim rings, and two-tone paint on lower bodysides. The 'X' package was dropped.

CONCORD — SERIES 01 — FOUR/SIX/V-8 — For 1978, the compact Hornet was reworked to become a luxurious Concord, with the same 108-inch wheelbase and four body styles: two- and four-door sedan, hatchback, or station wagon. The hatchback coupe was a particularly attractive design, with huge cargo space. Sporty too, with an optional 'X' package. Styling features included rectangular headlamps and bezels a bright six-section crosshatch grille with clear squarish parking lights behind the outer sections, and tri-color horizontal taillamps. All Concords had front disc brakes, front sway bar, inside hood release, rocker panel moldings, hood ornament, and full wheel covers. Walnut-vinyl inserts accented instrument panels. Base Concords ran with a 232 cu. in. six and three-speed floor shift. Automatic shift and a 304 V-8 were optional plus a four-cylinder engine (formerly on Gremlins alone) early in 1978. Sedans had Velveteen fabric bench seats in five colors; hatchbacks, soft-feel vinyl buckets. Standard equipment also included a heater/defroster, color-keyed carpeting, padded door trim panels, lighter, rear bumper guards, dual bodyside pin stripes, color-keyed scuff moldings, locking glovebox, and C78 x 14 blackwall tires. Wagons carried a space-saver spare tire and held a locking hidden compartment. Hatchbacks had a sports steering wheel and flipper-type rear vent windows; four-doors, roll-down rear windows. Concord's Sport package, available on all models with 258 six or 304 V-8, included soft-feel vinyl bucket seats, with individual reclining seats (vinyl or velveteen crush fabric) optional in sedans and wagons. It also included a sports steering wheel, slot-style wheels with DR78 x 14 blackwall steel-belted radials, brushed aluminum instrument panel overlays, wide rocker panel moldings, lower bodyside tape stripe and extra quiet insulation. For luxury, Concord offered the D/L package on all but the hatchback. It featured individual reclining seats in velveteen crush fabric (soft-feel vinyl in wagons), plus map pockets in custom door trim panels, woodgrain instrument panel overlays, light group, dual horns, hood pin stripes, parcel shelf, digital clock, wide rocker moldings, bumper nerfing strips front and rear, extra quiet insulation, day/night mirror, and DR78 x 14 whitewalls with color-keyed wheel covers. D/L sedans had a landau vinyl roof and color-keyed scuff moldings, plus trunk carpeting and spare tire cover; two-doors, opera windows with silver accents. D/L wagons came with woodgrain side overlays (which could be deleted) and cargo floor skid strips. A Touring Wagon package added unique door trim panels in beige with orange/brown accents, leather-wrapped steering wheel, and wide brown/orange scuff moldings.

AMX HATCHBACK — SERIES 01 — SIX/V-8 — Reviving a name associated with performance a few years earlier, AMC tried once again to capture a slice of the youth/performance market with a new AMX, first introduced as a Hornet option in 1977. Built on the Concord platform, with an all new, slightly wedge-shaped front, AMX came with a load of appealing features, heavy on black. They included: black fender flares front and rear, rear window louvers, an 'AMX' decal just to the rear of the doors, front air dam, painted bumpers with guards and nerfing strips, black scuff moldings, dual flat black mirrors (the left one remote-controlled), color-coordinated slot wheels—plus a blacked out grille with round signal lights and 'AMX' emblem in the center. Inside, drivers found a floor console, rally gauges with tachometer, map pockets in custom door trim panels, brushed aluminum instrument panel overlays, a black soft-feel sports steering wheel, day/night mirror, package tray, special graphics and inside hood release. Soft-feel vinyl bucket seats came in black, blue or beige, with "Levi's" trim package optional. A brushed aluminum roof band with special insignia helped make the AMX easy to spot. Five colors were offered: Alpine White, Firecracker Red, Sunshine Yellow, Quick Silver Metallic, and Classic Black. That black AMX (a $49 option) had unique gold rally striping on the roof band, front doors and fenders, plus gold stripe on black slot-styled wheels and black windshield reveal moldings. The optional decal package with Classic Black body included gold/orange decals (black/orange with other body colors). A 258 cu. in. six with four-speed floor shift was standard. Automatic shift was required for the optional 304 cu. in. V-8. Standard AMX equipment also included front disc brakes, front sway bar, and DR78 x 14 blackwall steel-belted radial tires.

MATADOR (COUPE) — SERIES 10 — SIX/V-8 — For their final year, Matador coupes changed little in outside appearance but added some luxury features. The list includes power steering, power front disc brakes, automatic transmission, coolant recovery system, electric clock, dual horns, and a 12-inch day/night mirror. Individual reclining seats were upholstered in velveteen crush fabric. The light group consisted of a glovebox light, engine compartment light, courtesy lights, and ashtray light. Matadors also had extra quiet insulation, front/rear bumper guards, and a front sway bar. The coupe's Barcelona package added individual reclining seats in velveteen crush fabric with woven accent strips, plus custom door trim panels, a unique headliner, 24-ounce carpeting, headlight bezels painted in accent color, black trunk carpet, a rear sway bar, body-colored front/rear bumpers, bumper nerfing strips, landau padded vinyl roof, opera quarter windows with accents, and dual remote-control mirrors painted in body color. Barcelona medallions stood on fenders and glovebox door. Two-tone combinations included Golden Ginger metallic on Sand Tan, or Autumn Red metallic on Claret. Standard engine was a 258 cu. in. six, with 360 V-8 optional.

MATADOR (SEDAN AND WAGON) — SERIES 80 — SIX/V-8 — Like the coupe, Matador sedans and wagons changed little outside, but added the new luxury items. Station wagon seats were upholstered in crush grain vinyl. Sedans came with a 258 cu. in. six, but wagons carried the 304 V-8 as standard equipment. Both had three-speed automatic transmission and door vent windows. Standard equipment was the same as the coupe, except for the coolant recovery system. Matadors came in 13 body colors, including new Quick Silver and Claret metallics, plus seven vinyl roof colors. The Barcelona package, formerly a coupe option only, was now available on sedans.

I.D. DATA: The 13-symbol Vehicle Identification Number (VIN), as before was embossed on a metal plate riveted to the upper corner of the instrument panel, behind the left wiper pivot and 'A' pillar, visible through the windshield. Coding was the same as 1976-77. Symbol one ('A') indicated American Motors Corp. Model year (second symbol) changed to '8' for 1978. The third symbol was a letter for transmission type: 'A' column-shift automatic; 'C' floor-shift automatic; 'E' three-speed floor shift; 'M' four-speed floor shift. Digits indicating series (fourth symbol) were now: '0' Concord/AMX; '1' Matador coupe; '4' Gremlin; '6' Pacer; and '8' Matador sedan/wagon. The body-type digit (symbol five) changed to: '3' two-door hatchback; '5' four-door sedan; '6' two-door sedan or hatchback; '8' station wagon. Symbol six indicated model/group: '4' Gremlin four-cylinder; '5' base Gremlin; '7' Pacer, Concord, Matador or Gremlin Custom; '9' AMX. Symbol seven showed engine type: 'A' 258-6 1Bbl.; 'C' 258-6 2Bbl.; 'E' 232-6 1Bbl.; 'G' 2.0-liter four 2Bbl.; 'H' 304 V-8 2Bbl.; 'N' 360 V-8 2Bbl. The final six digits were the sequential serial number: 100001 to 699999 for Kenosha manufacture; 700001 to 999999 for Brampton, Ontario. A non-removable Federal emission control information label in the engine compartment identified the engine family and gave basic tune-up specs. A non-removable safety sticker affixed to the edge of the left front door showed month and year built, the VIN and a safety compliance statement, as well as consumer information (vehicle class, acceleration/passing figures, tire reserve load, and stopping distance). A unit body identification plate riveted to the edge of the left front door showed: vehicle Body Number (K Kenosha, followed by a six-digit sequence number); the five-digit Model Number (model year, body, and standard appointment group); a four-digit Trim Number; Paint Code Number; and a Build Sequence Number preceded by a letter showing the production line at which the car was manufactured.

GREMLIN SERIES 40 (SIX-CYLINDER)

Series No.	Body/Style No.	Body Type & Seating	Factory Price	Shipping Weight	Prod. Total
40	7846-5	2-dr Sed-4P	3539	2834	Note 1
40	7846-7	2-dr Cust Sed-4P	3789	2822	Note 1

GREMLIN SERIES 40 (FOUR-CYLINDER)

40	7846-4	2-dr Cust Sed-4P	3789	2556	6,349

Note 1: Total model year production: 22,104 Gremlins (15,755 six-cylinder).

PACER SERIES 60

60	7866-7	2-dr Sed-4P	4048/4298	3197/3430	7,411
60	7868-7	2-dr Sta Wag-4P	4193/4443	3245/3478	13,820

Note 2: Of the 21,231 Pacers produced during the model year, 2,514 had a V-8 engine.

CONCORD SERIES 01

01	7803-7	2-dr Hatch-4P	3849/4099	3051/3284	2,572
01	7806-7	2-dr Sed-5P	3749/3999	3029/3262	50,482
01	7805-7	4-dr Sed-5P	3849/4099	3099/3332	42,126
01	7808-7	4-dr Sta Wag-5P	4049/4299	3133/3366	23,573

Note 2: Total model year Concord production, 121,293 units (110,972 with six-cylinder engine, 6,541 with V-8, and 3,780 with a four).

AMX SERIES 01

01	7803-9	2-dr Hatch-4P	4649/4899	3159/3381	2,540

MATADOR (COUPE) SERIES 10

10	7816-7	2-dr Cpe-5P	4799/4989	3709/3916	2,006

MATADOR (SEDAN AND WAGON) SERIES 80

80	7885-7	4-dr Sed-6P	4849/5039	3718/3921	4,824
80	7888-7	4-dr Sta Wag-6P	—/5299	—/4146	3,746

Note 3: Of the total model year production of 10,576 during the model year, only 23 came with a six-cylinder engine.

FACTORY PRICE AND WEIGHT NOTE: Figure before the slash in price columns (except Gremlin) is for six-cylinder engine, after slash for V-8 engine.

ENGINES: BASE FOUR (Gremlin): Same as 1977; see 1977 specifications. BASE SIX (Gremlin, Pacer, Concord): Inline. OHV. Six-cylinder. Cast iron block. Displacement: 232 cu. in. (3.8 liters). Bore & stroke: 3.75 x 3.50 in. Compression ratio: 8.0:1. Brake horsepower: 90 at 3400 R.P.M. Torque: 168 lb.-ft. at 1600 R.P.M. Taxable H.P.: 33.75. Seven main bearings. Hydraulic valve lifters. Carburetor: 1Bbl. Carter YF. BASE SIX (AMX, Matador sedan/coupe); OPTIONAL (Gremlin, Pacer, Concord): Inline. OHV. Six-cylinder. Cast iron block. Displacement: 258 cu. in. (4.2 liters). Bore & stroke: 3.75 x 3.90 in. Compression ratio: 8.0:1. Brake horsepower: 120 at 3600 R.P.M. Torque: 201 lb.-ft. at 1800 R.P.M. Seven main bearings. Taxable H.P.: 33.75. Hydraulic valve lifters. Carburetor: 2Bbl. Carter BBD. BASE SIX (California models): Same as 258 cu. in. six above, but with Carter YF 7235 1Bbl. carburetor. Brake horsepower: 100 at 3400 R.P.M. Torque: 200 lb.-ft. at 1600 R.P.M. OPTIONAL V-8 (Pacer, Concord, AMX): 90-degree, overhead valve V-8. Cast iron block. Displacement: 304 cu. in. (5.0 liters). Bore & stroke: 3.75 x 3.44 in. Compression ratio: 8.4:1. Brake horsepower: 130 at 3200 R.P.M. Torque: 238 lb.-ft. at 2000 R.P.M. Taxable H.P.: 45. Five main bearings. Hydraulic valve lifters. Carburetor: 2Bbl. Motorcraft 2100. BASE V-8 (Matador wagon); OPTIONAL (Matador coupe/sedan): 90-degree, overhead valve V-8. Cast iron block. Displacement: 360 cu. in. (5.9 liters). Bore & stroke: 4.08 x 3.44 in. Compression ratio: 8.25:1. Brake horsepower: 140 at 3350 R.P.M. Torque: 278 lb.-ft. at 2000 R.P.M. Taxable H.P.: 53.3. Five main bearings. Hydraulic valve lifters. Carburetor: 2Bbl. Motorcraft 2100.

CHASSIS DATA: Wheelbase: (Gremlin) 96 in.; (Pacer) 100 in.; (Concord/AMX) 108 in.; (Matador coupe) 114 in.; (Mat. sed/wagon) 118 in. Overall length: (Gremlin) 166.6 in.; (Pacer sedan) 172 in.; (Pacer wagon) 177 in.; (Concord) 183.6 in.; (AMX) 186 in.; (Matador coupe) 209.9 in.; (Matador sedan) 218.3 in.; (Matador wagon) 219.3 in. Height: (Gremlin) 51.5 in.; (Pacer sedan) 52.8 in.; (Pacer wagon) 53.2 in.; (Concord) 51.3-51.7 in.; (AMX) 52.2 in.; (Matador coupe) 51.6 in.; (Matador sedan) 53.9 in.; (Matador wagon) 56 in. Front Tread: (Gremlin/Concord) 57.5 in.; (Pacer) 61.4 in.; (Concord) 57.6 in.; (Matador) 59.6 in. Rear Tread: (Gremlin/Hornet) 57.1 in.; (Pacer) 60 in.; (Concord) 57.1-57.5 in.; (Matador) 60.6 in. Standard Tires: (Gremlin) B78 x 14 whitewall; (Pacer) D78 x 14; (Concord) C78 x 14 except with D/L package, D78 x 14; (AMX) DR78 x 14; (Matador coupe/sedan) F78 x 14; (Matador wagon) H78 x 14.

TECHNICAL: Three-speed manual floor-shift transmission was standard on Gremlin base six, Concords and Pacers. Four-speed floor-shift was standard on Gremlin Custom six, Gremlin four, and AMX. Matadors came with Torque Command three-speed column-shift automatic; optional on others. Automatic shift gear ratios: (1st) 2.45:1; (2nd) 1.45:1; (Rev) 2.20:1. Steering: (Pacer) rack and pinion; (others) recirculating ball. Suspension: independent front coil springs (Pacer springs mounted between the two control arms); semi-elliptic rear leaf springs except (Matador) coil springs. Brakes: front disc; rear drum. Fuel tank: (Gremlin) 21 gal. except four-cylinder, 13 gal.; (Pacer) 20 gal.; (Concord/AMX) 22 gal.

DRIVETRAIN OPTIONS: 258 cu. in. six-cylinder engine: Gremlin/Pacer/Concord ($120). 304 cu. in. V-8, 2Bbl.: Pacer/Concord/AMX ($233). 360 cu. in. V-8, 2Bbl.: Matador sedan/coupe ($190). Four-speed manual floor shift: Gremlin/Pacer/Concord ($111). Torque-Command automatic transmission, column shift: Gremlin ($270); Pacer/Concord ($296). Torque-Command with floor shift lever: Gremlin ($294); Pacer/Concord/AMX ($320); Matador coupe with V-8 and bucket seats ($70). Twin Grip differential ($55-$59). Heavy-duty engine cooling system ($29-$37) but standard with air conditioning. Maximum cooling system: Matador V-8 ($48), Matador V-8 with air ($19). Auxiliary automatic transmission oil cooler: Matador ($34). Heavy-duty suspension ($31-$36); incl. front sway bar on Gremlin/Pacer, rear on Matador. Front sway bar: Gremlin/Pacer ($18) but incl. with radial tires. Rear sway bar: Matador ($18). Air-adjustable shock absorbers: Matador ($44-$48). H.D. 70-amp battery ($17-$19). California emission system ($74). High altitude package ($23).

GREMLIN/CONCORD/MATADOR CONVENIENCE/APPEARANCE OPTIONS: 'X' package: Gremlin ($249). GT package: Gremlin ($649). Concord D/L package ($200). Concord Sport package: hatch ($289); sed/wag ($379). Barcelona package: Matador coupe ($849); Matador sedan ($699). "Levi's" trim package: AMX ($49). 'AMX' decal pkg. (black/orange decal on hood and liftgate): AMX ($49). Extra quiet insulation package: Gremlin/Concord/AMX ($45); included with Concord Sport and D/L pkg. Protection group: Gremlin ($42); Concord ($27). Interior decor/convenience group: Gremlin ($69); Concord ($79); Concord D/L ($54); AMX/Matador ($59). Gauge package: Gremlin Cust. six ($75); Concord ($99). Visibility group (remote control left mirror, manual right mirror, day/night mirror, intermittent wipers): Gremlin/Concord ($71). Visibility group (dual remote mirrors, deluxe wipers): Matador ($81). Remote control left mirror ($16-$17). Intermittent wipers ($30-$32). Power steering ($141-$147). Power front disc brakes ($64). Cruise control ($99); N/A on Gremlin four. Air conditioning system: Grem./Conc./AMX ($478). Air conditioning package (incl. tinted glass and power steering): Gremlin ($669); Conc./AMX ($679); Matador ($590). AM radio ($80-$81). AM/FM/Stereo four-speaker radio: Gremlin ($144); others ($224). AM/CB Radio: Gremlin ($119); others ($199). AM/FM/CB Radio ($299); N/A on Gremlin. Rear speaker for AM radio ($22-$23). Tape player and AM/FM/Stereo radio: Matador ($336). Digital clock: Gremlin/Concord ($25). Tachometer: Gremlin four ($49). Power windows: Matador sedan/wagon ($155). Power side and tailgate windows: Matador wagon ($202). Power tailgate window: Mat. wagon ($47); standard in three-seat. Console: Gremlin/Concord ($29). Hidden compartment: Concord hatch/AMX ($31). Individual reclining seats: Matador (NC). Vinyl bucket seats: Gremlin ($49); Concord ($69); Concord D/L and Matador coupe (NC). Third seat: Matador wagon ($143).

Stowage/litter containers ($10). Rear defroster ($81-$88). Dual horns: Gremlin/Concord ($12). Light group: Concord/AMX ($30). Sports steering wheel: Gremlin Cust./Concord/Matador ($20). Soft-feel sports steering wheel: Gremlin Cust., Conc. sed/wag, Matador ($31); Gremlin 'X', Concord hatch or Sport pkg. ($11). Tilt steering wheel: Concord ($64); Matador ($67). Tinted glass ($52-$64). Two-tone paint: Concord D/L ($75); Matador ($43). Delete two-tone: Matador Barcelona sedan (deduct $100). Special color combinations ($24) except AMX Classic Black ($49). Vinyl roof: Concord ($105); Matador ($118). Rally side stripes: Gremlin ($43); Mat. coupe ($46). Woodgrain wagon paneling: Concord ($75); Matador ($133). Delete woodgrain from Concord D/L wagon (deduct $75). Roof rack: Gremlin ($59); Matador wagon ($84). Roof rack and air deflector: Concord wagon ($85). Tailgate air deflector: Gremlin ($24). Matador ($27). Inside hood release: Gremlin ($16). Front bumper guards: Gremlin/Concord ($19). Bumper nerfing strips: Concord ($34). Side scuff molding: base Gremlin ($29). Protective inner coating ($95) except Matador ($106). Door edge guards: Matador ($11). Locking gas cap ($7). Engine block heater ($19-$20). Wheel covers (set of four): Gremlin ($36). Custom wheel covers ($23). Styled wheels for D-size tires ($136) except AMX, 'X' or Sport pkg. ($71). Aluminum styled wheels ($236) except AMX 'X' or Sport pkg. ($171). Space-Saver spare tire: Gremlin or Concord with regular wheels ($18); no charge with special wheels/tires. Tires: B78 x 14 whitewall; Gremlin (NC). D78 x 14: Grem. (NC); Conc. ($18). D78 x 14 whitewall: Grem. ($36); Conc. ($63). DR78 x 14 SBR: Gremlin ($112); Concord ($139); with Conc. D/L ($16); Gremlin Cust. 'X' (NC). DR78 x 14 white SBR: Gremlin ($157); Concord ($184); Conc. D/L ($121); AMX, Conc. Sport, Gremlin 'X' ($45). DR78 x 14 white-letter SBR: Gremlin Cust. ($172); Concord ($199); Conc. D/L ($136); AMX, Conc. Sport, 'X' pkg. ($60);. DR78 x 14 white GBR: Gremlin ($36); Concord ($159); Concord Sport ($165); Conc. D/L ($96). F78 x 14 whitewall: Matador coupe/sedan ($48). FR78 x 14 white SBR: Matador ($175). H78 x 14 whitewall: Matador wagon ($48). HR78 x 14 white SBR: Matador ($198); wagon ($175).

PACER CONVENIENCE/APPEARANCE OPTIONS: Sport package ($165); N/A on wagon or w/232 engine. Interior decor/convenience group ($59). Visibility group: remote left mirror, right mirror, intermittent wipers ($61). Left remote mirror ($16). Gauge package ($99). Intermittent wipers ($30). Power steering ($147). Power disc brakes ($64). Cruise control ($99). Air conditioning ($478). Air conditioning pkg.: tinted glass and power steering ($679). AM radio ($80). AM/FM/Stereo four-speaker radio ($224). AM/CB Radio ($199). AM/FM/CB Radio ($299). Rear speaker ($22). Tape player and AM/FM/Stereo radio ($336). Console ($29). Hidden compartment hatch ($35). Individual reclining seats: velveteen crush or reflection print fabric, or soft-feel vinyl (NC). Vinyl bucket seats (NC). Stowage/litter compartment ($10). Rear defroster ($81). Rear wiper/washer ($59). Sports steering wheel ($20); incl. with Sport pkg. Soft-feel sports steering wheel ($31), with Sport pkg. ($11). Tilt steering wheel ($64). Tinted glass ($58). Door vent windows ($34). Two-tone color: hatch ($84). Special color combinations ($24). Woodgrain wagon paneling ($111). Protective inner coating ($95). Vinyl roof ($118). Roof rack ($59). Bumper guards ($38). Locking gas cap ($7). Custom wheel covers ($23). Styled wheels ($136); with Sport hatch pkg. ($71). Aluminum styled wheels ($236); with Sport hatch ($171). Tires: DR78 x 14 SBR ($76). DR78 x 14 white SBR ($121). DR78 x 14 white-letter SBR ($136). DR78 x 14 white GBR ($96). E78 x 14 whitewall ($18). ER78 x 14 SBR ($94). ER78 x 14 white SBR ($139). ER78 x 14 white-letter SBR ($154). Tires with Sport hatchback package: DR78 x 14 white SBR ($45); DR78 x 14 white-letter SBR ($60); ER78 x 14 ($18); ER78 x 14 white ($63); ER78 x 14 white-letter ($78).

HISTORY: Introduced: Sept. 9, 1977, except the new Concord, in October; modified Gremlins and Concords debuted later. Model year production: (U.S.) 137,860, for 1.55 percent of the industry total North American production for U.S. market, 175,204 units (10,129 four-cylinder, 145,467 six-cylinder and 19,608 V-8). Calendar year production: (U.S.) 164,351, led by Concord with 108,414 cars manufactured. Calendar year sales by U.S. dealers: 170,739 (1.8 percent of industry total).

HISTORICAL FOOTNOTES: AMC's fiscal picture improved again during the 1978 model year, with net earnings at their highest point since 1973. Much of the company's strength, however, continued to stem from its Jeep subsidiary. Except for the new Concord, North American production slipped substantially in every division. Gremlin prices were cut in November 1977. Promise for the future came in the form of negotiations with Regie Nationale des Usines Renault, the French firm that produced the Renault. The arrangement reached between the two companies in January 1979 would permit AMC to distribute the Renault Le Car, and perhaps allow Renault to distribute AMC Jeep vehicles. Far more significant, though, was the announcement that AMC planned to produce a joint-venture Renault vehicle in the United States. Gerald C. Meyers took over as the new chairman and CEO at AMC, while W. Paul Tippett stepped into his former role as president and chief operating officer. James L. Tolley moved from PR director at Chevrolet to vice-president of public relations at AMC. Passenger car operations were consolidated at Kenosha during the year. The Milwaukee body plant turned to stamping, while the Brampton, Ontario, facility converted to Jeep production. Four-cylinder engines had first been purchased intact from Volkswagenwerk. During 1977, AMC initiated a plan to assemble the engines itself, on an assembly line bought from VW. But as the 1978 model year began, AMC contracted instead to purchase 'Iron Duke' fours from Pontiac.

1979

American Motors left the mid-size market by abandoning the Matador, which had been selling poorly. Meanwhile, the Gremlin was replaced by a similar, but more stylish, subcompact, the new Spirit; and the performance oriented AMX moved to the shorter Spirit chassis. Spirit, Concord and Pacer base models included as standard equipment a high-pressure compact spare tire, manual front disc brakes, inside hood release, lighted ashtray, full wheel covers, rear bumper guards, custom steering wheel, and color-keyed 12-ounce carpeting. A new, upscale trim level was added: the Limited. This signaled AMC's move away from austerity and toward a touch of luxury, even in economy cars. Standard colors for all models (except AMX) were Olympic White Classic Black, Quick Silver metallic, Cumberland Green metallic, Wedgewood Blue, Starboard Blue metallic, Khaki, British Bronze metallic, Saxon Yellow, Morocco Buff, Alpaca Brown metallic, Sable Brown metallic, Firecracker Red, Russet metallic and Bordeaux metallic. Torque-Command transmissions (supplied by Chrysler) with V-8 engines received a lockup torque converter. Over two-thirds of AMC passenger cars had air conditioning.

SPIRIT — SERIES 40 — FOUR/SIX — Gremlin's more luxurious replacement kept the same engine choices and basic design as its subcompact predecessor, but with much larger rear side windows on the two-door sedan. New quad rectangular headlamps flanked a clean four-row, horizontally ribbed grille with center medallion. Clear, wide parking lights sat below the headlights. Horizontal amber reflectors were mounted at the forward end of the front fenders, 'Spirit' emblems at their rear. Slightly rounded rectangular taillamps held inset backup lights. Aluminum bumpers had black end caps. Joining that familiar sedan was a good-looking two-door Liftback coupe. Front styling was similar, but the rear end held extra-wide four-section taillamps that stretched from the license plate to the outer edge of the panel. The liftback's big pop-up hatch sloped much more sharply than the sedan's back end. Basic engine was the Volkswagen/Audi 121 cu. in. four-cylinder, with 232 and 258 cu. in. sixes optional. Liftbacks could also have a 304 V-8. A four-speed floor shift transmission was standard; floor or column shift automatics optional. A three-speed manual shift was available with the 232 six at reduced price. Base Spirit standard equipment included blackwall C78 x 14 tires, vinyl bucket seats, four-spoke steering wheel, lighter, locking glovebox, folding rear seat, spare tire cover, dual paint stripes, plus moldings for wheel lip, drip rail, hood front edge, windshield surround and rocker panels. Liftbacks included a front sway bar to improve handling. The DL model added custom bucket seats in Caberfae Corduroy fabric or Sport Vinyl, walnut burl woodgrain instrument panel overlay, woodgrain steering wheel, day/night mirror, digital clock, extra quiet insulation, dual horns, courtesy lights, package shelf, folding split rear seatback, front/rear bumper guards, and whitewall tires with color-keyed styled wheel covers. For more luxury, Spirit's Limited included leather bucket seats, an AM radio, power door locks, power steering, power liftback release, dual remote mirrors, light and visibility groups, convenience and protection groups, tilt steering wheel, full-length console with center armrest, 18-ounce carpeting, and P195/75R14 glass-belted whitewalls. DL and Limited liftbacks could also have the sporty GT package that included a black full-length console, black leather-wrapped steering wheel, black instrument panel with woodgrain overlay, woodgrain door panel accents, tachometer, black bumpers with nerfing strips and guards, twin black remote mirrors, black exterior trim moldings, black grille insert and headlight bezels, and black rear venturi area. GT models carried P195/75R14 steel-belted radials on spoke style wheels; V-8s with manual shift even had a Performance Tuned exhaust sound. 'GT' emblems were placed below the 'Spirit' badges on front fenders. For handling to match the sharp looks, a GT Rally Tuned Suspension Package added a tuned front sway bar, rear sway bar, heavy-duty adjustable Gabriel "Strider" shocks, tuned strut rod bushings and rear spring iso-clamp pads, Hi-Control rear leaf springs, unique steering gears, and heavy-duty brakes.

AMX — SERIES 40 — SIX/V-8 — AMX liftbacks entered the 1979 model year sitting on a short (96 inch) Spirit wheelbase, rather than the previous Concord platform. "Expect to be noticed," the factory declared. To make sure, every AMX had front/rear black bumpers with guards and nerfing strips, a front air dam and rear deck spoiler with accent stripes, front/rear fender flares, a new rectangular blackout grille with center 'AMX' emblem, twin remote mirrors, and Turbocast II aluminum wheels with white letter ER60 x 14 radial tires. Eye-catching graphics included 'AMX' decals on doors and rear spoiler, plus a huge flame decal on the hood. Quad headlamps sat over clear rectangular signal/parking lights. Inside, drivers sat in Sport Vinyl or Caberfae Corduroy bucket seats, gripped a leather-wrapped steering wheel, watched a full gauge array with brushed aluminum instrument panel overlays, and enjoyed a center console with armrest. Standard engine was the 258 cu. in. six (304 V-8 optional) with four-speed floor shift. A Rally Tuned suspension system helped handling, while V-8s with manual shift included a performance-tuned exhaust sound. That suspension included Gabriel 'Strider' shocks, front sway bar, heavy-duty rear sway bar, and Hi-Control rear leaf springs. AMX colors were Olympic White, Classic Black, Wedgewood Blue, Saxon Yellow, Morocco Buff, and Firecracker Red.

PACER — SERIES 60 — SIX/V-8 — Except for an upright hood ornament above the upward-bulging grille, changes to the Pacer hatchback sedan and wagon consisted mainly of a larger (258 cu. in.) base engine and the addition of a Limited upgrade to the basic D/L model. Standard D/L equipment included individual reclining seats in Caberfae Corduroy or Sport Vinyl, windsplit molding, front/rear bumper guards, folding rear seat back, extra quiet insulation, day/night inside mirror, electric clock, dual horns, courtesy lights, two-speed wiper/washers, custom steering wheel with woodgrain overlays, and woodgrain-overlay instrument panel. D/L models had color-keyed wheel covers, P195/75R14 whitewall glass-belted radials, front sway bar, and color-keyed wide scuff moldings. Bucket seats upholstered in Caberfae Corduroy fabric were also offered on D/L Pacers. Beyond those features, the Limited included power steering, power windows and door locks, an AM radio, leather reclining seats with beige corduroy accents, woodgrain tilt steering wheel, dual remote-control mirrors, visibility and convenience groups, light and protection groups, folding center armrest, 18-ounce color-keyed carpeting, and color-keyed styled wheel covers. In addition to the standard colors, Pacers were available with Misty Beige clearcoat and in six two-tone combinations. Four-speed manual shift was standard (with floor lever); column- or floor-shift automatic optional. Once again, a 304 cu. in. V-8 was available, which required power steering and brakes. According to industry sources, only 184 Pacers had a sunroof; 347 had vinyl tops.

CONCORD — SERIES 01 — FOUR/SIX/V-8 — Front end styling changed appreciably on the compact, luxurious Concord, with wide clear parking/signal lights setting below quad rectangular headlamps. The restyled formal grille was considerably taller, with seven vertical bars. Bright aluminum bumpers had black end caps and guards. Standard engine remained the 232 cu. in. six, but a 258 six, 304 V-8 and 121 four were all optional. Four-speed manual floor shift was standard; column-shift automatic transmission optional. Concords now came in three trim levels: base, D/L, and Limited (no Limited for the hatchback body). Base Concords were equipped with a front sway bar, lighted ashtray, sport vinyl notched bench seat (Striped Knit fabric available with automatic transmission), color-keyed 12-ounce carpeting, full wheel covers, dual bodyside pin stripes, hood ornament, and moldings for drip rail, wheel lip, hood front edge, and windshield surround. Tires were D78 x 14 blackwalls. D/L versions had individual reclining seats in Velveteen Crush fabric or Sport Vinyl, as well as a day/night mirror, digital clock, extra quiet insulation, dual horns, courtesy lights, underhood light, walnut burl woodgrain instrument panel overlay, custom steering wheel with woodgrain overlays, custom headliner and sunvisors, package shelf, front/rear bumper guards, color-keyed wheel covers, and whitewall tires. D/L sedans and hatchbacks also sported a landau vinyl roof; wagons had woodgrain bodyside overlays. Genuine leather individual reclining seats with beige corduroy accents came on the plush Limiteds, as did an AM radio, power door locks, twin remote mirrors, adjustable tilt woodgrain steering wheel, light group, visibility group, convenience and protection groups, styled wheel covers, 18-ounce carpeting, and P195/75R14 whitewall glass-belted radials (except hatchbacks).

I.D. DATA: The 13-symbol Vehicle Identification Number (VIN) again was embossed on a metal plate riveted to the top left surface of the instrument panel, visible through the windshield. Coding was the same as 1976-78. Model year code (symbol two) changed to '9' for 1979. Series code (symbol four) now included: '0' Concord; '4' Spirit/AMX; '7' Limited; and '9' AMX.

SPIRIT SERIES 40

Series No.	Body/Style No.	Body Type & Seating	Price Four/Six	Shipping Weight	Prod. Total
40	7943-7	2-dr Lift-4P	3999/4049	2545/2762	Note 1
40	7946-7	2-dr Sed-4P	3899/3949	2489/2706	Note 1
SPIRIT DL					
40	7943-7	2-dr Lift-4P	4199/4249	2635/2852	Note 1
40	7946-7	2-dr Sed-4P	4099/4149	2579/2796	Note 1
SPIRIT LIMITED					
40	7943-7	2-dr Lift-4P	5199/5249	2732/2949	Note 1
40	7946-7	2-dr Sed-4P	5099/5149	2676/2893	Note 1
AMX SERIES 40					
40	7943-9	2-dr Lift-4P	5899/6149	2899/3092	3,657

Note 1: Total Spirit/AMX model year production: 52,714 cars (16,237 four-cylinder, 36,241 six-cylinder, 3,893 V-8).

PACER DL SERIES 60

Series No.	Body/Style No.	Body Type & Seating	Price Six/V-8	Shipping Weight	Prod. Total
60	7966-7	2-dr Hatch-4P	4699/5177	3133/3360	2,863
60	7968-7	2-dr Sta Wag-4P	4849/5327	3170/3397	7,352
PACER LIMITED					
60	7966-7	2-dr Hatch-4P	5699/6177	3218/3445	Note 2
60	7968-7	2-dr Sta Wag-4P	5849/6327	3255/3482	Note 2

Note 2: Production totals above include both DL and Limited models. Of the 10,215 Pacers made during the model year, 1,014 carried a V-8 engine.

CONCORD SERIES 01

Series No.	Body/Style No.	Body Type & Seating	Price Six/V-8	Shipping Weight	Prod. Total
01	7903-7	2-dr Hatch-4P	4149/4399	2888/3095	2,331
01	7906-7	2-dr Sed-5P	4049/4299	2873/3080	40,110
01	7905-7	4-dr Sed-5P	4149/4399	2939/3146	40,134
01	7908-7	4-dr Sta Wag-5P	4349/4599	2977/3184	20,278
CONCORD DL					
01	7903-7	2-dr Hatch-4P	4448/4698	3003/3210	Note 3
01	7906-7	2-dr Sed-5P	4348/4598	2982/3189	Note 3
01	7905-7	4-dr Sed-5P	4448/4698	3040/3247	Note 3
01	7908-7	4-dr Sta Wag-5P	4648/4898	3072/3279	Note 3
CONCORD LIMITED					
01	7906-7	2-dr Sed-5P	5348/5598	3090/3297	Note 3
01	7905-7	4-dr Sed-5P	5448/5698	3146/3253	Note 3
01	7908-7	4-dr Sta Wag-5P	5648/5898	3177/3384	Note 3

Note 3: Production totals shown include base, DL and Limited models. Total Concord model year production: 102,853 (6,355 four-cylinder, 91,842 six-cylinder and 4,656 V-8).

Note 4: Four-cylinder engine was offered on Concords at six-cylinder price.

FACTORY PRICE AND WEIGHT NOTE: Figure before the slash is for six-cylinder engine, after slash for V-8 engine: except Spirit, which is four-cylinder and six-cylinder.

ENGINES: BASE FOUR (Spirit); OPTIONAL (Concord hatchback/sedan): Inline. Overhead cam. Four-cylinder. Cast iron block; cast aluminum alloy head. Displacement: 121 cu. in. (2.0 liters). Bore & stroke: 3.41 x 3.32 in. Compression ratio: 8.2:1. Brake horsepower: 80 at 5000 R.P.M. Torque: 105 lb.-ft. at 2800 R.P.M. Five main bearings. Solid valve lifters. Carburetor: 2Bbl. Holley 5210. BASE SIX (Concord); OPTIONAL (Spirit): Inline. OHV. Six-cylinder. Cast iron block. Displacement: 232 cu. in. (3.8 liters). Bore & stroke: 3.75 x 3.50 in. Compression ratio: 8.0:1. Brake horsepower: 90 at 3400 R.P.M. Torque: 168 lb.-ft. at 1600 R.P.M. Seven main bearings. Hydraulic valve lifters. Carburetor: 1Bbl. Carter YF. BASE SIX (AMX, Pacer); OPTIONAL (Spirit, Concord): Inline. OHV. Six-cylinder. Cast iron block. Displacement: 258 cu. in. (4.2 liters). Bore & stroke: 3.75 x 3.90 in. Compression ratio: 8.3:1. Brake horsepower: 110 at 3200 R.P.M. Torque: 210 lb.-ft. at 1800 R.P.M. Seven main bearings. Hydraulic valve lifters. Carburetor: 2Bbl. Carter BBD. OPTIONAL SIX (California models): Same as 258 cu. in. six above, but with 1Bbl. Carter YF carburetor. Brake horsepower: 100 at 3400 R.P.M. Torque: 200 lb.-ft. at 1600 R.P.M. Compression ratio: 8.1:1. OPTIONAL V-8 (Spirit liftback, AMX, Pacer, Concord): 90-degree, overhead valve V-8. Cast iron block. Displacement: 304 cu. in. (5.0 liters). Bore & stroke: 3.75 x 3.44 in. Compression ratio: 8.4:1. Brake horsepower: 125 at 3200 R.P.M. Torque: 220 lb.-ft. at 2400 R.P.M. Five main bearings. Hydraulic valve lifters. Carburetor: 2Bbl. Motorcraft 2100.

CHASSIS DATA: Wheelbase: (Spirit/AMX) 96 in.; (Pacer) 100 in.; (Concord) 108 in. Overall length: (Spirit/AMX liftback) 168.5 in.; (Spirit sedan) 166.8 in.; (Pacer hatchback) 172.7 in.; (Pacer wagon) 177.7 in.; (Concord) 186 in. Height: (Spirit/AMX) 51.6 in.; (Pacer hatch) 52.8 in.; (Pacer wagon) 53.1 in.; (Concord) 51.1-51.6 in. Front Tread: (Spirit/AMX) 58.1 in.; (Pacer) 61.2 in.; (Concord) 57.6 in. Rear Tread: (Spirit/AMX/Concord) 57.5 in.; (Pacer) 60.0 in. Standard Tires: (Spirit) C78 x 14; (AMX) ER60 x 14 Flexten belted radial OWL; (Pacer) P195/75R14 GBR; (Concord) D78 x 14 except Limited, P195/75R14 GBR.

TECHNICAL: Four-speed manual transmission with floor shift was standard. Three-speed available on Spirit. Column-shift automatic available on Spirit/Concord/Pacer. Floor-shift automatic available on Spirit/AMX/Pacer. Three-speed manual shift gear ratios: (1st) 2.99:1; (2nd) 1.75:1; (3rd) 1.00:1; (Rev) 3.17:1. Four-speed gear ratios: (1st) 3.98:1; (2nd) 2.14:1; (3rd) 1.42:1; (4th) 1.00:1; (Rev) 3.99:1. Standard axle ratio: (Spirit four) 3.08:1 with four-speed, 3.31:1 with automatic; (Spirit six) 2.53:1 exc. 232 with three-speed, 2.73:1; (Spirit/AMX/V-8) 2.87:1 exc. 2.56:1 with automatic, w/o Twin-Grip differential; (AMX six) 2.53:1; (Pacer six) 2.53:1; (Concord four) 3.31:1 w/four-speed, 3.58:1 w/automatic; (Concord six) 2.53:1 except wagon w/automatic, 2.73:1; (Pacer/Concord V-8) 2.56:1 exc. 2.87:1 w/Twin-Grip differential. Steering: (Pacer) rack and pinion; (others) recirculating ball. Suspension: independent front coil springs; semi-elliptic rear leaf springs. Brakes: front disc, rear drum. Fuel tank: (Spirit four-door sedan) 13 gal.; (Spirit/AMX/Pacer) 21 gal.; (Concord) 22 gal.

1979 AMC, AMX (Series 40), liftback coupe, OCW

1979 AMC, Concord Limited (Series 01), station wagon, OCW

1980 AMC, Eagle 4WD (Series 30), station wagon (with Sport option package), OCW

1979 AMC, Concord DL (Series 01), sedan (American Motors Silver Anniversary Edition), OCW

1980 AMC, Eagle 4WD (Series 30), sedan, OCW

1981 AMC, Spirit DL (Series 40), sedan, OCW

1981 AMC, Eagle SX/4 4WD (Series 50), liftback sedan (with Sport option package), OCW

DRIVETRAIN OPTIONS: 232 cu. in. six-cylinder engine: Spirit ($50). 258 cu. in. six-cylinder engine: Spirit/Concord ($130). 304 cu. in. V-8 ($250); N/A in Spirit sedan. Three-speed manual floor shift: Spirit with 232 six (deduct $50). Torque-Command automatic transmission, column shift: Spirit six ($296); Pacer/Concord ($323). Torque-Command with floor shift: Spirit ($321); Pacer ($348); AMX ($296). Twin Grip differential ($63). Heavy-duty engine cooling system: Pacer ($31); Concord/AMC ($39) but standard with air conditioning. Maximum cooling system: Concord V-8 ($59); Concord V-8 with air ($20). Auxiliary automatic transmission oil cooler: Pacer/Concord V-8 ($36). Handling package (unique front sway bar, rear sway bar): Concord six ($30). Air shock absorbers, rear: Concord ($98). Heavy-duty shock absorbers: Pacer/Concord ($14). H.D. 70-amp battery ($18); N/A on Spirit, 56-amp with Pacer V-8. Cold climate group (H.D. battery and alternator, engine block heater): Pacer/Concord/AMX ($96); with air cond. or rear defroster ($38). California emission system ($78).

SPIRIT/CONCORD/AMX CONVENIENCE/APPEARANCE OPTIONS: Spirit liftback GT package ($469); with Limited ($200-$469). Spirit liftback GT rally tuned suspension package ($99). Extra quiet insulation package: Concord ($48). Protection group: Concord ($87); Concord DL ($21); AMX ($27). Convenience group incl. headlight on buzzer, intermittent wipers, dual vanity mirrors ($75). Gauge package (incl. parcel shelf): Spirit six/V-8 ($104). Spirit GT ($52). Visibility group (remote control left/right mirrors, day/night mirror): Spirit/Concord ($62); DL models ($50); std. on Spirit GT. Remote control left mirror: Spirit/Concord ($17). Power steering ($152-$158); std. On Ltd. models. Power front disc brakes ($70). Cruise control ($104). Air conditioning system: Spirit V-8/Concord/AMX ($513). Air conditioning package (incl. tinted glass and power steering): Spirit/Concord/AMX ($722-$731); N/A on Concord Ltd. AM radio ($84); std. on Concord Ltd. AM/FM/Stereo four-speaker radio: Concord/AMX ($236); Concord Ltd. exc. hatch ($152). AM/FM/CB Radio ($314) exc. Ltd. ($230). Rear speaker for AM radio ($24). Digital clock: Spirit/Concord ($40) but std. on Ltd. Tachometer: Spirit/Concord ($52); std. with Spirit GT pkg. Power door locks: Spirit/AMX ($72); std. on Ltd. Power liftback release: Spirit ($30) std. on Ltd. Caberfae corduroy fabric bucket seats: AMX (NC). Bench seat: Spirit sedan (NC). Bucket seats: Spirit (NC). Console: Spirit ($75); std. w/GT. Hidden compartment: Concord hatch ($33). Rear defroster ($89). Dual horns: Spirit/Concord ($13) std. on DL and Ltd. Light group: Spirit ($45); Spirit DL, AMX ($35); Concord ($49); Concord DL ($39); std. on Ltd. models. Leather-wrapped sport steering wheel: Concord ($49) exc. Ltd. ($20). Woodgrain steering wheel: Concord DL ($29); std. on Ltd. Tilt steering wheel ($72); std. on Ltd. models. Tinted glass ($57-$60). Two-tone paint: Spirit liftback ($65); Concord DL and Ltd. ($100). Special color combinations: ($26) exc. AMX. Pop-up moonroof ($178). Rally side stripes: Spirit ($46). Delete woodgrain from Concord DL wagon (deduct $75). Roof rack: Spirit sed. ($62); Concord wagon ($90). Tailgate air deflector: Spirit sed. ($26). Front bumper guards: Concord ($21); std. on DL and Ltd. Side scuff molding: AMX ($31). Protective inner coating ($100) exc. Spirit. Locking gas cap ($8) exc. Spirit. Styled wheel covers: Concord ($35); N/A on Ltd. Color-keyed wheel covers: Concord DL exc. wgn ($45); std. on Ltd. Spoke style 14 x 6 in. wheels with trim rings: Concord ($145); Concord Ltd. exc. hatch ($100). Turbine forged aluminum wheels: Concord ($300); Concord Ltd. except hatch ($255). Tires: C78 x 14 whitewall: base Spirit ($48). D78 x 14: base Spirit ($19); D78 x 14 whitewall: Spirit ($67); Spirit DL ($19); Concord ($48). P195/75R14 GBR: Spirit ($120); Spirit DL ($72); Concord ($101); Concord DL ($53). P195/75R14 white GBR: Spirit ($168); Spirit DL ($120); Concord ($149); Concord DL ($101). P195/75R14 SBR; Spirit ($168); Spirit DL ($120); Spirit Ltd. (NC); Concord ($149); Concord DL ($101); Concord Ltd. sed/wgn (NC). P195/75R14 white SBR: Spirit ($216); Spirit DL ($168); Spirit Ltd. ($8); Concord ($197); Concord DL ($149); Concord Ltd. sed/wgn ($48). DR70 x 14 Flexten radial: Spirit ($238); Spirit DL ($190); Spirit Ltd. ($70); Concord ($219); Concord DL ($171); Concord Ltd. ($70). DR70 x 14 OWL Flexten radial: Spirit ($302); Spirit DL ($254); Spirit Ltd. ($134); Concord ($283); Concord DL ($235); Concord Ltd. ($34).

PACER CONVENIENCE/APPEARANCE OPTIONS: Convenience group: headlight on buzzer, intermittent wipers, dual lighted vanity mirrors ($75); std. on Ltd. Visibility group: remote left and right mirrors ($50); std. on Ltd. Left remote mirror ($17). Gauge package ($129); N/A w/Ltd. or center armrest. Power steering ($158); std. on Ltd. Power disc brakes ($70). Cruise control ($104). Air conditioning ($513). Air conditioning pkg. with tinted glass and power steering ($734); N/A w/Ltd. AM radio ($84); std. w/Ltd. AM/FM/Stereo four-speaker radio ($236); w/Ltd. ($152). AM/FM/CB Stereo Radio ($314); w/Ltd. ($230). Rear speaker ($24). Tape player and AM/FM/Stereo radio ($353); w/Ltd. ($269). Center armrest ($49); std. on Ltd. Hidden compartment: hatch ($37). Caberfae corduroy bucket seats (NC). Power door locks ($72). Power window and door locks ($194). Light group ($39); std. on Ltd. Rear defroster ($89). Rear wiper/washer ($62). Leather-wrapped sport steering wheel ($49); w/Ltd. ($20). Woodgrain steering wheel ($29); incl. w/Ltd. Tilt steering wheel ($72); std. w/Ltd. Tinted glass ($63). Door vent windows ($36). Two-tone color: black rocker panels deleted ($65). Special color combinations ($26); N/A w/two-tone or Ltd. Misty beige clearcoat: Ltd. ($60). Woodgrain wagon paneling ($117). Protective inner coating ($100). Pop-up moonroof: hatch ($178). Vinyl roof: hatch ($124). Roof rack ($62). Locking gas cap ($8). Styled wheel covers ($35); N/A on Ltd. Spoke style 14 x 6 in. wheels ($145); w/Ltd. ($100). Turbine forged aluminum 14 x 6 in. wheels ($300); w/Ltd. ($255). Tires: P195/75R14 black SBR (NC). P195/75R14 white SBR ($48).

HISTORY: Introduced: September 19, 1978. Model year production (U.S.): 169,439 (1.8 percent of the industry total). Calendar year production: 184,636 cars, including 88,581 Concords. Calendar year sales by U.S. dealers: 162,057 (1.9 percent of industry total). Concords sold the best (85,432), Pacers the worst (only 8,168).

HISTORICAL FOOTNOTES: Record-breaking profits highlighted AMC's year, along with a strengthened tie to Renault, the French-owned automaker. Renault paid $200 million for an interest in AMC, carrying forward the agreement that had begun the previous year. Plans were made to begin assembling Renault autos at Kenosha for the 1982 model year, with Renault supplying the engines and transmissions. Meanwhile, Pacer sales continued to slip, due in part to marginal fuel economy, but mainly to the fact that its curious design never quite caught on. This was true even though Pacer had been, according to *Automotive Industries* magazine, "widely acclaimed as a daring innovation in design." Perhaps too daring for popular tastes. As Renault became AMC's major stockholder, the company looked forward to major changes in the coming years. A three-year corrosion warranty debuted in May 1979.

1980

Major news for the 1980 model year was the appearance of the Eagle. Based on the Concord chassis, it was the first major four-wheel-drive passenger car produced in the U.S. in modern times. Otherwise, the lineup remained the same as in 1979, though this would be the final year for both Pacer and AMX. The V-8 engine was gone for good. All models had front disc brakes, standard four-speed floor shift, a high-pressure compact spare tire, inside hood release, dome light, cigar lighter, front stabilizer bar (except Spirit sedan), high level ventilation, and a parking brake warning light. To improve corrosion resistance, rust-prone regions used more galvanized materials and special coatings. One-side galvanized steel went inside hoods, deck lids, and door panels. Front fenders were plastic-lined, while petroleum wax coatings went on door panel bottoms, fender bottoms. and rear seam areas. Four-cylinder engines used a Delco High Energy Ignition system. Standard colors for all models were Cardinal Red, Cameo Blue, Navy Blue, Saxon Yellow, Cameo Tan, Medium Brown metallic, Classic Black, and Olympic White. All models except the AMX could also be obtained in Russet Bordeaux, Medium Blue, Dark Brown, Quick Silver or Smoke Gray metallic. One noteworthy new option: a leather-wrapped steering wheel, offered on all models. Premium sound systems could include a cassette tape player.

SPIRIT — SERIES 40 — FOUR/SIX — For its second year, Spirit continued with little change except for a new beltline molding on DL sedans, extending just below the front fender nameplates. The original 121 cu. in. four departed, so base Spirits were now powered by a 2.5-liter (151 cu. in.) four from Pontiac, with four-speed manual floor shift, and rode on C78 x 14 whitewalls. A 258 six remained optional, but the V-8 was dropped. Standard equipment included manual front disc brakes, full wheel covers, dual paint stripes, energy-absorbing bumpers, custom steering wheel, lighted ashtray, locking glovebox, Sport vinyl bench seats (buckets in liftback), anodized aluminum bumpers with black end caps, and quad rectangular headlamps. In addition to the colors above, Spirits were available in Caramel. Spirit buyers could step up to a DL and get reclining bucket seats up front and split folding seat in back, with Caberfae Corduroy or Sport vinyl upholstery; an AM radio and day/night mirror; digital clock; luxury woodgrain steering wheel; woodgrain instrument panel overlay; premium cloth headliner and visors; parcel shelf; full-styled wheel covers; front/rear bumper guards; dual horns; extra quiet insulation; plus blackout rocker panels and wide lower body side moldings. Topping the line was the Spirit Limited, with reclining leather bucket seats and split folding rear seat, power steering, woodgrain-accent door panels, 18-ounce carpeting, console with center armrest, tilt steering wheel, power door locks and liftback release, bumper nerfing strips, protection and convenience groups, visibility group with dual remote mirrors, lights-on buzzer, and P195/75R14 whitewall glass-belted radials with wire wheel covers. Performance fans could again get a Spirit GT liftback with tachometer and sport steering wheel inside, black bumpers and rear venturi area, blackout grille and headlight bezels, blackout moldings, black left remote mirror, dual pin stripes, and spoke styled wheels with P195/75R14 fiberglass-belted radial tires. Six-cylinder GT models with manual shift also included deep-tone exhaust. The GT package was available on base and DL Spirits. Once again, a Rally-tuned suspension package was offered for six-cylinder GT models.

AMX — SERIES 40 — SIX — The 'AMX' badge on the grille moved from the corner to the center for 1980, but other changes for the sporty performance AMC model were minor in its final outing. Base engine was the 258 cu. in. six with four-speed manual shift. Standard gear included a GT Rally-tuned suspension system, tachometer, black left remote mirror, sports steering wheel, deep-tone exhaust (with manual shift), dual note horns, and extra quiet insulation. An 'AMX' nameplate was on the glovebox door as well as on the grille, rear spoiler, and entry doors. Spoke style wheels held DR70 x 14 white-letter tires. As before, black accents set the tone for AMX. It had black bumpers, guards and nerfing strips; front/rear fender flares with accent stripes; front air dam; grille insert and headlight bezels; door, quarter window and rear window surround moldings; and windshield wiper arms. The color-keyed rear spoiler had accent stripes. A floor-shift automatic transmission was optional. An AMX custom interior package included reclining bucket seats in Sport vinyl or Caberfae corduroy.

PACER — SERIES 60 — SIX — Striking and innovative when it first appeared in 1975, Pacer sales never met expectations; so it was dropped after 1980. As before, the top two rows of the four-row grille bulged up into the hood area. Subdued blackout vertical grille elements were dominated by the horizontal bars. Pacer was the only AMC model that never received quad headlamps. DL Pacers came equipped with individual reclining seats in Sport vinyl, woodgrain-accent door trim panels, woodgrain instrument panel overlays, custom steering wheel with woodgrain accents, 12-ounce color-keyed full carpeting, rear seat armrests and ashtray, day/night mirror, clock courtesy lights, key warning buzzer, locking glovebox, extra-quiet insulation, and dual note horns. Tires were P195/75R14 fiberglass-belted radial whitewalls with styled wheel covers. Pacers also had front and rear bumper guards, a squarish hood ornament, wide color-keyed bodyside scuff moldings, and wide rocker panel moldings. Upgrading to a Limited brought Chelsea leather reclining seats, a folding vinyl center armrest, woodgrain tilt steering wheel, and 18-ounce carpeting. Limiteds also had power steering, power windows and door locks, dual remote mirrors, an AM radio dome/map light, glovebox and under-hood lights, intermittent wipers, and lighted passenger visor mirror. In addition to the standard colors, Pacers were offered in Caramel and Misty Beige Clearcoat.

CONCORD — SERIES 01 — FOUR/SIX — AMC's compact gained a new horizontal-bar grille for 1980, with quad rectangular headlamps and big full-width wraparound taillamps. 'Concord' badges sat at the side of the grille, as well as the trailing edge of the front fenders and the trunk lid. Only the front-fender amber reflectors remained. New, distinctive opera windows on DL Concords added both elegance and visibility for rear passengers. A four-cylinder 151 cu. in. Pontiac engine was now standard, with the 258 six optional. In addition to the basic body colors, Concords came in Dark Green metallic. Added to the option list: six-way power seats, automatic-leveling air shocks, power windows, and power deck lid release. Wagons could now have a rear window wiper/washer. Base Concords rode D78 x 14 blackwall tires with full wheel covers. Standard equipment included anodized aluminum bumpers with black end caps, dual bodyside pin stripes, narrow wheel lip and rocker panel moldings, bench seats in Stripe Knit fabric or Sport vinyl, front/rear ashtrays, hood ornament, narrow black side scuff moldings, and 12-ounce full carpeting. DL Concords added a day/night mirror, digital clock, courtesy light, dual note horns, extra quiet insulation, front/rear bumper guards, individual reclining seats in Sport vinyl, full woodgrain instrument panel overlay, woodgrain-accented steering wheel, trunk carpeting, wide wheel lip and rocker panel moldings, 'B' pillar crests, and whitewall tires. Four-door DL sedans had rear opera windows and full vinyl roof, while two-doors featured a landau roof with stylish half-covered opera windows. Concord Limited sedans and wagons offered power steering, power door locks, tilt steering wheel, AM radio, dual remote mirrors, dome/map light, under-hood and trunk lights, lighted visor mirror, lights-on buzzer, intermittent wipers, woodgrain steering wheel, and bumper nerf strips. Their individual reclining seats were upholstered in either Chelsea leather or St. Lauren deep plush fabric. Limited tires were P195/7514 fiberglass-belted whitewall radials with wire wheel covers.

EAGLE — SERIES 30 — SIX — Eagles arrived to the tune of a jingle, called "The Eagle Has Landed On All Fours." The Concord-based 4WD specialty vehicle was intended to combine the traction and handling of a truck with the comforts and conveniences of a luxurious passenger auto. Measuring 109.3 inches, its wheelbase was an inch longer than Concord's. The Eagle also sat three inches higher off the ground, making it easy to spot from a distance. Tires were 15-inch size. Three bodies were offered: two- and four-door sedans and a four-door wagon. Grilles had seven narrow horizontal bars and an 'Eagle' badge in the upper corner, plus an 'AMC' emblem on the wide upper bar (at the opposite end). 'AMC' and 'Eagle' nameplates stood on the deck lid: '4 Wheel Drive' (or 'Automatic 4WD') on rear quarter panels. Distinctive opera windows were half concealed, as on Concords. Hood ornaments were made up of twin rectangles. Eagles soon became noticed not only for their increased height and ground clearance, but for their accent-colored lower body treatment. That darker area stretched the full body length, over wide fender flares, set apart by a bright molding. Both the lower rocker sill strips and three inch fender flares (front and rear) were made of Krayton, a durable injection-molded plastic that was also used for bumper ends. Eagle's special bumpers had to match truck standards. A stone/gravel deflector formed the lower section of the front-end panel. AMC's Eagle was the first volume-produced 4WD with independent front suspension, allowing a lower center of gravity, smooth ride and improved stability. The advanced 4WD system could interpret road conditions automatically distributing power to the wheels (front or rear) that needed help most. A viscous coupling with 43 plates in the transfer case provided the necessary slippage, while it also absorbed vibration in the driveline. Standard equipment for the four-wheel-drive Eagle included a 258 cu. in. six with two-barrel carburetor and Torque-Command automatic transmission, plus power disc brakes, power steering, inside hood release, dual horns, front/rear bumper guards, electric clock, lighter, heavy-duty cooling system, and wheel opening moldings. Four-doors wore a full vinyl roof; two-doors a landau vinyl roof. Eagles rode P195/75R15B whitewall glass-belted radials with argent styled wheel covers. Body colors were the same as Concord's. Eagle's Limited added power windows, a parcel shelf, upgraded carpeting, premium door trim, a luxury woodgrain steering wheel, visibility group, and individual reclining seats. Eagle's Sport package, available for all but the four-door sedan, included low-gloss black Krayton flares and rocker panels; black bumpers with nerfing strips; black taillamp treatment, grille insert, windshield/liftgate moldings, and remote-control twin mirrors; halogen headlamps and foglamps (except Limited), and blackwall all-weather Goodyear Tiempo steel-belted radials. Sport models wore a '4x4' silver decal on the lower door.

I.D. DATA: As in 1976-79, the 13-symbol VIN was embossed on a metal plate riveted to the top left surface of the instrument panel, visible through the windshield. Coding was the same as before. The model year code (symbol two) changed to '0' for 1980. Under series (symbol four) a '3' code was added for the Eagle. Only two engine codes (seventh symbol) were used: 'B' 151-4; 'C' 258-6.

SPIRIT SERIES 40

Series No.	Body/Style No.	Body Type & Seating	Factory Price	Shipping Weight	Prod. Total
40	8043-0	2-dr Lift-4P	4293/4422	2556/2758	Note 1
40	8046-0	2-dr Sed-4P	4193/4322	2512/2714	Note 1
SPIRIT DL					
40	8043-5	2-dr Lift-4P	4592/4721	2656/2854	Note 1
40	8046-5	2-dr Sed-4P	4492/4621	2611/2813	Note 1
SPIRIT LIMITED					
40	8043-7	2-dr Lift-4P	5091/5220	2675/2877	Note 1
40	8046-7	2-dr Sed-4P	4991/5120	2630/2832	Note 1

Note 1: Total production for the model year: 71,032 Spirits (37,799 four-cylinder and 33,233 six-cylinder). Model year sales: 55,392.

Series No.	Body/Style No.	Body Type & Seating	Factory Price	Shipping Weight	Prod. Total
AMX SERIES 40					
40	8043-9	2-dr Lift-4P	5653	2901	N/A
PACER DL SERIES 60					
60	8066-5	2-dr Hatch-4P	5407	3147	405
60	8068-5	2-dr Sta Wag-4P	5558	3195	1,341
PACER LIMITED					
60	8066-7	2-dr Hatch-4P	6031	3172	Note 2
60	8068-7	2-dr Sta Wag-4P	6182	3220	Note 2

Note 2: Production totals for Pacer DL also include Limited.

Series No.	Body/Style No.	Body Type & Seating	Factory Price	Shipping Weight	Prod. Total
CONCORD SERIES 01					
01	8006-0	2-dr Sed-5P	4753/4882	2646/2844	27,845
01	8005-0	4-dr Sed-5P	4878/5007	2712/2910	35,198
01	8008-0	4-dr Sta Wag-5P	5078/5207	2741/2939	17,413
CONCORD DL					
01	8006-5	2-dr Sed-5P	5052/5181	2764/2962	Note 3
01	8005-5	4-dr Sed-5P	5177/5306	2834/3032	Note 3
01	8008-5	4-dr Sta Wag-5P	5377/5506	2855/3053	Note 3
CONCORD LIMITED					
01	8006-7	2-dr Sed-5P	5551/5680	2789/2987	Note 3
01	8005-7	4-dr Sed-5P	5676/5805	2859/3057	Note 3
01	8008-7	4-dr Sta Wag-5P	5876/6005	2886/3084	Note 3

Note 3: Production totals under base model include DL and Limited. Total model year production: 80,456 Concords (9,949 four-cylinder, 70,507 six-cylinder). Model year sales: 70,336.

Series No.	Body/Style No.	Body Type & Seating	Factory Price	Shipping Weight	Prod. Total
EAGLE SERIES 30					
30	8036-5	2-dr Sed-5P	6999	3382	10,616
30	8035-5	4-dr Sed-5P	7249	3450	9,956
30	8038-5	4-dr Sta Wag-5P	7549	3470	25,807
EAGLE LIMITED					
30	8036-7	2-dr Sed-5P	7396	3397	Note 4
30	8035-7	4-dr Sed-5P	7646	3465	Note 4
30	8038-7	4-dr Sta Wag-5P	7946	3491	Note 4

Note 4: Production totals shown under base Eagle include Limited. Model year Eagle sales: 34,041.

FACTORY PRICE AND WEIGHT NOTE: Figure before the slash in Spirit and Concord prices is for four-cylinder engine, after slash for six-cylinder.

ENGINES: BASE FOUR (Spirit, Concord): Inline. OHV. Four-cylinder. Cast iron block and head. Displacement: 151 cu. in. (2.5 liters). Bore & stroke: 4.0 x 3.0 in. Compression ratio: 8.2:1. Brake horsepower: 82 at 4000 R.P.M. Torque: 128 lb.-ft. at 2400 R.P.M. Five main bearings. Hydraulic valve lifters. Carburetor: 2Bbl. Rochester 2SE. Manufactured by Pontiac. BASE SIX (AMX, Pacer, Eagle); OPTIONAL (Spirit, Concord): Inline. OHV. Six-cylinder. Cast iron block. Displacement: 258 cu. in. (4.2 liters). Bore & stroke: 3.75 x 3.90 in. Compression ratio: 8.3:1. Brake horsepower: 110 at 3200 R.P.M. Torque: 210 lb.-ft. at 1800 R.P.M. Seven main bearings. Hydraulic valve lifters. Carburetor: 2Bbl. Carter BBD.

CHASSIS DATA: Wheelbase: (Spirit/AMX) 96 in.; (Pacer) 100 in.; (Concord) 108 in.; (Eagle) 109.3 in. Overall length: (Spirit/AMX) 167 in.; (Pacer hatchback) 173.9 in.; (Pacer wagon) 178.8 in.; (Concord) 185 in.; (Eagle) 184 in. Height: (Spirit/AMX) 51.5 in.; (Pacer hatchback) 52.7 in.; (Pacer wagon) 53.1 in.; (Concord) 51.3-52.6 in.; (Eagle) 55-55.8 in. Front Tread: (Spirit/AMX) 58.1 in.; (Pacer) 61.2 in.; (Concord) 57.6 in.; (Eagle) 59.6 in. Rear Tread: (Spirit/AMX) 57.0 in.; (Pacer) 60.0 in.; (Concord) 57.1 in.; (Eagle) 57.6 in. Standard Tires: (Spirit) C78 x 14; (AMX) DR70 x 14; (Pacer) P195/75R14; (Concord) D78 x 14; (Eagle) P195/75R15.

TECHNICAL: Four-speed floor-shift manual transmission standard; three-speed Torque-Command automatic transmission optional (floor or column shift) on all models except Eagle, which had standard automatic shift. Manual shift gear ratios: Four-cylinder (1st) 3.50:1, (2nd) 2.21:1, (3rd) 1.43:1, (4th) 1.00:1, (Rev) 3.39:1. Six-cylinder (1st) 4.07:1; (2nd) 2.57:1; (3rd) 1.66:1; (4th) 1.00:1; (Rev) 3.95:1. Standard axle ratios: (Spirit/Concord four/Eagle) 3.08:1; (other models) 2.53:1. Steering: recirculating ball. Suspension: independent front coil springs; semi-elliptic rear leaf springs. Brakes: front disc, rear drum. Fuel tank: (Spirit/AMX/Pacer) 21 gal.; (Concord) 22 gal.

DRIVETRAIN OPTIONS: 258 cu. in. six-cylinder engine: Spirit/Concord ($129). Torque-Command automatic transmission, column shift: Spirit ($305); Pacer/Concord ($333). Torque-Command with floor shift: Spirit/AMX ($331), Pacer ($359). Optional 3.54:1 axle ratio: Eagle ($19). Twin-Grip differential ($65); N/A Eagle. Heavy-duty engine cooling system (H.D. radiator, viscous fan): Spirit/Concord six ($41) but std. w/air conditioning. H.D. cooling system (H.D. radiator, seven-blade flex fan/shroud): Pacer ($37). Extra-duty suspension pkg. (rear sway bar, H.D. shocks/springs): Eagle ($65). Handling package (unique front sway bar, rear sway bar): Spirit/Concord six exc. GT ($31). Front sway bar: Spirit six sed. ($20). Front suspension skid plate: Eagle ($65). Automatic load-leveling (air shocks): Concord six, Eagle ($145). Air shock absorbers, rear: Spirit ($52). Heavy-duty shock absorbers: Pacer/Concord ($15). H.D. battery ($19). Cold climate group: H.D. battery and alternator, engine block heater ($107); with air cond. or rear defroster ($47). California emission system ($250). Trailer towing package 'A' (to 2000 pounds): Concord/Eagle ($85).

SPIRIT/CONCORD/AMX/EAGLE CONVENIENCE/APPEARANCE OPTIONS: Spirit liftback GT package: base/DL ($249). Spirit liftback GT Rally-tuned suspension package ($109). AMX custom interior package (reclining vinyl bucket seats, custom door panels, split rear seat, day/night mirror, courtesy lights, parcel shelf): AMX w/vinyl trim ($149); w/fabric trim ($179). Eagle Sport package; base two-door/wgn ($299). Extra quiet insulation package; base Spirit/Concord ($50); Concord DL wgn ($19). Protection group (stainless door edge guards, front bumper guards and nerf strips, front mats): Spirit ($111); Spirit DL ($67); Spirit GT, AMX ($31). Protection group w/front and rear guards and mats: Concord ($114); Concord DL ($70). Eagle protection group (stainless door edge guards, front/rear bumper nerf strips, front/rear mats): Eagle ($70) exc. w/Sport pkg. ($34). Convenience group incl. headlight-on buzzer, intermittent wipers, vanity mirror ($63). Gauge package (clock, tach, oil, amp, vacuum): Spirit six ($129) exc. DL/Ltd. ($77); AMX GT ($75); N/A base Spirit. Visibility group (remote control left/right mirrors, day/night mirror): Spirit/Concord/AMX ($64); DL or GT ($52). Eagle visibility group (remote left/right mirrors) ($52). Remote control left mirror ($18); N/A AMX. Pop-up moonroof: Spirit/AMX/Concord ($195). Power steering ($164). Power front disc brakes ($74). Cruise control ($108). Air conditioning system ($529). Air conditioning package (incl. tinted glass and power steering); Spirit/AMX ($752); Concord ($758). Halogen headlamps ($20). Fog lamps (dealer-installed): Eagle ($69). Light group ($37-$53). A MX hood decal ($60). AM radio ($89). AM/FM/stereo radio ($219) exc. Spirit DL/Ltd. ($130). AM/FM/stereo radio w/cassette ($335) exc. Spirit DL/Ltd. ($246). AM/FM/CB stereo radio ($475) exc. Spirit DL/Ltd. ($386). Premium sound system ($95). Digital clock: Spirit/Concord ($52). Tachometer: Spirit/Concord/Eagle ($54); std. with Spirit GT pkg. Power door locks: Spirit, AMX, Concord/Eagle two-door DL/Ltd. ($75); Concord/Eagle four-door DL/Ltd. ($108), N/A base Spirit. Power door/window locks: Concord DL, base Eagle ($199-$289). Power liftback release: Spirit ($32). Power decklid release: Eagle/Concord sed/wgn ($32). Power six-way driver's seat: Concord DL/Ltd. ($149). Power driver/pass. seat: Concord DL/Ltd. ($249). Caberfae corduroy fabric bucket seats: Spirit DL ($29). Vinyl bench seat: Spirit sedan (NC); Concord w/striped knit fabric ($29). Vinyl reclining seats: Concord DL (NC). Rochelle velour stripe fabric reclining seats: Concord DL ($29). Leather reclining seats: Concord Ltd. (NC). Silver knit fabric reclining seats: Concord/Eagle Ltd. (deduct $100). Plaid fabric seats: Eagle ($29); N/A Ltd. Console: Spirit/AMX ($78). Rear defroster ($93). Rear wiper/washer: Eagle wgn ($79). Dual horns: Spirit/Concord ($14): std. on DL and Ltd. Leather-wrapped sport steering wheel: Spirit/Concord/Eagle ($51); Spirit DL/Ltd./GT, Concord Ltd., AMX ($21). Woodgrain steering wheel: Concord DL, Eagle ($30). Parcel shelf ($22). Tilt steering wheel ($75-$78). Tinted glass ($59-$65). Two-tone paint: Spirit GT ($84); Concord D/L and Ltd. ($103). Special color combinations: ($30) exc. AMX. Eagle Ltd. Rally side stripes: Spirit ($65). Delete woodgrain from Concord DL/Ltd. or Eagle wgn (deduct $75). Roof rack: Spirit sed ($64); Concord/Eagle wgn ($93). Tailgate air deflector: Spirit sed ($27). Front/rear bumper guards: Spirit/Concord ($44). Side scuff molding: Spirit ($32). Locking gas cap ($9). Styled wheel covers: Spirit/AMX/Concord ($35); N/A on Ltd. Spoke style 14 x 6 in. wheels with trim rings: Spirit/Concord ($150) exc. DL ($115); Ltd. ($15). Turbine forged aluminum wheels: Spirit/Concord ($310) exc. DL ($275); Ltd. ($175); Spirit GT ($160). Turbocast II aluminum 14 x 7 in. wheels: Spirit ($350) exc. DL ($315); Ltd. ($215); GT, AMX ($200). Wire wheel covers: Spirit/Concord ($135) exc. DL ($100). Spirit/Concord/AMX Tires: D78 x 14: Spirit (NC). D78 x 14 whitewall: Spirit ($23); Concord ($49). P195/75R14 GBR: Spirit ($75); Concord ($101); Concord DL/Ltd. ($52). P195/75R14 white GBR: Spirit ($124); Spirit GT ($50); Concord ($150); Concord DL/Ltd. ($101). P195/75R14 SBR: Spirit ($125); Spirit GT ($130); Concord ($151); Concord DL/Ltd. ($102). P195/75R14 white SBR: Spirit ($174); Spirit GT ($195); Concord ($200); Concord DL/Ltd. ($151). DR70 x 14 Flexten radial: Spirit ($205); Concord ($231); Concord DL/Ltd. ($182). DR70 x 14 OWL Flexten radial: Spirit ($270); Concord ($296); Concord DL/Ltd. ($247). ER60 x 14 OWL Flexten radial: AMX w/Turbocast II wheels ($53). Eagle Tires: P195/75R15 SBR Tiempo ($42). P195/75R15 white SBR Tiempo ($91) exc. Sport ($49).

PACER CONVENIENCE/APPEARANCE OPTIONS: Convenience group incl. headlight-on buzzer, intermittent wipers, right lighted vanity mirror ($63). Visibility group: remote left and right mirrors ($52). Protection group: front/rear bumper nerf strips, door edge guards, front/rear floor mats ($70). Left remote mirror ($18). Power steering ($164). Power front disc brakes ($74). Cruise control ($108). Air conditioning ($529). Air conditioning pkg. with tinted glass and power steering ($761). AM radio ($89). AM/FM/stereo four-speaker radio ($219). AM/FM/stereo radio w/8-track ($335). AM/FM/CB stereo radio ($475). Center armrest ($51): std. on Ltd. Rochelle velour stripe fabric seats: DL ($29). Vinyl sport seat trim: DL (NC). Power door locks ($75). Power window/door locks ($199). Light group ($43). Rear defroster ($93). Rear wiper/washer ($79). Leather-wrapped sport steering wheel ($31); w/Ltd. ($21). Woodgrain steering wheel ($30). Tilt steering wheel ($78). Tinted glass ($68). Door vent windows ($50). Two-tone color: black rocker panels deleted ($67). Special color combinations ($30); N/A w/two-tone or Ltd. Misty beige clearcoat: Ltd. ($90). Woodgrain wagon paneling ($121). Pop-up moonroof: hatch ($195). Roof rack ($78). Locking gas cap ($9). Wire wheel covers ($100). Spoke style 14 x 6 in. wheels ($115); w/Ltd. ($15). Turbine forged aluminum 14 x 6 in. wheels ($275); w/Ltd. ($175). Tires: P195/75R14 white SBR ($49).

HISTORY: Introduced: (Eagle) September 27, 1979; (others) October 11. Model year production (U.S.): 199,613, which was 2.9 percent of the industry total. Calendar year production (U.S.): 164,728 cars. Model year sales by U.S. dealers: 163,502. Calendar year sales: 149,438 (2.3 percent of total).

HISTORICAL FOOTNOTES: For rating purposes, the new Eagle was declared a "four wheel-drive automobile" rather than a passenger car. Thus, its so-so gas mileage didn't count in AMC's corporate average fuel economy (CAFE) rating because it was classed as a light truck. And for meeting safety standards, Eagle ranked as a multi-purpose vehicle. The new Eagles were assembled in the same Kenosha production line as passenger cars, however. Early in the model year (December 1979), AMC announced that the slow-selling Pacer would be dropped to allow for increased Eagle production at the Kenosha facility. Eagle sold well, though not to AMC's 50,000-unit expectations. Eagle's 4WD had been developed by FF Developments in Britain, but made by Chrysler's New Process Gear Division. Four-wheel-drive passenger cars weren't entirely new. Britain's limited-production Jensen Interceptor had used 4WD in the 1960s. But as the '80s decade began, Subaru's version introduced in 1975 in wagon form, was Eagle's sole competition for the all-wheel fancier's dollars. During 1980 contract talks, AMC became the second domestic auto company (after Chrysler) to accept a member of the United Auto Workers union on its board. After record-breaking profits in the previous year, AMC ended the 1980 period with a loss of $155.7 million. Yet continued strong Jeep sales (with increased outlets worldwide) and a cash inflow from Renault, plus plans to market several French-built models in the U.S., helped keep AMC's prospects on the bright side. AMC's rust-out warranty was extended to five years.

INNOVATIONS: Four-wheel-drive passenger car. New microprocessor-controlled feedback carburetor system developed.

1981

With the Pacer gone, AMC's lineup dwindled to just three models. But the four-wheel-drive Eagle, which appeared the year before on a modified Concord platform, added a Spirit-based version for 1981. All models came with a standard 151 cu. in. four-cylinder engine. The optional 258 cu. in. six was redesigned using aluminum and other lightweight materials, cutting 90 pounds from its previous heft. Camshaft alterations reduced its valve overlap, allowing slower, smoother idling and more low-speed torque. Three-speed automatic transmissions now included a lockup torque converter. Galvanized steel (one-sided) outer body panels provided improved rust protection and AMC continued its five-year no-rust-through warranty, introduced the previous year. Upper deck panels were now two-sided galvanized steel. Standard 1981 colors were: Classic Black, Olympic White, Cameo Tan, Montana Blue, Moonlight Blue, Autumn Gold, Oriental Red, and Beige; plus 13 metallics (Quick Silver, Medium Blue, Medium or Dark Brown, Copper Brown, Chestnut Brown, Vintage Red, Deep Maroon, Steel Gray, Blue, Silver, Sherwood Green, and Dark Green).

SPIRIT—SERIES 40—FOUR/SIX— Styling changes on the subcompact Spirit included a new crossbar-style grille with emblem on lower corner, rally stripes, altered wheel covers, and a new selection of body colors. Power windows and radio antenna were optional for the first time. Spirits were now equipped with P185/75R14 blackwall glass-belted radial tires and had wheel covers, front disc brakes, a lighted front ashtray and lighter, carpeting, vinyl bucket front seats, vinyl spare tire cover, and rear bumper guards. In addition to whitewalls and an AM radio, DL models offered extra quiet insulation, dual horns, custom door panels with map pockets, a luxury woodgrain steering wheel, day/night inside mirror, electric clock, front bumper guards, styled wheel covers, and a carpeted spare tire cover. A GT package with full instrumentation was available again this year.

CONCORD—SERIES 01—FOUR/SIX— For improved rust protection, all exterior Concord body panels were now galvanized steel. Glass-belted P195/75R14 blackwall radial tires with wheel covers were standard; steel-belted tires and wire wheel covers optional. The restyled grille used three vertical bars to accent the five horizontal bars. Opera windows were restyled. New colors and fabrics were offered. Base engine was the 151 cu. in. four with four-speed manual floor shift. Standard equipment included a stowaway spare tire, front and rear armrests, lighter, carpeting, bench seats, folding rear wagon seat, rear bumper guards, and moldings for drip rail, wheel lip, hood front edge, windshield and rear window surrounds, rocker panels, and bodyside scuff area. An optional retractable cargo area cover could hide luggage in Concord wagons. A vinyl landau roof highlighted Concord's DL sedans. DL models also had stainless steel wheel covers, individual reclining seats, a custom steering wheel, day/night mirror, cargo area skid strips, electric clock, trunk carpeting, front bumper guards, striping, dual horns, woodgrain wagon side panels, extra sound insulation, and whitewall tires. Two-doors featured opera quarter windows. The luxurious Limited added visibility and light groups as well as a luxury woodgrain steering wheel and styled wheel covers, plus premium seat and door trim.

EAGLE SX AND KAMMBACK—SERIES 50—FOUR/SIX— Since the original 4WD Eagle showed promise, AMC added a shrunken version for 1981, based on the Spirit chassis. Billed as "the sports car that doesn't always need a road," the SX/4 two-door hatchback had a sporty look, but hardly qualified as a sports car. Also in the lineup was a Kammback wagon, derived from the Spirit/Gremlin sedan design. Both rode a 97.2-inch wheelbase but carried 15 inch tires, which gave three inches more ground clearance than the Spirits. Front-end styling focused on a new 8x3 checkerboard-style grille, like the senior Eagles. An 'Eagle' nameplate was up front, as well as at the usual front fender locations. An 'AMC' badge sat atop the grille. 'SX/4' decals were on lower front doors, part of the wide accent-colored Krayton plastic body striping that ran from front to back, over the fender flares. A bright molding separated the two body colors. '4WD' emblems stood on quarter panels. Subcompact Eagles came with a 2.5-liter (151 cu. in.) four-cylinder engine, four-speed floor shift and transfer case, the same as their bigger brothers. Three-speed automatic shift was optional, as was the 258 cu. in. six. The smaller Eagles rode well enough to rate with ordinary passenger cars—far more smoothly than the typical off-road vehicle—and performed with reasonable liveliness and impressive gas mileage. Eagles had power front disc brakes, power steering, front sway bar, high energy ignition, 42-amp alternator, 55-380 (cold crank rating) battery, quad rectangular headlamps, 21-gallon fuel tank, and compact spare tire. Standard equipment also included P195/75R15 blackwall glass-belted radial tires with wheel covers, vinyl front bucket seats and fold-down rear bench seat, two-speed wipers, carpeting, locking glovebox, front armrests, lighted front ashtray, lighter, coat hooks, inside hood release, dome light, body pin stripes, spare tire cover, and front/rear bumper nerf strips. The DL upgrade added custom vinyl reclining bucket seats up front and a split vinyl rear seat, Alpine cloth custom headliner and visors, woodgrain instrument panel overlay, woodgrain horn cover on a custom steering wheel, day/night mirror, and digital clock. It also featured left/right remote-control chrome mirrors, chrome side marker lights, dual horns, extra quiet insulation, and P195/75R15 whitewall glass-belted radials with argent styled wheel covers. DL liftbacks had blackout window frames, belt moldings, and door/quarter frame moldings. Off-road enthusiasts could elect an optional Sport package that included a floor shift console, parcel shelf, and vinyl sport steering wheel inside. Outside they featured a 'Sport' nameplate plus low gloss black Krayton flares and rocker panels, black bumpers with guards and nerf strips, black grille insert, moldings, taillamp treatment, and left/right remote sport mirrors. Sport models rode P195/75RIS blackwall steel-belted radial Goodyear Arriva tires with styled wheel covers, and carried halogen headlamps and foglamps.

EAGLE—SERIES 30—FOUR/SIX— Eagle's new checkerboard grille, with an 8x3 pattern, differed considerably from its Concord cousin. Like their new smaller companions, the big Eagles were noteworthy for their dark Krayton lower body treatment. With standard four-speed manual shift, Eagle rated 22 mpg in the EPA fuel economy rankings. Outside body panels were now one-side galvanized steel for added rust protection. Standard equipment was the same as the smaller Eagle 50, but with individual vinyl reclining front seats, dual horns, the extra quiet insulation package, whitewall P195/75R15 glass-belted radials and argent styled wheel covers. Eagle 30s also had front/rear armrests with woodgrain overlay, cargo area skid strips, day/night mirror, digital clock, Alpine cloth headliner and visors, locking cargo compartment, woodgrain steering wheel and instrument panel overlays, and front/rear bumper nerf strips. Two-door sedans sported a landau roof design; four-doors, a full vinyl roof. Wagon rear seats folded down. The Eagle 30 Limited added leather reclining seats, 18-ounce carpeting, luxury woodgrain steering wheel and a parcel shelf. The Sport package, highlighted by a '4x4' silver decal on the lower door and a 'Sport' nameplate, contained a leather-wrapped sport steering wheel; low-gloss black flares and rocker panels; plus black bumpers/guards, nerf strips, hood molding, taillamp treatment, grille insert, headlamp bezels, door frames, moldings, and remote-control dual sport mirrors. Also halogen headlamps and foglamps, and P195/75R15 blackwall steel-belted Arriva radial tires.

I.D. DATA: A new 17 symbol Vehicle Identification Number (VIN) was embossed on a metal plate riveted to the upper left surface of the instrument panel, visible through the windshield. It began with a digit indicating country of manufacture: '1' U.S.; '2' Canada. The second symbol identified the manufacturer: 'A' AMC; 'C' American Motors (Canada). Third symbol showed vehicle type: 'M' passenger car; 'C' multi purpose vehicle (Eagle); 'E' export. Symbol four denoted engine type: 'B' 151 cu. in. (2.5-liter) four (from Pontiac); 'C' 258 cu. in. (4.2-liter) six. The fifth symbol identified transmission (and transfer case) type: 'M' four-speed manual floor shift; 'H' four-speed with 4WD; 'G' four-speed with full time 4WD; 'W' five-speed floor shift; 'N' five-speed with 4WD; 'A' column shift automatic; 'C' floor-shift automatic; and 'K' floor shift automatic with 4WD. The next two digits identified the line and body type: '05' Concord four-door; '06' Concord two-door; '08' Concord wagon; '35' Eagle four-door sedan; '36' Eagle two-door sedan; '38' Eagle four-door wagon; '43' Spirit two-door Liftback; '46' Spirit two-door sedan; '53' Eagle SX/4 two-door liftback; '56' Eagle (Kammback) two-door sedan. The eighth symbol identified trim level: '0' base model; '5' DL; '7' Limited. Next came a check digit to mathematically determine validity of car's VIN. Symbol ten was a letter indicating model year: 'B' 1981. Symbol eleven showed manufacturing plant: 'K' Kenosha; 'B' Brampton, Ontario. Finally came a six digit sequence number. An engine Build Code was stamped on a machined surface of the block of six-cylinder engines, between cylinders two and three, and at the rear of the engine, near the flywheel on 151 cu. in. fours. The fourth symbol of that code was identical to the engine code of the VIN. Symbol one is year ('1' 1981); symbols 2-3, the month built (01-12); symbols 5-6, the day of the month. The VIN is also on the Federal Safety Label attached to the edge of the left door, above the door lock or on the bottom line of a metal plate attached to upper left corner of firewall under the hood. A Unit Body/Trim Plate on left door edge shows Body Number, Model Number, Trim Number, Paint Code and Build Sequence Number.

SPIRIT SERIES 40

Series No.	Body/Style No.	Body Type & Seating	Factory Price	Shipping Weight	Prod. Total
40	8143-0	2-dr Lift-4P	5190/5326	2587/2716	42,252
40	8146-0	2-dr Sed-4P	5090/5226	2542/2671	2,367

SPIRIT DL

Series No.	Body/Style No.	Body Type & Seating	Factory Price	Shipping Weight	Prod. Total
40	8143-5	2-dr Lift-4P	5589/5725	2673/2802	Note 1
40	8146-5	2-dr Sed-4P	5489/5625	2627/2756	Note 1

Note 1: Production totals include base and DL models. Total model year production: 44,599 Spirits (26,075 four-cylinder and 18,524 six-cylinder). Model year sales: 38,334.

CONCORD SERIES 01

Series No.	Body/Style No.	Body Type & Seating	Factory Price	Shipping Weight	Prod. Total
01	8106-0	2-dr Sed-5P	5819/5955	2672/2798	15,496
01	8105-0	4-dr Sed 5P	5944/6080	2738/2864	24,403
01	8108-0	4-dr Sta Wag-5P	6144/6280	2768/2894	15,198

CONCORD DL

01	8106-5	2-dr Sed-5P	6218/6354	2767/2893	Note 2
01	8105-5	4-dr Sed-5P	6343/6479	2837/2963	Note 2
01	8108-5	4-dr Sta Wag-5P	6543/6679	2852/2978	Note 2

CONCORD LIMITED

01	8106-7	2-dr Sed-5P	6665/6801	2789/2915	Note 2
01	8105-7	4-dr Sed-5P	6790/6926	2859/2985	Note 2
01	8108-7	4-dr Sta Wag-5P	6990/7126	2880/3006	Note 2

Note 2: Production totals shown for base Concord include DL and Limited models. Total model year production 55,097 Concords (7,067 four-cylinder and 48,030 six-cylinder). Model year sales: 63,732.

EAGLE SERIES 50

50	8153-0	2-dr SX/4 Lift-4P	6717/6853	2967/3123	17,340
50	8156-0	2-dr Kamm Sed-4P	5995/6131	2919/3015	5,603

EAGLE DL SERIES 50

50	8153-5	2-dr SX/4 Lift-4P	7119/7255	3040/3196	Note 3
50	8156-5	2-dr Kamm Sed-4P	6515/6651	2990/3146	Note 3

Note 3: Production totals include both base and DL models.

EAGLE SERIES 30

30	8136-5	2-dr Sed-5P	7847/7983	3104/3260	2,378
30	8135-5	4-dr Sed-5P	8097/8233	3172/3328	1,737
30	8138-5	4-dr Sta Wag-5P	8397/8533	3184/3340	10,371

EAGLE LIMITED

30	8136-7	2-dr Sed-5P	8244/8380	3114/3270	Note 4
30	8135-7	4-dr Sed-5P	8494/8630	3180/3336	Note 4
30	8138-7	4-dr Sta Wag-5P	8794/8930	3198/3354	Note 4

Note 4: Production totals shown under base Eagle include Limited. Total model year production: 37,429 Eagles (11,344 four-cylinder and 26,085 six-cylinder). Model year sales: 42,904.

FACTORY PRICE AND WEIGHT NOTE: Figure before the slash is for four-cylinder engine, after slash for six-cylinder.

ENGINES: BASE FOUR (all models): Inline. OHV. Four-cylinder. Cast iron block and head. Displacement: 151 cu. in. (2.5 liters). Bore & stroke: 4.0 x 3.0 in. Compression ratio: 8.24:1. Brake horsepower: 82 at 3800 R.P.M. Torque: 125 lb.-ft. at 2600 R.P.M. Five main bearings. Hydraulic valve lifters. Carburetor: 2Bbl. Rochester 2SE. OPTIONAL SIX (all models): Same as 1980 specifications (258 cu. in. inline OHV).

CHASSIS DATA: Wheelbase: (Spirit) 96 in.; (Concord) 108 in.; (Eagle 50) 97.2 in.; (Eagle 30) 109.3 in. Overall length: (Spirit) 167 in.; (Concord) 185 in.; (Eagle 50 SX/4) 164.6 in.; (Eagle 50 Kammback) 164.4 in.; (Eagle 30) 184 in. Height: (Spirit) 51.5 in.; (Concord) 51.3-51.5 in.; (Eagle 50) 55.3-55.5 in.; (Eagle 30) 55.0-55.8 in. Width: (Spirit) 72 in.; (Concord) 71 in.; (Eagle 50) 73 in.; (Eagle 30) 71.9 in. w/flares. Front Tread: (Spirit) 58.1 in.; (Concord) 57.6 in.; (Eagle) 59.6 in. Rear Tread: (Spirit) 57 in.; (Concord) 57.1 in.; (Eagle) 57.6 in. Standard Tires: (Spirit) P185/75R14 BSW GBR; (Concord) P195/75R14 BSW GBR; (Eagle) P195/75R15 BSW GBR.

TECHNICAL: Four-speed manual floor shift standard. Gear ratios: (1st) 4.07:1; (2nd) 2.39:1; (3rd) 1.49:1; (4th) 1.00:1; (Rev) 3.95:1. Torque-Command three-speed automatic transmission optional; lock-up torque converter. Standard axle ratio: (Spirit/Concord four) 3.08:1; (Spirit/Concord six) 2.37:1; (Eagle four) 3.54:1; (Eagle six) 2.73:1. Steering: recirculating ball. Suspension: independent front coil springs; semi-elliptic rear leaf springs. Clutch dia.: 9.12 in. Brakes: front disc, rear drums: (Spirit) 10.3 in. disc; (Concord) 10.8 in. disc; (Eagle) 11 in. disc. Electronic ignition.

SPIRIT/CONCORD/EAGLE DRIVETRAIN OPTIONS: 258 cu. in. six-cylinder engine ($136). Column-shift automatic transmission: Spirit/Concord ($350). Floor-shift automatic transmission: Spirit/Eagle ($350). Optional 3.08:1 axle ratio: Eagle 30 six with automatic ($20). Twin-Grip differential: Spirit/Concord ($69). Heavy-duty engine cooling system (H.D. radiator, viscous fan/shroud, coolant recovery system): Spirit/Concord six ($61) but std. w/air cond. Eagle four ($51). Maximum cooling system (H.D. radiator and viscous fan): Eagle ($62). Handling package (unique front sway bar, rear sway bar): Spirit, Concord six ($42); N/A w/Spirit GT. H.D. shock absorbers: Spirit/Concord ($16); N/A with Spirit GT Rally-tuned pkg. Automatic load leveling (air shocks): Concord/Eagle six ($153). Extra duty suspension pkg. (rear sway bar and H.D. shocks/springs): Eagle 50 ($37); Eagle 30 ($69). Extra heavy-duty suspension (H.D. springs shocks, control arms/bushings): Concord ($59). Front suspension skid plate: Eagle ($69). Trailer towing package A (to 2000 pounds): Concord/Eagle 30 ($90). Trailer towing package B (to 3500 pounds): Eagle 30 ($195). H.D. (56-450 cold crank) battery ($20). 80-amp battery: Concord/Eagle ($32). H.D. alternator ($63). Cold climate group incl. H.D. battery/alternator, engine block heater ($113); w/air cond. or rear defroster: Spirit/Concord ($50). California emission system ($50).

CONVENIENCE/APPEARANCE OPTIONS: Spirit liftback GT package ($372); DL ($272). Spirit liftback GT Rally-tuned suspension package ($119). Eagle Sport package: Eagle 30 two-door/wgn ($314); Eagle 50 liftback ($472); Eagle 50 DL liftback ($367). Extra quiet insulation package ($53). Protection group (stainless door edge guards, front/rear bumper guards and nerfing strips, front/rear floor mats): Spirit ($117); Concord ($120): DL/Ltd. ($71-$74); Spirit GT ($33). Eagle protection group incl. stainless door edge guards, front/rear bumper guards, front/rear floor mats ($79-$82); w/Sport pkg. ($33-$36). Convenience group: headlight-on buzzer, intermittent wipers, right lighted vanity mirror ($67). Gauge package (clock, tach, oil, amp or volt, vacuum): Spirit, Eagle 50 ($136); Spirit GT/DL ($79-$81); Eagle 30 or DL ($81). Pop-up sunroof w/tinted glass ($246). Rear spoiler: Spirit GT, Eagle Sport liftback ($99). Light group ($46-$56). Left remote control mirror ($19) exc. GT; N/A on Eagle 30. Left/right remote chrome mirrors ($56) exc. Spirit GT/DL; std. on Concord DL/Ltd.; N/A Eagle 30. Left/right remote sport mirrors: Spirit, Eagle 50 ($56); Eagle 50 DL (NC). Left/right electric remote chrome mirrors: Spirit/Concord ($132); Concord DL and Eagle 30 ($76-$77). Day/night ($13); std. on DL/Ltd. Power steering: Spirit/Concord ($173). Power front disc brakes: Spirit/Concord ($80). Electronic cruise control ($132). Air conditioning system ($531-$585). Air conditioning package incl. tinted glass and power steering: Spirit ($774); Concord ($833). Halogen headlamps ($40). Foglamps (dealer-installed): Eagle ($73). Dual horns: Spirit/Concord ($15). AM radio ($92). AM/FM/CB stereo four-speaker radio ($456) exc. Spirit DL ($364). AM/FM/stereo four-speaker radio ($192) exc. Spirit DL ($100). AM/FM/cassette stereo radio ($356) exc. Spirit DL ($264). Premium audio system incl. power amplifier, four hi-fi speakers, fader ($100). Power antenna ($53). Power door locks: Spirit DL, Concord DL/Ltd. two-door sed, Eagle 30 two-door ($90); Concord DL/Ltd. and Eagle 30 four-door/wgn ($130-$131). Power windows and door locks: Spirit DL, Concord DL/Ltd. two-door sed, Eagle 30 two-door, 50 DL ($231); Concord DL/Ltd. and Eagle 30 four-door/wgn ($330). Power liftback release: Spirit/Eagle 50 ($34). Power decklid release: Concord/Eagle 30 sed ($34). Power six-way driver's seat: Concord DL/Ltd., Eagle 30 ($157). Power six-way driver/pass. seat: Concord DL/Ltd., Eagle 30 ($262). Center console w/armrest: Spirit ($82). Floor shift console: Eagle ($52). Parcel shelf ($24). Bench seat (striped knit fabric): Concord ($48). H.D. seat frame assembly for bench seat: Concord ($31). H.D. vinyl seat trim: Concord ($60); N/A w/DL or four-speed. Coventry Check seat fabric, reclining bucket seats: Spirit DL, Eagle 50 ($31). Velour stripe fabric on reclining seats: Concord DL, Eagle 30 ($58). Durham plaid fabric or Rochelle sculptured velour on reclining seats: Eagle 30 ($58). Cargo area cover: Concord/Eagle wgn ($62). Digital clock ($55); std. on DL/Ltd. Rear wiper/washer ($99). Rear defroster ($102-$107). Vinyl sport steering wheel: Spirit/Eagle 50 ($34). Woodgrain steering wheel: Spirit/Concord DL, Eagle 30 ($32). Leather-wrapped sport steering wheel ($54) exc. GT/Ltd., Eagle 50 Sport ($20-$34). Tilt steering wheel: Spirit ($79); Eagle ($82). Tinted glass ($70-$75). Two-tone paint (w/o pin stripes): Spirit, Concord DL/Ltd. ($109). Special color combinations ($32). Rally side stripes: Spirit ($79). Woodgrain paneling: Eagle wgn ($128). Delete woodgrain from Concord DL/Ltd. wgn (deduct $75). Side scuff moldings ($44). Roof rack: Spirit sed, Eagle 50 ($74); Concord/Eagle 30 wgn ($98). Locking gas cap ($10). Tailgate air deflector: Spirit/Eagle 50 sed ($29). Front/rear bumper guards ($47). Styled wheel covers (argent): Spirit ($37) exc. GT, Concord ($74); Concord DL ($37); Eagle ($48). Custom wheel covers: Concord ($37); std. on DL. Wire wheel covers: Spirit/Concord ($142); DL ($105); N/A on GT. Spoke style 14 x 6 in. wheels w/trim rings: Spirit/Concord ($158) exc. DL ($121); Concord Ltd. ($16). Turbocast II aluminum 14 x 7 in. wheels: Spirit ($368) exc. DL ($331-$345); Spirit GT ($210); Concord Ltd. ($226). Aluminum 15 x 6 in. wheels: Eagle ($310-$357). Spirit/Concord Tires: P185/75R14/B white GBR: Spirit ($52). P195/75R14/B black GBR: Spirit ($25) exc. DL (NC). P195/75R14/B white GBR: Spirit ($76); Spirit DL ($25); Concord ($52). P195/75R14/B white SBR Arriva: Spirit ($129); Spirit DL ($77); Concord ($104); Concord DL/Ltd. ($53). P195/70R14/B RWL polysteel radial: Spirit ($229); Spirit DL ($178); Concord ($205); Concord DL/Ltd. ($154). Eagle Tires: P195/75R15 white GBR: Eagle 50 ($52). P195/75R15 black SBR Arriva ($52-$53). P195/75R15 white SBR Arriva: Eagle 30 ($96); Eagle 50 ($104); Eagle DL ($96); Eagle Sport ($52). P215/65R15 OWL SBR Eagle GT: Eagle 30 ($245); Eagle Sport ($201). P215/75R15 OWL SBR Eagle GT: Eagle 50 ($254); Eagle DL ($245).

HISTORY: Introduced: September 25, 1980. Model year production: 137,125 (44,486 fours and 92,639 sixes), which came to 2.1 percent of the industry total. Calendar year production (U.S.): 109,319. Model year sales by U.S. dealers: 145,206 (including 236 leftover Pacers). Calendar year sales: 136,682 cars. Concords sold the best, followed by Eagles, then Spirits.

HISTORICAL FOOTNOTES: Strengthening its tie with the French automaker, AMC marketed as a "captive import" the new Renault 18i. On December 16, 1980, AMC stockholders approved the arrangement that would give Renault a 46 percent share of the corporation. Three more Renault officers joined the AMC board making a total of five. Skyrocketing interest rates received part of the blame for sluggish sales of AMC domestic cars, which slipped 8.2 percent from 1980. Still, the company's market share was down only slightly. Operation resumed at AMC's Milwaukee plant in August 1981, after a nine-month closure. One of the two Kenosha production lines shut down to retool for manufacturing the planned Renault/AMC joint-venture front-wheel-drive subcompact model. Eagle sales edged out those of the 4WD Subaru, but that flash of popularity wasn't destined to last long.

1982

Both the compact Concord and subcompact Spirit had slipped further down in sales volume, but returned for another try in 1982, along with both Eagle 4WD versions. Styling changed little from 1981. The foremost technical change was the availability of a T5 five-speed overdrive manual transmission from Warner Gear, which boosted fuel economy ratings. Its overdrive fifth gear (0.76:1 or 0.86:1) was in the rear housing of the transmission. Four-speed manual and three-speed automatic transmissions were redesigned; as before the automatics came from Chrysler. Lower final drive ratios on all models were intended to improve economy. Sixes with automatic received wider-ratio gearboxes. The optional 258 cu. in. six-cylinder engine gained a serpentine accessory drive system for added fuel savings. One belt powered the alternator, water pump, air pump, and power steering pump. GM cars using Pontiac's "Iron Duke" four gained fuel injection this year, but AMC's version stuck to carburetion. Front disc brakes gained low-drag calipers. New body colors were added: Topaz Gold metallic, Sea Blue metallic, Deep Night Blue, Slate Blue metallic, Jamaican Beige, Mist Silver metallic, and Sun Yellow. Carryover metallic colors were Deep Maroon, Vintage Red, Copper Brown, Sherwood Green and Dark Brown; plus Oriental Red, Olympic White and Classic Black.

SPIRIT — SERIES 40 — FOUR/SIX — Spirits looked the same outside, but could be purchased with the new five-speed overdrive transmission—the first domestic subcompact to offer that option. Once again, base and DL trim were available, along with the sporty GT package. Base powertrain was the 2.5-liter (151 cu. in.) four-cylinder "Iron Duke" engine from Pontiac, with four-speed floor shift, manual front disc brakes, and P185/75R14 black glass-belted radial tires. Standard equipment also included two-speed wiper/washers, front sway bar, compact spare tire, lighter, color-keyed carpeting, inside hood release, locking glovebox, dome light, vinyl bucket front seats, fold-down rear bench seat, energy-absorbing bumpers, side pin striping and wheel covers. DL Spirits rode P185/75R14 whitewall glass-belted radials on argent styled wheel covers and added reclining vinyl bucket seats, a premium split rear seat, Alpine fabric headliner and visors, AM radio, woodgrain dash overlay, day/night mirror, extra quiet insulation package, dual horns and a digital clock. Black rocker panel moldings, chrome side marker lights, a chrome remote-control left mirror and front/rear bumper guards also marked the DL. Liftback buyers could choose a Spirit GT package, which included spoke style 14 x 6-inch wheels with P185/75R14 blackwall glass-belted radial tires; tachometer; sport steering wheel; left-hand remote sport mirror; black body trim moldings at windshield and rear window surround, belt drip and B pillar; black grille insert, headlight bezels, bumpers with nerfing strips and rear venturi; and GT nameplates.

CONCORD — SERIES 01 — FOUR/SIX — Base Concords again were powered by a 151 cu. in. four with four-speed floor shift and had manual disc brakes, bench seats, a front sway bar, P195/75R14 blackwall glass-belted radial tires with wheel covers, and a compact high-pressure spare tire. They also had the option of a five-speed overdrive floor shift, which produced a 37 mpg EPA highway rating with the four. A reworked, wider-ratio automatic transmission also helped mileage when coupled to the optional 258 six with a lower final axle ratio. External appearance was unchanged. Standard equipment also included two-speed wiper/washers, dome light, lighter, carpeting, a hood ornament, dual body pin stripes, and black scuff moldings on body sides. Concord DL models added individual vinyl reclining seats, molded fiberglass headliner and visors (Alpine fabric), a day/night inside mirror, dual rear ashtrays, digital electronic clock, woodgrain instrument panel overlay, dual horns, extra quiet insulation, bumper guards front and rear, a remote-control left mirror, and custom wheel covers with whitewall tires. As before, DL two-doors carried opera windows and a landau vinyl roof while four-doors had a full vinyl roof and wagons sported woodgrain side panels. Moving another step up, the Limited included leather reclining seats, heavy carpeting (18-ounce in passenger area), a luxury woodgrain steering wheel, parcel shelf, chrome right-hand remote-control mirror, and wire wheel covers with whitewall tires.

EAGLE — SERIES 50 — FOUR/SIX — 'Select Drive' let motorists switch easily between two-wheel-drive and full-time 4WD on the short-wheelbase, Spirit-based Eagle. That was formerly an option. Although the 151 cu. in. four still served as base engine, with four-speed floor shift, Eagles could also get the new five-speed manual or three-speed automatic, along with the 258 cu. in. six-cylinder powerplant. All Eagles included power steering and brakes and a front sway bar, and rode on 15-inch tires with wheel covers. P195/75R15 blackwall glass-belted radials were standard, with a compact spare tire. Eagles also came with color-keyed carpeting, custom vinyl bucket front seats (fold-down rear bench seat), front/rear bumper nerfing strips, inside hood release, dome light, locking glovebox, wheelwell and rocker panel moldings, and body pin striping. Lower door sections were painted in accent color. Eagle DL models added reclining bucket seats up front, a split rear seat, woodgrain dash overlay, day/night mirror, digital clock, Alpine fabric headliner/visors, remote-control left mirror (chrome), extra quiet insulation, twin horns, and argent styled wheel covers with whitewall tires. Appearing again on the SX/4 Liftback option list was an Eagle Sport package, including low-gloss black Krayton rocker panels and flares; black bumpers with guards and nerf strips; colored inserts in lower bodyside moldings; black grille insert, windshield, headlamp bezels, liftgate, drip/belt moldings, and taillamp treatment; a black remote-control left sport mirror; plus halogen headlamps and foglamps. Inside, Sport models had a floor-shift console, parcel shelf, and vinyl sport steering wheel. They wore P195/75R15 blackwall steel-belted Arriva radial tires with styled wheel covers.

EAGLE — SERIES 30 — FOUR/SIX — Concord based Eagle sedans and wagons also had switch-selected 2WD/4WD with optional five-speed overdrive transmission. The 151 cu. in. four with four-speed floor shift remained standard; 258 six optional (with automatic). Base model big Eagles were a bit more luxurious than their smaller brothers, fitted with standard equipment that required a model upgrade in the 50 series. The list included individual reclining front seats, extra quiet insulation, dual horns, day/night mirror, lighter, Alpine fabric headliner/visors, digital clock, vinyl door trim, left remote chrome mirror, and woodgrain dash overlay. Two-doors featured opera quarter windows with landau roof, four-doors a full vinyl roof, and wagons held a fold-down rear seat. Standard Eagles rode P195/75R15 whitewall glass-belted radials with argent styled wheel covers. Eagle Limiteds contained leather reclining seats and heavy carpeting, plus a woodgrain steering wheel, parcel shelf, 'Limited' nameplate on front fender, and twin remote-control mirrors. The Sport package included a leather-wrapped steering wheel; black bumpers and guards; black headlamp bezels, grille insert, windshield/liftgate moldings, door frames, B pillars and remote left sport mirror; low-gloss black rocker panels and flares; halogen headlamps and foglamps; colored inserts in lower bodyside moldings, hood molding and nerf strip; a '4x4' silver decal on lower door; and steel-belted blackwall radial tires. The Sport package was available only on base Eagle two-door sedans and wagons. Two trailer towing packages were available, for light or medium loads.

I.D. DATA: The 17-symbol VIN, visible through the windshield, used the same coding as in 1981.

SPIRIT SERIES 40

Series No.	Body/Style No.	Body Type & Seating	Factory Price	Shipping Weight	Prod. Total
40	8243-0	2-dr Lift-4P	5576/5726	2588/2687	20,063
40	8246-0	2-dr Sed-4P	5476/5626	2538/2637	119
SPIRIT DL					
40	8243-5	2-dr Lift-4P	5959/6109	2666/2765	Note 1
40	8246-5	2-dr Sed-4P	5859/6009	2614/2713	Note 1

Note 1: Production totals shown under base Spirit include DL models. Total model year production: 20,182 Spirits (9,290 four-cylinder and 10,892 six-cylinder). Model year sales: 18,161.

CONCORD SERIES 01

Series No.	Body/Style No.	Body Type & Seating	Factory Price	Shipping Weight	Prod. Total
01	8206-0	2-dr Sed-5P	5954/6104	2693/2773	6,132
01	8205-0	4-dr Sed-5P	6254/6404	2752/2842	25,572
01	8208-0	4-dr Sta Wag-5P	7013/7163	2786/2876	12,106
CONCORD DL					
01	8206-5	2-dr Sed-5P	6716/6866	2768/2858	Note 2
01	8205-5	4-dr Sed-5P	6761/6911	2841/2931	Note 2
01	8208-5	4-dr Sta Wag-5P	7462/7612	2940/3030	Note 2
CONCORD LIMITED					
01	8206-7	2-dr Sed-5P	7213/7363	2790/2880	Note 2
01	8205-7	4-dr Sed-5P	7258/7408	2862/2952	Note 2
01	8208-7	4-dr Sta Wag-5P	7959/8109	2892/2982	Note 2

Note 2: Production totals under base Concord include DL and Limited. Total model year production: 33,693 Concords (2,038 four-cylinder and 31,655 six-cylinder) including Canadian output for U.S. market. Model year sales: 36,505.

EAGLE SX/4 SERIES 50

Series No.	Body/Style No.	Body Type & Seating	Factory Price	Shipping Weight	Prod. Total
50	8253-0	2-dr SX/4 Lift-4P	7451/7601	2972/3100	10,445
50	8256-0	2-dr Kamm Sed-4P	6799/6949	2933/3061	520
EAGLE DL					
50	8253-5	2-dr SX/4 Lift-4P	7903/8053	3041/3169	Note 3
50	8256-5	2-dr Kamm Sed-4P	7369/7519	3000/3128	Note 3

Note 3: Production totals shown under base Eagle 50 include DL models. Of the 10,965 Eagle 50s manufactured, 3,529 had four-cylinder engine.

Series No.	Body/Style No.	Body Type & Seating	Factory Price	Shipping Weight	Prod. Total
EAGLE SERIES 30					
30	8236-5	2-dr Sed-5P	8719/8869	3107/3235	1,968
30	8235-5	4-dr Sed-5P	8869/9019	3172/3300	4,091
30	8238-5	4-dr Sta Wag-5P	9566/9716	3199/3327	20,899
EAGLE LIMITED					
30	8236-7	2-dr Sed-5P	9166/9316	3115/3243	Note 4
30	8235-7	4-dr Sed-5P	9316/9466	3180/3308	Note 4
30	8238-7	4-dr Sta Wag-5P	10013/10163	3213/3341	Note 4

Note 4: Production totals shown under base Eagle 30 include Eagle Limited. They include Canadian output for U.S. market. Only 6,056 Eagle 30 sedans and two wagons were made in U.S. Model year Eagle sales: 37,797.

FACTORY PRICE AND WEIGHT NOTE: Figure before the slash is for four-cylinder engine, after slash for six-cylinder.

ENGINES: BASE FOUR (all models): Inline. OHV. Four-cylinder. Cast iron block and head. Displacement: 151 cu. in. (2.5 liters). Bore & stroke: 4.0 x 3.0 in. Compression ratio: 8.2:1. Brake horsepower: 82 at 3800 R.P.M. Torque: 125 lb.-ft. at 2600 R.P.M. Five main bearings. Hydraulic valve lifters. Carburetor: 2Bbl. Rochester 2SE, exc. E2SE with automatic transmission. OPTIONAL SIX (all models): Inline. OHV. Six-cylinder. Cast iron block and head. Displacement: 258 cu. in. (4.2 liters). Bore & stroke: 3.75 x 3.90 in. Compression ratio: 8.6:1. Brake horsepower: 110 at 3000 R.P.M. Torque: 205 lb.-ft. at 1800 R.P.M. Seven main bearings. Hydraulic valve lifters. Carburetor: Carter BBD 2Bbl.

CHASSIS DATA: Wheelbase: (Spirit) 96 in.; (Concord) 108 in.; (Eagle 50) 97.2 in.; (Eagle 30) 109.3 in. Overall length: (Spirit) 167 in.; (Concord) 185 in.; (Eagle 50) 164.5 in. but 166.5 in. w/bumper guards; (Eagle 30) 184 in. but 186.3 in. w/bumper guards. Height: (Spirit) 51.5 in.; (Concord) 51.3-51.5 in.; (Eagle 50) 55.4 in.; (Eagle 30) 55.0-55.8 in. Front Tread: (Spirit) 58.1 in.; (Concord) 57.6 in.; (Eagle) 59.6 in. Rear Tread: (Spirit) 57.0 in.; (Concord) 57.1 in.; (Eagle) 57.6 in. Standard Tires: (Spirit) P185/75R14 GBR; (Concord) P195/75R14 GBR; (Eagle) P195/75R15 GBR.

TECHNICAL: Four-speed manual floor shift standard; five-speed overdrive transmission optional; three-speed automatic optional. Eagles: "Select Drive" 4WD with transfer case. Four-speed manual gear ratios: (1st) 4.03:1; (2nd) 2.37:1; (3rd) 1.50:1; (4th) 1.00:1; (Rev) 3.78:1. Five-speed gear ratios: same as four-speed with additional fifth gear (0.86:1 for four-cylinder, 0.76:1 for sixes). Standard axle ratio: (four-cylinder engine) 3.08:1; (Spirit/Concord six) 2.35:1 exc. w/auto trans. 2.21:1; (Concord) 2.21:1; (Eagle 50 six) 2.35:1; (Eagle 30 six) 2.73:1 exc. w/auto trans. 2.35:1. Steering: recirculating ball. Suspension: independent front with coil springs, upper/lower control arms, anti-roll bar, semi-elliptic rear leaf springs with "live" (rigid) rear axle. Brakes: front disc, rear drum; (Spirit/Concord) 10.8 in. disc, 9 in. drum exc. Concord wagon: 10 in. drum; (Eagle) 11 in. disc, 10 in. drum. Electronic ignition. Fuel tank (Spirit/Eagle 50) 21 gal.; (Concord/Eagle 30) 22 gal.

DRIVETRAIN OPTIONS: 258 cu. in. six-cylinder engine ($150). Five-speed floor shift with overdrive ($199). Column shift automatic transmission: Spirit/Concord ($411). Floor-shift automatic transmission: Spirit/Eagle ($411). Optional axle ratios: Concord six (2.73:1) or Eagle 30 six (3.08:1); with automatic and trailer towing pkg. ($21). Twin-Grip differential: Spirit/Concord ($75-$79). Heavy-duty engine cooling system (H.D. radiator, viscous fan, coolant recovery system): Spirit six, Concord ($75) but std. w/Concord air cond.; Eagle ($65). Maximum cooling system: Eagle ($68). Handling package: Spirit/Concord ($46). H.D. shock absorbers: Spirit/Concord ($17); N/A with Spirit GT Rally-tuned pkg. or load-leveling. Automatic load leveling: Concord six ($163). Extra duty suspension package: Eagle 30 ($75). Extra duty suspension pkg. incl. rear sway bar and H.D. shocks: Eagle 50 ($40). Front suspension skid plate: Eagle ($75). Trailer towing package A: Concord/Eagle 30 ($101). Trailer towing package B: Eagle 50 six ($215). H.D. battery ($25). Cold climate group incl. H.D. battery and engine block heater ($56). California emission system ($50).

CONVENIENCE/APPEARANCE OPTIONS: Spirit GT package: on DL liftback ($399). Spirit GT Rally-tuned suspension package: liftback ($129). Eagle Sport package: Eagle 30 two-door/wgn ($333); Eagle 50 liftback ($499); Eagle 50 DL liftback ($394). Extra quiet insulation package: Spirit/Concord/Eagle 50 ($59); std. on Concord DL/Ltd., Eagle DL. Protection group (stainless door edge guards, bumper guards and nerfing strips, front mats): Spirit/Concord ($128); DL/Ltd. ($78); Spirit GT ($42). Eagle protection group incl. stainless door edge guards, bumper guards, floor mats ($92); w/Sport pkg. ($42). Convenience group (headlight-on buzzer, intermittent wipers, lighted vanity mirror) ($71). Gauge package (clock, tach, oil, amp or volt, vacuum): Spirit, Eagle 50 ($147); Spirit GT/DL, Eagle 30 or DL ($88). Pop-up sunroof: sedans, Eagle 50 ($279). Rear spoiler: Spirit GT, Eagle 50 Sport liftback ($101). Light group ($59). Left remote control mirror ($30) exc. GT; std. on DL models; N/A on Eagle 30. Right remote mirror (chrome): DL models, Eagle 30 ($31). Left/right remote chrome mirrors ($61) exc. Spirit GT/DL; std. on Concord Ltd.; N/A Eagle 30. Right remote sport mirror (black): Spirit GT liftback, Eagle Sport ($31). Left/right electric remote chrome mirrors ($142) exc. DL and Eagle 30 ($112); Eagle 30/Concord Ltd. ($81). Day/night mirror ($14); std. on DL/Ltd.; N/A Eagle 30. Power steering: Spirit/Concord ($199). Power front disc brakes ($99). Electronic cruise control ($159). Air conditioning ($609-$679). Air conditioning package incl. tinted glass and power steering: Spirit/Concord ($890-$973). Halogen headlamps ($41). Halogen foglamps: Eagle ($79). Dual horns ($16) exc. Eagle 30; std. on DL/Ltd. AM radio ($99). AM/FM/CB stereo four-speaker radio ($456) exc. Spirit DL ($357). AM/FM/Stereo four-speaker radio ($208) exc. Spirit DL ($109). AM/FM/cassette stereo radio ($356) exc. Spirit DL ($257). Electronically tuned AM/FM/cassette stereo radio w/power amplifier and four coax speakers ($499); Spirit DL ($400). Premium audio system incl. power amplifier, 4 hi-fi speakers, fader ($115). Power antenna ($56). Power door locks: Spirit DL, Concord DL/Ltd. two-door sed, Eagle DL ($106); Concord DL/Ltd. and Eagle 30 four-door/wgn ($152). Power door locks and windows: Spirit DL, Concord DL/Ltd. two-door sed, Eagle DL ($275); Concord DL/Ltd. and Eagle 30 four-door/wgn ($391). Power liftback release: Spirit/Eagle 50 ($37) but incl. w/rear spoiler. Power decklid release: Concord/Eagle sed ($37). Power six-way driver's seat: Concord DL/Ltd., Eagle 30 ($171). Power six-way driver/pass. seat: Concord DL/Ltd., Eagle 30 ($281). Center console w/armrest: Spirit ($89). Floor shift console: Eagle ($56). Parcel shelf ($26). Coventry Check fabric reclining bucket seats: Spirit/Eagle 50 ($32). Individual reclining seats (Castilian sculptured fabric): Concord DL, Eagle 30 ($59). Individual reclining seats (Durham plaid fabric): Eagle 30 ($59). Cargo area cover: Concord/Eagle wgn ($68). Digital clock ($59); std. on DL/Ltd.; N/A Eagle 30. Rear wiper/washer ($119). Rear defroster ($125). Vinyl sport steering wheel: Spirit/Eagle 50 ($39) but std. w/GT. Woodgrain steering wheel: DL models, Eagle 30 ($35). Leather-wrapped sport steering wheel ($58) exc. GT/Ltd., Eagle 50 Sport ($19-$23). Tilt steering wheel ($99). Tinted glass ($82-$95). Two-tone accent color: Spirit exc. GT, Concord DL/Ltd. ($119). Special color combinations ($33). Rally stripes: Spirit ($85). Woodgrain paneling: Eagle 30 wgn ($139). Delete woodgrain from Concord DL/Ltd. wgn (deduct $75). Scuff moldings ($47). Roof rack: Spirit sed/Eagle 50 ($85); Concord/Eagle 30 wgn ($105). Locking gas cap ($10). Tailgate air deflector: Spirit sed, Eagle kammback ($32). Bumper guards ($50) but std. w/DL, GT, Ltd., Eagle Sport pkg. Styled wheel covers (argent): Spirit ($40) exc. GT; std. on Spirit DL, Concord ($84); Concord DL ($43); Eagle 50 ($52). Custom wheel covers: Concord ($41); std. on DL. Wire wheel covers ($155); Spirit DL exc. GT ($115); Concord DL ($114). Spoke style 14 x 6 in. wheels w/trim rings ($172) exc. DL ($131-$132); Concord Ltd. ($17). Turbocast II aluminum 14 x 7 in. wheels ($398) exc. DL ($357-$358); Spirit GT ($226); Concord Ltd. ($243). Sport aluminum 15 x 6 in. wheels: Eagle ($335-$387). Spirit/Concord Tires: P185/75R14 white GBR: Spirit ($66). P185/75R14 black GBR: Spirit GT sed (NC). P195/75R14 black GBR: Spirit ($40). P195/75R14 white GBR: Spirit ($108); Spirit DL ($40); Concord ($66). P195/75R14 white SBR Arriva: Spirit ($177); Spirit DL ($111); Concord ($137); Concord DL/Ltd. ($71); P205/70R14 RWL polysteel radial: Spirit ($252); Spirit DL ($186); Concord ($227); Concord DL/Ltd. ($161). Eagle Tires: P195/75R15 white GBR: Eagle 50 ($60). P195/75R15 black SBR Arriva: Eagle 30 ($25); Eagle 50 ($85); Eagle DL ($25). P195/75R15 white SBR Arriva: Eagle 30 ($85); Eagle 30 Sport ($60); Eagle 50 ($145); Eagle DL ($85); Eagle Sport ($60). P215/65R15 OWL SBR Eagle GT: Eagle 30 ($200); Eagle 30 Sport ($175); Eagle 50 ($260); Eagle DL ($200); Eagle Sport ($175).

HISTORY: Introduced: September 24, 1981. Model year production (U.S.): 70,898 (1.4 percent of industry total). Of that number, 14,972 were four-cylinder, 55,926 six-cylinder. Calendar year production (U.S.): 109,746 (including new Alliances for 1983). Model year sales by U.S. dealers: 99,300 (including 6,837 new Alliances) for a market share of 1.8 percent. Calendar year sales: 112,433 (2.0 percent share of industry sales).

HISTORICAL FOOTNOTES: On June 15, 1982, production of the new Renault-designed, front-drive Alliance finally began at the Kenosha, Wisconsin, plant. Its acceptance in the marketplace could signal whether AMC's passenger car operation would continue to survive. The Alliance would not debut until September, as a 1983 model. Even including its captive import Renault models (Fuego, 18i and LeCar),

AMC's market share declined to well under two percent for the '82 model year. Sales of the 4WD Eagle dipped too, though not nearly so badly as the other models in the lineup. Only the Renault connection, it seemed, had a reasonable charge of rescuing the ailing company. With the assistance of early Alliance sales in the fall, AMC managed to beat Volkswagen of America to recapture fourth place in the domestic rankings, for the first time since 1978. In October, the company announced a reduction in the white-collar workforce, relying on attrition and early retirement as well as layoffs. An unusual 1982 agreement with the UAW allowed AMC to invest up to $2,000 from workers' paychecks in new product programs, to be repaid starting in 1985 with 10 percent interest. W. Paul Tippett, Jr., was installed as chairman and CEO, replacing Gerald C. Meyers, who resigned in January 1982. In late September, all Spirit and Eagle SX/4 production moved to the plant at Brampton, Ontario. Big Eagles continued to be made in Kenosha. Concords were built at both factories.

INNOVATIONS: Switchable two-/four-wheel-drive. Built-in computer in electronic fuel feedback carburetion on system to assist mechanics with swift diagnosis.

1983

Both Spirit and Concord prepared for their final outings, but American Motors entered the 1983 model year with a Small French Hope: the front-drive Alliance. Mixing driver conveniences with technological sophistication, the AMC/Renault joint-venture soon would be the only two-wheel-drive offering from AMC. The venerable 258 cu. in. six gained a fuel feedback system with oxygen (knock) sensor, along with a healthy jump to 9.2:1 compression. Gearing changed slightly to achieve better performance, in response to 1982 alterations that boosted mileage.

(Renault) ALLIANCE — SERIES 90 — FOUR — Drivetrains for the new subcompact Alliance came from France, but cars were assembled in Wisconsin. A fuel-injected version of the 1.4-liter four-cylinder engine, as used on the imported LeCar, provided the power through a four-speed overdrive manual shift. Alliances featured rack-and-pinion steering and front-drive, with fully independent (front and rear) suspension. A five-speed manual transmission was optional; also a three-speed automatic. Two- and four-door hatchback sedans were offered with standard power front disc brakes. Quad rectangular headlamps flanked a horizontal-bar grille with center emblem. Parking lights were below the bumpers. An 'Alliance' emblem sat ahead of the front doors, as on other AMC models. MacPherson struts and coil springs made up the front suspension design, which included front (and rear) stabilizer bars. Alliances rode on 155/80GR13 blackwall glass-belted radials with semi-styled wheels and hub covers. Body features included moldings for roof drip rail, rear window, rocker panels, body sides, and windshield surrounds. Inside were vinyl bucket seats (non-reclining), a console with lighter, fabric-covered headliner, a trip odometer, electric wipers with pulse action, and soft-feel steering wheel. Trunks were carpeted; hoods released from inside the car. A microcomputer monitored engine functions, sending signals to a dashboard indicator. The pedestal front seats rocked on curved tracks, adding to leg room for rear passengers. One unusual option, an infra-red door locking/unlocking device, was similar to a remote-controlled garage door opener. Another was a "Systems Sentry" that warned (via lights) of low fluid levels and brake pad wear. Three upgrades were available. The L Alliance added dual accent pin stripes, a bright grille and hub covers, day/night mirror, and blacked out rocker panels. It also carried moldings for beltline, bumper inserts and taillamps. DL models included deluxe six-way cloth bucket rocker/recliner seats, door panels with 'hockey stick' armrests, a soft-hub steering wheel, extra quiet insulation, tinted glass, dual rear ashtrays, tachometer, color-keyed remote left mirror, dual-note horn, and digital clock. The five-speed transmission was standard on DL models, which wore 175/705R13 blackwalls with wheel trim rings. Topping the line was the Limited, with textured fabric bucket rocker/recliner seats and luxury door panels. Extras included a rear center armrest, light group, bright wheel lip moldings, luxury wheel covers, visibility group, and halogen headlamps. Alliance body colors were: Almond Beige; Olympic White; Night Blue; Jade Mist; Sebring Red; and Sterling, Garnet, Cinnamon, Amberglow or Diamond Blue metallic clearcoat. Later in the model year an MT edition appeared, painted in special charcoal gray metallic clearcoat with 'MT' decals and a black rear panel. Additional gear included a decklid luggage rack, right-hand remote mirror, bright instrument panel molding, bodyside and hood pin striping, painted aluminum wheels, and leather-wrapped steering wheel. Inside the MT were Limited fabric rocker/recliner seats and a six-speaker, electronic-tuning stereo radio.

SPIRIT — SERIES 40 — SIX — Not much changed on the body of the Spirit in its final year, but it gained bigger tires (P195/75R14 whitewalls), styled wheel covers, and a push-button AM radio as standard DL fittings. The sedan was gone; only the liftback remained. Rather than the previous four, AMC's 258 cu. in. six-cylinder engine (now with knock sensor) became the sole powerplant. Four-speed manual floor shift was standard; five-speed overdrive or automatic (column or floor shift) optional. Mixing the standard goodies from the previous base and DL models, this year's Spirit came with vinyl reclining bucket seats, lighted ashtray (and lighter), front armrest, locking glovebox, dome light, day/night mirror, digital clock, bumper guards, remote left mirror, styled wheel covers, a front sway bar, and extra quiet insulation package. Formerly an option package, the Spirit GT became a separate model this year. Performance extras included a handling package, gauge package with tachometer, and P195/75R14 SBR Arriva tires on Turbocast II aluminum wheels. Among its other goodies: a leather-wrapped sport steering wheel, black bumpers with guards and nerfing strips, black pin stripes, fog lamps, black moldings and dual remote-control sport mirrors, and center console with armrest. GT Spirits had no clock or radio as standard equipment.

CONCORD — SERIES 01 — SIX — Like the Spirit, the Concord carried a standard 258 cu. in. six for 1983, abandoning the four-cylinder. That engine now had a new fuel feedback system and knock sensor for added efficiency. Only the twin four-door models remained: sedan and station wagon, in base or DL trim (plus a Limited wagon). DL sedans sported a full vinyl roof and opera windows. The enlarged standard equipment list included a front sway bar, front and rear ashtrays, lighter, coat hooks, color-keyed carpeting, Alpine fabric headliner and sun visors, energy absorbing front/rear bumpers, a hood ornament, drip rail and windshield moldings, wide rocker panel moldings, and scuff belt moldings. DL and Limited equipment was similar to 1982. The 'Concord' nameplate was on the upper corner of the grille, as well as on front fenders.

EAGLE — SERIES 50 — FOUR/SIX — Only the four-wheel-drive Eagles kept the old 151 cu. in. (Pontiac) four-cylinder engine as base powerplant, with an optional 258 six. And only the Liftback SX/4 model remained, with body graphics to prove it. Base models included a padded horn bar; DL versions a custom woodgrain steering wheel. Otherwise, equipment remained similar to the previous year. A Sport package was offered again, with halogen headlamps and fog lamps (the latter mounted above the front bumper). The package included a 'Sport' nameplate and red or silver inserts in lower bodyside moldings. Other details were the same as the 1982 Sport package, with a heavy emphasis on black accents. Shorter (3.54:1) gearing with the four-cylinder engine boosted performance.

EAGLE — SERIES 30 — FOUR/SIX — Senior Eagles lost several models this year: the two-door sedan, and the Limited four-door. Standard engine was the familiar 151 cu. in. four with four-speed manual shift; the 258 six was optional, along with five-speed overdrive gearbox or floor-shift automatic. At mid-year, a new AMC-built four, measuring 150 cu. in., replaced the Pontiac "Iron Duke." Base Eagles were well equipped, including armrests, Alpine fabric headliner/visors, digital clock, trunk and cargo area carpeting, day/night rearview mirror, dome light, locking glove compartment, a custom woodgrain steering wheel, woodgrain instrument panel, bumper nerf strips, wheel opening and rocker panel moldings, and chrome remote-control left mirror. Reclining front seats were upholstered in deluxe grain vinyl. Wagons had a fold-down rear bench seat and flip-up tailgate, plus a retractable cargo area cover. Sedans included a full vinyl roof. Whitewall P195/75R15B glass-belted radials came with full wheel covers. Accenting Eagle bodies was molding on the drip rail, beltline, backlight, and windshield. All Eagles had power steering and power brakes. The Limited wagon held Chelsea leather reclining seats and other extras similar to the 1982 version: 18-ounce carpeting, woodgrain steering wheel, parcel shelf, and a second remote control mirror. The Sport package was offered again, but only on the station wagon. Its contents were the same as in 1982, with red or silver inserts in the lower bodyside moldings, a silver '4x4' decal on the lower door, and P195/75R15 blackwall Arriva steel-belted radials.

I.D. DATA: The 17-symbol VIN, embossed on a metal plate on the top surface of the instrument panel, used the same coding as in 1981-82; see previous section for details. The model year code changed to 'D' for 1983. Engine codes for the 151 cu. in. four were on a pad at the right side of the block, below the cylinder head. Six-cylinder codes were on a pad between cylinders two and three. Alliance's 17-symbol VIN was similar. The first three symbols ('1AM') indicated U.S., AMC, and passenger car. The fourth symbol showed fuel-injection type: 'D' Bendix TBI; 'E' Bosch multi-point. Symbol five showed transmission type: 'M' four-speed manual; 'W' five-speed; 'C' automatic. Digits 6-7 indicated body style: '95' four-door sedan; '95' two-door sedan. Digit eight showed trim level: '0' base model; '3' L; '6' DL; '8' Limited. Ninth is a check digit; tenth, the model year code ('D' 1983). In eleventh position, 'K' Kenosha manufacture. Finally comes a six digit sequence number.

ALLIANCE (BASE) SERIES 90

Series No.	Body/Style No.	Body Type & Seating	Factory Price	Shipping Weight	Prod. Total
90	8396-0	2-dr Sed-5P	5595	1945	Note 1

ALLIANCE L

Series No.	Body/Style No.	Body Type & Seating	Factory Price	Shipping Weight	Prod. Total
90	8396-3	2-dr Sed-5P	6020	1945	55,556
90	8395-3	4-dr Sed-5P	6270	1980	86,649

ALLIANCE DL

Series No.	Body/Style No.	Body Type & Seating	Factory Price	Shipping Weight	Prod. Total
90	8396-6	2-dr Sed-5P	6655	1945	Note 1
90	8395-6	4-dr Sed-5P	6905	1980	Note 1
ALLIANCE LIMITED					
90	8395-8	4-dr Sed-5P	7470	1980	Note 1
ALLIANCE MT					
90	8396-6	2-dr Sed-5P	7450	N/A	Note 1
90	8395-6	4-dr Sed-5P	7700	N/A	Note 1

Note 1: Production totals shown under Alliance L include base DL and Limited models. Model year sales: 124,687 Alliances.

SPIRIT DL SERIES 40

Series No.	Body/Style No.	Body Type & Seating	Factory Price	Shipping Weight	Prod. Total
40	8343-5	2-dr Lift-4P	5995	2732	Note 2
SPIRIT GT SERIES 40					
40	8343-9	2-dr Lift-4P	6495	2756	Note 2

Note 2: Total model year production: 3,491. Model year sales: 6,487.

CONCORD (BASE) SERIES 01

Series No.	Body/Style No.	Body Type & Seating	Factory Price	Shipping Weight	Prod. Total
01	8305-0	4-dr Sed-5P	6724	2820	4433
01	8308-0	4-dr Sta Wag-5P	7449	2864	867
CONCORD DL					
01	8305-5	4-dr Sed-5P	6995	2900	Note 3
01	8308-5	4-dr Sta Wag-5P	7730	2938	Note 3
CONCORD LIMITED					
01	8308-7	4-dr Sta Wag-5P	8117	2990	Note 3

Note 3: Production totals shown under base Concord include DL and Limited models. Model year sales: 16,576 Concords.

EAGLE SX/4 SERIES 50

Series No.	Body/Style No.	Body Type & Seating	Factory Price	Shipping Weight	Prod. Total
50	8353-0	2-dr Lift-4P	7697/7852	2956/3084	2259
EAGLE SX/4 DL					
50	8353-5	2-dr Lift-4P	8164/8319	3025/3153	Note 4

Note 4: Production total includes SX/4 base and DL models.

EAGLE SERIES 30

Series No.	Body/Style No.	Body Type & Seating	Factory Price	Shipping Weight	Prod. Total
30	8335-5	4-dr Sed-5P	9162/9317	3181/3309	3,093
30	8338-5	4-dr Sta Wag-5P	9882/10037	3201/3329	12,378
EAGLE LIMITED					
30	8338-7	4-dr Sta Wag-5P	10343/10498	3215/3343	Note 5

Note 5: Station wagon production total shown includes base and Limited models. Total Eagle model year production: 17,730 (only 464 of them with four-cylinder engine). Model year sales: 31,604.

EAGLE FACTORY PRICE AND WEIGHT NOTE: Figure before the slash is for four-cylinder engine, after slash for six-cylinder.

ENGINES: BASE FOUR (Eagle): Inline. OHV. Four-cylinder. Cast iron block and head. Displacement: 151 cu. in. (2.5 liters). Bore & stroke: 4 0 x 3.0 in. Compression ratio: 8.2:1. Brake horsepower: 84 at 4000 R.P.M. Torque: 125 lb.-ft. at 2600 R.P.M. Five main bearings. Hydraulic valve lifters. Carburetor: 2Bbl. Rochester 2SE. REPLACEMENT FOUR (Eagle): Inline. OHV. Four-cylinder. Cast iron block. Displacement: 150 cu. in. (2.46 liters). Bore & stroke: 3.88 x 3.19 in. Compression ratio: 9.2:1. Brake horsepower: N/A. Torque: 132 lb.-ft. at 3200 R.P.M. Five main bearings. Hydraulic valve lifters. Carburetor: 1Bbl. electronic feedback Carter YFA. BASE SIX (Spirit, Concord); OPTIONAL (Eagle): Inline. OHV. Six-cylinder. Cast iron block and head. Displacement: 258 cu. in. (4.2 liters). Bore & stroke: 3.75 x 3.90 in. Compression ratio: 9.2:1. Brake horsepower: 110 at 3200 R.P.M. Torque: 210 lb.-ft. at 1800 R.P.M. Seven main bearings. Hydraulic valve lifters. Carburetor: 2Bbl. Carter BED. BASE FOUR (Alliance): Inline. OHV. Four-cylinder. Cast iron block; aluminum head. Transverse mounted. Displacement: 85.2 cu. in. (1.4 liters). Bore & stroke: 2.99 x 3.03 in. Compression ratio: 8.8:1. Brake horsepower: 56 at 4200 R.P.M. Torque: 75 lb.-ft. at 2500 R.P.M. Five main bearings. Solid valve lifters. Single-point Bendix (throttle-body) fuel injection.

CHASSIS DATA: Wheelbase: (Alliance) 97.8 in.; (Spirit) 96 in.; (Concord) 108 in.; (Eagle 50) 97.2 in.; (Eagle 30) 109.3 in. Overall length: (Alliance) 163.8 in.; (Spirit) 167.2 in.; (Concord) 185 in.; (Eagle 50 SX/4) 164.6 in.; (Eagle 30) 183.2 in. Height: (Alliance) 54.5 in.; (Spirit) 51.5 in.; (Concord) 51-51.6 in.; (Eagle SX/4) 55 in.; (Eagle 30) 55.4 in.; (Eagle 30 wagon) 55 in. Width: (Alliance) 65.0 in.; (Spirit) 71.9 in.; (Concord) 71 in.; (Eagle SX/4) 73 in.; (Eagle 30) 72.3 in. Front Tread: (Alliance) 55.2 in.; (Spirit/Concord) 57.6 in.; (Eagle) 59.6 in. Rear Tread: (Alliance) 52.8 in.; (Spirit/Concord) 57.1 in.; (Eagle) 57.6 in. Standard Tires: (Alliance) P155/80GR13 GBR; (Spirit/Concord) P195/75R14 GBR; (Eagle) P195/75R15 GBR.

TECHNICAL: Transmission: four-speed manual floor shift standard; five-speed manual and automatic optional. Alliance transaxle: four-speed; five-speed and automatic optional. Manual transmission gear ratios (Alliance four-speed): (1st) 3.73:1; (2nd) 2.06:1; (3rd) 1.27:1; (4th) 0.90:1. (Alliance five-speed): (1st) 3.73:1; (2nd) 2.06:1; (3rd) 1.27:1; (4th) 0.90:1; (5th) 0.73:1. Spirit/Concord/Eagle (Borg-Warner T4) manual shift gear ratios: (1st) 4.03:1; (2nd) 2.37:1; (3rd) 1.50:1; (4th) 1.00:1; (Rev) 3.76:1. Borg-Warner T5 five-speed: same but 0.86:1 (four-cyl.) or 0.76:1 (six-cyl.) top gear. Standard axle ratio: (Alliance) 3.56:1 w/automatic; 3.29:1 w/4-spd.; 3.87:1 w/5-spd. (Spirit) 2.35:1; (Concord) 2.35:1 exc. 5-spd., 2.73:1. (Eagle four) 3.54:1; (Eagle SX/4 six) 2.35:1; (Eagle 50 six) 2.73:1 exc. w/auto, 2.35:1. Drive: (Alliance) front; (Spirit/Concord) rear; (Eagle) 2/4. Clutch dia.: (Alliance) 7.1 in.; (others) 9.1 in. exc. six- cyl., 9.5 in. Transverse-mounted engine (Alliance). Steering: (Alliance) rack and pinion; (others) recirculating ball. Suspension: (Spirit/Concord/Eagle) independent front coil springs with anti-roll bar, semi-elliptic rear leaf springs; (Alliance) fully independent—MacPherson strut front, twin transverse torsion bar rear, anti-roll bars. Brakes: front disc, rear drum: (Alliance) 9.4 in. disc, 8 in. drum; (Spirit/Concord) 10.8 in. disc, 9.2 in. drum; (Concord wagon) 10x1.75 in. drum; (Eagle) 11 in. disc, 10x1.75 in. drum. Electronic ignition. Unibody construction. Fuel tank: (Alliance) 12.5 gal.; (Spirit, SX/4) 21 gal.; (Concord/Eagle) 22 gal.

SPIRIT/CONCORD/EAGLE DRIVETRAIN OPTIONS: 258 cu. in. six-cylinder engine: Eagle ($155). Five-speed floor shift with overdrive: Spirit/Concord ($125). Five-speed floor shift with overdrive and Select Drive: Eagle ($219). Column-shift automatic transmission: Spirit/Concord ($423). Floor-shift automatic transmission: Spirit ($423); Eagle ($437). Optional axle ratios: Concord/Eagle six (2.73:1); Eagle 30 six (3.08:1) with automatic and trailer towing pkg. ($30). Twin-Grip differential: Spirit/Concord ($82). Heavy-duty engine cooling system (H.D. radiator, viscous fan/shroud, coolant recovery system): Spirit/Concord ($77) but std. w/air cond. H.D. engine cooling (H.D. radiator, viscous fan): Eagle four ($67). Maximum cooling system: Eagle six ($70). Handling package (unique front sway bar; rear sway bar): Spirit/Concord ($48). Automatic load leveling (air shocks): Concord/Eagle 30 ($169). Extra duty suspension pkg (special front sway bar, rear sway bar and H.D. shocks): Eagle SX/4 ($65); also incl. H.D. springs, Eagle 30 ($77). Front suspension skid plate: Eagle ($77). Trailer towing package A (to 2000 pounds): Concord/Eagle 30 ($104). Trailer towing package B (to 3500 pounds): Eagle 30 ($222). H.D. battery ($26). Cold climate group incl. H.D. battery and engine block heater ($58). California emission system ($65).

SPIRIT/CONCORD/EAGLE CONVENIENCE/APPEARANCE OPTIONS: Eagle Sport package: Eagle SX/4 ($516); Eagle SX/4 DL ($407); Eagle 30 wgn ($344). Extra quiet insulation package: Concord/Eagle SX/4 ($61); std. on Concord DL/Ltd. Protection group (stainless door edge guards, bumper guards and nerfing strips, front mats): Spirit ($30-$40). Protection group w/o nerfing strips: Concord ($132); Concord DL/Ltd. ($81). Eagle protection group (stainless door edge guards, bumper guards, floor mats): Eagle 30 ($75); w/Sport pkg. ($23). Eagle protection group with front mats only: SX/4 ($72); w/Sport pkg. ($20). Convenience group: headlight-on buzzer, intermittent wipers, right lighted vanity mirror ($73). Gauge package (clock, tach, oil, amp or volt, vacuum): Eagle SX/4 ($152); Spirit, Eagle 30, SX/4 DL ($91). Pop-up sunroof ($295). Rear spoiler (incl. power liftback release): Spirit, Eagle SX/4 ($104). Light group ($61). Left remote control mirror: Concord, Eagle SX/4 ($32); std. on DL models. Right remote mirror (chrome): DL models, Eagle 30 ($32). Left/right remote chrome mirrors: Concord, Eagle SX/4 exc. Sport/DL ($64). Right remote sport mirror (black): Eagle 30 Sport wgn or SX/4 Sport ($32). Left/right electric remote chrome mirrors: SX/4 ($147); DL models ($115-$116); Ltd. wgn ($83). Day/night mirror: Concord, SX/4 ($15). Power steering: Spirit/Concord ($212). Power front disc brakes: Spirit/Concord ($100). Electronic cruise control ($170). Air conditioning system ($670-$725). Halogen headlamps ($20). Halogen foglamps: Eagle ($82). Dual horns: Concord, SX/4 ($17); std. on DL/Ltd. AM radio ($82-$83). AM/FM/CB stereo four-speaker radio ($471) exc. Spirit DL ($389). AM/FM/Stereo four-speaker radio ($199) exc. Spirit DL ($117). AM/FM/cassette stereo radio ($329) exc. Spirit DL ($247). Electronically tuned AM/FM/cassette stereo radio w/power amplifier and four coax speakers ($499). Spirit DL ($417). Power door locks: Spirit, SX/4 DL ($120); Concord DL/Ltd. and Eagle 30 ($170). Power windows and door locks: Spirit, SX/4 DL ($300); Concord DL/Ltd. and Eagle 30 ($425). Power liftback release: Eagle SX/4 ($40); incl. w/rear spoiler. Power decklid release: Concord/Eagle sed ($40). Power six-way driver's seat: Concord DL/Ltd., Eagle 30 ($189). Power six-way driver/pass. seat: Concord DL/Ltd., Eagle 30 ($302). Center console w/armrest: Spirit DL ($92). Floor shift console: Eagle ($65). Parcel shelf ($27). Coventry Check fabric bucket seat trim: Spirit/Eagle SX/4 ($39). Castilian sculptured fabric seat trim: Concord DL, Eagle 30 ($67). Durham plaid fabric seat trim: Eagle 30 ($67). Digital clock: Concord, SX/4 ($61); std. on DL/Ltd. Rear wiper/washer ($124). Rear defroster ($135). Vinyl sport steering wheel: Spirit DL, Eagle SX/4 ($40). Woodgrain steering wheel: DL models, Eagle 30 ($36). Leather-wrapped sport steering wheel ($60) exc. Concord Ltd., wgn and Eagle 30 Ltd. ($24); SX/4 Sport ($20); N/A Spirit DL.

1981 AMC, Eagle 4WD (Series 50), Kammback sedan, OCW

1981 AMC, Concord DL (Series 01), sedan, OCW

1984 AMC, Eagle Limited 4WD (Series 30), station wagon, OCW

1984 AMC, Eagle 4WD (Series 30), sedan, OCW

1986 AMC, (Renault) Alliance DL (Series 90), sedan, OCW

1986 AMC, (Renault) Alliance DL (Series 30), convertible, OCW

1988 AMC, Eagle 4WD (Series 30), station wagon, OCW

Tilt steering wheel ($106). Tinted glass ($95-$105). Two-tone accent color: Spirit exc. GT, Concord DL/Ltd. ($135). Special color combinations ($49). Rally stripes: Spirit DL ($88). Woodgrain paneling: Eagle 30 wgn ($144). Delete woodgrain from Concord DL/Ltd. wgn (deduct $75). Scuff moldings ($55). Roof rack: Concord/Eagle 30 wgn ($115). Locking gas cap ($10). Bumper guards: Concord/Eagle ($52) but std. w/DL, Ltd., Eagle Sport pkg. Styled wheel covers (argent): Concord ($87); Concord DL ($45); Eagle SX/4 ($54); N/A Concord Ltd. Custom wheel covers: Concord ($42), std. on DL. Wire wheel covers: Spirit DL ($119); Concord ($160). Spoke style 14 x 6 in. wheels w/trim rings: Spirit/Concord DL ($136); Concord ($178); Concord Ltd. wgn ($18). Turbocast II aluminum 14 x 7 in. wheels: Spirit DL ($370); Concord ($411); Concord DL/Ltd. wgn ($251). Sport aluminum 15 x 6 in. wheels: Eagle ($346-$400).

Spirit/Concord Tires: P195/75R14B white GBR: Spirit DL (NC). P195/75R14B black SBR Arriva: Spirit GT (NC). P195/75R14B white SBR Arriva: Spirit DL, Concord DL/Ltd. ($73); Concord ($142). P205/70R14B RWL polysteel radial: Spirit/Concord DL/Ltd. ($192); Spirit GT ($188); Concord ($281).

Eagle Tires: P195/75R15B white GBR: SX/4 ($69). P195/75R15B black SBR Arriva: Eagle 30, SX/4 DL ($20); SX/4 ($73). P195/75R15B white SBR Arriva: SX/4 ($142); Eagle 30, SX/4 DL ($73); Sport ($69). P215/65R15B OWL SBR Eagle GT: SX/4 ($269); Eagle 30, SX/4 DL ($200); Eagle Sport ($196).

ALLIANCE OPTIONS: Five-speed manual transmission, floor shift, w/overdrive: L ($95). Floor-shift automatic transmission ($420) exc. DL/MT/Ltd. ($325). H.D. battery ($25). Cold climate group ($36-$79). H.D. cooling ($67). Systems Sentry (monitors for low oil, coolant, brake fluid, disc wear, washer/power steering fluid, transaxle oil) ($125). Extra quiet insulation package: L ($62). Protection group incl. door edge guards, carpeted mats, locking gas cap ($52); N/A base. Visibility group (dual remote mirrors, lighted visor mirror, intermittent wipers): L ($160); DL ($129); MT ($97). Light group ($46). Halogen headlamps: L/DL/MT ($20). Tachometer: L ($82). Power steering ($199). Speed control ($170); N/A base. Air conditioning ($630). Power windows ($300-$350). Intermittent wipers: L/DL/MT ($50). Keyless entry system ($95). Power door locks ($120-$170) exc. base model. Rear defroster ($130). Tinted glass ($90). AM radio exc. MT ($82). AM/FM radio exc. MT ($135). AM/FM stereo radio: L/DL/Ltd. ($199). Electronic-tuning AM/FM stereo four-speaker radio w/cassette: L/DL/Ltd. ($465). Speaker for left I.P. ($28). Vinyl reclining bucket seats: base/L ($65). Vinyl rocker/reclining buckets: DL (NC). Cloth bucket seats: L ($30). Cloth reclining bucket seats: L ($95). Leather rocker/reclining bucket seats: Ltd./MT ($413). Two-tone paint: L/DL/Ltd. ($160). Metallic accent paint: DL/Ltd. (NC); L ($62). Black leather-wrapped sport steering wheel: L/DL/Ltd. ($60). Luxury wheel covers: L ($88); DL ($36). Wheel trim rings: L ($52). Aluminum wheels: L/DL/Ltd. ($249-$337). Tires: 155/80GR13 white GBR: base/L ($61). 175/70SR13 SBR: L ($72). 175/70SR13 white SBR: L ($132); DL/Ltd. ($60). Spare tire (to replace polyspare): L/DL/MT/Ltd. ($35).

HISTORY: Introduced: September 22, 1982. Model year production (U.S.): 168,726, which amounted to nearly three percent of the industry total—more than double the 1982 percentage. Of that number, 142,669 were four-cylinder, 25,057 six-cylinder. Calendar year production (U.S.): 201,993 (including new Encores for 1984). Eagle production of 6,979 units was dwarfed by the 152,581 Alliances made during 1983. But 23,012 Eagles were built in Canada. Model year sales by U.S. dealers: 183,005 (including 3,651 new Encores). Calendar year sales: 193,251 for a 2.8 percent market share, up substantially from the 1.9 percent in 1982.

HISTORICAL FOOTNOTES;Designed by Renault in France, but manufactured in Kenosha Wisconsin, the subcompact front-drive Alliance set the stage for other joint ventures between American and foreign companies. Promoted as combining "advanced European technology with American expertise," Alliance attempted to lure buyers from both the domestic and import ranks. Its design evolved from the Renault 9, acclaimed "Car of the Year" by the European press in 1982. Tooling had begun in August 1981. Some $200 million was spent on development and production, over a 2-1/2-year period. Ample changes were made to adapt the car for American tastes, including the addition of American designed power steering and brake systems, Bendix fuel injection, and electronic controls. Meanwhile, the Spirit and Concord quietly disappeared as AMC focused on its joint-venture and the 4WD Eagle. AMC registered a loss of $146.7 million for the year, nearly as bad as 1982, though the final quarter showed a modest profit—perhaps pointing toward a better year ahead. In July, AMC sold its defense subsidiary, AM General Corp.; next month, its lawn tractor operation, Wheel Horse Products. Corporate headquarters in Southfield, Michigan, was sold too, then leased back—all in an attempt to raise cash for product development. Production of a new 150 cu. in. four-cylinder engine began in February 1983, installed on Eagles starting at mid-year.

1984

The slimmed-down AMC lineup, reduced to a single Eagle model and the Kenosha-built French subcompact, had one major addition for 1984. A hatchback Encore, with three or five doors, joined the original twin front-drive Alliance sedans.

Note: By this time, many automakers (including AMC) had begun to count the rear hatch of their small cars as a door: thus, a three-door hatchback has only two "real" doors; and a five-door has only four doors suitable for people to enter. Listings in this catalog follow the numbering used by the manufacturer.

(Renault) ENCORE — SERIES 90 — FOUR — Built on the same 97.8 in. wheelbase as the Alliance, the sportier Encore hatchback stood three inches shorter in overall length. It was AMC's attempt to attract youthful buyers, now that the Spirits and GTs were gone. Encores used the same 1.4-liter four-cylinder engine as the Alliance, with a standard four-speed (overdrive) manual transmission; five-speed optional. Three- and five-door versions were offered (see note above). Each had a stubby rear end with distinctive backlight and taillamp structure. Encore's emblem sat on the side of the grille, while Alliance's was at the center. Base Encores were nicely fitted inside with carpeting, fabric-covered headliner molding and visors, a day/night rearview mirror, lighter, inside hood release, console with stowage box, plus vinyl bucket front seats and 60/40 fold-down rear seat. Externally, they featured quad rectangular halogen headlamps and a horizontal-bar style black grille with bright molding, with blackout rocker panels and liftgate. Encores also had pulse wiper/washers, front and rear stabilizer bars, flip-out rear windows, power brakes, and P155/80GR13 glass-belted radials on semi-styled wheels with black hubcaps. Stored in back was a polyspare tire. The engine had electronic ignition and fuel injection. Suspension was fully independent, with MacPherson struts. Rack-and-pinion steering helped handling. Three upgrades were offered. S models held an AM radio, with dual accent pin stripes, cargo area cover, bright grille and wheel covers; the five-door had roll-down rear windows. LS Encores moved up to 175/70SR13 steel-belted radial tires (blackwall) with luxury sport wheel covers, plus a five-speed overdrive transmission. Other LS luxuries included tinted glass, digital clock, extra quiet insulation, dual-note horn, oil level gauge, tachometer, 'hockey stick' armrests, and rocker/recliner bucket seats in deluxe striped fabric. A chime warned of key left in ignition, headlamps-on, and seat belts unbuckled. A black rear spoiler and left remote mirror completed the LS package. Sporty GS Encores added light and visibility groups and Westchester fabric rocker/recliner bucket seats, plus black luxury sport wheel covers, black accent stripes, black sport steering wheel, and pin stripes along hood, bodyside and tailgate. Five-door Encores came only in S or LS versions. A Diamond Edition Encore, added later, featured gold bumper inserts and gold aluminum wheels, plus special pin striping on hood and bodysides. Painted Olympic White or Classic Black, the Diamond Encore's wing seats were upholstered in honey fabric, while its dash held an electronic-tuning AM/FM/stereo radio with cassette player.

(Renault) ALLIANCE — SERIES 90 — FOUR — After a strong start in the marketplace, Alliance changed little for its second year—though its price rose in several jumps. External niceties included blackout rocker panels and a black grille (with bright surround). Inside, a day/night mirror became standard on the base model, which wore P155/80GR13 blackwall tires. L models added dual accent pin stripes, bright grille and hub covers, and childproof rear door locks. DL rocker/recliner seats now held Lucerne fabric upholstery, while DL dashes contained low-fuel and oil level gauges. Calais fabric upholstery went on Limited rocker/recliner seats, which also offered hood pin stripes, a blackout lower back panel, and bright decklid luggage rack. Otherwise, standard equipment for each trim level was about the same as in 1983. Three colors were added and radio operation was improved. A second windshield washer outlet was added. Alliance's Diamond Edition was equipped like that of the Encore hatchback.

EAGLE — SERIES 30 — FOUR/SIX — Only the larger Eagle survived into 1984, in four-door sedan and wagon form, powered by the new AMC-manufactured four-cylinder engine. The new 150 cu. in. (2.46 liter) four, introduced during the 1983 model run, featured a single-barrel electronic feedback carburetor. Also standard on Jeeps, it replaced the GM-built 151 cu. in. four, which had powered Spirits and Concords as well as Eagles. The standard four- speed manual transmission now included an upshift indicator light to warn drivers when a gear change was wise. As before, the 258 cu. in. six-cylinder engine was optional. The "live" rear axle suspension consisted of computer-selected springs and telescoping shock absorbers. Front suspension included full coil springs and stabilizer bar. Standard equipment was similar to the 1983 Eagle 30, including the familiar Krayton protective treatment on lower bodysides, argent styled wheel covers, dual pin stripes, dual horns, and a lockable wagon cargo compartment. Moldings highlighted drip and quarter window areas, plus the belt surround. Power brakes and steering were standard, as was a hood ornament. Taillamps were large wraparound style. Leather reclining seats served as the main attraction on the Limited wagon. Eagle's Sport package, on base station wagons only, consisted of a leather-wrapped sport steering wheel, low-gloss black rocker panels and fender flares, black bumpers with guards and nerf strips, red or silver inserts in lower bodyside and hood moldings, black taillamp treatment, black windshield/liftgate moldings, black B pillars and door frames, a left-side remote-controlled black sport mirror, and halogen headlamps. Halogen fog lamps sat above the front bumper. Sport tires were blackwall P195/75R15 steel-belted Arriva radials. A silver '4x4' decal highlighted the lower door, as did the 'Sport' nameplate.

I.D. DATA: Eagle's 17-symbol Vehicle Identification Number (VIN) was embossed on a metal plate riveted to the top left surface of the instrument panel, visible through the windshield. Coding was the same as 1981-83: see 1981 for breakdown details. Engine codes (symbol four) for 1984 were: 'C' 258-6; 'U' 150-4. Model year code (symbol ten) changed to 'E' for 1984. Alliance/Encore's 17-symbol VIN was also similar to 1983 coding, but with additions for the new Encore. Symbols 6-7 (body style) were now: '93' three-door liftback; '99' five-door liftback; '95' four-door sedan; '96' two-door sedan. Symbol eight (trim level) included: '0' base model; '3' Alliance L or Encore S; '6' Alliance DL or Encore LS; '8' Limited; '9' Encore GS. Model year code (symbol ten) changed to 'E' for 1984.

ENCORE (BASE) SERIES 90

Series No.	Body/Style No.	Body Type & Seating	Factory Price	Shipping Weight	Prod. Total
90	8493-0	3-dr Lift-5P	5755	1974	Note 1
ENCORE S					
90	8493-3	3-dr Lift-5P	6365	1985	55,343
90	8499-3	5-dr Lift-5P	6615	2008	32,266
ENCORE LS					
90	8493-6	3-dr Lift-5P	6995	2033	Note 1
90	8499-6	5-dr Lift-5P	7195	2059	Note 1
ENCORE GS					
90	8493-9	3-dr Lift-5P	7547	2043	Note 1

ENCORE DIAMOND EDITION

Series No.	Body/Style No.	Body Type & Seating	Factory Price	Shipping Weight	Prod. Total
90	8493-6	3-dr Lift-5P	7570	N/A	N/A
90	8499-6	5-dr Lift-5P	7770	N/A	N/A

Note 1: Production totals under S series include base, LS and GS Encore models. Model year sales: 72,076 Encores.

Series No.	Body/Style No.	Body Type & Seating	Factory Price	Shipping Weight	Prod. Total
ALLIANCE (BASE) SERIES 90					
90	8496-0	2-dr Sed-5P	5959	1934	Note 2
ALLIANCE L					
90	8496-3	2-dr Sed-5P	6465	1936	50,978
90	8495-3	4-dr Sed-5P	6715	1964	70,037
ALLIANCE DL					
90	8496-6	2-dr Sed-5P	7065	1975	Note 2
90	8495-6	4-dr Sed-5P	7365	2002	Note 2
ALLIANCE LIMITED					
90	8495-8	4-dr Sed-5P	8027	2019	Note 2
ALLIANCE DIAMOND EDITION					
90	8496-6	2-dr Sed-5P	7715	N/A	N/A
90	8495-6	4-dr Sed-5P	8015	N/A	N/A

Note 2: Production totals under L series include base, DL and Limited Alliance models. Model year sales: 105,340.

EAGLE SERIES 30

Series No.	Body/Style No.	Body Type & Seating	Factory Price	Shipping Weight	Prod. Total
30	8435-5	4-dr Sed-5P	9495/9666	3189/3307	4,241
30	8438-5	4-dr Sta Wag-5P	10225/10396	3220/3338	21,294
EAGLE LIMITED SERIES 30					
30	8438-7	4-dr Sta Wag-5P	10695/10866	3236/3354	Note 3

Note 3: Production total shown for Eagle wagon includes base and Limited models. Of the 25,535 Eagles manufactured in the model year, only 184 had four-cylinder engine. Model year sales: 23,137.

FACTORY PRICE AND WEIGHT NOTE: Figure before the slash in Eagle listings is for four-cylinder engine, after slash for six-cylinder.

ENGINES: BASE FOUR (Alliance/Encore): Inline. OHV. Four-cylinder. Cast iron block; aluminum head. Transverse mounted. Displacement: 85.2 cu. in. (1.4 liters). Bore & stroke: 2.99 x 3.03 in. Compression ratio: 9.0:1. Brake horsepower: 56 at 4200 R.P.M. Torque: 75 lb.-ft. at 2500 R.P.M. Five main bearings. Solid valve lifters. Single-point Bendix (throttle-body) fuel injection. BASE FOUR (Eagle): Inline. OHV. Four-cylinder. Cast iron block. Displacement: 150 cu. in. (2.46 liters). Bore & stroke: 3.88 x 3.19 in. Compression ratio: 9.2:1. Brake horsepower: N/A. Torque: 132 lb.-ft. at 3200 R.P.M. Five main bearings. Hydraulic valve lifters. Carburetor: 1Bbl. electronic feedback Carter YFA. OPTIONAL SIX (Eagle): Same as 1983 specifications (258 cu. in. inline OHV).

CHASSIS DATA: Wheelbase: (Encore/Alliance) 97.8 in.; (Eagle) 109.3 in. Overall length: (Encore) 160.6 in.; (Alliance) 163.8 in.; (Eagle) 180.9 in. Height: (Encore/Alliance) 54.5 in.; (Eagle) 54.4 in. Width: (Alliance/Encore) 65 in.; (Eagle) 72.3 in. Front Tread: (Encore/Alliance) 55.2 in.; (Eagle) 59.6 in. Rear Tread: (Encore/Alliance) 52.8 in.; (Eagle) 57.6 in. Standard Tires: (Encore/Alliance) P155/80GR13 GBR; (Eagle) P195/75R15 GBR.

TECHNICAL: Transmission: four-speed manual standard; five-speed manual and three-speed automatic optional. Floor shift lever. Eagle 4WD: selectable 2/4 wheel. Alliance manual transmission gear ratios: (1st) 3.73:1; (2nd) 2.06:1; (3rd) 1.27:1; (4th) 0.90:1; (5th) 0.73:1; (Rev) 3.54:1. Eagle manual gear ratios: (1st) 4.03:1; (2nd) 2.37:1; (3rd) 1.50:1; (4th) 1.00:1; (5th) 0.86:1 exc. 0.76:1 w/six-cyl. engine: (Rev) 3.54:1. Clutch dia.: (Alliance/Encore) 7.14 in.; (Eagle four) 9.1 in.; (Eagle six) 10.3 in. Standard axle ratio: (Alliance/Encore) 3.29:1 w/4-spd; 3.87:1 w/5-spd; 3.27:1 w/automatic; (Eagle four) 3.54:1; (Eagle six) 2.73:1 exc. w/towing pkg. 3.08:1. Steering: (Alliance/Encore) rack and pinion; (Eagle) power assisted recirculating ball. Suspension: (Alliance/Encore) fully independent: front, MacPherson struts w/lower control arms, coil springs, anti-roll bar; rear, transverse semi-torsion bars, swinging longitudinal trailing arms, anti-roll bar; (Eagle) independent front coil springs with anti-roll bar; semi-elliptic rear leaf springs. Brakes: front disc, rear drum; (Alliance) 9.4 in. disc, 8 in. drum; (Eagle) 11 in. disc, 10 in. drum. Electronic ignition. Fuel tank: (Alliance/Encore) 12.5 gal.; (Eagle) 22 gal.

EAGLE DRIVETRAIN OPTIONS: 258 cu. in. six-cylinder engine ($171). Five-speed floor shift with overdrive and select drive ($227). Floor-shift automatic transmission: six ($452). Optional axle ratios (2.73:1 or 3.08:1); Eagle six ($31). H.D. engine cooling (H.D. radiator, viscous fan); Eagle four ($69). Maximum cooling system: Eagle six ($72). Automatic load leveling (air shocks): six ($175). Extra duty suspension pkg. (special front sway bar, rear sway bar, H.D. shocks and springs ($80). Front suspension skid plate ($80). Trailer towing package A (to 2000 pounds) ($108). Trailer towing package B (to 3500 pounds) ($230). H.D. battery ($27). Cold climate group incl. H.D. battery and engine block heater ($60). California emission system ($78).

EAGLE — CONVENIENCE/APPEARANCE — OPTIONS: Eagle Sport package ($356). Protection group (stainless door edge guards, bumper guards, floor mats) ($78); w/Sport pkg. ($24). Convenience group (headlight-on buzzer, intermittent wipers, right lighted vanity mirror) ($76). Gauge package (clock, tach, oil, volt, vacuum) ($94). Light group ($63). Right remote mirror: black or chrome ($33). Left/right remote chrome mirrors ($119); Ltd. wgn ($86); N/A w/Sport pkg. Electronic cruise control ($176). Air conditioning system ($750). Halogen headlamps ($15). Halogen foglamps ($85). AM radio ($86). AM/FM/Stereo four-speaker radio ($206). AM/FM/cassette stereo radio ($340). Electronically tuned AM/FM/cassette stereo radio w/power amplifier and four coax speakers ($516). Power door locks ($176). Power windows and door locks ($440). Power decklid release ($41). Power six-way driver's seat ($196). Power six-way driver/pass. seat ($313). Floor shift console ($67). Parcel shelf ($28). Fabric seat trim ($69). Rear wiper/washer: wgn ($128). Rear defroster ($140). Woodgrain steering wheel ($37); N/A w/Sport pkg. Leather-wrapped sport steering wheel ($62) exc. Ltd. wgn ($25). Tilt steering wheel ($110). Tinted glass ($109). Woodgrain paneling: wgn ($149). Black scuff moldings ($57). Roof rack: wgn ($119). Locking gas cap ($10). Bumper guards ($54). Sport aluminum 15 x 6 in. wheels ($358). Tires: P195/75R15B black SBR Arriva ($21). P195/75R15B white SBR Arriva ($76); Sport wgn ($72). P215/65R15B OWL SBR Eagle GT ($207); Sport wgn ($203).

ALLIANCE/ENCORE OPTIONS: Five-speed manual transmission, floor-shift, w/overdrive: Alliance L, Encore S ($97). Three-speed floor-shift automatic transmission ($435) exc. Alliance DL/Ltd., Encore LS/GS ($338). H.D. battery ($27). H.D. engine cooling ($69); std. w/air cond. Cold climate group (H.D. battery/alternator, engine coolant heater) ($38-$81). Systems Sentry (monitors for low oil, coolant. brake fluid, disc wear, washer/power steering fluid, transaxle oil) ($128); N/A base models. Extra quiet insulation package: L/S ($64). Rear black spoiler: Encore base/S ($72). Protection group (door edge guards, front/rear carpeted mats, locking gas cap) ($53); N/A base models. Visibility group (dual remote mirrors, lighted visor mirror, intermittent wipers): L/S ($164); DL/LS ($133). Light group ($47); N/A base models. Fog lamps ($77). Tachometer: L/S ($84). Power steering ($215). Cruise control ($174); N/A base. Air conditioning ($653). Intermittent wipers ($51). Keyless entry system ($97); N/A base. Power door locks ($123-$174). Power windows and door locks ($308-$359). Power liftgate lock release: Encore S/LS ($31). Digital clock ($58); N/A base. Rear wiper/washer: Encore ($120). Rear defroster ($133). Tinted glass ($92). AM radio: base models ($84). AM/FM radio: base models ($147); others ($63). AM/FM four-speaker stereo radio ($120); N/A base. Electronic-tuning AM/FM stereo four-speaker radio w/cassette ($427); N/A base. Vinyl reclining bucket seats: base/L/S ($67). Vinyl rocker/reclining bucket seats: LS/DL (NC). Cloth bucket seats: L/S ($75). Cloth reclining bucket seats: L/S ($142). Luxury cloth rocker/reclining bucket seats: Ltd. ($299). Leather rocker/reclining bucket seats: DL/LS ($349); GS/Ltd. ($299). Metallic paint: L/S ($150); LS/GS/DL/Ltd. (NC). Black leather-wrapped sport steering wheel ($62); N/A base. Decklid luggage rack: Alliance L/DL ($108). Luxury wheel covers: Alliance L ($90); DL ($37). Wheel trim rings: base/L/S ($53). Aluminum wheels: L/S ($345); DL ($292); Ltd./LS/GS ($255). Tires: P155/80GR13 white GBR; base/L/S ($63). P175/70SR13 SBR: base/L/S ($74). P175/70SR13 white SBR: base/L/S ($135); others ($61). Conventional spare tire: Alliance exc. base ($36).

HISTORY: Introduced: September 25, 1983. Model year production: 234,159 (208,808 four-cylinder and 25,351 Eagle six-cylinder). U.S. production totaled 208,624 cars, which amounted to more than 2.5 percent of the industry total. Calendar year production (U.S.): 192,196 Encores and Alliances made in Kenosha, Wisconsin; (Canada) 22,982 Eagles. Model year sales by U.S. dealers: 201,275 (including 336 leftover Concords and 386 Spirits). Calendar year sales: 190,255 for a 2.4 percent share of the market.

HISTORICAL FOOTNOTES: When Eagle was introduced for 1980, its only competitor for the 4WD market was Subaru. Four years later, Toyota had introduced its Tercel 4WD, while Audi brought out its costly versions. Yet AMC continued to push the Eagle, which remained the only domestic-built 4WD model, despite sagging sales and rumors that it would abandon production and sell the Brampton, Ontario plant to Chrysler. As Renault/Jeep Sport vice-president R.C. Lund insisted, the Eagle "brought a whole new dimension of functional improvement to highway driving while still retaining the off-road capabilities.... Many consumers coming from the two-wheel-drive segments were buying the vehicles for the security they offered for on-highway driving." (That Sport group had recently been created to promote AMC's sporty image.) For the time being, at least, Eagle remained the only domestically-built 4WD passenger auto. Still, Eagle sales had declined to little more than half their 1981 level. A glance at sales figures demonstrated that the company's financial survival had to rely on the Renault front-drives. Renault now owned over 46 percent of AMC stock. The corporation showed a modest profit ($15.5 million) for the year, after a disastrous loss of $146.7 million for 1983. Even though Alliance sold strongly from the start, beating predictions by 31 percent, AMC had to halt production at Kenosha during 1984, to reduce its inventory. Encore/Alliance prices were cut late in 1984, following three price increases. Renault gradually abandoned the imported LeCar, to focus on the U.S.-built Encore. Although W. Paul Tippett, Jr., remained AMC chairman, president Jose Dedeurwaerder was named CEO. Roy D. Chapin, Jr., went into retirement.

1985

Renault-designed AMC models gained a new engine choice for 1985; a 1.7-liter overhead cam four, in addition to the previous 1.4-liter OHV. Alliance also gained a new convertible body style. New to the option list: Keyless Entry, which used infrared waves to lock and unlock the car doors remotely.

(Renault) ENCORE — SERIES 90 — FOUR — The new 1.7-liter engine and five-speed transmission went into all Encore GS models. Others kept the 1.4-liter four and four-speed as standard, but could get the bigger engine as an option. All Encores had power disc brakes and halogen headlamps. Base Encores came with a black grille, color-keyed bumpers, carpeting, lighter, console with stowage box, cloth headliner, front courtesy lights, left-hand black remote-control mirror, day/night inside mirror, pulse wiper/washers, front/rear stabilizer bars, trip odometer, and vinyl bucket seats. Black semi-styled wheels held standard P155/80GR13 glass-belted radial tires. Encores added an AM radio, bright grille, 60/40 split rear seat, dual pin stripes, removable carpeted cargo cover, plus moldings for bumper insert, lower liftgate and windshield surround. Stepping up a notch, the LS offered five-speed manual overdrive transmission, digital clock, rear ashtray, dual note horn, extra quiet insulation, tachometer, black rear spoiler, bright belt moldings, and cloth-covered rocker/reclining bucket seats. Tires were P175/705R13 steel-belted with sport wheel covers. This year's sporty Encore GS featured a black front air dam, black grille, light and visibility groups, black belt moldings, black sport steering wheel, and black pin stripes on the hood, liftgate and bodysides. Aluminum wheels added to looks, a power liftgate release brought convenience, while a handling package helped performance and fog lamps added a practical touch.

(Renault) ALLIANCE — SERIES 90 — FOUR — AMC's biggest news was the addition of a convertible to the Alliance lineup—the first AMC ragtop since the Rebel, back in 1968. Built entirely at the Kenosha, Wisconsin, plant, on the same assembly line as other Alliance/Encore models, the convertible adopted the new 1.7-liter Renault engine as standard powerplant, with five-speed manual overdrive transmission. AMC president Jose Dedeurwaerder expected that it would "enhance the image that young, new-value buyers already have of the Alliance and Encore." With a $10,295 (minimum) base price tag, it was promoted as the "lowest-priced domestic convertible" on the market. Three-speed automatic shift was optional, as on all models. Base and L sedans retained the smaller 1.4-liter four, but all DL Alliances also had the 1.7 four as standard. Convertibles came in two trim levels and six colors: white, beige and red, plus Mica Red, Light Blue and Gold metallic clearcoat. Folding tops were white or almond color. Interior trim was blue or almond. DL convertibles could also have honey or garnet, in vinyl or cloth. The less-costly L ragtop included a black grille and front air dam, tinted glass, heavy-duty battery, twin ashtrays, locking lighted glovebox, extra quiet insulation, dual black remote-controlled mirrors, black bumper insert moldings, roll-down quarter windows, and bright wheel trim rings. Five-speed manual transmission was standard. The power-operated top had a black inner liner and zip-out rear window. Color-keyed top boots used hidden fasteners. DL convertibles came with standard AM/FM stereo radio, digital clock, dual note horn, cloth rocker/recliner bucket seats, power steering, leather-wrapped steering wheel, door storage bins, luxury wheel covers, and a tachometer. Both had black trim moldings and color-keyed sun visors. Base Alliance equipment was similar to the Encore liftback's, but included blackout rocker panels with bright moldings. L sedans had a bright grille and bumper insert moldings, plus an AM radio and dual accent pin stripes. DL Alliance sedans were similar to Encore's LS, with full luggage compartment trim, color-keyed mirror, bright decklid and quarter window moldings, door storage bins, and bright wheel trim rings. They rode on steel-belted P175/70SR13 radial tires. Stepping all the way up to the Limited brought buyers a rear center armrest, blackout lower back panel, light and visibility groups, decklid luggage rack, wheel lip moldings, hood pin stripes, intermittent wipers, plus luxury cloth rocker/recliner bucket seats. Entertainment options stretched to a six-speaker electronically-tuned stereo radio with cassette player.

EAGLE — SERIES 30 — SIX — Eagles no longer had to be stationary to switch from two-wheel to four-wheel drive (and back again). "Shift-on-the-fly" capability let drivers change between the two while the car was moving. Only the 258 cu. in. six-cylinder engine was offered this year, with standard five-speed overdrive manual transmission. Alternator capacity jumped to 56 amps (from 42). Hoods lost their former ornament, but added a scoop effect along the top surface. Full-face radios with four speakers became standard. Other base equipment was similar to that of 1984. Eagle's Limited added a right remote chrome mirror, parcel shelf, woodgrain steering wheel and leather reclining seats, plus a new extra this year: wire wheel covers. The Sport package was similar to 1984, with dual mirrors. Two new body colors, Medium Blue and Dark Blue metallic, joined Garnet, Silver, Autumn Brown, Almond, and Mocha Dark Brown, for a total of seven choices. Interiors came in garnet, honey or almond, plus—this year—blue.

I.D. DATA: Eagle's 17 symbol Vehicle Identification Number (VIN) was again embossed on a metal plate riveted to the top left surface of the instrument panel, visible through the windshield. Coding was the same as in 1981-84. Alliance/Encore also used a 17-symbol VIN, with coding the same as in 1984. Model year code (symbol ten) changed to 'F' for 1985. Engine codes were now: 'D' 1.4-liter four; 'E' California 1.4-liter four; 'A' 1.7-liter four; and 'C' 258 cu. in. six. The two-digit identifier for body style (symbols 6-7) now included '97' convertible.

ENCORE (BASE) SERIES 90

Series No.	Body/Style No.	Body Type & Seating	Factory Price	Shipping Weight	Prod. Total
90	8593-0	3-dr Lift-5P	5895	1946	Note 1
ENCORE S					
90	8593-3	3-dr Lift-5P	6360	1953	38,623
90	8599-3	5-dr Lift-5P	6610	2007	19,902
ENCORE LS					
90	8593-6	3-dr Lift-5P	7060	1997	Note 1
90	8599 6	5-dr Lift-5P	7310	2055	Note 1
ENCORE GS					
90	8593-9	3-dr Lift-5P	7560	2046	Note 1

Note 1: Production totals under S series include base, LS and GS Encore models. Model year sales: 46,923 Encores.

Series No.	Body/Style No.	Body Type & Seating	Factory Price	Shipping Weight	Prod. Total
ALLIANCE (BASE) SERIES 90					
90	8596-0	2-dr Sed-5P	5995	1922	Note 2
ALLIANCE L					
90	8596-3	2-dr Sed-5P	6400	1929	33,617
90	8595-3	4-dr Sed-5P	6650	1964	50,906
90	8597-3	2-dr Conv-4P	10295	2153	7,141
ALLIANCE DL					
90	8596-6	2-dr Sed-5P	7000	1962	Note 2 & 3
90	8595-6	4-dr Sed-5P	7250	2001	Note 2
90	8597-6	2-dr Conv-4P	11295	2190	Note 2

ALLIANCE LIMITED

Series No.	Body/Style No.	Body Type & Seating	Factory Price	Shipping Weight	Prod. Total
90	8595-8	4-dr Sed-5P	7750	2190	Note 2

Note 2: Production totals under L series include base, DL and Limited Alliance models. Model year sales: 75,208 Alliances.

Note 3: Add $103 for 1.7-liter four-cylinder engine (except Encore GS, Alliance convertible and Alliance Limited, which had it as standard equipment).

EAGLE SERIES 30

30	8535-5	4-dr Sed-5P	10457	3306	2,655
30	8538-5	4-dr Sta Wag-5P	11217	3337	13,535

EAGLE LIMITED

30	8538-7	4-dr Sta Wag-5P	11893	3368	Note 3

Note 3: Production total shown for Eagle wagon includes base and Limited models. All Eagles had six-cylinder engine. Model year sales: 15,362 Eagles.

ENGINES: BASE FOUR (Alliance/Encore): Inline. OHV. Four-cylinder. Cast iron block; aluminum head. Transverse mounted. Displacement: 85.2 cu. in. (1.4 liters). Bore & stroke: 2.99 x 3.03 in. Compression ratio: 9.0:1. Brake horsepower: 56 at 4200 R.P.M. Torque: 75 lb.-ft. at 2500 R.P.M. Five main bearings. Solid valve lifters. Single point Bendix (throttle-body) fuel injection. OPTIONAL FOUR (Alliance/Encore): Inline. Overhead cam. Four-cylinder. Cast iron block. Displacement: 105 cu. in. (1.7 liters). Bore & stroke: 3.19 x 3.29 in. Compression ratio: 9.5:1. Brake horsepower: 77.5 at 5000 R.P.M. Torque: 96 lb.-ft. at 3000 R.P.M. Five main bearings. Throttle-body fuel injection (Bendix). BASE SIX (Eagle): Inline. OHV. Six-cylinder. Cast iron block. Displacement: 258 cu. in. (4.2 liters). Bore & stroke: 3.75 x 3.90 in. Compression ratio: 9.2:1. Brake horsepower: 110 at 3200 R.P.M. Torque: 210 lb.-ft. at 1800 R.P.M. Seven main bearings. Hydraulic valve lifters. Carburetor: 2Bbl.

CHASSIS DATA: Wheelbase: (Encore/Alliance) 97.8 in.; (Eagle) 109.3 in. Overall length: (Encore) 160.6 in.; (Alliance) 163.8 in.; (Eagle) 180.9 in. Height: (Encore/Alliance) 54.5 in. exc. conv., 53.1 in.; (Eagle) 54.4 in. Width: (Encore/Alliance) 65.0 in.; (Eagle) 72.3 in. Front Tread: (Encore/Alliance) 55.2 in.; (Eagle) 59.6 in. Rear Tread: (Encore) 52.8 in.; (Eagle) 57.6 in. Standard Tires: (Encore/Alliance) P155/80GR13 GBR; (Eagle) P195/75R15 GBR.

TECHNICAL: Transmission: (Alliance/Encore) four-speed overdrive manual shift standard; five-speed manual and three speed automatic optional. (Eagle) five-speed overdrive manual shift standard; three-speed automatic optional. Floor shift lever. Alliance/Encore manual transmission gear ratios: (1st) 3.73:1; (2nd) 2.05:1; (3rd) 1.32:1; (4th) 0.97:1; (5th) 0.79:1; (Rev) 3.56:1. Eagle manual transmission gear ratios: (1st) 4.03:1; (2nd) 2.73:1; (3rd) 1.50:1; (4th) 1.00:1; (Rev) 3.76:1. Clutch dia.: (Alliance/Encore) 7.1 in.; (Eagle) 10.3 in. Standard axle ratio: (Alliance/Encore) 3.29:1 except 3.56:1 w/5-spd transmission; (Eagle) 2.73:1. Steering: (Alliance/Encore) rack and pinion; (Eagle) recirculating ball. Suspension: (Alliance/Encore) fully independent with MacPherson front struts and stabilizer bar, trailing rear arms with transverse torsion bars and stabilizer bar; (Eagle) independent front coil springs, semi-elliptic rear leaf springs. Brakes: (Alliance/Encore) 9.4 in. front disc, 8 in. rear drum; (Eagle) 11 in. front disc, 10 in. rear drum. Electronic ignition. Fuel tank: (Alliance/Encore) 12.5 gal.; (Eagle) 22 gal.

EAGLE DRIVETRAIN OPTIONS: Three-speed floor shift automatic transmission ($366). Optional 2.73:1 or 3.08:1 axle ratio ($32). H.D. engine cooling ($75). Automatic load leveling ($182). Extra-duty suspension pkg. ($83). Front suspension skid plate ($83). Trailer towing package A (to 2000 pounds) ($112). Trailer towing package B (to 3500 pounds) ($239). H.D. battery ($28). Cold climate group ($62). California emission system ($81).

EAGLE CONVENIENCE/APPEARANCE OPTIONS: Eagle Sport package: base wgn ($416). Protection group: bumper guards, floor mats and door edge guards ($81); w/Sport pkg. ($25). Convenience group: headlight-on buzzer, intermittent wipers, lighted vanity mirror ($79). Gauge package ($98). Light group ($66). Right remote mirror (black or chrome): base ($34). Left/right remote chrome mirrors ($90-$124). Cruise control ($183). Air conditioning system ($781). Halogen headlamps ($16). Halogen foglamps ($88). AM radio ($94). AM/FM/stereo radio ($235). Electronically-tuned AM/FM/cassette stereo radio ($432). Electronically-tuned AM/FM stereo radio w/cassette and Dolby sound ($537). Power door locks ($183). Power windows and door locks ($458). Keyless entry system ($101). Power decklid release: sed ($43). Power six-way driver's seat ($204). Power six-way driver/pass. seat ($326). Console ($70). Parcel shelf ($29). Cloth reclining seats: base ($72). Rear wiper/washer: wgn ($133). Rear defroster ($146). Woodgrain steering wheel ($39). Leather-wrapped sport steering wheel ($65) exc. Ltd. ($26). Tilt steering wheel ($115). Tinted glass ($113). Woodgrain paneling: wgn ($155). Special color combinations ($53). Black scuff moldings ($59). Roof rack: wgn ($124). Bumper guards ($56). Sport aluminum 15 x 6 in. wheels ($373) exc. Ltd. ($217). Wire wheel covers ($156). Tires: P195/75R15B black SBR Arriva ($22). P195/75R15B white SBR Arriva ($75-$79). P215/65R15B OWL SBR Eagle GT ($211-$215).

ALLIANCE/ENCORE OPTIONS: 1.7-liter four-cylinder engine ($103). Five-speed manual transmission, floor shift, w/overdrive: Alliance L, Encore S ($100). Three-speed floor-shift automatic transmission ($448) exc. Alliance L conv., DL/Ltd., Encore LS/GS ($348); N/A base. Encore handling package: S/LS three-door ($31). H.D. battery ($28). H.D. cooling ($71). Cold climate group ($62-$83). Systems Sentry: monitors for low oil, coolant, brake fluid, disc wear, washer/power steering fluid, transaxle oil ($132); N/A base models. Extra quiet insulation package: L/S ($66). Rear spoiler: Encore base/S ($74). Sunshine package (sunroof, aluminum wheels and leather-wrapped steering wheel): DL/LS (5359). Pop-up sunroof ($324). Protection group ($55). Visibility group (dual remote mirrors, lighted visor mirror, intermittent wipers): L/S ($169); DL/LS ($137). Light group ($48). Fog lamps ($79). Tachometer: L/S ($87). Power steering ($221). Cruise control ($179); N/A base. Air conditioning ($673). Intermittent wipers ($53). Keyless entry system ($100). Power door locks ($127-$179). Power door/window locks ($318-$370). Power liftback release: S/LS ($32). Rear defroster ($137). Rear wiper/washer: Encore ($124) exc. GS ($70). Tinted glass ($95). AM radio: base models ($91). AM/FM radio: base models ($160); others ($69). AM/FM stereo radio ($144); N/A base. Electronic-tuning AM/FM stereo four-speaker radio w/cassette ($335) exc. DL conv. ($191); N/A base. Electronic-tuning AM/FM stereo radio w/cassette and Dolby ($440) exc. DL conv. ($296). Digital clock: L/S ($60). Vinyl reclining bucket seats: LS/base Alliance ($69). Vinyl rocker/reclining buckets: DL/LS (NC). Cloth bucket seats: L/S ($77). Cloth reclining bucket seats: L/S ($146). Leather rocker/reclining bucket seats: LS/DL ($359); GS/Ltd. ($308). Door storage bins: L/S ($21). Metallic paint ($155) incl. clearcoat. Leather-wrapped sport steering wheel ($64); N/A base. Decklid luggage rack: Alliance L/DL ($111). Luxury sport wheel covers ($93) exc. L conv., DL ($38). Wheel trim rings ($55). Aluminum wheels ($216-$309). Tires: P155/80R13 white GBR ($65). P175/705R13 SBR ($76). P175/70SR13 white SBR ($63-$139). P185/60R14 SBR RBL: base/S/L ($155); others ($79). Spare tire (to replace polyspare): Alliance ($37).

HISTORY: Introduced: October 1, 1984. Model year production (U.S.): 150,189 Encores and Alliances made in Kenosha, which came to 1.9 percent of the industry total; (Canada) 16,190 Eagles. Calendar year production (U.S.): 111,138 Encores and Alliances; (Canada) 11,311 Eagles. Model year sales by U.S. dealers: 137,493. Calendar year sales: 123,449, for a 1.6 percent market share.

HISTORICAL FOOTNOTES: Sales dropped sharply for the model year, as consumers turned toward bigger cars—partly a result of moderate, stable gasoline prices. First year mechanical problems also turned some prospective buyers away from AMC's French-designed duo, especially as they rose in price. After a modest profit ($15.5 million in the previous year, AMC posted a $125.3 million loss for fiscal 1985. Alliance/Encore prices were cut in December 1984. Then, in February 1985, AMC cut the financing rate to 8.5 percent—the first domestic company to offer such incentives, which soon became almost normal. AMC helped pioneer extended warranties, too, with new 5-year/50,000-mile coverage on the powertrain, plus five years for rust-through. The new Alliance convertible was a joint project of AMC and American Sun Roof corporation. On a special subassembly line at Kenosha, metal tops and 'B' and 'C' pillars were sliced off two-door sedans. Then, a series of reinforcing operations strengthened the cut-down bodies before they returned to the line for paint and trim. Eagle, meanwhile, continued its downhill slide that had begun in 1981—the only year AMC beat out Subaru in 4WD passenger car sales. Unlike most 4WD imports, which were efficient front-drive designs with transfer mechanisms in their transaxles, Eagle was essentially a rear-drive vehicle with front-drive axle and transfer case hooked on. In short, a clumsy mechanism in an aged body, its design reaching back to 1969. Production fell to just 85 Eagles per day at the Brampton, Ontario, factory. Just after New Year's, AMC cut production at Kenosha, laying off 600 workers. Another slash came in February, with more to follow by the start of 1986 model production in July. The June labor contract cut AMC workers' wages to a level on a par with those at General Motors and Ford; the agreement was accepted only after AMC took steps to close down the Kenosha plant.

INNNOVATIONS; "Shift-on-the-fly" four-wheel-drive. Convertible body style.

1986

All models added the high-mounted stop light required by law, and ashtrays left the standard equipment lists. Additions included gas-charged shock absorbers, a restyled instrument cluster, and larger-diameter stabilizer bars. New to the option lineup, a four-position tilt steering wheel.

ENCORE — SERIES 90 — FOUR — Base model Encores left the lineup so S was the lowest-priced liftback. One new model was added: the top-level Electronic, whose instrument cluster held an array of hi-tech doodads. It included both digital and analog speedometers; a trip computer; tachometer; fuel gauge; oil level, temperature and pressure lights; plus a bar graph display that monitored engine functions. Elsewhere in the lineup, about the most thrilling change was an increase in alternator output from 50 to 60 amps. Only S and LS Encores were offered in five-door liftback form; the GS and Electronic were three-door (actually two passenger doors) only. The 1.4-liter four-cylinder engine was standard; 1.7-liter optional. Entry level (S) Encores now sported black bumpers, cargo area carpeting, clearcoat paint, and an AM radio. Back seats were 60/40 split fold-down type. In addition to fancy instrumentation, Encore Electronics had cloth bucket seats, a color-keyed steering wheel, bright wheel trim rings and a five-speed overdrive transmission. LS models lost their dual note horns, but added twin pin stripes. The top-level GS now featured dual exhaust and a soft-feel steering wheel, as well as the extras offered in 1985.

ALLIANCE — SERIES 90 — FOUR — The luxurious Limited Alliance left the lineup for 1986. A revised L and DL grille used dark horizontal bars over five vertical bars, with center emblem. Extended taillamps were new, headlamps smaller, interior altered. A new base four-door sedan joined the 1985 two-door. Convertibles again carried the larger 1.7-liter four, which was optional on other Alliances. Base Alliances added black bumpers and clearcoat paint to their standard equipment list. L Alliances now included a color-keyed steering wheel and bumpers, plus bright grille and Sebring Red body paint. Except for semi-styled bright wheels, black belt molding and bright rocker panel and windshield moldings, the L convertible equipment was the same as in 1985. DL convertibles gained metallic paint and black bodyside scuff moldings with bright inserts, dual pin stripes, and a black soft-feel steering wheel. DL sedans lost their dual note horns, but added dual accent pin stripes.

EAGLE — SERIES 30 — SIX — Once again, Eagle was powered by the 258 six with five-speed overdrive transmission. A modest price increase was its only real change from 1985. Base models now had tinted glass (formerly an option), but lost a few minor items including twin armrests and ashtrays. Extras on the Limited were the same as in 1985. The Sport package for base Eagle wagons was also the same as 1985, but included only the left-hand remote mirror.

I.D. DATA: Eagle's 17-symbol Vehicle Identification Number (VIN) was embossed on a metal plate riveted to the top left surface of the instrument panel, visible through the windshield. See coding details in 1981 listing. Model year (symbol ten) changed to 'G' for 1986. Alliance/Encore's VIN used the same coding as 1984-85. Model year code (tenth digit) changed to 'G' for 1986. The code for the Limited ('8' in the eighth digit position) was no longer used.

ENCORE S SERIES 90

Series No.	Body/Style No.	Body Type & Seating	Factory Price	Shipping Weight	Prod. Total
90	8693-3	3-dr Lift-5P	6710	1970	12,239
90	8699-3	5-dr Lift-5P	6960	2003	6,870
ENCORE LS					
90	8693-6	3-dr Lift-5P	7310	1974	Note 1
90	8699-6	5-dr Lift-5P	7560	2007	Note 1
ENCORE ELECTRONIC					
90	8693-4	3-dr Lift-5P	7498	1974	Note 1
ENCORE GS					
90	8693-9	3-dr Lift-5P	7968	1977	Note 1

Note 1: Production totals under S series include LS, Electronic and GS Encore models. Model year sales: 17,671 Encores.

ALLIANCE (BASE) SERIES 90

Series No.	Body/Style No.	Body Type & Seating	Factory Price	Shipping Weight	Prod. Total
90	8696-0	2-dr Sed-5P	5999	1923	Note 2
90	8695-0	4-dr Sed-5P	6199	1957	Note 2
ALLIANCE L					
90	8696-3	2-dr Sed-5P	6510	1928	23,204
90	8695-3	4-dr Sed-5P	6760	1962	42,891
90	8697-3	2-dr Conv-4P	10557	2222	2,015
ALLIANCE DL					
90	8696-6	2-dr Sed-5P	7110	1935	Note 2
90	8695-6	4-dr Sed-5P	7360	1969	Note 2
90	8697-6	2-dr Conv-4P	11557	2228	Note 2

Note 2: Production totals under L series include base and DL Alliance models. Model year sales: 55,603.

Note 3: Prices shown are for 1.4-liter engine. Add $264 for 1.7-liter four-cylinder engine (except Alliance convertible, which had it as standard equipment).

EAGLE SERIES 30

Series No.	Body/Style No.	Body Type & Seating	Factory Price	Shipping Weight	Prod. Total
30	8635-5	4-dr Sed-5P	10719	3307	1,274
30	8638-5	4-dr Sta Wag-5P	11489	3341	6,943
EAGLE LIMITED SERIES 30					
30	8638-7	4-dr Sta Wag-5P	12179	3372	Note 4

Note 4: Production total shown for Eagle wagon includes base and Limited models. All Eagles had six-cylinder engine. Model year sales: 9,020 Eagles.

ENGINES: BASE FOUR (Alliance/Encore): Inline. OHV. Four-cylinder. Cast iron block; aluminum head. Transverse mounted. Displacement: 85.2 cu. in. (1.4 liters). Bore & stroke: 2.99 x 3.03 in. Compression ratio: 9.0:1. Brake horsepower: 56 at 4200 R.P.M. Torque: 75 lb.-ft. at 2500 R.P.M. Five main bearings. Solid valve lifters. Single-point Bendix (throttle-body) fuel injection. BASE FOUR (Alliance convertible, Encore Electronic/GS); OPTIONAL (other Alliance/Encore): Inline. Overhead cam. Four-cylinder. Cast iron block. Displacement: 105 cu. in. (1.7 liters). Bore & stroke: 3.19 x 3.29 in. Compression ratio: 9.5:1. Brake horsepower: 77.5 at 5000 R.P.M. Torque: 96 lb.-ft. at 3000 R.P.M. Five main bearings. Bendix throttle-body fuel injection. BASE SIX (Eagle): Same specifications as 1985.

CHASSIS DATA: Wheelbase: (Encore/Alliance) 97.8 in.; (Eagle) 109.3 in. Overall length: (Encore) 160.6 in.; (Alliance) 163.8 in.; (Eagle) 180.9 in. Height (Encore/Alliance) 54.5 in. exc. conv., 53.1 in.; (Eagle) 54.4 in. Width: (Encore/Alliance) 65.0 in.; (Eagle) 72.3 in. Front Tread: (Encore/Alliance) 55.2 in.; (Eagle) 59.6 in. Rear Tread: (Encore) 52.8 in.; (Eagle) 57.6 in. Standard Tires: (Encore/Alliance) P155/80GR13 GBR; (Eagle) P195/75R15 GBR.

TECHNICAL: Transmission: (Alliance/Encore) four-speed overdrive manual shift standard; five-speed manual and three-speed automatic optional; (Eagle) five-speed overdrive manual shift standard; three-speed automatic optional. Floor shift lever. Standard axle ratio: (Alliance/Encore) 3.29:1 except 3.56:1 w/5-spd transmission; (Eagle) 2.73:1. Steering: (Alliance/Encore) rack and pinion; (Eagle) recirculating ball. Suspension: (Alliance/Encore) fully independent with MacPherson front struts and stabilizer bar, trailing rear arms with transverse torsion bars and stabilizer bar; (Eagle) independent front coil springs, semi-elliptic rear leaf springs. Brakes: (Alliance/Encore) 9.4 in. front disc, 8 in. rear drum; (Eagle) 11 in. front disc, 10 in. rear drum. Electronic ignition. Fuel tank: (Alliance/Encore) 12.5 gal.; (Eagle) 22 gal.

EAGLE DRIVETRAIN OPTIONS: Three-speed floor-shift automatic transmission ($379). Optional 2.73:1 axle ratio ($33). H.D. engine cooling ($78). Automatic load leveling ($188). Extra-duty suspension pkg. ($86). Front suspension skid plate ($86). Trailer towing package A (to 2000 pounds) ($116). Trailer towing package B (to 3500 pounds) ($247). H.D. battery ($32). Cold climate group ($64). California emissions pkg. ($84).

EAGLE CONVENIENCE/APPEARANCE OPTIONS: Eagle Sport package: base model ($431). Protection group: front/rear bumper guards, front/rear mats, stainless steel door edge guards ($84); wgn w/Sport pkg. ($26). Convenience group: headlight-on buzzer, intermittent wipers, lighted vanity mirror ($82). Gauge package ($101). Light group ($68). Right remote mirror (black or chrome) ($35). Left/right remote chrome mirrors ($128) exc. Ltd. ($93). Cruise control ($189). Air conditioning system ($795). Halogen headlamps ($17). Halogen fog lamps ($91). AM/FM radio ($186). Electronic-tuning AM/FM/Stereo radio ($243). Electronic-tuning AM/FM/cassette stereo radio ($447). Power door locks ($189). Power windows and door locks ($474). Keyless entry system ($105). Power decklid release: sed ($45). Power six-way driver's seat ($211). Power six-way driver/pass. seat ($337). Floor shift console ($72). Parcel shelf ($30). Cloth seat upholstery: base ($75). Rear wiper/washer: wgn ($138). Rear defroster ($151). Woodgrain steering wheel: base ($40). Leather-wrapped sport steering wheel ($67) exc. Ltd. ($27). Tilt steering wheel ($119). Woodgrain paneling: wgn ($160). Black scuff moldings ($61). Roof rack: wgn ($128). Bumper guards ($58). Sport aluminum 15 x 6 in. wheels ($386) exc. Ltd. ($225). Wire wheel covers ($161). Tires: P195/75R15B black SBR Arriva ($23). P195/75R15B white SBR Arriva ($78-$82). P215/65R15B OWL SBR Eagle GT ($218-$223).

ALLIANCE/ENCORE OPTIONS: 1.7-liter four-cylinder engine: Alliance L/DL, Encore S/LS ($164). Five-speed manual transmission, floor-shift, w/overdrive: L/S ($100). Three-speed floor-shift automatic transmission ($469) exc. Alliance DL/conv., Encore LS/GS/Electronic ($369). Handling package: Encore three-door exc. GS ($32). Cold climate group ($85) exc. ($64) w/air cond. H.D. engine cooling ($73). H.D. alternator and engine cooling ($107). H.D. battery ($29). Extra quiet insulation package: L/S/Electronic ($68). Sunshine package (sunroof, soft-feel steering wheel and 14-inch aluminum wheels): DL exc. conv. ($407); L/S ($541); LS ($368). Pop-up sunroof ($332). Rear spoiler: Electronic/S ($76). Protection group: door edge guards and carpeted floor mats ($56). Visibility group (dual remote mirrors, intermittent wipers): L/S/Electronic ($173); DL/LS ($140); N/A conv. Light group ($65). Fog lamps ($81). Tachometer: L/S ($89). Power steering ($227). Cruise control ($183); N/A Alliance base. Air conditioning ($685). Digital clock: L/S/Electronic ($62). Keyless entry system ($103); N/A Alliance base/conv. Power door locks ($130-$183). Power windows and door locks: conv. ($326). Power liftgate lock release: Encore ($40). Rear wiper/washer: Encore ($127). Rear defroster

($140). Tinted glass ($99). AM radio: base Alliance ($93). AM/FM radio ($71) exc. base Alliance ($164). Electronic-tuning AM/FM stereo radio ($192). Electronic-tuning AM/FM stereo radio w/cassette ($357) exc. DL conv. ($165); N/A base Alliance. Electronic-tuning AM/FM stereo radio w/cassette and (Dolby) Jensen Accusound ($614) exc. DL conv. ($422); N/A base Alliance. Vinyl reclining bucket seats: base/L Alliance, Encore S/Electronic ($71). Cloth bucket seats: base/L Alliance, Encore S ($79). Cloth reclining bucket seats: L/S ($150); Electronic ($71). Cloth rocker/reclining wing back seats: DL ($105); N/A conv. Sebring Red paint: Alliance ($50). Metallic paint ($159); DL conv. (NC). Black soft-feel sport steering wheel ($66). Tilt steering wheel: L/DL, Encore ($115). Decklid luggage rack: Alliance DL ($114). Luxury sport wheel covers ($39) exc. base/L Alliance, Encore S ($95); N/A GS. Wheel trim rings: base/L Alliance, S ($56). Aluminum wheels ($221-$316). Tires: P155/80GR13 white GBR ($67). P175/70SR13 SBR ($78). P175/70SR13 white SBR ($65-$143). P185/60R14 SBR RBL: DL/LS ($81); L/S/Electronic ($159); w/Sunshine pkg. (NC). Spare tire (to replace polyspare): L/DL sed ($65).

HISTORY: Introduced: October 1, 1985. Model year production (U.S.): 64,873, down to only 0.8 percent of the industry total; 8,217 Eagles. Calendar year production (U.S.): 49,435 Encores and Alliances made at Kenosha. Model year sales by U.S. dealers: 82,294. Calendar year sales: 72,849 for a market share of only 0.9 percent.

HISTORICAL FOOTNOTES; AMC president Jose Dedeurwaerder believed "the worst is over" after rough times early in the model year. But corporate fortunes and prospects continued to decline, registering a $91.3 million loss for 1986. Model year sales dropped to only 1.0 percent of the domestic market, from 1.6 the year before. Struggling to stay alive, the company even slashed financing rates all the way down to zero interest (on two-year loans, that is). But both American Honda and Volkswagen of America beat AMC in sales, and Nissan came close. By year's end, the Encore was dropped and replaced by a hatchback Alliance. Eagle sales fell below the 10,000 mark, though AMC insisted the tired old 4WD would stay in production in Canada a while longer. The irony is that Eagle's failure came at a time when interest in 4WD passenger cars was rising. On the positive side, Chrysler Corp. agreed to build its M-body cars at AMC's Kenosha plant, which helped pave the way for the Chrysler takeover a year later. Joseph E. Cappy became AMC president and CEO; Pierre Semerena (from Renault) was named chairman. Jose Dedeurwaerder combined duties of AMC vice-chairman with those of executive vice-president of Renault worldwide sales and marketing. Rumors flurried over the next year, until the Chrysler deal was finally concluded.

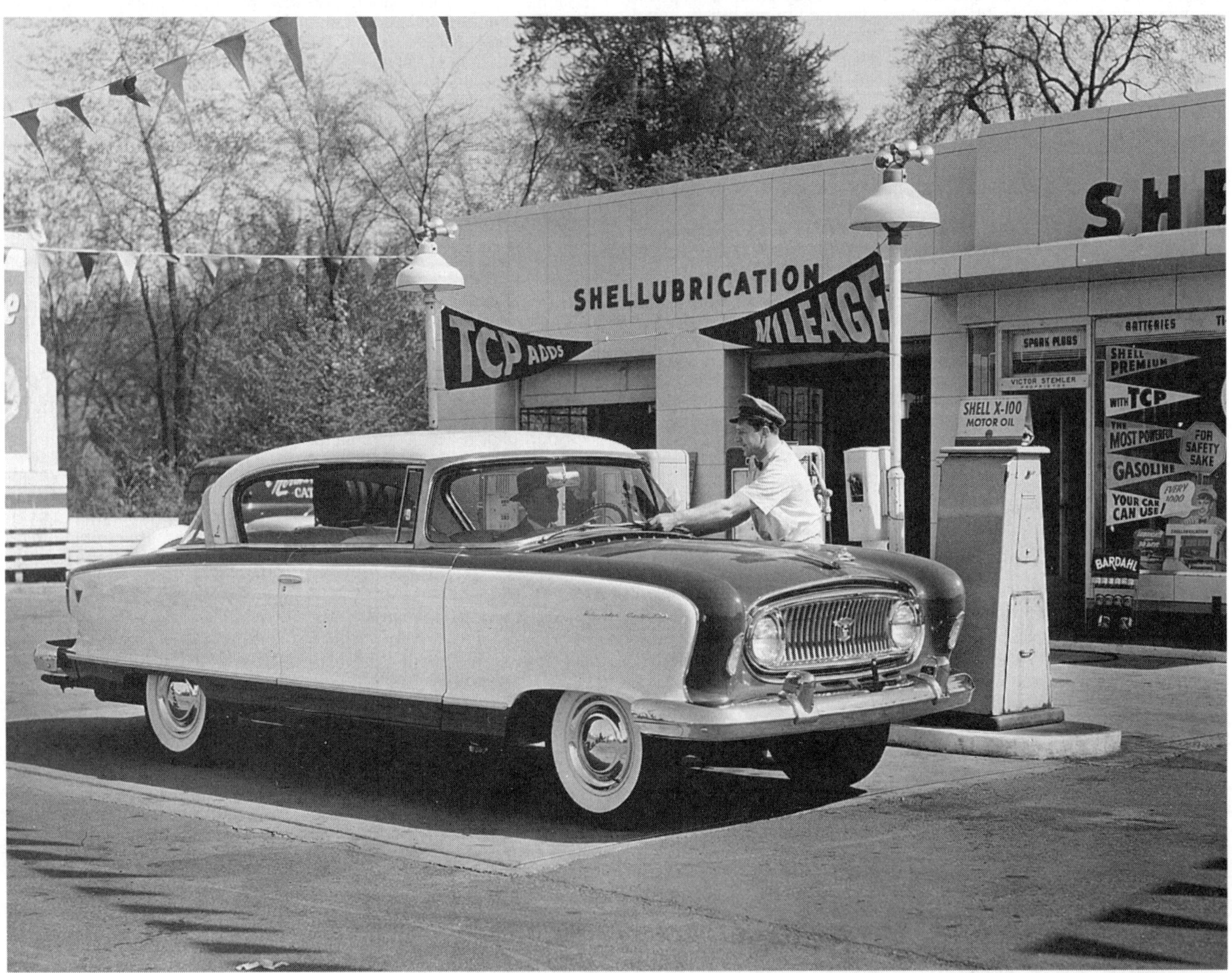

The long history of what eventually evolved into American Motors Corp. includes the Nash Motors Co., which originated in 1916 with Charles Nash at the helm. One of the many automobiles produced by Nash during its more than 40 years as an automaker was this 1955 Ambassador Country Club, getting checked out by a Shell attendant when service stations still provided actual service.

PACKARD

PACKARD — Warren, Ohio — (1899-1903)/Detroit, Michigan — (1903-1942 et seq.) — "Mr. Winton ... replied ... to the effect that the Winton waggon as it stood was the ripened and perfected product of many years of lofty thought, aided by mechanical skill of the highest grade, and could not be improved in any detail, and that if Mr. Packard wanted any of his own cats and dogs worked into a waggon, he had better build it himself, as he, Winton, would not stultify himself by any departure whatever from his own incontestably superior productions." Thus did automotive journalist Hugh Dolnar write in 1901 of the conversational exchange that had occurred two years previous and that led inexorably to the building of the first Packard. That James Ward Packard had encountered numerous problems with the Winton he had purchased in 1898 is documented in his and his brother William Doud's diaries, that he thought he could do better is very much evident, and that incontestably he did is a fact that Packard people today will not even deign to argue. Two men from Winton's camp, George Weiss and William A. Hatcher, defected to help him — and on November 6, 1899, the first Packard was completed in the shops of the brothers' New York and Ohio Company, a successful manufacturer of incandescent lamps and transformers in Warren, Ohio. Detail refinements followed in the four additional Model As built in 1899 and the Model B that followed in 1900, of which 49 were produced. The 7 hp single-cylinder four-stroke engine that powered these early Packards was conventional, as was the car's two-speed planetary transmission and center chain drive. Most unusual, however, and only years later to become standard automobile practice, were the Packard's automatic spark advance and "H" gear slot. On September 10, 1900, the Ohio Automobile Company was officially organized for the manufacture of the Packard automobile, with the Packard brothers, Weiss, Hatcher and James P. Gilbert (from the Packards' electric business) as stockholders. "Ask the Man Who Owns One" became the company's slogan in the fall of 1901. Among Packard owners already were William D. Rockefeller, who previously had favored Wintons but who purchased his first two (of many subsequent) Packards at the New York Automobile Show in November 1900. Exhibited there was the new 1901 12 hp Model C, with wheel steering, which would be followed in 1902 by the Model F in which a three-speed sliding gear transmission replaced the former planetary. Purchasing a Model F (his second Packard) was a wealthy Detroit businessman named Henry B. Joy, who also began purchasing quantities of stock in the Ohio Automobile Company. The stage was being set. On October 13, 1902, the Ohio Automobile Company became the Packard Motor Car Company, with 2,500 additional shares of stock authorized for sale, all of them bought by Henry Joy and his associates. One year later — on October 10, 1903 — the Packard Motor Car Company moved to Detroit. The decision to relocate there had been made in January 1903, with construction begun that spring on a huge and modern reinforced concrete factory designed by Albert Kahn. Meanwhile, in Warren, the Model K, Packard's first four, was in production, replacing Packard's first twin, the Model G introduced during the summer of 1902. Still, it was the venerable single-cylinder Model F that provided the most news for Packard during the summer of 1903 with the epic 61-day drive from San Francisco to New York made by Tom Fetch in the car nicknamed Old Pacific, which beat the Winton's record set the month previous by two days. Fetch's companion on the trip had been Marius Krarup, editor of *The Automobile;* the press coverage, needless to say, was lavish. By early fall the Packard making news was a racing Model K, called Gray Wolf driven by the man who had designed it and the production Model K: former Mors engineer Charles Schmidt. Schmidt tended to crash the car on occasion but his straightaway mile record of 77.6 mph at Daytona (subsequently broken by Henry Ford's 999) in January 1904, and his fourth place in the inaugural Vanderbilt Cup that October, were fine efforts. (Schmidt, who had been hired by Joy, would leave Packard for Peerless in January of 1905, being replaced as chief engineer by Russell Huff, who had joined the company at the turn of the century.) By the time of the Vanderbilt, Packard had been in Detroit a year, where production of the new Model L (introduced in November of 1903) was ongoing. And by now too, the future course of Packard was being indelibly writ. Neither Weiss nor Hatcher had made the move to Detroit, and the Packards themselves would soon be out of the Packard picture. Further, the Model L introduced the radiator configuration that would become a Packard hallmark for decades to follow. The L and the subsequent N were L-head fours, the first T-head Packard arrived with the S in 1906, superseded by the famous Model Thirty, which began its five-year run in model year 1907, accompanied by the smaller companion Model Eighteen for 1909. Packard was solidly established with these cars: Total company production through the Model S had been 1,691 cars, there would be 11,818 Models Thirty and Eighteen built. Among the very fine cars being produced in America, there were three Ps now: Packard, Pierce-Arrow and Peerless. Packard's first six, a four-main-bearing T-head introduced in April 1911 at 74 bhp, was up to 82 bhp in 1912, when a smaller seven-main-bearing L-head 60 hp six — with electric starter and lights, and left-hand drive — joined the line in December that year. Spiral bevel gears were introduced on the larger six in April 1914. By now Packard had the services of two men who would be inextricably linked with the marque for decades thereafter: In 1911, Henry Joy had hired Alvan Macauley, general manager of the Burroughs Adding Machine Company, as Packard's general manager; and Macauley (who would succeed to Packard's presidency in 1916) in turn hired a Burroughs colleague, Jesse G. Vincent, to head Packard engineering in 1912. The Twin Six arrived for 1916. The first 12-cylinder car put into series production anywhere in the world, and attractively priced as low as $2,600 at introduction in 1915, the Twin Six would be built until 1923, by which time more than 35,000 (four times that of the preceding sixes) had been sold. An L-head 60 degree, the engine was refined in subsequent years, detachable cylinder heads arriving for 1917 and the Fuelizer added for 1920. The Twin Six years were heady ones for Packard, though not heady enough for Henry Joy, whose expansionist tendencies had brought Packard to eminence but who left the Packard chairmanship in 1917 purportedly because his further ideas for broadening Packard's place in the industry included merger, and few members of the board then believed it would benefit Packard to merge with anyone. The World War I years saw Packard's eminence enhanced even further via the company's role in development of the Liberty, the finest airplane engine produced up to that time (according to Orville Wright), which, installed in a special Packard racer, broke all existing track records at Sheepshead Bay in 1917, and powered hundreds of aircraft sent "Over There" prior to the Armistice. By 1920, the Packard Motor Car Company stood ready to roar with the Twenties. Introduced that year was the L-head Single Six joining the Twin Six, the latter car replaced by the L-head Single Eight for 1924, during which year four-wheel brakes were introduced. Packard production for calendar year 1925 was 32,027, twice that of 1924. By now Packard was being flattered by imitation, its classic radiator shape adapted by Buick and Dagmar among others, though when Dagmar also adopted red hexagonal hubcaps, Packard's legal department was not so flattered to avoid mentioning that the Packard hubs were a registered trademark. "Original Creations by Master Designers" was the phrase Packard used in 1926 to announce its inauguration of series custom cars designed by custom coachbuilders. Bijur chassis lubrication had been introduced in 1925; hypoid gears followed in 1927. In 1928, in memory of James Ward Packard who died that year, the Packard family crest became the official Packard emblem. In 1929, all Packards had eight cylinders. Aware of Cadillac's forthcoming V-16, Packard had built an experimental Monobloc Twelve in 1929, but for production in 1930 countered Cadillac's multi-cylinders with the eight-cylinder 734 Speedster series, which could be had with a high compression head for 145 bhp at 3400 rpm. But in 1932, the Twin Six arrived with 160 hp, as Packard went 12 again. (Twin Six would be the car's designation only in 1932, incidentally; it became simply the Twelve for the remainder of its production run through 1939.) Interestingly, this car was initially planned for front-wheel drive, but the prototype (designed by Cornelius Van Ranst, who had been part of the L-29 Cord team) was as far as that project proceeded. Front-wheel drive had been considered because it would have made feasible a multi-cylinder automobile at an attractive price, but with the reversion to a standard chassis (featuring synchromesh and vacuum-boosted four-wheel brakes), Packard's 12-cylinder car was brought to market with price tags from $3,650 to $7,950. Joining it in 1932 was a popularly-priced Packard, the 110 hp Light Eight introduced at $1,750 and surviving one year only. From a calendar year production in 1928 that just missed the 50,000 mark, Packard plunged precipitously to 9,010 in 1932, 9,893 in 1933, 6,265 in 1934, ironically these years producing what many people today believe to be the most beautiful Packards ever. In 1935, the One-Twenty arrived with 110 hp L-head eight-cylinder engine, independent front suspension, hydraulic brakes and a price range of $980-$1,095 — vis-à-vis the Eight/Super Eight range that year of $2,385-$5,815 and the Twelves at $3,820-$6,435. Packard had moved into the lower-priced range. An even less expensive ($795-$1,295 at introduction) L-head 100 hp six was added for 1937. Calendar year production soared: 52,045 cars in 1935, 80,987 in 1936, 109,518 in 1937. That the Junior Packards (as these lesser-priced cars became known, the more expensive cars of course becoming the Seniors) resulted in a loss of prestige to the Packard luxury car image from which the company never recovered has since been vigorously debated. But undoubtedly the Packard company could not have survived the Depression without this product line. From 1935 to 1942, a total of 479,500 Junior Packards were produced, about 42,000 of the Senior cars. Whether Packard should have called its cheaper car something else is really the only factor worthy of argument — and could be debated both ways; Marmon did poorly with its cheaper Roosevelt, Cadillac did well with its LaSalle though not in numbers approaching the output of the Junior Packards. By the late Thirties, the Senior Packards were being produced in rapidly diminishing numbers. The Twelve was discontinued after 1939; 1940 saw 7,500 Senior eights built, 1941 not quite 4,500. Custom coachwork was still available on these cars, the most memorable perhaps the Packards designed by Howard "Dutch" Darrin, who also plied his art on Junior

Packard chassis. The Weather-Conditioner — an air conditioning unit only partially effective — was introduced as an option for 1940, and 1941 brought the Clipper, a strikingly good-looking car whose design is credited chiefly to Darrin, though others kibitzed. Priced midway between the top-rung Junior and bottom-rung Senior Packard, the Clipper was designed to give a shot in the arm to company sales, which had languished since the 1938 recession year, principally because Packard styling had not kept pace with the industry. That it succeeded is indicated by 1941 calendar year figures when more Clippers (16,600) were sold than any other model in the Packard line. Overall, in 1941, Packard outproduced Cadillac Division. During World War II the Packard Motor Car Company sold the dies for both the Junior and Senior Packards to the U.S.S.R., where the Packard would serve as inspiration for the Russian Z.I.S. In 1946, all Packards of necessity had to be the Clipper, which given its prewar welcome could not be regarded as unfortunate. Unfortunate, however, were the problems that befell the company postwar and the tragic mistakes made — which ultimately resulted in the proud name of Packard being forever stilled in the industry in the late Fifties.

Packard Data Compilation by Dr. William Bell

1899

PACKARD — MODEL A — ONE: The first test run of the first Packard was November 6, 1899, the *Warren* (Ohio) *Tribune* reporting, "the successful completion of the machine will probably mean a factory for automobiles in this city." Five Model A Packards were built, with construction on all of them having begun by the end of 1899. Ostensibly all of these cars might be regarded as prototypes for production, since there were differences in each and continuing refinements. The famous Packard H-gate shift lever was installed on the first car soon after the test run. The fifth and final Model A was the first Packard sold, to George D. Kirkham, a Warren businessman.

Model A, 1-cyl.

Model No.	Body Type & Seating	Factory Price	Shipping Weight	Prod. Total
A	Rds	—	—	5

ENGINE: Horizontal. One, four-cycle. Cast iron block. B & S: 5-1/2 x 6 in. Disp.: 142.6 cu. in. Brake H.P.: 9 @ 800 R.P.M. Valve lifters: mechanical exhaust, intake suction. Carb.: float-feed.

CHASSIS: W.B.: 71-1/2 in. Tires: 34 x 3.

TECHNICAL: Planetary transmission. Speeds: 2F/1R. Chain drive. Bicycle-type wheels.

1900

PACKARD — MODEL B — ONE: The first production Packard was the Model B, introduced during the spring of 1900, with 49 built by the end of the year. Engineering features included an automatic spark advance with rotating governor and a foot pedal to control engine speed. Only one body style, a single-seat roadster, was available at $1,200, though dos-a-dos seating was available as an option. Steering was by spade handle lever, upon which a bulb horn was fitted. A foot chime was also provided. A single solar light was mounted in front. The Model B was displayed at the New York Automobile Show in November 1900, and it continued to be listed in the 1901 Packard catalog as a "lower horsepower" companion to the new Model C.

Model B, 1-cyl.

Model No.	Body Type & Seating	Factory Price	Shipping Weight	Prod. Total
B	Rds	1200	—	49

ENGINE: Horizontal. One, four-cycle. Cast iron block. B & S: 5-1/2 x 6 in. Disp.: 142.6 cu. in. Brake H.P.: 9 @ 800 R.P.M. Valve lifters: mechanical exhaust, intake suction. Carb.: float-feed.

CHASSIS: W.B.: 76 in. Tires: 34 x 3.

TECHNICAL: Planetary transmission. Speeds: 2F/1R. Chain drive. Wire spoke wheels.

OPTIONS: Dos-a-Dos seat ($50.00). Tops (50.00-75.00).

1901

PACKARD — MODEL C — ONE: The Model C was the first Packard to feature a steering wheel that, with its spoke-mounted bulb horn, was mounted on the right side of the car. The foot chime was continued as standard. A pair of Dietz oil lamps replaced the single solar lamp provided in the Model B. Horsepower was now up to 12. The dos-a-dos body style was standard, with a forward-facing rear seat also available, in addition to a surrey. Prices for these three body styles was a uniform $1,500. Three factory and two private Packards were entered in the New York to Buffalo race of 1901, four of them receiving first-class certificates. Top speed of the Model C was 25 mph, though Packard offered a third gear "for up to 30 miles per hour ... if desired." A total of 81 of these cars was built.

I.D. DATA: Engine numbers. Starting: 29. Ending: 140.

Model C, 1-cyl.

Model No.	Body Type & Seating	Factory Price	Shipping Weight	Prod. Total
C	Rds.-single seat	1500	—	Note 1
C	Rds.-dos-a-dos seat	1500	—	Note 1
C	Surrey-4P	1500	—	Note 1
C	Rds.-w/rear seat	1500	—	Note 1

Note 1: Packard Model C production for 1901 totaled 81 with no body style breakout available.

ENGINE: Horizontal. One, four-cycle. Cast iron block. B & S: 6 x 6-1/2 in. Disp.: 183.8 cu. in. Brake H.P.: 12 @ 850 R.P.M. Net H.P.: 12. Main bearings: two. Valve lifters: mechanical exhaust, intake suction. Carb.: float-feed.

CHASSIS: W.B. 76 in. Tires: 34 x 4.

TECHNICAL: Planetary. Speeds: 2F/1R. Chain drive. Wire spoke wheels.

OPTIONS: Top grade leather seat cover. Tops ($50.00-$75.00).

HISTORICAL: Introduced November 1900. Model year production: 81.

1902

PACKARD — MODEL F — ONE: Though retaining the same engine as the Model C, the Model F was a vastly changed car and marked the beginning of Packard's evolution from buggy-type to automobile. Wheelbase was 84 inches, a rear tonneau was available, wooden artillery wheels were used, and the transmission was now a three-speed selective. Two acetylene headlights were added, the side oil lamps being retained. In an economy contest, a Model F averaged 27-1/2 mpg. At $2,500 for the tonneau, this was the most expensive Packard to date. The Model F was continued into the 1903 model year, with detail refinements (including a four-inch increase in wheelbase) and lower prices ($2,300 for tonneau). It was a Model F named Old Pacific that made the celebrated run from San Francisco to New York during the summer of 1903, Tom Fetch driving, Marius Krarup assisting.

I.D. DATA: Engine numbers. Starting: 141. Ending: 241.

Model F, 1-cyl.

Model No.	Body Type & Seating	Factory Price	Shipping Weight	Prod. Total
F	Rds.-2P	2250	—	Note 1
F	Rear Tonneau-5P	2500	—	Note 1

Note 1: Packard Model F production for 1902 and into 1903 is estimated at 179 with no body style breakout available.

Note: Prices reduced to $2,000 and $2,300 for 1903 model year.

ENGINE: Horizontal. One, four-cycle. Cast iron block. B & S: 6 x 6-1/2 in. Disp.: 183.8 cu. in. Brake H.P.: 12 @ 850 R.P.M. Net H.P.: 12. Main bearings: two. Valve lifters: intake suction. Carb.: float-feed.

CHASSIS: W.B.: 84 in., increased to 88 in. for 1903 model year. Tires: 34 x 4.

TECHNICAL: Sliding gear transmission. Speeds: 3F/1R. Clutch: Chain drive with spur differential. Hand and foot brakes, on rear wheels only. Wood artillery wheels.

OPTIONS: Tonneau seating ($250.00). Top grain leather seat covers.

HISTORICAL: Introduced November 1901. Model year (1902-1903) sales: 179.

PACKARD — MODEL G — TWO: The Model G was Packard's first and only two-cylinder car, though it was essentially arrived at by simply joining together two singles, each with its own carburetor. Large bulbous hubs extended out from the artillery wheels, and the cars were weighty at about 4,000 pounds. Only four were built.

Model G, 2-cyl.

Model No.	Body Type & Seating	Factory Price	Shipping Weight	Prod. Total
G	Rear Tonneau-8P	—	—	Note 1
G	Surrey-4P	—	—	Note 1

Note 1: Packard Model G production for 1902 totaled four with no body style breakout available.

ENGINE: Horizontal, opposed. Two. Cast iron block. Brake H.P.: 24. Net H.P.: 24. Valve lifters: suction intake. Carb.: float-feed.

CHASSIS: W.B.: 91 in. Tires: 36 x 4-1/2.

TECHNICAL: Sliding gear transmission. Speeds: 3F/1R. Mechanical brakes on two wheels. Artillery wheels.

OPTIONS: Front instruments. Speedometer. Sight oil and gas gauges. Ignition switch.

HISTORICAL: Introduced late summer 1902. Model year production: 4.

1903

PACKARD — MODEL F — ONE: The Model F was continued with detail refinements as a 1903 model. Included among the changes was a more sloping Renault-type hood and a longer (88-inch) wheelbase. See 1902 for further description.

PACKARD — MODEL K — FOUR: At more than $7,000, the Model K was one of the most expensive cars in America in 1903. No regular production Packard would ever again be priced that high. The first Packard with its engine located in front, and the first four-cylinder Packard as well, the K also featured the company's first use of a four-speed transmission. Thoroughly disliked by Henry Joy, production totaled just 34 units. Packard engineer Charles Schmidt did enjoy some success racing the Model K Gray Wolf, however, including a run at Ormond-Daytona Beach where he put up a 77.6 mph mile.

Model K, 4-cyl.

Model No.	Body Type & Seating	Factory Price	Shipping Weight	Prod. Total
K	Rear Tonneau	7300	—	Note 1
K	King of Belgium Tonneau	7300	—	Note 1

Note 1: Packard Model K production for 1903 totaled 34 with no body style breakout available.

ENGINE: Inline. Four. Cast iron block. B & S: 4 x 5 in. Brake H.P.: 24 @ 1000 R.P.M. Net H.P.: 24. Valve lifters: automatic inlet. Carb.: float-feed.

CHASSIS: W.B.: 92 in. Tires: 36 x 4.

TECHNICAL: Sliding gear transmission. Speeds: 4F/1R. Shaft drive. Bevel gear differential. Mechanical brakes, on two rear wheels. Artillery wheels.

HISTORICAL: Introduced November 1902. Model year production: 34.

1904

PACKARD — MODEL L — FOUR: The distinctive Packard radiator outline and flat-hood configuration arrived with the Model L. A combination transmission-differential was located over the rear axle. The body was aluminum over wood, with aluminum also used for the crankcase. Top speed of the car was 40 mph, though widely touted was the "1000 Miles at 33-1/2 Miles Per Hour" that had been achieved in a company test. The standard paint combination for the Model L was Richelieu blue body with black molding and cream yellow striping, the running gear cream yellow with black and blue striping. Standard equipment included two side oil lamps, one rear oil lamp, bulb horn and tube, front and rear storm aprons, and a tool kit.

I.D. DATA: Engine numbers. Starting: 501. Ending: 705.

Model L, 4-cyl.

Model No.	Body Type & Seating	Factory Price	Shipping Weight	Prod. Total
L	Tonneau	3000	1900	Note 1
L	Surrey	3000	1900	Note 1
L	Runabout	3000	1900	Note 1

Note 1: Packard Model L production for 1904 totaled 207 with no body style breakout available.

ENGINE: L-head. Four. Cast iron block. B & S: 3-7/8 x 5-1/8 in. Disp.: 241.7 cu. in. Brake H.P.: 22 @ 900 R.P.M. Net H.P.: 22. Main bearings: three. Carb.: float-feed.

CHASSIS: W.B.: 94 in. Tires: 34 x 4.

TECHNICAL: Sliding gear transmission on rear axle. Speeds: 3F/1R. Bevel gear differential. Mechanical brakes on two rear wheels. Artillery wheels.

OPTIONS: Wicker side baskets. Head lamps, sight feed oil gauge.

HISTORICAL: Introduced November 1903. Model year production: 207.

1905

PACKARD — MODEL N — FOUR: The Model N marked the beginning of Packard's expansion of body styles, five being offered this year ranging from runabout to limousine in a price range from $3,400 to $4,600. The wheelbase was extended a foot, and the four-cylinder engine had six more horses than the previous Model L. A single-jet carburetor with auxiliary automatic inlet and warm water jacket was a new feature. In addition, tonneaus were now double-side-entrance instead of the previous rear-entrance. Standard equipment included two side oil lamps, one rear oil lamp, brackets for headlights, complete tool kit, tire repair kit, front and rear storm aprons.

I.D. DATA: Engine numbers. Starting: 1002. Ending: 1405.

Model N, 4-cyl.

Model No.	Body Type & Seating	Factory Price	Shipping Weight	Prod. Total
N	Brgm.	4100	—	Note 1
N	Tr.	3600	—	Note 1
N	Rbt.	3400	—	Note 1
N	Limo.	4600	—	Note 1
N	Tonneau	3675	—	Note 1

Note 1: Packard Model N production for 1905 totaled 403 with no body style breakout available.

ENGINE: L-head. Four. Cast iron block. B & S: 4-1/16 x 5-1/8 in. Disp.: 265.7 cu. in. Brake H.P.: 28 @ 900 R.P.M. Net H.P.: 28. Main bearings: three. Valve lifters: mechanical. Carb.: float-feed.

CHASSIS: W.B.: 106 in. Tires: 34 x 4.

TECHNICAL: Sliding gear transmission on rear axle. Speeds: 3F/1R. Expanding flywheel clutch. Shaft drive. Bevel gear differential. External clamping and internal expanding brakes on two rear wheels. Wood artillery wheels.

OPTIONS: Cowl lamps. Head lamps. Wicker side baskets.

HISTORICAL: Introduced November 1904. Model year production: 403.

1906

PACKARD — MODEL S or 24 — FOUR: The Model S was also known as the 24, indicating horsepower ostensibly although tests showed as much as 40-50 hp being developed by the S's four-cylinder engine. First of the Packard T-heads, this engine also marked the first use of magneto jump spark ignition. A hydraulic governor was fitted to the engine. Wheelbases were stretched to 119 inches (except for the runabout) and made for considerably more commodious tonneaus. Introduced this year was the soon-to-be-famous Packard hexagon-shaped hubcap; their centers were painted black on the Model S and ensuing models, until 1913 when the black was changed to red and remained so for the next 40 years.

I.D. DATA: Engine Numbers. Starting: 2003. Ending: 2739.

Model S/24, 4-cyl.

Model No.	Body Type & Seating	Factory Price	Shipping Weight	Prod. Total
24	Tr.	4000	—	Note 1
24	Rbt.	4000	—	Note 1
24	Limo.	5200	—	Note 1
24	Land.	5225	—	Note 1
24	Victoria	4189	—	Note 1

Note 1: Packard Model 24 production for 1906 is estimated at 728 with no body style breakout available.

1899 Packard, Model A, runabout, OCW

1902 Packard, Model F, runabout (special for J.W. Packard), OCW

1905 Packard, Model N, limousine, OCW

1910 Packard, Model 30 UCS, runabout, OCW

1901 Packard, Model C, runabout, OCW

1904 Packard, Model L, runabout, OCW

1908 Packard, Model 30 UA, runabout, OCW

1911 Packard, Model 18 NC, close coupled touring, OCW

ENGINE: T-head. Four. Cast iron block. B & S: 4-1/2 x 5-1/2 in. Disp.: 349.9 cu. in. Brake H.P.: 24 @ 650 R.P.M. Net H.P.: 24. Main bearings: three. Valve lifters: solid. Carb.: float-feed with water jacket.

CHASSIS: W.B.: 119 in. (rbt. 108 in.) Tires: 34 x 4 front, 34 x 4-1/2 rear.

TECHNICAL: Sliding gear transmission on rear axle. Speeds: 3F/1R. Expanding flywheel clutch. Shaft drive. Bevel gear differential. Mechanical brakes on two rear wheels. Wood artillery wheels.

OPTIONS: Single sidemount.

HISTORICAL: Introduced September 1905. Model year sales: 728.

1907

PACKARD — MODEL THIRTY (U) — FOUR: The new Thirty was basically a refinement over the previous S. Cylinder tops and valve chambers now had a flat top instead of the previous dome, and valves were larger. Front wheels now ran on ball instead of roller bearings. The wheelbase was slightly longer, most of the added length in the hood. Added to the usual standard equipment were headlights, irons for an extension cape cart top, and the tire repair kit now included jack and pump, and irons for carrying extra tires.

I.D. DATA: Engine numbers. Starting: 3003. Ending: 4134.

Model 30/U, 4-cyl.

Model No.	Body Type & Seating	Factory Price	Shipping Weight	Prod. Total
30 (U)	Rbt.	4200	—	Note 1
30 (U)	Tr.	4200	2600	Note 1
30 (U)	Limo.	5500	—	Note 1
30 (U)	Land.	5600	—	Note 1

Note 1: Packard Model 30 production for 1907 is estimated at 1,128 with no body style breakout available.

ENGINE: T-head. Four. Cast iron block. B & S: 5 x 5-1/2 in. Disp.: 431.9 cu. in. Brake H.P.: 30 @ 650 R.P.M. Net H.P.: 30. Main bearings: three. Valve lifters: solid. Carb.: float-feed, warm water jacket.

CHASSIS: W.B.: 122 in. Tires: 34 x 4 front, 34 x 4-1/2 rear. Runabout W.B.: 108 in. Tires: 34 x 3-1/2 front, 34 x 4 rear.

TECHNICAL: Sliding gear transmission on rear axle. Speeds: 3F/1R. Expanding flywheel clutch. Shaft drive. Bevel gear differential. Mechanical brakes on rear wheels only. Wood, artillery wheels.

HISTORICAL: Introduced August 1906. Model year sales: 1,128.

1908

PACKARD — MODEL THIRTY (UA) — FOUR: A longer wheelbase and larger wheels were among the few changes in the UA model of 1908. The frame was slightly lowered. A bayonet-type locking radiator cap (also seen on some of the final 1907 cars) became standard, replacing the former screw cap. One new body style was introduced, a close-coupled touring with one-person rumbleseat.

I.D. DATA: Engine numbers. Starting: 5006. Ending: 6311.

Model 30/UA, 4-cyl.

Model No.	Body Type & Seating	Factory Price	Shipping Weight	Prod. Total
30 (UA)	Rbt.	4200	—	Note 1
30 (UA)	Tr.	4200	2600	Note 1
30 (UA)	Limo.	5500	—	Note 1
30 (UA)	Limo.	5600	—	Note 1
30 (UA)	Close-coupled Tr.	NA	—	Note 1

Note 1: Packard Model 30 production for 1908 totaled 1,303 with no body style breakout available.

ENGINE: T-head. Four. Cast iron block. B & S: 5 x 5-1/2 in. Disp.: 431.9 cu. in. Brake H.P.: 30 @ 650 R.P.M. Net H.P.: 30. Main bearings: three. Valve lifters: solid. Carb.: float-feed, warm water jacket.

CHASSIS: W.B.: 123-1/2 in. Tires: 36 x 4 front, 36 x 4-1/2 rear. Runabout W.B.: 108 in. Tires: 36 x 3-1/2 front, 36 x 4 rear.

TECHNICAL: Sliding gear transmission on rear axle. Speeds: 3F/1R. Expanding ring clutch. Shaft drive and bevel gear differential. Mechanical brakes on rear wheels. Wood artillery wheels.

OPTIONS: Victoria top ($325.00). Glass-back canopy top (470.00). Adjustable glass windshield (70.00). Special colors, body and gear (50.00).

HISTORICAL: Introduced May 1907. Model year production: 1,303.

1909

PACKARD — MODEL EIGHTEEN (NA) — FOUR: The Model Eighteen was the first attempt to downsize a Packard. It was built with the same "quality at all costs" that typified the Model Thirty. The car featured a smaller engine and shorter wheelbase — and price tags about $1,000 less. It was not as successful as the company had hoped, being outsold by the Model Thirty by about two to one this year, even more in succeeding years. Initially offered in runabout, limousine, landaulet and touring body styles, a demi-limousine was added to the line in December of 1909.

I.D. DATA: Engine numbers. Starting: 9001. Ending: 9801.

Model 18/NA, 4-cyl.

Model No.	Body Type & Seating	Factory Price	Shipping Weight	Prod. Total
18 (NA)	Rbt.	3200	—	Note 1
18 (NA)	Limo.	4300	—	Note 1
18 (NA)	Land.	2900	—	Note 1
18 (NA)	Tr.	3200	2900	Note 1
18 (NA)	Demi. Limo.	NA	—	Note 1

Note 1: Packard Model 18 production for 1909 totaled 802 with no body style breakout available.

ENGINE: T-head. Four. Cast iron block. B & S: 4-1/16 x 5-1/8 in. Disp.: 265.7 cu. in. Brake H.P.: 18 @ 650 R.P.M. Net H.P.: 18. Main bearings: three. Valve lifters: solid. Carb.: float-feed, warm water jacket.

CHASSIS: W.B.: 112 in. Tires: 34 x 4. Runabout W.B.: 102 in. Tires: 34 x 3-1/2 front, 34 x 4 rear.

TECHNICAL: Sliding gear transmission on rear axle. Speeds: 3F/1R. Expanding flywheel clutch. Shaft drive and bevel gear differential. Mechanical brakes on two rear wheels. Wood artillery wheels.

OPTIONS: Cape cart top ($135.00). Victoria top (150.00). Material seat covers (67.50 touring, 32.50 runabout). Special colors, body and gear (50.00).

HISTORICAL: Introduced summer 1908. Model year production: 802.

PACKARD — MODEL THIRTY (UB, UBS) — FOUR: Changes were few in the Thirty for 1909. The radiator was revised to a cellular type, and a four-gallon gasoline reserve tank was added. A redesigned linkage eliminated the necessity for the separate reverse lever that had been present on all Packards since 1904. The front fenders were hooded, with a mud guard placed between frame and runningboards. UB was the designation for all body styles (including the new demi-limousine introduced in December), except for the short wheelbase runabout that was designated UBS.

I.D. DATA: Engine numbers. Starting: 6481 and 7501. Ending: 7086 and 8999.

Model No.	Body Type & Seating	Factory Price	Shipping Weight	Prod. Total
Model 30/UBS, 4-cyl.				
30 UBS	Rbt.	4200	2600	Note 1
Model 30/UB, 4-cyl.				
30 UB	Tour.	4200	2600	Note 1
30 UB	Limo.	5500	—	Note 1
30 UB	Land.	5600	—	Note 1
30 UB	Close-Coupled Tour.	NA	—	Note 1
30 UB	Demi-Limo.	NA	—	Note 1

Note 1: Packard Model UB/UBS production for 1909 totaled 1,501 with no body style breakout available.

ENGINE: T-head. Four. Cast iron block. B & S: 5 x 5-1/2 in. Disp.: 431.9 cu. in. Brake H.P.: 30 @ 650 R.P.M. Net H.P.: 30. Main bearings: three. Valve lifters: mechanical. Carb.: float-feed, warm water jacket.

CHASSIS: [Thirty UB] W.B.: 123-1/2 in. Tires: 36 x 4 front, 36 x 4-1/2 rear. [Thirty UBS] W.B.: 108 in. [Runabout] Tires: 36 x 3-1/2 front, 36 x 4-1/2 rear.

TECHNICAL: Sliding gear transmission on rear axle. Speeds: 3F/1R. Expanding flywheel clutch. Shaft drive and bevel gear differential. Mechanical brakes on rear wheels only. Wood, artillery wheels.

HISTORICAL: Introduced summer 1908. Model year production: 1,501.

1910

PACKARD — MODEL EIGHTEEN (NB) — FOUR: The Model Eighteen for 1910 shared the same refinements as the Model Thirty. The new phaeton body style that was provided on the Thirty was not made available on the Eighteen, however, nor was the demi-limousine continued as a cataloged Eighteen model. Model Eighteen body styles now numbered just four. This year the Model Thirty outsold the Eighteen by more than three to one.

I.D. DATA: Engine numbers. Starting: 12001. Ending: 12837.

Model 18/NB, 4-cyl.

Model No.	Body Type & Seating	Factory Price	Shipping Weight	Prod. Total
18 (NB)	Rbt.	3200	—	Note 1
18 (NB)	Tr.	3200	3000	Note 1
18 (NB)	Limo.	4400	—	Note 1
18 (NB)	Land.	4500	—	Note 1

Note 1: Packard Model 18 production for 1910 totaled 766 with no body style breakout available.

ENGINE: T-head. Four. Cast iron block. B & S: 4-1/16 x 5-1/8 in. Disp.: 267.5 cu. in. Brake H.P.: 18 @ 650 R.P.M. Net H.P.: 18. Main bearings: three. Valve lifters: solid. Carb.: float-feed, warm water jacket.

CHASSIS: W.B.: 112 in. Tires: 34 x 4. [Runabout] W.B.: 102 in. Tires: 34 x 3-1/2 front, 34 x 4 rear.

TECHNICAL: Sliding gear transmission. Speeds: 3F/1R. Dry plate clutch. Bevel gear differential. Mechanical brakes on two rear wheels. Wood artillery wheels.

HISTORICAL: Introduced summer 1909. Model year production: 766.

PACKARD — MODEL THIRTY (UC, UCS) — FOUR: Engineering changes for the Thirty UC included replacement of the expanding ring clutch (which had been fitted for a half decade) with a dry plate type, and the addition of shock absorbers as standard equipment to smooth out the suspension. The front fenders were more massive, the mud guard between them and the body deeper. Also enlarged was the steering wheel, its wood rim now extending to the wheel's periphery and to part of the spokes. A phaeton was a new body style.

I.D. DATA: Engine numbers. Starting: (UC) 10000, (UCS) 13001. Ending: (UC) 11999, (UCS) 13518.

Model 30/UCS, 4-cyl.

Model No.	Body Type & Seating	Factory Price	Shipping Weight	Prod. Total
30 (UCS)	Rbt.	4200	3600	Note 1
Model 30/UC, 4-cyl.				
30 (UC)	Tr.	4200	3600	Note 1
30 (UC)	Limo.	5500	—	Note 1
30 (UC)	Land.	5600	—	Note 1
30 (UC)	CC. Twn. Car	NA	—	Note 1
30 (UC)	Demi-Limo.	NA	—	Note 1
30 (UC)	Phae.	NA	—	Note 1

Note 1: Packard Model 30 production for 1910 totaled 2,493 with no body style breakout available.

ENGINE: T-head. Four. Cast iron block. B & S: 5 x 5-1/2 in. Disp.: 431.9 cu. in. Brake H.P.: 30 @ 650 R.P.M. Net H.P.: 30. Main bearings: three. Valve lifters: mechanical.

CHASSIS: [Model 30 UC] W.B.: 123-1/2 in. Tires: 36 x 4 front, 36 x 4-1/2 rear. [Model 30 UCS] W.B.: 108 in. Tires: 36 x 3-1/2 front, 36 x 4-1/2 rear.

TECHNICAL: Sliding gear transmission. Speeds: 3F/1R. Dry plate clutch. Bevel gear differential. Mechanical brakes on two rear wheels. Wood artillery wheels.

HISTORICAL: Introduced summer 1909. Model year production: 2,493.

1911

PACKARD — MODEL EIGHTEEN (NC) — FOUR: The Eighteen NC shared the changes made to the Thirty UD. Although the smaller Packard did not share the variety of body styles available for the Thirty, it did receive a new close-coupled touring and coupe this year. Sales of fewer than 400 cars was disappointing, however, vis-à-vis the Thirty's more than 1,800.

I.D. DATA: Engine numbers. Starting: 18001. Ending: 19176.

Model 18/NC, 4-cyl.

Model No.	Body Type & Seating	Factory Price	Shipping Weight	Prod. Total
18 (NC)	Rbt.	3200	—	Note 1
18 (NC)	Tr.	3200	3100	Note 1
18 (NC)	Limo.	4400	—	Note 1
18 (NC)	Land.	4500	—	Note 1
18 (NC)	Close-Coupled	3200	—	Note 1
18 (NC)	Coupe	3900	—	Note 1

Note 1: Packard Model 18 production for 1911 totaled 360 with no body style breakout available.

ENGINE: T-head. Four. Cast iron block. B & S: 4-1/16 x 5-1/8 in. Disp.: 267.5 cu. in. Brake H.P.: 18 @ 650 R.P.M. Net H.P.: 18. Main bearings: three. Valve lifters: solid. Carb.: float-feed, warm water jacket.

CHASSIS: W.B.: 112 in. Tires: 34 x 4. [Runabout] W.B.: 102 in. Tires: 34 x 3-1/2 front, 34 x 4 rear.

TECHNICAL: Sliding gear transmission. Speeds: 3F/1R. Dry plate clutch. Bevel gear differential. Mechanical brakes on two rear wheels. Wood artillery wheels.

OPTIONS: Fore-doors for limousine and landaulet ($200.00). Seat covers (30.00 to 60.00). Storm-tilt windshield (60.00).

HISTORICAL: Introduced summer 1910. Model year production: 360.

PACKARD — MODEL THIRTY (UD, UDS) — FOUR: The big news from Packard this year was a new standard paint scheme, Packard blue with gray striping for bodies; moldings, frame, hood, radiator, fenders, battery and tool boxes in black. For open cars, the wheels, axles and below-frame running gear were gray with black striping; the reverse was used on closed cars. Fore-doors were available optionally. Open cars were upholstered in tufted straight-grain leather; enclosed bodies had untufted straight-grain leather in front; in the rear, tufted blue goatskin was used below the belt, with untufted blue broadcloth for roof and quarters. Engineering changes were minimal, the rear semi-elliptic suspension being beefed up with the addition of three short leaves. New options included combination oil and electric side and rear lights, and the second battery necessary for them. Two new body styles were a coupe and a brougham, for the latter of which all metal parts were nickel-plated and the interior outfitted in gray checked broadcloth.

I.D. DATA: UD engine numbers. Starting: 15001. Ending: 15999. UDS engine numbers. Starting: 16000. Ending: 16884.

Model 30/UDS, 4-cyl.

Model No.	Body Type & Seating	Factory Price	Shipping Weight	Prod. Total
30 (UDS)	Rbt.	4200	3800	Note 1
Model 30/UD, 4-cyl.				
30 (UD)	Tr.	4200	3800	Note 1
30 (UD)	Limo.	5450	—	Note 1
30 (UD)	Close-Coupled Twn. Car	4200	—	Note 1
30 (UD)	Brgm.	4200	—	Note 1
30 (UD)	Phae.	5550	—	Note 1
30 (UD)	Cpe.	4900	—	Note 1
30 (UD)	Brgm.	NA	—	Note 1

Note 1: Packard Model 30 production for 1911 totaled 1,865 with no body style breakout available.

ENGINE: T-head. Four. Cast iron block. B & S: 5 x 5-1/2 in. Disp.: 431.9 cu. in. Brake H.P.: 30 @ 650 R.P.M. Net H.P.: 30. Main bearings: three. Valve lifters: mechanical. Carb.: float-feed, warm water jacket.

CHASSIS: [Thirty UD] W.B.: 123 in. Tires: 36 x 4-1/2. [Thirty UDS] W.B.: 108 in. Tires: 36 x 4-1/2.

TECHNICAL: Sliding gear transmission over rear axle. Speeds: 3F/1R. Dry plate clutch. Mechanical brakes on two wheels. Wood artillery wheels.

OPTIONS: Fore-doors for limousine and landaulet ($200.00), seat covers (30.00 to 60.00), storm-tilt windshield (60.00).

HISTORICAL: Introduced summer 1910. Model year production: 1,865.

1912

PACKARD — MODEL EIGHTEEN (NE) — FOUR: The re-engineered clutch design of the Thirty UE was incorporated in the Eighteen NE. (The ND designation was skipped for conformity's sake in this the last model year of the Thirty and Eighteen.) The oil and electric side and rear light combination was standard; headlights were gas. There was a reshuffling of body styles, and the runabout was given a six-inch-longer wheelbase than previously.

I.D. DATA: Engine numbers. Starting: 26001. Ending: 27000.

Model 18/NE, 4-cyl.

Model No.	Body Type & Seating	Factory Price	Shipping Weight	Prod. Total
NE	Tr.	3200	3400	Note 1
NE	Rbt.	3200	3000	Note 1
NE	Limo.	4400	3300	Note 1
NE	Land.	4500	NA	Note 1
NE	Imp. Limo.	4600	3300	Note 1
NE	Cpe.	3900	3000	Note 1

Note 1: Packard Model 18 production for 1912 totaled 350 with no body style breakout available.

ENGINE: T-head. Four. Cast iron block. B & S: 4-1/16 x 5-1/8 in. Disp.: 267.5 cu. in. Brake H.P.: 18 @ 650 R.P.M. Net H.P.: 18. Main bearings: three. Valve lifters: solid. Carb.: float-feed, warm water jacket.

CHASSIS: W.B.: 112 in. Tires: 34 x 4. [Runabout] W.B.: 108 in. Tires: 34 x 3-1/2 front, 34 x 4 rear.

TECHNICAL: Sliding gear transmission. Speeds: 3F/1R. Dry plate clutch. Bevel gear differential. Mechanical brakes on two rear wheels. Wood artillery wheels.

HISTORICAL: Introduced summer 1911. Model year production: 350.

PACKARD — MODEL THIRTY (UE) — FOUR. — The most important engineering change in the Thirty UE was the remounting of the dry disc clutch directly behind the engine, the clutch and flywheel now a rigid extension of the crankcase. Using the "S" sub-designation for the runabout was discontinued; the standard wheelbase was now 123-1/2 inches, the runabout's was six inches longer at 114, and the limousine and landaulet were now on a 129-1/2-inch wheelbase all their own. A brougham was a new body style. The combination oil and electric side and rear lights that were available optionally in 1911 were now fitted as standard equipment; headlights were gas.

I.D. DATA: Engine numbers. Starting: 20001. Ending: 23000.

Model 30/UE, 4-cyl.

Model No.	Body Type & Seating	Factory Price	Shipping Weight	Prod. Total
UE	Phae.	4200	3600	Note 1
UE	Cape Cart Tr.	4200	NA	Note 1
UE	Tr.	4200	3700	Note 1
UE	Rbt.	4200	3300	Note 1
UE	Limo.	5450	3900	Note 1
UE	Land.	5550	NA	Note 1
UE	Imp. Limo.	5650	4000	Note 1
UE	Imp. Land.	5750	NA	Note 1
UE	Brgm.	5500	3900	Note 1
UE	Cpe.	4900	3500	Note 1

Note 1: Packard Model 30 production for 1912 totaled 1,250 with no body style breakout available.

ENGINE: T-head. Four. Cast iron block. B & S: 5 x 5-1/2 in. Disp.: 431.9 cu. in. Brake H.P.: 30 @ 650 R.P.M. Net H.P.: 30. Main bearings: three. Valve lifters: mechanical. Carb.: float-feed, warm water jacketed.

CHASSIS: [Thirty UE] W.B.: 123-1/2 in. Tires: 36 x 4-1/2 front, 37 x 5 rear. [Thirty Runabout] W.B.: 114 in. Tires: 36 x 4-1/2 front, 37 x 5 rear. [Limousine/Landaulet] W.B.: 129-1/2 in. Tires: 36 x 4-1/2 front, 37 x 5 rear.

TECHNICAL: Sliding gear transmission on rear axle. Speeds: 3F/1R. Dry plate clutch. Bevel gear differential. Mechanical brakes on two rear wheels. Wood artillery wheels.

HISTORICAL: Introduced summer 1911. Model year production: 1,250.

PACKARD — SERIES 1-48 — SIX: This new car was introduced simply as the Packard Six, receiving its 1-48 series designation in retrospect with the arrival of succeeding models. Cast in three blocks of two, the T-head six developed 74 brake horsepower. In road testing, a top speed of about 80 mph was recorded, with 0-60 mph acceleration time at 30 seconds. Three differential ratios were available. Main and reserve gas tanks were mounted under the front seat. Combination oil and electric side and taillamps, and gas headlamps, were fitted. The number of body styles available was 13, and in addition to the standard Packard paint scheme, a customer could have virtually his heart's desire optionally.

I.D. DATA: Engine numbers. Starting: 23001. Ending: 26000.

Model 1-48, 6-cyl.

Model No.	Body Type & Seating	Factory Price	Shipping Weight	Prod. Total
1-48	Tr.-7P	5000	3900	Note 1
1-48	Phae.-5P	5000	3800	Note 1
1-48	Rbt.-2P	5000	3300	Note 1
1-48	Close-Coupled-5P	5000	4175	Note 1
1-48	Victoria Tr.-7P	5250	3900	Note 1
1-48	Victoria Phae.-5P	5215	3800	Note 1
1-48	Canopy Tr.-7P	5445	4000	Note 1
1-48	Limo.-7P	6250	4100	Note 1
1-48	Land.-7P	6350	4395	Note 1
1-48	Imp. Limo.-7P	6450	4200	Note 1
1-48	Imp. Land.-7P	6550	4495	Note 1
1-48	Brgm.-4P	6300	4100	Note 1
1-48	Cpe.	5700	3700	Note 1

Note 1: Packard Model 1-48 production for 1912 totaled 1,329 with no body style breakout available.

ENGINE: T-head. Six. Cast iron block. B & S: 4-1/2 x 5-1/2 in. Disp.: 525 cu. in. Brake H.P.: 74 @ 1720 R.P.M. Net H.P.: 48. Main bearings: four. Valve lifters: mechanical. Carb.: Packard combined float-feed and automatic mixture regulation.

CHASSIS: W.B.: 133 in. O.L.: 183-1/2 in. Tires: 36 x 4-1/2 front, 37 x 5 rear. [Phaeton & Brougham] W.B.: 139 in. O.L.: 189-1/2 in. Tires: 36 x 4-1/2 front, 37 x 5 rear. [Coupe & Runabout] W.B.: 121-1/2 in. O.L.: 172-1/2 in. Tires: 36 x 4-1/2 front, 37 x 5 rear.

TECHNICAL: Rear mounted, sliding gear transmission. Speeds: 3F/1R. Packard multi-disc clutch. Overall ratio: 3.27:1. Optional: 3.05:1 and 3.52:1. Internal expanding and external contracting brakes on two rear wheels. Wood artillery wheels.

HISTORICAL: Introduced April 1911. Model year production: 1,329.

1913

PACKARD — SERIES 1-38 — SIX: Introduced as the "38" (the Series 1-38 designation arriving later), this Packard was an L-head six cast in three blocks of two. Unlike the preceding "48," its valves were located on the right and enclosed by aluminum covers. The Series 1-38 was noteworthy as the first Packard to use an electric starter and the first to have left-hand drive. Introduced in December of 1912, it was succeeded in February of 1913 by the "1438," which was essentially a continuation of the previous car.

I.D. DATA: Engine numbers. Starting: 38000. Ending: 42000.

Model 1-38, 6-cyl.

Model No.	Body Type & Seating	Factory Price	Shipping Weight	Prod. Total
1-38	Tr.-5P	4150	4070	Note 1
1-38	Phae.-5P	4150	4110	Note 1
1-38	Imp. Limo.-5P	5400	4510	Note 1
1-38	Imp. Land.-5P	5500	4495	Note 1
1-38	Limo.-5P	5200	4400	Note 1
1-38	Land.-5P	5300	4430	Note 1
1-38	Phae.-4P	4150	4070	Note 1
1-38	Brgm.-4P	5200	4375	Note 1
1-38	Imp. Cpe.-4P	4900	4175	Note 1
1-38	Rbt.-2P	4050	3820	Note 1
1-38	Cpe.-2P	4500	4070	Note 1

Note 1: Packard Model 1-38 production totaled 1,618, which includes production of the carryover Model 1438 in 1914. No body style breakout is available.

ENGINE: L-head. Six. Cast iron block. B & S: 4 x 5-1/2 in. Disp.: 415 cu. in. Brake H.P.: 60 @ 1720 R.P.M. Net H.P.: 38. Main bearings: seven. Valve lifters: mechanical. Carb.: Packard, float-feed, acetylene primer.

CHASSIS: W.B.: 134 in. O.L.: 175-1/2 in. Tires: 36 x 4-1/2 front, 37 x 5 rear. [Phaeton & Brougham series] W.B.: 138 in. O.L.: 179-1/4 in. Tires: 36 x 4-1/2 front, 37 x 5 rear. [Runabout series] W.B.: 115-1/2 in. O.L. 156-3/4 in. Tires: 34 x 4-1/2 front, 37 x 5 rear.

TECHNICAL: Rear mounted, sliding gear transmission. Speeds: 3F/1R. Dry, multi-disc clutch. Overall ratio: 3.8:1. Mechanical brakes on two rear wheels. Wood artillery wheels.

HISTORICAL: Introduced December 1912. Model year production: 1,618 (includes the 1914 "1438' model, which was merely the continuation of the Model 1-38, introduced in February 1913).

PACKARD — SERIES 2-48 (1348) — SIX: Although an electric generator (no starter) was incorporated on the 2-48 (which also bore the designation "1348"), the car retained right-hand drive. Retained, too, were the combination oil and electric side and rear lights, but the handles on the former were now located on the side rather than on top of the lamp bodies. Electric headlights replaced the previous gas units. Engineering changes included direct lubrication of piston pin bearings. Motor support was now three point instead of four; the water pump and dual magneto moved to the rear. The fuel tank was removed from under the seat to the back of the car; the battery and toolbox moved from the runningboard to under the driver's seat. Horsepower of the T-head six was up to 82. The touring car now joined the phaeton and brougham on the 139-inch wheelbase; the runabout and coupe remained on the 121-1/2-inch chassis; the 133-inch chassis was retained for all other body styles.

I.D. DATA: Engine numbers. Starting: 35026. Ending: 37999.

Model 2-48/1348, 6-cyl.

Model No.	Body Type & Seating	Factory Price	Shipping Weight	Prod. Total
2-48 (1348)	Brgm.-5P	5800	—	Note 1
2-48 (1348)	Cpe.-3P	5100	—	Note 1
2-48 (1348)	Tr.-7P	4850	4560	Note 1
2-48 (1348)	Imp. Limo.-7P	6050	—	Note 1
2-48 (1348)	Land.-7P	5950	—	Note 1
2-48 (1348)	Phae.-5P	4750	4450	Note 1
2-48 (1348)	Rbt.-5P	4650	4010	Note 1
2-48 (1348)	Limo.	5850	—	Note 1

Note 1: Packard Model 2-48 production for 1913 totaled 1,000 with no body style breakout available.

ENGINE: T-head. Six. Cast iron block. Brake H.P.: 82 @ 1720 R.P.M. Net H.P.: 48. Main bearings: four. Valve lifters: mechanical. Carb.: float-feed, mixture regulation, acetylene primer added.

CHASSIS: W.B.: 121-1/2 - 139 in. O.L.: 172-1/2 - 189-1/2 in. Tires: 36 x 4-1/2 front, 37 x 4 rear.

TECHNICAL: Rear mounted, sliding gear transmission. Speeds: 3F/1R. Multi-disc clutch. Bevel gear rear axle. Overall ratio: 3.27:1. Mechanical brakes on two rear wheels. Wood artillery wheels.

HISTORICAL: Introduced June 1912. Model year production: 1,000.

1914

PACKARD — SERIES 1-38 — SIX: This Packard, introduced in February 1913 ostensibly as a 1914 model, was simply a continuation of the L-head 1-38 of the previous season. Company owners manuals for 1914 used the same description for this car as for the 1913 1-38. Little further data is available. One reference indicates a total of 678 cars produced.

PACKARD — SERIES 2-38 — SIX: A new L-head engine cast in two blocks of three was the big news for the 2-38, together with the adoption of spiral bevel gears. Further engineering refinements included a hot water jacketed intake manifold, mud webs cast integrally with the crankcase, pressure-fed lubrication to 35 points, brake drums increased to 17 inches, and dual exhausts. Spare tires were now carried at the rear. The gas pedal was repositioned to the right of the brake pedal. Headlights were complete with dimmer switch. All body styles were now placed on a single 140-inch wheelbase chassis.

I.D. DATA: Engine numbers. Starting: 53026. Ending: 56000.

Model 2-38, 6-cyl.

Model No.	Body Type & Seating	Factory Price	Shipping Weight	Prod. Total
27	Tr.-7P	3850	4426	Note 1
46	Spec. Tr.-6P	3350	4395	Note 1
30	Salon Tr.-6P	3850	4376	Note 1
28	Phae.-4P	3750	4293	Note 1
51	Phae.-5P	3750	4360	Note 1
29	Rbt.-2P	3750	4113	Note 1
42	Limo.-6P	4900	4677	Note 1
40	Limo.-7P	4950	4712	Note 1
44	Cab Sides Limo.-7P	5000	4757	Note 1
43	Land.-6P	4900	4660	Note 1
41	Land.-7P	4950	4700	Note 1
34	Cab Sides Land.-7P	5000	4747	Note 1
NA	All Weather Conv-7P	4525	NA	Note 1
50	Imp. Limo.-6P	5100	4785	Note 1
31	Imp. Limo.-7P	5150	4818	Note 1
33	Salon Limo.-7P	5100	4763	Note 1
36	Brgm.-6P	5000	4735	Note 1
37	Salon Brgm.-6P	4950	4685	Note 1
38	Coupe-3P	4450	4382	Note 1

Note 1: Packard Model 2-38 production for 1914 totaled 1,501 with no body style breakout available.

ENGINE: L-head. Six. Cast iron block. B & S: 4 x 5-1/2 in. Disp.: 415 cu. in. Brake H.P.: 60 @ 1720 R.P.M. Net H.P.: 38. Main bearings: seven. Valve lifters: mechanical. Carburetor: float-feed, acetylene primer.

CHASSIS: W.B.: 140 in. O.L.: 198 in. (touring-201 in.). Tires: 37 x 4-1/2 front, 37 x 5 rear.

TECHNICAL: Rear mounted, sliding gear transmission. Speeds: 3F/1R. Dry disc clutch. Spiral bevel gears. Overall ratio: 3.9:1. Optional: 3.53:1. Mechanical brakes on two rear wheels. Wood artillery wheels.

HISTORICAL: Introduced December 1913. Model year production: 1,501.

PACKARD — SERIES 3-48 (1448) — SIX: The 3-48 went left-hand drive, necessitating a 180 degree remounting of the T-head six-cylinder engine. The exhaust now vented on the right with the carburetion complex on the left. A combination self-starter and generator was fitted. Driver controls were mounted on the steering column. Spiral bevel gears were incorporated with the rear axle. A 139-inch wheelbase carried all bodies except the runabout, which was 121-1/2 in. Bodies were wider, body styles more numerous, and 42 exterior color combinations were available.

I.D. DATA: Engine numbers. Starting: 50026. Ending: 52000.

Model 3-48/1448, 6-cyl.

Model No.	Body Type & Seating	Factory Price	Shipping Weight	Prod. Total
3-48 (1448)	Tr.-7P	4850	—	Note 1
3-48 (1448)	Phae.-5P	4750	—	Note 1
3-48 (1448)	Phae- Rbt.-2P	4700	—	Note 1
3-48 (1448)	Rbt.-2P (+ rumble)	4650	—	Note 1
3-48 (1448)	Limo.-7P	5900	—	Note 1
3-48 (1448)	Imp. Limo.-7P	6100	—	Note 1
3-48 (1448)	Salon Limo.-7P	6050	—	Note 1
3-48 (1448)	Land.-7P	5900	—	Note 1
3-48 (1448)	Cabette-4P	5800	—	Note 1
3-48 (1448)	Brgm.-4P	5900	—	Note 1
3-48 (1448)	Salon Brgm.-4P	5850	—	Note 1
3-48 (1448)	Cpe.-2P	5400	—	Note 1
3-48 (1448)	Imp. Cpe.-4P	5600	—	Note 1
3-48 (1448)	Vic. Tr.-7P	5065	—	Note 1

Note 1: Packard Model 3-48 production in 1914 totaled 1,499 with no body style breakout available.

ENGINE: T-head. Six. Cast iron block. B & S: 4-1/2 x 5-1/2 in. Disp.: 525 cu. in. Brake H.P.: 82 @ 1720 R.P.M. Main bearings: four. Valve lifters: solid. Carb.: float-feed and automatic mixture regulation with primer.

CHASSIS: W.B.: 139 to 121-1/2 in. O.L.: 202 to 180 in.

TECHNICAL: Rear mounted, sliding gear transmission. Speeds: 3F/1R. Disc clutch. Shaft drive with spiral bevel gears. Mechanical brakes on two rear wheels. Wood artillery wheels.

OPTIONS: Clock. Speedometer. Trunk rack. Klaxon horn. Tire covers. Hat box. Trunk with three leather cases. Power tire pump. Seat covers for open cars. Ammeter. Speaking tubes. Sterling silver trim (inside).

HISTORICAL: Introduced April 1913. Model year production: 1,499.

PACKARD — SERIES 4-48 — SIX: From a four-main-bearing T-head, the 48 was now a seven-main-bearing L-head. The intake manifold was water jacketed. Seventeen-inch brake drums replaced the former 15s. The 2-38's lubrication system was adopted. Dual exhaust were fitted. All body styles (including runabout) were carried on a huge 144-inch wheelbase. A Warner speedometer, Klaxon horn and Waltham clock were fitted as standard, and the spare tires were now rear-mounted. Seventy-two man hours were required to assemble each engine. Each car was road tested prior to delivery. Prices ranged from $4,750 to $6,510.

I.D. DATA: Engine numbers. Starting: 63026. Ending: 66000.

Model 4-48, 6-cyl.

Model No.	Body Type & Seating	Factory Price	Shipping Weight	Prod. Total
73	Cab Sides Limo.-7P	6000	4954	Note 1
77	Cab Sides Land.-7P	6000	4944	Note 1
72	Limo.-6P	5900	4874	Note 1
74	Cab Sides Limo.-6P	5950	4916	Note 1
76	Land.-6P	5900	4857	Note 1
69	Imp. Limo.-6P	6100	4982	Note 1
79	Brgm.-6P	6000	4932	Note 1
66	Phae.-4P	4750	4490	Note 1
59	Cpe.-2P	5450	4577	Note 1

Note 1: Packard Model 4-48 production for 1914 totaled 441 with no body style breakout available.

ENGINE: L-head. Six. Cast iron block. B & S: 4-1/2 x 5-1/2 in. Disp.: 525 cu. in. Brake H.P.: 60 @ 1200 R.P.M. Main bearings: seven. Valve lifters: mechanical.

CHASSIS: W.B.: 144 in. O.L.: 204-3/4 in. Tires: 37 x 5.

TECHNICAL: Rear-mounted sliding gear transmission. Speeds: 3F/1R. Rear mounted, disc clutch. Overall ratio: 3.53:1. Optional: 3.28:1. Mechanical brakes on two rear wheels. Wood artillery wheels.

HISTORICAL: Introduced February 1914. Model year production: 441.

1915

PACKARD — SERIES 3-38 — SIX: An increase of five horsepower (to 65) was the most significant engineering difference of the 3-38 over its 2-38 predecessor. Lighting was now completely electric, with

1912 Packard, Model 2-48 (1348), limousine (with body by Kimball), OCW

1914 Packard, Model 4-48, touring (with Barney Oldfield, driving, and Harvey Firestone up front), OCW

1917 Packard, Twin Six (Model 2-25), limousine, OCW

1920 Packard, Twin Six (Model 3-35), sedan, OCW

1913 Packard, Model 1-38, touring, OCW

1916 Packard, Twin Six (Model 1-35), cab sides limousine (with body by Kimball), OCW

1919 Packard, Twin Six (Model 3-25), coupe, OCW

1923 Packard, Single Six (Model 126), touring, HAC

headlights incorporating a mini auxiliary light within the overall design. A "combination rear lamp and license tag illuminator" was new and located on the left. A limousine with cab sides was a new body style.

I.D. DATA: Engine numbers. Starting: 75026. Ending: 76999.

Model 3-38, 6-cyl.

Model No.	Body Type & Seating	Factory Price	Shipping Weight	Prod. Total
65	Phae.-5P	3750	4410	Note 1
66	Phae.-4P	3750	4343	Note 1
67	Rbt.-2P	3750	4163	Note 1
79	Brgm.-6P	5000	4785	Note 1
80	Salon Brgm.-4P	4950	4735	Note 1
59	Cpe.-3P	4450	4432	Note 1
74	Cab Sides Limo.-6P	4950	4769	Note 1
63	Tour.-7P	3850	4476	Note 1
68	Imp. Limo.-7P	5150	4868	Note 1
70	Salon Limo.-7P	5100	4813	Note 1
NA	All W. Conv.-7P	—	—	Note 1
72	Limo.-7P	4950	4762	Note 1
73	Cab Sides Limo.-7P	5000	4807	Note 1
76	Land.-6P	4900	4710	Note 1
77	Cab Sides Land.-7P	5000	4797	Note 1
60	Salon Tour.-6P	3850	4426	Note 1
61	Spec. Tour.-6P	3850	4445	Note 1
76	Land.-6P	4900	4710	Note 1
69	Imp. Limo.-6P	5100	4835	Note 1
71	Limo.-6P	4900	4727	Note 1
75	Land.-7P	4950	4750	Note 1

Note 1: Packard Model 3-38 production for 1915 totaled 1,801 with no body style breakout available.

ENGINE: L-head. Six. Cast iron block. B & S: 4 x 5-1/2 in. Disp.: 415 cu. in. Brake H.P.: 65 @ 1720 R.P.M. Net H.P.: 38. Main bearings: seven. Valve lifters: mechanical. Carb.: float-feed, acetylene primer.

CHASSIS: W.B.: 140 in. O.L.: 198-1/2 in. (touring-201 in.). Tires: 37 x 4-1/2 front, 37 x 5 rear.

TECHNICAL: Rear mounted sliding gear transmission. Speeds: 3F/1R. Dry disc clutch. Spiral bevel gears. Overall ratio: 3.9:1. Mechanical brakes on two rear wheels, 17 in. drums. Wood, artillery wheels.

HISTORICAL: Introduced September 1914. Model year production: 1,801.

PACKARD — SERIES 5-48 — SIX: The 5-48 was little changed from the 4-48. All-electric lighting was featured, the main headlight incorporating a smaller auxiliary in the front, the tail-license plate light moved to the left at the rear. The wheelbase remained a gargantuan 144 inches, with some Packards stretching out overall to a length of almost 17 feet, and the heaviest weighing in at over 2-1/2 tons. A high-speed rear axle ratio (3.11:1) was available optionally.

I.D. DATA: Engine numbers. Starting: 78026. Ending: 78586.

Model 5-48, 6-cyl.

Model No.	Body Type & Seating	Factory Price	Shipping Weight	Prod. Total
63	Tr.-7P	4850	4623	Note 1
60	Salon Tr.-7P	4850	4573	Note 1
66	Phae.-5P	4750	4557	Note 1
65	Phae.-4P	4750	4490	Note 1
67	Rbt.-2P	4750	4310	Note 1
72	Limo.-7P	5950	4909	Note 1
75	Land.-7P	5950	4897	Note 1
71	Limo.-6P	5900	4874	Note 1
76	Land.-6P	5900	4857	Note 1
69	Imp. Limo.-6P	6100	4982	Note 1
68	Imp. Limo.-7P	6150	5015	Note 1
70	Salon Limo.-7P	6100	4960	Note 1
79	Brgm.-6P	6000	4932	Note 1
80	Salon Brgm.-4P	5950	4882	Note 1
59	Cpe.-3P	5450	4577	Note 1

Note 1: Packard Model 5-48 production for 1915 totaled 360 with no body style breakout available.

ENGINE: L-head. Six. Cast iron block. B & S: 4-1/2 x 5-1/2 in. Disp.: 525 cu. in. Brake H.P.: 60 @ 1200 R.P.M.

CHASSIS: W.B.: 144 in. O.L.: 202-1/4 in. (touring-204-3/4 in.)

TECHNICAL: Rear mounted sliding gear transmission. Speeds: 3F/1R. Disc clutch. Overall ratio: 3.28:1. Optional: 3.11:1. Mechanical brakes on two rear wheels. Wood, artillery wheels.

HISTORICAL: Introduced October 1914. Model year production: 360.

1916

PACKARD — TWIN SIX (1-25, 1-35) — TWELVE: This was the first year of the famous Twin Six, the model designations corresponding to the two wheelbase lengths of 125 and 135 inches. With this car, Packard relocated its gearbox from the rear axle to a position behind the clutch housing (although the shift lever was still to the left of the driver). Top speed was 70 miles an hour, this model being noted for its smooth acceleration in high from a sedate 4 mph. The Twin Six standard paint scheme for open cars was Packard blue striped with cream yellow for body and door panels; underbody, body front, hood, radiator, frame, fenders, splashers, moldings and all running gear parts were black with no striping; wheels were cream yellow striped with black. For closed cars, the standard was Packard blue striped with black for body and door panels, with exterior hardware in black. Exterior hardware on open bodies was furnished in nickel only. Standard equipment included a one-man top, side curtains, windshield, Sparton horn, complete tool kit, Warner speedometer, Waltham clock, tire carrier, power tire pump.

I.D. DATA: Engine numbers. Starting: 80000. Ending: 87787.

Model 1-25, Twin Six, 12-cyl., 125" wb

Model No.	Body Type & Seating	Factory Price	Shipping Weight	Prod. Total
82	Rbt.-2P	2600	3910	Note 1
84	Cpe.-3P	3550	4175	Note 1
118	Tr.-7P	2950	4190	Note 1
119	Salon Tr.-7P	2950	4180	Note 1
81	Phae.-5P	2950	4130	Note 1
117	Salon Phae.-5P	2950	4120	Note 1
114	Limo.-6P	4350	4415	Note 1
115	Land.-6P	4350	4395	Note 1
83	Brgm.-4P	4400	4365	Note 1
Model 1-35, Twin Six, 12-cyl., 135" wb				
90	Tr.-7P	3150	4285	Note 1
91	Salon Tr.-7P	3150	4275	Note 1
94	Phae.-5P	3150	4220	Note 1
95	Salon Phae.-5P	3150	4210	Note 1
100	Limo.-6P	4550	4550	Note 1
102	Land.-6P	4550	4540	Note 1
111	Brgm.-4P	4600	4475	Note 1
105	Limo.-7P	4600	4585	Note 1
101	Cab Sides Limo.-7P	4650	4630	Note 1
98	Imp. Limo.-7P	4800	4715	Note 1

Note 1: Packard Model 1-25 and Model 1-35 combined production for 1916 totaled 3,606 with no model breakout or body style breakout available.

ENGINE: L-head, 60 degree V-12. Two cast iron blocks of six. B & S: 3 x 5 in. Disp.: 424.1 cu. in. Brake H.P.: 88 @ 2600 R.P.M. Net H.P.: 43.2. Main bearings: three. Valve lifters: mechanical, solid. Carb.: Packard pressure-feed.

CHASSIS: [Model 1-25]: W.B.: 125 in. Tires: 36 x 4-1/2 front, 37 x 5 rear. [Model 1-35]: W.B.: 135 in. Tires: 36 x 4-1/2 front, 37 x 5 rear.

TECHNICAL Sliding gear transmission. Speeds: 3F/1R. Multi-disc clutch. Mechanical brakes only on rear wheels. Artillery wheels.

HISTORICAL: Introduced May 1915. Model year production: 3,606.

1917

PACKARD — TWIN SIX (2-25, 2-35) — TWELVE: Engineering refinements to the second series of the Twin Six included detachable cylinder heads and removal of the thermostat from the block to the upper tank of the radiator. With smaller (35 x 5) wheels used all around, these new cars appeared considerably lower than their predecessors. The 2-25's wheelbase was increased an inch-and-a-half, and a four-passenger runabout was a new body style. As in the previous year, no runabout was offered in the longer-wheelbase 2-35 line.

I.D. DATA: Engine numbers. Starting: 125051. Ending: 150000.

Model 2-25, Twin Six, 12-cyl., 126-1/2" wb

Model No.	Body Type & Seating	Factory Price	Shipping Weight	Prod. Total
151	Cpe.-3P	4150	4425	Note 1
149	Rbt.-2P	2865	4150	Note 1
167	Rbt.-4P	2865	4250	Note 1
145	Tr.-7P	3265	4460	Note 1
146	Phae.-5P	3265	4375	Note 1
147	Salon Phae.-5P	3265	4365	Note 1
152	Limo.-6P	4665	4700	Note 1
153	Land.-6P	4715	4680	Note 1
150	Brgm.-4P	4715	4550	Note 1
Model 2-35, Twin Six, 12-cyl., 135" wb				
154	Tr.-7P	3500	4562	Note 2
155	Salon Tr.-7P	3500	4552	Note 2
156	Phae.-5P	3500	4450	Note 2
157	Salon Phae.-5P	3500	4450	Note 2
160	Limo.-6P	4900	4800	Note 2
161	Limo.-7P	4950	4850	Note 2
164	Cab Sides Limo.-7P	5000	4900	Note 2

Model No.	Body Type & Seating	Factory Price	Shipping Weight	Prod. Total
158	Imp. Limo.-7P	5150	4970	Note 2
159	Salon Limo.-7P	5100	4910	Note 2
163	Land.-7P	5000	4800	Note 2
165	Cab Sides Land.-7P	5050	4850	Note 2
162	Land.-6P	4950	4790	Note 2
166	Salon Brgm.-4P	4950	4740	Note 2

Note 1: Packard Model 2-25 production for 1917 totaled 4,950 with no body style breakout available.

Note 2: Packard Model 2-35 production for 1917 totaled 4,049 with no body style breakout available.

ENGINE: L-head, 60 degree V-12. Two cast iron blocks of six. B & S: 3 x 5 in. Disp.: 424.1 cu. in. Brake H.P.: 88 @ 2600 R.P.M. Net H.P.: 43.2. Main bearings: three. Valve lifters: mechanical. Carb.: Packard pressure-feed.

CHASSIS: [Model 2-25]: W.B.: 126-1/2 in. [2-35, 135 in.] Tires: 35 x 5.

TECHNICAL: Sliding gear transmission. Speeds: 3F/1R. Multi-disc clutch. Spiral bevel gear. Mechanical brakes on rear wheels. Artillery wheels.

HISTORICAL: Introduced August 1916. Model year production: [2-25] 4,950 units; [2-35] 4,049 units.

1918-1919

PACKARD — TWIN SIX (3-25, 3-35) — TWELVE: The third series Twin Six was an evolution of the second series. Improved head design of the 12-cylinder engine provided better breathing and a modest horsepower increase. The gearshift lever was relocated from the driver's left to the center of the floor. The speedometer cable drive was moved from the front wheel to the rear of the transmission. Wheelbases of both the 3-25 and 3-35 were lengthened slightly. Interestingly, there were more 3-25 body styles offered than 3-35 body styles, a reverse of the previous seasons. The third series Twin Six was introduced June 1, 1917, for the 1918 model year, and was continued through 1919. Production for the period totaled 4,180 units of the 3-25, 5,406 units of the 3-35.

I.D. DATA: Engine numbers. Starting: 150051. Ending: N/A.

Model 3-25, Twin Six, 12-cyl., 128" wbl

Model No.	Body Type & Seating	Factory Price	Shipping Weight	Prod. Total
168	Tr.-7P	3450	4435	Note 1
169	Salon Tr.-7P	3450	4400	Note 1
181	Phae.-5P	3450	4280	Note 1
183	Salon Phae.-5P	3450	4250	Note 1
171	Rbt.-4P	3450	4210	Note 1
174	Cpe.-4P	4800	4326	Note 1
172	Limo.-7P	5000	4710	Note 1
173	Land.-7P	5050	4745	Note 1
175	Imp. Limo.-7P	5200	4860	Note 1
184	Brgm.-6P	5050	4372	Note 1
185	Brgm.-7P	5150	4755	Note 1
Model 3-35, Twin Six, 12-cyl., 136" wb				
194	Tr.-7P	3850	4490	Note 2
177	Salon Tr.-7P	3850	4465	Note 2
207	Limo.-7P	5400	4780	Note 2
180	Land.-7P	5450	4825	Note 2
178	Imp. Limo.-7P	5600	4920	Note 2
185	Brgm.-7P	5500	4845	Note 2

Note 1: Packard Model 3-25 production totaled 4,180 over three years of availability: 1,788 for 1917; 1,518 for 1918; and 874 for 1919. No body style breakout is available.

Note 2: Packard Model 3-35 production totaled 5,406 over three years of availability: 1,470 for 1917; 1,221 for 1918; and 2,715 for 1919. No body style breakout is available.

ENGINE: L-head, 60 degree V-12. Two cast iron blocks of six. B & S: 3 x 5 in. Disp.: 424.1 cu. in. Brake H.P.: 90 @ 2600 R.P.M. Net H.P.: 43.2. Main bearings: three. Valve lifters: mechanical, solid. Carb.: Packard pressure-feed.

CHASSIS: W.B.: [3-25] 128 in. [3-35] 136 in.

TECHNICAL: Sliding gear transmission. Speeds: 3F/1R. Multi-disc clutch. Spiral bevel gear. Mechanical brakes on rear wheels. Artillery wheels.

HISTORICAL: Introduced June 1917. Model 3-25 production: 1,788 cars (1917), 1,518 (1918), 874 (1919). Model 3-35 production: 1,470 cars (1917), 1,221 (1918), 2,715 (1919).

1920-1923

PACKARD — TWIN SIX (3-35) — TWELVE: Following the end of the World War I, the 3-25 was phased out in 1919, one final car being built in 1920. The 3-35 continued to be built through 1923, with prices progressively reduced in the wake of the postwar recession. The Packard company came to the conclusion that the Twin Six was simply too expensive to build. New to the 3-35 in 1920 was the "Fuelizer" incorporating a spark plug in the intake manifold to help vaporize the gasoline, with "Fuelizer" kits provided for the earlier models. In 1921, Warren G. Harding became the first U.S. President to travel to his inaugural in an automobile. The automobile was a Packard Twin Six. A total of 8,750 Twin Sixes were built from 1920 until discontinuation in 1923.

I.D. DATA: Engine numbers. Starting: 21000. Ending: N/A.

Model 3-35, Twin Six, 12-cyl., 136" wb

Model No.	Body Type & Seating	Factory Price	Shipping Weight	Prod. Total
1920				
176	Tr.-7P	6000	4470	Note 1
195	Phae.-5P	6000	4300	Note 1
196	Rbt.-4P	6000	4245	Note 1
185	Cpe.-5P	NA	4430	Note 1
209	Duplex Cpe.-5P	8200	4580	Note 1
177	Sed.-7P	NA	4520	Note 1
208	Duplex Sed.-7P	8450	4670	Note 1
178	Limo.-7P	8350	4595	Note 1
1921				
176/194	Tr.-7P	4850	4470	Note 1
195	Phae.-5P	4850	4300	Note 1
196	Rbt.-4P	4850	4245	Note 1
185	Cpe.-5P	6600	4430	Note 1
209/227	Duplex Cpe.-5P	6600	4580	Note 1
177	Sed.-7P	6850	4520	Note 1
208/226	Duplex Sed.-7P	6850	4670	Note 1
179	Limo.-7P	6650	4595	Note 1
1922-1923				
194	Tr.-7P	3850	4470	Note 1
195	Phae.-5P	3850	4300	Note 1
196	Rbt.-4P	3850	4245	Note 1
185	Cpe.-5P	5240	4430	Note 1
227	Duplex Cpe.-5P	5250	4580	Note 1
177	Sed.-7P	5400	4520	Note 1
226	Duplex Sed.-7P	5400	4670	Note 1
207	Limo.-7P	5275	4595	Note 1

Note 1: Packard Model 3-35 production for 1920-23 totaled 8,750: 5,193 in 1920; 1,310 in 1921; 1,944 in 1922; and 303 in 1923. No body style breakout is available.

ENGINE: L-head, 60 degree V-12. Two cast iron blocks of six. B & S: 3 x 5 in. Disp.: 424.1 cu. in. Brake H.P.: 90 @ 2600 R.P.M. Net H.P.: 43.2. Main bearings: three. Valve lifters: solid. Carb.: Packard downdraft with Fuelizer.

CHASSIS: W.B.: 136 in. Tires: 33 x 5.

TECHNICAL: Selective-sliding gear transmission. Speeds: 3F/1R. Multiple disc clutch. Spiral bevel gears. Overall ratio: 4.36:1. Mechanical brakes on rear wheels. Artillery wheels on detachable rims.

HISTORICAL: Introduced August 1919. Calendar year production: 5,193 cars in 1920; 1,310 in 1921; 1,944 in 1922, 303 in 1923.

1921-1922

PACKARD — SINGLE SIX (116) — SIX: The Single Six was introduced to provide a more economical alternative to the Twin Six, both for Packard to build and customers to buy. Benefiting from the company's Liberty aero engine development during World War I, its L-head 241.5-cubic inch straight six developed 52 hp, nearly as much power as a prewar six at twice the displacement and twice the weight. Both cast aluminum crankcase and oil pan were bolted to the cast iron cylinder block, the oil pan easily removable. The Fuelizer introduced on the Twin Six was retained. The handbrake was placed on the driver's left. Closed bodies used whipcord with leather for the front seat and doors; open cars were completely leather upholstered. Unfortunately, the Single Six's development had been costly, with the result that the car was introduced with price tags dangerously close to the Twin Six's. Still, price was not the Single Six's principal problem, as successive price reductions during the model year proved. The principal problem was that this new Packard didn't seem to be a Packard at all. Its wheelbase was a short 116 inches, which made for a boxy look; its body styles were only four, none of which seated more than five passengers. The standard paint scheme was Packard blue for body, black for fenders and running gear, no striping. The Single

Six was introduced in September 1920, with 1,042 cars built in the remainder of that year; only 6,374 cars were sold for the whole of the 1921 calendar year. In February of 1922, rumors spread that a new version of the Single Six was imminent. The official announcement arrived in April. Only 1,384 Single Six 116s were built in calendar year 1922 — for a total production for the model of just 8,800 units.

I.D. DATA: Engine numbers. Starting: 26. Ending: 8850.

Single Six/Model 116, 6-cyl.

Model No.	Body Type & Seating	Factory Price	Shipping Weight	Prod. Total
190	Tr.-5P	3640	2920	Note 1
191	Rbt.-2P	3640	2790	Note 1
192	Sed.-5P	4950	3170	Note 1
193	Cpe.-4P	4835	2990	Note 1

Note 1: Packard Single Six production for 1920-22 totaled 8,800: 1,042 for 1920; 6,374 for 1921; and 1,384 for 1922. No body style breakout is available.

Note: Single Six prices were reduced several times, and by October 1921 the cars were selling for $2,350 (touring and runabout), $3,350 (sedan), $3,125 (coupe).

ENGINE: L-head, straight six. Cast enbloc. B & S: 3-3/8 x 4-1/2 in. Disp.: 241.5 cu. in. Brake H.P.: 52 @ 2400 R.P.M. Net H.P.: 27.3. Main bearings: seven. Carb.: Packard-updraft with Fuelizer.

CHASSIS: W.B.: 116 in. Tires: 33 x 4-1/2.

TECHNICAL: Selective transmission. Speeds: 3F/1R. Seven plate, eight-inch clutch. Bevel gears. Overall ratio: 4.31:1. Mechanical brakes on rear wheels. Wood spoke wheels.

HISTORICAL: Introduced September 1920. Model year production: 8,800.

1922-1923

PACKARD — SINGLE SIX (126, 133) — SIX: Although this new Single Six incorporated such engineering revisions as a somewhat complicated nine-plate clutch, a slight increase in stroke for 54 hp and the removal of the water pump to the front of the engine, the really big news was wheelbase and body styling, and the number of body styles available. There were five now on a 126-inch chassis, including a debonair four-passenger Sport Model that was two inches lower and rode on disc wheels as standard. Three seven-passenger body styles were also added, on a 133-inch chassis. A new belt molding ran the entire length of open car bodies, a feature other manufacturers would soon imitate. The standard paint scheme was Packard Blue striped with gold, fenders and running gear in black enamel. Closed cars were black above the belt. To the original eight body styles introduced in April 1922, a coupe and sedan-limousine for five passengers were added in October of that year, a five-passenger touring sedan following in June of 1923. Total Single Six 126-133 production was 26,560 cars, a healthy increase over the 116 that preceded it.

I.D. DATA: Engine numbers. Starting: 9000. Ending: 35942.

Single Six, Model 126, 6-cyl.

Model No.	Body Type & Seating	Factory Price	Shipping Weight	Prod. Total
220	Tr.-5P	2485	3225	Note 1
223	Rbt.-2P	2485	3030	Note 1
224	Spt. Mod.-4P	2650	3165	Note 1
222	Cpe.-4P	3175	3305	Note 1
221	Sed.-5P	3275	3455	Note 1
230	Cpe.-5P	3550	3360	Note 1
231	Sed. Limo.-5P	3325	3525	Note 1
232	Tr. Sed.-5P	2750	3360	Note 1
Single Six, Model 133, 6-cyl.				
225	Tr.-7P	2685	3355	Note 2
229	Sed. Limo.-7P	3575	3680	Note 2
228	Sed.-7P	3525	3555	Note 2

Note 1: Packard Model 126 production for 1922-23 totaled 18,192. No body style breakout is available.

Note 2: Packard Model 133 production for 1922-23 totaled 8,368. No body style breakout is available.

ENGINE: L-head. Straight Six. Cast enbloc. B & S: 3-3/8 x 5 in. Disp.: 268.4 cu. in. C.R.: 4.8:1. Brake H.P.: 54 @ 2700 R.P.M. Main bearings: seven. Carb.: Packard-updraft with Fuelizer.

CHASSIS: W.B.: 126 in. and 133 in. Tires: 33 x 4-1/2.

TECHNICAL: Selective transmission. Speeds: 3F/1R. Nine-plate, eight-inch clutch. Bevel gear, spiral type rear axle. Overall ratio: [126] 4.3:1, [133] 4.66:1. Mechanical brakes on rear wheels. Wood and disc wheels.

OPTIONS: Disc wheels ($35.00) — standard on only the Sport Model.

HISTORICAL: Introduced April 20, 1922. Model year production: (126) 18,192, (133) 8,368.

1924

PACKARD — SINGLE EIGHT (136,143) — EIGHT: Eight cylinders and four-wheel brakes were introduced to Packard with this model. Like the Single Six, its 136 and 143 model designations reflected the two wheelbase lengths, which were 10 inches longer than the six, with all of that length put up front in the hood. Again, seven-passenger models were on the longer wheelbase. Packard's new nine-bearing straight-eight developed 85 bhp. The Fuelizer was retained, and a Lanchester vibration damper fitted on the front end of the crankshaft. There was four-point mounting of the engine. An air tire pump ran off the transmission; the service brake activated rear stoplights. Watson stabilizers were installed front and rear. Front and rear bumpers were standard, as were a moto-meter and disc wheels. The Winterfront, standard initially, was discontinued as such in December, available thereafter only as an option. A divided windshield with built-in hand-operated windshield wiper was fitted, as was a center-mounted rear view mirror inside. Single Eight bodies were essentially the same as the Single Six, but interior trim and upholstery was more luxurious and appointments more elegant. Black remained the standard for fenders and running gear, and above the belt for closed cars. Closed bodies were Packard blue striped with red until December, the striping thereafter Azure blue. Open cars were a vermilion-striped Dust Proof gray, with upholstery in hand crushed brown Spanish leather. Particularly rakish was the runabout with rumbleseat and golf bag compartment.

I.D. DATA: Engine numbers. Starting: 200001. Ending: 208428.

Single Eight, Model 136, 8-cyl.

Model No.	Body Type & Seating	Factory Price	Shipping Weight	Prod. Total
244	Touring-5P	3650	3990	Note 1
234	Runabout-2/4P	3850	3879	Note 1
246	Sport Model-4P	3800	3810	Note 1
239	Coupe-4P	4550	4125	Note 1
242	Coupe-5P	4725	4204	Note 1
237	Sedan-5P	4650	4260	Note 1
243	Sedan Limousine-5P	4700	4275	Note 1
Single Eight, Model 143, 8-cyl.				
245	Touring-7P	3850	4074	Note 2
240	Sedan-7P	4900	4379	Note 2
241	Sedan Limousine-7P	4950	4434	Note 2

Note 1: Packard Model 136 production totaled 7,871 with no body style breakout available.

Note 2: Packard Model 143 production totaled 4,894 with no body style breakout available.

ENGINE: L-head. Straight eight. Cast enbloc. B & S: 3-3/8 x 5 in. Disp.: 357.8 cu. in. C.R.: 4.51:1. Brake H.P.: 85 @ 3000 R.P.M. Net H.P.: 36.4. Main bearings: nine. Valve lifters: mechanical. Carb.: Packard updraft with Fuelizer.

CHASSIS: W.B.: 136 and 143 in. Tires: 35 x 5.

TECHNICAL: Selective transmission. Speeds: 3F/1R. Nine-plate clutch. Shaft drive to spiral bevel gears. Overall ratio: 4.7:1 (4.8:1 on roadster and sport models). Mechanical brakes on all wheels. Disc wheels.

HISTORICAL: Introduced June 14, 1923. Model year sales: (136) 7,871; (143) 4,894.

PACKARD — SINGLE SIX (226, 233) — SIX: Introduced in December of 1923, six months after the Single Eight, the new Packard Single Six incorporated many of the larger car's features: four-wheel brakes, service brake-activated stoplight, rear view mirror and divided windshield with windshield wiper among them. A battery box was fitted into the right front fender. The general $100 increase in prices was to accommodate the addition of the four-wheel braking system. Operating economy of the new Single Six was stressed, as much as 20 mpg and 20,000 miles on a set of tires being advertised. Open cars featured a tonneau light, and long grain black leather upholstery. Though not as elegantly appointed, closed car interiors did include vanity cases and smoking sets. Body styles on the longer 133-inch wheelbase remained the same three seven-passenger cars as the year previous. Four new body styles were added on the 126-inch wheelbase, though the touring sedan would be discontinued before the end of the model run. The former two-passenger runabout had been replaced with a rumbleseat version with golf bag compartment.

I.D. DATA: Engine numbers. Starting: 37000. Ending: 48917.

Single Six, Model 226, 6-cyl.

Model No.	Body Type & Seating	Factory Price	Shipping Weight	Prod. Total
220	Touring-5P	2585	3317	Note 1
223	Runabout-2/4P	2785	3317	Note 1
230	Coupe-5P	3450	3438	Note 1
232	Touring Sed.-5P	2850	3360	Note 1
222	Coupe-4P	3275	3438	Note 1
221	Sedan-5P	3375	3582	Note 1
231	Sedan Limousine-5P	3425	3682	Note 1
224	Sport Model-4P	2750	3323	Note 1
Single Six, Model 233, 6-cyl.				
225	Touring Sedan-7P	2785	3432	Note 2
229	Sedan Limousine-7P	3675	3817	Note 2
228	Sedan-7P	3625	3715	Note 2

Note 1: Packard Model 226 production totaled 8,094 with no body style breakout available.

Note 2: Packard Model 233 production totaled 3,131 with no body style breakout available.

ENGINE: L-head. Straight six. Cast iron block. B & S: 3-3/8 x 5 in. Disp.: 268.4 cu. in. C.R.: 4.8:1. Brake H.P.: 54 @ 2700 R.P.M. Net H.P.: 27.34. Main bearings: seven. Valve lifters: mechanical. Carb.: Packard updraft with Fuelizer.

CHASSIS: W.B.: 126 in. and 133 in. Tires: 33 x 5.

TECHNICAL: Selective transmission. Speeds: 3F/1R. Nine-plate, eight-inch clutch. Bevel gear, spiral type rear axle. Overall ratio: 4.36:1. Mechanical brakes on four wheels. Wood wheels.

HISTORICAL: Introduced December 27, 1923. Model year production: [226] 8,094, [233] 3,131.

1925-1926

PACKARD — SECOND SERIES (236, 243) — EIGHT: The Single Eight designation was dropped, the cars being simply called the Eight now. Bijur chassis lubrication was a fine and progressive new addition, the Skinner Oil Rectifier was not. Disc wheels and balloon tires were standard. Hotchkiss drive was adopted during the spring of 1926. Though weighing in at an average of 4,000 pounds, these cars could do as much as 80 mph. The cars had been introduced in February 1925 in the usual Packard paint schemes, but by that summer, with the availability of pyroxylin lacquers, the colors available were broadened. Mid-model run, too, saw revision to a simplified Bendix braking system and the replacement of the former divided windshield with a one-piece. A club sedan was the first five-passenger car to be cataloged on the longer 143-inch wheelbase. A Holbrook Coupe was the first custom car to be cataloged on the 133-inch chassis. But available from the spring of 1926 too, was a variety of custom cars, advertised as "Original Creations by Master Designers," on the 143-inch wheelbase. These were presented in a special custom catalog and included a four-passenger Sedan Cabriolet by Judkins (Style No. 6413), a five-passenger Stationary Town Cabriolet by Derham (Style No. 3509), a five-passenger Stationary Town Cabriolet by Fleetwood (Style No. 1509), a seven-passenger Inside Drive Limousine Sedan by Holbrook (Style No. 2711), and the following designs by Dietrich: five-passenger Stationary Town Cabriolet (Style No. 1177), two-passenger Convertible Coupe (Style No. 1222), four-passenger Sedan (Style No. 1176).

I.D. DATA: Engine numbers. Starting: 208997. Ending: 219002.

Model 236, 8-cyl.

Model No.	Body Type & Seating	Factory Price	Shipping Weight	Prod. Total
239	Coupe-4P	4650	4147	Note 1
242	Coupe-5P	4825	4337	Note 1
281	Holbrook-2P	3750	4178	Note 1
234	Runabout-4P	3950	3965	Note 1
253	Sedan-5P	4750	4433	Note 1
257	Sedan Limousine-5P	4850	4535	Note 1
246	Sport-4P	3900	4023	Note 1
244	Touring-5P	3750	4090	Note 1
Model 243, 8-cyl.				
254	Sedan-7P	5000	4560	Note 2
255	Club Sedan-5P	4890	4573	Note 2
256	Sedan Limousine-7P	5100	4615	Note 2
245	Touring-7P	3950	4104	Note 2

Note 1: Packard Model 236 production totaled 2,794 with no body style breakout available.

Note 2: Packard Model 243 production totaled 5,118 with no body style breakout available.

ENGINE: L-head. Straight eight. Cast iron block. B & S: 3-3/8 x 5 in. Disp.: 357.8 cu. in. C.R.: 4.51:1. Brake H.P.: 85 @ 3000 R.P.M. Net H.P.: 36.4. Main bearings: nine. Valve lifters: mechanical. Carb.: Packard updraft with Fuelizer.

CHASSIS: W.B.: 136 and 143 in. Tires: 33 x 6.75.

TECHNICAL: Selective transmission. Speeds: 3F/1R. Multi-disc clutch. Shaft drive and bevel gear rear axle. Overall ratio: 4.66:1 (4.08:1 for roadster and sport models). Mechanical brakes on all wheels. Disc wheels.

HISTORICAL: Introduced February 2, 1925. Model year production: (236) 2,794, (243) 5,118.

PACKARD — THIRD SERIES (326, 333) — SIX: The Single Six became simply the Six this year, its engine bored out to 3-1/2 inches for an increase in horsepower to 60. Disc wheels were standard. The Six enjoyed the Eight's engineering changes, including Bijur and Skinner Oil Rectifier—and the wider color availability with lacquer. Phaeton was a new body style for the 126-inch wheelbase, as was a four-passenger coupe with separate trunk though it was discontinued by the end of 1925. The club sedan was a new addition on the longer 133-inch wheelbase. The introduction of the custom catalog during the spring of 1926 saw these body styles available also on the Six's 133-inch wheelbase, and the Holbrook Coupe became available at that time on the 126-inch chassis as well.

I.D. DATA: Engine numbers. Starting: 49501. Ending: 90463.

Model 326, 6-cyl.

Model No.	Body Type & Seating	Factory Price	Shipping Weight	Prod. Total
268	Coupe-2P	2660	3590	Note 1
222	Coupe-4P	3275	3658	Note 1
230	Coupe-5P	3450	3876	Note 1
226	Phaeton-5P	3450	3558	Note 1
223	Runabout-4P	2785	3458	Note 1
221	Sedan-5P	3375	3842	Note 1
231	Sedan Limousine-5P	3425	3974	Note 1
224	Sport Model-5P	2750	3595	Note 1
220	Touring-5P	2585	3653	Note 1
Model 333, 6-cyl.				
265	Club Sedan-5P	2725	4080	Note 2
266	Sedan-7P	2785	3948	Note 2
267	Sedan Limousine-7P	3675	4038	Note 2
225	Touring-7P	2785	3698	Note 2

Note 1: Packard Model 326 production totaled 24,668 with no body style breakout available.

Note 2: Packard Model 333 production totaled 15,690 with no body style breakout available.

ENGINE: L-head. Straight six. Cast enbloc. B & S: 3-1/2 x 5 in. Disp.: 288.6 cu. in. C.R.: 4.8:1. Brake H.P.: 60 @ 3200 R.P.M. Net H.P.: 29.4. Main bearings: seven. Valve lifters: mechanical. Carb.: Packard updraft with Fuelizer.

CHASSIS: W.B.: 126 in. O.L.: 16 ft. Tires: 33 x 5.7. W.B.: 133 in. Tires: 33 x 5.7.

TECHNICAL: Selective transmission. Speeds: 3F/1R. Nine-plate, eight-inch clutch. Hotchkiss rear axle. Overall ratio: 4.31:1. Mechanical brakes on four wheels. Disc wheels.

HISTORICAL: Introduced February 2, 1925. Model year production: (326) 24,668, (333) 15,690.

1927

PACKARD — THIRD SERIES (336, 343) — EIGHT: Massive engineering changes to Packard's straight-eight — including aluminum pistons, turbohead combustion chamber, revised manifolding, a boring out to 3-1/2 inches — resulted in a considerable increase of horsepower to 109. The Fuelizer was dropped at introduction in August 1926, with the Skinner Oil Rectifier discontinued during the model run. The two-plate clutch and hypoid differential were new. The phaeton replaced the sport model, and all cars featured full crown one-piece fenders. The Holbrook Coupe was transferred to the custom department. Body styles on the 136-inch wheelbase were reduced to three: phaeton, runabout, sedan. A four-passenger coupe joined the previous offerings on the 143-inch chassis.

I.D. DATA: Engine numbers. Starting: 220000. Ending: 224999.

Model 336, 8-cyl.

Model No.	Body Type & Seating	Factory Price	Shipping Weight	Prod. Total
291	Phaeton-5P	3750	4130	Note 1
292	Runabout-2/4P	3850	4110	Note 1
293	Sedan-5P	4750	4430	Note 1

Model 343, 8-cyl.

Model No.	Body Type & Seating	Factory Price	Shipping Weight	Prod. Total
294	Sedan-7P	5000	4660	Note 2
295	Sedan Limousine-7P	5100	4700	Note 2
296	Club Sedan-5P	4890	4550	Note 2
297	Coupe-4P	4750	4475	Note 2
290	Touring-7P	3950	4250	Note 2

Note 1: Packard Model 336 production totaled 1,245 with no body style breakout available.

Note 2: Packard Model 343 production totaled 3,241 with no body style breakout available.

ENGINE: L-head. Straight eight. Cast enbloc. B & S: 3-1/2 x 5 in. Disp.: 384.8 cu. in. Brake H.P.: 109 @ 3200 R.P.M. Net H.P.: 39.2. Main bearings: nine. Valve lifters: mechanical. Carb.: Packard updraft.

CHASSIS: W.B.: 136 and 143 in. Tires: 33 x 6.75.

TECHNICAL: Selective transmission. Speeds: 3F/1R. Two plate clutch. Shaft drive and hypoid differential. Overall ratio: 4.33:1 (4.66:1 and 4.1:1 optional). Mechanical brakes. Disc wheels.

HISTORICAL: Introduced August 1926. Model year production: (336) 1,245, (343) 3,241.

PACKARD — FOURTH SERIES (426, 433) — SIX: The same engineering changes that made a phenomenally better performer of the Packard Eight accomplished the same thing on the Six: Though bore/stroke measurements and displacement remained the same, horsepower was now up to 81. The Fuelizer was dropped immediately, the Skinner Oil Rectifier later in the year. The two-plate clutch and hypoid differential were new. A reorganization of body styles eliminated many on the 126-inch wheelbase, with a five-passenger sedan the only closed car available on that chassis. All other closed cars — the new four-passenger coupe included — were on the 133-inch wheelbase.

I.D. DATA: Engine numbers. Starting: 950007. Ending: 120407.

Model 426, 6-cyl.

Model No.	Body Type & Seating	Factory Price	Shipping Weight	Prod. Total
301	Phaeton-5P	2585	3590	Note 1
302	Runabout-4P	2685	3545	Note 1
303	Sedan-5P	2585	3925	Note 1

Model 433, 6-cyl.

Model No.	Body Type & Seating	Factory Price	Shipping Weight	Prod. Total
300	Touring 7P	2785	3790	Note 2
304	Sedan-7P	2785	4070	Note 2
305	Sedan Limousine-7P	2885	4130	Note 2
306	Club Sedan-5P	2725	4015	Note 2
307	Coupe-4P	2685	3925	Note 2

Note 1: Packard Model 426 production totaled 14,401 with no body style breakout available.

Note 2: Packard Model 433 production totaled 10,934 with no body style breakout available.

ENGINE: L-head. Straight eight. Cast enbloc. B & S: 3-1/2 x 5 in. Disp.: 288.6 cu. in. Brake H.P.: 81 @ 3200 R.P.M. Net H.P.: 29.4. Main bearings: seven. Valve lifters: mechanical. Carb.: Packard updraft.

CHASSIS: W.B.: 126 and 133 in. Tires: 33 x 5.70.

TECHNICAL: Selective transmission. Speeds: 3F/1R. Two plate clutch. Shaft drive and hypoid differential. Overall ratio: 4.66:1 (5.10:1 and 4.33:1 optional). Mechanical brakes on all wheels. Disc wheels.

HISTORICAL: Introduced August 1926. Model year production: (426) 14,401, (433) 10,934.

1928

PACKARD — FOURTH SERIES, CUSTOM AND STANDARD MODEL (443) — EIGHT: A single wheelbase, 143 inches in length, carried all eight-cylinder Packards in the Fourth Series. The Custom Eight was introduced in July 1927, and was really a misnomer since the real custom cars were in Packard's custom coachwork catalog: 20 designs from eight coachbuilders (Rollston, Holbrook, Dietrich, LeBaron, Judkins, Derham, Murphy and Fleetwood). The nine production styles available in the Custom Eight 443 were repeated in the Standard Model that was introduced seven months later, on March 1, 1928. The Standard Model 443 was essentially the Custom 443 in a less luxurious and significantly less pricier car. Side-mounted spares and a full range of color options were offered in the Custom 443 rear-mounted spares and fewer color options were offered on the Standard Model 443. The Packard straight-eight engine now had dual coils and an oil spray cylinder lubrication device. An oil filter and rubber engine mounts were new this year, too. The wisdom of introducing a less expensive eight-cylinder Packard was reflected in the production totals: only 4,486 Packard eights had been built during the 1927 model year; the figure for 1928 would be 7,800 cars.

I.D. DATA: Engine numbers. Starting: 225013. Ending: 232815.

Model 443 Custom, 8-cyl.

Model No.	Body Type & Seating	Factory Price	Shipping Weight	Prod. Total
311	Phaeton-5P	3975	4295	Note 1
312	Runabout-2/4P	3975	4290	Note 1
318	Coupe-2/4P	4150	4626	Note 1
317	Coupe-4P	4950	4510	Note 1
319	Convertible Coupe-2/4P	4250	4380	Note 1
316	Club Sedan-5P	4950	4585	Note 1
314	Sedan-7P	5150	4825	Note 1
315	Sedan Limousine-7P	5250	4900	Note 1
310	Touring-7P	4040	4395	Note 1

Model 443 Standard, 8-cyl.

Model No.	Body Type & Seating	Factory Price	Shipping Weight	Prod. Total
381	Phaeton-5P	3650	4130	Note 1
382	Runbout-2/4P	3650	4110	Note 1
388	Coupe-2/4P	3550	4400	Note 1
387	Coupe-4P	3750	4400	Note 1
389	Convertible Coupe-2/4P	3650	4345	Note 1
386	Club Sedan-5P	3750	4360	Note 1
384	Sedan-7P	3750	4550	Note 1
385	Sedan Limousine-7P	3850	4710	Note 1
380	Touring-7P	3550	4200	Note 1

Note 1: Packard Model 443 (Custom and Standard combined) production totaled 7,800 with no body style breakout available.

ENGINE: L-head. Straight eight. Cast enbloc. B & S: 3-1/2 x 5 in. Disp.: 384.8 cu. in. Brake H.P.: 109 @ 3200 R.P.M. Net H.P.: 39.2. Main bearings: nine. Valve lifters: mechanical. Carb.: Packard updraft.

CHASSIS: W.B.: 143 in. Tires: 32 x 6.75.

TECHNICAL: Selective transmission. Speeds: 3F/1R. Two-plate clutch. Hypoid differential. Overall ratio: 4.33:1 (closed cars), 4.07:1 (open cars). Mechanical brakes on all wheels. Disc wheels.

HISTORICAL: Introduced July 1927. Model year production: 7,800 units.

PACKARD — FIFTH SERIES (526, 533) — SIX: These would be the last six-cylinder Packards until 1937. New cylinder lubrication (choke operated), an oil filter and four-point engine mounting (instead of the former three) were featured. Although few were ordered, the coach-built body styles in Packard's custom car catalog were available on the longer 133-inch Six wheelbase. A phaeton and two-passenger runabout were new production bodies on that chassis; a coupe and convertible coupe were added on the 126-inch Six wheelbase.

I.D. DATA: Engine numbers. Starting: 125013. Ending: 166770.

Model 526, 6-cyl.

Model No.	Body Type & Seating	Factory Price	Shipping Weight	Prod. Total
301	Phaeton-5P	2275	3665	Note 1
302	Runabout-4P	2275	3620	Note 1
303	Sedan-5P	2285	4000	Note 1
308	Coupe-2/4P	2350	3950	Note 1
309	Convertible Coupe-2/4P	2425	3875	Note 1

Model 533, 6-cyl.

Model No.	Body Type & Seating	Factory Price	Shipping Weight	Prod. Total
300	Touring-7P	2485	3865	Note 2
304	Sedan-7P	2685	4145	Note 2
306	Club Sedan-5P	2685	4085	Note 2
305	Sedan Limousine-7P	2785	4205	Note 2
307	Coupe-4P	2685	4000	Note 2
321	Phaeton-5P	2385	3745	Note 2
322	Runabout-4P	2385	3700	Note 2

Note 1: Packard Model 526 production totaled 28,336 with no body style breakout available.

Note 2: Packard Model 533 production totaled 13,414 with no body style breakout available.

ENGINE: L-head. Straight six. Cast enbloc. B & S: 3-1/2 x 5 in. Brake H.P.: 81 @ 3200 R.P.M. Net H.P.: 29.4. Main bearings: seven. Valve lifters: mechanical. Carb.: Packard updraft.

CHASSIS: [Model 526] W.B.: 126 in. Tires: 32 x 6. [Model 533] W.B.: 133 in. Tires: 32 x 6.75.

TECHNICAL: Selective transmission. Speeds: 3F/1R. Two-plate clutch. Hypoid differential. Overall ratio: 4.33:1. Mechanical brakes on all wheels. Disc wheels.

OPTIONS: Single sidemount. Cowl lights ($45.00).

HISTORICAL: Introduced July 1, 1927. Model year production: (526) 28,336, (533) 13,414.

1924 Packard, Single Eight (Model 143), sedan, HAC

1927 Packard, Model 426, runabout, AA

1928 Packard, Model 443, dual cowl phaeton (with body by LeBaron), AA

1929 Packard, Deluxe Eight (Model 645), runabout (with body by Rollston), AA

1930 Packard, Standard Eight (Model 733), roadster, AA

1932 Packard, Twin Six (Model 906), convertible sedan (with body by Dietrich), AA

1932 Packard, Deluxe Eight (Model 903), coupe roadster, AA

1935 Packard, Eight (Model 1201), phaeton, AA

1935 Packard, Twelve (Model 1208), sedan, JAC

1929

PACKARD — SIXTH SERIES, STANDARD EIGHT (626, 633) — EIGHT: Packard went straight-eight across the board in 1929. The new Standard Eight replaced the former Six, retaining its two chassis lengths though with a half-inch increment to 126-1/2 and 133-1/2 inches. Packard-designed shock absorbers replaced the Watson Stabilizers. The new 319.2-cubic inch engine was basically a smaller brother to the 348.8-cubic inch Custom and DeLuxe Eight, sharing the same stroke but with a slightly smaller bore. Many parts were interchangeable. The moto-meter was gone, replaced by a temperature gauge on the dash. Parabolic headlamps replaced the former drum types. All brightwork on the car was now chrome-plated, rather than nickel as previously. Disc wheels remained standard. The Standard Eight Model 626 offered a sedan, coupe and convertible coupe. All other body styles were on the longer Standard Eight Model 633.

I.D. DATA: Engine numbers. Starting: 233017. Ending: 276166.

Model 626, 8-cyl.

Model No.	Body Type & Seating	Factory Price	Shipping Weight	Prod. Total
333	Sedan-5P	2285	4185	Note 1
338	Coupe-2/4P	2350	4100	Note 1
339	Convertible Coupe-2/4P	2425	4020	Note 1
Model 633, 8-cyl.				
351	Phaeton-5P	2385	3905	Note 2
352	Runabout-2/4P	2385	3805	Note 2
330	Touring-7P	2485	3950	Note 2
334	Sedan-7P	2685	4440	Note 2
335	Sedan Limousine-7P	2785	4473	Note 2
336	Club Sedan-5P	2685	4340	Note 2
337	Coupe-4P	2575	4225	Note 2

Note 1: Packard Model 626 production totaled 26,070 with no body style breakout available.

Note 2: Packard Model 633 production totaled 17,060 with no body style breakout available.

ENGINE: L-head. Straight eight. Cast enbloc. B & S: 3-3/16 x 5 in. Disp.: 319.2 cu. in. Brake H.P.: 90 @ 3200 R.P.M. Main bearings: nine. Vibration damper. Carb.: Packard updraft.

CHASSIS: W.B.: 126-1/2 in. (626); 133-1/2 in. (633). Tires: 32 x 6.00 [626], 32 x 7.00 [633].

TECHNICAL: Selective transmission. Speeds 3F/1R. Single-plate clutch. Shaft drive and hypoid differential. Overall ratio: 4.38:1 (4.69:1 and 5.08:1 optional). Disc wheels.

HISTORICAL: Introduced August 1928. Model year production: 26,070 [626], 17,060 [633].

PACKARD — SIXTH SERIES, SPEEDSTER (626) — EIGHT: This was the hot Packard for 1929. Ostensibly it was the big eight engine in the small eight chassis, but it was much more than that. A high-lift camshaft, high compression head, metric plugs and a high-speed vacuum pump, amid other fine tuning, provided for 130 bhp and a 100 mph top speed. Even a muffler cutout was provided. Production was limited to just 70 cars of which only one has been confirmed as extant today.

I.D. DATA: Engine numbers. Starting: 166942. Ending: 167012.

Model 626, 8-cyl.

Model No.	Body Type & Seating	Factory Price	Shipping Weight	Prod. Total
391	Phae.-4P	NA	4300	Note 1
392	Rds.-2/4P	NA	4435	Note 1

Note 1: Packard Model 626 production for 1929 totaled 70 with no body style breakout available.

ENGINE: L-head. Straight eight. Cast enbloc. B & S: 3-1/2 x 5 in. Disp.: 384.4 cu. in. Brake H.P.: 130 @ 3200 R.P.M. Main bearings: nine. Valve lifters: solid. Carb.: Packard.

CHASSIS: W.B.: 126-1/2 in. Tires: 32 x 6.00.

TECHNICAL: Selective transmission. Speeds 3F/1R. Two-plate clutch. Shaft drive and hypoid differential. Overall ratio: 3.31.1. Mechanical brakes on all wheels. Disc wheels.

HISTORICAL: Introduced 1929. Model year production: 70.

PACKARD — SIXTH SERIES, CUSTOM EIGHT (640), DELUXE EIGHT (645) — EIGHT: Packard's big straight-eight was offered in the 140-1/2-inch wheelbase Custom Eight 640 and 145-1/2-inch wheelbase DeLuxe Eight 645. Body styles proliferated, with most available on either chassis, though the sport phaeton was strictly for the 645, the convertible coupe strictly for the 640. In addition, the "Individual Custom Line" featured 13 body designs from Dietrich, LeBaron and Rollston on the 645 chassis, three Dietrich designs on the 640 chassis. As with the Standard Eight, the moto-meter had given way to a temperature gauge on the dash, parabolic headlamps replaced the former drum types and all brightwork was chrome-plated. Disc wheels remained standard, however.

I.D. DATA: Engine numbers. Starting: 167001. Ending: 178879.

Model 640 Custom, 8-cyl.

Model No.	Body Type & Seating	Factory Price	Shipping Weight	Prod. Total
342	Rbt.-2/4P	3175	4285	Note 1
341	Phae.-5P	3175	4370	Note 1
348	Cpe.-2/4P	3250	4560	Note 1
340	Tour.-7P	3275	4390	Note 1
349	Conv. Cpe.-2/4P	3350	4475	Note 1
347	Cpe.-4P	3750	4535	Note 1
346	Club Sed.-5P	3750	4655	Note 1
344	Sed.-7P	3750	4835	Note 1
345	Sed. Limo.-7P	3850	4910	Note 1
Model 645 Deluxe, 8-cyl.				
372	Rbt.-2/4P	4585	4785	Note 2
371	Phae.-5P	4585	4870	Note 2
378	Cpe.-2/4P	5385	5060	Note 2
373	Spt. Phae.-5P	4935	4890	Note 2
370	Tour.-7P	4585	4890	Note 2
377	Cpe.-5P	5735	5125	Note 2
376	Club Sed.-5P	5785	5155	Note 2
374	Sed.-7P	5785	5335	Note 2
375	Sed. Limo.-7P	5985	5410	Note 2

Note 1: Packard Model 640 production totaled 9,801 with no body style breakout available.

Note 2: Packard Model 645 production totaled 2,061 with no body style breakout available.

ENGINE: L-head. Straight eight. Cast iron, cast enbloc. B & S: 3-1/2 x 5 in. Disp.: 384.8 cu. in. Brake H.P.: 105 @ 3200 R.P.M. Net H.P.: 39.2. Main bearings: nine. Valve lifters: mechanical. Carb.: Packard.

CHASSIS: [Custom] W.B.: 140-1/2 in. Tires: 32 x 7. [DeLuxe] W.B.: 145-1/2 in. Tires: 32 x 7.

TECHNICAL: Selective transmission. Speeds: 3F/1R. Two-plate clutch. Shaft drive and hypoid differential. Overall ratio: 4.07:1 open cars, 4.38:1 closed. Mechanical brakes on all wheels. Disc wheels.

OPTIONS: Dual Sidemount ($240.00). Sidemount cover(s). Wire wheels (80.00). Wood spoke (102.00).

HISTORICAL: Introduced August 1, 1928 [Custom]. September 1, 1928 [Deluxe]. Model year production: [640] 9,801, [645] 2,061.

1930

PACKARD — SEVENTH SERIES, STANDARD EIGHT (726, 733) — EIGHT: Wheelbases for the Standard Eight were increased an inch this year to accommodate the redesigned water pump, now with dual fan belts. The motor thermostat was eliminated, thermostatically controlled radiator shutters taking over temperature control completely. Horsepower was up to 90, the new carburetor was an updraft Detroit Lubricator, and the transmission now a four-speed with the addition of an extra low gear. Hoods of the Standard Eight featured louvered vents as previously, though an accessory hood with three louver doors was available to provide the Standard Packards more of the look of their four-door-louvered big brothers. A single body style was offered in the 127-1/2-inch wheelbase Model 726, and it was the five-passenger sedan. All other body styles were on the longer 134-1/2-inch wheelbase Model 733.

I.D. DATA: Engine numbers. Starting: 277013. Ending: 305283.

Model 726, 8-cyl.

Model No.	Body Type & Seating	Factory Price	Shipping Weight	Prod. Total
403	Sed.-5P	2375	4265	15,731
Model 733, 8-cyl.				
402	Rds.-2/4P	2425	3945	Note 1
401	Phae.-4P	2425	3935	Note 1
431	Spt. Phae.-4P	2725	4130	Note 1

Model No.	Body Type & Seating	Factory Price	Shipping Weight	Prod. Total
400	Tr.-7P	2525	4055	Note 1
408	Cpe.-2/4P	2525	4180	Note 1
409	Conv. Cpe.-2/4P	2550	4100	Note 1
407	Cpe.-5P	2675	4255	Note 1
406	Clb. Sed.-5P	2675	4325	Note 1
404	Sed.-7P	2675	4500	Note 1
405	Sed. Limo.-7P	2775	4555	Note 1

Note 1: Packard Model 733 production totaled 12,531 with no body style breakout available.

ENGINE: L-head, straight eight. Cast enbloc. B & S: 3-3/16 x 5 in. Disp.: 319.2 cu in. Brake H.P.: 90 @ 3200 R.P.M. Net H.P.: 32.5. Main bearings: nine. Valve lifters: solid. Carb.: Detroit Lubricator updraft.

CHASSIS: [Model 726] W.B.: 127-1/2 in. Tires: 20 x 6.00. [Model 733] W.B.: 134-1/2 in. Tires: 20 x 6.50.

TECHNICAL: Selective transmission. Speeds: 4F/1R. Single-plate clutch. Shaft drive and hypoid differential. Overall ratio: 4.38:1, 4.69:1, 5.08:1. Mechanical brakes on all wheels. Disc wheels.

OPTIONS: Three louver-door hood. Dual sidemount. Trunk rack. Fender parking lights ($20.00)

HISTORICAL: Introduced August 1929. Model year production: [726] 15,731, [733] 12,531.

PACKARD — SEVENTH SERIES, SPEEDSTER (734) — EIGHT: The 734 Speedster was Packard's answer to Cadillac's new V-16. Basically, it was a highly modified Standard Eight chassis of 134-1/2 inches into which was stuffed an equally modified DeLuxe eight engine. Different gear ratios and cylinder heads were provided, the choice up to the customer and at no extra cost. The hottest combination, the 8.0 head and the 3.3 differential, made for a Packard capable of better than 100 mph. A dual updraft carburetor was unique to the Speedster Series. Most speedsters came complete with a tachometer. Their bodies were lower and narrower than the Packard norm, and cataloged body styles numbered four: speedster runabout (the two-passenger boattailed version and the most famous), phaeton, victoria and sedan. A runabout version with rumbleseat was made available later, as was the 734 chassis to outside coachbuilders. Quite obviously, the 734 Speedster Series had its parentage in the 626 Speedster, the limited production model of the year previous. For reasons unknown, Packard chose not to promote its new 734 Speedster, and its production was limited as well. Only 113 of these cars were built.

I.D. DATA: Engine numbers. Starting: 184003. Ending: 184120.

Model 734, 8-cyl.

Body No.	Body Type & Seating	Factory Price	Shipping Weight	Prod. Total
422	Speedster Rbt.-2P	5200	4210	Note 1
452	Rbt.-4P	5200	4295	Note 1
445	Phae.-4P	5200	4300	Note 1
447	Vic.-4P	6000	4525	Note 1
443	Sed.-4P	6000	4580	Note 1

Note 1: Packard Model 734 production totaled 113 with no body style breakout available.

ENGINE: L-head, straight eight. Cast enbloc. B & S: 3-1/2 x 5 in. Disp.: 384.8 cu. in. C.R.: 4.85:1 standard, 6.00:1 high compression head. Brake H.P.: 125 @ 3400 with standard compression; with high compression head 145 @ 3400 R.P.M. Main bearings: nine. Carb.: dual updraft Detroit Lubricator.

CHASSIS: W.B.: 134-1/2 in. Tires: 19 x 6.50.

TECHNICAL: Selective transmission. Speeds: 4F/1R. Shaft drive, hypoid differential. Overall ratio: 3.33:1 and 4.66:1. Mechanical brakes on all wheels. Wire or disc wheels.

HISTORICAL: Introduced January 1930. Model year production: 113.

PACKARD — SEVENTH SERIES, CUSTOM EIGHT (740), DELUXE EIGHT (745) — EIGHT: Wheelbases remained the same for the big Packards this year, but the four-speed transmission was new and a 4.69:1 rear axle ratio was added. The carburetor was a Detroit updraft, and dual fan belts were fitted. A vacuum booster pump was added mid-year. Non-shatter laminated glass was in all windows, there was a glove compartment on each side of the dashboard, and both driver's seat and steering wheel were adjustable. Parking lamps were now fender-mounted, and headlamps exchanged their former parabolic look for one resembling half a cantaloupe. Dual mounted spares were standard on the 745, an option on the 740. Fifteen designs were offered in the Individual Custom line: six from LeBaron, five from Brewster, and two each from Rollston and Dietrich.

I.D. DATA: Engine numbers. Starting: 179001 & 184501. Ending: 184000 & 187508.

Model 740 Custom, 8-cyl.

Body No.	Body Type & Seating	Factory Price	Shipping Weight	Prod. Total
418	Cpe.-2/4P	3295	4500	Note 1
417	Cpe.-5P	3650	4555	Note 1
419	Conv. Cpe.-2/4P	3350	4425	Note 1
411	Phae.-4P	3190	4250	Note 1
441	Spt. Phae.-4P	3490	4450	Note 1
412	Rds.-2/4P	3190	4245	Note 1
410	Tr.-7P	3325	4345	Note 1
413	Sed.-5P	3585	4560	Note 1
416	Club Sed.-5P	3750	4580	Note 1
414	Sed.-7P	3785	4765	Note 1
415	Sed. Limo.-7P	3885	4810	Note 1
Model 745 Deluxe, 8-cyl.				
422	Rds.-2/4P	4585	4695	Note 2
421	Phae.-4P	4585	4695	Note 2
451	Spt. Phae.-4P	4885	4845	Note 2
420	Tr.-7P	4585	4745	Note 2
428	Cpe.-2/4P	4785	4875	Note 2
429	Conv. Cpe.-2/4P	4885	4745	Note 2
427	Cpe.-5P	5100	4995	Note 2
423	Sed.-5P	4985	4805	Note 2
426	Clb. Sed.-5P	5150	5000	Note 2
424	Sed.-7P	5185	5095	Note 2
425	Sed. Limo.-7P	5350	5140	Note 2

Note 1: Packard Model 740 production totaled 6,200 with no body style breakout available.

Note 2: Packard Model 745 production totaled 1,789 with no body style breakout available.

ENGINE: L-head, straight eight. Cast enbloc. B & S: 3-1/2 in. x 5 in. Disp.: 384.8 cu. in. Brake H.P.: 106 @ 3200 R.P.M. Net H.P.: 39.2. Main bearings: nine. Valve lifters: mechanical. Carb.: Detroit Lubricator updraft.

CHASSIS: [Model 740] W.B.: 140-1/2. in. Tires: 19 x 7.00. [Model 745] W.B.: 145-1/2 in. Tires: 19 x 7.00.

TECHNICAL: Sliding gear transmission. Speeds: 4F/1R. Two-plate clutch. Shaft drive, hypoid differential. Overall ratio: 4.07:1, 4.38:1, 4.69:1. Mechanical brakes on all wheels. Disc wheels.

OPTIONS: Spotlight. Wire wheels ($90.00). Spoke wheels (110.00)

HISTORICAL: Introduced August 1929. Model year production: [740] 6,200, [745] 1,789.

1931

PACKARD EIGHTH SERIES, STANDARD EIGHT (826, 833), INDIVIDUAL CUSTOM EIGHT (833) — EIGHT: With the adoption of valves and manifolding from the 734 Speedster, horsepower of the Standard Eight engine was up to 100. A 4.07:1 rear axle ratio was added to the former 4.38:1, 4.69:1 and 5.08:1. A Stewart Warner fuel pump replaced the former vacuum tank. The Bijur lubrication went automatic (vacuum-operated). Hubcaps were larger, tires smaller, disc wheels still standard though with wire or wood optional. Steering wheels dropped the number of spokes to three. The Model 826, again, was a single body style on a 127-1/2-inch wheelbase: the $2,385 price-leading sedan. All Standard Eight 833s were on the 134-1/2 inch wheelbase, with 11 body styles offered. There were nine body styles in the Individual Custom 833, the same as offered for the big Packard eight and an attempt to stimulate custom sales during this Great Depression year.

I.D. DATA: Engine numbers. Starting: 320001. Ending: 332111.

Model 826, 8-cyl.

Body No.	Body Type & Seating	Factory Price	Shipping Weight	Prod. Total
463	Sed.-5P	2385	4479	6,009
Model 833, 8-cyl.				
462	Rds.-2/4P	2425	4140	Note 1
461	Phae.-4P	2425	4185	Note 1
481	Spt. Phae.-4P	2725	4285	Note 1
460	Tr.-7P	2525	4256	Note 1
468	Cpe.-2/4P	2525	4360	Note 1
469	Conv. Cpe.-2/4P	2550	4290	Note 1
467	Cpe.-5P	2675	4308	Note 1
466	Club Sed.-5P	2675	4488	Note 1
464	Sed.-7P	2785	4732	Note 1
465	Sed. Limo.-7P	2885	4638	Note 1
483	Conv. Sed.-5P	3445	4555	Note 1
Model 833 Individual Custom, 8-cyl.				
1879	Conv. Vict.	4275	4186	Note 1
1881	Conv. Sed.	4375	4442	Note 1
3000	All W. Cab.	4850	4614	Note 1

Body No.	Body Type & Seating	Factory Price	Shipping Weight	Prod. Total
3001	All W. Land.	5050	4684	Note 1
3002	All W. Twn. Car	4975	4744	Note 1
3003	All W. Twn. Car Land.	5175	4744	Note 1
3004	Cab. Sed. Limo.	4490	4485	Note 1
3008	All W. Spt. Cab.	4850	4614	Note 1
3009	All W. Spt. Land.	5050	4614	Note 1

Note 1: Packard Model 833 production totaled 6,096 with no body style breakout available.

ENGINE: L-head, straight eight. Cast iron block. B & S: 3-3/16 x 5 in. Disp.: 319.2 cu. in. Brake H.P.: 100 @ 3200 R.P.M. Net H.P.: 32.5. Main bearings: nine. Carb.: Detroit Lubricator.

CHASSIS: [Standard Eight (826)] W.B.: 127-1/2 in. Tires: 19 x 6.50. [Standard Eight (833)] W.B.: 134-1/2 in. Tires: 19 x 6.50. [Individual Custom Eight (833)] W.B.: 134-1/2 in. Tires: 19 x 6.50.

TECHNICAL: Selective transmission. Speeds: 4F/1R. Single plate clutch. Shaft drive and hypoid differential. Overall ratio: 4.38:1, 4.69:1, 5.08:1 and 4.07:1. Mechanical brakes on all wheels. Disc wheels.

OPTIONS: Dual sidemounts. Sidemount cover(s). Bumper guards. Spotlight.

HISTORICAL: Introduced August 1930. Model year production: [Standard 826] 6,009. [Standard 833] 6,096.

PACKARD — EIGHTH SERIES, DELUXE EIGHT (840, 845), INDIVIDUAL CUSTOM EIGHT (840) — EIGHT: Engineering refinements for the Standard Eight were adopted on the larger eights, its horsepower now up to 120. The former "Custom" designation was dropped, both 840 and 845 now being called DeLuxe. Wheelbase lengths remained the same, but the longer 145-1/2-inch 845 now offered only two seven-passenger body styles: sedan and sedan-limousine. All other DeLuxe body styles were carried on the shorter 140-1/2-inch chassis. The Individual Custom line was on the shorter wheelbase as well, and offered two Dietrich designs (convertible victoria and convertible sedan) and seven "Custom Made by Packard" styles. This represented the finalization of the Packard company's long-desired resolve to make the Individual Custom line an in-house operation.

I.D. DATA: Engine numbers. Starting: 188001. Ending: 191345.

Model 840 Deluxe, 8-cyl.

Body No.	Body Type & Seating	Factory Price	Shipping Weight	Prod. Total
472	Rds.-2/4P	3490	4383	Note 1
471	Phae.-4P	3490	4439	Note 1
491	Spt. Phae.-4P	3790	4535	Note 1
470	Tr.-7P	3595	4507	Note 1
478	Cpe.-2/4P	3545	4592	Note 1
479	Conv.Cpe.-2/4P	3595	4523	Note 1
473	Cpe.-5P	3850	4673	Note 1
476	Sed.-5P	3795	4955	Note 1
Model 845 Deluxe, 8-cyl.				
474	Club Sed.-5P	3950	4720	Note 2
475	Sed.-7P	4150	5010	Note 2
Model 840 Individual Custom, 8-cyl.				
1879	Sed. Limo.-7P	4285	5080	Note 1
1881	Conv. Vict.	5175	4674	Note 1
3000	Conv. Sed.	5275	4916	Note 1
3001	All Weather Cabr.	5750	4916	Note 1
3002	All Weather Land.	5950	4976	Note 1
3003	All Weather Twn. Car	5875	4976	Note 1
3004	All Weather Twn. Car Land.	6075	4717	Note 1
3009	All Weather Sport Land.	5750	4846	Note 1
3008	All Weather Sport Cabr.	5390	4846	Note 1

Note 1: Packard Model 840 production totaled 2,035 with no body style breakout available.

Note 2: Packard Model 845 production totaled 1,310 with no body style breakout available.

ENGINE: L-head, straight eight. Cast enbloc. B & S: 3-1/2 x 5 in. Disp.: 384.8 cu. in. Brake H.P.: 120 @ 3200 R.P.M. Net H.P.: 39.2. Main bearings: nine. Valve lifters: mechanical. Carb.: Detroit Lubricator.

CHASSIS: [Deluxe Eight (840) and Individual Custom Eight] W.B.: 140-1/2 in. Tires: 19 x 7.00. [Deluxe Eight (845)] W.B.: 145-1/2 in. Tires: 19 x 7.00.

TECHNICAL: Selective transmission. Speeds: 4F/1R. Single plate clutch. Shaft drive, hypoid differential. Overall ratio: 4.38:1, 4.69:1, 5.08:1 and 4.97:1. Mechanical brakes on all wheels. Disc wheels.

OPTIONS: Dual sidemount ($148.00). Luggage rack. Wire wheels (60.00). Stone guard (27.50). Deluxe emblem (10.00). Windwings (25.00). Trunk (125.00).

HISTORICAL: Introduced September 9, 1930. Model year production: [840] 2,035, [845] 1,310.

1932

PACKARD — NINTH SERIES, LIGHT EIGHT (900) — EIGHT: The Light Eight was Packard's first attempt to truly counter the Depression with a lower priced model. The car failed to do this, through no fault of its own, and was produced for less than a year. The Light Eight's problem was that it was too expensive to build and not significantly enough lower-priced to introduce an all-new clientele for the company. But it was nonetheless a remarkable car. Its engine featured a block thermostat with no shutters and a warm-air heater for the carburetor intake. Bijur lubrication was absent, only grease fittings being needed and used. The chassis featured ride control, angleset differential, automatic clutch and vacuum-powered brakes. Horsepower was 110, top speed was 72 mph. The Light Eight was perhaps most memorable for its sweeping modern lines and its distinctive "shovel nose."

I.D. DATA: Engine numbers. Starting: 360009. Ending: 366794.

Model 900 Light Eight, 8-cyl.

Body No.	Body Type & Seating	Factory Price	Shipping Weight	Prod. Total
569	Cpe.-Rds.-2/4P	1795	3930	Note 1
568	Cpe.-2/4P	1795	3990	Note 1
553	Sed.-5P	1750	4115	Note 1
563	Cpe.Sed-5P	1795	4060	Note 1

Note 1: Packard Model 900 production totaled 6,750 with no body style breakout available.

Note 2: The price of the sedan was raised to $1,895, the other body styles to $1,940 during the model year.

ENGINE: L-head. Straight eight. Cast enbloc. B & S: 3-3/16 x 5 in. Disp.: 319.2 cu. in. C.R.: 6.1:1. Brake H.P.: 110 @ 3200 R.P.M. Net H.P.: 32.5. Main bearings: nine. Valve lifters: solid. Carb.: Packard.

CHASSIS: W.B.: 127-3/4 in. Tires: 17 x 6.50.

TECHNICAL: Selective synchromesh. Speeds: 3F/1R. Floor shift controls. Single plate clutch. Shaft drive and angleset hypoid differential. Mechanical brakes on all wheels. Steel disc wheels. Freewheeling. Vacuum clutch.

OPTIONS: Dual sidemounts. Sidemount cover(s). Cigar lighter. Right-hand taillight. Dual rear mounted spares. Luggage rack, sidemount spares, full rear bumper and fender park lights ($65.00).

TECHNICAL: Introduced January 1932. Model year production: 6,750 units.

PACKARD — NINTH SERIES, STANDARD EIGHT (901, 902) — EIGHT: The Standard Eight had new numerical designations with no reference to wheelbase, and two new wheelbases this year that were two inches longer at 129-1/2 inches for Model 901 (the $2,485 five-passenger sedan) and 136-1/2 inches for the Model 902, which was offered in 12 body styles. Individual Customs were unavailable for the Standard Eight this year. But engineering refinements were many. The standard compression ratio was raised to 6.0:1 (with lower or higher ratios available optionally); horsepower was boosted to 110. The frame was a new double-drop design with X-bracing. Ride control was standard, and the harmonic stabilizer front bumper an option. The cars were introduced with the four-speed transmission, but late in the model run a three-speed with synchromesh and vacuum clutch was fitted.

I.D. DATA: Engine numbers. Starting: 340057. Ending: 347720.

Model 901, 8-cyl.

Body No.	Body Type & Seating	Factory Price	Shipping Weight	Prod. Total
503	Sed.-5P	2485	4570	3,922
Model 902, 8-cyl.				
508	Cpe.-2/4P	2675	4420	Note 1
507	Cpe.-5P	2795	4505	Note 1
509	Cpe. Rds.-2/4P	2650	4420	Note 1
501	Phae.-4P	2650	4300	Note 1
521	Sport Phae.-4P	2950	4400	Note 1
543	Sed.-5P	2685	4590	Note 1
504	Sed.-5/7P	2885	4735	Note 1
506	Club Sed.-5P	2775	4555	Note 1
523	Conv. Sed.-5P	3445	4573	Note 1
505	Sed. Limo.-5/7P	2985	4770	Note 1
500	Tr.-5/7P	2775	4345	Note 1
527	Conv. Vic.-5P	3395	4317	Note 1

Note 1: Packard Model 902 production totaled 3,737 with no body style breakout available.

ENGINE: L-head, straight eight. Cast enbloc. B & S: 3-3/16 x 5 in. Disp.: 319.2 cu. in. C.R.: 6.0:1. Brake H.P.: 110 @ 3200 R.P.M. Net H.P.: 32.5. Main bearings: nine. Valve lifters: solid. Carb.: Detroit Lubricator updraft.

CHASSIS: [Standard Eight (901)] W.B.: 129-1/2 in. Tires: 17 x 7.00. [Standard Eight (902)] W.B.: 136-1/2 in. Tires: 17 x 7.00.

TECHNICAL: Selective (synchromesh with three-speed). Speeds: 4F/1R, later 3F/1R. Floor shift controls. Single plate clutch. One-piece driveshaft to hypoid differential. Overall ratio: 4.41:1, 4.69:1 and 5.07:1 opt. on four-speed. Mechanical brakes on all wheels. Disc wheels.

OPTIONS: Harmonic stabilizer front bumper. Dual sidemount. Sidemount cover(s). Cigar lighter. Spotlight. Fender lights and trunk rack ($97.00). Trunk (45.00). Wire wheels (50.00). Special paint (110.00). Front stone guard (35.00). Whitewall tires (10.00).

TECHNICAL: Introduced June 1931. Model year production: (901) 3,922, (902) 3,737.

PACKARD — NINTH SERIES, DELUXE EIGHT (903, 904), INDIVIDUAL CUSTOM EIGHT (904) — EIGHT: Horsepower was up to 135, and wheelbases now measured 142-1/2 for the 903 and 147-1/2 for the 904. The frame was a new double-drop design with X-bracing. Ride control and the harmonic stabilizer front bumper were standard. Also standard were fender lamps and dual trumpet horns mounted under the headlights. The four-speed transmission was fitted to the cars at introduction, but late in the model year was replaced with a three-speed with synchromesh and vacuum clutch. Top speed was 85 mph, with 0 to 60 mph in 18.8 seconds. With radios becoming popular, the company tested various types in this series. The Dietrich-designed Convertible Sedan and Convertible Victoria, which the year previous had been in the Individual Custom line, were moved to the DeLuxe Eight 903 line this year, joining nine other body styles. The long-wheelbase DeLuxe Eight 904 carried only the five/seven-passenger sedan and sedan-limousine. The Individual Custom 904 offered five Dietrich designs (stationary coupe, convertible coupe, sport phaeton, convertible sedan and convertible victoria), together with 10 "Custom Made by Packard" body styles.

I.D. DATA: Engine numbers. Starting: 193051. Ending: 194708.

Model 903 Deluxe, 8-cyl.

Body No.	Body Type & Seating	Factory Price	Shipping Weight	Prod. Total
518	Cpe.-2/4P	3725	4890	Note 1
517	Cpe.-5P	3850	4985	Note 1
519	Cpe. Rds.-2/4P	3750	4890	Note 1
511	Phae.-4P	3690	4715	Note 1
531	Sport Phae.-4P	3990	4795	Note 1
513	Sed.-5P	3845	5045	Note 1
516	Club Sed.-5P	3890	5000	Note 1
533	Conv. Sed.-5P	4550	4983	Note 1
510	Tr.-5/7P	3795	4760	Note 1
537	Conv. Vic.-5P	4495	4727	Note 1

Model 904 Deluxe, 8-cyl.

Body No.	Body Type & Seating	Factory Price	Shipping Weight	Prod. Total
514	Sed.-5/7P	4150	5195	Note 2
515	Sed. Limo.-5/6P	4285	5240	Note 2

Model 904 Individual Custom, 8-cyl.

Body No.	Body Type & Seating	Factory Price	Shipping Weight	Prod. Total
2068	Sta. Cpe.-2/4P	5900	5000	Note 2
2071	Conv. Cpe.-2/4P	6050	4965	Note 2
2069	Spt. Phae.-4P	5800	4800	Note 2
2070	Conv. Sed.-5P	6250	5100	Note 2
2072	Conv. Vic.-4P	6150	4815	Note 2
4000	All W. Cab.-5/7P	6850	5250	Note 2
4001	All W. Land.-5/7P	7250	5250	Note 2
4002	All W. Town Car-5/7P	6850	5310	Note 2
4003	All W. Town Car Land.- 5/7P	7250	5310	Note 2
4004	Sed. Cab. Limo.-6P	6850	5050	Note 2
4005	Spt. Sed.-5P	6850	5030	Note 2
4006	All W. Brgm.-5/7P	6850	5293	Note 2
4007	Limo. Sed.-6P	6850	5075	Note 2
4008	All W. Cab. Sport Cab.-5/7P	6850	5180	Note 2
4009	All W. Land.-5/7P	7250	5180	Note 2

Note 1: Packard Model 903 production totaled 955 with no body style breakout available.

Note 2: Packard Model 904 production totaled 700 with no body style breakout available.

Note 3: For the Individual Custom 904 cars, the "2000" digits represent the Dietrich designs, the "4000" digits the "Custom Made by Packard."

ENGINE: L-head, straight eight. Cast enbloc. B & S: 3-1/2 x 5 in. Disp.: 384.8 cu. in. C.R.: 6.0:1. Brake H.P.: 135 @ 3200 R.P.M. Main bearings: nine. Valve lifters: solid. Carb.: Detroit Lubricator updraft.

CHASSIS: [Deluxe Eight (903)] W.B.: 142-1/2 in. Tires: 19 x 7.00. [Deluxe Eight (904) & Individual Custom Eight (904)] W.B.: 147-1/2 in. Tires: 19 x 7.00.

TECHNICAL: Selective transmission. Speeds: 4F/1R, later changed to 3F/1R. Two plate clutch. Split driveshaft to hypoid differential. Overall ratio: 4.06:1, 4.41:1, 4.69:1 and 5.07:1 opt. with four-speed. Mechanical brakes on all wheels. Disc wheels. Freewheeling. Vacuum clutch.

OPTIONS: Front bumper. Rear bumper. Dual sidemounts. Sidemount cover(s). Clock. Cigar lighter.

HISTORICAL: Introduced June 1931. Model year production: [903] 955, [904] 700.

PACKARD — NINTH SERIES, TWIN SIX (905, 906) — TWELVE: Introduced together with the Light Eight at New York Automobile Show time in January 1932, the Twin Six was Packard's entry in the multi-cylinder race, its designation a nostalgic remembering of the World War I-era Twin Sixes, and used this first year only. The wheelbases were 142-1/2 inches for the 905, 147-1/2 inches for the 906, which included the Individual Custom cars. Prices began at $3,650 and rose from there to $7,950, but they bought a lot of car. Horsepower was 160, and though a Twin Six five-passenger sedan was clocked at 101 mph, Packard brochures understated the car's performance and claimed a speed only in excess of 85. Interior appointments were lavish. Ten body styles were offered on the 905 chassis; the 11 body styles on the 906 chassis included a five/seven-passenger sedan and sedan-limousine, the remainder of the line being the Individual Custom cars.

I.D. DATA: Serial numbers located on a rectangular plate mounted on the firewall. Starting: 900001. Ending: 901000. The vehicle number was the body type followed by the production number of that particular car.

Model 905 Twin Six, 12-cyl.

Body No.	Body Type & Seating	Factory Price	Shipping Weight	Prod. Total
570	Tr.-5/7P	3895	5315	Note 1
571	Phae.-5P	3790	5275	Note 1
581	Spt. Phae.-5P	4090	5375	Note 1
573	Sed.-5P	3745	5635	Note 1
583	Conv. Sed.-5P	4395	5255	Note 1
576	Clb. Sed.-5P	3895	5585	Note 1
577	Cpe.-5P	3850	5485	Note 1
587	Conv. Vict.-5P	4325	5180	Note 1
578	Cpe.-2/4P	3650	5425	Note 1
579	Cpe. Rds.-2/4P	3750	5350	Note 1

Model 906 Twin Six, 12-cyl.

Body No.	Body Type & Seating	Factory Price	Shipping Weight	Prod. Total
574	Sed.-5/7P	3995	5765	Note 2
575	Sed. Limo.-5/7P	4195	5830	Note 2

Model 906 Individual Custom, 12-cyl.

Body No.	Body Type & Seating	Factory Price	Shipping Weight	Prod. Total
4000	All W. Cabr.-5/7P	7550	5430	Note 2
4001	All W. Land'let.-5/7P	7950	5430	Note 2
4002	All W. Twn. Car.-5/7P	7550	5490	Note 2
4003	All W. Twn. Car Lan.-5/7P	7950	5490	Note 2
2068	Stat. Cpe. Dietrich-2/4P	6600	5180	Note 2
2069	Spt. Phae. Dietrich-4P	6500	4980	Note 2
2070	Conv. Sed. Dietrich-5P	6950	5280	Note 2
2071	Conv. Rds. Dietrich-2/4P	6750	5145	Note 2
2072	Conv. Vict. Dietrich-4P	6850	4995	Note 2
2069	Spt. Phae. Dietrich-4P	6500	4980	Note 2

Note 1: Packard Model 905 production totaled 311 with no body style breakout available.

Note 2: Packard Model 906 production totaled 238 with no body style breakout available.

ENGINE: 67 degree V-block. Modified L. Twelve. Cast iron monobloc. Aluminum alloy pistons, four ring. B & S: 3-7/16 x 4 in. Disp.: 445.5 cu. in. C.R.: 6.0:1. Brake H.P.: 160 @ 3200 R.P.M. Net H.P.: 56.7. Main bearings: four. Zero lash automatic valve silencers. Carb.: Stromberg-Duplex.

CHASSIS: [905 Series] W.B.: 142-1/8 in. Tires: 7.50 x 18. [906 Series] W.B.: 147-1/8 in. Tires: 7.50 x 18.

TECHNICAL: Selective synchromesh transmission. Speeds: 3F/1R. Outer floor-cane controls. Double plate clutch. Overall ratio: open cars, 4.41:1; closed, 4.69:1, opt. 4.06:1 or 5.07:1. Mechanical brakes on four wheels. Wire or wood spoke wheels. Freewheeling finger control on steering column.

HISTORICAL: Introduced January 1932. Model year production: 311 (905), 238 (906).

1933

PACKARD — TENTH SERIES, EIGHT (1001, 1002) — EIGHT: The Standard Eight became simply the Eight this year, with horsepower now up to 120 courtesy of such engine refinements as a new dual downdraft Stromberg carburetor, revised manifolding, an automatic choke and smaller flywheel. Three-point motor suspension was adopted. The Bendix-BK vacuum booster brakes of the Twin Six were fitted. Wire wheels were now standard, with disc and wood optional. The angleset hypoid differential introduced on the Light Eight was incorporated. The former vacuum-plate clutch was replaced by a single-plate, with automatic clutch control available optionally. The fender-mounted battery and toolboxes were gone, and the new pivoted pane window ventilation would be offered this one model year only on all eights and twelves. Whereas the 127-1/2-inch wheelbase had previously carried only a five-passenger sedan, now in the Eight Model 1001 it carried the four body styles offered the previous year in the Light Eight. The Eight Model 1002's wheelbase was 136 inches, and it carried 13 body styles.

I.D. DATA: Serial numbers. Starting: 370001. Ending: 373010.

Model 1001, 8-cyl.

Body No.	Body Type & Seating	Factory Price	Shipping Weight	Prod. Total
603	Sed.-5P	2150	4335	Note 1
602	Cpe. Sed.-5P	2190	4245	Note 1
608	Cpe.-2/4P	2160	4200	Note 1
609	Cpe. Rds.-2/4P	2250	4150	Note 1
Model 1002, 8-cyl.				
618	Cpe. Rds.-2/4P	2350	4450	Note 2
617	Cpe.-5P	2440	4500	Note 2
611	Phae.-5P	2370	4270	Note 2
613	Sed.-5P	2385	4590	Note 2
614	Sed.-5/7P	2455	4640	Note 2
616	Club Sed.-5P	2390	4545	Note 2
623	Conv. Sed.-5P	2890	4515	Note 2
627	Conv. Vic.-5P	2780	4540	Note 2
610	Tr.-5/7P	2390	4275	Note 2
615	Sed. Limo.-5/7P	2550	4725	Note 2
5633	Formal Sed.-5/7P	3085	4900	Note 2

Note 1: Packard Model 1001 production totaled 1,881 with no body style breakout available.

Note 2: Packard Model 1002 production totaled 1,099 with no body style breakout available.

ENGINE: L-head. Straight eight. Cast enbloc. B & S: 3-3/16 x 5 in. Disp.: 319.2 cu. in. C.R.: 6.0:1 standard, 6.38:1 and 5.0:1 optional. Brake H.P.: 120 @ 3200 R.P.M. Net H.P.: 32.5. Main bearings: nine. Valve lifters: solid. Carb.: Stromberg.

CHASSIS: [Tenth Series (1001)] W.B.: 127-1/2 in. Tires: 17 x 7.00. [Tenth Series (1002)] W.B.: 136 in. Tires: 17 x 7.00

TECHNICAL: Selective synchromesh transmission. Speeds: 3F/1R. Single plate clutch. Shaft drive and angleset hypoid differential. Overall ratio: 4.36:1 standard, 4.69:1 and 4.07:1 optional. Mechanical brakes on all wheels. Wire wheels.

OPTIONS: Dual sidemounts. Sidemount cover(s). Spotlight.

HISTORICAL: Introduced January 1933. Model year production: (1001) 1,881, (1002) 1,099.

PACKARD — TENTH SERIES, SUPER EIGHT (1003, 1004) — EIGHT: The former DeLuxe Eight was now the Super Eight. It featured the same engineering refinements given the Tenth Series Eight. Wheelbases were revised to 135 inches for Model 1003, which remained in a single five-passenger sedan body style. Thirteen body styles were available in Model 1004, which now was on a 142-inch wheelbase. The former 147-1/2-inch wheelbase was dropped, with the result that all custom cars now were offered only on a 12-cylinder chassis.

I.D. DATA: Serial numbers. Starting: 750000. Ending: 751327.

Model 1003 Super Eight, 8-cyl.

Body No.	Body Type & Seating	Factory Price	Shipping Weight	Prod. Total
653	Sed.-5P	2750	4815	512
Model 1004 Super Eight, 8-cyl.				
658	Cpe.-2/4P	2780	4670	Note 1
657	Cpe.-5P	2980	4780	Note 1
659	Cpe. Rds.-2/4P	2870	4625	Note 1
651	Phae.-5P	2890	4490	Note 1
661	Spt. Phae.-5P	3150	4690	Note 1
673	Formal Sed.-5P	3600	5155	Note 1
654	Sed.-5/7P	3090	4965	Note 1
656	Club Sed.-5P	2975	4830	Note 1
663	Conv. Sed.-5P	3590	4840	Note 1
667	Conv. Vic.-5P	3440	4795	Note 1
650	Tr.-5/7P	2890	4610	Note 1
655	Sed. Limo-5/7P	3280	4795	Note 1

Note 1: Packard Model 1004 production totaled 788 with no body style breakout available.

ENGINE: L-head. Straight eight. Cast enbloc. B & S: 3-1/2 x 5 in. Disp.: 384.8 cu. in. C.R.: 6.0:1 standard, 6.38:1 and 5.0:1 optional. Brake H.P.: 145 @ 3200 R.P.M. Net H.P.: 39.2. Main bearings: nine. Carb.: Stromberg.

CHASSIS: [Super Eight (1003)] W.B.: 135 in. Tires: 17 x 7.00. [Super Eight (1004)] W.B.: 142 in. Tires: 17 x 7.00.

TECHNICAL: Selective synchromesh transmission. Speeds: 3F/1R. Single plate clutch. Shaft drive, angleset hypoid differential. Overall ratio: 4.36:1 standard, 4.69:1 and 4.07:1 optional. Mechanical brakes on all wheels. Wire wheels.

HISTORICAL: Introduced January 1933. Model year production: (1003) 512, (1004) 788.

PACKARD — TENTH SERIES, TWELVE (1005, 1006) — TWELVE: The double-drop frame of the Twin Six became a tapered frame in the Twelve, which was the new designation for Packard's multi-cylindered car. Refinements included a single dry-plate clutch replacing the former two-plate, with vacuum control freewheeling an option. The Stromberg carburetor was given an automatic choke with fast idle. The Model 1005 was on a 142-inch wheelbase offering touring, phaeton, sport phaeton, sedan, convertible sedan, formal sedan, club sedan, convertible victoria, coupe-roadster and five-passenger as well as two/four-passenger coupe body styles. The Model 1006 on a 147-inch wheelbase included a five/seven-passenger sedan and sedan limousine together with the custom cars. The designation "Individual Custom" was no longer used, and the dropping of the long wheelbase chassis for the Super Eight meant that anyone desiring a custom Packard this year had to go for 12 cylinders.

I.D. DATA: Serial number located on a rectangular plate mounted on the firewall. Starting: 901001. Ending: 901600.

Model 1005, 12-cyl.

Body No.	Body Type & Seating	Factory Price	Shipping Weight	Prod. Total
631	Phae.-5P	3790	5095	Note 1
641	Spt. Phae.-5P	4090	5175	Note 1
633	Sed.-5P	3860	5385	Note 1
643	Conv. Sed.-5P	4650	5405	Note 1
5633	Formal Sed.-5P	4560	5690	Note 1
636	Clb. Sed.-5P	3960	5400	Note 1
637	Cpe.-5P	3890	5300	Note 1
647	Conv. Vict.-5P	4490	5225	Note 1
638	Cpe.-2/4P	3720	5255	Note 1
639	Cpe. Rds.-2/4P	3850	5160	Note 1
Model 1006, 12-cyl.				
634	Sed.-5/7P	4085	5600	Note 1
635	Sed. Limo.-5/7P	4285	5650	Note 1
Model 1006 Custom, 12-cyl.				
4000	All W. Cabr.-5/7P	6030	5650	Note 1
D-758	All W. Cabr. LeB.-5/7P	7000	5610	Note 1
4001	All W. Land'let.-5/7P	6250	5650	Note 1
4002	All W. Twn. Car-5/7P	6080	5610	Note 1
D-759	All W. Twn. Car LeB.-5/7P	7000	5670	Note 1
4003	All W. Twn. Car-Lan.-5/7P	6250	5610	Note 1
4004	Cab. Sed. Limo.-6P	6000	5650	Note 1
4005	Spt. Sed.-5P	6000	5330	Note 1
4007	Sed. Limo.-5/7P	6045	5650	Note 1
3068	Stat. Cpe. Dietrich-2/4P	6000	5360	Note 1
3069	Spt. Phae. Dietrich-4P	5875	5160	Note 1
3070	Conv. Sed. Dietrich-5P	6570	5460	Note 1
3071	Conv. Rbt. Dietrich-2/4P	6080	5325	Note 1
3072	Conv. Vict. Dietrich-4P	6070	5175	Note 1
3182	Spt. Sed. Dietrich-5/7P	7000	5735	Note 1/2

Note 1: Packard Model 1005 and Model 1006 production combined totaled 520 with no body style breakout available.

Note 2: It was a Dietrich Sport Sedan (3182) that became the basis for the famous "Car of the Dome" exhibited at the Century of Progress Exposition in Chicago.

ENGINE: 67 degree V-block. Modified L. Twelve. Cast iron monobloc. B & S: 3-7/16 x 4 in. Disp.: 445.5 cu. in., 7.5 liters. C.R.: 6.0:1. Brake H.P.: 160 @ 3200 R.P.M. Net H.P.: 56.7. Main bearings: four. Valve lifters: zero lash. Carb.: Stromberg.

CHASSIS: [1005 Series] W.B.: 142 in. Tires: 7.50 x 17. [1006] W.B.: 147 in. Tires: 7.50 x 17.

TECHNICAL: Selective synchromesh transmission. Speeds: 3F/1R. Floor shift controls. Single dry plate clutch. Shaft drive. Overall ratio: open cars: 4.41:1, closed: 4.69:1, optional: 4.06:1 or 5.07:1. Mechanical brakes on four wheels. Wire or wood spoke wheels.

OPTIONS: Front bumper w/vibration dampers. Rear bumper. Dual sidemount. Sidemount cover(s). Heater. Spotlight (included on open cars, optional on others).

HISTORICAL: Introduced January 1933. Model year production: 520.

1934

PACKARD — ELEVENTH SERIES, EIGHT (1100, 1101, 1102) — EIGHT: Many detail changes highlighted the Eleventh Series. An oil temperature regulator was added, and the gas tank filler was built into the left rear taillight assembly. The new bumpers were slotted, simulating a double-bar look. The car was re-engineered for radio, necessitating a larger, heavy-duty generator, with a vacuum-tube radio becoming an option. The pivot window treatment of the year previous gave way to an angle vent wing. The three model numbers for the Eleventh Series Packard Eight reflected three new wheelbase lengths. Model 1100 was 129-1/2 inches, and once again was provided with only a single five-passenger sedan. Model 1102 was 141-1/4 inches and offered a sedan and sedan-limousine for seven passengers. Model 1101 was 136-1/4 inches, with 10 body styles offered.

I.D. DATA: Serial numbers. Starting: 374001. Ending: 379149.

Body No.	Body Type & Seating	Factory Price	Shipping Weight	Prod. Total
Model 1100, 8-cyl.				
703	Sed.-5P	2350	4640	Note 1
Model 1101, 8-cyl.				
719	Cpe. Rds.-2/4P	2580	4430	Note 1
711	Phae.-4P	2570	4350	Note 1
710	Tr.-7P	2590	4400	Note 1
718	Cpe.-2/4P	2550	4500	Note 1
717	Cpe.-5P	2640	4580	Note 1
716	Clb. Sed.-5P	2670	4730	Note 1
713	Sed.-5P	2585	4660	Note 1
723	Conv. Sed.-5P	3090	4680	Note 1
712	Formal Sed.-5P	3285	4760	Note 1
727	Conv. Vict.-5P	2980	4710	Note 1
Model 1102, 8-cyl.				
714	Sed.-7P	2655	4945	Note 1
715	Sed. Limo.-7P	2790	5000	Note 1

Note 1: Packard Model 1100, 1101 and 1102 production combined totaled 5,120 with no body style breakout available.

ENGINE: L-head. Straight eight. Cast enbloc. B & S: 3-3/16 x 5 in. Disp.: 319.2 cu. in. Brake H.P.: 120 @ 3200 R.P.M. Net H.P.: 32.5. Main bearings: nine. Valve lifters: solid. Carb.: Stromberg.

CHASSIS: [Eleventh Series (1100)] W.B.: 129-1/2 in. Tires: 17 x 700. [Eleventh Series (1101)] W.B.: 136-1/4 in. Tires: 17 x 7.00. [Eleventh Series (1102)] W.B.: 141-1/2 in. Tires: 17 x 7.00.

TECHNICAL: Selective synchromesh transmission. Speeds: 3F/1R. Single plate clutch. Shaft drive, angleset hypoid differential. Overall ratio: 4.35:1 standard, 4.69:1 and 4.07:1 optional. Mechanical brakes on all wheels. Wire wheels. Drivetrain options: Freewheeling.

OPTIONS: Dual sidemounts. Sidemount cover(s). Radio ($79.50). Cigar lighter. Chrome-plate wheel covers (10.00 each). Deluxe radiator ornament (10.00). Pelican radiator ornament (20.00). Six disc wheels (25.00). Six wood wheels (78.00). Six chrome wire wheels (192.00). Six chrome disc wheels (85.00). Six chrome wheel trimming (12.00). Side mirrors (16.00 pair).

HISTORICAL: Introduced August 1933. Model year production: 5,120.

PACKARD — ELEVENTH SERIES, SUPER EIGHT (1103, 1104, 1105) — EIGHT: Though the same refinements made to the Eight were incorporated in the Super Eight as well, the big news this year was the return of custom cars to the Super Eight line. The Model 1103 remained the bread-and-butter sedan, at a new low price of $2,350. The Model 1104 offered 11 body styles, the same lineup as the previous year with the exception of the seven-passenger sedan and sedan-limousine. These now moved to the 147-inch wheelbase that was newly reinstated for the Super Eight Model 1105, which also carried all the custom bodies provided the Twelve except for the LeBaron Sport Runabout and Sport Coupe by Packard.

I.D. DATA: Serial numbers. Starting: 752001. Ending: 753946.

Body No.	Body Type & Seating	Factory Price	Shipping Weight	Prod. Total
Model 1103, 8-cyl.				
753	Sed.-5P	2950	4890	Note 1
Model 1104, 8-cyl.				
759	Cpe. Rds.-2/4P	3070	4680	Note 1
751	Phae.-5P	3090	4645	Note 1
761	Spt. Phae.-4P	3350	4740	Note 1
750	Tr.-7P	3180	4720	Note 1
758	Cpe.-2/4P	2980	4800	Note 1
757	Cpe.-5P	3180	4885	Note 1
756	Club Sed.-5P	3255	4985	Note 1
763	Conv. Sed.-5P	3790	4390	Note 1
752	Formal Sed.-5P	3800	5010	Note 1
767	Conv. Vict.-5P	3640	4875	Note 1
Model 1105 Standard, 8-cyl.				
754	Sed.-7P	3290	5245	Note 1
755	Limo.-7P	3480	5275	Note 1

Note: The following are Custom cars that were returned to the Eleventh Series Model 1105 Super Eight line:

Body No.	Body Type & Seating	Factory Price	Shipping Weight	Prod. Total
Model 1105 Dietrich, 8-cyl.				
4068	Stat. Cpe. by Dietrich-2/4P	5445	4955	Note 1
4071	Conv. Rbt. by Dietrich-2/4P	5363	4920	Note 1
4070	Conv. Sed. by Dietrich-5P	5800	5055	Note 1
4072	Conv. Vict. by Dietrich-5P	5345	4770	Note 1
4182	Spt. Sed. by Dietrich-5P	6295	5380	Note 1
Model 1105 LeBaron, 8-cyl.				
858	All W. Cabr. by LeBaron-5/7P	5450	5205	Note 1
859	All W. Twn. Car by LeBaron-5/7P	5450	5265	Note 1
280	Spt. Phae. by LeBaron-5P	7065	4755	Note 1

Note 1: Packard Model 1103, Model 1104 and Model 1105 production combined totaled 1,920 with no body style breakout available.

ENGINE: L-head. Straight eight. Cast enbloc. B & S: 3-1/2 x 5 in. Disp.: 384.8 cu. in. C.R.: 6.0:1 standard, 6.38:1 and 5.0:1 optional. Brake H.P.: 145 @ 3200 R.P.M. Net H.P.: 39.2. Main bearings: nine. Carb.: Stromberg.

CHASSIS: [Super Eight (1103)] W.B.: 134-7/8 in. Tires: 17 x 7.00. [Super Eight (1104)] W.B. 141-7/8 in. Tires: 17 x 7.00. [Super Eight (1105)] W.B.: 146-7/8 in. Tires: 17 x 7.00.

TECHNICAL: Selective synchromesh transmission. Speeds: 3F/1R. Single plate clutch. Shaft drive, angleset hypoid differential. Overall ratio: 4.36:1 standard, 4.69:1 and 4.07:1 optional. Mechanical brakes on all wheels. Wire wheels. Drivetrain options: vacuum clutch.

OPTIONS: Dual sidemount. Sidemount cover(s). Deluxe radio ($79.50). Clock. Cigar lighter. Spotlight. Mirrors. Luggage rack (144.00). Rumbleseat windshield (175.00). Vee-lensed headlight and parking lights.

HISTORICAL: Introduced August 1933. Model year production: 1,920.

PACKARD — ELEVENTH SERIES, TWELVE (1106, 1107, 1108) — TWELVE: Three wheelbases carried the Packard Twelve this year. The Model 1106 LeBaron Runabout Speedster was a Twelve on the Super Eight's 135-inch wheelbase chassis. Model 1107 was the 142-inch wheelbase and carried 11 production body styles. Model 1108 was the long 147-inch wheelbase and offered the seven-passenger production sedan and sedan-limousine, as well as a variety of LeBaron and Dietrich custom cars. There were engineering refinements throughout the Twelve model lines. In the interior the instrument panel was redesigned, and radio was a popular new option. Though weighing well over 5,000 pounds, these Packard Twelves were fine performing cars, with 0 to 60 mph in 20.4 seconds.

I.D. DATA: Serial numbers located on a rectangular plate mounted on the firewall. Starting: 901601. Ending: 903000.

Body No.	Body Type & Seating	Factory Price	Shipping Weight	Prod. Total
Model 1106, 12-cyl.				
275	Rbt. Spd. LeB.-2P	7746	5400	Note 1
Model 1107, 12-cyl.				
730	Tr.-5/7P	3980	5415	Note 1
731	Phae.-5P	3890	5325	Note 1
741	Spt. Phae.-5P	4190	5400	Note 1
733	Sed.-5P	3960	5530	Note 1
743	Conv. Sed.-5P	4750	5470	Note 1
732	Fml. Sed.-5P	4660	5630	Note 1

Body No.	Body Type & Seating	Factory Price	Shipping Weight	Prod. Total
736	Clb. Sed.-5P	4060	5660	Note 1
737	Cpe.-5P	3990	5530	Note 1
747	Conv. Vict.	4590	5440	Note 1
738	Cpe.-2/4P	3820	5585	Note 1
739	Cpe. Rds.-2/4P	3850	5330	Note 1
Model 1108 Standard, 12-cyl.				
734	Sed.-5/7P	4185	5700	Note 1
735	Sed. limo.-5/7P	4385	5750	Note 1
Model 1108 Dietrich, 12-cyl.				
4002	All W. Twn. Car Dietrich	5695	5715	Note 1
4068	Stationary Cpe. Dietrich-2/4P	6185	5405	Note 1
4069	Spt. Phae. Dietrich-4P	5180	5400	Note 1
4070	Conv. Sed. Dietrich-5P	6555	5505	Note 1
4071	Conv. Rbt. Dietrich-2/4P	6100	5370	Note 1
4072	Conv. Vict. Dietrich-4P	6080	5220	Note 1
4182	Spt. Sed. Dietrich-5P	7060	5130	Note 1
Model 1108 LeBaron, 12-cyl.				
858	All W. Cabr. LeB.-5/7P	6150	5655	Note 1
859	All W. Twn. Car LeB.	6150	5715	Note 1
280	Spt. Phae. LeB.-4P	7580	5130	Note 1

Note 1: Packard Model 1106, 1107 and 1108 production combined totaled 960 with no body style breakout available.

ENGINE: 67 degree V-block. Modified L. Twelve. Cast iron monobloc. B & S: 3-7/16 x 4 in. Disp.: 445.5 cu. in., 7.5 liters. C.R.: 6.0:1 with cast heads, 6.0:1 and 6.8:1 with aluminum heads. Brake H.P.: 160 @ 3200 R.P.M. Net H.P.: 56.7. Main bearings: four. Valve lifters: mechanical zero lash. Carb.: Stromberg.

CHASSIS: [1106 Series] W.B.: 134-7/8 in. Tires: 7.00 x 17. [1107 Series] W.B.: 141-7/8 in. Tires: 7.50 x 17. [1108 Series] W.B.: 146-7/8 in. Tires: 7.50 x 17.

TECHNICAL: Selective synchromesh transmission. Speeds: 3F/1R. Floor shift controls. Single dry plate clutch with vacuum assist. Shaft drive. Overall ratio: 4.41:1 open cars, 4.69:1 closed, 4.06:1 or 5.07:1 optional. Mechanical, vacuum assisted brakes on four wheels. Wire or wood spoke wheels.

OPTIONS: Sidemount cover(s). Radio ($79.50). Heater. Radio antenna. Spotlight.

HISTORICAL: Introduced August 1933. Model year production: 960.

1935

PACKARD — TWELFTH SERIES, ONE TWENTY (120-A) — EIGHT: With this car, Packard indelibly entered the medium-priced field. Its engine was typically Packard, an L-head straight eight delivering 110 horsepower. The wheelbase was 120 inches, hence the new model's designation. Nearly 25,000 were sold in 1935, during which year not quite 7,000 of all the other cars Packard was producing found buyers. The One Twenty was a smash hit in the marketplace, and it was a medium-priced car of total Packard integrity. Independent front suspension and hydraulic brakes were two of the One Twenty's features that would not be adopted on the larger cars for several years.

I.D. DATA: Serial number located on a metal firewall plate. The plate also showed the body type number and the production number of that particular car, starting with a 200 base number. Starting: body type number plus 201. Engine numbers located on boss on upper left corner of cylinder block. Starting: X-1501. Ending: X-27499.

Model 120, 8-cyl.

Body No.	Body Type & Seating	Factory Price	Shipping Weight	Prod. Total
898	Bus. Cpe.-2P	980	3400	Note 1
899	Conv. Cpe.-2/4P	1070	3385	Note 1
895	Spt. Cpe.-2/4P	1020	3435	Note 1
894	Tr. Cpe.-5P	1025	3455	Note 1
893	Sed.-5P	1060	3510	Note 1
896	Clb. Sed.-5P	1085	3515	Note 1
892	Tr. Sed.-5P	1095	3550	Note 1

Note 1: Packard Model 120 production for 1935 totaled 24,995 with no body style breakout available.

ENGINE: L-head. Straight eight. Cast iron. B & S: 3-1/4 x 3-7/8 in. Disp.: 256.16 cu. in. C.R.: 6.5:1 standard, 7.0:1 optional. Brake H.P.: 110 @ 3850 R.P.M. Net H.P.: 33.8. Main bearings: five. Valve lifters: mechanical. Carb.: Stromberg.

CHASSIS: [120 Series] W.B.: 120 in. Tires: 7.00 x 16. [Commercial] W.B.: 158 in. Tires: 7.00 x 16.

TECHNICAL: Selective synchromesh transmission. Speeds: 3F/1R. Floor shift controls. Dry plate clutch. Shaft drive. Overall ratio: 4.36:1 or 4.54:1 (depending on body style). Hydraulic brakes on four wheels. Disc wheels.

OPTIONS: Dual sidemounts. Sidemount cover(s). Bumper guards. Radio. Heater. Clock. Radio antenna. Spotlight.

HISTORICAL: Introduced January 1935. Model year production: 24,995.

PACKARD — TWELFTH SERIES, EIGHT (1200, 1201, 1202) — EIGHT: Aluminum cylinder heads were standard, the compression ratio was changed to 6.5:1, and horsepower was up to 130 with the Twelfth Series Eight. Top speed was over 90 mph. In the chassis, the X-member was extended to form boxed side rails, eliminating the traditional tubular front crossmember. On the outside, there was a new look to the car beginning up front with a five-degree slant to the radiator and carrying to the pontoon fenders in the rear. Chrome side louvers were a distinguishing feature. Sidemounts could be ordered, but if they were not, the spare tire was concealed in the sloping rear panel. The 127-inch wheelbase Model 1200 remained the five-passenger sedan. Body styles on the 134-inch wheelbase Model 1201 were nine in number and included a LeBaron Cabriolet. On Model 1202's 139-inch wheelbase were seven body styles, including a new "business" sedan and limousine and just one custom, the LeBaron Town Car.

I.D. DATA: Serial number located on metal rectangular plate on the firewall. The plate also showed body type number plus the production number for that particular car starting with a base number of 200. Starting: body type number plus 201. Engine numbers located on base on upper left corner of cylinder block. Starting: 385001. Ending: 390499.

Model 1200, 8-cyl.

Body No.	Body Type & Seating	Factory Price	Shipping Weight	Prod. Total
803	Sed.-5P	2385	4780	Note 1
Model 1201, 8-cyl.				
818	Cpe.-2/4P	2470	4475	Note 1
817	Cpe.-5P	2560	4760	Note 1
819	Cpe. Rds.-2/4P	2580	4725	Note 1
811	Phae.-5P	2870	4475	Note 1
813	Sed.-5P	2585	4815	Note 1
816	Clb. Sed.-5P	2580	4820	Note 1
812	Formal Sed.-5/7P	3285	5035	Note 1
807	Conv. Vict.-5P	3200	4835	Note 1
195	Cabr. LeB.-5/7P	5240	5185	Note 1
Model 1202, 8-cyl.				
814	Sed.-5/7P	2755	4955	Note 1
814	Bus. Sed.-5/8P	2630	4985	Note 1
815	Limo.-5/7P	2890	5045	Note 1
815	Bus. Limo.-5/8P	2765	5150	Note 1
863	Conv. Sed.-5P	3300	5140	Note 1
810	Tr.-5/7P	3170	4400	Note 1
194	Tr. Car LeB.-5/7P	5385	5225	Note 1

Note 1: Packard Model 1200, Model 1201 and Model 1202 production combined totaled 4,781 with no body style breakout available.

ENGINE: L-head. Straight eight. B & S: 3-3/16 x 5 in. Disp.: 320 cu. in. C.R.: 6.5:1 standard, 6.0:1 optional. Brake H.P.: 130 @ 3200 R.P.M. Net H.P.: 32.5. Main bearings: nine. Valve lifters: roller cam. Carb.: Stromberg-Duplex.

CHASSIS: [1200] W.B.: 127 in. Tires: 7.00 x 17 low pressure. [1201] W.B.: 134 in. Tires: 7.00 x 17 low pressure. [1202] W.B.: 139 in. (commercial vehicles - 160 in.) Tires: 7.00 x 17 low pressure.

TECHNICAL: Selective synchromesh transmission. Speeds: 3F/1R. Floor shift controls. Single disc clutch. Shaft drive. Overall ratio: 4.69:1 standard, 4.36:1 and 4.07:1 optional. Mechanical brakes on four wheels. Welded spoke wheels.

OPTIONS: Dual sidemounts. Sidemount cover(s). Bumper guards. Radio. Heater. Clock. Radio antenna. Spotlight. Disc and wood wheels.

HISTORICAL: Introduced August 1934. Model year production: 4,781.

PACKARD — TWELFTH SERIES, SUPER EIGHT (1203, 1204, 1205) — EIGHT: With the same engineering refinements as the Eight, the Super Eight for 1935 enjoyed a horsepower increase to 150. The new body styling theme of the Eight was followed on the Super Eight; the

1935 Packard, Eight (Model 1201), coupe roadster, OCW

1935 Packard, Eight (Model 1201), coupe, AA

1936 Packard, 120 (Model 120-B), sedan, AA

1936 Packard, Super Eight (Model 1404), coupe roadster, AA

1936 Packard, Twelve (Model 1408), convertible sedan, JAC

1937 Packard, Six (Model 115-C), station wagon, OCW

1937 Packard, Twelve (Model 1507), five-passenger coupe, JAC

only sedan with a trunk bulge was the club sedan. The handbrake was relocated under the cowl, which was a good idea; the front doors were hinged at the rear, which arguably was not — both these features in the Eight as well. Like the Eight, the Super Eight was offered in three wheelbases. The 132-inch Model 1203 was the five-passenger sedan. The 139-inch Model 1204 was offered in nine body styles, including the LeBaron Cabriolet. The 144-inch Model 1205 was offered in seven body styles, including a new "business" sedan and limousine, and the LeBaron Town Car.

I.D. DATA: Serial number located on metal rectangular plate on the firewall. The plate also showed body type number plus the production number of that particular car starting with a base number of 200. Starting: body type number plus 201. Engine numbers located on upper half of crankcase, left side, front end. Upper cylinder left side front on Twelve only. Starting: 755001. Ending: 756999.

Model 1203, 8-cyl.

Body No.	Body Type & Seating	Factory Price	Shipping Weight	Prod. Total
843	Sed.-5P	2990	5030	Note 1

Model 1204, 8-cyl.

Body No.	Body Type & Seating	Factory Price	Shipping Weight	Prod. Total
858	Cpe.-2/4P	2880	4935	Note 1
857	Cpe.-5P	3080	5015	Note 1
859	Cpe. Rds.-2/4P	3070	5045	Note 1
851	Phae.-5P	3390	5120	Note 1
841	Spt. Phae.-5P	3650	5350	Note 1
856	Clb. Sed-5P	3170	5150	Note 1
852	Fml. Sed.-5/7P	3800	5250	Note 1
847	Conv. Vict.-5P	3860	5095	Note 1
195	Cabr. LeB.-5/7P	5670	5300	Note 1

Model 1205, 8-cyl.

Body No.	Body Type & Seating	Factory Price	Shipping Weight	Prod. Total
854	Sed.-5/7P	3390	5300	Note 1
854	Bus. Sed.-5/8P	3265	5320	Note 1
855	Limo.-5/7P	3580	5350	Note 1
855	Bus. Limo-5/8P	3455	5380	Note 1
883	Conv. Sed.-5P	4010	5050	Note 1
850	Tr.-5/7P	3690	4729	Note 1
194	Twn. Car LeB.-5/7P	5815	5525	Note 1

Note 1: Packard Model 1203, Model 1204 and Model 1205 production combined totaled 1,392 with no body style breakout available.

ENGINE: L-head. Straight eight. Cast enbloc. B & S: 3-1/2 x 5 in. Disp.: 384.4 cu. in. C.R.: 6.3:1 standard, 6.9:1 optional. Brake H.P.: 150 @ 3200 R.P.M. Net H.P.: 39.2. Main bearings: nine. Valve lifters: roller cam. Carb.: Stromberg-Duplex.

CHASSIS: [1203 Series] W.B.: 132 in. Tires: 7.00 x 17. [1204 Series] W.B.: 139 in. Tires: 7.00 x 17. [1205 Series] W.B.: 144 in.; (commercial vehicles - 165 in.) Tires: 7.00 x 17.

TECHNICAL: Selective synchromesh transmission. Speeds: 3F/1R. Floor shift controls. Single disc clutch. Shaft drive. Overall ratio: 4.41:1. Mechanical brakes on four wheels. Welded spoke wheels.

OPTIONS: Front bumper (stabilizer). Dual sidemounts. Sidemount cover(s). Bumper guards. Radio. Heater. Spotlight.

HISTORICAL: Introduced August 1934. Model year production: 1,392.

PACKARD — TWELFTH SERIES, TWELVE (1207, 1208) — TWELVE: Aluminum heads and an increase in stroke to 4-1/4 inches were among the refinements resulting in a horsepower increase to 175 for the Twelve. With the optional high compression head, 180 bhp was on tap. Three-point rubber suspension of the engine was adopted. Chassis and body styling changes followed the Eight and Super Eight theme. Model 1207 was on the 139-1/4-inch wheelbase and featured 10 body styles, a LeBaron All-Weather Cabriolet the only custom. Model 1208 was on the 144-1/4-inch chassis, and offered five body styles with a LeBaron All-Weather Town Car the only custom.

I.D. DATA: Serial number located on a rectangular plate mounted on the firewall. Starting: 903001. Ending: 903587. There was also a body type number and the production number of that particular car, starting with a base number of 200. Starting: body number plus 201.

Model 1207, 12-cyl.

Body No.	Body Type & Seating	Factory Price	Shipping Weight	Prod. Total
831	Phae.-5P	4190	5475	Note 1
821	Spt. Phae.-5P	4490	5830	Note 1
833	Sed.-5P	3960	5700	Note 1
832	Formal Sed.-5P	4660	5695	Note 1
836	Clb. Sed.-5P	4060	5640	Note 1
837	Cpe.-5P	3990	5545	Note 1
827	Conv. Vict.-5P	4890	5605	Note 1
838	Cpe.-2/4P	3820	5535	Note 1
839	Cpe. Rds.-2/4P	3850	5480	Note 1
195	All W. Cabr. LeB.-5/7P	6290	5930	Note 1

Model 1208, 12-cyl.

Body No.	Body Type & Seating	Factory Price	Shipping Weight	Prod. Total
830	Tr.-7P	4490	5415	Note 1
873	Conv. Sed.-5P	5050	5990	Note 1
834	Sed.-7P	4285	5790	Note 1
835	Limo.-7P	4485	5840	Note 1
194	All W. Twn. Car LeB.-7P	6435	5950	Note 1

Note 1: Packard Model 1207 and Model 1208 production combined totaled 788 with no body style breakout available.

ENGINE: 67 degree V-block. Modified L. Twelve. Cast iron monobloc. B & S: 3-7/16 x 4-1/4 in. Disp.: 473.3 cu. in. C.R.: 6.0:1, 6.25:1, 7.0:1. Brake H.P.: 175 @ 3200 R.P.M. Net H.P.: 56.7. Main bearings: four. Valve lifters: mechanical with zero lash take-up mechanisms. Carb.: Stromberg-Duplex.

CHASSIS: [1206] W.B.: 132-1/2 in. [1207] W.B.: 139-1/4 in. Tires: 7.50 x 17. [1208] W.B.: 144-1/4 in. Tires: 7.50 x 17.

TECHNICAL: Selective synchromesh transmission. Speeds: 3F/1R. Floor shift control. Single plate clutch with vacuum assist. Shaft drive. Overall ratio: 4.41:1 standard, 4.06:1, 4.69:1, 5.07:1 optional. Mechanical vacuum assist brakes on four wheels. Wire or wood spoke wheels. Vacuum clutch.

OPTIONS: Dual sidemount ($65.00). Sidemount cover(s). Bumper guards. Radio. Heater. Spotlight.

HISTORICAL: Introduced August 1934. Model year production: 788.

1936

PACKARD — FOURTEENTH SERIES, ONE TWENTY (120-B) — EIGHT: Engineering refinements including an increase in stroke to 4-1/2 inches made for 120 hp—and the rather neat fact that now both horsepower and wheelbase matched the One Twenty's designation. The cars were capable of a genuine 85 mph, and 0 to 60 mph in 19.9 seconds. The suicide doors were gone, and the 120-B's sales of 55,000 cars more than doubled the previous year's figure. The convertible sedan was a new body style.

I.D. DATA: Serial numbers located on a metal firewall plate. The plate also showed the body type number and the production number of that particular car, starting with a base number of 200. Starting: body type number plus 201. Engine numbers located on boss on upper left corner of cylinder block. Starting: X-27500. Ending: 99999.

Model 120, 8-cyl.

Body No.	Body Type & Seating	Factory Price	Shipping Weight	Prod. Total
998	Bus. Cpe.-2P	990	3380	Note 1
999	Conv. Cpe.-2/4P	1110	3525	Note 1
995	Spt. Cpe.-2/4P	1030	3455	Note 1
994	Tr. Cpe.-5P	1040	3475	Note 1
993	Sed.-5P	1075	3505	Note 1
996	Clb. Sed.-5P	1090	3495	Note 1
992	Tr. Sed.-5P	1115	3560	Note 1
997	Conv. Sed.-5P	1395	3660	Note 1

Note 1: Packard Model 120 production for 1936 totaled 55,042 with no body style breakout available.

ENGINE: L-head. Straight eight. Cast iron. B & S: 3-1/4 x 4-1/2 in. Disp.: 282 cu. in. C.R.: 6.5:1 standard, 7.0:1 optional. Brake H.P.: 120 @ 3800 R.P.M. Net H.P.: 33.8. Main bearings: five. Valve lifters: mechanical. Carb.: Stromberg.

CHASSIS: W.B. 120 in. Tires: 7.00 x 16.

TECHNICAL: Selective synchromesh transmission. Speeds: 3F/1R. Floorshift control. Clutch: 10 in. plate. Shaft drive. Overall ratio: 4.09:1 standard, 4.54:1 and 4.7:1 optional. Hydraulic brakes on four wheels. Disc or steel artillery wheels.

OPTIONS: Single sidemount. Sidemount cover(s). Radio. Heater. Clock. Radio antenna.

HISTORICAL: Introduced August 1935. Model year production: 55,042.

PACKARD — FOURTEENTH SERIES, EIGHT (1400, 1401, 1402) — EIGHT: Except for numerical designation, the Fourteenth Series Eights were essentially a reprise of the Twelfth Series. (Superstition had resulted in there being no Thirteenth Series.) Chrome strip ribs were added to the headlights, the radiator was sloped another five degrees and the front fenders modified accordingly — but that was about it. Engineering changes included Delco-Remy ignition with octane selector and clutch bearings that were now permanently lubricated. Body styles remained the same, on the same three wheelbase lengths.

I.D. DATA: Serial number located on a metal rectangular plate on the firewall. The plate also showed body type number plus the production number of that particular car, starting with a base number of 200. Starting: body type number plus 201. Engine numbers located on boss on upper left corner of cylinder block. Starting: 390500. Ending: 395499.

Body No.	Body Type & Seating	Factory Price	Shipping Weight	Prod. Total
Model 1400, 8-cyl.				
903	Sed.-5P	2385	4815	Note 1
Model 1401, 8-cyl.				
918	Cpe.-2/4P	2470	4735	Note 1
917	Cpe.-5P	2560	4745	Note 1
919	Cpe. Rds.-2/4P	2730	4740	Note 1
911	Phae.-5P	3020	4990	Note 1
913	Sed.-5P	2585	4978	Note 1
916	Clb. Sed.-5P	2580	4815	Note 1
912	Formal Sed.-5/7P	3285	4958	Note 1
907	Conv. Vict.-5P	3200	4810	Note 1
294	Cabr. LeB.-5/7P	5240	5185	Note 1
Model 1402, 8-cyl.				
914	Sed-5/7P	2755	4950	Note 1
914	Bus. Sed.-5/8P	2630	5020	Note 1
915	Limo.-5/7P	2890	5035	Note 1
915	Bus. Limo.-5/8P	2765	5068	Note 1
963	Conv. Sed.-5P	3400	5103	Note 1
910	Tr.-5/7P	3270	5060	Note 1
295	Twn. Car LeB.-5/7P	5385	5517	Note 1

Note 1: Packard Model 1400, Model 1401 and Model 1402 production combined totaled 3,973 with no body style breakout available.

ENGINE: L-head. Straight eight. Cast enbloc. B & S: 3-3/16 x 5 in. Disp.: 320 cu. in. C.R.: 6.5:1 standard, 6.0:1 optional. Brake H.P.: 130 @ 3200 R.P.M. Net H.P.: 32.5. Main bearings: nine. Valve lifters: roller cam. Carb.: Stromberg-Duplex.

CHASSIS: [1400 Series] W.B.: 127 in. Tires: 7.00 x 17. [1401 Series] W.B.: 134 in. Tires: 7.00 x 17. [1402 Series] W.B.: 139 in.; (commercial vehicles - 160 in.) Tires: 7.00 x 17.

TECHNICAL: Selective synchromesh transmission. Speeds: 3F/1R. Floor shift control. Clutch: Single disc. Shaft drive rear axle. Overall ratio: 4.69:1 standard, 4.36:1 and 4.07:1 optional. Mechanical brakes on four wheels. Welded spoke wheels.

OPTIONS: Dual sidemounts. Sidemount cover(s). Bumper guards. Radio. Heater. Spotlight.

HISTORICAL: Introduced August 1935. Model year production: 3,973.

PACKARD — FOURTEENTH SERIES, SUPER EIGHT (1403, 1404, 1405) — EIGHT: The few changes accorded the Eight were also accorded the Super Eight. Body styles and wheelbases remained the same. The Fourteenth Series was memorable as Packard's last for Bijur lubrication, ride control, semi-elliptic suspension, mechanical brakes—and the big 384-cubic inch engine.

I.D. DATA: Serial number located on a metal rectangular plate on the firewall. The plate also showed body type number plus the production number of that particular car, starting with a base number of 200. Starting: body type number plus 201. Engine numbers located on upper half of crankcase, left side, front end. Starting: 757000. Ending: 758499.

Body No.	Body Type & Seating	Factory Price	Shipping Weight	Prod. Total
Model 1403, 8-cyl.				
943	Sed.-5P	2990	5080	Note 1
Model 1404, 8-cyl.				
958	Cpe.-2/4P	2880	4933	Note 1
957	Cpe.-5P	3080	5010	Note 1
959	Cpe. Rds.-2/4P	3070	4993	Note 1
951	Phae.-5P	3390	5080	Note 1
941	Spt. Phae.-5P	3650	5200	Note 1
956	Clb. Sed.-5P	3170	5178	Note 1
952	Formal Sed.-5/7P	3800	5245	Note 1
947	Conv. Vict.-5P	3860	5122	Note 1
294	Cabr. LeB.-5/7P	5670	5300	Note 1
Model 1405, 8-cyl.				
954	Sed.-5/7P	3390	5280	Note 1
954	Bus. Sed.-5/8P	3265	5380	Note 1
955	Limo.-5/7P	3580	5328	Note 1
955	Bus. Limo.-5/8P	3455	5380	Note 1
983	Conv. Sed.-5P	4010	5430	Note 1
950	Tr.-5/7P	3690	5200	Note 1
295	Town Car LeB.-5/7P	5815	5525	Note 1

Note 1: Packard Model 1403, Model 1404 and Model 1405 production combined totaled 1,330 with no body style breakout available.

ENGINE: L-head. Straight eight. Cast enbloc. B & S: 3-1/2 x 5 in. Disp.: 384.4 cu. in. C.R.: 6.3:1 standard, 6.0:1 optional. Brake H.P.: 150 @ 3200 R.P.M. Net H.P.: 39.2. Main bearings: nine. Valve lifters: roller cam. Carb.: Stromberg-Duplex.

CHASSIS: [1403] W.B.: 132 in. Tires: 7 x 17. [1404] W.B.: 139 in. Tires: 7 x 17. [1405] W.B.: 144 in. Tires: 7 x 17.

TECHNICAL: Selective synchromesh transmission. Speeds: 3F/1R. Floor shift control. Single disc clutch. Shaft drive. Overall ratio: 4.41:1. Mechanical brakes on four wheels. Welded spoke wheels.

OPTIONS: Dual sidemounts. Sidemount cover(s). Bumper guards. Radio. Heater. Spotlight.

HISTORICAL: Introduced August 1935. Model year production: 1,330.

PACKARD — FOURTEENTH SERIES, TWELVE (1407, 1408) — TWELVE: The Twelve's engine now had a conventionally designed oil temperature regulator, but further engineering changes were virtually nil. Styling changes for the Eight and Super Eight were also accorded the Twelve. Body styles and wheelbases remained the same. LeBaron's All Weather Cabriolet and All Weather Town Car continued to be the priciest Twelves in the line, at more than $6,000.

I.D. DATA: The body type code plus the production number (vehicle number) was used on the rectangular plate mounted on the firewall. In 1936 the body type and production numbers started with a 200 base. Body type number plus 201. Engine serial numbers. Starting: 904000. Ending: 905499.

Body No.	Body Type & Seating	Factory Price	Shipping Weight	Prod. Total
Model 1407, 12-cyl.				
931	Phae.-5P	4190	5480	Note 1
921	Spt. Phae.-5P	4490	5785	Note 1
933	Sed.-5P	3960	5695	Note 1
932	Fml. Sed.-6P	4660	5880	Note 1
936	Clb. Sed.-5P	4060	5760	Note 1
937	Cpe.-5P	3990	5495	Note 1
927	Conv. Vict.-5P	4890	5585	Note 1
938	Cpe.-2/4P	3820	5495	Note 1
939	Cpe. Rds.-2/4P	3850	5495	Note 1
294	All W. Cabr. LeB.-5/7P	6290	5900	Note 1
Model 1408, 12-cyl.				
930	Tr.-7P	4490	5460	Note 1
973	Conv. Sed.-5P	5050	5945	Note 1
934	Sed.-7P	4285	5790	Note 1
935	Sed. Limo.-7P	4485	5890	Note 1
295	All W. Twn. Car LeB.-7P	6435	5950	Note 1

Note 1: Packard Model 1407 and Model 1408 production combined totaled 682 with no body style breakout available.

ENGINE: 67 degree V-block. Modified L. Twelve. B & S: 3-7/16 x 4-1/2 in. Disp.: 473.3 cu. in. C.R.: 6.0:1, 6.25:1 , 7.0:1. Brake H.P.: 175 @ 3200 R.P.M. (180 @ 3200 with high compression heads). Net H.P.: 56.7. Main bearings: four. Valve lifters: mechanical with zero lash. Carb.: Stromberg-Duplex.

CHASSIS: [1407] W.B.: 139-1/4 in. Tires: 7.50 x 17. [1408] W.B.: 144-1/2 in. Tires: 7.50 x 17.

TECHNICAL: Selective synchromesh transmission. Speeds: 3F/1R. Floor shift control. Single plate clutch. Shaft drive. Overall ratio: 4.41:1 standard, 4.06:1, 4.69:1 and 5.07:1 optional. Mechanical-vacuum assist brakes on four wheels. Wire spoke wheels.

OPTIONS: Dual sidemounts. Sidemount cover(s). Bumper guards. Radio. Heater. Spotlight.

HISTORICAL: Introduced August 1935. Model year production: 682.

1937

PACKARD — FIFTEENTH SERIES, SIX (115-C) — SIX: Packard's first six-cylinder car since the Fifth Series in 1927 was introduced as a lower-priced companion to the wildly successful One Twenty. Its engine was basically the One Twenty's minus two cylinders, a 237-cubic inch L-head six good for 100 mph. Its wheelbase was five inches shorter at 115 inches. From the cowl back, the two Junior Packards looked quite alike, distinguishing differences appearing in the shorter hood and front fenders of the new Six, in addition to trim variations (the ornamental hood louvers on the One Twenty were chrome-plated, whereas on the Six they were sheet metal stampings). Interiors were less expensively appointed, with no chrome trim on the dashboard. Sidemounts were not available. But the price was right at $795 to $1,295. And the range of body styles included both a convertible coupe and a station wagon, the latter introduced mid-model year.

I.D. DATA: Serial number located on metal firewall plate. The plate also showed body type number plus the actual production number of that body type, starting with a base number of 200. Starting: body type number plus 201. Engine numbers located on boss on upper left corner of cylinder block. Starting: T-1500. Ending: 99999.

Model 115-C, 6-cyl.

Body No.	Body Type & Seating	Factory Price	Shipping Weight	Prod. Total
1088	Bus. Cpe.-2P	795	3140	Note 1
1089	Conv. Cpe.-2/4P	910	3285	Note 1
1085	Spt, Cpe.-2/4P	840	3215	Note 1
1084	Tr. Cpe.-5P	860	3235	Note 1
1083	Sed.-5P	895	3265	Note 1
1086	Clb. Sed.-5P	900	3275	Note 1
1082	Tr. Sed.-5P	910	3310	Note 1
1060	Sta. Wag.	1295	NA	Note 1

Note 1: Packard Model 115-C production totaled 65,400 with no body style breakout available.

ENGINE: L-head. Inline six. Cast iron block. B & S: 3-7/16 x 4-1/4 in. Disp.: 237 cu. in. C.R.: 6.3:1 standard, 7.0:1 optional. Brake H.P.: 100 @ 3600 R.P.M. Net H.P.: 29.4. Main bearings: four. Valve lifters: mechanical. Carb.: Chandler-Grove.

CHASSIS: [115C] W.B.: 115 in. Tires 16 x 6.50.

TECHNICAL: Selective synchromesh transmission. Speeds: 3F/1R. Floor shift control. Single disc clutch. Shaft drive. Overall ratio: 4.36:1 standard, 4.54:1 optional. Hydraulic brakes on four wheels. Disc or optional steel artillery wheels.

OPTIONS: Clock ($11.50). Windshield defroster (6.75). Fender lights (13.50). Radiator screen (1.75). Vanity mirror (95 cents). Radio (59.50). Cigar lighter (2.50). Deluxe emblem (6.00).

HISTORICAL: Introduced September 1936. Model year production: 65,400.

PACKARD — FIFTEENTH SERIES, ONE TWENTY (120-C, 120-CD, 138-CD) — EIGHT: A station wagon was a One Twenty addition for 1937, but so also were three body styles (touring coupe, club sedan and touring sedan) designated 120 CD, the "d" translating to "deluxe" and providing such luxuries as a clock, deluxe radiator ornament, prettier trim, whitewall tires, full Marshall springs in the seats, a banjo spoke steering wheel, sponge-backed carpets and automatic radiator shutters. Then, late in the model year, two more versions of the One Twenty joined the model line, these on a 138-inch wheelbase, seven-passenger touring sedan and limousine in the $2,000 range. Despite competition from its new six-cylinder companion Junior Packard, One Twenty sales for the model year were above the 50,000 mark.

I.D. DATA: Serial number located on a metal firewall plate. The plate also showed the body type number and the actual production number of that body type, starting with a base number of 200. Starting: body type numbers plus 201. Engine numbers located on boss on upper left corner of cylinder block. Starting: X-100000. Ending: 199999.

Body No.	Body Type & Seating	Factory Price	Shipping Weight	Prod. Total
Model 120-C, 8-cyl.				
1098	Bus. Cpe.-2P	1130	3340	Note 1
1095	Spt. Cpe.-2/4P	1175	3415	Note 1
1094	Tr. Cpe.-5P	1200	3435	Note 1
1903	Sed.-5P	1235	3465	Note 1
1096	Clb. Sed.-5P	1240	3455	Note 1
1099	Conv. Cpe.-2/4P	1250	3485	Note 1
1092	Tr. Sed.-5P	1250	3520	Note 1
1097	Conv. Sed.-5P	1550	3630	Note 1
1070	Sta. Wag.-8P	1335	3590	Note 1
Model 120-CD, 8-cyl.				
1094CD	Tr. Cpe.-5P	1415	3465	Note 1
1096CD	Clb. Sed.-5P	1455	3485	Note 1
1092CD	Tr. Sed.-5P	1465	3550	Note 1
Model 138-CD, 8-cyl.				
1091CD	Tr. Sed.-7P	1900	3835	Note 1
1090CD	Tr. Limo.-7P	2050	3900	Note 1

Note 1: Packard Model 120-C, Model 120-CD and Model 138-CD production combined totaled 50,100 with no body style breakout available.

ENGINE: L-head. Straight eight. Cast iron block. B & S: 3-1/4 x 4-1/2 in. Disp.: 282 cu. in. C.R. 6.5:1 standard, 7.0:1 optional. Brake H.P.: 120 @ 3800 R.P.M. Net H.P.: 33.8. Main bearings: five. Valve lifters: mechanical. Carb.: Stromberg or Carter.

CHASSIS: [120C Series] W.B.: 120 in. Tires: 7.00 x 16. [120CD Series.] W.B.: 120 in. Tires: 7.00 x 16. [138CD] W.B.: 138 in. Tires: 7.00 x 16.

TECHNICAL: Selective synchromesh transmission. Speeds: 3F/1R. Floor shift control. Shaft drive rear axle. Overall ratio: 4.09:1 standard, 4.54:1 and 4.7:1 optional. Hydraulic brakes on four wheels. Disc and optional steel artillery wheels.

OPTIONS: Rear bumper. Single sidemount. Sidemount cover(s). Bumper guards. Radio. Heater. Clock (optional 120C, standard 120CD and 138CD). Cigar lighter. Radio antenna. Spotlight.

HISTORICAL: Introduced September 1936. Model year production: 50,100.

PACKARD — FIFTEENTH SERIES, SUPER EIGHT (1500, 1501, 1502) — EIGHT: The Super Eight received the Fourteenth Series Eight's 320-cubic inch engine, and what had been the Eight in the Fourteenth Series was now called a Super Eight, too. These were among many changes. Bijur lubrication was no more. But independent front suspension arrived, as did hydraulic brakes with centrifuse drums. And the rear-hinged doors were gone. Bumpers were new front and rear, and the radiator was given a 30 degree slant. The 127-inch wheelbase Model 1500 Super Eight was the bread-and-butter five-passenger sedan priced at $2,335. The 134-inch wheelbase Model 1501 included eight body styles ranging in price from $2,420 to $4,850 for the LeBaron Cabriolet. The 139-inch wheelbase Model 1502 offered six body styles ranging from a $2,705 touring sedan to the $4,990 LeBaron Town Car.

I.D. DATA: Serial number located on a metal rectangular plate on the firewall. The plate also showed body type number plus the production number of that particular car, starting with a base number of 200. Starting: body type number plus 201. Engine numbers located on left side of crankcase near starter. Starting: 395500. Ending: 449999.

Body No.	Body Type & Seating	Factory Price	Shipping Weight	Prod. Total
Model 1500, 8-cyl.				
1003	Tr. Sed.-5P	2335	4530	Note 1
Model 1501, 8-cyl.				
1018	Cpe.-2/4P	2420	4585	Note 1
1017	Cpe.-5P	2510	4595	Note 1
1019	Cpe. Rds.-2/4P	2680	4580	Note 1
1016	Clb. Sed.-5P	2530	4600	Note 1
1012	Formal Sed.-5P	3235	4795	Note 1
1017	Conv. Vict.-5P	3150	4650	Note 1
1013	Tr. Sed.-5P	2535	4670	Note 1
L-394	Cabr. LeB.-5/7P	4850	4965	Note 1
Model 1502, 8-cyl.				
1014	Tr. Sed.-5/7P	2705	4700	Note 1
1014B	Bus. Sed.-5/8P	2580	4755	Note 1
1015	Limo.-5/7P	2840	4815	Note 1
1015B	Bus. Limo.-5/8P	2715	4925	Note 1
1063	Conv. Sed.-5P	3350	4945	Note 1
L-395	Twn. Car. LeB.-5/7P	4990	5360	Note 1

Note 1: Packard Model 1500, Model 1501 and Model 1502 production combined totaled 5,793 with no body style breakout available.

ENGINE: L-head. Straight eight. Cast enbloc. B & S: 3-3/16 x 5 in. Disp.: 320 cu. in. C.R.: 6.5:1 standard, 7.0:1 optional. Brake H.P.: 135 @ 3200 R.P.M. Net H.P.: 32.5. Main bearings: nine. Valve lifters: roller cam. Carb.: Stromberg.

CHASSIS: [1500] W.B.: 127 in. Tires: 7.50 x 16. [1501] W.B.: 134 in. Tires: 7.50 x 16. [1502] W.B.: 139 in. (commercial vehicles - 165 in.) Tires: 7.50 x 16.

TECHNICAL: Selective synchromesh transmission. Speeds: 3F/1R. Floor shift control. Single disc clutch. Shaft drive. Overall ratio: 4.69:1. Hydraulic brakes on four wheels. Disc wheels.

OPTIONS: Dual sidemounts. Sidemount cover(s). Bumper guards. Radio. Heater and defroster. Spotlight.

HISTORICAL: Introduced September 1936. Model year production: 5,793.

PACKARD — FIFTEENTH SERIES, TWELVE (1506, 1507, 1508) — TWELVE: Generally, the Twelve received the same changes as the Super Eight: independent front suspension and hydraulic brakes were fitted; Bijur lubrication was gone, as were the rear-hinged doors. Wheelbases were 132-1/4 inches for the five-passenger sedan in

Model 1506. The 139-1/4-inch wheelbase Model 1507 had eight body styles ranging from $3,560 to $5,700 for the LeBaron All-Weather Cabriolet. The four body styles in the 144-1/4-inch wheelbase Model 1508 were convertible sedan, touring sedan, touring limousine and LeBaron All Weather Town Car. Since the longest wheelbase available in a Fifteenth Series Super Eight was 139 inches, anybody wanting a longer Packard had to take a 12-cylinder engine with it. The Packard Twelve enjoyed its best sales year in 1937: 1,300 cars.

I.D. DATA: Serial number located on a rectangular plate mounted on the firewall. They used the body type number and production number for that body type. These started with a 200 base. Starting: body number plus 201. Engine numbers located on left side of block below distributor. Starting: 905500. Ending: 919999.

Model 1506, 12-cyl.

Body No.	Body Type & Seating	Factory Price	Shipping Weight	Prod. Total
1023	Tr. Sed.-5P	3490	5335	Note 1
Model 1507, 12-cyl.				
1033	Tr. Sed.-5P	3560	5525	Note 1
1032	Formal Sed.-6P	4260	5550	Note 1
1036	Clb. Sed.-5P	3660	5520	Note 1
1037	Cpe.-5P	3590	5415	Note 1
1027	Conv. Vict.-5P	4490	5345	Note 1
1038	Cpe.-2/4P	3420	5255	Note 1
1039	Cpe. Rds.-2/4P	3450	5255	Note 1
L-394	All W. Cabr. LeB.-5/7P	5700	5740	Note 1
Model 1508, 12-cyl.				
1073	Conv. Sed.-5P	4650	5680	Note 1
1034	Tr. Sed.-7P	3885	5600	Note 1
1035	Tr. Limo.-7P	4085	5660	Note 1
L-395	All W. Twn. Car LeB.-5/7P	5900	5790	Note 1

Note 1: Packard Model 1506, Model 1507 and Model 1508 production combined totaled 1,300 with no body style breakout available.

Note: touring, phaeton and sport phaeton were available on special order only.

ENGINE: 67 degree V block. Modified L. Twelve. Cast iron monobloc. B & S: 3-7/16 x 4-1/4 in. Disp.: 473.3 cu. in. C.R.: 6.0:1 standard, 6.4:1 and 7.0:1 optional. Brake H.P.: 175 @ 3200 R.P.M. (180 @ 3200 with high compression heads). Net H.P.: 56.7. Main bearings: four. Valve lifters: mechanical with zero lash take-up mechanism. Carb.: Stromberg.

CHASSIS: [1506] W.B.: 132-1/4 in. Tires: 8.25 x 16. [1507] W.B.: 139-1/4 in. Tires: 8.25 x 16. [1508] W.B.: 144-1/4 in. Tires: 8.25 x 16.

TECHNICAL: Selective synchromesh transmission. Speeds: 3F/1R. Floor shift control. Single plate vacuum assist clutch. Shaft drive. Overall ratio: 4.41:1 standard, 4.06:1, 4.69:1 and 5.07:1 optional. Hydraulic brakes with vacuum booster, handbrake mechanical to rear drums. Steel disc wheels.

OPTIONS: Dual sidemount w/covers and luggage rack ($240.00). Bumper guards. Radio. Heater. Spotlight.

HISTORICAL: Introduced September 1936. Model year production: 1,300.

1938

PACKARD — SIXTEENTH SERIES, SIX (1600) — SIX: The Six's engine was bored out to 3-1/2 inches, which increased displacement to 245 cubic inches; though horsepower remained 100, low speed torque was improved. A Six could now accelerate from 0 to 50 mph in 15.8 seconds, and 78 mph was top. A heavier water pump, redesigned fan and increased radiator capacity were among the other engineering changes. The wheelbase was increased to 122 inches, and the all-steel bodies were all-new. There were not as many of them, however; though a two-door touring sedan and club coupe were added to the line, five body styles were dropped, including the station wagon. The most distinctive aspect of the new body styling was the chrome strip that ran the length of the hood, up the windshield and into the roof of the car.

I.D. DATA: Serial number located on decal, which also indicated the body type number plus production number starting with a base number of 2000. Starting: body type number plus 2001. Engine numbers located on boss on upper left corner of cylinder block. Starting: B-1501. Ending: 99999.

Model 1600, 6-cyl.

Body No.	Body Type & Seating	Factory Price	Shipping Weight	Prod. Total
1188	Bus. Cpe.-2P	975	3450	Note 1
1185	Clb. Cpe.-2/4P	1020	3425	Note 1
1189	Conv. Cpe.-2/4P	1135	3500	Note 1
1184	2-dr. Tr. Sed.-5P	1040	3475	Note 1
1182	4-dr. Tr. Sed.-5P	1070	3525	Note 1

Note 1: Packard Model 1600 production totaled 30,050 with no body style breakout available.

ENGINE: L-head. Inline six. Cast iron block. B & S: 3-1/2 x 4-1/4 in. Disp.: 245 cu. in. C.R.: 6.52:1 standard, 7.05:1 optional. Brake H.P.: 100 @ 3600 R.P.M. Net H.P.: 29.4. Main bearings: four. Valve lifters: pressure lubricated. Carb.: Chandler-Grove.

CHASSIS: W.B.: 122 in. Tires: 16 x 6.50.

TECHNICAL: Selective synchromesh transmission. Speeds: 3F/1R. Floor shift control. Single plate clutch. Shaft drive rear axle. Overall ratio: 4.54:1. Hydraulic brakes on four wheels. Disc wheels.

OPTIONS: Radio. Heater. Clock. Spotlight.

HISTORICAL: Introduced September 1937. Model year production: 30,050.

PACKARD — SIXTEENTH SERIES, EIGHT (1601, 1601D, 1602) — EIGHT: The One Twenty became the Eight this year. Like the Six, its wheelbase was increased seven inches (to 127, the same length as the shortest Senior Packard) for the 1601 cars, with a 148-inch chassis arriving for Model 1602. Compression ratio was changed to 6.6:1, with a 7.05:1 aluminum option available. Only the four-door touring sedan was available as a DeLuxe model, though any of the body styles could be "deluxed" via the extensive accessory catalog. Though the station wagon was dropped, the Eight did not lose as many body styles as the Six—and among the new ones were three elegant custom creations from Rollston. These were $5,000-range cars, the most expensive Junior Packards ever. The long-wheelbase Model 1602 limousine and sedan remained in the $2,000 range. Cars in the 1601 line could be purchased for $1,225 to $1,650.

I.D. DATA: Serial number located on a decal vehicle plate. It contained the body type number plus the production number, starting with a base number of 2000. Starting: body type number plus 2001. Engine numbers located on boss on upper left corner of cylinder block. Starting: A-300001. Ending: 399999.

Model 1601, 8-cyl.

Body No.	Body Type & Seating	Factory Price	Shipping Weight	Prod. Total
1198	Bus. Cpe.-2P	1225	3570	Note 1
1195	Clb. Cpe.-2/4P	1270	3550	Note 1
1199	Conv. Cpe.-2/4P	1365	3625	Note 1
1197	Conv. Sed.-5P	1650	3775	Note 1
1194	2-dr. Tr. Sed.-5P	1295	3600	Note 1
1192	4-dr. Tr. Sed.-5P	1325	3650	Note 1
Model 1601-D, 8-cyl.				
1172	4-dr. Tr. Sed. Deluxe-5P	1540	3685	Note 1
Model 1601 Rollston, 8-cyl.				
1665	All W. Cabr. Roll.-5/7P	4810	NA	Note 1
1669	All W. Twn. Car Roll.-5/7P	4885	NA	Note 1
1668	All W. Brgm. Roll.-4P	5100	NA	Note 1
Model 1602, 8-cyl.				
1190	Tr. Limo.-5/7P	2110	4245	Note 1
1191	Tr. Sed.-5/7P	1955	4195	Note 1

Note 1: Packard Model 1601, Model 1601-D, Model 1601 Rollston and Model 1602 production combined totaled 22,624 with no body style breakout available.

ENGINE: L-head. Straight eight. Cast iron. B & S: 3-1/4 x 4-1/2 in. Disp.: 282 cu. in. C.R.: 6.6:1 standard, 7.05:1 optional. Brake H.P.: 120 @ 3800 R.P.M. Net H.P.: 33.8. Main bearings: five. Valve lifters: pressure lubricated. Carb.: Stromberg.

CHASSIS: [1601 Series] W.B.: 127 in. Tires: 7.00 x 16. [1602] W.B.: 148 in.

TECHNICAL: Selective synchromesh transmission. Speeds: 3F/1R. Floor shift control. Shaft drive rear axle. Overall ratio: 4.36:1 standard. Hydraulic brakes on four wheels. Disc wheels.

OPTIONS: DeLuxe steering wheel ($12.50). Gearshift ball (50 cents). Radiator emblem (6.75). Electric clock (11.75). Chrome wheel discs (20.00). Custom radio (65.75). Heater (19.85). Luggage (29.50).

HISTORICAL: Introduced September 1937. Model year production: 22,624.

PACKARD — SIXTEENTH SERIES, SUPER EIGHT (1603, 1604, 1605) — EIGHT: Engineering changes were minimal. Appearance changes were prominent, many of them (split vee windshield with chrome center strip, for example) introduced also on the Junior Pack-

1938 Packard, Eight (Model 1601), sedan, JAC

1938 Packard, Twelve (Model 1608), all-weather town car (with body by Rollston), JAC

1938 Packard, Eight (Model 1602), touring limousine, AA

1938 Packard, Super Eight (Model 1604), convertible victoria, AA

1939 Packard, Super Eight (Model 1703), convertible coupe (with drophead coupe top), JAC

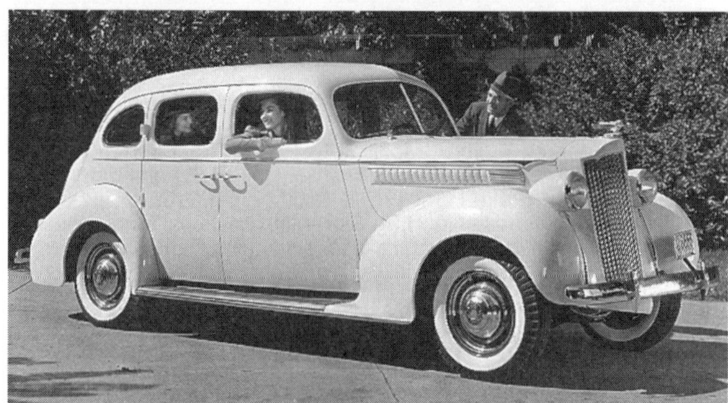

1939 Packard, Six (Model 1700), touring sedan, JAC

1940 Packard, Eight/120 (Model 1801), club sedan, JAC

1940 Packard, Six/110 (Model 1800), station wagon, OCW

1940 Packard, Eight/120 (Model 1801), convertible victoria (with body by Darrin), OCW

1940 Packard, Super Eight/180 (Model 1803), convertible sedan, JAC

ards. Fenders were pontoon, enveloping the sidemount on those cars carrying same. The radiator cap was pressurized, its filler moved under the hood. Super Eight standard equipment continued to include such niceties as an electric clock and cigar lighter, and package purchases of the "Custom Accessory Group" or "DeLuxe Accessory Group" added further amenities. Whitewall tires were $17.50 for a set of five, $23.50 for six and the extensive accessory catalog offered a new item this year: a "Guest Speaker" to be mounted in the center of the driver's seat back, which ensured "perfect radio reception for rear seat passengers." Wheelbases remained the same, though model numbers were 1603 (the former 1500), 1604 (the former 1501) and 1605 (the former 1502) now that the Junior Packards had been brought into the company numbering code. A Rollston All-Weather Cabriolet was a new entry for Model 1604. A Rollston Town Car and two Brunn customs were added to the Model 1605 line.

I.D. DATA: Serial number located on a decal vehicle plate that was placed on the firewall. (The decal tended to disintegrate over the years). The decal showed the body type number plus the production number for that particular car starting with a base number of 2000. Starting: body type number plus 2001. Engine numbers located on left side of crankcase near starter. Starting: A-500001. Ending: 599999.

Note: The decal had the unfortunate tendency to chip away and become illegible. This was the only year Packard used the decal in lieu of an engraved plate.

Model 1603, 8-cyl.

Body No.	Body Type & Seating	Factory Price	Shipping Weight	Prod. Total
1103	Tr. Sed.-5P	2790	4530	Note 1
Model 1604, 8-cyl.				
1118	Cpe.-2/4P	2925	4585	Note 1
1117	Cpe.-5P	2965	4595	Note 1
1119	Conv. Cpe.-2/4P	3210	4580	Note 1
1116	Clb. Sed.-5P	2990	4600	Note 1
1112	Fml. Sed.-5P	3710	4795	Note 1
1107	Conv. Vict.-5P	3670	4650	Note 1
1113	Tr. Sed.-5P	2995	4670	Note 1
494	All W. Cabr. Roll.-5/7	5790	NA	Note 1
Model 1605, 8-cyl.				
1114	Tour. Sed.-5/7P	3165	4700	Note 1
1114	Bus. Sed.-5/8P	3165	4815	Note 1
1115	Limo.-5/7P	3305	4815	Note 1
1115	Bus. Limo.-5/8P	3305	4815	Note 1
1143	Conv. Sed.-5P	3970	4945	Note 1
3087	All W. Cabr. Brunn-5/7P	7475	NA	Note 1
3086	Tour. Cabr. Brunn-5/6P	7475	NA	Note 1
495	Twn. Car Roll.-5/7P	5890	NA	Note 1

Note 1: Packard Model 1603, Model 1604 and Model 1605 production combined totaled 2,478 with no body style breakout available.

ENGINE: L-head. Straight eight. Cast enbloc. B & S: 3-3/16 x 5 in. Disp.: 320 cu. in. C.R.: 6.5:1 standard, 7.0:1 optional. Brake H.P.: 130 @ 3200 R.P.M. Net H.P.: 32.5. Main bearings: nine. Valve lifters: roller cam. Carb.: Stromberg.

CHASSIS: [1603] W.B.: 127 in. Tires: 7.50 x 16. [1604] W.B.: 134 in. Tires: 7.50 x 16. [1605] W.B.: 139 in. Tires: 7.50 x 16.

TECHNICAL: Selective synchromesh transmission. Speeds: 3F/1R. Floor shift control. Single plate clutch. Semi-floating rear axle. Overall ratio: 4.69:1. Hydraulic brakes on four wheels. Disc wheels.

OPTIONS: Spotlight ($18.50). Chrome wheel discs (20.00). Fog lights (6.95). Bumper guards (2.95). Windshield defroster (7.95). DeLuxe heater (19.85). DeLuxe radio (78.50). DeLuxe emblem (6.75). Pelican (10.00).

HISTORICAL: Introduced September 1937. Model year production 2,478.

PACKARD — SIXTEENTH SERIES, TWELVE (1607, 1608) — TWELVE: Not only did the Twelve share the same changes as the Super Eight, but it also joined the latter car on the same chassis. Gone were the Twelve's 132-, 139- and 144-inch wheelbases. Presumably there was a Twelve five-passenger sedan offered on the Super Eight's 127-inch wheelbase as Model 1606 (which would have been logical given the company's new numbering code), but that car failed to show up in Packard brochures. On the 134-inch wheelbase Model 1607 were seven production body styles and the Rollston All-Weather Cabriolet. On the 139-inch Model 1608 were three production and three custom cars. Just 566 Twelves were produced during the model year.

I.D. DATA: Serial number was on a vehicle decal that was located on the cowl. The number was the body type number and the production number for that particular car, starting with a base number of 2000. Starting: body number plus 2000. Engine numbers located on left side of block below distributor. Starting: A-600001. Ending: 620999.

Note: The decal had the unfortunate tendency to chip away and become illegible. This was the only year Packard used the decal in lieu of an engraved plate.

Model 1607, 12-cyl.

Body No.	Body Type & Seating	Factory Price	Shipping Weight	Prod. Total
1132	Formal Sed.-5P	4865	5550	Note 1
1133	Tr. Sed.-5P	4155	5525	Note 1
1136	Clb. Sed.-5P	4255	5520	Note 1
1137	Cpe.-5P	4185	5415	Note 1
1138	Cpe.-2/4P	4135	5255	Note 1
1139	Conv. Cpe.-2/4P	4370	5255	Note 1
1127	Conv. Vict.-5P	5320	5345	Note 1
494	All W. Cabr. Roll.-5/7P	6730	5740	Note 1
Model 1608, 12-cyl.				
1134	Tour. Sed.-7P	4485	5600	Note 1
1135	Sed. Limo. Tr.-7P	4690	5660	Note 1
1153	Conv. Sed.-5P	5390	5680	Note 1
495	All W. Twn. Car Roll.-5/7P	6880	5735	Note 1
3087	All W. Cabr. Brunn-5/7P	8510	5730	Note 1
3086	Tr. Cabr. Brunn-5/7P	8510	5725	Note 1

Note 1: Packard Model 1607 and Model 1608 production combined totaled 566 with no body style breakout available.

ENGINE: 67 degree V-block. Modified L. Twelve. Cast iron monobloc. B & S: 3-7/16 x 4-1/4 in. Disp.: 473.3 cu. in. C.R.: 6.0:1 standard, 6.4:1 and 7.0:1 optional. Brake H.P.: 175 @ 3200 R.P.M. Main bearings: four. Valve lifters: mechanical with zero lash take-up mechanisms. Carb.: Stromberg.

CHASSIS: [1607 Series] W.B.: 134-3/8 in. Tires: 8.25 x 16. [1608 Series] W.B.: 139-3/8 in. Tires: 8.25 x 16.

TECHNICAL: Selective synchromesh transmission. Speeds: 3F/1R. Floor shift control. Twelve inch single-plate vacuum clutch - vacuum assisted. Shaft drive. Overall ratio: 4.41:1. Hydraulic brakes with vacuum booster, handbrake mechanical to rear drums.

HISTORICAL: Introduced September 1938. Model year production: 566.

1939

PACKARD — SEVENTEENTH SERIES, SIX (1700) — SIX: Outside the look was substantially the same, but inside the Six for 1939 the gearshift was column mounted (called Handishift) and a new option was overdrive (called Econo-Drive). Another option was called No-Rol, a device to aid in starting and holding the car on an incline. The rear-leaf springs introduced in 1938 were given a "fifth" leaf in 1939. The body styles offered previously were brought back, but brought back too, was the station wagon that had been missing in 1938.

I.D. DATA: Serial number located on metal plate on firewall. This also included body type number plus the production number of that particular car, starting with a base number of 2000. Starting: body type number plus 2001. Engine number located on boss on upper left corner of cylinder block. Starting B-1501. Ending: 99999.

Model 1700, 6-cyl.

Body No.	Body Type & Seating	Factory Price	Shipping Weight	Prod. Total
1288	Bus. Cpe.-2P	888	3295	Note 1
1285	Clb. Cpe.-2/4P	944	3365	Note 1
1289	Conv. Cpe.-2/4P	1092	3385	Note 1
1284	2-dr Tr. Sed.-5P	964	3390	Note 1
1282	4-dr Tr. Sed.-5P	995	3400	Note 1
NA	Sta. Wag.-7P	1404	3652	Note 1

Note 1: Packard Model 1700 production totaled 24,350 with no body style breakout available.

ENGINE: L-head. Inline six. Cast iron block. B & S: 3-1/2 x 4-1/4 in. Disp.: 245 cu. in. C.R.: 6.52:1 standard, 7.05:1 optional. Brake H.P.: 100 @ 3200 R.P.M. Net H.P.: 29.4. Main bearings: four. Valve lifters: pressure lubricated. Carb.: Chandler-Grove.

CHASSIS: [1700] W.B.: 122 in. Tires: 6.50 x 16.

TECHNICAL: Selective synchromesh transmission. Speeds: 3F/1R. Column-mounted gearshift control. Single plate clutch. Shaft drive. Overall ratio: 4.54:1 standard. Hydraulic brakes on four wheels. Disc wheels.

OPTIONS: Radio. Heater. Clock. Spotlight. No-Rol. Tachometer.

HISTORICAL: Introduced September 1938. Model year production: 24,350.

PACKARD — SEVENTEENTH SERIES, ONE TWENTY (1701, 1702) — EIGHT: The One Twenty name was back for the eight-cylinder Junior Packard. The car shared the same new features as the Six: Handishift standard, and Econo-Drive, No-Rol and tachometer optional. Compression ratios were revised to 6.40:1 standard, with 6.85:1 optional and the former aluminum cylinder head replaced by cast iron. The station wagon returned to the line, and the long-wheelbase sedan and limousine were retained.

I.D. DATA: Serial number located on metal plate on firewall. This also included the body type number plus production number of that particular model, the last number having a starting base of 2000. Starting: body type number plus 2001. Engine numbers located on boss on upper left corner of cylinder block. Starting: B-300001. Ending: 399999.

Model 1701, 8-cyl.

Body No.	Body Type & Seating	Factory Price	Shipping Weight	Prod. Total
1298	Bus. Cpe.-2P	1099	3490	Note 1
1295	Clb. Cpe.-2/4P	1145	3535	Note 1
1299	Conv. Cpe.-2/4P	1288	3545	Note 1
1297	Conv. Sed.-5P	1600	3780	Note 1
1294	2-dr. Tr. Sed.-5P	1166	3595	Note 1
1292	4-dr. Tr. Sed.-5P	1196	3605	Note 1
1293	Sta. Wag.-7P	1636	3850	Note 1
Model 1702, 8-cyl.				
1290	Tr. Limo.-7P	1856	4185	Note 1
1291	Tr. Sed.-7P	1702	4100	Note 1

Note 1: Packard Model 1701 and Model 1702 production combined totaled 17,647 with no body style breakout available.

ENGINE: L-head. Straight eight. Cast iron block. B & S: 3-1/4 x 4-1/2 in. Disp.: 282 cu. in. C.R.: 6.41:1 standard, 6.85:1 optional. Brake H.P.: 120 @ 3800 R.P.M. Net H.P.: 33.8. Main bearings: five. Valve lifters: pressure lubricated. Carb.: Duplex or Stromberg.

CHASSIS: [1701 Series] W.B.: 127 in. Tires: 7.00 x 16. [1702 Series] W.B.: 148 in. Tires: 7.00 x 16.

TECHNICAL: Selective synchromesh transmission. Speeds: 3F/1R. Column shift control. Single plate clutch. Regular differential. Overall ratio: 4.36:1 standard; 4.09:1, 4.54:1, 4.70:1 and 4.90:1 optional; 4.54:1 standard with overdrive. Hydraulic brakes on four wheels. Disc wheels.

OPTIONS: Dual sidemounts. Sidemount cover(s). Radio. Clock. Spotlight. Econo-Drive (overdrive). No-Rol. Tachometer.

HISTORICAL: Introduced September 1938. Model year production: 17,647.

PACKARD — SEVENTEENTH SERIES, SUPER EIGHT (1703, 1705) — EIGHT: There was a drastic reduction in Super Eight body styles this year, from 15 in 1938, there were now just six (four on the 127-inch wheelbase, two on the 148-inch wheelbase) and custom cars were gone. Like the Junior Packards, the Super Eight had a column-mounted gearshift and offered overdrive, the hill-holding device and a tachometer among many options. Cylinder heads were now all cast iron, and both compression ratios and rear axle ratios were revised. By now the Super Eight was close to being simply a Junior Packard with more elaborate appointments and 10 extra horsepower. This would be the final year for the Super Eight's venerable 130 hp engine.

I.D. DATA: Serial number located on a metal rectangular plate on the firewall. The plate also showed the body type number plus the production number of that particular car, starting with a base number of 2000. Starting: body type number plus 2001. Engine numbers located on upper half of crankcase, left side, front end. Starting: B-500001. Ending: 599999.

Model 1703, 8-cyl.

Body No.	Body Type & Seating	Factory Price	Shipping Weight	Prod. Total
1275	Clb. Cpe.-2/4P	1650	3860	Note 1
1279	Conv. Cpe.-2/4P	1875	3870	Note 1
1272	Tr. Sed.-5P	1732	3930	Note 1
1277	Conv. Sed.-5P	2130	4005	Note 1
Model 1705, 8-cyl.				
1270	Tr. Limo.-5/8P	2294	4510	Note 1
1271	Tr. Sed.-5/8P	2156	4425	Note 1

Note 1: Packard Model 1703 and Model 1705 production combined totaled 3,962 with no body style breakout available.

ENGINE: L-head. Straight eight. Cast enbloc. B & S: 3-3/16 x 5 in. Disp.: 320 cu. in. C.R.: 6.45:1 standard, 6.85:1 optional. Brake H.P.: 130 @ 3200 R.P.M. Net H.P.: 32.5. Main bearings: nine. Valve lifters: roller cam. Carb.: Stromberg.

CHASSIS: [1703] W.B.: 127 in. Tires: 16 x 7.00. [1705] W.B.: 148 in. Tires: 16 x 7.00.

TECHNICAL: Selective synchromesh transmission. Speeds: 3F/1R. Column-mounted gearshift control. Single plate clutch. Floating rear axle. Overall ratio: 4.36:1 (1703), 4.54:1 (1705). Hydraulic brakes on four wheels. Steel disc wheels. Drivetrain options: hill-holder.

HISTORICAL: Introduced September 1938. Model year production: 3,962.

PACKARD — SEVENTEENTH SERIES, TWELVE (1707, 1708) — TWELVE: Fewer than 500 cars would be built in this the last year of the Packard Twelve. Wheelbases and body styles remained the same, including the custom cars. The only customs this year in the entire Packard lineup were Twelves. The column-mounted gearshift was an option on the Twelve, together with a host of others including a burled walnut instrument panel and a push-button radio.

I.D. DATA: Serial number located on rectangular plate on the firewall. In 1939 this plate showed the body type code plus the production number for that body type starting with a 2000. Starting: body type number plus 2001. Engine numbers located on left side of block below distributor. Starting: B-600001. Ending: 620999.

Model 1707, 12-cyl.

Body No.	Body Type & Seating	Factory Price	Shipping Weight	Prod. Total
1232	Formal Sed.-5P	4865	5745	Note 1
1233	Tr. Sed.-5P	4155	5670	Note 1
1236	Clb. Sed.-5P	4255	5590	Note 1
1237	Cpe.-5P	4185	5425	Note 1
1238	Cpe.-2/4P	4140	5400	Note 1
1239	Conv. Cpe.-2/4P	4375	5540	Note 1
1227	Conv. Vict.-5P	5230	5570	Note 1
594	All W. Cabr. Roll.-5/7P	6730	4950	Note 1
Model 1708, 12-cyl.				
1234	Tr. Sed.-7P	4485	5750	Note 1
1235	Sed. Limo. Tr.-7P	4690	5825	Note 1
1253	Conv. Sed.-5P	5395	5890	Note 1
595	All W. Twn. Car Roll.-5/7P	6880	5075	Note 1
4087	All W. Cabr. Brunn-5/7P	8355	5845	Note 1
4086	Tr. Cabr. Brunn-5/7P	8355	5845	Note 1

Note 1: Packard Model 1707 and Model 1708 production combined totaled 446 wlth no body style breakout available.

ENGINE: 67 degree V-block. Modified L-head. Twelve. Cast iron monobloc. B & S: 3-7/16 x 4-1/4 in. Disp.: 473.3 cu. in. C.R.: 6.0:1 standard, 6.4:1 and 7.0:1 optional. Brake H.P.: 175 @ 3200 R.P.M. Net H.P.: 56.7. Main bearings: four. Valve lifters: mechanical with zero lash take-up mechanisms. Carb.: Stromberg.

CHASSIS: [1707 Series] W.B.: 134-3/8 in. Tires: 8.25 x 16. [1708 Series] W.B.: 139-3/8 in. Tires: 8.25 x 16.

TECHNICAL: Selective synchromesh transmission. Speeds: 3F/1R (with optional column shift), floor-mounted gearshift control. Vacuum assist - 12 in. clutch. Shaft drive. Overall ratio: 4.41:1. Hydraulic brakes with vacuum booster.

OPTIONS: Dual sidemount mirrors ($20.00). Sidemount cover(s). Radio. Heater and defroster (40.00). Clock. Cigarette lighter. Radio antenna. Spotlight. Luggage rack (240.00). Auxiliary front bumper guard (40.00). Deluxe steering wheel (20.00). Optional column shift (240.00).

HISTORICAL: Introduced September 1938. Model year production: 446.

1940

PACKARD — EIGHTEENTH SERIES, ONE-TEN (1800) — SIX: The One-Ten designation was new, and so was this Junior Packard's look this year, with the tall Packard radiator grille flanked by two vertical side grilles, and the side hood louvers being given a step design. Sealed beam headlights were fitted directly on the fenders, with parking lights mounted on the fender crowns. Engineering changes were few, with revisions to compression ratios and rear axle ratios among them. The overdrive was now a Warner Gear. Standard equipment included bumpers and bumper guards front and rear, assist cords in both sedans, and a robe rail in the four-door version.

I.D. DATA: Serial number located on a metal plate on the firewall. Also included on the plate is the body type number plus the production number of that particular car, using a base number of 2000. Starting: body type number plus 2001. Engine numbers located on a boss on left side of cylinder block between No. 2 and No. 3 cylinder. Starting: C-1501. Ending: 64111.

Model 1800, 6-cyl.

Body No.	Body Type & Seating	Factory Price	Shipping Weight	Prod. Total
1388	Bus. Cpe.-2P	867	3110	Note 1
1385	Clb. Cpe.-2/4P	940	3165	Note 1
1389	Conv. Cpe.-2/4P	1104	3230	Note 1
1384	2-dr Tr. Sed.-5P	964	3190	Note 1
1382	4-dr Tr. Sed.-5P	996	3200	Note 1
1383	Sta. Wag.-8P	1200	3380	Note 1

Note 1: Packard Model 1800 production totaled 62,300 with no body style breakout available.

ENGINE: L-head. Inline. Six. Cast iron block. B & S: 3-1/2 x 4-1/4 in. Disp.: 245 cu. in. C.R.: 6.39:1 standard, 6.71:1 optional. Brake H.P.: 100 @ 3200 R.P.M. Net H.P.: 29.4. Main bearings: four. Valve lifters: adjustable tappet. Carb.: Stromberg Model BXOV-26.

CHASSIS: [1800] W.B.: 122 in. Tires: 6.25 x 16.

TECHNICAL: Selective synchromesh transmission. Speeds: 3F/1R. Column-mounted gearshift controls. Single plate clutch. Shaft drive. Overall ratio: 4.3:1 standard. Hydraulic brakes on four wheels. Disc wheels.

OPTIONS: Radio. Heater. Clock. Cigar lighter. Spotlight.

HISTORICAL: Introduced August 1939. Model year production: 62,300.

PACKARD — EIGHTEENTH SERIES, ONE-TWENTY (1801) — EIGHT: The One-Twenty designation was hyphenated this year, and the car enjoyed the same engineering and styling changes as the new One-Ten. Cylinder heads were redesigned for better intake gas flow. The greater length of the hood allowed for easier mounting of spare wheels for those ordering them. Window moldings were described as a "stunningly grained" luxury feature, and there were more options than ever, including a rear-seat center armrest. The long-wheelbase model was discontinued. But "Dutch" Darrin, who had begun customizing the One-Twenty in California in 1938, came aboard officially with a convertible victoria.

I.D. DATA: Serial number located on metal plate on firewall. The plate also included the body type number plus the production number of that particular car, starting with a base number of 2000. Starting: body type number plus 2001. Engine numbers located on boss on upper left corner of cylinder block. Starting: C-300001. Ending: 328320.

Model 1801, 8-cyl.

Body No.	Body Type & Seating	Factory Price	Shipping Weight	Prod. Total
1398	Bus. Cpe.-2P	1038	3340	Note 1
1395	Clb. Cpe.-2/4P	1111	3405	Note 1
1399	Conv. Cpe.-2/4P	1277	3585	Note 1
1396	4-dr. Clb. Sed.-5P	1239	3460	Note 1
1397	Conv. Sed.-5P	1573	3640	Note 1
1394	2-dr. Tr. Sed.-5P	1135	3440	Note 1
1393	Sta. Wag.-8P	1404	3590	Note 1
1392	4-dr. Tr. Sed.-5P	1166	3550	Note 1
700	Conv. Vict. Darrin-5P	3819	3826	Note 1
Model 1801 Deluxe, 8-cyl.				
1395-DE	Clb. Cpe.-2/4P	1161	3400	Note 1
1399-DE	Conv. Cpe.-2/4P	1318	3470	Note 1
1396-DE	Clb. Sed.-5P	1314	3480	Note 1
1392-DE	Tr. Sed.-5P	1246	3495	Note 1

Note 1: Packard Model 1801 and Model 1801 Deluxe production combined totaled 28,138 with no body style breakout available.

ENGINE: L-head. Inline. Eight. Cast iron block. B & S: 3-1/4 x 4-1/2 in. Disp.: 282 cu. in. C.R.: 6.41:1 standard, 6.85:1 optional. Brake H.P.: 120 @ 3600 R.P.M. Net H.P.: 33.8. Main bearings: five. Valve lifters: pressure lubricated.

CHASSIS: [1801 Series] W.B.: 127 in. Tires: 6.50 x 16.

TECHNICAL: Selective synchromesh transmission. Speeds: 3F/1R. Column shift control. Single plate clutch. Shaft drive. Overall ratio: 4.09:1 standard. Hydraulic brakes on four wheels. Disc wheels.

OPTIONS: Dual sidemounts. Radio. Spotlight.

HISTORICAL: Introduced August 1939. Model year production: 28,138.

PACKARD — EIGHTEENTH SERIES, SUPER EIGHT, ONE-SIXTY (1803, 1804, 1805) — EIGHT: One-Sixty designated the horsepower of the new engine powering all Senior Packards this year. Styling generally followed Junior Packard themes, with differences between the One-Sixty and the One-Eighty being in hood louvers, hubcaps and the mascot in front (the One-Sixty had the goddess, the One-Eighty the pelican). The One-Sixty was provided three wheelbases, the 127-inch Model 1803 carrying most of the body styles, the 138-inch Model 1804 offering just a five-passenger sedan, and the 148-inch Model 1805 providing a touring limousine and a sedan with accommodations for up to eight passengers. Air conditioning "Cooled by Mechanical Refrigeration," as Packard said—was an option, which did not work too well.

I.D. DATA: Serial number located on a rectangular plate on the firewall. The plate also showed the body type number plus the production number of that particular car, starting with a base number of 2000. Starting: body type number plus 2001. Engine numbers located on upper left side of cylinder block between No. 3 and No. 4 cylinder. Starting: 500001. Ending: 507697.

Model 1803, 8-cyl.

Body No.	Body Type & Seating	Factory Price	Shipping Weight	Prod. Total
1378	Bus. Cpe.-2P	1524	3665	Note 1
1375	Clb. Cpe.-2/4P	1595	3735	Note 1
1379	Conv. Cpe.-4P	1775	3795	Note 1
1376	Clb. Sed.-5P	1717	3780	Note 1
1377	Conv. Sed.-5P	2050	3990	Note 1
1372	Tr. Sed.-5P	1632	3825	Note 1
Model 1804, 8-cyl.				
1362	Tr. Sed.-5P	1895	4070	Note 1
Model 1805, 8-cyl.				
1370	Tr. Limo.-5/8P	2154	4460	Note 1
1371	Tr. Sed-5/8P	2026	4350	Note 1

Note 1: Packard Model 1803, Model 1804 and Model 1805 production combined totaled 5,662 with no body style breakout available.

ENGINE: L-head. Straight eight. Cast iron block. B & S: 3-1/2 x 4-5/8 in. Disp.: 356 cu. in. C.R.: 6.45:1 standard, 6.85:1 optional. Brake H.P.: 160 @ 3200 R.P.M. Net H.P.: 39.2. Main bearings: nine. Valve lifters: silent, hydraulic. Aluminum pistons.

CHASSIS: [1803 Series] W.B.: 127 in. Tires: 7.00 x 16. [1804 Series] W.B.: 138 in. Tires: 7.00 x 16. [1805 Series] W.B.: 148 in. Tires: 7.00 x 16.

TECHNICAL: Selective synchromesh transmission. Speeds: 3F/1R. Column-mounted gearshift control. Single plate clutch. Shaft drive rear axle. Overall ratio: 3.92:1 standard (1803), 4.09:1 (1804), 4.36:1 (1805). Hydraulic brakes on four wheels. Disc wheels.

OPTIONS: Dual sidemounts. Bumper guards. Radio. Heater. Spotlight. Steel spoke wheels.

HISTORICAL: Introduced August 1939. Model year production: 5,662.

PACKARD — EIGHTEENTH SERIES, CUSTOM SUPER EIGHT ONE-EIGHTY (1806, 1807, 1808) — EIGHT: The One-Eighty's engine was the same as the One-Sixty, as were the three chassis on which all body styles were carried. As successor to the Twelve, however, the One-Eighty was considerably more lavish in trim and appointments, and it was the model that carried the custom cars in the Senior Packard line. The Rollston offerings were updated variations of the cars previously available on the Twelve; the Darrins were all-new and the most widely promoted. "Glamour Car of the Year!" was the company's advertising headline. The Darrin Convertible Victoria was on the 127-inch Model 1806 chassis, joining a Club Sedan, the Darrin Convertible Sedan was on the 138-inch Model 1807 chassis, together with the Rollston All-Weather Cabriolet and touring and formal sedans. The long 148-inch wheelbase Model 1808 carried a limousine and sedan in addition to the Rollston All-Weather Town Car.

I.D. DATA: Serial number located on metal rectangular plate on the firewall. The plate also showed the body type number plus the production number of that particular car, starting with a base number of 2000. Starting: body type number plus 2001. Engine numbers located on upper left side of cylinder block between No. 3 and No. 4 cylinder. Starting: CC-500001. Ending: 507697.

Model 1806, 8-cyl.

Body No.	Body Type & Seating	Factory Price	Shipping Weight	Prod. Total
1356	Clb. Sed.-5P	2243	3900	Note 1
700	Conv. Vict. Darrin-5P	4570	4121	Note 1
Model 1807, 8-cyl.				
1342	Tr. Sed.-5P	2410	4175	Note 1
1332	Formal Sed.-5P	2840	4210	Note 1
694	All W. Cabr. Roll.-5/7P	4450	4050	Note 1
710	Conv. Sed. Darrin-5P	6300	4050	Note 1
720	Spt. Sed. Darrin-5P	6100	4215	Note 1
Model 1808, 8-cyl.				
1350	Tr. Limo.-5/8P	2669	4585	Note 1
1351	Tr. Sed.-5/8P	2541	4510	Note 1
695	All W. Twn. Car Roll.-7P	4574	4175	Note 1

Note 1: Packard Model 1806, Model 1807 and Model 1808 production combined totaled 1,900 with no body style breakout available.

ENGINE: L-head. Straight eight. Cast enbloc. B & S: 3-1/2 x 4-5/8 in. Disp.: 356 cu. in. C.R.: 6.45:1. Brake H.P.: 160 @ 3500 R.P.M. Net H.P.: 39.2. Main bearings: nine. Valve lifters: silent, hydraulic.

CHASSIS: [1806] W.B.: 127 in. Tires: 7.00 x 16. [1807] W.B.: 138 in. Tires: 7.00 x 16. [1808] W.B.: 148 in. Tires: 7.00 x 16.

TECHNICAL: Selective synchromesh transmission. Speeds: 3F/1R. Column-mounted gearshift control. Single plate clutch. Shaft drive. Overall ratio: 3.92:1 (1806), 4.90:1 (1807), 4.36:1 (1808). Hydraulic brakes on four wheels. Disc wheels.

OPTIONS: Single sidemount. Bumper guards. Radio. Heater. Spotlight.

HISTORICAL: Introduced August 1939. Model year production: 1,900.

1941

PACKARD — NINETEENTH SERIES, ONE-TEN (1900) — SIX: Because of blockbuster sales in 1940, the most junior of the Junior Packards was offered in a wide variety of body styles for 1941, with DeLuxe versions available for every One-Ten except the business coupe. A new 133-inch six-cylinder chassis was added as well, with Packard now entering the taxicab business in earnest. "Electromatic" was Packard's name for the new semi-automatic clutch, and overdrive was now called Aero-Drive. Two-tone paint schemes were new, and the runningboards were off (though still remaining available optionally). The shortened hood louvers also served as hood releases.

I.D. DATA: Serial number located on metal plate on firewall. Also included on the plate was the body type number plus the production number of that particular car, starting with a base number of 2000. Starting: body type number plus 2001. Engine numbers located on a boss on left side of cylinder block between No. 2 and No. 3 cylinder. Starting: D-1501. Ending: 36327.

Model 1900, 6-cyl.

Body No.	Body Type & Seating	Factory Price	Shipping Weight	Prod. Total
1488	Bus. Cpe.-2P	927	3150	Note 1
1485	Clb. Cpe.-2/4P	1020	3200	Note 1
1489	Conv. Cpe.-2/4P	1195	3310	Note 1
1484	2-dr. Tr. Sed.-5P	1010	3245	Note 1
1482	4-dr. Tr. Sed.-5P	1076	3250	Note 1
1483	Sta. Wag.-8P	1251	3460	Note 1
1462	Taxicab-5P	NA	3950	Note 1
Model 1900 Deluxe, 6-cyl.				
1485-DE	Clb. Cpe.-2/4P	1058	3205	Note 1
1489-DE	Conv. Cpe.-2/4P	1229	3315	Note 1
1484-DE	2-dr. Tr. Sed.-5P	1070	3270	Note 1
1482-DE	4-dr, Tr. Sed.-5P	1136	3270	Note 1
1463-DE	Sta. Wag.-8P	1326	3470	Note 1

Note 1: Packard Model 1900 and Model 1900 Deluxe production combined totaled 34,700 with no body style breakout available.

ENGINE: L-head. Inline. Six. Cast iron block. B & S: 3-1/2 x 4-1/4 in. Disp.: 245 cu. in. C.R.: 6.39:1 standard, 6.71:1 optional. Brake H.P.: 100 @ 3200 R.P.M. Net H.P.: 29.4. Main bearings: four. Valve lifters: adjustable tappet. Carb.: Stromberg Model BXOV-26.

CHASSIS: [1900 Series] W.B.: 122 in. Tires: 6.50 x 15. [Taxi] W.B.: 133 in. Tires: 6.50 x 15.

TECHNICAL: Selective synchromesh transmission. Speeds: 3F/1R. Column shift control. Disc clutch. Shaft drive rear axle. Overall ratio: 4.30:1 standard. Hydraulic brakes on four wheels. Disc wheels.

OPTIONS: Radio. Heater. Spotlight. Air conditioning.

HISTORICAL: Introduced September 1940. Model year production 34,700.

PACKARD — NINETEENTH SERIES, ONE-TWENTY (1901) — EIGHT: What was given to the One-Ten was taken away from the One-Twenty in 1941. Body styles were reduced to eight. Styling changes were common to the two cars. Headlights now settled completely into the fenders, and the one-piece sidemounts (when ordered) were sunk even deeper therein. The former divided rear window was now a one-piece.

I.D. DATA: Serial number located on metal plate on firewall. Also included was the body type number plus the production number of that particular car, starting with a base number of 2000. Starting: body type number plus 2001. Engine numbers located on a boss upper left side of cylinder block—boss is painted white. Starting: D-300001. Ending: 317238.

Model 1901, 8-cyl.

Body No.	Body Type & Seating	Factory Price	Shipping Weight	Prod. Total
1498	Bus. Cpe.-2P	1142	3385	Note 1
1495	Clb. Cpe.-2/4P	1235	3430	Note 1
1499	Conv. Cpe.-2/4P	1407	3585	Note 1
1497	Conv. Sed.-5P	1753	3725	Note 1
1494	2-dr. Tr. Sed.-5P	1260	3504	Note 1
1492	4-dr. Tr. Sed.-5P	1291	3510	Note 1
1493	Sta. Wag.-8P	1466	3720	Note 1
1473	Sta. Wag. DeL.-8P	1541	3730	Note 1

Note 1: Packard Model 1901 production totaled 17,100 with no body style breakout available.

ENGINE: L-head. Straight eight. Cast iron block. B & S: 3-1/4 x 4-1/2 in. Disp.: 282 cu. in. C.R.: 6.41:1 standard, 6.85:1 optional. Brake H.P.: 120 @ 3600 R.P.M. Net H.P.: 33.8. Main bearings: five. Valve lifters: pressure lubricated. Carb.: Carter Model WA1.

CHASSIS: [1901 Series] W.B.: 127 in. Tires: 7.00 x 15.

TECHNICAL: Selective synchromesh transmission. Speeds: 3F/1R. Column shift control. Conventional clutch. Shaft drive. Overall ratio: 4.09:1 standard. Hydraulic brakes on four wheels. Disc wheels.

OPTIONS: Dual sidemounts. Radio. Heater. Spotlight. Turn signals. Air conditioning ($275.00).

HISTORICAL: Introduced September 1940. Model year production: 17,100.

PACKARD — NINETEENTH SERIES, SUPER EIGHT ONE-SIXTY (1903, 1904, 1905) — EIGHT: Engineering changes were minimal, but the look was different this year throughout the Packard line. The Senior cars appeared longer (which they were by five inches), though the wheelbases remained the same. Radiators were pushed forward, and headlamps were now completely inset into the fenders, with the parking lamps mounted directly above them. Two-toning was in, if a customer wished; and runningboards were out, also at customer request. In their place a black rubber gravel shield was given the rear fender of One-Sixty closed cars (the shield was chrome on the convertibles). Models 1904 and 1905 offered the same body styles as the year previous; in Model 1903 the club sedan and the touring sedan were eliminated, but DeLuxe versions of both the convertible sedan and coupe were added.

I.D. DATA: Serial number located on a metal rectangular plate on the firewall. The plate also showed the body type number plus the production number of that particular car, starting with a base number of 2000. Starting: body type number plus 2001. Engine numbers located on a boss upper left side of cylinder block—boss is painted white. Starting: D-500001. Ending: 504550.

Model 1903, 8-cyl.

Body No.	Body Type & Seating	Factory Price	Shipping Weight	Prod. Total
1478	Bus. Cpe.-2P	1594	3875	Note 1
1475	Clb. Cpe.-4P	1709	3800	Note 1
1479	Conv. Cpe.-4P	1892	3965	Note 1
1479-DE	Conv. Cpe. DeL.-4P	2067	3985	Note 1
1477	Conv. Sed.-5P	2180	4140	Note 1
1477-DE	Conv. Sed. DeL.-5P	2405	4160	Note 1
1472	Tr. Sed.-5P	1750	3865	Note 1
Model 1904, 8-cyl.				
1462	Tr. Sed.-5P	2009	4305	Note 1
Model 1905, 8-cyl.				
1471	Tr. Sed.-7P	2161	4495	Note 1
1470	Tr. Limo.-7P	2289	4570	Note 1

Note 1: Packard Model 1903, Model 1904 and Model 1905 production combined totaled 3,525 with no body style breakout available.

ENGINE: L-head. Straight eight. Cast iron block. B & S: 3-1/2 x 4-5/8 in. Disp.: 356 cu. in. C.R.: 6.45:1 standard, 6.85:1 optional. Brake H.P.: 160 @ 3500 R.P.M. Net H.P.: 39.2. Main bearings: nine. Valve lifters: silent hydraulic.

CHASSIS: [1903] W.B.: 127 in. Tires: 7.00 x 16. [1904] W.B.: 138 in. Tires: 7.00 x 16. [1905] W.B.: 148 in. Tires: 7.00 x 16.

TECHNICAL: Selective synchromesh transmission. Speeds: 3F/1R. Column-mounted gearshift control. Single plate clutch. Shaft drive. Overall ratio: 3.92:1. Hydraulic brakes on four wheels. Disc wheels.

OPTIONS: Dual sidemounts. Fender skirts. Radio ($63.50). Heater and defroster. Spotlight. Air conditioning (275.00). Electromagnetic clutch (37.50). Aero-Drive.

HISTORICAL: Introduced September 1940. Model year production: 3,525.

PACKARD — NINETEENTH SERIES, SUPER EIGHT ONE-EIGHTY (1906, 1907, 1908) — EIGHT: Though the One-Sixty and the One-Eighty were essentially the same cars save for trim and appointments, the Packard company this year strove to make the most of the difference. Catalogs specified that all One-Eighty models were custom cars available on special order. Independent coachbuilders accounted for 6 of the 11 body styles available, Packard providing the rest. Windows were larger in the One-Eighty, and hydraulically-operated in the closed cars. In the closed cars too, wood replaced the wood-grained metal moldings of the year previous. And all One-Eighty cars were provided chrome gravel shields when runningboards were not ordered. Wheelbases remained the same, though body styles available were revised. In the Model 1906 the club sedan was dropped, leaving only the Darrin Convertible Victoria—in the Model 1907 the Darrin Convertible Sedan was replaced by a LeBaron Sport Brougham. The Model 1908 line was augmented with a new touring sedan and touring limousine by LeBaron.

I.D. DATA: Serial number located on metal rectangular plate on the firewall. The plate also showed the body type number plus the production number of that particular car, starting with a base number of 2000. Starting: body type number plus 2001. Engine numbers located on a boss upper left side of cylinder block—boss is painted white. Starting: CD-500001. Ending: 504550.

Model 1906, 8-cyl.

Body No.	Body Type & Seating	Factory Price	Shipping Weight	Prod. Total
1429	Conv. Vict. Darrin-5P	4595	4040	Note 1
Model 1907, 8-cyl.				
1452	Spt. Brgm. LeB.-5P	3545	4450	Note 1
1422	Spt. Sed. Darrin-5P	4795	4490	Note 1
794	All W. Cabr. Roll.-7P	4695	4075	Note 1
1432	Formal Sed.-6P	3095	4380	Note 1
1442	Tr. Sed.-5P	2632	4350	Note 1
Model 1908, 8-cyl.				
1451	Tr. Sed.-7P	2769	4590	Note 1
1450	Tr. Limo.-7P	2913	4650	Note 1
1421	Tr. Sed. LeB.-7P	5345	4740	Note 1
1420	Tr. Limo. LeB.-7P	5595	4850	Note 1
795	All W. Twn. Car Roll.-7P	4820	4200	Note 1

Note 1: Packard Model 1906, Model 1907 and Model 1908 production combined totaled 930 with no body style breakout available.

ENGINE: L-head. Straight eight. Cast enbloc. B & S: 3-1/2 x 4-5/8 in. Disp.: 356 cu. in. C.R.: 6.45:1 standard, 6.85:1 optional. Brake H.P.: 160 @ 3500 R.P.M. Net H.P.: 39.2. Main bearings: nine. Valve lifters: silent hydraulic.

CHASSIS: [1905 Series] W.B.: 127 in. Tires: 7.00 x 16. [1906 Series] W.B.: 138 in. Tires: 7.00 x 16. [1907 Series] W.B.: 148 in. Tires: 7.00 x 16.

TECHNICAL: Selective synchromesh transmission. Speeds: 3F/1R. Column shift control. Single plate clutch. Shaft drive rear axle. Overall ratio: 3.92:1. Hydraulic brakes on four wheels. Disc wheels.

OPTIONS: Dual sidemounts. Sidemount cover(s). Fender skirts. Radio ($63.50). Heater and defroster. Spotlight. Electromagnetic clutch. AeroDrive. Air conditioning.

HISTORICAL: Introduced September 1940. Model year production: 930.

PACKARD — NINETEENTH SERIES, CLIPPER (1951) — EIGHT: The Clipper borrowed the One-Twenty's engine, though a new compression ratio provided five more horsepower. The Clipper's wheelbase was 127 inches as was the One-Twenty and the smallest Super Eight, though the chassis was thoroughly redesigned. What the Clipper did not borrow from any other Packard, of course, was its unique new look. Only one body style was available in Model 1951 (a four-door sedan), and it was priced at $1,420 (midway between the One-Twenty and One-Sixty). The Clipper was lower than any other Packard on the market, and wider than virtually any other car in the industry. Its pace-setting styling would be carried in many Junior and Senior Packards for the Twentieth Series.

I.D. DATA: Serial number located on metal plate on firewall. Also included on the plate was the body type number and the production number for that particular car, starting with a base number of 2000. Starting: body type number plus 2001. Engine numbers located on a boss upper left side of cylinder block—boss is painted white. Starting: D-400001. Ending: 499999.

Model 1951, 8-cyl.

Body No.	Body Type & Seating	Factory Price	Shipping Weight	Prod. Total
1401	Tr. Sed.-5P	1420	3725	16,600

ENGINE: L-head. Straight eight. Cast iron block. B & S: 3-1/4 x 4-1/2 in. Disp.: 282 cu. in. C.R.: 6.85:1. Brake H.P.: 125 @ 3600 R.P.M. Net H.P.: 33.8. Main bearings: five. Valve lifters: adjustable. Carb.: Carter Model WDO 512 S.

CHASSIS: [1951] W.B.: 127 in. Tires: 7.00 x 15.

TECHNICAL: Selective, synchronized transmission. Speeds: 3F/1R. Column-mounted gearshift control. Disc clutch. Shaft drive. Packard-Hypoid Angleset differential. Overall ratio: 4.09:1 standard, 4.36:1 optional. Hydraulic brakes on four wheels. Disc wheels.

OPTIONS: Fender skirts. Bumper guards. Radio. Spotlight. Air conditioning. Electromatic clutch. AeroDrive.

HISTORICAL: Introduced April 1941. Model year production: 16,600.

1942

PACKARD — TWENTIETH SERIES, SIX (2000, 2010, 2020, 2030) — SIX: The former One-Ten was once again renamed the Six, with the Clipper engine in all cars and Clipper styling in most. The station wagon and the convertible sedan offered the previous year were dropped; the convertible coupe (2020) and taxi (2030) were the only cars to retain the traditional One-Ten look. All bodies in the Special (2000) and Custom (2010) featured Clipper styling. Dish-shaped wheelcovers without the Packard name were fitted this year. And wheelbases were three: 120 inches for Models 2000 and 2010, 122 inches for Model 2020, 133 inches for Model 2030.

I.D. DATA: Serial number located on metal plate on firewall. Also included was the body type number plus the production number of that particular car, starting with a base of 2000. Starting: body type number plus 2001. Engine numbers located on a boss upper left side of cylinder block—boss is painted white. Starting: E-1501. Ending: 12906.

Model 2000, 6-cyl.

Body No.	Body Type & Seating	Factory Price	Shipping Weight	Prod. Total
1588	Bus. Cpe.-3P	1248	3365	Note 1
1585	Clb. Sed.-6P	1283	3415	Note 1
1582	Tr. Sed.-6P	1318	3435	Note 1
Model 2010, 6-cyl.				
1505	Clb. Sed.-6P	1353	3440	Note 1
1502	Tr. Sed.-6P	1388	3460	Note 1
Model 2020, 6-cyl.				
1589	Conv. Cpe.-5P	1468	3315	Note 1
Model 2030, 6-cyl.				
1584	Taxicab-6P	NA	3980	Note 1

Note 1: Packard Model 2000, Model 2010, Model 2020 and Model 2030 production combined totaled 11,325 with no body style breakout available.

ENGINE: L-head. Inline six. Cast iron block. B & S: 3-1/4 x 4-1/4 in. Disp.: 245 cu. in. C.R.: 6.39:1 standard, 6.71:1 optional. Brake H.P.: 105 @ 3600 R.P.M. Net H.P.: 29.4. Main bearings: four. Valve lifters: adjustable. Carb.: Carter Model WA1-530-S.

CHASSIS: [2000, 2010] W.B.: 120 in. Tires: 6.50 x 15. [2020] W.B.: 122 in. Tires: 6.50 x 15. [2030] W.B.: 133 in. Tires: 6.50 x 15.

TECHNICAL: Selective synchromesh transmission. Speeds: 3F/1R. Column-mounted gearshift control. Disc clutch. Shaft drive. Overall ratio: 4.30:1 standard, 4.55:1 optional. Hydraulic brakes on four wheels. Disc wheels.

OPTIONS: Radio. Vacuum radio antenna. Electromatic. Turn signals (standard on the Custom).

HISTORICAL: Introduced August 1941. Model year production: 11,325.

PACKARD — TWENTIETH SERIES, EIGHT (2001, 2011, 2021) — EIGHT: This series, formerly the One-Twenty, was as "Clipperized" as the One-Ten. Again, only a single production car—the Model 2021 convertible coupe—retained the One-Twenty styling, and on the traditional 127-inch wheelbase. All other cars rode on a 120-inch wheel-

1941 Packard, Eight/120 (Model 1901), club coupe, JAC

1941 Packard, Six/110 (Model 1900), station wagon, OCW

1942 Packard, Special Six (Model 2020), convertible coupe, JAC

1948 Packard, Standard Eight (Series 2201), station sedan, AA

1948 Packard, Custom Eight (Series 2206), sedan (with body by Derham), AA

1941 Packard, Deluxe Six/110 (Model 1900), convertible coupe, OCW

1942 Packard, Clipper, Super Eight/180 (Model 2006), sedan, OCW

1947 Packard, Deluxe Clipper Eight (Series 2111), sedan, OCW

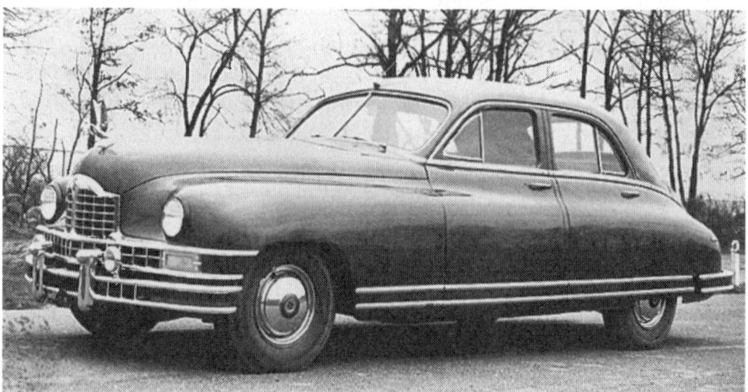

1948 Packard, Deluxe Eight (Series 2211), sedan, AA

1949 Packard, Custom Eight (Series 2333), convertible, OCW

base and carried Clipper styling, these designated the Special (2001) and the Custom (2011). Turn signals, automatic courtesy lights, electric clock and automatic cigar lighter were among the amenities supplied as standard equipment on the Eight Custom, available optionally on the Eight Special.

I.D. DATA: Serial number located on metal plate on firewall. The body type number plus the production number for that particular car was also included on the plate, starting with a base number of 2000. Starting: body type number plus 2001. Engine numbers located on a boss upper left side of cylinder block—boss is painted white. Starting: E-300001. Ending: 319350.

Model 2001, 8-cyl.

Body No.	Body Type & Seating	Factory Price	Shipping Weight	Prod. Total
1598	Bus. Cpe.-3P	1303	3490	Note 1
1595	Clb. Sed.-6P	1338	3540	Note 1
1592	Tr. Sed.-6P	1373	3560	Note 1
Model 2011, 8-cyl.				
1515	Clb. Sed.-6P	1408	3565	Note 1
1512	Tr. Sed.-6P	1443	3585	Note 1
Model 2021, 8-cyl.				
1599	Conv. Cpe.-6P	1578	3585	Note 1

Note 1: Packard Model 2001, Model 2011 and Model 2021 production combined totaled 19,199 with no body style breakout available.

ENGINE: L-head. Straight eight. Cast iron block. B & S: 3-1/4 x 4-1/2 in. Disp.: 282 cu. in. C.R.: 6.85:1. Brake H.P.: 125 @ 3600 R.P.M. Net H.P.: 33.8. Main bearings: five. Valve lifters: adjustable.

CHASSIS: [2001, 2011] W.B.: 120 in. Tires: 6.50 x 15. [2021] W.B.: 127 in. Tires: 6.50 x 15.

TECHNICAL: Selective synchromesh transmission. Speeds: 3F/1R. Column-mounted gearshift control. Disc clutch. Shaft drive. Overall ratio: 4.10:1 standard. Hydraulic brakes on four wheels. Disc wheels.

OPTIONS: Radio. Heater. Vacuum radio antenna. Electromatic. Air conditioning. Turn signals.

HISTORICAL: Introduced August 1941. Model year production: 19,199.

PACKARD — TWENTIETH SERIES, SUPER EIGHT ONE-SIXTY (2003, 2004, 2005, 2023, 2055) — EIGHT: Turn indicators and dish-shaped hubcaps that did not say Packard were common to both Junior and Senior Packards for 1942. There was news unique to the Seniors, however; the cars' straight-eight engine now generated 165 hp, though that fact was not publicized during a year when the big Packard word was "Clipper." Clipper styling came to the One-Sixty in a club sedan and touring sedan on the 127-inch wheelbase, the convertible coupe being the only traditionally-styled One-Sixty now on that chassis. The traditional One-Sixty look remained on the 138-inch and 148-inch cars, the latter chassis now including a new business sedan and limousine. There was a nod to the Clipper even in these models, however, with the change from vertical to horizontal in the grilles flanking the radiator (all non-Clippers featured this). Electric windshield wipers and an accelerator pedal starter were also new to the One-Sixty this year.

I.D. DATA: Serial number located on a metal rectangular plate on the firewall. The plate also showed the body type number plus the production number of that particular car, starting with a base number of 2000. Starting: body type number plus 2001. Engine numbers on a boss upper left side of cylinder block—boss is painted white. Starting: F500000. Ending: E504000.

Model 2003, 8-cyl.

Body No.	Body Type & Seating	Factory Price	Shipping Weight	Prod. Total
1575	Clb. Sed.-6P	1635	3985	Note 1
1572	Tr. Sed.-6P	1695	4005	Note 1
Model 2023, 8-cyl.				
1579	Conv. Cpe.-5P	1795	3905	Note 1
Model 2004, 8-cyl.				
1562	Tr. Sed.-6P	1905	4090	Note 1
Model 2005, 8-cyl.				
1571	Tr. Sed.-5/7P	2050	4325	Note 1
1570	Tr. Limo.-5/7P	2175	4445	Note 1

Model 2055, 8-cyl.

Body No.	Body Type & Seating	Factory Price	Shipping Weight	Prod. Total
1591	Bus. Sed.-5/7P	1900	4315	Note 1
1590	Bus. Limo.-5/7P	2025	4435	Note 1

Note 1: Packard Model 2003, Model 2023, Model 2004, Model 2005 and Model 2055 production combined totaled 2,580 with no body style breakout available.

ENGINE: L-head. Straight eight. Cast enbloc. B & S: 3-1/2 x 4-5/8 in. Disp.: 356 cu. in. C.R.: 6.85:1. Brake H.P.: 165 @ 3600 R.P.M. Net H.P.: 39.2. Main bearings: nine. Valve lifters: hydraulic.

CHASSIS: [2003] W.B.: 127 in. Tires: 7.00 x 16. [2023] W.B.: 127 in. Tires: 7.00 x 16. [2004] W.B.: 138 in. Tires: 7.00 x 16. [2005, 2055] W.B.: 148 in. Tires: 7.00 x 16.

TECHNICAL: Selective synchromesh transmission. Speeds: 3F/1R. Column-mounted gearshift control. Single plate clutch. Shaft drive. Overall ratio: 3.92:1. Hydraulic brakes on four wheels. Disc wheels.

HISTORICAL: Introduced August 25, 1941. Model year production: 2,580.

PACKARD — TWENTIETH SERIES, SUPER EIGHT ONE-EIGHTY (2006, 2007, 2008) — EIGHT: The One-Eighty was provided the same changes as the One-Sixty—and the same neglect in the wake of the attention-getting Clipper. As with the One-Sixty, Clipper styling arrived in two body styles on the 127-inch wheelbase, the Darrin Convertible Victoria the sole non-Clipper now on that chassis. Though the Darrin Sport Sedan and LeBaron Sport Brougham were dropped, LeBaron remained represented with two custom bodies, as did Rollson. This was, of course, the last year for the Super Eight.

I.D. DATA: Serial number located on a metal rectangular plate on the firewall. The plate also showed the body type number plus the production number of that particular car, starting with base number of 2000. Starting: body type number plus 2001. Engine numbers located on a boss upper left side of cylinder block—boss is painted white. Starting: CE-500001. Ending: 503371.

Model 2006, 8-cyl.

Body No.	Body Type & Seating	Factory Price	Shipping Weight	Prod. Total
1525	Clb. Sed.-6P	2115	4010	Note 1
1522	Tr. Sed.-6P	2215	4030	Note 1
Model 2006 Special, 8-cyl.				
1529	Darrin Conv. Vic.-5P	4595	3920	Note 1
Model 2007, 8-cyl.				
1532	Formal Sed.-6P	3050	4390	Note 1
1542	Tr. Sed.-6P	2465	4280	Note 1
894	All W. Cabr. Roll.-7P	4875	4525	Note 1
Model 2008, 8-cyl.				
1551	Tr. Sed.-7P	2550	4525	Note 1
1550	Tr. Limo.-7P	2675	4540	Note 1
1521	Tr. Sed. LeB.-7P	5545	4740	Note 1
1520	Tr. Limo. LeB.-7P	5795	4850	Note 1
895	All W. Twn. Car Roll.-7P	4975	4200	Note 1

Note 1: Packard Model 2006, Model 2006 Special, Model 2007 and Model 2008 production combined totaled 672 with no body style breakout available.

ENGINE: L-head. Straight eight. Cast enbloc. B & S: 3-1/2 x 4-5/8 in. Disp.: 356 cu. in. C.R.: 6:85:1. Brake H.P.: 165 @ 3600 R.P.M. Net H.P.: 39.2. Main bearings: nine. Valve lifters: hydraulic.

CHASSIS: [2006] W.B.: 127 in. Tires: 7.00 x 16. [2007] W.B.: 138 in. Tires: 7.00 x 16. [2008] W.B.: 148 in. Tires: 7.00 x 16.

TECHNICAL: Selective synchromesh transmission. Speeds: 3F/1R. Column-mounted gearshift control. Single plate clutch. Shaft drive. Overall ratio: 3.92:1 Hydraulic brakes on four wheels. Disc wheels.

OPTIONS: Dual sidemounts. Fender skirts. Radio ($57.50). Heater with defroster (40.00). Clock. Radio. Spotlight. Turn indicators (9.75). Overdrive (60.00).

HISTORICAL: Introduced August 25, 1941. Model year production: 672.

PACKARD 1946-1958

The postwar history of Packard Motor Car Co. is a sad tale to relate. One of America's oldest carmakers, Packard continued to create outstanding automobiles from 1946 to 1958. The cars failed to find popularity with a new breed of buyers who wanted a radically different type of product after the fighting in Europe and Asia subsided.

By G. Marshall Naul

For years, Packard's business philosophy was built on the foundation of thought that high-priced car buyers did not care for radical change on an annual, model year basis. The directors of the company felt that such customers preferred a quality product that could retain its style value one season after the next. This was no longer the case in the industry, after 1949, when style consciousness came to play an ever more important role in the marketing of cars on a high-volume basis.

Also contributing to the eventual demise of the Packard nameplate was the company's independent status. Without full-range market coverage and the resources of a giant corporation to back it up, Packard was unable to adjust quickly to the new postwar trends. This meant that even after the problems had been identified, there was no feasible way to solve them. Packard simply could not afford to create all new styling one year and sufficiently change it the next.

Of course, for the modern enthusiast, yesterday's problems have turned into a blessing of sorts. This is because many of those tradition-bound, quality-constructed Packards of the late-1940s and early-1950s now represent valuable collectors' items. Endowed with the magic of the Packard name, such automobiles are durable, beautiful and rare.

The first postwar Packards saw daylight on a chilly, gray October morning in 1945 and were, indeed, cars built to the same high standards held by this manufacturer since 1899. All of America wanted a new car at this time, so the fact that these Packards looked much like the 1942 models had little effect on sales. It was due to other factors, such as labor unrest and difficulty getting raw materials, that only 30,793 Twenty-First Series (1946) Packards were sold. Even at that, Packard was able to keep pace with other competitors within its own price class.

For 1947, the Packard saw little change, but began losing precious ground in terms of keeping abreast of new trends. The problem was not of major proportion yet, since the only all-new cars to be had were those from smaller companies such as Studebaker and Kaiser-Frazer. In fact, the company's longtime rival, Cadillac, was merely one notch up in the charts. (Only about three percent of the 1946-1950 Packards were in the Cadillac price range, however, and the company actually saw Buick as the big competitor in that period.)

The year 1948 brought a different ballgame. That was when Cadillac introduced P-38-type tailfins and sleekly-styled sheet metal on a few of its lines. Packard countered with a new look as well. It was one that seemed to have mass appeal. Praised and honored by a number of internationally respected design organizations, the Twenty-Second Series models earned 146,441 deliveries for calendar 1948 and 1949.

Suddenly it was late 1949 and three things began to happen. First, production by all manufacturers got back into full swing, satisfying just about all demand for new cars. Second, the large makers came forth with completely new and much modernized styling. The General Motors' hardtops were the fashion hit of the season. The third factor was one where Packard's weakness began to show. Though labeled as new, Twenty-Third Series "Golden Anniversary" models, the late-1949 and 1950 offerings looked basically the same as before. One important innovation was Ultramatic transmission, a type considered the best of its day by the public and auto experts alike.

In contrast to the models from other firms, buyers began viewing Packard as old-fashioned in a brave, new world. Helping little to combat the image, was a lack of a modern overhead valve V-8 engine, although Packard made the largest straight eight available at the time. It was standard on the 23rd Series Custom Eights of 1949 and an option on all '49 Packards by year's end.

Avoiding or neglecting the need for a V-8 engine, Packard made a valiant attempt to get back on the right track in 1951. There was an almost completely new car, except for the huge straight eight. It featured all-new sheet metal and trim, new frames and updated interior styling. The addition of the handsome Mayfair hardtop was a move in the right direction, along with increased acceptance of Ultramatic. The result was a 115 percent increase in business over 1950. This should have been a sign of the proper pattern to follow year after year.

Unfortunately, the indicators were ignored. Despite some wonderfully creative reworkings that resulted in flashier and fancier models in 1953 and 1954, the new Packards remained virtually unchanged in basic terms.

Sales and production figures, in themselves, did not paint an exceptionally bleak picture until 1954. Packard was the 16th largest producer in 1951, selling some 76,000 cars. The following season, it was 16th again, with 63,000 deliveries. It even achieved 14th rank and found 81,000 customers for 1953. Yet, the overall market was consistently expanding. Packard's business was not keeping pace with that of the major firms. There was no real growth. When a general downturn hit after the Korean War, 1954 assemblies peaked at 27,593 cars. It was yet another bad sign.

Forced into a corner, Packard went to new body shells and V-8 power for 1955. There were three-tone color combinations, hooded headlights, torsion bars, wraparound windshields, a hint of tailfins and, even, a medium-priced Clipper line.

As in the past, the high degree of change brought immediate benefits. Sales climbed to 70,000 cars. The new Packards drew rave reviews. But, the revisions came with bills for new tooling, technology and factory expansion. These were costs that Packard could no longer bear alone, so the company's president, James Nance, went looking for a financial partner in 1954. This culminated in the purchase of Studebaker, a move that seemed logical on the surface, but actually brought more problems.

Like the other independent manufacturers at this time, Studebaker was overextended in trying to compete with the 'Big Three' automakers and actually pulled a somewhat healthy parent to its grave. When sales dropped to 13,000 cars in the depressed market of 1956, Nance bailed out. Curtiss-Wright Corp. gained management control of Studebaker-Packard, primarily as a tax write-off, and quickly decided to consolidate its holdings at Studebaker's South Bend, Ind., facilities. Many profitable aspects of the auto company (defense contracts, etc.) were acquired by Curtiss-Wright. What remained of Studebaker-Packard was eventually released under its own management.

For the next two years, the Packard became a badge-engineered car to fulfill dealer contracts and was built off a Studebaker platform. Though technically a fine automobile, and certainly rare and unique, this new type of Packard was unable to attract repeat customers due to its lack of identity and some controversial styling. After 1958, the name Packard disappeared from the automotive scene. Many say the passing was unavoidable. "How could a car with enduring quality and grace survive in an age in which the basis of success is planned obsolescence?," they asked.

1946

CLIPPER SIX — (6-CYL) — SERIES 2100 — Although given a new designation as Twenty-First Series models, the 1946 Packards were an extension of the 1942 Clipper line with practically no changes. The Clipper design had been started in 1941, but with pent-up demand for new cars built-up over four war years, there was no time nor any need for all-new models. A single body stamping was used for Packards, even though length of the wheelbase varied by series. Changes in length were taken up ahead of the firewall with longer front end sheet metal. Clippers were easy to spot. Unlike other models, the horizontal grille extension bars running below the headlights did not wrap around the front body corners. In addition, the six did not carry model identification script below the vent windows on the front doors. Available body types included a two-door Club Sedan with a fastback roofline and a conventional four-door sedan with a notchback (or 'trumped' back) look. Also provided, with six-cylinder power only, were a taxicab sedan and a taxicab sedan with a driver's partition.

CLIPPER SIX SERIES

Series Number	Body/Style Number	Body Type & Seating	Factory Price	Shipping Weight	Production Total
2100	1685	2-dr Clb Sed-6P	1680	3450	Note 1
2100	1682	4-dr Tr Sed-6P	1730	3495	Note 1
2100	1686	4-dr Taxi-6P	1945	3670	Note 1
2100	1684	4-dr Part. Taxi-6P	2069	3730	Note 1

NOTE 1: 15,892 Clipper Sixes were built with no body style breakout available.

PACKARD I.D. NUMBERS: Packard engine numbers were the most important of three types of manufacturer's codes. They were stamped on a white-painted boss on the upper left-hand side of the cylinder block. A vehicle number was also stamped on a plate attached to the left top side of the cowl and was the same as a Body/Style Number, since it identified the model or style. These numbers correspond to the Body/Style Number in the second column of the charts below, with the first two symbols changing from 16 to 21 to indicate Twenty-First Series. A Body Number was provided and was also stamped on the plate attached to the left top side of the cowl, below the hood. The Body Number does not provide model identification, but seems to represent a production sequence record used mainly for factory purposes. The Body/Style Number appeared as the first four digits of the Packard serial number, followed by the engine number. Engine numbers for the Clipper Six were F-1501 to F-14999. Engine numbers for Clipper and Clipper Deluxe Eights were F-300001 to F-319999. Engine numbers for Super Clipper and Custom Clipper Eights ranged from F-500001 to F-505999 with both built in mixed production and sharing the same range of numbers.

CLIPPER STANDARD/DELUXE EIGHT — (8-CYL) — SERIES 2101/2111 — The basic Clipper Eight was marketed only in four-door trunk sedan (notchback) form. It carried a door script to identify the series designation and was listed as the only car in the 2101 Series. A Deluxe 2111 Series included both this model and the fastback Club Sedan. Identification for the fancier cars was achieved by placing special bi-level script on the door, below the front vent window. Deluxes also featured wraparound-type grille extension bars; fancier wheel trim treatments; more window moldings and richer interior trim. Taxicabs were not normally provided on the eight-cylinder chassis.

CLIPPER EIGHT SERIES

Series Number	Body/Style Number	Body Type & Seating	Factory Price	Shipping Weight	Production Total
STANDARD					
2101	1692	4-dr Tr Sed-6P	1802	3575	1,500
DELUXE					
2111	1615	2-dr Clb Sed-6P	1817	3625	Note 1
2111	1612	4-dr Tr Sed-6P	1869	3670	Note 1

NOTE 1: 5,714 Clipper Deluxe Eights were built with no body style breakout available.

SUPER CLIPPER EIGHT — (8-CYL) — SERIES 2103 — The Super Clipper Eight was on a seven inch longer wheelbase than lower-priced Packards. It featured wraparound grille extension bars, upgraded wheel trim treatments a "humpier' looking rear deck and a single level door signature script reading 'Super Clipper'. In terms of body styles, both a four-door and two-door were offered in a single level of trim. The Club Sedan was a fastback.

SUPER CLIPPER EIGHT SERIES

Series Number	Body/Style Number	Body Type & Seating	Factory Price	Shipping Weight	Production Total
2103	1675	2-dr Clb Sed-6P	2241	3950	Note 1
2103	1672	4-dr Tr Sed-6P	2290	3995	Note 1

Note 1: 4,924 Super Clipper Eights were built with no body style breakout available.

CUSTOM SUPER CLIPPER EIGHT — (8-CYL) — SERIES 2106/2126 — In a case of subtle prestige, Packard's top-flight cars appeared without front door script to identify their upper crust status. They did, however, have wraparound grille extension bars to help avoid confusion with low-priced Clipper Sixes on the behalf of buyers unable to detect differences in size. Of course, a look at the rich interior appointments served to further distinguish the high-dollar machines. As might be expected, they were built on two of Packard's longest platforms, either the 127-inch wheelbase chassis, shared with Super Clippers, or the 148-inch wheelbase extended chassis used for seven-passenger sedans and limousines. The biggest Packard engine, with its smooth nine bearing crankshaft and silent hydraulic lifters was nestled under the hoods of these cars. Like all Packards, they had a six-volt, positive ground electrical system.

CUSTOM SUPER CLIPPER EIGHT SERIES

Series Number	Body/Style Number	Body Type & Seating	Factory Price	Shipping Weight	Production Total
STANDARD WHEELBASE LINE					
2106	1625	2-dr Clb Sed-6P	2913	4000	Note 1
2106	1622	4-dr Tr Sed-6P	3047	4060	Note 1
EXTENDED WHEELBASE LINE					
2126	1651	4-dr Sed-7P	4332	4870	Note 2
2126	1650	4-dr Limo-7P	4496	4900	Note 2

Note 1: 1,472 standard wheelbase Custom Super Clippers were built with no body style breakout available.

Note 2: 1,291 extended wheelbase Custom Super Clippers were built with no body style breakout available.

ENGINES:

(CLIPPER SIX) Inline. L-head. Displacement: 245.3 cid. Bore and stroke: 3-1/2 x 4-1/4 inches. Compression ratio: 6.7:1. Brake hp: 105 at 3600 rpm. Four main bearings. Solid valve lifters. Carburetor: Carter Type WA1 one-barrel Model 530S.

(CLIPPER STANDARD/DELUXE EIGHT) Inline. L-head. Displacement: 282.04 cid. Bore and stroke: 3-1/4 x 4-1/4 inches. Compression ratio: 6.85:1. Brake hp: 125 at 3600 rpm. Five main bearings. Solid valve lifters. Carburetor: Carter Type WDO two-barrel Model 512S.

(SUPER/CUSTOM SUPER CLIPPER EIGHT) Inline. L-head. Displacement: 356 cid. Bore and stroke: 3-1/2 x 4-5/8 inches. Compression ratio: 6.85:1. Brake hp: 165 at 3600 rpm. Nine main bearings. Hydraulic valve lifters. Carburetor: Carter Type WDO two-barrel Model 531S.

CHASSIS FEATURES: Wheelbase: (Series 2100, 2101 and 2111) 120 inches; (Series 2103 and 2106) 127 inches; (Series 2126) 148 inches. Overall length: (Series 2100, 2101 and 2111) 208.4 inches; (Series 2103 and 2106) 215.5 inches. Front tread: (all) 59-1/4 inches. Rear tread: (Series 2100) 60-9/16 inches; (Series 2101 and 2111) 60-13/16 inches; (Series 2103, 2106 and 2126) 60-11/16 inches. Tires: (Series 2103, 2106) 7.00 x 15; (Series 2126) 7.50 x 16; (other series) 6.50 x 15. Packard advertising for 1946 highlighted such chassis features as roll control bar; fifth shock absorber; car wider than high and low center of gravity.

OPTIONS: Heater. Radio. Fender skirts. Wheel trim rings. Roof-mount radio antenna. Two-tone paint. Electromatic clutch. Overdrive.

HISTORICAL FOOTNOTES: Postwar Packards were reintroduced to the market in October 1945. A limited number of standard body styles were available at first. The full line of standard Packards was seen in production by about April 1946. Super Eights started rolling from the assembly line a month later, followed by manufacture of a complete line by June of the same year. A total of 30,793 cars found buyers. Calendar year deliveries peaked at 42,102 units, making Packard America's 14th largest producer. Instruments were said to be grouped in a newly redesigned panel offering "at-a-glance" readability. Highly promoted were such beneficial devices as automatic chokes, rotary door catches, safety glass, counter-balanced trunk lids and "chatterproof' glove compartments. The Classic Car Club of America accepts 1946-1947 Custom Super Clippers as authentic Classic cars upon individual application by owners. The Milestone Car Society and Veteran Motor Car Club of America have designated the Custom Super Clipper as a Milestone Car.

1947

CLIPPER SIX — (6-CYL) — SERIES 2100 — There were virtually no changes in Packard models for 1947, save for serial numbers, price and weight increases. Taxi sedans, with or without driver's partitions, continued to be offered as six-cylinder-only models.

PACKARD I.D. NUMBERS: Packard engine numbers were the most important of three types of manufacturer's codes. They were stamped on a white-painted boss on the upper left-hand side of the cylinder block. A vehicle number was also stamped on a plate attached to the left top side of the cowl and was the same as a Body/Style Number, since it identified the model or style. These numbers correspond to the Body/Style Number in the second column of the charts below with the first two symbols changing from 16 to 21 to indicate Twenty-First Series. A Body Number was provided and was also stamped on the plate attached to the left side of the cowl below the hood. The Body Number does not provide model identification, but seems to represent a production sequence record used mainly for factory purposes. The Body/Style Number appeared as the first four digits of the Packard serial number, followed by the engine number. Engine numbers for the Clipper Six were F-15001 to F-50999. Engine numbers for Clipper and Clipper Deluxe Eights were F-320001 to F-399999. Engine numbers for Super Clipper and Custom Clipper Eights ranged from F-506001 to F-521999 with both built in mixed production and sharing the same range of numbers.

CLIPPER SIX SERIES

Series Number	Body/Style Number	Body Type & Seating	Factory Price	Shipping Weight	Production Total
2100	2182	4-dr Sed-6P	1745	3495	Note 1
2100	2185	2-dr Clb Sed-6P	1695	3480	Note 1
2100	2186	4-dr Taxi-6P	2024	3705	Note 1
2100	2184	4-dr Part. Taxi-6P	2148	3765	Note 1

Note 1: 14,949 Clipper Sixes were built with no body style breakout available.

Note 2: Prices increased to $1,912 (Club Sedan) and $1,937 (four-door sedan) at midyear.

CLIPPER EIGHT — (8-CYL) — SERIES 2111 — A standard Clipper Eight, Series 2101 model, is listed by some 1947 references, but no prices, weights or other data are provided for this car. This suggests that the model was either dropped, or that no examples were sold. For all practical purposes, only the two Clipper Deluxe Eights remained. Both were unchanged from their 1946 specifications.

CLIPPER DELUXE EIGHT SERIES

Series Number	Body/Style Number	Body Type & Seating	Factory Price	Shipping Weight	Production Total
2111	2115	2-dr Clb Sed-6P	1895	3625	Note 1
2111	2112	4-dr Sed-6P	1947	3670	Note 1

NOTE 1: 23,855 Deluxe Clipper Eights were built with no body style breakout available.

NOTE 2: Prices increased to $2,124 (Club Sedan) and $2,149 (four-door sedan) at midyear.

SUPER CLIPPER EIGHT — (8-CYL) — SERIES 2103 — As with the other 1947 models, there was virtually no change in the new Super Clipper Eight models. Cars in this series continued to sell with the biggest Packard engine and the middle-sized platform. Once again, they took their identification from script placed on the upper part of the front door, below the ventipanes.

SUPER CLIPPER EIGHT SERIES

Series Number	Body/Style Number	Body Type & Seating	Factory Price	Shipping Weight	Production Total
2103	2175	2-dr Clb Sed-6P	2342	3950	Note 1
2103	2172	4-dr Sed-6P	2391	3995	Note 1

Note 1: 4,802 Super Clipper Eights were built with no body style breakout available.

Note 2: Prices increased to $2,747 (Club Sedan) and $2,772 (four-door sedan) at midyear.

CUSTOM SUPER CLIPPER EIGHT — (8-CYL) — SERIES 2106/2126 — Customs continued to come with distinctive interior trims and no external identifiers, such as door script. Special carpeting was featured again, along with upholstery in rich broadcloth and leather combinations. Imitation wood paneling was used on the interior of Custom models to add an even finer flavor. The model lineup was the same as provided the previous season.

CUSTOM SUPER CLIPPER EIGHT SERIES

Series Number	Body/Style Number	Body Type & Seating	Factory Price	Shipping Weight	Production Total
STANDARD WHEELBASE LINE					
2106	2125	2-dr Clb Sed-6P	3140	4000	Note 1
2106	2122	4-dr Sed-6P	3274	4060	Note 1
EXTENDED WHEELBASE LINE					
2126	2151	4-dr Sed-7P	4357	4870	Note 2
2126	2150	4-dr Limo-7P	4521	4900	Note 2

Note 1: 5,690 standard wheelbase Custom Super Clippers were built with no body style breakout available.

Note 2: 1,790 extended wheelbase Custom Super Clippers were built with no body style breakout available.

Note 3: Prices increased to $3,384 (Club Sedan); $3,449 (six-passenger sedan); $4,504 (seven-passenger sedan); and $4,668 (limousine) at midyear.

ENGINES:

(CLIPPER SIX) Inline. L-head. Displacement: 245.3 cid. Bore and stroke: 3-1/2 x 4-1/4 inches. Compression ratio: 6.7:1. Brake hp: 105 at 3600 rpm. Four main bearings. Solid valve lifters. Carburetor: Carter Type WA1 one-barrel Model 530S.

(CLIPPER STANDARD/DELUXE EIGHT) Inline. L-head. Displacement: 282.04 cid. Bore and stroke: 3-1/4 x 4-1/4 inches. Compression ratio: 6.85:1. Brake hp: 125 at 3600 rpm. Five main bearings. Solid valve lifters. Carburetor: Carter Type WDO two-barrel Model 512S.

(SUPER/CUSTOM SUPER CLIPPER EIGHT) Inline. L-head. Displacement: 356 cid. Bore and stroke: 3-1/2 x 4-5/8 inches. Compression ratio: 6.85:1. Brake hp: 165 at 3600 rpm. Nine main bearings. Hydraulic valve lifters. Carburetor: Carter Type WDO two-barrel Model 531S.

CHASSIS FEATURES: Wheelbase: (Series 2100, 2101 and 2111) 120 inches; (Series 2103 and 2106) 127 inches; (Series 2126) 148 inches. Overall length: (Series 2100, 2101 and 2111) 208.4 inches; (Series 2103 and 2106) 215.5 inches. Front tread: (all) 59-1/4 inches. Rear tread: (Series 2100) 60-9/16 inches; (Series 2101 and 2111) 60-13/16 inches; (Series 2103, 2106 and 2126) 60-11/16 inches. Tires: (Series 2103, 2106) 7.00 x 15; (Series 2126) 7.50 x 16; (other series) 6.50 x 15. Packard advertising for 1947 highlighted such chassis features as roll control bar; fifth shock absorber; car wider than high and low center of gravity.

OPTIONS: White sidewall tires ($21). Heater. Radio. Fender skirts. Wheel trim rings. Roof mount radio antenna. Two-tone paint. Electromatic clutch. Overdrive.

HISTORICAL FOOTNOTES: Packard slipped into the 16th spot on auto industry sales charts this season. Sales rankings were based on calendar year deliveries of 55,477 vehicles, as opposed to a strong model year production total of 81,879 cars. The unusually large spread between the two is related to the changeover to the all-new Twenty-Second Series (1948-1949) models that were manufactured late in the 1947 calendar year. The Classic Car Club of America accepts the 1946-1947 Custom Super Clipper as a full Classic, upon individual application by owners. The Milestone Car Society and the Veteran Motor Car Club of America have designated the Custom Super Clipper a Milestone Car. The one-millionth Packard was built during 1947. It was a 22nd Series Super Eight convertible.

1948

STANDARD EIGHT/DELUXE EIGHT — (8-CYL) — SERIES 2201/2211 — The Twenty-Second Series Packards were merchandised as 1948 and 1949 models, since Packard did not adhere to a model year changeover system. Effective Nov. 1, 1948, for purposes of registration, 1948 Series 2200 Packards became 1949 Series 2200-9 models. When they were first introduced these were all-new postwar cars. General appearance changes included a longer hood; an "ox-yoke" shaped upper grille; full-width, wraparound lower grille; a pair of simplified, vertical front bumper guards and smoother, rounded bodylines. Their styling is often referred to as the "inverted bathtub" or "pregnant elephant" look. Standard Eights were the base offering (except for six-cylinder taxi and export-only models). They came in two conventional passenger car versions: Club Sedan or touring sedan. They had the plainest and cheapest looking Packard hood ornament; single rocker panel strips; upper belt moldings running from below the front ventipanes to the rear; and no lower belt moldings at mid-body level. Deluxe Eights were the same basic cars with extra exterior trim and shared some richer interior appointments with Super Eights. Most had more elaborate, horizontally 'veed' hood ornaments (with disc-shaped protrusions at the forward tip). These were called 'Winged Goddess' mascots. (Four styles of ornaments were available.) Fancier wheel trim treatments were another common aid in spotting Deluxe Eights. An almost all-steel, station wagon-like Station Sedan was provided as a Standard Eight model only. It had genuine northern birch wood body paneling that was structural only in the tailgate region.

PACKARD I.D. NUMBERS: Packard engine numbers were the most important of three types of manufacturer's codes. They were stamped on a white-painted boss on the upper left-hand side of the cylinder block. A vehicle number was also stamped on a plate attached to the left top side of the cowl and was the same as a Body/Style Number, since it identified the model or style. These numbers correspond to the Body/Style Number in the second column of the charts below, with the first two symbols changing from 21 to 22 to indicate Twenty-Second series. A Body Number was provided and was also stamped on the plate attached to the left top side of the cowl, below the hood. The Body Number does not provide model identification, but seems to represent a production sequence record used mainly for factory purposes. The Body/Style Number appeared as the first four digits of the Packard serial number, followed by the engine number. Engine numbers for six-cylinder taxis and exported sixes were G-1501 to G-10000. Engine numbers for the Standard/Deluxe Eights were G-200001 to G-303000 for 1948 (Series 2200) models and continuing through G-350000 for 1949 (Series 2200-9) models. Engine numbers for Super Eights were G-400001 to G-432000 for 1948 (Series 2200) models and continuing through G-475000 for 1949 (Series 2200-9) models. Engine numbers for Custom Eights were G-600001 to G-612000 for 1948 (Series 2200) models and continuing through G-650000 for 1949 (Series 2200-9) models.

PACKARD EIGHT SERIES

Series Number	Body/Style Number	Body Type & Seating	Factory Price	Shipping Weight	Production Total
STANDARD LINE					
2201	2292	4-dr Sed-6P	2150	3815	Notes 1/2
2201	2295	2-dr Clb Sed-6P	2125	3755	Notes 1/2
2201	2293	4-dr Sta Sed-6P	3350	4080	Notes 1/2
DELUXE LINE					
2211	2262	4-dr Sed-6P	2375	3850	Notes 3/4
2211	2265	2-dr Clb Sed-6P	2350	3770	Notes 3/4

Note 1: 12,803 Series 2200 (1948) Standard Eights were built. No breakout per body type available.

Note 2: 12,532 Series 2200-9 (1949) Standard Eights were built. No breakout per body type available.

Note 3: 47,790 Series 2200 (1948) Deluxe Eights were built. No breakout per body type available.

Note 4: 27,438 Series 2200-9 (1949) Deluxe Eights were built. No breakout per body type available.

SUPER EIGHT — (8-CYL) — SERIES 2202/2222/2232 — Packard's middle line emphasized technical benefits, as indicated by 1948 promotional messages such as: "A new performance thrill awaits the buyers of the spirited Super Eight ... the motor car that makes distance disappear." These cars came with enriched interior appointments and streamlined 'Goddess of Speed' hood ornaments. Exterior trim was not much different than that of the Standard Eights, except on the Super Deluxe sedan, which was trimmed in the manner of the Deluxe Eight and also had slightly fancier taillamp doors with short chrome divider bars. Three subseries were coded. The first included Club and touring sedans on a 120-inch wheelbase chassis. The second featured four closed body styles on an extended 141-inch wheelbase. An all-new Victoria Convertible was the third entry. It was Packard's first open car since 1942. The Super convertible had single rocker panel strips and fender skirts were standard. It was built on the standard wheelbase chassis, but drew much buyer interest.

SUPER EIGHT SERIES

Series Number	Body/Style Number	Body Type & Seating	Factory Price	Shipping Weight	Production Total
STANDARD WHEELBASE (CLOSED)					
2202	2272	4-dr Sed-6P	2690	3855	Notes 1/2
2202	2275	2-dr Clb Sed-6P	2665	3790	Notes 1/2
LONG WHEELBASE (CLOSED)					
2222	2277	4-dr Sed-7P	3300	4460	Notes 3/4
2222	2271	4-dr Del Sed-7P	3650	4590	Notes 3/4
2222	2276	4-dr Limo-7P	3450	4525	Notes 3/4
2222	2270	4-dr Del Limo-7P	3800	4610	Notes 3/4
VICTORIA CONVERTIBLE COUPE					
2232	2279	2-dr Conv-6P	3250	4025	Notes 5/6

Note 1: 12,929 Series 2200 (1948) standard wheelbase Super Eights were built. No breakout per body type available.

Note 2: 5,871 Series 2200-9 (1949) standard wheelbase Super Eights were built. No breakout per body type available.

Note 3: 1,740 Series 2200 (1948) extended wheelbase Super Eights were built. No breakout per body type available.

Note 4: 865 Series 2200-9 (1949) extended wheelbase Super Eights were built. No breakout per body type available.

Note 5: 4,750 Series 2200 (1948) Super Eight Victoria Convertibles were built.

Note 6: 4,250 Series 2200-9 (1949) Super Eight Convertible Victorias were built.

CUSTOM EIGHT — (8-CYL) — SERIES 2206/2226/2233 — Packard's luxury line had the highest horsepower, but not the highest power-to-weight ratio. The luxury-per-pound factor was excellent though. Egg-crate-style grille insert designs were exclusive to these cars and a beauty panel of similar patterning stretched across the lower rear body to encase the taillamps with its bright metal gridwork. Rear wheel shrouds (fender skirts) were standard equipment and double rocker panel trim strips underscored the body sides. A graceful, vertical cormorant or pelican mascot was seen raising its wings over the nose of the car. Interiors were done in rich cloth and leather combinations and all-leather on the Victoria Convertible. The standard Custom wheelbase was 127 inches. Seven-passenger styles had a 148-inch stance.

CUSTOM EIGHT SERIES

Series Number	Body/Style Number	Body Type & Seating	Factory Price	Shipping Weight	Production Total
STANDARD WHEELBASE (CLOSED)					
2206	2252	4-dr Sed-6P	3750	4175	Notes 1/2
2206	2255	2-dr Clb Sed-6P	3700	4110	Notes 1/2
LONG WHEELBASE (CLOSED)					
2226	2251	4-dr Sed-7P	4704	4860	Notes 3/4
2226	2250	4-dr Limo-7P	4868	4880	Notes 3/4

VICTORIA CONVERTIBLE COUPE

Series Number	Body/Style Number	Body Type & Seating	Factory Price	Shipping Weight	Production Total
2233	2259	2-dr Conv-6P	4295	4380	Notes 5/6

Note 1: 5,935 Series 2200 (1948) standard wheelbase Custom Eights were built. No breakout per body type available.

Note 2: 2,989 Series 2200-9 (1949) standard wheelbase Custom Eights were built. No breakout per body type available.

Note 3: 231 Series 2200 (1948) long wheelbase Custom Eights were built. No breakout per body type available.

Note 4: 49 Series 2200-9 (1949) long wheelbase Custom Eights were built. No breakout per body type available.

Note 5: 1,103 Series 2200 (1948) Custom Eight Victoria Convertibles were built.

Note 6: 215 Series 2200-9 (1949) Custom Eight Victoria Convertibles were built.

ENGINES:

(STANDARD/DELUXE EIGHT) Inline. L-head. Cast iron block. Displacement: 288 cid. Bore and stroke: 3-1/2 x 3-3/4 inches. Compression ratio: 7.0:1. Brake hp: 130 at 3600 rpm. Five main bearings. Solid valve lifters. Carburetor: Carter Type WDO two-barrel Model 644SA.

(SUPER EIGHT) Inline. L-head. Cast iron block. Displacement: 327 cid. Bore and stroke: 3-1/2 x 4-1/4 inches. Compression ratio: 7.0:1. Brake hp: 145 at 3600 rpm. Solid valve lifters. Five main bearings. Carburetor: Carter Type WDO two-barrel Model 643SA.

(CUSTOM EIGHT) Inline L-head. Cast iron block. Displacement: 356 cid. Bore and stroke: 3-1/2 x 4-5/8 inches. Compression ratio: 7.0:1. Brake hp: 160 at 3600 rpm. Nine main bearings. Hydraulic valve lifters. Carburetor: Carter Type WDO two-barrel Model 531S or 531SA.

CHASSIS FEATURES: Wheelbase: (Standard/Deluxe/Super Eight 2202/2232) 120 inches; (Super Eight 2222) 141 inches; (Custom Eight 2206 and 2233)127 inches; (Custom Eight 2226) 148 inches. Overall length: (Standard/Deluxe/Super Eight 2202/2232) 204-5/8 inches; (Super Eight 2222) 225-5/8 inches; (Custom Eight 2206 and 2233) 212-5/8 inches; (Custom Eight 2226) 233-5/8 inches. Front tread: (Standard Deluxe) 59-11/32; (Super) 59-19/32; (Custom) 60-3/32 inches. Rear tread: (Standard /Deluxe) 60-15/32; (Super) 60-23/32; (Custom) 60-47/64 inches. Tires: (Standard/Deluxe) 6.50 x 16; (Super) 7.60 x 15, except seven-passenger styles had size 7.00 x 15; (Custom) 7.00 x 15, except convertible had size 7.00 x 16.

OPTIONS: Comfort-Aire ventilation system. Radio. Cowl mount radio antenna. Rear fender shrouds (standard on Custom and both convertibles). Rear master bumper guards and protection rail. Front master bumper guard assembly. Exhaust pipe chrome extensions. License plate frames. Front fog lamps. Outside rearview mirror (left-hand or/and right-hand). Wheel trim rings. White sidewall tires. Overdrive ($87). Electromatic clutch with overdrive ($123). Oil bath air cleaner ($7, standard on Super and Custom). Available rear axle ratios included: 3.54:1, 3.90:1, 4.09:1, 4.10:1 and 4.36:1.

HISTORICAL FOOTNOTES: The first 22nd Series Packards to appear in August 1947 were the new convertibles. Packard did not adhere to a model year coding system until 1951. The company's official posture was that its traditional series production system wasn't relative to model year changeovers. The so-called "948" models were actually built from August 1947 through May 1949. In November 1948, dealers were instructed to remove data plates on all unsold 22nd Series Packards and return them to the factory. They were replaced by similar plates with the suffix '9' added to the Body/Style Number. Retail prices were then increased on some models. Packard 2201/2211 models went up an average $125 on 1949 price sheets; 2202 models went up $137; 2222 models went up $200; and convertibles and Custom Eight model prices remained unchanged. The 2200-9 coded cars were considered 1949 Packards for registration purposes. The total production of 22nd Series models hit 146,441 cars. Calendar year sales of 98,898 Packards was good for the 14th rank in industry. The new Packard body styling was awarded a 'Fashion Car of the Year' gold medal by the New York Fashion Academy. At automobile salons and concours d'elegance exhibits throughout the world, the new Custom Victoria Convertible Coupe was honored for its beauty and elegance. A dashboard with black-lighted 'Flite-Glo' instrumentation was a gimmicky new feature. Tool kits were still provided with each new Packard sold. On April 19, 1948, Alvan Macauley retired. He had served as Packard president from 1916 to 1938 and chairman from 1938 to 1948. George T. Christopher moved from the position of company president to replace him. A total of 1,317 (1948) and 24 (recoded 1949) taxicabs were built. A total of 1,927 (1948) and 683 (recoded 1949) export units were built. All of these were six-cylinder powered. Packard Custom Eights built through 1950 are certified Milestone Cars.

1949

STANDARD EIGHT/DELUXE EIGHT — (8-CYL) — SERIES 2301 — Twenty-Third Series "Golden Anniversary" models went on sale in May 1949. They looked much like the previous cars, but had some noticeable differences. The front bumpers had chromed centers instead of the painted type used in 1948. A thin spear of chrome ran down the middle of the bodysides, stopping just forward of the taillamps on base Packard Eights. Above this molding, on the front fenders, Packard block lettering appeared and was underlined in chrome. The taillight lenses were set in protruding oval-shaped bright metal housings except on Station Sedans. The size of the rear window (backlight) was enlarged 33 percent. Inside, oval clutch/brake pedals were used. A Packard nameplate was placed between the speedometer and clock opening. A new illuminated switch turned on the engine. The Deluxe Eight had chromed 13-inch diameter hubcaps. The Standard Eight had 10-inch diameter hubcaps. A "Goddess of Speed" hood mascot was standard with both levels of trim. Automatic transmission was introduced in November 1949 for all models. The 120-inch wheelbase continued.

PACKARD I.D. NUMBERS: Packard engine numbers were the most important of three types of manufacturer's codes. They were stamped on a white-painted boss on the upper left-hand side of the cylinder block. A vehicle number was also stamped on a plate attached to the left top side of the cowl and was the same as a Body/Style Number, since it identified the model or style. These numbers correspond to the Body/Style Number in the second column of the charts below, with the first two symbols changing from 22 to 23 to indicate Twenty-Third series. A Body Number was provided and was also stamped on the plate attached to the left top side of the cowl, below the hood. The Body Number does not provide model identification, but seems to represent a production sequence record used mainly for factory purposes. The Body/Style Number appeared as the first four digits of the Packard serial number, followed by the engine number. Engine numbers for the Standard/Deluxe Eights were H-200001 to H-291000 for 1949 (Series 2300) models and continued through H-295000 for 1950 (Series 2300-5) models. Engine numbers for Super Eights were H-400001 to H-416000 for 1949 (Series 2300) models and continued through H-425000 for 1950 (Series 2300-5) models. Engine numbers for Custom Eights were H-600001 to H-602000 for 1949 (Series 2300) models and continued through H-610000 for 1950 (Series 2300-5) models.

PACKARD EIGHT SERIES

Series Number	Body/Style Number	Body Type & Seating	Factory Price	Shipping Weight	Production Total
STANDARD LINE					
2301	2392	4-dr Sed-6P	2249	3815	Note 1
2301	2395	2-dr Clb Sed-6P	2224	3740	Note 1
2301	2393	4-dr Sta Sed-6P	3449	4075	Note 1
DELUXE LINE					
2301	2362	4-dr Sed-6P	2383	3840	Note 1
2301	2365	2-dr Clb Sed-6P	2358	3770	Note 1

Note 1: 49,280 Series 2300 (1949) Standard/Deluxe Eights were built with no breakout per body style available.

SUPER/SUPER DELUXE EIGHT — (8-CYL) — SERIES 2302/2322/2332 — The Super Eight was trimmed somewhat like lower series cars. It shared the same horizontal grille, "Goddess of Speed" hood ornament and a chrome molding below the windows that stopped at the rear fender center. However, it had a slightly longer bodyside molding that overlapped the taillamp housings. The Super Deluxe was a new model, approximating a Custom Eight. For example, it had front and rear eggcrate grilles; cast chromium extensions from the upper belt molding to windshield wipers; bullet-type bumper guards; pelican hood ornament; and an ivory-colored Tenite steering wheel with plated inlaid handgrips. Seats were upholstered in rich, pin striped wool cloth with bolster-type back rests and door panels. The instrument board, upper seatback panels and window frames had a woodgrain finish. Standard equipment included fender shrouds; wheel trim rings; day/night rearview mirror; Select-O-Matic spring cushions and added acoustical insulation. The Convertible Victoria was appointed in similar fashion, but limousines had the standard Super-type bar grille.

SUPER SERIES

Series Number	Body/Style Number	Body Type & Seating	Factory Price	Shipping Weight	Production Total
STANDARD LINE					
2302	2382	4-dr Sed-6P	2633	3870	Note 1
2302	2385	2-dr Clb Sed-6P	2608	3800	Note 1
DELUXE LINE					
2302	2372	4-dr Sed-6P	2919	3925	Note 1
2302	2375	2-dr Clb Sed-6P	2894	3855	Note 1
LONG WHEELBASE (CLOSED)					
2322	2371	4-dr Sed-7P	3950	4600	Note 2
2322	2370	4-dr Limo-7P	4100	4620	Note 2
VICTORIA CONVERTIBLE COUPE					
2332	2379	2-dr Conv-6P	3350	4260	671

Note 1: 8,565 Series 2300 (1949) Super Eights were built with no breakout per body style available.

Note 2: Four Series 2322 (1949) seven-passenger sedans and limos were built. No breakout per body style available for Series 2322 models.

CUSTOM EIGHT — (8-CYL) — SERIES 2306/2333 — On Custom Eights, the chrome molding below the windows extended completely down the rear fenders and around the trunk lid. This was about the only external distinction over Super Deluxe Eights, plus the use of cloisonne hubcap medallions as a standard feature. Color-keyed Bedford cloth and leather upholstery combinations were exclusive trims found inside Custom Eights. Ultramatic transmission became standard equipment on Custom Eights before November 1949. It was then made optional on other Packards.

CUSTOM EIGHT SERIES

Series Number	Body/Style Number	Body Type & Seating	Factory Price	Shipping Weight	Production Total
2306	2352	4-dr Sed-6P	3750	4310	810
2333	2359	2-dr Conv-6P	4295	4530	60

ENGINES:

(STANDARD/DELUXE EIGHT) Inline. L-head. Cast iron block. Displacement: 288 cid. Bore and stroke: 3-1/2 x 3-3/4 inches. Compression ratio: 7.0:1. Brake hp: 130 at 3600 rpm. Five main bearings. Solid valve lifters. Carburetor: Carter Type WDO two-barrel Model 644SA.

(SUPER EIGHT) Inline. L-head. Cast iron block. Displacement: 327 cid. Bore and stroke: 3-1/2 x 4-1/4 inches. Compression ratio: 7.0:1. Brake hp: 145 at 3600 rpm. Solid valve lifters. Five main bearings. Carburetor: Carter Type WDO two-barrel Model 643SA.

(CUSTOM EIGHT) Inline. L-head. Cast iron block. Displacement: 356 cid. Bore and stroke: 3-1/2 x 4-5/8 inches. Compression ratio: 7.0:1. Brake hp: 160 at 3600 rpm. Nine main bearings. Hydraulic valve lifters. Carburetor: Carter Type WDO two-barrel Model 531S or 531SA.

CHASSIS FEATURES: Wheelbase: (2301 Eights) 120 inches; (Super Series 2322) 141 inches; (other Supers and Customs) 127 inches. Overall length: (2301 Eights) 204-11/16 inches; (Super Series 2322) 225-11/16 inches; (other Supers) 211-11/16 inches; (Customs) 213-1/4 inches. Front tread: (Customs) 60-3/32 inches; (all others) 59-19/32 inches. Rear tread: (all) 60-23/32 inches. Tires: (Station Sedan) 7.00 x 15; (other 2301 Eights and Super Eights) 7.60 x 15; (Super Deluxe) 8.00 x 15; (Super 2322 and all Customs) 8.20 x 15.

OPTIONS: Heater and defroster. Six-tube radio. Deluxe eight-tube radio. Roof-mount radio antenna. Cowl-mount radio antenna. Custom sun visor. Traffic light viewfinder. White sidewall tires. Coat hooks. Dual vanity mirrors. Emergency brake alarm. Cormorant hood ornament (unless standard). Rear wheel shrouds (unless standard). Tissue dispenser. Road lamps. Fog lamps. Rear seat draft deflectors on four-door sedans. Cloisonne hubcap medallions (except standard Customs). Vent-I-Shades. License plate frames. Gasoline filler panel guard. Door edge guards. Spare tire valve extension. Outside rear view mirrors (right- and/or left-hand). Plaque with original owner's initials. Vacuum-type radio antenna. Fuse kit. Trouble light. Exhaust deflector. Wheel blocks. Curb feelers. Underhood light. Spotlight. Wheel trim rings. Rear bumper guard and protection rail. Select-O-Spring seat inserts. Two-tone finish. Ultramatic trunk logo (standard on cars with Ultramatic Drive).

HISTORICAL FOOTNOTES: Both model year and calendar year sales totals were 59,390 vehicles. This includes only the 23rd Series models sold as late 1949 cars. Packard celebrated its 50th year as an automaker this season, a most notable achievement. As part of the ceremonies surrounding this accomplishment, a total of 2,000 cars were finished in Custom gold paint, a non-standard color. These cars were driven from the Packard Proving Grounds, in Utica, Mich., by dealers and salesmen. The dealers and salesmen took them to locations throughout North America as part of a driveaway honoring the company's longevity. In October 1949, George T. Christopher retired from the company. Hugh Ferry was elected to fill the open post in December 1949. He would soon try to hire James J. Nance away from General Electric Co. to assume the presidency of Packard. Custom Eights built to 1949 specifications are recognized Milestone Cars.

1950

STANDARD/DELUXE EIGHT — (8-CYL) — SERIES 2301-5 — Beginning on Oct. 1, 1949, the "Golden Anniversary" Packards were redesignated 1950 models for purposes of registration. At almost the same time, Ultramatic Drive was made available (as an option) on the low-priced Eights. This was about the only major change, with even retail prices and weights staying the same. Also, a Carter WGD two-barrel carburetor replaced the WDO type as standard equipment. Several new options, including Select-O-Seat spring inserts (June 14);

1950 Packard, Super Eight (Series 2322-5), long wheelbase limousine, AA

1951 Packard, 200 Deluxe (Series 2401), club sedan, AA

1951 Packard, Patrician 400 (Series 2406), sedan, AA

1952 Packard, 250 (Series 2531), convertible, AA

1952 Packard, 300 (Series 2502), sedan, AA

1952 Packard, Patrician 400 (Series 2506), sedan, AA

1953 Packard, Mayfair (Series 2631), hardtop, AA

sedan rear seat draft deflectors (June 21); accelerator pedal wear pads (June 21) and woodgrain tissue dispenser (July 1) were made running additions to the list of available accessories during the summer of 1949. Consequently such items are most commonly seen on 1950 models. Quick identification of Packard's economical products was possible by spoting the "Goddess of Speed" ornament on the hood. Deluxe Eights continued to be distinguished by three-inch-larger hubcaps than Standard Eights used.

PACKARD I.D. NUMBERS: Packard engine numbers were the most important of three types of manufacturer's codes. They were stamped on a white-painted boss on the upper left-hand side of the cylinder block. A vehicle number was also stamped on a plate attached to the left top side of the cowl and was the same as a Body/Style Number, since it identified the model or style. These numbers correspond to the Body/Style Number in the second column of the charts below, with the first two symbols 23 to indicate Twenty-Third Series and a suffix -5 to indicate 1950 model year registration. A Body Number was provided and was also stamped on the plate attached to the left top side of the cowl, below the hood. The Body Number does not provide model identification, but seems to represent a production sequence record used mainly for factory purposes. The Body/Style Number appeared as the first four digits of the Packard serial number, followed by the engine number. Engine numbers for the Standard/Deluxe Eights were H-200001 to H-291000 for 1949 (Series 2300) models and continued through H-295000 for 1950 (Series 2300-5) models. Engine numbers for Super Eights were H-400001 to H-416000 for 1949 (Series 2300) models and continued through H-425000 for 1950 (Series 2300-5) models. Engine numbers for Custom Eights were H-600001 to H-602000 for 1949 (Series 2300) models and continued through H-610000 for 1950 (Series 2300-5) models. According to research by Dick Bachman, engines built after Feb. 8, 1950, also had an F in the suffix to indicate the use of hydraulic valve lifters.

PACKARD EIGHT SERIES

Series Number	Body/Style Number	Body Type & Seating	Factory Price	Shipping Weight	Production Total
STANDARD LINE					
2301-5	2392-5	4-dr Sed-6P	2249	3815	Note 1
2301-5	2395-5	2-dr Clb Sed-6P	2224	3740	Note 1
2301-5	2393-5	4-dr Sta Sed-6P	3449	4075	Note 1
DELUXE LINE					
2301-5	2362-5	4-dr Sed-6P	2383	3840	Note 1
2301-5	2365-5	2-dr Clb Sed-6P	2358	3770	Note 1

Note 1: 40,359 Series 2300-5 (1950) Standard/Deluxe Eights were built with no breakout per body style available.

SUPER/SUPER DELUXE EIGHT — (8-CYL) — SERIES 2302-5/ 2322-5/ 2332-5 — Supers could be identified by the window molding that stopped at the center of the rear fender, in combination with a sweep spear that touched the taillamp housing. No other line had both features. Super Deluxes had chrome wheel rims and pelican hood ornaments as standard equipment. Hydraulic valve lifters were adopted, as a running production change for Supers, on Feb. 8, 1950. For an undetermined reason, standard reference sources indicate the weight of the 1950 convertible dropped by 150 pounds. The convertible and Super Deluxes continued to use eggcrate grilles and matching rear beauty panels.

SUPER SERIES

PACKARD EIGHT SERIES

Series Number	Body/Style Number	Body Type & Seating	Factory Price	Shipping Weight	Production Total
STANDARD LINE					
2302-5	2382-5	4-dr Sed-6P	2633	3870	Note 1
2302-5	2385-5	2-dr Clb Sed-6P	2608	3800	Note 1
DELUXE LINE					
2302-5	2372-5	4-dr Sed-6P	2919	3925	Note 1
2302-5	2375-5	2-dr Clb Sed-6P	2894	3855	Note 1
LONG WHEELBASE (CLOSED)					
2322-5	2371-5	4-dr Sed-7P	3950	4600	0
2322-5	2370-5	4-dr Limo-7P	4100	4620	0
VICTORIA CONVERTIBLE COUPE					
2332-5	2379-5	2-dr Conv-6P	3350	4110	614

Note 1: 4,722 Series 2300-5 (1950) Super Eights were built with no breakout per body style available, except convertible.

CUSTOM EIGHT — (8-CYL) — SERIES 2306-5/2333-5 — Custom Eights continued with eggcrate grilles front and rear; pelican hood ornaments; extra-rich Bedford cloth and leather trims; and extended upper belt moldings that looped around the deck lid. Base price was increased by $225, on both models, to cover the inclusion of Ultramatic transmission as standard equipment. It should be noted that this was the same as the cost of this optional transmission the previous year, although the 1950 price was lowered to $185 on other series. In other words, Custom Eight buyers were spending $40 more to have this feature than those who purchased it separately in lower-rung Packards. A Super Deluxe Sedan with automatic transmission would cost $3,104, compared to a Custom Eight sedan at $3,975, though both would be practically the same car with slightly different interiors and powerplants.

CUSTOM EIGHT SERIES

Series Number	Body/Style Number	Body Type & Seating	Factory Price	Shipping Weight	Production Total
PACKARD EIGHT SERIES					
2306-5	2352-5	4-dr Sed-6P	3975	4310	870
2333-5	2359-5	2-dr Conv-6P	4520	4539	85

ENGINES:

(STANDARD/DELUXE EIGHT) Inline. L-head. Cast iron block. Displacement: 288 cid. Bore and stroke: 3-1/2 x 3-3/4 inches. Compression ratio: 7.0:1. Brake hp: 135 at 3600 rpm. Five main bearings. Solid valve lifters. Carburetor: Carter Type WGD two-barrel Model 728S or 728SA. (Carburetor change took place October 1949 with engine number H-238000. This may have been the starting number for "1950" Series 2300-5 models).

(SUPER EIGHT) Inline. L-head. Cast iron block. Displacement: 327 cid. Bore and stroke: 3-1/2 x 4-1/4 inches. Compression ratio: 7.0:1. Brake hp: 150 at 3600 rpm. Solid valve lifters (hydraulic lifters after Feb. 8, 1950). Five main bearings. Carburetor: Carter Type WDO two-barrel Model 643SA.

(CUSTOM EIGHT) Inline. L-head. Cast iron block. Displacement: 356 cid. Bore and stroke: 3-1/2 x 4-5/8 inches. Compression ratio: 7.0:1. Brake hp: 165 at 3600 rpm. Nine main bearings. Hydraulic valve lifters. Carburetor: Carter Type WDO two-barrel Model 531S or 531SA.

CHASSIS FEATURES: Wheelbase: (2301 Eights) 120 inches; (Super Series 2322) 141 inches; (other Supers and Customs) 127 inches. Overall length: (2301 Eights) 204-11/16 inches; (Super Series 2322) 225-11/16 inches; (other Supers) 211-11/16 inches; (Customs) 213-1/4 inches. Front tread: (Custom) 60-3/32 inches; (Super Convertible) 60 inches; (all others) 59-19/32 inches. Rear tread: (all) 60-23/32 inches. Tires: (Station sedan) 7.00 x 15; (other 2301 Eights and closed Super Eights) 7.60 x 15; (Super Eight Deluxe) 8.00 x 15; (Super Eight Convertible) 8.20 x 15; (all Customs) 8.20 x 15.

OPTIONS: Heater and defroster. Six-tube radio. Deluxe eight-tube radio. Roof-mount radio antenna. Cowl-mount radio antenna. Custom sun visor. Traffic light viewfinder. White sidewall tires. Coat hooks. Dual vanity mirrors. Emergency brake alarm. Cormorant hood ornament (unless standard). Rear wheel shrouds (unless standard). Tissue dispenser. Road lamps. Fog lamps. Rear seat draft deflectors on four-door sedans. Cloisonne hubcap medallions (except standard Customs). Vent-I-Shades. License plate frames. Gasoline filler panel guard. Door edge guards. Spare tire valve extension. Outside rearview mirrors (right- and/or left-hand). Plaque with original owner initials. Vacuum-type radio antenna. Fuse kit. Trouble light. Exhaust deflector. Wheel blocks. Curb feelers. Underhood light. Spotlight. Wheel trim rings. Rear bumper guard and protection rail. Select-O-Spring seat inserts. Two-tone finish. Ultramatic trunk logo (standard on cars with Ultramatic Drive). Overdrive ($92). Electronic clutch with overdrive ($128). Ultramatic Drive ($185-$225). Oil bath air cleaner ($7; standard on Super and Custom). Available rear axle ratios included: 3.54:1, 3.90:1, 4.09:1, 4.10:1 and 4.36:1.

HISTORICAL FOOTNOTES: Colonel Jesse G. Vincent retired as executive vice-president at the end of the year. He had been with the firm since 1912. Vincent continued service as an engineering consultant and member of the board of directors. Packard obtained several choice military contracts on the verge of war's outbreak in Korea. Model year sales peaked at 106,040 cars. Calendar year production was 72,138 units, giving Packard the 16th industry ranking. A new R-11-type overdrive was used on 23rd series cars and was said to provide three extra miles of driving on each gallon of gasoline. On March 2, 1950, Packard adopted 14mm spark plugs for its straight eight engines. Milestone Car status applies to 23rd Series Custom Eights sold as 1950 models.

1951

PACKARD 200 — (8-CYL) — SERIES 2401 — August 24, 1950, saw the introduction of an all-new 24th Series Packard line. Styling more contemporary to the 1950s appeared on these cars designed by John Reinhart. According to sales literature, "Packards, for 1951, are only 5-foot 2-1/2 inches high, for in-the-groove roadability with 'hats on' headroom in front and back. New low bonnets (hoods) and high crown fenders give the outlook of a sports car." This was not too great an exaggeration, when compared to the look of the past. The base model range was the Packard 200 line, identified by a single strip of chrome across the front fenders and door and a 'toothless' grille. A low, single-fin hood mascot was seen. The 200 Deluxe was further distinguished by its chrome wheel rings and turn indicators. Standard equipment on all Packards included twin horns; two sun visors; two variable speed windshield wipers; horn blow ring; front and rear bumper guards; jack and tools.

PACKARD I.D. NUMBERS: The Vehicle Identification Number is found on a plate attached to the left front door post. Engine serial numbers were located on a boss at the upper left-hand side of the cylinder block. VINs began with the Body/Style Number suffixed by the engine serial number. Body/Style Numbers started with the first two symbols '24' to indicate 24th Series. The second pair of symbols indicated body style. All four symbols conformed to those in the second column of the charts below. Engine serial numbers: [PACKARD 200/200 Deluxe] J-200001 to J-275000. [PACKARD 250] J-400001 to J-425000. [PACKARD 300] J-400001 to J-425000. [PATRICIAN 400] J-600001 to J-610000.

PACKARD 200 SERIES

Series Number	Body/Style Number	Body Type & Seating	Factory Price	Shipping Weight	Production Total
STANDARD LINE					
2401	2492	4-dr Sed-6P	2469	3665	Note 1
2401	2495	2-dr Clb Sed-6P	2416	3600	Note 1
2401	2498	2-dr Bus Cpe-3P	2302	3550	Note 1
DELUXE LINE					
2401	2462	4-dr Sed-6P	2616	3660	Note 2
2401	2465	2-dr Clb Sed-6P	2563	3605	Note 2

Note 1: 24,310 Packard 200s were built with no body style breakout available.

Note 2: 47,052 Packard 200 Deluxes were built with no body style breakout available.

PACKARD 250 — (8-CYL) — SERIES 2401 — The Packard 250 was on the same wheelbase platform as more modestly priced models, but utilized a 327-cid straight eight. Packard's only convertible and first hardtop coupe were included. Trim identification was provided by chrome moldings across the front fender and door. A toothy-looking grille insert and pelican hood mascot were seen. Especially colorful and rich upholstery was used for both these sporty cars. Fender skirts were standard on both.

PACKARD 250 SERIES

Series Number	Body/Style Number	Body Type & Seating	Factory Price	Shipping Weight	Production Total
2401	2467	2-dr HT Cpe-6P	3234	3820	Note 1
2401	2469	2-dr Conv-6P	3391	4040	Note 1

Note 1: 4,640 Packard 250s were built with no body style breakout available.

PACKARD 300 — (8-CYL) — SERIES 2402 — Identification for the Packard 300 sedan came from a straight chrome molding running across the rear doors, rear fenders and taillights in a horizontal plane. Standard equipment included all Packard 200 features plus oil bath; air cleaner; tilt-type glare proof rearview mirror; chrome-plated wheel discs; trunk compartment light and robe rail. Double lens taillamps were used. A wide variety of interior trims was provided.

PACKARD 300 SERIES

Series Number	Body/Style Number	Body Type & Seating	Factory Price	Shipping Weight	Production Total
2402	2472	4-dr Sed-6P	3034	3875	15,309

PATRICIAN 400 — (8-CYL) — SERIES 2406 — The Patrician was the replacement for the fancy Custom Eight. It was identified by wide, vertically ribbed, chrome gravel shields on the lower front region of the rear fender bulge; three 'jet louvers' on the middle of the rear fenders; a chrome spear high on the front fenders and doors; a second chrome spear running from the gravel shield to the extreme rear of car; chrome, finned moldings atop the rear fenders and double lens horizontal taillamps. A wraparound-style backlight provided a hardtop roof look. The grille insert had vertical "teeth" and the tip of the hood had a cormorant. Luxurious "fashion forum" interiors were featured, with special carpeting and a chrome-plated steering column. All features of the Packard 300 were incorporated plus cloisonne wheel cover center medallions. This was the model for buyers seeking an elite machine.

PATRICIAN 400 SERIES

Series Number	Body/Style Number	Body Type & Seating	Factory Price	Shipping Weight	Production Total
2406	2452	4-dr Sed-6P	3662	4115	9,001

Note : Custom Formal Sedans on the Patrician 400 platform were available.

ENGINES:

(PACKARD 200/200 DELUXE EIGHT) Inline. L-head. Cast iron block. Displacement: 288 cid. Bore and stroke: 3-1/2 x 3-3/4 inches. Compression ratio: 7.0:1. Brake hp: 135 at 3600 rpm. Solid valve lifters. Five main bearings. Carburetor: Carter Type WGD two-barrel Model 784S.

(PACKARD 250/300 EIGHT) Inline. L-head. Cast iron block. Displacement: 327 cid. Bore and stroke: 3-1/2 x 4-1/4 inches. Compression ratio: 7.0:1. Brake hp: 150 at 3600 rpm. Five main bearings. Hydraulic valve lifters. Carburetor: Carter Type WGD two-barrel Model 767S.

(PATRICIAN 400 EIGHT) Inline. L-head. Cast iron block. Displacement: 327 cid. Bore and stroke: 3-1/2 x 4-1/4 inches. Compression ratio: 7.8:1. Brake hp: 155 at 3600 rpm. Nine main bearings. Hydraulic valve lifters. Carburetor: Carter Type WGD two-barrel Model 767S.

CHASSIS FEATURES: Wheelbase: (Series 2401) 122 inches; (all others) 127 inches. Overall length: (Series 2401) 209-3/8 inches; (all others) 217-3/4 inches. Front tread: (Packard 200) 59-1/2 inches; (Packard 250/300/Patrician 400) 60 inches. Rear tread: (Packard 200) 60-23/32 inches; (Packard 250/300/Patrician 400) 61-7/32 inches. Tires: (Packard 200) 7.60 x 15; (all others) 8.00 x 15.

OPTIONS: Whitewall tires ($28 exchange). Heater and defroster ($77). Signal-Seeking radio with electric antenna and rear speaker ($125.80). Rear fender shrouds ($21). Cloisonne wheel hub shell covers ($16). Pelican hood ornament ($13). Windshield washer ($9). Foam cushion rear seat ($12). Backup lights and trunk light ($14). Robe cord ($12). Two-tone finish ($20). Genuine leather trim ($153). Rear window wiper. Exterior sun shade. Traffic light view finder. Visor vanity mirrors. Emergency brake alarm. Tissue dispenser. Road and fog lamps. Vent-I-Shades. License plate frame. Gas door guard. Door edge guards. Spare tire valve extension. Extension rearview mirror. Fuse kit. Trouble light. Exhaust deflector. Wheel blocks. Curb feelers. Spotlight. Underhood lamps. Ultramatic rear fender nameplates (standard on cars with automatic transmission). NOTE: Car collectors have documented several cases where extra 'jet louvers' were added to Patrician 400s (and possibly other models) by company dealers. This was an attempt to bolt-on a little extra prestige by dressing-up the exterior appearance at minimal cost. Overdrive transmissions ($100). Utramatic Drive was standard in Patrician 400s, optional on other models ($189 extra cost). When equipped with Ultramatic, the Packard 300 was delivered with a 7.8:1 high-compression head that increased the hp output to 155. This was still, however, the type of 327-cid engine with five main bearings. (The 327-cid Patrician engine had nine main bearings.) Also, when equipped with Ultramatic, the Packard 200/200 Deluxe was delivered with a 7.5:1 high-compression cylinder head. It increased output of the 288-cid engine to 138 hp. The 327-cid Packard 300 engine was a $45 option in lower-priced models. Oil bath air cleaner ($9). Oil filter ($12). The 327-cid Patrician 400 engine could not be made optional in other lines because it was too long to fit comfortably in the shorter wheelbase chassis.

HISTORICAL FOOTNOTES: Introduction of 1951 Packards in the 200, 200 Deluxe, 300 and Patrician 400 series began in August 1950. The Packard 250 line with the convertible and hardtop was added in March 1951. On Oct. 12, 1950, the Society of Motion Picture Art Directors proclaimed the 24th Series Packard as "The most beautiful car of the year." The midyear two-door hardtop acquired the name Mayfair after its release. An experimental Phantom II sports car was constructed for Packard design chief Ed Macauley, based on a highly-modified Club Sedan. It featured a long, wide hood scoop; wide, ebbed bright metal underscores; similarly ribbed fender skirts; Custom concentric circle wheel discs; hardtop coupe styling and two-place seating. A Packard 200 touring sedan exhibited average fuel consumption of 22.023 mpg while participating in the 1951 Mobilgas Economy Run. This was better than 12 other entries in the same class. A total of 100,132 Packards were supplied to buyers during the 1951 model run. Calendar year totals were counted at 76,075 cars, good for 16th position on industry sales charts. Milestone Cars include the Patrician 400 sedans.

1952

PACKARD 200 — (8-CYL) — SERIES 2501 — As indicated previously, annual model year changes were adopted after 1951. Therefore, the 1952 Packards were 25th Series cars. General styling was modestly changed. Packard block lettering, seen along the lower edge of the 1951 hood, was removed this year. A medallion bearing the company crest was set into the middle of the upper grille surround. 'Base level' Packard 200s were identified by single chrome spears across the front fender and door; single-fin "jet plane" hood ornaments; hood edge lettering; and exclusive use of the same toothless grille seen last season. Upholstery trims were in plain-looking quality cloth. Standard equipment was comprised of twin horns; two sun visors; two variable-speed vacuum windshield wipers; horn blow ring; front and back bumper guards; bumper jack; tools; map lights; front door courtesy lights; and front seat armrests. The Packard 200 Deluxe, for 1952, had some additional points of distinction. It was provided with the toothy-type grille; three "jet louvers" on the rear quarter of the body and chrome wheel trim rings. It had all Packard 200 features plus foam rubber front seat cushions; turn indicators; glovebox lamp; and electric clock. Upholstery was in gray or brown pin striped cloth. The base level 200 business coupe was dropped.

PACKARD I.D. NUMBERS: The Vehicle Identification Number was found on a plate attached to the left front door post. Engine serial numbers were located on a boss at the upper left-hand side of the cylinder block. VINs began with the Body/Style Number suffixed by the engine serial number. Body/Style Numbers started with the first two symbols '25' to indicate 25th Series. The second pair of symbols indicated body style. All four symbols conformed to those in the second column of the charts below. Engine serial numbers: [PACKARD 200/200 Deluxe] K-200000 to K-250000. [PACKARD 250/PACKARD 300] K-400001 to K-415000. [PATRICIAN 400] K-600000 to K-605000.

PACKARD 200 SERIES

Series Number	Body/Style Number	Body Type & Seating	Factory Price	Shipping Weight	Production Total
STANDARD LINE					
2501	2592	4-dr Sed-6P	2528	3680	Note 1
2501	2595	2-dr Clb Sed-6P	2475	3640	Note 1
DELUXE LINE					
2501	2562	4-dr Sed-6P	2675	3685	Note 2
2501	2565	2-dr Clb Sed-6P	2632	3660	Note 2

Note 1: 46,720 Packard 200s were built with no body style breakout available.

Note 2: About 7,000 cars included in the 46,720 total were Deluxe models.

PACKARD 250 — (8-CYL) — SERIES 2531 — The Packard 250 was again on the same platform as more modestly-priced models and used the five main bearing 327-cid straight eight. However, it had separate series coding this year. Trim and ornamentation features included a new pelican hood ornament (with lower wings); chrome wheel discs; rear fender shields; single spear molding on the front fenders and door; unlettered lower hood edge; three 'jet louvers' on rear fendersides and a vertical-tooth-type grille. Standard equipment included all 200 Deluxe items plus hydraulic valve lifters; oil filter; oil bath air cleaner; trunk compartment lamp; tilt-type rearview mirror; front and rear wool carpeting and rear seat armrests. The Mayfair hardtop was provided with six interior upholstery combinations of ribbed nylon and leather materials, while the convertible had seats covered with a combination of genuine top grain leather and washable woven leather-like plastic.

PACKARD 250 SERIES

Series Number	Body/Style Number	Body Type & Seating	Factory Price	Shipping Weight	Production Total
2531	2577	2-dr HT Cpe-6P	3293	3805	Note 1
2531	2579	2-dr Conv-6P	3450	4000	Note 1

Note 1: 5,201 Packard 250s were built with no body style breakout available.

PACKARD 300 — (8-CYL) — SERIES 2502 — The Packard 300 sedan was on the 127-inch wheelbase again. It could be identified by the straight chrome spear running across the rear doors and fenders, in addition to the spear on the front doors and fenders. The toothy grille; non-lettered hood; low-wing pelican; chrome wheel discs; rear fender shields; and wraparound backlight were among other visual distinctions. Seen again were twin-lens taillamps horizontally positioned behind a flare at the middle edge of the rear fenders, plus fin-like bands of chrome atop the fender peak. Standard equipment included all 200 Deluxe items plus glare-proof inside rearview mirror; robe rail and rear seat foam rubber cushions. The interior was trimmed with striped fabric and had embossed, pleated door panels. The number '300', in chrome, appeared at the base of the rear roof pillar.

PACKARD 300 SERIES

Series Number	Body/Style Number	Body Type & Seating	Factory Price	Shipping Weight	Production Total
2502	2572	4-dr Sed-6P	3094	3880	6,705

PATRICIAN 400 — (8-CYL) — SERIES 2506 — Packard called the Patrician 400 the "Most Luxurious Motor Car in the World." It was like a Packard 300 with both appearance and performance improvements. Identification could most easily be made through the rear fender trim treatment. At the bottom of the rear door "pontoon" was a form-fitting gravel deflector that was vertically ribbed at its trailing edge. A strip of chrome molding traced the upper contour of the gravel deflector to the door line break where it met a straight extension molding that swept along the top of the fender shield to the back bumper. Also, on the upper rear fender tip there was a blade of fin-like chrome that dropped down to the horizontal taillamp. The section of this molding directly above the red lens was embellished with short, horizontal ribbing. At the base of the wrapover roof pillar was placed '400' numbering. Cloisonne-type wheel hub shell covers were used. Standard equipment was comprised of all other Packard 300 styling, trim and equipment features plus hassock foot rests; chrome exhaust extensions; the nine bearing crankshaft engine; Ultramatic Drive; and four "jet louvers" (three on the fenderside centerline and one on the rear door). Interior appointments included a special steering wheel, Wilton carpeting and color-keyed two-tone Bedford cord upholstery with a pattern of alternating pleated and plain sections.

PATRICIAN 400 SERIES

Series Number	Body/Style Number	Body Type & Seating	Factory Price	Shipping Weight	Production Total
2506	2552	4-dr Sed-6P	3797	4100	3,975

Note: Packard dealer literature indicates it was possible for a buyer to negotiate the purchase of a Custom Formal Sedan on the Patrician 400 platform.

ENGINES:

(PACKARD 200/200 DELUXE EIGHT) Inline. L-head. Cast iron block. Displacement: 288 cid. Bore and stroke: 3-1/2 x 3-3/4 inches. Compression ratio: 7.0:1. Brake hp: 135 at 3600 rpm. Five main bearings. Solid valve lifters. Carburetor: Carter Type WGD two-barrel Model 784S. (This engine was optionally available with hydraulic valve lifters, a 7.5:1 high-compression cylinder head and 138 hp at 3600 rpm.)

(PACKARD 250/300 EIGHT) Inline. L-head. Cast iron block. Displacement: 327 cid. Bore and stroke: 3-1/2 x 4-1/4 inches. Compression ratio: 7.0:1. Brake hp: 150 at 3600 rpm. Five main bearings. Hydraulic valve lifters. Carburetor: Carter Type WGD two-barrel Model 928S. Besides a carburetor model change, this engine featured a new timing chain, new vertical-type air cleaner and higher output 45-ampere generator. (This engine was optionally available with a 7.8:1 high-compression cylinder head and 155 hp at 3600 rpm.)

(PATRICIAN 400 EIGHT) Inline. L-head. Cast iron block. Displacement: 327 cid. Bore and stroke: 3-1/2 x 4-1/4 inches. Compression ratio: 7.8:1. Brake hp: 155 at 3600 rpm. Nine main bearings. Hydraulic valve lifters. Carburetor: Carter Type WGD two-barrel Model 928S. Besides a carburetor model change, this engine featured a new timing chain, new vertical-type air cleaner and higher output 45-ampere generator. (This engine was optionally available with a 7.0:1 low-compression cylinder head and 150 hp at 3600 rpm.)

CHASSIS FEATURES: Wheelbase: (Series 2501 and 2531) 122 inches; (Series 2502 and 2506) 127 inches. Overall length: (Series 2501 and 2531) 212-3/4 inches; (Series 2502 and 2506) 217-3/4 inches. Front tread: (200/200 Deluxe) 59.5 inches; (all other models) 60 inches. Rear tread: (200/200 Deluxe) 60-23/32 inches; (all other models) 61-7/32 inches. Tires: (200/200 Deluxe) 7.60 x 15; (all other models) 8.00 x 15.

OPTIONS: Whitewall tires, when available ($27.60). Genuine leather upholstery ($153). Heater and defroster ($76.50). Two-tone exterior finish ($20). Signal-seeking radio with electric antenna and rear speaker ($125.80). Rear fender shrouds ($21.45). Wheel hub shell covers ($16.35). Pelican hood mascot ($13.45). Robe cord ($12.35). Windshield washer ($9.40). Non-glare rearview mirror ($5.95). Patrician 400 steering wheel ($14.25). Foam rubber rear seat cushions ($12.25). Back-up lights and trunk compartment lamp ($13.85). Solex tinted glass ($45.20). Easamatic power brakes ($39.45). Rear window wipers. Fog lamps. Spotlight. Woodgrain tissue dispenser. Exterior sun shade. Traffic light viewfinder. Visor vanity mirror. Road lamps. Vent-I-Shades. Chrome exhaust deflector. Curb feelers. Gas door guard. Locking gas door. Door edge guards. Spare tire valve extension. Exterior rearview mirror, left-hand and/or right-hand. Fuse kit. Trouble light. Underhood lamp. Wheel blocks. Overdrive transmission ($102). Ultramatic Drive, standard in Patrician 400, optional on other models at extra cost ($189). When equipped with Ultramatic, changes in relation to use of high-compression cylinder head were the same as detailed under 1951 Packard powertrain options. The 327-cid five main bearing Packard 300 engine was available in Packard 200/200 Deluxes at extra cost ($45). Oil bath air cleaner ($8.70). Oil filter ($11.80). On cars equipped with overdrive transmissions (not available in Patrician 400) a new clutch driven member and tailshaft mounting were used.

HISTORICAL FOOTNOTES: Model year production was 69,921 cars. Calendar year sales were 69,988 cars. Packard was the 16th ranked automaker. In May 1952, Hugh Ferry announced that James J. Nance would become his successor as president and general manager of Packard Motor Car Corp. The 25th Series was introduced Nov. 14, 1951, on the nationwide television comedy show hosted by Red Skelton. Packard's first special non-production-type show car was exhibited this year. It was called the Pan American convertible. Lightly plated 'Korean War' chrome (with reduced nickel content) was used on Packards this year, due to Korean War material restrictions. Such chrome deteriorated much more rapidly than the conventional type, a fact that old car hobbyists usually must deal with in restorations of such models. According to standard reference sources listing U.S. calendar year car production by body styles, Packard built 3,730 hardtops, 1,133 convertibles, and no station wagons in 1952. The Patrician 400 is a Milestone Car.

1953

CLIPPER SPECIAL/CLIPPER DELUXE — (8-CYL) — SERIES 2601/2611 — When 1953 Packards were introduced on Nov. 21, 1952, the Clipper was back. It was the base Packard nameplate, in a year marked by model expansions. Changes for the 26th Series were a grille with full-width curved center bar; new hood ornaments; wraparound backlights on all cars; and noticeable trim revisions. The Clipper Special was most like the old styles as plain, rounded rear fenders were retained. A straight chrome molding with barbed tip sat high on the front fenders and doors. A second straight molding was set lower on the rear fenders and back door of the touring sedan. Jet plane hood ornaments and plain cloth interiors appeared. The basic Packard equipment assortment included twin horns; twin visors and wipers; horn ring; front and back bumper guards; jack and tools. The Clipper Special added turn signals, glovebox light and clock to the list. A fancier Clipper Deluxe seemed to have the front and rear bodyside moldings linked via a staggered chrome plate. It was actually part of one long, continuous arrangement of chrome strips. The Deluxe had all the same features found on Clipper Specials plus chrome wheel trim rings and fin-shaped rear fendertop chrome blades that Packard called "fishtails." Beginning this year, the relationship between Packards and Clippers was de-emphasized.

PACKARD I.D. NUMBERS: The Vehicle Identification Number was found on a plate attached to the left front door post. Engine serial numbers were located on a boss at the upper left-hand side of the cylinder block. VINs began with the Body/Style Number suffixed by the engine serial number. The Body/Style Number forming the first part of the VIN started with the symbols '26' to indicate 26th Series. The next two symbols indicated body style. All four symbols appear in the second column of the charts below. Engine serial numbers for 1953 were: [CLIPPER SPECIAL] L-200000 to L-233778. [CLIPPER DELUXE] L-300000 to L-330920. [CAVALIER/PACKARD 2631] L-400000 to L-418552; [PATRICIAN/EXECUTIVE] L-600000 to L-607829.

PACKARD 2600 SERIES

CLIPPER/CLIPPER DELUXE SERIES

Series Number	Body/Style Number	Body Type & Seating	Factory Price	Shipping Weight	Production Total
CLIPPER SPECIAL					
2601	2692	4-dr Sed-6P	2588	3715	23,126
2601	2695	2-dr Clb Sed-6P	2534	3685	6,370
2601	2697	2-dr Sptster-6P	2795	3685	3,671
CLIPPER DELUXE					
2611	2662	4-dr Sed-6P	2735	3745	26,037
2611	2665	2-dr Clb Sed-6P	2681	3705	4,678

CAVALIER/PACKARD 2631 — (8-CYL) — SERIES 2602/2631 — The basic Cavalier series included a sedan that was comparable to the former Packard 300. However, a few more sporty Packards were listed in a Cavalier sub-series. They were the convertible, the Mayfair hardtop and the new semi-custom Caribbean convertible inspired by the Pan American show car of 1952. All three were grouped in the Packard 2631 Series. The Cavalier had horizontal taillights; "fishtail" rear fender treatments; Packard lettering on the rear fenders; and an arrangement of side moldings that somewhat resembled a lightning bolt with a short upper slash on front fenders and a long lower slash from behind the front wheelwell to the rear of the car. The two slashes were connected by a curved, fluted piece of chrome that slanted forward, along the front wheelhousing's rear lip. The Mayfair was trimmed in the same manner as Clipper Deluxes on the outside, but came with richer interiors. The regular convertible also had the Clipper Deluxe (staggered) type molding treatment, but with three "jet louvers" added under the rear fender spear. Both had "fishtail" rear treatments; fender skirts; stylized pelican hood ornaments; chrome wheel discs; tilt-type rearview mirrors and trunk lights. The Caribbean convertible was a show car brought to life via body modifications by Mitchell-Bentley Corp., of Ionia, Mich. Its unique standard features list included a full-leather interior; chrome-plated wire wheels; enlarged wheel openings with flared lips; full-length, full-width front hood scoop; "de-chromed" body look; horizontal taillights; integrated "fishtail" rear fender treatment; chrome wheelwell moldings, front and rear; continental tire kit; and Custom finish in one of just four shades of paint: Polaris blue, Gulf green metallic, Matador maroon metallic or Sahara sand. A Packard script nameplate appeared on the rear-mounted spare tire, which was encased in a metal cover. It had a center cutout to show off a wire wheel with a Packard center wheel disc.

CAVALIER 2602/PACKARD 2631 SERIES

Series Number	Body/Style Number	Body Type & Seating	Factory Price	Shipping Weight	Production Total
CAVALIER					
2602	2672	4 dr Sed-6P	3234	3975	10,799
MAYFAIR HARDTOP					
2631	2677	2-dr HT Cpe-6P	3278	3905	5,150
CAVALIER CONVERTIBLE					
2631	2679	2-dr Conv-6P	3234	3960	1,518
CARIBBEAN CUSTOM CONVERTIBLE					
2631	2678	2-dr Cus Conv-6P	5210	4110	750

PATRICIAN/CORPORATE-EXECUTIVE — (8-CYL) — SERIES 2606/2626 — Identification features of 1953 Packard Patricians included the manufacturer's name in script on the rear upper portion of the back fenders. They also had the standard pelican/cormorant-type hood ornaments; horizontal taillights; and a side molding treatment similar to that seen on Cavaliers, but with chrome gravel shields added. Standard equipment included all items found on Clipper Deluxes plus tilt-type rearview mirror; chrome wheel discs; trunk compartment light and robe rails. Long wheelbase models reappeared in the Packard catalog this year and were called Executive Sedans and Corporate Limousines. They were actually built by Henney Motor Co., a maker of professional cars, hearses and ambulances. These eight-passenger models used the lightning bolt-style arrangement of moldings, with the rear streak extending a long way toward the back of the car. The house of Derham, a custom body firm, also created a limited number of Custom Formal Sedans on the 1953 platform. These cars carried Patrician style trim.

PATRICIAN/CORPORATE-EXECUTIVE SERIES

Series Number	Body/Style Number	Body Type & Seating	Factory Price	Shipping Weight	Production Total
PATRICIAN					
2606	2652	4-dr Sed-6P	3735	4190	7,456
2606	2653	4-dr Derham Fml Sed-6P	6531	4335	25
HENNEY CORPORATE-EXECUTIVE					
2626	2651	4-dr Exec Sed-8P	6900	4650	100
2626	2650	4-dr Corp Limo-8P	7100	4720	50

ENGINES:

(CLIPPER SPECIAL EIGHT) Inline. L-head. Cast iron block. Displacement: 288.6 cid. Bore and stroke: 3-1/2 x 3-3/4 inches. Compression ratio: 7.7:1. Brake hp: 150 at 4000 rpm. Five main bearings. Solid or hydraulic valve lifters (cars with hydraulic valve lifters had a 'H' suffix on engine number). Carburetor: Carter Type WGD two-barrel Model 784S.

(CLIPPER DELUXE EIGHT) Inline. L-head. Cast iron block. Displacement: 327 cid. Bore and stroke: 3-1/2 x 4-1/4 inches. Compression ratio: 8.0:1. Brake hp: 160 at 3600 rpm. Five main bearings. Solid or hydraulic valve lifters (cars with hydraulic valve lifters had an 'H' suffix on engine number). Carburetor: Carter Type WGD two-barrel Model 928S or 2102S.

(CAVALIER/MAYFAIR EIGHT) Inline. L-head. Cast iron block. Displacement: 327 cid. Bore and stroke: 3-1/2 x 4-1/4 inches. Compression ratio: 8.0:1. Brake hp: 180 at 4000 rpm. Five main bearings. Hydraulic valve lifters. Carburetor: Carter Type WCFB four-barrel Model 2084S or Model 985S.

(PATRICIAN/CORPORATE-EXECUTIVE) All specifications for this engine were the same as those given for the Cavalier engine, except that a nine main bearing crankshaft was used in the Patrician and Corporate-Executive powerplant.

CHASSIS FEATURES: Wheelbase: (Series 2601, 2611 and 2631) 122 inches; (Series 2602 and 2606) 127 inches; (Series 2626) 149 inches. Overall length: (Series 2601, 2611 and 2631) 213-3/32 inches; (Series 2602 and 2606) 218-5/32 inches; (Series 2626) 240-5/32 inches. Front tread: (Clippers) 59-1/2 inches; (all others) 60 inches. Rear tread: (Clippers) 60-23/32 inches; (all others) 61-7/32 inches. Tires: (Clipper) 7.60 x 15; (Executives) 8.20 x 15; (all others) 8.00 x 15.

OPTIONS: Power steering ($195). Easamatic power brakes ($39). Push-button radio with manual antenna ($97); with electric antenna ($109). Signal-seeking radio with manual antenna ($118); with electric antenna ($132). Rear compartment speaker ($16). Power windows and front seat ($153). Windshield washers ($9.40). Back-up lights ($11). Size 7.60 x 15 whitewalls, exchange ($30). Size 8.00 x 15 whitewalls, exchange ($33). Two-tone paint ($20). Fresh air heater and defroster ($80). Tinted Solex glass ($45). Overdrive ($110). Ultramatic

1953 Packard, Cavalier (Series 2602), sedan, AA

1953 Packard, Patrician Custom (Series 2606), formal sedan (with body by Derham), AA

1954 Packard, Super Clipper Panama (Series 5411), sport coupe, AA

1954 Packard, Caribbean Custom (Series 5431), convertible, AA

1955 Packard, "The" Four Hundred (Series 5580), hardtop, AA

1953 Packard, Caribbean Custom (Series 2631), convertible, AA

1954 Packard, Clipper Deluxe (Series 5401), club sedan, AA

1954 Packard, (Series 5431), convertible, AA

1955 Packard, Clipper Custom Constellation (Series 5560), hardtop, AA

1955 Packard, Clipper Panama Super (Series 5540), hardtop, AA

was standard in Patricians only, optional in other models at extra cost ($199). Available rear axle gear ratios included: (conventional) 3.90:1; (overdrive) 4.00:1 and (Ultramatic) 3.54:1.

HISTORICAL FOOTNOTES: Factory introductions were made Nov. 28, 1952. The model run brought production of 89,730 cars. Calendar year sales hit 81,341 vehicles. Packard was ranked 14th among automakers in industry sales. Body/Style 2697, the Clipper Sportster, used the two-door Club Sedan body with Mayfair trim features including chrome interior roof bows; extra heavy side window moldings and staggered-type side trim to give the car a pillarless hardtop look. Packard Clipper was lettered above the body side moldings on the upper rear quarters and the "fishtail" type rear fender treatment was seen. The special Caribbean convertible was not introduced until midyear, appearing in January 1953. A unique Packard Balboa show car was constructed this year and put on exhibit on August 31, 1953. It was based on the Caribbean body with a reverse sloping fiberglass roof and roll-down rear window. Air conditioning, not offered since 1942, was released as a $625 option (for four models) on July 1, 1953. The first two air-conditioners were, however, installed in two White House fleet cars on May 19, 1953. The limousine was introduced on March 14, 1953. The Patrician 400 is a Milestone car.

1954

CLIPPER SPECIAL — (8-CYL) — SERIES 5400 — The 1954 Packard products were introduced to the public on Jan. 15, 1954, with the Clipper Special four-door sedan added on March 29. General styling changes for an expanded line of Clippers included revised sweep spear patterns; redesigned rear fenders; new taillights set into the rear fender tips; and the addition of wraparound chrome plates between the horizontal grille bar extensions and outer edges of the front bumper. The Clipper Special continued with two separate sweep spears. Seen on the rear door or fender was a Clipper nameplate under the spear. In addition, a Clipper Special nameplate was located on the trunk lid. Standard equipment included twin horns; twin sun visors; two variable-speed vacuum windshield wipers; horn blow ring; front and back bumper guards; bumper jack and tools. These cars were marketed as Clippers, with the Packard tie-in de-emphasized.

PACKARD I.D. NUMBERS: The Vehicle Identification Number was found on a plate attached to the left front door post. Engine serial numbers were located on a boss at the upper left-hand side of the cylinder block. VINs began with the Body/Style Number suffixed by the engine serial number. The Body/Style Number forming the first part of the VIN was revised and no longer used consecutive series numbering. Packard switched to using the last two digits of the calendar year as the first two symbols of the series and model designations. Therefore, the first two symbols used to identify cars, series and models were '54'. The second pair of symbols indicated body style. All four symbols conformed to those in the second column of the charts below. Engine serial numbers: [CLIPPER SPECIAL] M-200000 to M-202019. [CLIPPER DELUXE] M-300000 to M-321199. [CAVALIER/PACKARD 5431] M-400000 to M-402638. [PATRICIAN/EXECUTIVE] M-600000 to M-605618.

CLIPPER SPECIAL SERIES

Series Number	Body/Style Number	Body Type & Seating	Factory Price	Shipping Weight	Production Total
5400	5482	4-dr Sed-6P	2594	3650	970
5400	5485	2-dr Clb Sed-6P	2544	3585	912

DELUXE CLIPPER/SUPER CLIPPER — (8-CYL) — SERIES 5401/5411 — There were now two extra-fancy, extra-powerful lines of Clippers on the same 122-inch wheelbase as Clipper Specials. They had the larger 327 cid/165 hp Packard engine under their hoods. The Deluxe was trimmed with a continuous sweep spear molding running high on the bodysides from behind the headlights to the bottom of the taillights. Clipper Deluxe lettering appeared on the trunk lid. The Sportster coupe continued, now as a Deluxe. It was actually a pillared Club Coupe, but had wide exterior window frame moldings that gave it a hardtop appearance. It also had a sporty interior and chrome headliner bows. Except for the bigger engine, Deluxe equipment features were similar to those of Special Clippers. An all-new line was the Super Clipper series, which was identified with model name lettering on the trunk and added a glovebox light to the features list. It included a sporty business coupe with two separate sweep spears, such as Clipper Specials had. This model had a "Panama" script under the forward section of the rear fender spear. It was trimmed about the same as the Deluxe Sportster. The next step up was the Panama Sports Coupe (two-door hardtop) in the Super Clipper line. It used the same roofline as the all-new Packard Pacific and was otherwise similar to Deluxe/Super Clippers outside. Inside was a different story, as rich appointments were used. In total, over 20 trim combinations (genuine leather, broadcloth, nylon cord and nylon matelasse in a rainbow of colors) were provided for Clippers this year. Packard was pushing the Clipper as a stronger entry in the hot medium-price market, which had a lot to do with its new models and enrichments.

DELUXE/SUPER CLIPPER SERIES

Series Number	Body/Style Number	Body Type & Seating	Factory Price	Shipping Weight	Production Total
DELUXE SERIES					
5401	5492	4-dr Sed-6P	2695	3660	7,610
5401	5495	2-dr Clb Sed-6P	2645	3590	1,470
5401	5497	2-dr Sptster-6P	2830	3595	1,336
SUPER SERIES					
5411	5462	4-dr Sed-6P	2815	3695	6,270
5411	5465	2-dr Clb Sed-6P	2765	3610	887
PANAMA SUB-SERIES					
5411	N/A	2-dr Bus Cpe-6P	N/A	N/A	Note 1
5411	5467	2-dr HT Spt Cpe-6P	3125	3805	3,618

Note 1: The two-door Business Coupe is a Panama Body/Style Number. Factory delivered price and shipping weight data for this model was not provided. The production of Panama business coupes is combined in the total for the 5467 model.

CAVALIER — (8-CYL) — SERIES 5402 — The Cavalier was now the lowest-priced true Packard and the only one to utilize the five main bearing engine. Basic Packard styling changes included new "horned" headlamp rims; curvier rear fender "fishtails"; and new side spear treatments. On the Cavalier, the forward spear was placed high on the body and ran from behind the headlamps to a point just below the rear ventipanes. A rear spear was positioned much lower and traveled from the forward edge of the fender pontoon, almost to the rear of the car, passing just above the fender skirts. The area between where the two moldings passed each other was decorated with three short, parallel strips of chrome. A Packard medallion was placed on the base of the rear roof pillar. A Packard script appeared on the rear fendersides. On Packards, but not Clippers, the center horizontal grille bar had vertical fluting on both sides of the center vertical grille post. The taillight clusters were placed halfway up the rear fenders. Standard Cavalier extras included directional signals; tilt-type rearview mirror; chrome-plated wheel discs; trunk compartment light and robe rail. This model was on the 127-inch wheelbase.

CAVALIER SERIES

Series Number	Body/Style Number	Body Type & Seating	Factory Price	Shipping Weight	Production Total
5402	5472	4-dr Sed-6P	3344	3955	2,580

PACKARD LINE — (8-CYL) — SERIES 5431 — To emphasize the difference between Packards and Clippers, the company's three sportiest Packards were provided with the nine main bearing straight eight engine this year and called the "Packard Line." Included were the Packard convertible, Pacific hardtop and Caribbean convertible coupe. The new names stressed a luxury tie-in, but still gave each of these attention-getting models a distinct identity. James Nance felt that if all models had their own names they would not be forgotten or confused. The conventional convertible had the same type of side trim featured on the Cavalier, except that the Packard script was moved from the rear fenders to the deck lid. Standard equipment also included a pelican-style hood mascot and rear fender shields. The interior was trimmed in a combination of leather and leather-grained plastic. The Pacific looked much like the ragtop, except that the roof did not fold away. However, it did have rear fender script, as well as medallions near the base of the rear roof pillar. The 1954 Caribbean had the new type headlamp rims; a chrome trim band along the edge of the hood scoop; lower rear wheel cutouts; two-tone finish, color-keyed to interior tones; Caribbean script on the sides of the front fenders; sweep spear moldings that began above the split taillamps and ran straight to the front of the fender pontoon, then arched up and into the upper beltline and new, integral taillamps. Standard equipment, on this model only, included power steering; power brakes; windshield washers; white sidewall tires; power windows; power seat; dual heaters and defrosters; three-way radio with electric antenna; continental spare tire; chromed wire wheels; and wide chrome wheelhousing surrounds with body sill and rear quarter panel extensions.

PACKARD LINE

Series Number	Body/Style Number	Body Type & Seating	Factory Price	Shipping Weight	Production Total
PACKARD PACIFIC					
5431	5477	2-dr HT Cpe-6P	3827	4040	1,189
PACKARD					
5431	5479	2-dr Conv-6P	3935	4260	863
CARIBBEAN CUSTOM					
5431	5478	2-dr Cus Conv-6P	6100	4400	400

PACKARD PATRICIAN CUSTOM/HENNEY LINE — (8-CYL) — SERIES 5406/5426 — A staggered (or step-down) type sweep spear molding, connected by ribbed diagonal chrome ornaments, was used on Patrician models and the Henney-built eight-passenger sedans and limousines. Also on these models, chrome bumper strips appeared on the rocker sills to underscore the stately beauty of the most luxurious Packards. The Packard Patrician had round medallions on the rear roof pillar and many rich appointments.

PACKARD PATRICIAN CUSTOM/HENNEY LINE

Series Number	Body/Style Number	Body Type & Seating	Factory Price	Shipping Weight	Production Total
5426	5451	4-dr Exec Sed-8P	6900	4650	65
5426	5450	4-dr Limo-8P	7250	4720	35
5426	5452	4-dr Sed-8P	3890	4190	2,760

Note 1: Prices for the Henney-built Executive Sedan and Corporate Limousine were factory delivered prices at Henney Motor Car plant in Freeport, Ill.

ENGINES:

(CLIPPER SPECIAL EIGHT) Inline. L-head. Cast iron block. Displacement: 288 cid. Bore and stroke: 3-1/2 x 3-3/4 inches. Compression ratio: 7.7:1. Brake hp: 150 at 4000 rpm. Five main bearings. Solid or hydraulic valve lifters. (Cars with hydraulic valve lifters had an 'H' engine number suffix). Carburetor: Carter Type WGD two-barrel Model 986S.

(DELUXE/SUPER CLIPPER EIGHT) Inline. L-head. Cast iron block. Displacement: 327 cid. Bore and stroke: 3-1/2 x 4-1/4 inches. Compression ratio: 8.0:1. Brake hp: 165 at 3600 rpm. Five main bearings. Hydraulic or solid valve lifters. (Cars with hydraulic valve lifters had an 'H' engine number suffix). Carburetor: Carter Type WGD two-barrel Model 2102S.

(CAVALIER EIGHT) Inline. L-head. Cast iron block. Displacement: 327 cid. Bore and stroke: 3-1/2 x 4-1/4 inches. Compression ratio: 8.0:1. Brake hp: 185 at 4000 rpm. Five main bearings. Hydraulic valve lifters. Carburetor: Carter Type WCFB four-barrel Model 2103S.

(PACKARD LINE 5431/5406/5426 EIGHT) Inline. L-head. Cast iron block. Displacement: 359 cid. Bore and stroke: 3-9/16 x 4-1/2 inches. Compression ratio: 8.7:1. Brake hp: 212 at 4000 rpm. Nine main bearings. Hydraulic valve lifters. Carburetor: Carter WCFB four-barrel Model 2212S.

CHASSIS FEATURES: Wheelbase: (Series 5400, 5401, 5411 and 5431) 122 inches; (Series 5402 and 5406) 127 inches; (Series 5426) 149 inches. Overall length: (Clippers) 215-1/2 inches; (Cavalier and Patrician) 216-1/2 inches; (Pacific/Packard convertible/Caribbean) 211-1/2 inches; (Henney models) 238-1/2 inches. Front tread: (Clippers) 59-3/4 inches; (all others) 60 inches. Rear tread: (Clippers) 59.9 inches; (Packard) 60.8 inches; (Henney Custom) 60.9 inches. Tires: (Clippers) 7.60 x 15; (Cavalier) 8.00 x 15; (Henney models) 8.20 x 15; (all others) 8.00 x 15.

OPTIONS: Power steering ($177.50). Power brakes ($43). Four-Way power seat ($75). Windshield washer ($16.75). Sun visor ($31.50). Spotlight ($28.50). Pelican hood ornament ($13.45). Curb signals ($1.75). Hydraulic windows ($153). Standard radio ($102). Three-way tuning radio with electric antenna ($132). Ultramatic ($199). Heater/defroster ($79.50). White sidewall tires ($32.50 exchange). Backing lights ($13). Rear seat speaker ($16.80). Solex glass ($45.20). Molding mirror ($5.10). Continental tire carrier ($270). Overdrive ($110). Ultramatic drive was standard in the Caribbean and Patrician, optional on other models at extra cost.

HISTORICAL FOOTNOTES: Factory introduction of 1954 models was held Jan. 15, 1954. Model year sales were 30,965 cars; calendar year sales reached 27,593 cars. Packard was America's 16th ranked maker again. The Panther-Daytona (or Grey Wolf II) experimental Packard sports car was driven by Dick Rathmann at Daytona Speed-Weeks. It hit 110.9 mph (officially) and clocked 131 mph (unofficially) later. Experimentation with supercharged straight eights began in 1953 and continued this season. Packard did a lightning-like conversion of its Conner Ave. plant in the fall of 1954. In just 62 days, this factory was turned into a modern body assembly facility, so that the company could build its own bodies for the first time in many years. On June 22, 1954, after months of preliminary discussions, an agreement to merge Packard with Studebaker was signed by the presidents of these two companies. On Oct. 1, 1954, The Studebaker-Packard Corp. came into official existence, with its headquarters in Detroit. Packard models recognized by the Milestone Car Society include the 1954 Caribbean and Patrician 400 sedan.

1955

CLIPPER DELUXE/SUPER — (V-8) — SERIES 5540 — Everything seemed new this year, including the former straight eight engines giving way to V-8 power. There were massive bumpers with bullet-shaped guards. There were full-width grilles with bowed upper bars and "ship's wheel" center medallions. Fine, vertical blades were seen on Clipper grilles. The front fenders were "bent-over" to hood the headlamps. Sweep-around windshields appeared. The fact that this was merely a face lift of previous bodies showed only at the rear of the Clipper, where a 1954 look was retained. At the middle of the rear deck was another "ship's wheel" medallion and, on either side, model identification script was placed. The left-hand signature read Clipper; the right-hand one read either Deluxe or Super. Side moldings curved down and back from the front ventipane to the rear edge of front doors, then ran straight to the taillamps. With "integrated two-toning," everything above and behind this molding was painted one color, everything else was done in another color. Clipper script decorated the hood and the fender area above the front bumper's wraparound edges. The only Packard identification was a small script on the right corner of the trunk. Deluxes had small hubcaps and lacked rocker panel moldings. Supers had chrome wheel discs and bright metal steps on the rockers, along with upgraded nylon and vinyl interiors.

PACKARD I.D. NUMBERS: The Vehicle Identification Number was found on a plate attached to the left front door post. Engine serial numbers were located on a boss at the upper left-hand side of the cylinder block. VINs began with the Body/Style Number suffixed by the engine serial number. The Body/Style Number forming the first part of the VIN was revised and no longer used consecutive series numbering. Packard switched to using the last two digits of the calendar year as the first two symbols of the series and model designations. Therefore, the first two symbols used to identify cars, series and models were '55'. The second pair of symbols indicated body style. All four symbols conformed to those in the second column of the charts below. Engine serial numbers: [CLIPPER DELUXE] 5522-1001 to 5522-9039. [CLIPPER SUPER] 5542-1001 to 5542-8979. [PANAMA HARDTOP] 5547-1001 to 5547-8016. [CLIPPER CUSTOM] 5562-1001 to 5562-9702. [CONSTELLATION] 5567-1001 to 5567-7678. [PATRICIAN] 5582-1001 to 5582-10127. [PACKARD 400 HARDTOP] 5587-1001 to 5587-8206. [CARIBBEAN CONVERTIBLE] 5588-1001 to 5588-1500.

CLIPPER DELUXE/SUPER SERIES

Series Number	Body/Style Number	Body Type & Seating	Factory Price	Shipping Weight	Production Total
DELUXE SERIES					
5540	5522	4-dr Sed-6P	2586	3680	8,309
SUPER SERIES					
5540	5542	4-dr Sed-6P	2686	3670	7,979
PANAMA SUPER SUB-SERIES					
5540	5547	2-dr HT Spt Cpe-6P	2776	3700	7,016

CLIPPER CUSTOM — (V-8) — SERIES 5560 — Chrome wheel discs; rocker panel moldings and fender skirts were standard Clipper Custom equipment, except for the Constellation model. This two-door hardtop had no skirts, but featured a chrome molding on the fender openings. A Custom script was placed on the right-hand side of the trunk. Interior materials ranged all the way up to the same genuine leather used in Patricians, although the trim patterns varied between the two cars. Two-tone Constellation hardtops came standard with a side molding treatment that gave a double color sweep effect. This was done by extending the lower front spear (which ran straight from the upper bumper bar to mid-door on other Clippers) in a downward curve toward the rocker molding, near the rear of the front door. Then, the region below this molding was colored to match the roof and the panels above the upper rear side spear. It looked novel and could be ordered, as an option, on the Clipper Custom touring sedan.

CLIPPER CUSTOM SERIES

Series Number	Body/Style Number	Body Type & Seating	Factory Price	Shipping Weight	Production Total
CLIPPER CUSTOM					
5560	5562	4-dr Sed-6P	2926	3885	8,708
CLIPPER CONSTELLATION					
5560	5567	2-dr HT Spt Cpe-6P	3076	3865	6,672

PACKARD LINE — (V-8) — SERIES 5580 — Senior Packards had the same shape grille opening as Clippers, but used a grid-type insert. New features included wraparound parking lamps; sweep-around windshields; Packard rear fenderside script and hood ornaments. All-new rear fenders with cathedral-shaped taillights and a flat, rounded tailfin look were used. At the leading edge were vertical, simulated vent panels finished in chrome. Trim and decoration varied between models. The Four-Hundred was a hardtop. It had Packard block letters on the hood; gold trunk ornaments; a modified pelican hood ornament; roof medallions and 'Four Hundred' signatures on the deck and front fenders. A straight spear of chrome ran from the corner of the upper grille bar, over the wheel opening, then across the door to the vertical "vent'. A second spear ran from the back bumper, over the fender skirt, straight to the front wheelhousing. It touched the bottom of the vertical 'vent' thus, a rectangular panel was formed where the higher

1955 Packard, Caribbean Custom (Series 5580), convertible, AA

1956 Packard, Clipper Custom (Series 5660), sedan, AA

1956 Packard, Caribbean Custom (Series 5688), hardtop, AA

1957 Packard, Clipper Country Sedan (Series 57L), station wagon, AA

1958 Packard, (Series 58L), station wagon, AA

1956 Packard, Super Panama (Series 5640), hardtop, AA

1956 Packard, "The" Patrician (Series 5680), sedan, AA

1957 Packard, Clipper Country Sedan (Series 57L), station wagon, AA

1958 Packard, (Series 58L), hardtop, AA

1958 Packard, Hawk (Series 58LS), sport coupe, AA

molding passed over the lower one. This allowed for a three-tone finish with one color on the roof and under the bottom molding; a second within the parallel moldings; and a third on all other areas. The Caribbean convertible had a twin-scoop hood with no ornamentation, except on the front edge of the scoops. An overlapping, fender-within-fender treatment was seen at the rear. The "shorter' fender was banded with a thin molding that dropped to gas filler door level, then ran straight to the headlamps. The 'long' fender dropped to the bumper exhaust pod, at which level another horizontal spear ran forward to the front wheel housing. To achieve three-tone finish, everything above the upper molding was one color; everything between the moldings (plus the fender extension area) was a second color and all panels below the bottom molding were painted a third color. Except for air conditioning, every choice option including dual outside mirrors and rear antennae was standard. In comparison, Patricians looked elegantly simple. They had one straight molding on the back fender (which hit the vertical 'vent' at right angles) and a separate front molding that ran straight from the upper grille bar edge to the rear of the front door. A split-fin hood ornament was seen and two-toning meant a different color for the roof. However, optional trim was offered to make the Patrician look more like the '400'. With this treatment, the higher molding was simply extended back to the 'vent', thereby forming a horizontal rectangle that was finished with the same color used on the roof. It had a Patrician script placed inside it. All senior Packards came with rocker moldings, fender skirts, chrome wheel discs and Ultramatic Drive. All Patricians had "tinfoil" side trim.

PACKARD LINE

Series Number	Body/Style Number	Body Type & Seating	Factory Price	Shipping Weight	Production Total
FOUR-HUNDRED					
5580	5587	2-dr HT Cpe-6P	4080	4250	7,206
CARIBBEAN					
5580	5588	2-dr Cus Conv-6P	5932	4755	500
PATRICIAN					
5580	5582	4-dr Sed-6P	4040	4275	9,127

ENGINES:

(CLIPPER DELUXE/SUPER V-8) Overhead valve. Cast iron block. Displacement: 320 cid. Bore and stroke: 3-13/16 x 3-1/2 inches. Compression ratio: 8.5:1. Brake hp: 225 at 4600 rpm. Five main bearings. Hydraulic valve lifters. Carburetor: Carter Type WCFB four-barrel (with cylinder head No. 440689) Model 2232S; (with cylinder head No. 440854) Model 2284S.

(CLIPPER CUSTOM/PACKARD LINE V-8) Overhead valve. Cast iron block. Displacement: 352 cid. Bore and stroke: 4 x 3-1/2 inches. Compression ratio: 8.5:1. Brake hp: 245 at 4600 rpm. Five main bearings. Hydraulic valve lifters. Carburetor: Carter Type WCFB four-barrel Models 2232S or 2284S. Packard Line models used the same engine with carburetion changes for higher output. The Patrician and Four-Hundred had a Rochester Type 4GC four-barrel Model 440823 carburetor. It gave 260 hp at 4600 rpm. The Caribbean had two Rochester Type 4GC four-barrel carburetors as follows: (front) Model 476010; (rear) Model 476011. They helped produce 275 hp at 4800 rpm.

CHASSIS FEATURES: Wheelbase: (Clipper) 122 inches; (Packard) 127 inches. Overall length: (Clipper) 214.8 inches; (Packard) 218.5 inches. Front tread: (Clipper) 59.7 inches; (Packard) 60 inches. Rear tread: (Clipper) 60 inches; (Packard) 60-63/64 inches. Tires: (Clipper) 7.60 x 15 tubeless; (Packard) 8.00 x 15 tubeless. Torsion-Level suspension was standard on Clipper Custom and Packard, not available on other models, which came with conventional layout. A 12-volt positive ground electrical system was new. Power brakes were standard on Caribbean.

OPTIONS: Radio ($102). Heater ($80). Power steering ($115). Power brakes ($40). Power seat ($70). Power windows ($108). Air conditioning ($647). Power antenna. Tinted glass. Wonderbar radio. Rear window defogger. Roll-up trunk light. Bolt-on wire wheel covers. Remote spare tire filler. Locking gas cap door. Rain vent shades. Curb feelers. Traffic light viewfinder. License plate frames. Door edge guards. Lighted vanity mirror. Drink holder and pocket pouch. Snap-in Car-Pet mats. Chrome rocker arm covers. Remote master cylinder filler. Fog lamps. A three-speed manual transmission was standard on all Clippers. Ultramatic Drive was optional on all Clippers at $199. Ultramatic Drive was standard and mandatory on all Packards. Overdrive transmission was optional on Clippers at $110. An oil bath air cleaner was standard with Packard; optional with Clipper. All Packards had dual exhaust with reverse flow mufflers and resonators. Available rear axle gear ratios included: (standard) 3.90:1; (Ultramatic) 3.23:1 and (overdrive) 3.90:1.

HISTORICAL FOOTNOTES: Factory introduction of 1955 models took place Jan. 17, 1955. Model year output was 55,247 cars. Calendar year sales were 69,667 units. Packard was America's 14th ranked automaker. A Patrician ran 25,000 miles at an average speed of 104.737 mph in an AAA-supervised test at the company's Utica Proving Ground in Utica, Mich. The Packard Request show car with a "classic" grille was built this year. Packard supplied V-8 engines and Ultramatic transmissions to American Motors Corp. for use in Nash and Hudson Eights. Richard Teague was now chief stylist at Studebaker-Packard Corp.

1956

CLIPPER DELUXE/SUPER — (V-8) — SERIES 5640 — In 1956, the Clipper grille was given fine horizontal blades instead of the short vertical type. A mesh-type insert was installed in the front bumper "air scoop" opening. The hood and deck lid were redesigned and wrap-around parking lamps were seen. Bumper guards were moved further outward, below the headlights. New chrome trims and horizontal two-toning were adopted. Identifying the Deluxe sedan was a Deluxe script on front fenders and separate side spears front and rear. The front spear ran straight from the upper grille molding to the rear edges of front doors. The second molding was positioned higher on the rear body, running from under the back ventipane to the taillamp cluster. Clipper Supers had model identifying front fender script, but now lacked rocker panel moldings. Two full-length rub rail moldings were used on the side of the new body. The first ran straight from mid-headlamp level to the rear of the body. The second ran from the upper grille bar edge straight to the middle of the front door, then dipped to the same level as the top of the rear wheelhousing in a curve. Upon hitting the forward bulge of the rear fender this molding straightened out again and ran back to the bumper, passing right over the top of the fender skirt. On all Clippers the rear fenders were redone and ended in a V-shaped notch (referred to as a reverse vertical sweep) that housed 'boomerang-shaped' cathedral taillights. A more massive rear bumper was seen.

PACKARD I.D. NUMBERS: The Vehicle Identification Number was found on a plate attached to the left front door post. Engine serial numbers were located on a boss at the upper left-hand side of the cylinder block. VINs began with the Body/Style Number suffixed by the engine serial number. The Body/Style Number forming the first part of the VIN was revised and no longer used consecutive series numbering. Packard again used the last two digits of the calendar year as the first two symbols of the series and model designations. Therefore, the first two symbols used to identify cars, series and models were '56'. The second pair of symbols indicated body style. All four symbols conformed to those in the second column of the charts below. Engine serial numbers: [CLIPPER DELUXE] 5622-1001 to 5622-6715. [CLIPPER SUPER] 5642-1001 to 5642-6173. [PANAMA HARDTOP] 5647-1001 to 5647-4999. [CLIPPER CUSTOM] 5662-1001 to 5662-3130. [CONSTELLATION] 5667-1001 to 5667-2494. [PATRICIAN] 5682-1001 to 5682-4775. [PACKARD 400 HARDTOP] 5687-1001 to 5687-4224. [CARIBBEAN CONVERTIBLE] 5699-1001 to 5699-1276. [CARIBBEAN HARDTOP] 5697-1001 to 5697-1263.

CLIPPER DELUXE/SUPER SERIES

Series Number	Body/Style Number	Body Type & Seating	Factory Price	Shipping Weight	Production Total
DELUXE					
5640	5622	4-dr Del Sed-6P	2731	3955	5,715
SUPER					
5640	5642	4-dr Sup Sed-6P	2866	4010	5,173
SUPER PANAMA					
5640	5647	2-dr Sup HT Cpe-6P	2916	4035	3,999

CLIPPER CUSTOM — (V-8) — SERIES 5660 — Custom script on the front fenders and chrome rocker panel moldings help in identifying Clipper Customs. The balance of trim on these cars was similar to that used on Clipper Supers, including twin rub rails with the lower molding having a curved dip near the rear quarters. Interior appointments were the richest offered on Clippers, the Constellation hardtop having leather trim options available and standard chrome roof bows.

CLIPPER CUSTOM SERIES

Series Number	Body/Style Number	Body Type & Seating	Factory Price	Shipping Weight	Production Total
CLIPPER CUSTOM					
5660	5662	4-dr Cus Sed-6P	3069	4070	2,129
CLIPPER CUSTOM CONSTELLATION					
5660	5667	2-dr Cus HT-6P	3164	4070	1,466

EXECUTIVE LINE — (V-8) — SERIES 5670 — The Executive line was introduced on April 9, 1956, as a replacement for the entire Clipper Custom lineup. This car was designed to fill a marketing gap existing between the lowest-priced Packard and the Clipper Deluxe. The Executive had a Packard grille and Packard-inspired side body trim, but was more closely related to Clippers. The 352-cid Clipper V-8 was used for power and the body was the Clipper-type (with reverse vertical sweep fenders and taillights). Body ornamentation had a Packard look. The Executive was trimmed with two straight horizontal rub rails running from behind the headlights to ahead of the taillights. In two-tone color schemes, the area between the parallel moldings was painted to match the roof. There was no vertical simulated 'vent' strip on the rear quarter of this car. Rocker panel moldings were used between the wheel openings only.

EXECUTIVE LINE

Series Number	Body/Style Number	Body Type & Seating	Factory Price	Shipping Weight	Production Total
5670	5672A	4-dr Sed-6P	3465	4185	1,784
5670	5677A	2-dr HT Cpe-6P	3560	4185	1,031

PACKARD LINE — (V-8) — SERIES 5680 — Changes in the Packard body, from 1955, included a redesigned grille with a mesh-type insert having a gridwork of vertical and horizontal chrome bars placed against it. Both the mesh and the grille could also be seen in the "air scoop' opening under the main horizontal bumper bar. Wraparound parking lamps were seen again, but had rounded rear edges. The headlamp hoods were lowered by one inch. Front fenders were extended on all Packards and Executives. Packard hood letters no longer appeared, being replaced by a centrally mounted crest. Due to the redesigned bumper, the guards were spaced wider apart, placing them directly under the headlights. Included in this series were the Patrician sedan and the Four-Hundred hardtop coupe. Both had vertical vents on the rear fenders and the same arrangement of side trim. This consisted of a wide, ribbed chrome band extending the full length of the car between two horizontal rub rails. The first rail ran from the front edge of the upper grille bar to the rear edge of the back fender; the second was parallel to it, about eight inches lower. Both moldings intersected the vent ornament and outside door courtesy/safety lamps were placed at this spot. Also seen on both cars were model identification script, set into the contrast panel, behind the front wheelhousing. In addition, both were highlighted by bright metal body underscores that continued across the fender skirts and had wide, ribbed chrome rear extension panels. The Ultramatic transmission offered an electronic push-button selector mounted on the steering column.

PACKARD LINE

Series Number	Body/Style Number	Body Type & Seating	Factory Price	Shipping Weight	Production Total
PATRICIAN					
5680	5682	4-dr Sed-6P	4160	4255	3,775
FOUR-HUNDRED					
5680	5687	2-dr HT Cpe-6P	4190	4290	3,224

CARIBBEAN SUB-SERIES — (V-8) — SERIES 5688 — The Caribbean was now a separate Packard sub-series having two models with special styling and engineering. General styling changes from 1955 Caribbeans were minimal. The deeper hooded headlight look was used; the rear edge of parking lamps was rounded; the Caribbean script was colored gold and gridwork in the grille insert was of slightly wider squares so that several divisions were eliminated both horizontally and vertically. In addition, the new Packard 'air scoop' bumper (with the center cutout revealing a portion of the grille insert) was used. This located the bumper guard bullets directly under the headlights. Also, new three-tone color combinations were offered, such as maroon, light blue and ivory white. The hardtop was a new addition and its roof had a pair of lengthwise ribs, one on each side. Use of a dual four-barrel induction system was continued with the 374 cid/310 hp Caribbean V-8. Caribbeans had reversible seat cushions that could be unsnapped and repositioned.

CARIBBEAN SUB-SERIES

Series Number	Body/Style Number	Body Type & Seating	Factory Price	Shipping Weight	Production Total
5688	5697	2-dr Cus HT Cpe-6P	5495	4590	263
5688	5699	2-dr Cus Conv-6P	5995	4960	276

ENGINES:

(CLIPPER DELUXE/SUPER V-8) Overhead valve. Cast iron block. Displacement: 352 cid. Bore and stroke: 4 x 3-1/2 inches. Compression ratio: 9.5:1. Brake hp: 240 at 4600 rpm. Five main bearings. Hydraulic valve lifters. Carburetor: Carter Type WGD two-barrel Model 2393S.

(CLIPPER CUSTOM/EXECUTIVE V-8) Overhead valve. Cast iron block. Displacement: 352 cid. Bore and stroke: 4 x 3-1/2 inches. Compression ratio: 9.5:1. Brake hp: 275 at 4600 rpm. Five main bearings. Hydraulic valve lifters. Carburetor: Rochester Type 4GC four-barrel carburetor Model 6480253.

(PACKARD LINE V-8) Overhead valve. Cast iron block. Displacement: 374 cid. Bore and stroke: 4-1/8 x 3-1/2 inches. Compression ratio: 10.0:1. Brake hp: 290 at 4600 rpm. Five main bearings. Hydraulic valve lifters. Carburetor: Rochester Type 4GC four-barrel Model 6480253.

(CARIBBEAN V-8) Overhead valve. Cast iron block. Displacement: 374 cid. Bore and stroke: 4-1/8 x 3-1/2 inches. Compression ratio: 10.0:1. Brake hp: 310 at 4600 rpm. Five main bearings. Hydraulic valve lifters. Carburetor: Two Rochester Type 4GC four-barrel units were used as follows: (front) Model 6489090; (rear) Model 6489091.

CHASSIS FEATURES: Wheelbase: (Clipper/Executive) 122 inches; (Packard) 127 inches. Overall length: (Clipper/Executive) 215.3 inches; (Packard) 218.6 inches. Front tread: (Clipper/Executive) 59.7 inches; (Packard) 60 inches. Rear tread: (Clipper/Executive) 60 inches; (Packard) 60.8 inches. Tires: (Clipper/Executive) 7.60 x 15 tubeless; (Packard) 8.00 x 1 5 tubeless. Electrical ground was changed to negative.

OPTIONS: Torsion suspension, Clipper ($150, but by the end of the production run, all models had Torsion-Level suspension as standard equipment). Radio with manual antenna ($103). Three-way tuning radio with electric antenna and rear speaker ($135). Front seat heater ($46). Power steering ($115). Power brakes ($40). Four-Way power seat ($70). Electric windows ($70). Air conditioning ($647). Power antenna. Solex glass with filter ($45.20). Whitewall tires ($33 exchange). Hub shells ($15). Dual exhaust ($35). Spotlight with mirror ($28.50). Tilt-type mirror ($3.65). Tinted glass. Wonderbar radio. Rear window defogger. Roll-up trunk light. Bolt-on wire wheel covers. Remote spare tire filler. Locking gas cap door. Rain vent shades. Curb feelers. Traffic light viewfinder. License plate frames. Door edge guards. Lighted vanity mirror. Drink holder and pocket pouch. Snap-in Car-Pet mats. Chrome rocker arm covers. Remote master cylinder filler. Fog lamps. Three-speed manual transmission was standard on Clippers; not available on Packards (except Clipper-based Executives). Overdrive was optional on Clippers and Executives at $110. Limited-slip differential was optional on all models. Oil bath air cleaner standard on all models. Twin Ultramatic Drive was a mandatory option in Packards except Clipper/Executive models ($199 extra). Torsion-Level suspension standard on all models by the end of year. Available as a no-cost option on Deluxe models was conventional suspension. Power brakes were standard on all senior Packards; optional on Clipper and Executive. Electronically-controlled, push-button Ultramatic gear selection was standard in Caribbean, optional on all cars with automatics. Available rear axle gear ratios included: (standard) 3.90:1; (Ultramatic) 3.23:1 and (overdrive) 3.90:1.

HISTORICAL FOOTNOTES: Factory introductions were held Nov. 3, 1955, for Clippers and Packards and April 9, 1956, for Executives. The total model run of Packards was a mere 28,835 cars. Calendar year sales dropped to 13,432. Packard slid to the 15th industry ranking. These figures did not combine Packard and Studebaker sales. (Studebaker was ranked 13th). The 1955-1956 Four-Hundred/Patrician and Caribbean are Milestone Cars. The 1956 Caribbean convertible came with reversible seat upholstery that was brocade on one side and leather on the other. The futuristic Predictor show car was constructed this year. On July 27, 1956, Studebaker-Packard Corp. entered a joint management agreement with Curtiss-Wright Corp. Shortly thereafter, James Nance resigned as chief executive officer. On Aug. 15, 1956, Packard operations in Detroit were brought to a halt. For 1957 and 1958, a limited range of Packards would be built off of Studebaker platforms at Studebaker's South Bend, Ind., plant. The 1957 models were called Clippers and the 1958 models had Packard nameplates and trim. Both were far different than Packard products of the past.

1957

CLIPPER — (V-8) — SERIES 57L — The 1957 Packard Clipper was a badge-engineered automobile built off a Studebaker President chassis. Packard modifications included finned rear fenders, a special rear wheel panel treatment and more elaborate trim. The Packard name appeared in individual block letters on the front of the hood. A Clipper script was placed on the rear fenders. Packard and Clipper script was also affixed to the deck lid or station wagon tailgate. The traditional Clipper "ship's wheel" medallion decorated the grille and the rear of the cars. Side trim distinctive to the Packard Clipper consisted of a wide, grooved bright metal band extending the full length of the car and across the tailgate of the station wagon. Standard equipment included modified 1956 Clipper chrome wheel discs; chrome drip moldings; two-speed electric wipers; turn signals; back-up lights; front bumper guards; padded dashboard; deep-dish steering wheel; electric clock; cigar lighter; glovebox lamp; front and rear carpeting; foam rubber seat cushions; and a rear seat center armrest on the Town Sedan.

PACKARD I.D. NUMBERS: The serial number plate was located on the left-hand front door hinge pillar facing. Engine numbers were stamped on a machined pad at the left of the oil filler tube mounting on top of the cylinder block. The first two symbols, '57', indicated the model year. The third symbol was an alphabetical series code and was 'L' for all 1957 models. Serial numbers were 57L L-1001 to L-5809. Engine numbers were LS-101 and up. Body/Style Numbers utilized the first three symbols of the above codes, a dash, a letter indicating the model and a number. 57L-Y8 identified the Town Sedan; 57L-P8 identified the Country Sedan station wagon. Only these two styles were offered.

CLIPPER SERIES 57L

Series Number	Body/Style Number	Body Type & Seating	Factory Price	Shipping Weight	Production Total
TOWN SEDAN					
57L	57L-Y8	4-dr Sed-6P	3212	3570	3,940
COUNTRY SEDAN					
57L	57L-P8	4-dr Sta Wag-6P	3384	3650	869

ENGINE:

(CLIPPER V-8) Overhead valve. Cast iron block. Displacement: 289 cid. Bore and stroke: 3-9/16 x 3-5/8 inches. Compression ratio: 7.8:1. Brake hp: 275 at 4800 rpm. Five main bearings. Solid valve lifters. Carburetor: Stromberg WW6121 two-barrel. Included as standard equipment on this engine was a McCulloch Model VS-57S supercharger designed to cut in at 3000 rpm.

CHASSIS FEATURES: Wheelbase: (Town Sedan) 120.5 inches; (Country Sedan) 116.5 inches. Overall length: (Town Sedan) 211.8 inches; (Country Sedan) 204.8 inches. Front tread: 56-11/16 inches. Rear Tread: 55-11/16 inches. Tires: 7.60 x 15.

OPTIONS: Tinted glass ($32). White sidewall tires ($28). Power steering ($98). Power brakes ($38). Power windows ($103). Power seat ($45). Dual rear antennae (electric for sedan, manual for station wagon). Front seat belts, pair ($25). Padded sun visors. Country Sedan luggage carrier ($60). Air conditioning, Town Sedan only ($325). Rear radio speaker ($13). Flight-O-Matic transmission was standard equipment. Limited-slip differential was optional at extra cost. Conventional suspension was featured, with helper springs on Country Sedan station wagon. Available axle ratios included: (standard) 3.31:1; (optional at no-cost) 3.07:1 or 3.54:1.

HISTORICAL FOOTNOTES: The Studebaker-based Packard Clipper was introduced on Jan. 31, 1957. The possibility of a marketing program between Studebaker-Packard and Mercedes-Benz was explored in the spring of 1957. H.D. Churchill was president of Studebaker-Packard in 1957. The corporation lost $43.3 million this year. The supercharger used on the 1957 engine was built by McCulloch Motors, best known as a chainsaw manufacturer. While often identified as a Paxton supercharger, it was not until March 1962 that the supercharger branch became the Paxton Products Division of Studebaker-Packard Corp.

1958

PACKARD — (V-8) — SERIES 58L — The 1958 Packards were marketed as a midyear line introduced in January 1958. The Clipper designation was dropped. Four models were available with a Packard Hawk hardtop and Packard hardtop being added to the line. Only the Packard Hawk V-8 was supercharged. General changes from 1957 included new bodies with an unusual "shovel nose." This low, wide air-intake-type grille surround was actually a fiberglass bolt-on item. New dual headlamps were on all models, except Hawks. Radical pointed tailfins took the fender-within-fender theme of earlier Caribbeans to the extreme. There were now fins on top of fins, with the top one curving sharply upward. The bottom fin jutted out further at the rear and housed "boomerang-shaped" taillights with integral back-up lights. The lower fin turned into a sweep spear contrast panel that tapered as it ran the full length of the body from above the rear bumper to just below the front fender tip. The cars were fitted with 14-inch wheels to make them lower. A scoop appeared on the hood, along with Packard block lettering. Packard script was affixed to the fins and rear deck lid. Styling on the Packard Hawk was distinctive and it is described below, as a separate sub-series. Standard equipment was the same as 1957, except the Packard engine was not supercharged.

PACKARD I.D. NUMBERS: The serial number plate was located on the left-hand front door hinge pillar facing. Engine numbers were stamped on a machined pad at the left of the oil filler tube mounting on top of the cylinder block. The first two symbols, '58', indicated the model year. The third symbol was an alphabetical series code and was 'L' for all 1958 models. Serial numbers were 58L-6101 and up. Body/Style Number for the sedan was J8; for the hardtop Y8 and for the station wagon P8. The station wagon was no longer called the Country Sedan. [PACKARD HAWK] The serial numbering system and code locations were the same. Serial Numbers were 58LS-K91001 and up. Engine numbers were 58L LS-101 and up. The new Body/Style Number for the Packard Hawk was K9.

PACKARD SERIES 58L

Series Number	Body/Style Number	Body Type & Seating	Factory Price	Shipping Weight	Production Total
58L	58L-J8	4-dr Sed-6P	3212	3505	1,200
58L	58L-Y8	2-dr HT Cpe-6P	3262	3480	675
58L	58L-P8	4-dr Sta Wag-6P	3384	3555	159

PACKARD HAWK — (V-8) — SERIES 58LS — The Packard Hawk had the same fiberglass, bolt-on air-intake-type grille as other Packards. It was, however, bolted onto the Studebaker Hawk sports car body, a sleek two-door hardtop coupe-style car. A number of special extras were included. For example, padded 'armrests' on the outside of the doors; a continental tire impression stamped on the deck lid; genuine leather interior with sports car-type instrument board and full instrumentation; simulated and integrated hood scoop; front fender markers; Mylar sweep panel inserts; Packard emblem hubcaps; wide chromed 'halo' roof band over backlight; tachometer; vacuum gauge; supercharger pressure gauge and 275-hp supercharged engine. The Hawk was lettered and 'scripted' like other Packards but had a different trim arrangement. A thin band of chrome outlined the concave rear tailfins and a straight spear stretched from the single headlights to almost the rear edge of the door. A flap-type vertical air vent door appeared behind the front wheel cutout.

PACKARD HAWK SERIES 58LS

Series Number	Body/Style Number	Body Type & Seating	Factory Price	Shipping Weight	Production Total
58LS	58LS-K9	2-dr HT Spt Cpe-5P	3995	3470	588

ENGINES:

(PACKARD V-8) Overhead valve. Cast iron block. Displacement: 289 cid. Bore and stroke: 3.56 x 3.63 inches. Compression ratio: 8.3:1. Brake hp: 225 at 4500 rpm. Five main bearings. Solid valve lifters. Carburetor: Carter Model 2575S four-barrel. Non-supercharged. (Low compression 7.0:1 cylinder heads were optional for this engine.)

(PACKARD HAWK V-8) Overhead valve. Cast iron block. Displacement: 289 cid. Bore and stroke: 3.56 x 3.63 inches. Compression ratio: 7.8:1. Brake hp: 275 at 4800 rpm. Five main bearings. Solid valve lifters. Carburetor: Stromberg WWG-122A two-barrel. Included as standard equipment on this engine was a McCulloch Model VS-57S supercharger designed to cut in at 3000 rpm.

CHASSIS FEATURES: Wheelbase: (Packard Hawk and sedan) 120.5 inches; (Packard hardtop and station wagon) 116.5 inches. Overall length: (Hawk) 205.1 inches; (sedan) 213.2 inches; (hardtop) 209.2 inches; (station wagon) 206.2 inches. Front tread: 56-11/16 inches. Rear tread: 55-11/16 inches. Tires: 8.00 x 14.

OPTIONS: Power steering ($68.86). Power brakes ($37.66). Power windows, in two-doors ($54); in four-doors ($102.60). Power seat ($45.19). Oil filter ($21.52). Seven-tube push-button radio ($79.90). Six-tube manual radio ($60.50). Rear speaker ($12.95). Climatizer heater ($71). Whitewall tires ($27.91 exchange). Two-tone paint ($21.50). Tinted glass ($32). Station wagon luggage carrier ($59.95). Hill Holder ($15.06). Dealer-installation air conditioner ($325). Trunk installation air conditioner ($275). Pair of front seat safety belts ($24.95). Rideaway third seat for station wagon ($101.68). Undercoating ($12.75). Flight-O-Matic was 'standard' on all models in that it was considered 'normal' equipment, but it still cost $189 extra. Overdrive was a $110.40 option. Dual exhaust, standard on Packard Hawk; $23.43 on others. Twin-Traction differential was $34.90 extra. An oil bath air cleaner was $8.07. Available rear axle gear ratios were: (standard) 3.92:1 or 4.27:1; (overdrive) 4.09:1 and (Flight-O-Matic) 3.31:1.

HISTORICAL FOOTNOTES: Production of 1958 models stopped July 13, 1958. No Packard automobiles were built thereafter. The name Studebaker-Packard survived until 1962.

1954 Packard Caribbean convertible and Santa Fe line train.

PIERCE-ARROW

PIERCE-ARROW — Buffalo, New York — (1901-1938) — Among the more delightful anomalies in the history of the American automobile is that of the Pierce-Arrow, one of the most revered and prestigious motorcars ever to grace the highway, descended from a company engaged in the manufacture of birdcages. The company was Heintz, Pierce and Munschauer, founded in Buffalo in 1865, and it produced ice boxes and other varied household items as well. In 1872, the middle partner bought controlling interest in the firm, and it was reorganized as the George N. Pierce Company. By 1896, bicycles were an additional product, and there was a new addition to the company roster, Colonel Charles Clifton as treasurer. It was Clifton who first assayed the possibility of automobile manufacture, a steam car completed in the summer of 1900 being the company's first effort. It was a failure. Following a trip to Europe, Clifton recommended the French De Dion motor, and it powered the first gasoline car completed that November. Early in 1901, David Fergusson, an English-born engineer then employed by the E.C. Stearns Company in nearby Syracuse, stopped by Buffalo to offer his services—and the Pierce company had its chief engineer for the next two decades. By May, the first two examples of Fergusson's De Dion-engined design were completed, and the rest of the year was spent testing the cars and demonstrating them to Pierce bicycle agents throughout the country. Manufacture of the Motorette, as the single-cylinder models were called, was begun late in 1901, and 150 of them had been produced by the end of the year following. Two cylinders followed in 1903, the Arrow designation arrived for these cars in 1904, as well as the Great Arrow name for the four-cylinder cars also introduced that year. The first of the famed Glidden Tours© was held in July 1905, and the Great Arrow driven by Percy Pierce (son of George N.) won it. The company from Buffalo captured the next four events too, for an unrivaled conquest of the Glidden Trophy. The first six-cylinder car made its debut in 1907, and two years later both the company and the marque name were changed to Pierce-Arrow. Although the company would pioneer in the extensive use of aluminum and in power braking, would introduce the first hydraulic tappets, as well, and featured such idiosyncrasies as a steering wheel gear lever (until 1908) and right-hand drive (until 1920), the most famous of all Pierce-Arrow features arrived in 1913—and this was the fender headlamp, designed in-house and patented by Herbert M. Dawley. Drum headlamps would remain an option through 1932, but most purchasers opted instead for the standard, and exclusive, fender treatment. By January 1915, Pierce-Arrow had built its 12,000th motorcar and was preeminent in the highest echelon of the luxury car market in terms of both prestige and output. The big sixes, of which the 66 was the mightiest and one of the largest stock cars ever built in the United States, found their way into the most elegant garages in America. The Dual Valve Six was introduced in October 1918 and, in addition to retaining the preference for the cars among Pierce-Arrow's usual clientele, also became a favorite among rum-runners because of the reliability and quiet of its engine. By now Cadillac had its V-8 and Packard its Twin-Six, but Pierce-Arrow continued to believe six cylinders remained the optimum number a motorcar should have. Following the First World War, the Pierce-Arrow management retired, and the New York banking firm of Seligman Company took over. Among the bankers' ideas for the company was development of a sleeve-valve engine; Fergusson was furious and abruptly resigned. Barney Roos was his successor, but resigned almost as abruptly, and succeeding him was Charles L. Sheppy. In 1921, the Pierce-Arrow Motor Car Company had a new president as well, Myron E. Forbes, who had joined the firm as treasurer in 1919. A smaller six, the L-head Series 80, was introduced for 1924. Nineteen twenty-six brought four-wheel brakes incorporating the vacuum-powered booster developed by Victor Kliesrath and Caleb Bragg. But by now Pierce-Arrow was hurting, wounded in the marketplace by its clinging to the traditional both in styling and in paucity of cylinders, which still remained at only six. In 1928, Colonel Clifton died and Myron Forbes, believing that the day of the independent manufacturer was fast drawing to a close, got together with Albert R. Erskine and negotiated a merger between Studebaker and Pierce-Arrow. It would prove a happy marriage for neither party, though in the short run it did result in a doubling of Pierce-Arrow sales to 10,000 units in 1929. The new cars were straight-eights that had been in development in Buffalo for some time prior to the entrance of Studebaker upon the scene. Though Myron Forbes would resign in 1929, with Albert Erskine taking over the Pierce-Arrow presidency, Pierce-Arrow functioned as an independent operating entity. In the multi-cylinder race that followed the Wall Street crash, Pierce-Arrow's entry (a V-12 designed by new chief engineer Karl Wise) was introduced in November 1931. Although at Bonneville Ab Jenkins blithely broke 14 official international records with the Pierce-Arrow 12 (including a 24-hour mark following which Jenkins emerged from the car clean shaven, having wielded a safety razor during the final hour—at over 125 mph), the story in Buffalo was taking a tragic turn. In 1933, Studebaker was in receivership, and Albert Erskine committed suicide. The Pierce-Arrow company was acquired by a group of Buffalo bankers and businessmen and was an independent once again. Arthur J. Chanter, a former Studebaker man who held Pierce-Arrow's presidency for several months prior to Erskine's death, was retained in that position. Nineteen thirty-three brought hydraulic tappets, an industry first, and the startlingly streamlined Silver Arrow, which was the smash hit of the New York Automobile Show and a precursor of styling trends to come. But Pierce-Arrow sales for 1933 totaled 2,152 units, 500 less than the year previous and nearly a thousand less than the 3,000-unit break-even point. Only five Silver Arrows, priced at $10,000 each, were built. Their fastback styling and dual fender headlights were incorporated in Pierces of 1934, which were called Silver Arrow models, but they were more standard Pierce than revolutionary Silver Arrow cars. In 1935, pointed reference was made by Arthur Chanter to the fact that, alone among American manufacturers, Pierce-Arrow was devoted to luxury car production exclusively. Only 875 luxury Pierces were sold in 1935. The figure dwindled to 787 in 1936, and plummeted to 167 in 1937. In the spring of 1938—the 13th of May, a Friday—the Pierce-Arrow company was sold at auction. The last Pierce-Arrow was built that summer for chief engineer Karl Wise from parts he had secured from the receivers.

1901

1-cyl., 2-3/4 hp

Model No.	Body Type & Seating	Factory Price	Shipping Weight	Prod. Total
A	Motorette	600	750	1
1-cyl., 3-3/4 hp				
A	Motorette	—	—	1

1902

1-cyl., 3-1/2 hp, 58" wb

Model No.	Body Type & Seating	Factory Price	Shipping Weight	Prod. Total
D-E	Motorette	850	725	127

1903

1-cyl., 5 hp

Model No.	Body Type & Seating	Factory Price	Shipping Weight	Prod. Total
5H-K	Rbt	950	800	39
1-cyl., 6-1/2 hp				
6H-K	Stanhope	1150	1000	149
2-cyl., 15 hp				
15-J	Tr-5P	2500	1650	49

1904

1-cyl., 8 hp, 70" wb

Model No.	Body Type & Seating	Factory Price	Shipping Weight	Prod. Total
8-L	Stanhope	1275	1250	51*
8-M	Stanhope-2P	1275	1250	222
4 cyl., 24/28 hp, 93" wb				
24-28N	Great Arrow Tr-5P	4000	2600	50
2-cyl., 15 hp, 81" wb				
15J	Tr-5P	2500	1900	75

***Note:** Some 8-L production took place in 1903 with the 8-M a carry-over model with its tiller replaced with a steering wheel.

1905

1-cyl., 8 hp, 70" wb

Model No.	Body Type & Seating	Factory Price	Shipping Weight	Prod. Total
8-M	Stanhope	1275	1250	Note 1

Great Arrow — 4-cyl., 24/28 hp, 100" wb

Model No.	Body Type & Seating	Factory Price	Shipping Weight	Prod. Tota
24-28N	Tonneau-5P	3500	—	Note 1
24-28N	Canopy Tonneau-5P	3750	—	Note 1
24-28N	Vic-5P	3650	—	Note 1
24-28N	Cape Tonneau-5P	3650	—	Note 1

Great Arrow — 4-cyl., 28/32 hp, 104" wb

Model No.	Body Type & Seating	Factory Price	Shipping Weight	Prod. Total
28-32N	Tonneau-5P	4000	—	Note 1
28-32N	Canopy Tonneau-5P	4250	—	Note 1
28-32N	Vic-5P	4150	—	Note 1
28-32N	Cape Tonneau-5P	4150	—	Note 1

Great Arrow — 4-cyl., 28/32 hp, 109" wb

Model No.	Body Type & Seating	Factory Price	Shipping Weight	Prod. Total
28-32N	Lan'let-7P	5000	—	Note 1
28-32N	Sub-7P	5000	—	Note 1
28-32N	Opera Coach-8P	5000	—	Note 1

Great Arrow — 4-cyl., 40 hp, 104" wb

Model No.	Body Type & Seating	Factory Price	Shipping Weight	Prod. Total
40P	Tonneau-5P	5000	—	Note 1

Great Arrow — 4-cyl., 40 hp, 109" wb

Model No.	Body Type & Seating	Factory Price	Shipping Weight	Prod. Total
40P	Lan'let-7P	5000	—	Note 1
40P	Sub-7P	5000	—	Note 1
40P	Opera Coach-8P	5000	—	Note 1

Note 1: Estimated Pierce-Arrow production for 1905 totaled 500 with no body style breakout available.

1906

Motorette — 1-cyl., 8 hp, 70" wb

Model No.	Body Type & Seating	Factory Price	Shipping Weight	Prod. Total
8-M	Stanhope	1275	1250	Note 1

Great Arrow — 4-cyl., 28/32 hp, 107" wb

Model No.	Body Type & Seating	Factory Price	Shipping Weight	Prod. Total
28-32N	Tr-5P	4000	—	Note 1
28-32N	Vic-5P	4150	—	Note 1
28-32N	Open Coach-8P	5000	—	Note 1
28-32N	Sub-7P	5000	—	Note 1
28-32N	Lan'let-7P	5250	—	Note 1

Great Arrow — 4-cyl., 40/45 hp, 109" wb

Model No.	Body Type & Seating	Factory Price	Shipping Weight	Prod. Total
40-45PP	Tr-7P	5000	—	Note 1
40-45PP	Open Coach-8P	6000	—	Note 1
40-45PP	Sub-7P	6000	—	Note 1
40-45PP	Lan'let-7P	6250	—	Note 1

Note 1: Estimated Pierce-Arrow production for 1906 totaled 700 with no body style breakout available.

1907

Great Arrow — 4-cyl., 28/32 hp, 112" wb

Model No.	Body Type & Seating	Factory Price	Shipping Weight	Prod. Total
30NN	Tr-5P	4000	—	Note 1
30NN	Limo-5P	5000	—	Note 1
30NN	Sub-7P	5000	—	Note 1

Great Arrow — 4-cyl., 40/45 hp, 124" wb

Model No.	Body Type & Seating	Factory Price	Shipping Weight	Prod. Total
45PP	Tr-7P	5000	—	Note 1
45PP	Limo-7P	6250	—	Note 1
45PP	Sub-7P	6250	—	Note 1

Great Arrow — 6-cyl., 65 hp, 135" wb

Model No.	Body Type & Seating	Factory Price	Shipping Weight	Prod. Total
65Q	Tr-7P	6500	—	Note 1

Note 1: Estimated Pierce-Arrow production for 1907 totaled 950 with no body style breakout available.

1908

Great Arrow — 4-cyl., 30 hp, 112" wb

Model No.	Body Type & Seating	Factory Price	Shipping Weight	Prod. Total
30NN	Tr	4000	—	Note 1

Great Arrow — 4-cyl., 40 hp, 124" wb

Model No.	Body Type & Seating	Factory Price	Shipping Weight	Prod. Total
45PP	Tr	5000	—	Note 1
45PP	Sub	6250	—	Note 1

Great Arrow — 6-cyl., 40 hp, 130" wb

Model No.	Body Type & Seating	Factory Price	Shipping Weight	Prod. Total
40S	Tr	5500	—	Note 1
40S	Sub	—	—	Note 1
40S	Rds	—	—	Note 1

Great Arrow — 6-cyl., 65 hp, 135" wb

Model No.	Body Type & Seating	Factory Price	Shipping Weight	Prod. Total
65Q	Tr	6500	—	Note 1
65Q	Sub	—	—	Note 1
65Q	Rds	—	—	Note 1

Note 1: Estimated Pierce-Arrow production for 1908 totaled 1,000 with no body style breakout available.

1909

Model 24 — 4 cyl., 24 hp, 111-1/2" wb

Model No.	Body Type & Seating	Factory Price	Shipping Weight	Prod. Total
24T	Rbt-3P	3100	—	Note 1
24T	Vic Top Rbt-3P	3300	—	Note 1
24T	Rbt-2P	3050	—	Note 1
24T	Tr Car-4P	3150	—	Note 1
24T	Lan'let-5P	3950	—	Note 1
24T	Brgm-5P	4050	—	Note 1

Model 36 — 6-cyl., 36 hp, 119" wb

Model No.	Body Type & Seating	Factory Price	Shipping Weight	Prod. Total
36UU	Tr-5P	4000	—	Note 1
36UU	Cape Top Tr-5P	4175	—	Note 1
36UU	Rbt-2P	3700	—	Note 1
36UU	Rbt-3P	3750	—	Note 1
36UU	Tr-4P	3800	—	Note 1
36UU	Brgm-5P	4650	—	Note 1
36UU	Lan'let-5P	4700	—	Note 1

Model 40 — 4-cyl., 40 hp, 124" wb

Model No.	Body Type & Seating	Factory Price	Shipping Weight	Prod. Total
40PP	Sub-7P	5400	—	Note 1
40PP	Tr Car-4P	4100	—	Note 1
40PP	Tr-7P	4300	—	Note 1
40PP	Lan-7P	5500	—	Note 1

Model 48 — 6-cyl., 48 hp, 130" wb

Model No.	Body Type & Seating	Factory Price	Shipping Weight	Prod. Total
48SS	Tr-4P	4800	—	Note 1
48SS	Cape Top Tr-4P	5000	—	Note 1
48SS	Tr-2P	4700	—	Note 1
48SS	Tr-3P	4750	—	Note 1
48SS	Tr-7P	5000	—	Note 1
48SS	Lan-7P	6200	—	Note 1
48SS	Sub-7P	6100	—	Note 1

Model 60 — 6-cyl., 60 hp, 135" wb

Model No.	Body Type & Seating	Factory Price	Shipping Weight	Prod. Total
60QQ	Tr-7P	6000	—	Note 1
60QQ	Cape Top Tr-7P	6200	—	Note 1
60QQ	Sub-7P	7100	—	Note 1
60QQ	Lan-7P	7200	—	Note 1

Note 1: Estimated Pierce-Arrow production for 1909 totaled 950 with no body style breakout available.

Production Notes: The 1909 Model 24s received a new four-speed transmission. Three experimental cars, Model 30U, were constructed with 30-hp six-cylinder engines that featured three cylinders cast singly. The wheelbase of these experimental models was 125 inches.

1910

Model 36 — 6-cyl., 36 hp, 125" wb

Model No.	Body Type & Seating	Factory Price	Shipping Weight	Prod. Total
36UU	Lan'let-5P	5000	—	Note 1
36UU	Mini Tonneau-4P	4000	—	Note 1
36UU	Tr-5P	4000	—	Note 1
36UU	Brgm-5P	4900	—	Note 1
36UU	Rbt (119" wb)	3850	—	Note 1

Model 48 — 6-cyl., 48 hp, 134-1/2" wb

Model No.	Body Type & Seating	Factory Price	Shipping Weight	Prod. Total
48SS	Lan'let-7P	6200	—	Note 1
48SS	Mini Tonneau-4P	4850	—	Note 1
48SS	Tr-7P	5000	—	Note 1
48SS	Sub-7P	6100	—	Note 1
48SS	Rbt (128" wb)	4850	—	Note 1

Model 66 — 6-cyl., 66 hp, 140" wb

Model No.	Body Type & Seating	Factory Price	Shipping Weight	Prod. Total
66QQ	Tr-7P	6000	—	Note 1
66QQ	Mini Tonneau-4P	5850	—	Note 1
66QQ	Sub-7P	7100	—	Note 1
66QQ	Lan'let-7P	7200	—	Note 1
66QQ	Rbt (133-1/2" wb)	5850	—	Note 1

Note 1: Estimated Pierce-Arrow production for 1910 totaled 1,500 with no body style breakout available.

1911

Model 36 — 6-cyl., 36 hp, 125" wb

Model No.	Body Type & Seating	Factory Price	Shipping Weight	Prod. Total
36UU	Tr-5P	4000	—	Note 1
36UU	Rbt-3P	4000	—	Note 1
36UU	Mini Tonneau-4P	4000	—	Note 1
36UU	Brgm-5P	4900	—	Note 1
36UU	Lan'let-5P	5000	—	Note 1

Model 48 — 6-cyl., 48 hp, 134-1/2" wb

Model No.	Body Type & Seating	Factory Price	Shipping Weight	Prod. Total
48SS	Tr-7P	5000	—	Note 1
48SS	Rbt	4950	—	Note 1

1901 Pierce, motorette, WLB

1904 Pierce Great Arrow, touring, HAC

1905 Pierce Great Arrow, touring, LIAM

1909 Pierce Great Arrow, Model 40, touring, LIAM

1913 Pierce-Arrow, Model 38-C, landaulet, HAC

Model No.	Body Type & Seating	Factory Price	Shipping Weight	Prod. Total
48SS	Mini Tonneau-4P	4850	—	Note 1
48SS	Close Coupled-5P	5000	—	Note 1
48SS	Protected Tr-5P	5000	—	Note 1
48SS	Sub	6100	—	Note 1
48SS	Lan	6200	—	Note 1

Model 66 — 6-cyl., 66 hp, 140" wb

Model No.	Body Type & Seating	Factory Price	Shipping Weight	Prod. Total
66QQ	Tr-7P	6000	—	Note 1
66QQ	Rbt	5050	—	Note 1
66QQ	Mini Tonneau-4P	5850	—	Note 1
66QQ	Protected Tr-5P	6000	—	Note 1
66QQ	Close Coupled-5P	6000	—	Note 1
66QQ	Sub	7100	—	Note 1
66QQ	Lan	7200	—	Note 1

Note 1: Estimated Pierce-Arrow production for 1911 totaled 2,200 with no body style breakout available.

1912

Model 36 — 6 cyl., 36 hp, 127-1/2" wb

Model No.	Body Type & Seating	Factory Price	Shipping Weight	Prod. Total
36UU	Tr-4P	4000	—	Note 1
36UU	Tr-5P	4000	—	Note 1
36UU	Brgm	4900	—	Note 1
36UU	Lan'let	4900	—	Note 1
36UU	Rbt (119" wb)	4000	—	Note 1

Model 48 — 6-cyl., 48 hp, 134-1/2" wb

Model No.	Body Type & Seating	Factory Price	Shipping Weight	Prod. Total
48SS	Tr-4P	4850	—	Note 1
48SS	Tr-5P	4850	—	Note 1
48SS	Tr-7P	5000	—	Note 1
48SS	Brgm	5750	—	Note 1
48SS	Lan'let	5750	—	Note 1
48SS	Sub	6100	—	Note 1
48SS	Lan	6100	—	Note 1
48SS	Vestibule Sub	6450	—	Note 1
48SS	Rbt-3P (128" wb)	4850	—	Note 1

Model 66 — 6-cyl., 66 hp, 140" wb

Model No.	Body Type & Seating	Factory Price	Shipping Weight	Prod. Total
66QQ	Tr-4P	5850	—	Note 1
66QQ	Tr-5P	5850	—	Note 1
66QQ	Tr-7P	6000	—	Note 1
66QQ	Sub	7100	—	Note 1
66QQ	Lan	7100	—	Note 1
66QQ	Vestibule Sub	7450	—	Note 1
66QQ	Rbt (133-1/2" wb)	5850	—	Note 1

1913

Model 38 — 6-cyl., 38.4 hp, 132" wb

Model No.	Body Type & Seating	Factory Price	Shipping Weight	Prod. Total
38C	Rbt-3P	4300	—	Note 1
38C	Tr-4P	4300	—	Note 1
38C	Tr-5P	4300	—	Note 1
38C	Brgm-6P	5200	—	Note 1
38C	Lan'let-6P	5200	—	Note 1

Model 48 — 6-cyl., 48.6 hp, 142" wb

Model No.	Body Type & Seating	Factory Price	Shipping Weight	Prod. Total
48B	Tr-5P	4850	—	Note 1
48B	Rbt	4850	—	Note 1
48B	Tr-4P	4850	—	Note 1
48B	Brgm	6100	—	Note 1
48B	Lan'let	6100	—	Note 1
48B	Sub-7P	6100	—	Note 1
48B	Lan-7P	6100	—	Note 1
48B	Vestibule Sub	6300	—	Note 1
48B	Vestibule Lan	6300	—	Note 1
48D	Tr-7P	5000	—	134

Model 66 — 6-cyl., 60 hp, 147-1/2" wb

Model No.	Body Type & Seating	Factory Price	Shipping Weight	Prod. Total
66A	Tr-7P	6000	—	Note 1
66A	Rbt	5850	—	Note 1
66A	Tr-4P	5850	—	Note 1
66A	Tr-5P	5850	—	Note 1
66A	Brgm	7100	—	Note 1
66A	Lan'let	7100	—	Note 1
66A	Sub-7P	7100	—	Note 1
66A	Lan-7P	7100	—	Note 1
66A	Vestibule Sub	7300	—	Note 1
66A	Vestibule Lan	7300	—	Note 1

Note 1: Estimated Pierce-Arrow production for 1913 totaled 1,900 with no body style breakout other than Model 48D available.

1914

Series 38-2 — 6-cyl., 38.4 hp, 132" wb

Model No.	Body Type & Seating	Factory Price	Shipping Weight	Prod. Total
38C	Tr-5P	4300	—	Note 1
38C	Tr-4P	4300	—	Note 1
38C	Brgm-7P	5200	—	Note 1
38C	Lan'let-7P	5200	—	Note 1
38C	Vestibule Brgm	5400	—	Note 1
38C	Vestibule Lan	5400	—	Note 1
38C	Rbt-3P (127-1/2" wb)	4300	—	Note 1

Series 48-2 — 6-cyl., 48.6 hp. 142" wb

Model No.	Body Type & Seating	Factory Price	Shipping Weight	Prod. Total
48B	Tr-4P	4850	—	Note 1
48B	Tr-5P	4850	—	Note 1
48B	Tr-7P	5000	—	Note 1
48B	Sub-7P	6100	—	Note 1
48B	Lan-7P	6100	—	Note 1
48B	Vestibule Sub	6300	—	Note 1
48B	Vestibule Lan	6300	—	Note 1
48B	Brgm	5800	—	Note 1
48B	Lan	5800	—	Note 1
48B	Vestibule Brgm	6000	—	Note 1
48B	Vestibule Lan'let	6000	—	Note 1
48B	Rb-3P (134-1/2" wb)	4850	—	Note 1

Series 66-2 — 6-cyl., 60 hp, 147-1/2" wb

Model No.	Body Type & Seating	Factory Price	Shipping Weight	Prod. Total
66A	Tr-4P	5850	—	Note 1
66A	Tr-5P	5850	—	Note 1
66A	Tr-7P	5850	—	Note 1
66A	Sub-7P	7100	—	Note 1
66A	Lan-7P	7100	—	Note 1
66A	Vestibule Lan	7300	—	Note 1
66A	Brgm-7P	6800	—	Note 1
66A	Lan-7P	6800	—	Note 1
66A	Vestibule Brgm	7000	—	Note 1
66A	Vestibule Lan	7000	—	Note 1
66A	Rbt-3P	5850	—	Note 1

Note 1: Estimated Pierce-Arrow production for 1914 totaled 1,500 with no body style breakout available.

Production Note: Pierce-Arrow's trademark fender headlights appeared for the first time in 1914. Also new this model year was the Westinghouse electric starter which replaced the previously used compressed air starter.

1915

Series 38-3 — 6-cyl., 38.4 hp, 134" wb

Model No.	Body Type & Seating	Factory Price	Shipping Weight	Prod. Total
38C	Tr-5P	4300	—	Note 1
38C	Tr-4P	4300	—	Note 1
38C	Rbt-2P	4300	—	Note 1
38C	Cpe Rbt-2P	4575	—	Note 1
38C	Brgm-7P	5200	—	Note 1
38C	Lan'let-7P	5200	—	Note 1
38C	Sed-7P	5200	—	Note 1
38C	Brgm Lan'let-7P	5200	—	Note 1
38C	Vestibule Brgm	5350	—	Note 1
38C	Vestibule Lan'let	5350	—	Note 1
38C	Vestibule Brgm Lan'let	5350	—	Note 1

Series 48-3 — 6-cyl., 48.6 hp, 142" wb

Model No.	Body Type & Seating	Factory Price	Shipping Weight	Prod. Total
48B	Tr-5P	4900	—	Note 1
48B	Tr-4P	4900	—	Note 1
48B	Tr-7P	5000	—	Note 1
48B	Rbt-2P	4900	—	Note 1
48B	Rbt Cpe-2P	5175	—	Note 1
48B	Cpe	5700	—	Note 1
48B	Sub-7P	6000	—	Note 1
48B	Lan-7P	6000	—	Note 1
48B	Brgm-7P	5800	—	Note 1
48B	Sub Lan	6000	—	Note 1
48B	Vestibule Sub	6200	—	Note 1
48B	Vestibule Lan	6200	—	Note 1
48B	Vestibule Brgm	5950	—	Note 1
48B	Vestibule Sub Lan	6200	—	Note 1

Series 66-3 — 6-cyl., 60 hp, 147-1/2" wb

Model No.	Body Type & Seating	Factory Price	Shipping Weight	Prod. Total
66A	Tr-7P	6000	—	Note 1
66A	Tr-4P	5900	—	Note 1
66A	Tr-5P	5900	—	Note 1
66A	Rbt-2P	5900	—	Note 1
66A	Cpe Rbt-2P	5900	—	Note 1
66A	Sub-7P	7000	—	Note 1
66A	Lan-7P	7000	—	Note 1
66A	Brgm-7P	6800	—	Note 1
66A	Sub Lan-7P	7000	—	Note 1
66A	Vestibule Lan	7200	—	Note 1

1914 Pierce-Arrow, Model 48-B, tourlng, LIAM

1920 Pierce-Arrow, Model 31, coupe, AA

1922 Pierce-Arrow, Model 33, touring, AA

1926 Pierce-Arrow, Model 80, seven-passenger sedan, AA

1929 Pierce-Arrow, Model 133, coupe, AA

1917 Pierce-Arrow, Model 66, touring, AA

1920 Pierce-Arrow, Model 31, roadster, AA

1926 Pierce-Arrow, Model 80, runabout, AA

1929 Pierce-Arrow, Model 133, seven-passenger sedan, AA

1929 Pierce-Arrow, Model 133, club brougham, AA

Model No.	Body Type & Seating	Factory Price	Shipping Weight	Prod. Total
66A	Vestibule Sub	7200	—	Note 1
66A	Vestibule Brgm	6950	—	Note 1
66A	Vestibule			
	Sub Lan	7200	—	Note 1

Note 1: Estimated Pierce-Arrow production for 1915 totaled 1,500 with no body style breakout available.

1916

Series 38-4 — 6-cyl., 38.4 hp, 134" wb

Model No.	Body Type & Seating	Factory Price	Shipping Weight	Prod. Total
38C	Tr-5P	4300	—	Note 1
38C	Tr-4P	4300	—	Note 1
38C	Rbt-2P	4300	—	Note 1
38C	Rbt-3P	4300	—	Note 1
38C	Cpe-3P	5000	—	Note 1
38C	Cpe-2P	5000	—	Note 1
38C	Brgm-7P	5200	—	Note 1
38C	Lan'let-7P	5200	—	Note 1
38C	Sed-7P	5200	—	Note 1
38C	Brgm Lan'let	5200	—	Note 1
38C	Vestibule Brgm	5350	—	Note 1
38C	Vestibule Lan'let	5350	—	Note 1
38C	Vestibule			
	Brgm Lan'let	5350	—	Note 1

Series 48-4 — 6-cyl., 48.6 hp, 142" wb

Model No.	Body Type & Seating	Factory Price	Shipping Weight	Prod. Total
48B	Tr-7P	5000	—	Note 1
48B	Tr-4P	4900	—	Note 1
48B	Tr-5P	4900	—	Note 1
48B	Rbt-2P	4900	—	Note 1
48B	Rbt-3P	4900	—	Note 1
48B	Cpe-2P	5700	—	Note 1
48B	Cpe-3P	5700	—	Note 1
48B	Sub-7P	6000	—	Note 1
48B	Lan-7P	6000	—	Note 1
48B	Brgm-7P	5800	—	Note 1
48B	Sub Lan	6000	—	Note 1
48B	Vestibule Sub	6200	—	Note 1
48B	Vestibule Lan	6200	—	Note 1
48B	Vestibule Brgm	5950	—	Note 1
48B	Vestibule			
	Sub Lan	6200	—	Note 1

Series 66-4 — 6-cyl., 60 hp, 147-1/2" wb

Model No.	Body Type & Seating	Factory Price	Shipping Weight	Prod. Total
66A	Tr-7P	6000	—	Note 1
66A	Tr-4P	5900	—	Note 1
66A	Tr-5P	5900	—	Note 1
66A	Rbt-2P	5900	—	Note 1
66A	Rbt-3P	5900	—	Note 1
66A	Cpe-2P	6700	—	Note 1
66A	Cpe-3P	6700	—	Note 1
66A	Sub-7P	7000	—	Note 1
66A	Lan-7P	7000	—	Note 1
66A	Brgm-7P	6800	—	Note 1
66A	Sub Lan	7000	—	Note 1
66A	Vestibule Lan	7200	—	Note 1
66A	Vestibule Sub	7200	—	Note 1
66A	Vestibule Brgm	6950	—	Note 1
66A	Vestibule			
	Sub Lan	7200	—	Note 1

Note 1: Estimated Pierce-Arrow production for 1916 totaled 1,600 with no body style breakout available.

1917

Series 38-4 — 6-cyl., 38.4 hp, 134" wb

Model No.	Body Type & Seating	Factory Price	Shipping Weight	Prod. Total
38C	Tr-5P	4800	—	Note 1
38C	Rbt-2P	4800	—	Note 1
38C	Rbt-3P	4800	—	Note 1
38C	Cpe-2P	5700	—	Note 1
38C	Cpe-3P	5700	—	Note 1
38C	Tr-4P	4800	—	Note 1
38C	Brgm	5900	—	Note 1
38C	Lan'let	5900	—	Note 1
38C	Sed	5900	—	Note 1
38C	Vestibule Brgm	6100	—	Note 1
38C	Brgm Lan'let	5900	—	Note 1
38C	Vestibule			
	Brgm-Lan'let	6100	—	Note 1
38C	Fr Brgm	5900	—	Note 1
38C	Fr Brgm-Lan'let	5900	—	Note 1

Series 48-4 — 6-cyl., 48.6 hp, 142" wb

Model No.	Body Type & Seating	Factory Price	Shipping Weight	Prod. Total
48B	Tr-7P	5500	—	Note 1
48B	Rbt-2P	5400	—	Note 1
48B	Rbt-3P	5400	—	Note 1
48B	Cpe-2P	6400	—	Note 1
48B	Cpe-3P	6400	—	Note 1
48B	Tr-5P	5400	—	Note 1
48B	Tr-4P	5400	—	Note 1
48B	Brgm	6600	—	Note 1
48B	Sub	6800	—	Note 1
48B	Lan	6800	—	Note 1
48B	Sub-Lan	6800	—	Note 1
48B	Vestibule Sub	7000	—	Note 1
48B	Vestibule Lan	7000	—	Note 1
48B	Vestibule Brgm	6800	—	Note 1
48B	Vestibule			
	Sub-Lan	7000	—	Note 1

Series 66-4 — 6-cyl., 60 hp, 147-1/2" wb

Model No.	Body Type & Seating	Factory Price	Shipping Weight	Prod. Total
66A	Tr-7P	6560	—	Note 1
66A	Rbt-2P	6400	—	Note 1
66A	Rbt-3P	6400	—	Note 1
66A	Cpe-2P	7400	—	Note 1
66A	Cpe-3P	7400	—	Note 1
66A	Tr-4P	6400	—	Note 1
66A	Tr-5P	6400	—	Note 1
66A	Brgm	7600	—	Note 1
66A	Sub	7800	—	Note 1
66A	Lan	7800	—	Note 1
66A	Sub-Lan	7800	—	Note 1
66A	Vestibule Sub	8000	—	Note 1
66A	Vestibule Lan	8000	—	Note 1
66A	Vestibule Brgm	7800	—	Note 1
66A	Vestibule			
	Sub-Lan	8000	—	Note 1

Note 1: Estimated Pierce-Arrow production for 1917 totaled 1,800 with no body style breakout available.

1918

Series 38-4 — 6-cyl., 38.4 hp, 134" wb

Model No.	Body Type & Seating	Factory Price	Shipping Weight	Prod. Total
38C	Tr-5P	4800	—	Note 1
38C	Rbt-2P	4800	—	Note 1
38C	Rbt-3P	4800	—	Note 1
38C	Cpe-2P	5700	—	Note 1
38C	Cpe-3P	5700	—	Note 1
38C	Conv Rds-2P	5700	—	Note 1
38C	Conv Rds-3P	5700	—	Note 1
38C	Rds-4P	4800	—	Note 1
38C	Tr-4P	4800	—	Note 1
38C	Brgm	5900	—	Note 1
38C	Lan'let	5900	—	Note 1
38C	Sed	5900	—	Note 1
38C	Vestibule Brgm	6100	—	Note 1
38C	Brgm-Lan'let	5900	—	Note 1
38C	Vestibule Lan'let	6100	—	Note 1
38C	Vestibule			
	Brgm-Lan'let	6100	—	Note 1
38C	Fr Brgm	5900	—	Note 1
38C	Fr Brgm-Lan'let	5900	—	Note 1
38C	Twn Brgm	5900	—	Note 1

Series 48-4 — 6-cyl., 48.6 hp, 142" wb

Model No.	Body Type & Seating	Factory Price	Shipping Weight	Prod. Total
48B	Rbt-2P	5400	—	Note 1
48B	Rbt-4P	5400	—	Note 1
48B	Rbt-3P	5400	—	Note 1
48B	Cpe-2P	6400	—	Note 1
48B	Cpe-3P	6400	—	Note 1
48B	Conv Rds-2P	6400	—	Note 1
48B	Conv Rds-3P	6400	—	Note 1
48B	Tr-4P	5400	—	Note 1
48B	Tr-5P	5400	—	Note 1
48B	Brgm	6600	—	Note 1
48B	Sub	6800	—	Note 1
48B	Lan	6800	—	Note 1
48B	Sub Lan	6800	—	Note 1
48B	Vestibule Sub	7000	—	Note 1
48B	Vestibule Lan	7000	—	Note 1
48B	Vestibule Brgm	6800	—	Note 1
48B	Vestibule			
	Sub-Lan	7000	—	Note 1
48B	Fr Brgm	6600	—	Note 1
48B	Tr-7P	5500	—	Note 1
48B	Lan Sub-7P	6800	—	Note 1

Series 66-4 — 6-cyl., 60 hp, 147-1/2" wb

Model No.	Body Type & Seating	Factory Price	Shipping Weight	Prod. Total
66A	Rbt-2P	6400	—	Note 1
66A	Rbt-3P	6400	—	Note 1
66A	Cpe-2P	7400	—	Note 1
66A	Cpe-3P	7400	—	Note 1
66A	Con Rds-2P	7400	—	Note 1
66A	Con Rds-3P	7400	—	Note 1
66A	Tr-4P	6400	—	Note 1
66A	Tr-5P	6400	—	Note 1
66A	Tr-7P	6500	—	Note 1
66A	Brgm	7600	—	Note 1
66A	Sub	7800	—	Note 1
66A	Lan	7800	—	Note 1
66A	Sub-Lan	7800	—	Note 1

Model No.	Body Type & Seating	Factory Price	Shipping Weight	Prod. Total
66A	Vestibule Lan	8000	—	Note 1
66A	Vestibule Brgm	7800	—	Note 1
66A	Vestibule Sub	8000	—	Note 1
66A	Vestibule Sub Lan	8000	—	Note 1

Note 1: Estimated Pierce-Arrow production for 1918 totaled 2,000 with no body style breakout available.

1919

Series 48-5 — 6-cyl., 48.6 hp, 142" wb

Model No.	Body Type & Seating	Factory Price	Shipping Weight	Prod. Total
48B	Tr-7P	6500	—	Note 1
48B	Rbt-2P	6400	—	Note 1
48B	Rbt-3P	6400	—	Note 1
48B	Tr-4P	6400	—	Note 1
48B	Rds-4P	6400	—	Note 1
48B	Tr-5P	6400	—	Note 1
48B	Cpe-2P	7500	—	Note 1
48B	Cpe-3P	7500	—	Note 1
48B	Con Rds-2P	7500	—	Note 1
48B	Con Rds-3P	7500	—	Note 1
48B	Brgm	7800	—	Note 1
48B	Brgm Lan'let	7800	—	Note 1
48B	Fr Brgm	7800	—	Note 1
48B	Fr Brgm Lan'let	7800	—	Note 1
48B	Sub	8000	—	Note 1
48B	Sub Lan	8000	—	Note 1
48B	Vestibule Brgm	8000	—	Note 1
48B	Vestibule Brgm Lan	8000	—	Note 1
48B	Vestibule Sub	8200	—	Note 1
48B	Vestibule Lan	8200	—	Note 1
48B	Vestibule Sub Lan	8200	—	Note 1

Note 1: Estimated Pierce-Arrow production for 1919 totaled 1,000 with no body style breakout available.

Production Note: The Series 5 Pierce-Arrow debuted the dual-valve engine in 1918 to stay abreast of the competition that was mainly offering eight- and twelve-cylinder engines.

1920

Series 31 — 6 cyl., 38 hp, 134" wb

Model No.	Body Type & Seating	Factory Price	Shipping Weight	Prod. Total
31	Rbt-2P & 3P	7250	—	Note 1
31	Tr-4P	7250	—	Note 1
31	Rds-4P	7250	—	Note 1
31	Tr-5P	7250	—	Note 1
31	Tr-7P	7250	—	Note 1
31	Cpe-2P & 3P	8250	—	Note 1
31	Sed-4P	8550	—	Note 1
31	Sed-7P	8750	—	Note 1
31	Brgm	8550	—	Note 1
31	Fr Brgm	8550	—	Note 1
31	Brgm Lan'let	8550	—	Note 1
31	Tourer Brgm	8550	—	Note 1
31	Vestibule Brgm	8750	—	Note 1
Series 51 — 6-cyl., 48 hp, 142" wb				
51	Rbt-2P & 4P	7650	—	Note 1
51	Tr-4P	7650	—	Note 1
51	Rds-4P	7650	—	Note 1
51	Tr-5P	7650	—	Note 1
51	Tr-6P	7750	—	Note 1
51	Cpe-2P & 3P	8750	—	Note 1
51	Brgm-5P	9050	—	Note 1
51	Fr Brgm-7P	9050	—	Note 1
51	Sub-7P	9250	—	Note 1
51	Vestibule Sub-7P	9450	—	Note 1
51	Fr Sub-7P	9250	—	Note 1

Note 1: Estimated Pierce-Arrow production for 1920 totaled 3,000 with no body style breakout available.

1921

Series 32 — 6-cyl., 38 hp, 138" wb

Model No.	Body Type & Seating	Factory Price	Shipping Weight	Prod. Total
32	Tr-4P	7500	—	Note 1
32	Tr-6P	7500	—	Note 1
32	Tr-7P	7500	—	Note 1
32	Rds-3P	8000	—	Note 1
32	Cpe-4P	8500	—	Note 1
32	Brgm-7P	8500	—	Note 1
32	Limo-7P	8750	—	Note 1
32	Sed-6P	9000	—	Note 1
32	Vestibule Sed-6P	9000	—	Note 1
32	Lan-7P	9000	—	Note 1

Note1: Estimated Pierce-Arrow production for 1921 totaled 1,400 with no body style breakout available.

Production Note: Pierce-Arrows reverted to left-hand drive in 1919, which had been the industry standard beginning in 1912. Also, the dual-valve engine was now cast en bloc instead of in pairs as before, which helped to reduce vibration during operation.

1922

Series 33 — 6-cyl., 38 hp, 138" wb

Model No.	Body Type & Seating	Factory Price	Shipping Weight	Prod. Total
33	Tr-4P	6500	—	Note 1
33	Tr-7P	6500	—	Note 1
33	Rds-3P	7000	—	Note 1
33	Brgm-7P	8000	—	Note 1
33	Cpe Sed	8000	—	Note 1
33	Cpe-3P	8000	—	Note 1
33	Sed-4P	8250	—	Note 1
33	Lan'let	8240	—	Note 1
33	Limo	8250	—	Note 1
33	Fml Limo	8250	—	Note 1
33	Vestibule Sed	8500	—	Note 1
33	Sed	8500	—	Note 1

Note 1: Estimated Pierce-Arrow production for 1922 totaled 1,200 with no body style breakout available.

1923

Series 33 — 6-cyl., 38 hp, 138" wb

Model No.	Body Type & Seating	Factory Price	Shipping Weight	Prod. Total
33	Tr-7P	5250	—	Note 1
33	Tr-4P	5250	—	Note 1
33	Rbt-2P	5250	—	Note 1
33	Cpe-3P	6800	—	Note 1
33	Cpe Sed-4P	6800	—	Note 1
33	Brgm-6P	6800	—	Note 1
33	Sed-4P	6900	—	Note 1
33	Sed-7P	7000	—	Note 1
33	Lan-let-6P	7000	—	Note 1
33	Limo-7P	7000	—	Note 1
33	Encl Drive Limo-7P	7000	—	Note 1
33	Fml-Limo-7P Fml	7000	—	Note 1

Note 1: Estimated Pierce-Arrow production for 1923 totaled 1,600 with no body style breakout available.

1924

Series 33 — 6-cyl., 38 hp, 138" wb

Model No.	Body Type & Seating	Factory Price	Shipping Weight	Prod. Total
33	Tr-7P	5250	—	Note 1
33	Tr-6P	5250	—	Note 1
33	Tr-4P	5250	—	Note 1
33	Rbt	5250	—	Note 1
33	Brgm-6P	6800	—	Note 1
33	Cpe-3P	6800	—	Note 1
33	Cpe Sed-4P	6900	—	Note 1
33	4-dr Sed-4P	6900	—	Note 1
33	Encl Drive Limo-7P	7000	—	Note 1
33	Fml Limo-7P	7000	—	Note 1
33	Lan'let-6P	7000	—	Note 1
33	Limo-7P	7000	—	Note 1
33	Sed-7P	7000	—	Note 1
33	Fml Lan-7P	7500	—	Note 1
33	Limo Lan-7P	7500	—	Note 1
33	Sed Lan-4P	7500	—	Note 1
33	Cpe Lan-3P	8000	—	Note 1
33	Encl Drive Lan-7P	8000	—	Note 1
33	Sed Lan-7P	8000	—	Note 1

Note 1: Estimated Pierce-Arrow production for 1924 totaled 2,000 with no body style breakout available.

1925

Series 33 — 6-cyl., 38 hp, 138" wb

Model No.	Body Type & Seating	Factory Price	Shipping Weight	Prod. Total
33	Rbt-2P	5250	4350	Note 1
33	Tr-4P	5250	4500	Note 1
33	Tr-7P	5250	4590	Note 1
33	Brgm-4P	6800	4730	Note 1
33	Cpe-3P	6800	4730	Note 1
33	Sed-4P	6900	4800	Note 1
33	Lan'let-4P	7000	4850	Note 1
33	Sed-7P	7000	4960	Note 1
33	Encl Drive			
	Sed-7P	7000	5060	Note 1
33	Limo-7P	7000	4850	Note 1
33	Encl Drive			
	Lan-7P	7500	4780	Note 1
33	Fr Limo-7P	7000	4780	Note 1
Series 80 — 6-cyl., 70 hp, 130" wb				
80	Tr-7P	2895	3385	Note 1
80	Tr-4P	3095	3260	Note 1
80	Sed-5P	3895	3440	Note 1
80	Cpe-4P	3695	3335	Note 1
80	Sed-7P	3995	3560	Note 1
80	Encl Drive			
	Limo-7P	4045	3615	Note 1
80	Rbt-2P	2895	3205	Note 1
80	Coach-5P	3150	4330	Note 1

Note 1: Estimated Pierce-Arrow production for 1925 totaled 5,600 with no body style breakout available.

Production Note: Series 80 Pierce-Arrows featured the new "L" head six with unit transmission.

1926

Series 33 — 6-cyl., 100 hp, 138" wb

Model No.	Body Type & Seating	Factory Price	Shipping Weight	Prod. Total
33	Tr-4P	5250	4500	Note 1
33	Rbt-2P	5250	4350	Note 1
33	Tr-7P	5250	4590	Note 1
33	Brgm-6P	6800	4730	Note 1
33	Cpe-3P	6800	4730	Note 1
33	Sed-4P	6900	4800	Note 1
33	Cpe Sed-4P	6900	4750	Note 1
33	Encl Drive			
	Limo-4P	7000	5060	Note 1
33	Sed-7P	7000	4960	Note 1
33	Lan'let-6P	7000	4780	Note 1
33	Fr Limo-7P	7000	4780	Note 1
33	Sed Lan'let-4P	7500	4800	Note 1
33	Limo-7P	7000	4850	Note 1
33	Encl Drive			
	Limo-7P	7000	5060	Note 1
33	Encl Drive			
	Lan'let-7P	8000	4780	Note 1
Series 80 — 6-cyl., 70 hp, 130" wb				
80	Tr-7P	2895	3385	Note 1
80	Tr-4P	3095	3260	Note 1
80	Rbt-2P	2895	3205	Note 1
80	Cpe-4P	3695	3335	Note 1
80	Sed-7P	3995	3560	Note 1
80	Encl Drive			
	Limo-7P	4045	3615	Note 1
80	Sed-5P	3895	3440	Note 1
80	2-dr Coach-5P	2995	3430	Note 1
80	4-dr Coach-5P	3250	3525	Note 1
80	4-dr Coach-7P	3350	3620	Note 1
80	Coach Limo-7P	3450	3675	Note 1

Note 1: Estimated Pierce-Arrow production for 1926 totaled 8,000 with no body style breakout available.

1927

Series 36 — 6-cyl., 100 hp, 138" wb

Model No.	Body Type & Seating	Factory Price	Shipping Weight	Prod. Total
36	Rbt-2P	5875	4560	Note 1
36	Tr-4P	5875	4510	Note 1
36	Tr-7P	5875	4584	Note 1
36	Cpe-3P	6375	4760	Note 1
36	4-dr Sed-4P	6375	4830	Note 1
36	Cpe Sed-4P	6375	4795	Note 1
36	Encl Drive			
	Limo-4P	6375	4850	Note 1
36	Encl Drive			
	Lan-7P	6000	4895	Note 1
36	Sed-7P	5875	4815	Note 1
36	Fr Lan-7P	8000	4865	Note 1
36	Sed Lan-7P	6000	4840	Note 1
36	Sed Lan-4P	6600	4800	Note 1
36	Encl Drive			
	Limo-7P	5875	4870	Note 1
36	Fr Limo-7P	7500	4740	Note 1
36	Encl Drive			
	Lan-4P	6600	4800	Note 1
36	Cl Cpl Sed-5P	6475	4805	Note 1
36	Cpe-2P	6600	4745	Note 1
Series 80 — 6-cyl., 70 hp, 130" wb				
80	Cpe-2P	3100	3405	Note 1
80	Brghm-5P	2495	3540	Note 1
80	Cpe-4P	3200	3450	Note 1
80	Clb Sed-5P	3300	3565	Note 1
80	Lan Sed-5P	3400	3570	Note 1
80	Sed-5P	2895	3605	Note 1
80	Sed-7P	3350	3620	Note 1
80	Encl Dr			
	Limo-7P	3450	3660	Note 1
DeL 80	Rbt-4P	2495	3285	Note 1
DeL 80	Cpe-4P	3250	3420	Note 1
DeL 80	Tr-7P	2895	3440	Note 1
DeL 80	Tr-4P	3095	3300	Note 1
DeL 80	Encl Dr			
	Limo-7P	4045	3680	Note 1
DeL 80	Sed-5P	3895	3500	Note 1
DeL 80	Sed-7P	3995	3600	Note 1

Note 1: Estimated Pierce-Arrow production for 1927 totaled 6,000 with no body style breakout available.

Production Note: In April 1927, the Series 80 two-door coach was reclassified as a brougham (five-passenger). All other Series 80 coach models were also reclassified as sedans.

1928

Series 36 — 6-cyl., 100 hp, 138" wb

Model No.	Body Type & Seating	Factory Price	Shipping Weight	Prod. Total
36	Cpe-2P	6600	4745	Note 1
36	Rbt-2P	5875	4560	Note 1
36	Tr-4P	5875	4510	Note 1
36	Tr-7P	5875	4585	Note 1
36	Encl Drive			
	Limo-7P	5875	4870	Note 1
36	Sed-7P	5875	4815	Note 1
36	Encl Drive			
	Lan'let-7P	6000	4895	Note 1
36	Lan Sed-7P	6000	4840	Note 1
36	Cpe-3P	6375	4760	Note 1
36	Cpe Sed-4P	6375	4795	Note 1
36	Sed-4P	6375	4830	Note 1
36	Encl Drive			
	Limo-4P	6375	4880	Note 1
36	C.C.Sed-4P	6475	4805	Note 1
36	Lan Sed-4P	6600	4800	Note 1
36	Encl Drive			
	Lan-4P	6600	4880	Note 1
36	Fml Limo-7P	7500	4740	Note 1
36	Fr Lan-7P	8000	4865	Note 1
Series 81 — 6-cyl., 75 hp, 130" wb				
81	Rbt-2P	2600	3350	Note 1
81	Cpe M.B.-2P	2650	3460	Note 1
81	Cpe M.B.-2/4P	2750	3530	Note 1
81	Cpe M.B.-4P	2950	3490	Note 1
81	Conv Cpe-2P	2950	3455	Note 1
81	Conv Cpe-4P	2950	3525	Note 1
81	Tr-4P	2700	3365	Note 1
81	Brgm-5P	3250	3540	Note 1
81	Clb Brgm	2475	3540	Note 1
81	Clb Sed-5P	2750	3635	Note 1
81	Cpe L.B.-2P	2650	3490	Note 1
81	Cpe L.B.-2/4P	2750	3560	Note 1
81	Lan Sed-5P	2850	3605	Note 1
81	Lan Sed-7P	3700	3700	Note 1
81	Clb Lan Sed-5P	3400	3640	Note 1
81	Sed-5P	2750	3605	Note 1
81	Sed-7P	2850	3700	Note 1
81	Tr-7P	2850	3500	Note 1
81	Encl Drive			
	Lan-7P	3800	3755	Note 1
81	Encl Drive			
	Limo-7P	2950	3755	Note 1

Note 1: Estimated Pierce-Arrow production for 1928 totaled 5,500 with no body style breakdown available.

Production Note: Cash-strapped Pierce-Arrow merged with Studebaker on August 7, 1928, making the two merged automakers the fourth largest automobile group behind General Motors, Ford and Chrysler.

1929

Model 133 — 8-cyl., 125 hp, 133" wb

Model No.	Body Type & Seating	Factory Price	Shipping Weight	Prod. Total
133	Spt Rds-2/4P	2875	3675	Note 1
133	Spt. Phae-4P	2950	3865	Note 1
133	Tr-5P	2950	4160	Note 1
133	Clb Brgm-5P	2775	4300	Note 1
133	Clb Berl-5P	3490	4540	Note 1
133	Cpe-2/4P	2875	3990	Note 1
133	Conv Cpe-2/4P	3100	4480	Note 1
133	Sed-5P	2975	4350	Note 1
133	Clb Sed-5P	3125	4240	Note 1
133	Sed-7P	3150	4450	Note 1
133	Encl Drive Limo-7P	3350	4575	Note 1

Model 143 — 8-cyl., 125 hp, 143" wb

Model No.	Body Type & Seating	Factory Price	Shipping Weight	Prod. Total
143	Tr-7P	3750	3900	Note 1
143	Conv Cpe-2P	3750	4000	Note 1
143	Sed-7P	3975	4360	Note 1
143	Encl Drive Limo-7P	4250	4590	Note 1
143	All Wtr Sed-4P	5750	4390	Note 1

Note 1: Estimated Pierce-Arrow production for 1929 totaled 9,800 with no body style breakout available.

Production Note: All Pierce-Arrows were now powered by a new-design straight-eight engine rated at 366 cubic inches. Model 133 and Model 143 automobiles produced late in 1929 were registered as 1930 Pierce-Arrows, but are lumped in with 1929 to avoid confusion.

1930

Model C — 8-cyl., 115 hp, 132" wb

Model No.	Body Type & Seating	Factory Price	Shipping Weight	Prod. Total
C	Clb Brgm-5P	2695	4460	Note 1
C	Cpe-2/4P	2865	4450	Note 1
C	Sed-5P	2875	4525	Note 1

Model B — 8-cyl., 125 hp, 134" wb

Model No.	Body Type & Seating	Factory Price	Shipping Weight	Prod. Total
B	Rds-2/4P	3125	4290	Note 1
B	Tr-5P	3300	4375	Note 1
B	Spt Phaeton-5P	3600	4470	Note 1
B	Conv Cpe-2/4P	3350	4420	Note 1

Model B — 8-cyl., 125 hp, 139" wb

Model No.	Body Type & Seating	Factory Price	Shipping Weight	Prod. Total
B	Vic Cpe-5P	3475	4590	Note 1
B	Sed-5P	3495	4720	Note 1
B	Salon Sed-5P	3795	4780	Note 1
B	Salon Clb Sed-5P	3795	4770	Note 1
B	Sed-7P	3625	4790	Note 1
B	Salon Sed-7P	3925	4840	Note 1
B	Clb Sed-5P	3670	4730	Note 1
B	Encl Drive Limo-7P	3825	4820	Note 1
B	Encl Dr Salon Limo-7P	4125	4860	Note 1
B	Clb Berl-7P	3870	4790	Note 1
B	Salon Clb Berl-5P	3995	4840	Note 1

Model A — 8-cyl., 132 hp, 144" wb

Model No.	Body Type & Seating	Factory Price	Shipping Weight	Prod. Total
A	Tr-7P	3975	4510	Note 1
A	Conv Cpe-2P	3975	4540	Note 1
A	Sed-7P	4485	4820	Note 1
A	Salon Sed-7P	4835	4900	Note 1
A	Encl Drive Limo-7P	4685	4890	Note 1
A	Encl Dr Salon Limo-7P	5035	5040	Note 1
A	Twn Car-7P	6250	4800	Note 1

Note 1: Estimated Pierce-Arrow production for 1930 totaled 7,000 with no body style breakout available.

Production Note: Again, late-in-the-year-produced Model A, Model B and Model C automobiles were registered as 1931 Pierce-Arrows, but are lumped in with 1930 to avoid confusion.

1931

Model 43 — 8-cyl., 125 hp, 134" wb

Model No.	Body Type & Seating	Factory Price	Shipping Weight	Prod. Total
43	Rds-2/4P	2895	4332	Note 1
43	Tr-5P	2895	4372	Note 1
43	Cpe-2/4P	2685	4528	Note 1

Model 43 — 8-cyl., 125 hp, 137" wb

Model No.	Body Type & Seating	Factory Price	Shipping Weight	Prod. Total
43	Sed-5P	2685	4638	Note 1
43	Clb Sed-5P	2835	4654	Note 1
43	Sed-7P	2995	4717	Note 1
43	Encl Drive Limo-7P	3145	4819	Note 1
43	Conv Sed-5P	3650	4530	Note 1

Model 42 — 8-cyl., 132 hp, 142" wb

Model No.	Body Type & Seating	Factory Price	Shipping Weight	Prod. Total
42	Spt Rds-2/4P	3450	4563	Note 1
42	Tr-5P	3450	4605	Note 1
42	Spt Phae-4P	3750	4734	Note 1
42	Conv Cpe-2/4P	3650	4698	Note 1
42	Sed-5P	3695	4980	Note 1
42	Clb Sed-5P	3745	4931	Note 1
42	Sed-7P	3825	5046	Note 1
42	Clb Berl-5P	3945	4953	Note 1
42	Encl Drive Limo-7P	3995	5075	Note 1

Model 41 — 8-cyl., 132 hp, 147" wb

Model No.	Body Type & Seating	Factory Price	Shipping Weight	Prod. Total
41	Tr-7P	4275	4786	Note 1
41	Conv Cpe-2/4P	4275	4740	Note 1
41	Sed-7P	4785	5100	Note 1
41	Encl Drive Limo-7P	4985	5157	Note 1
41	Twn Car-7P	6250	5211	Note 1
41	Twn Brgm-7P	6250	5206	Note 1
41	Twn Lan-7P	6400	NA	Note 1
41	LeB Cpe-2/4P	5100	5428	Note 1
41	LeB Vict Cpe-5P	5100	5338	Note 1
41	LeB Conv Sed-5P	5200	5358	Note 1
41	LeB Spt Sed-5P	5375	5602	Note 1
41	LeB Encl Dr Limo-7P	5975	5851	Note 1

Note 1: Estimated Pierce-Arrow production for 1931 totaled 4,500 with no body style breakout available.

1932

Model 54 — 8-cyl., 125 hp, 137" wb

Model No.	Body Type & Seating	Factory Price	Shipping Weight	Prod. Total
54	Conv Rds-2/4P	3100	4650	Note 1
54	Tr-5P	3150	4775	Note 1
54	Spt Phae-4P	3350	4811	Note 1
54	Clb Brgm-5P	2850	4745	Note 1
54	Cpe-2/4P	2985	4735	Note 1
54	Sed-5P	2985	4819	Note 1
54	Clb Sed-5P	3150	4824	Note 1
54	Clb Berl-5P	3350	4854	Note 1
54	Conv Sed-5P	3450	4961	Note 1

Model 54 — 8-cyl., 125 hp, 142" wb

Model No.	Body Type & Seating	Factory Price	Shipping Weight	Prod. Total
54	Tr-7P	3450	NA	Note 1
54	Sed-7P	3185	5024	Note 1
54	Encl Drive Limo-7P	3450	5071	Note 1

Model 53 — 12-cyl., 140 hp, 137" wb

Model No.	Body Type & Seating	Factory Price	Shipping Weight	Prod. Total
53	Conv Rds-2/4P	3900	4949	Note 1
53	Tr-5P	3950	5060	Note 1
53	Spt Phae-4P	4150	5096	Note 1
53	Clb Brgm-5P	3650	5042	Note 1
53	Cpe-2/4P	3785	4983	Note 1
53	Sed-5P	3785	5080	Note 1
53	Clb Sed-5P	3950	5244	Note 1
53	Clb Berl-5P	4150	NA	Note 1
53	Conv Sed-5P	4250	5244	Note 1

Model 53 — 12-cyl., 140 hp, 142" wb

Model No.	Body Type & Seating	Factory Price	Shipping Weight	Prod. Total
53	Tr-7P	4250	NA	Note 1
53	Sed-7P	3985	5301	Note 1
53	Encl Drive Limo-7P	4250	5336	Note 1

Model 52 — 12-cyl., 150 hp, 142" wb

Model No.	Body Type & Seating	Factory Price	Shipping Weight	Prod. Total
52	Clb Sed-5P	4400	5370	Note 1
52	Sed-5P	4295	5395	Note 1
52	Clb Berl-5P	4600	5403	Note 1

Model 52 — 12-cyl., 150 hp, 147" wb

Model No.	Body Type & Seating	Factory Price	Shipping Weight	Prod. Total
52	Sed-7P	4535	5465	Note 1
52	Encl Drive Limo-7P	4800	5506	Note 1

Note 1: Estimated Pierce-Arrow production for 1932 totaled 2,700 with no body style breakout available.

Production Notes: Prices listed were reduced an average of $500 during the model year to help spur sales. The V-12 engine was introduced this year. It featured 5.05:1 compression and did not require anti-knock fuel to be used. Some historical accounts of Pierce-Arrow include the Model 51, with a 147-inch wheelbase, but no record of available body styles is listed in any of the automobile guides covering 1932. LeBaron and Brunn were also creating custom-bodied automobiles on Pierce-Arrow chassis in 1932.

1929 Pierce-Arrow, Model 143, touring, AA

1929 Pierce-Arrow, Model 143, all-weather town car, AA

above and below, 1931 Pierce-Arrow, Model 41, victoria coupe (with body by LeBaron), AA

1935 Pierce-Arrow, Model 1245, sedan, AA

1929 Pierce-Arrow, Model 143, seven-passenger sedan, AA

1931 Pierce-Arrow, Model 42, club sedan, AA

1931 Pierce-Arrow, Model 42, touring, AA

1932 Pierce-Arrow, Model 53, convertible coupe, AA

1935 Pierce-Arrow, Model 1245, town brougham (with body by Brunn), AA

1933

Model 836 — 8-cyl., 135 hp, 136" wb

Model No.	Body Type & Seating	Factory Price	Shipping Weight	Prod. Total
836	Conv Rds-2/4P	3100	4618	Note 1
836	Cpe-2/4P	2795	4663	Note 1
836	Clb Brgm-5P	2385	4622	Note 1
836	Sed-5P	2575	4660	Note 1
836	Clb Sed-5P	2695	4681	Note 1
836	Conv Sed-5P	2975	4958	Note 1

Model 836 — 8-cyl., 135 hp, 139" wb

Model No.	Body Type & Seating	Factory Price	Shipping Weight	Prod. Total
836	Sed-7P	2850	4780	Note 1
836	Encl Drive Limo-7P	2975	4819	Note 1

Model 1236 — 12-cyl., 160 hp, 136" wb

Model No.	Body Type & Seating	Factory Price	Shipping Weight	Prod. Total
1236	Conv Rds.-2/4P	3500	4729	Note 1
1236	Cpe-2/4P	3195	4922	Note 1
1236	Clb Brgm-5P	2785	4854	Note 1
1236	Sed-5P	2975	4892	Note 1
1236	Clb Sed-5P	3095	4929	Note 1
1236	Conv Sed-5P	3375	NA	Note 1

Model 1236 — 12-cyl., 160 hp, 139" wb

Model No.	Body Type & Seating	Factory Price	Shipping Weight	Prod. Total
1236	Sed-7P	3250	5027	Note 1
1236	Encl Drive Limo-7P	3375	5088	Note 1

Model 1242 — 12-cyl., 175 hp, 137" wb

Model No.	Body Type & Seating	Factory Price	Shipping Weight	Prod. Total
1242	Tr-5P	3950	5256	Note 1
1242	Spt Phae-5P	4150	5296	Note 1
1242	Clb Brgm-5P	3650	5198	Note 1
1242	Sed-5P	3785	5288	Note 1
1242	Clb Sed-5P	3950	5361	Note 1
1242	Clb Berl-5P	4150	5384	Note 1
1242	Cpe-2/4P	3785	5263	Note 1
1242	Conv Rds-4P	3900	5107	Note 1
1242	Conv Sed-5P	4250	5438	Note 1

Model 1242 — 12-cyl., 175 hp, 142" wb

Model No.	Body Type & Seating	Factory Price	Shipping Weight	Prod. Total
1242	Tr-7P	4250	5337	Note 1
1242	Sed-7P	3985	5471	Note 1
1242	Encl Drive Limo-7P	4250	5507	Note 1

Model 1247 — 12-cyl., 175 hp, 142" wb

Model No.	Body Type & Seating	Factory Price	Shipping Weight	Prod. Total
1247	Sed-5P	4295	5429	Note 1
1247	Clb Sed-5P	4400	5417	Note 1
1247	Clb Berl-5P	4600	5421	Note 1

Model 1247 — 12-cyl., 175 hp, 147" wb

Model No.	Body Type & Seating	Factory Price	Shipping Weight	Prod. Total
1247	Sed-7P	4535	5550	Note 1
1247	Encl Drive Limo-7P	4800	5550	Note 1
1247	LeB Cpe M.B.-2P	5300	5286	Note 1
1247	LeB Cpe L.B.-2P	5600	5286	Note 1
1247	LeB Conv Vict-5P	5200	5198	Note 1
1247	LeB Conv Sed-5P	5700	5466	Note 1
1247	LeB Conv Sed W.P.-5P	6100	5496	Note 1
1247	LeB Clb Sed-5P	5700	5391	Note 1
1247	LeB Encl Dr Limo-7P	6200	5778	Note 1
1247	Brn Twn Brgm-7P	6700	5768	Note 1
1247	Brn Twn Car-7P	6700	5768	Note 1
1247	Brn Cabr-7P	7200	NA	Note 1
1247	Brn Encl Dr Brgm-7P	7200	NA	Note 1

Note 1: Estimated Pierce-Arrow production for 1933 totaled 2,150 with no body style breakout available. This included the production of five "concept" Silver Arrows built for display on the auto show circuit.

Production Note: Pierce-Arrow ended its merger with Studebaker after that automaker declared bankruptcy in 1933.

1934

Model 836A — 8-cyl., 135 hp, 136" wb

Model No.	Body Type & Seating	Factory Price	Shipping Weight	Prod. Total
836A	Clb Brgm-5P	2495	4780	Note 1
836A	Clb Brgm Salon-5P	2595	4797	Note 1
836A	4-dr Sed-5P	2595	4923	Note 1
836A	4-dr Sed Salon-5P	2695	4940	Note 1

Model 840A — 8-cyl., 140 hp, 139" wb

Model No.	Body Type & Seating	Factory Price	Shipping Weight	Prod. Total
840A	Conv Rds-4P	2995	4817	Note 1
840A	Clb Brgm-5P	2795	4906	Note 1
840A	Sed-5P	2895	4964	Note 1
840A	Clb Sed-5P	2995	5042	Note 1
840A	Cpe-4P	2895	4913	Note 1

Model 840A — 8-cyl., 140 hp, 144" wb

Model No.	Body Type & Seating	Factory Price	Shipping Weight	Prod. Total
840A	Slvr Arw Sed-5P	3495	5046	Note 1
840A	Sed-7P	3200	5107	Note 1
840A	Encl Drive Limo-7P	3350	5183	Note 1
840A	Brn Metro Twn Brgm-5P	4995	5228	Note 1

Model 1240A — 12-cyl., 175 hp, 139" wb

Model No.	Body Type & Seating	Factory Price	Shipping Weight	Prod. Total
1240A	Conv Rds-4P	3395	NA	Note 1
1240A	Clb Brgm-5P	3195	5152	Note 1
1240A	Sed-5P	3295	5227	Note 1
1240A	Clb Sed-5P	3395	5315	Note 1
1240A	Cpe-4P	3295	5168	Note 1

Model 1240A — 12-cyl., 175 hp, 144" wb

Model No.	Body Type & Seating	Factory Price	Shipping Weight	Prod. Total
1240A	Slvr Arw Sed-5P	3895	5347	Note 1
1240A	Sed-7P	3600	5381	Note 1
1240A	Encl Dr Limo-7P	3750	5442	Note 1
1240A	Brn Metro Twn Brgm-5P	5395	5529	Note 1

Model 1248A — 12-cyl., 175 hp, 147" wb

Model No.	Body Type & Seating	Factory Price	Shipping Weight	Prod. Total
1248A	Sed-7P	4295	NA	Note 1
1248A	Encl Dr Limo-7P	4495	5494	Note 1
1248A	Brn Encl Dr Limo-7P	6000	NA	Note 1
1248A	Brn Twn Brgm-7P	6500	NA	Note 1
1248A	Brn Twn Cabr-7P	7000	NA	Note 1
1248A	Brn Twn Car-7P	6500	NA	Note 1
1248A	Brn Encl Dr Brgm-7P	7000	NA	Note 1

Note 1: Estimated Pierce-Arrow production for 1934 totaled 1,740 with no body style breakout available.

1935

Model 845 — 8-cyl., 140 hp, 139" wb

Model No.	Body Type & Seating	Factory Price	Shipping Weight	Prod. Total
845	Conv Rds-2/4P	2995	4809	Note 1
845	Clb Brgm-5P	2795	4906	Note 1
845	Cpe-2/4P	2895	4905	Note 1
845	Sed-5P	2895	4964	Note 1
845	Clb Sed-5P	2995	5034	Note 1

Model 845 — 8-cyl., 140 hp, 144" wb

Model No.	Body Type & Seating	Factory Price	Shipping Weight	Prod. Total
845	Sed-7P	3200	5099	Note 1
845	Encl Drive Limo-7P	3350	5175	Note 1
845	Slvr Arw Sed-5P	3495	5046	Note 1
845	Brn Metro Twn Brgm-7P	4995	5220	Note 1

Model 1245 — 12-cyl., 175 hp, 139" wb

Model No.	Body Type & Seating	Factory Price	Shipping Weight	Prod. Total
1245	Conv Rds-2/4P	3395	5078	Note 1
1245	Clb Brgm-5P	3195	5216	Note 1
1245	Cpe-2/4P	3295	5174	Note 1
1245	Sed-5P	3295	5233	Note 1
1245	Clb Sed-5P	3395	5321	Note 1

Model 1245 — 12-cyl., 175 hp, 144" wb

Model No.	Body Type & Seating	Factory Price	Shipping Weight	Prod. Total
1245	Sed-7P	3600	5387	Note 1
1245	Encl Drive Limo-7P	3750	5442	Note 1
1245	Slvr Arw Sed-5P	3895	5347	Note 1
1245	Brn Metro Twn Brgm-7P	5395	5487	Note 1

Model 1255 — 12-cyl., 175 hp, 147" wb

Model No.	Body Type & Seating	Factory Price	Shipping Weight	Prod. Total
1255	Sed-7P	4295	5439	Note 1
1255	Encl Drive Limo-7P	4495	5494	Note 1

Note 1: Estimated Pierce-Arrow production for 1935 totaled 875 with no body style breakout available.

Production Note: Pierce-Arrow produced 9- and 15-passenger commercial vehicles in 1935 to help stimulate cash flow to keep the company in business.

1936

Model 1601 — 8-cyl., 150 hp, 138" wb

Model No.	Body Type & Seating	Factory Price	Shipping Weight	Prod. Total
1601	Cpe-2/4P	3195	5535	Note 1
1601	Conv Rds-2/4P	3295	5480	Note 1
1601	Clb Sed-5P	3295	5490	Note 1
1601	Sed-5P	3195	5565	Note 1
1601	Clb Berl-5P	3445	NA	Note 1

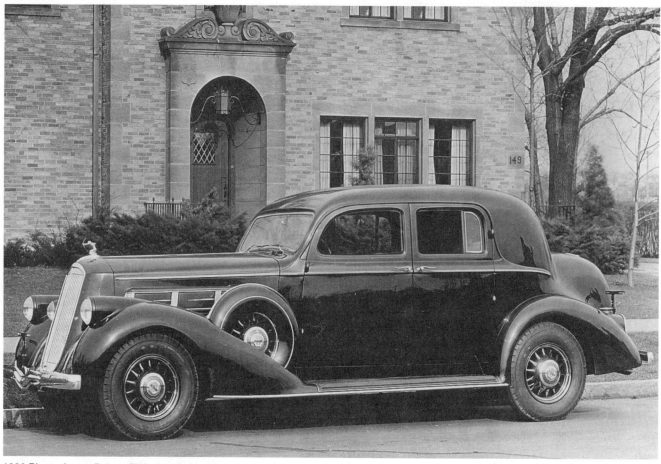

1936 Pierce-Arrow, Deluxe Eight (Model 1601), club sedan, AA

1936 Pierce-Arrow, Deluxe Eight, (Model 1601), five-passenger sedan, AA

1937 Pierce-Arrow, Twelve (Model 1702), convertible sedan, AA

1937 Pierce-Arrow, Twelve (Model 1702), Metropolitan town brougham (with body by Brunn), AA

Model 1601 — 8-cyl., 150 hp, 144" wb

Model No.	Body Type & Seating	Factory Price	Shipping Weight	Prod. Total
1601	Sed-7P	3500	5710	Note 1
1601	Encl Drive Limo-7P	3650	5750	Note 1
1601	Conv Sed-5P	4100	NA	Note 1
1601	Brn Metro Twn Brgm-7P	5295	5730	Note 1

Model 1602 — 12-cyl., 185 hp, 138" wb

Model No.	Body Type & Seating	Factory Price	Shipping Weight	Prod. Total
1602	Cpe-2/4P	3695	5745	Note 1
1602	Conv Rds-2/4P	3795	5690	Note 1
1602	Clb Sed-5P	3795	5740	Note 1
1602	Sed-5P	3695	5810	Note 1
1602	Clb Berl-5P	3945	NA	Note 1

Model 1602 — 12-cyl., 185 hp, 144" wb

Model No.	Body Type & Seating	Factory Price	Shipping Weight	Prod. Total
1602	Sed-7P	4000	5955	Note 1
1602	Conv Sed-5P	4600	5811	Note 1
1602	Encl Drive Limo-7P	4150	5995	Note 1
1602	Brn Metro Twn Brgm-7P	5795	5975	Note 1

Model 1603 — 12-cyl., 185 hp, 147" wb

Model No.	Body Type & Seating	Factory Price	Shipping Weight	Prod. Total
1603	Sed-7P	4795	6015	Note 1
1603	Encl Drive Limo-7P	4995	6035	Note 1

Note 1: Estimated Pierce-Arrow production for 1936 totaled 787 with no body style breakout available.

Production Note: In addition to automobiles and commercial vehicles, Pierce-Arrow began building travel trailers to, again, stimulate cash flow as the automaker was in dire straits financially.

1937

Model 1701 — 8-cyl., 150 hp, 138" wb

Model No.	Body Type & Seating	Factory Price	Shipping Weight	Prod. Total
1701	Cpe-4P	3195	5645	Note 1
1701	Sed-5P	3195	5675	Note 1
1701	Conv Rds-4P	3295	5590	Note 1
1701	Clb Sed-5P	3295	5600	Note 1
1701	Clb Berl-5P	3445	NA	Note 1
1701	Fml Sed-5P	3445	NA	Note 1

Model 1701 — 8-cyl., 150 hp, 144" wb

Model No.	Body Type & Seating	Factory Price	Shipping Weight	Prod. Total
1701	Fml Sed-5P	4300	5860	Note 1
1701	Sed-7P	3500	5820	Note 1
1701	Encl Dr Limo-7P	3650	5860	Note 1
1701	Conv Sed-5P	4100	5640	Note 1
1701	Brn Metro Twn Brgm-7P	5295	5840	Note 1

Model 1702 — 12-cyl., 185 hp, 138" wb

Model No.	Body Type & Seating	Factory Price	Shipping Weight	Prod. Total
1702	Cpe-4P	3695	5855	Note 1
1702	Sed-5P	3695	5920	Note 1
1702	Conv Rds-4P	3795	5800	Note 1
1702	Clb Sed-5P	3795	5850	Note 1
1702	Clb Berl-5P	3945	NA	Note 1
1702	Fml Sed-6P	3945	NA	Note 1

Model 1702 — 12-cyl., 185 hp, 144" wb

Model No.	Body Type & Seating	Factory Price	Shipping Weight	Prod. Total
1702	Sed-7P	4000	6065	Note 1
1702	Encl Dr Limo-7P	4150	6105	Note 1
1702	Conv Sed-5P	4600	5921	Note 1
1702	Brn Metro Twn Brgm-7P	5795	6085	Note 1

Model 1703 — 12-cyl., 185 hp, 147" wb

Model No.	Body Type & Seating	Factory Price	Shipping Weight	Prod. Total
1703	Sed-7P	4795	6125	Note 1
1703	Encl Drive Limo-7P	4995	6145	Note 1
1703	Encl Drive Opera Limo-7P	6760	6525	Note 1

Note 1: Estimated Pierce-Arrow production for 1937 totaled 167 with no body style breakout available.

1938

Model 1801 — 8-cyl., 150 hp, 138" wb

Model No.	Body Type & Seating	Factory Price	Shipping Weight	Prod. Total
1801	Sed-5P	3375	5675	Note 1
1801	Clb Sed-5P	3480	5600	Note 1
1801	Cpe-4P	3375	5590	Note 1
1801	Conv Rds-4P	3460	5645	Note 1
1801	Clb Berl-5P	3630	NA	Note 1
1801	Fml Sed-5P	3630	NA	Note 1

Model 1801 — 8-cyl., 150 hp, 144" wb

Model No.	Body Type & Seating	Factory Price	Shipping Weight	Prod. Total
1801	Fml Sed-5P	4300	5860	Note 1
1801	Sed-7P	3690	5820	Note 1
1801	Encl Dr Limo-7P	3840	5860	Note 1
1801	Conv Sed-5P	4300	5640	Note 1
1801	Brn Metro Twn Brgm-7P	5520	5840	Note 1

Model 1802 — 12-cyl., 185 hp, 138" wb

Model No.	Body Type & Seating	Factory Price	Shipping Weight	Prod. Total
1802	Cpe-4P	3895	5855	Note 1
1802	Sed-5P	3895	5920	Note 1
1802	Conv Rds-4P	4000	5800	Note 1
1802	Clb Sed-5P	4000	5850	Note 1
1802	Clb Berl-5P	4155	NA	Note 1
1802	Fml Sed-6P	4155	NA	Note 1

Model 1802 — 12-cyl., 185 hp, 144" wb

Model No.	Body Type & Seating	Factory Price	Shipping Weight	Prod. Total
1802	Sed-7P	4210	6065	Note 1
1802	Encl Dr Limo-7P	4360	6105	Note 1
1802	Conv Sed-5P	4820	5921	Note 1
1802	Brn Metro Twn Brgm-7P	6040	6085	Note 1

Model 1803 — 12-cyl., 185 hp, 147" wb

Model No.	Body Type & Seating	Factory Price	Shipping Weight	Prod. Total
1803	Sed-7P	5015	6125	Note 1
1803	Encl Drive Limo-7P	5220	6145	Note 1
1803	Encl Drive Opera Limo-7P	6760	6525	Note 1

Note 1: Estimated Pierce-Arrow production for 1938 totaled 17 with no body style breakout available.

Production Note: This was the final year of production for Pierce-Arrow automobiles as the company ceased to function in March 1938. Speculation is that many of the remaining parts in the factory were eventually scrapped for the metal collection drives held during World War II.

Five concept Pierce-Arrow automobiles called Silver Arrows were constructed for the 1933 auto show circuit. The Silver Arrow show cars were all designed and constructed in approximately 100 days, a phenomenal accomplishment when viewing the magnificence of the end result.

STUDEBAKER

STUDEBAKER — South Bend, Indiana — (1902-1942 et seq.) — The wagon-building Studebaker brothers of South Bend called themselves "The Largest Vehicle Builders in the World" in 1872 and launched themselves into the automobile business a half century later. There is some evidence they did this a little reluctantly. Having made a fortune supplying the army of the North in the Civil War, and British military forces in the Boer War, the Studebaker Brothers Manufacturing Company seemed content to reap profits in the horsedrawn field and experiment at its leisure in the burgeoning automotive arena. Though a horseless vehicle was developed as early as 1897, and the company built bodies for several electric car manufacturers, it was not until 1902 that John M. Studebaker's son-in-law Fred Fish persuaded the family to produce a car of its own. It was an electric designed by Thomas Alva Edison, 20 were built that year, and production continued in small numbers until 1912. In 1904, following the purchase of the assets of the defunct General (Cleveland), Fred Fish persuaded Studebaker to build gasoline cars, despite John Studebaker's opinion that "they stink to high heaven." The chassis were supplied by Garford in Elyria (Ohio), initially a two-cylinder 16 hp chain drive model, followed by a 20 hp shaft drive four in 1905. Until 1908, this collaboration with the Garford organization was retained. That year, Studebaker began its association with the Everitt-Metzger-Flanders Company that resulted in Studebaker's marketing of the E-M-F car, and subsequently the Flanders 20, and ultimately in 1911, the takeover of E-M-F by Studebaker and the formation of the Studebaker Corporation. The E-M-F and Flanders 20 were continued by Studebaker for 1912, but thereafter the brothers' name was affixed to all cars to come from the corporation. For 1913, the new Studebaker cars were sold in six models of four or six cylinders, the latter distinguished by their monoblock engine castings, Studebaker and Premier pioneering in this construction, and Studebaker claiming its six for less than $2,000 to be an American first. Though that fact could be mooted, the success of the Studebaker marketing strategy could not.

Studebaker Data Compilation by John A. Gunnell

Sales rose handsomely as year passed year. With the retirement from the Studebaker presidency of Fred Fish—his automotive enthusiasm had obviously paid off well personally, too—vice-president Albert Russel Erskine took over in July of 1915. Studebaker was a supplier first to Europe and then the U.S. government during the First World War. During this period the engineering department was in the charge of Fred M. Zeder, Owen R. Skelton and Carl Breer; they prepared the first postwar Studebakers, then left the company to set themselves up as consultants, and later to bring to reality the motorcar vision of Walter P. Chrysler. In 1920, all Studebakers were sixes, the Light, the Special and the Big Six. Robust vehicles that were difficult to break, these were the cars, in Erskine's words, that "made Studebaker famous." When Packard and Rickenbacker, among others, introduced four-wheel brakes in 1923, Studebaker was one of the most vociferous opponents, declaring them unsafe in full-page advertisements, but by 1926 four-wheel braking became standard on Studebaker products. It was in 1926, too, that Albert Erskine noticed something had been missing from South Bend—and that was style and class. This was a problem he attacked on several fronts. First, he hired the Rose Room of the Plaza Hotel in New York City during new car introduction time that summer and exhibited "special creations" by noted custom coachbuilders on various six-cylinder Studebaker chassis. Then in October he introduced a new motorcar called the Erskine, which had a European flair and was designed to carry the company fashionably into the lower-priced class. Those two ventures did not prove successful, but his third idea did—and this was an assault on the prestige segment of the marketplace. Eight cylinders was what he wanted, and when engineers Max Wollering and Guy Henry (who had taken over from the Zeder-Skelton-Breer triumvirate) objected, believing their sturdy and practical sixes quite sufficient, Erskine simply eased them out of the organization and brought in engineer Delmar G. "Barney" Roos who was happy to comply. The result was the Studebaker President, with a straight-eight engine initially delivering 100 bhp (raised to 132 by 1933 with the Speedway President line), styling upon which Ray Dietrich had consulted beautifully, and a price tag of $1,985-$2,485, a fine bargain in 1928. The new President was a smash. Lest the Studebaker six-cylinder line be forgotten, Erskine saw to it that those cars made news, too, by sending Commanders and Dictators to the races. Nineteen twenty-seven ended with Studebaker holding more stock car records than even the company could count, including 25,000 miles in less than 25,000 minutes by three Commanders. In 1928, a President sedan was sent to the board track at Atlantic City to take any records not broken by the Commanders, and a Dictator broke its own previous year's record (5,000 miles in less than 4,800 minutes) for good measure. "Builder of Champions," the ads read. The Commander and Dictator were given smaller eight-cylinder engines for 1929, and the big President eight took on the Indianapolis 500 in 1930 in two privately entered specials that performed so admirably that the company fielded its own factory-sponsored team in 1932 (most rare for a giant American manufacturer), with Cliff Bergere finishing a fine third. But the following year was a tragic one for Studebaker. Its purchase of the Pierce-Arrow company in 1928 had since been proven to be a financial mistake, the new car called the Rockne that had been introduced in 1932 was faring badly, and now Erskine was in the midst of the nightmare resulting from his ill-advised attempt to buy the White Motor Company. In March of 1933, Studebaker went into receivership; in July, Albert Erskine committed suicide. Picking up the pieces of the organization were Harold Vance and Paul Hoffman. Studebaker's Pierce-Arrow stock was sold for a million dollars, and $100,000 was spent on an ambitious "Studebaker Carries On" advertising campaign. Retrenchment meant the end for the big 337 cubic inch Studebaker President. For 1934, the line consisted of the Dictator six, the Commander eight and the President eight carrying the Commander engine upgraded from 221 cubic inches to 250 for 110 bhp. By March of 1935, Studebaker was out of receivership; Hoffman became the corporation's president, Vance chairman of the board. Synchromesh, freewheeling and X-braced frames had been introduced in 1934, followed by planar independent front suspension and hydraulic brakes in 1935, and Hill Holder in 1936. For 1937, an optional fully automatic overdrive followed the semi-automatic offered in 1935, and a new hypoid rear axle became standard. The innovation of windshield washers followed in 1938 models. But the best news from Studebaker arrived in 1939, and it was called the Champion. To prove it worthy of the name, this new six from Studebaker put up 15,000 miles at Indianapolis in under 15,000 minutes. More than 200,000 Champions were built prior to Pearl Harbor. By now, Raymond Loewy had begun his collaboration with Studebaker, and it was his design studio that would be responsible for the first all-new car to arrive from any major American company after the Second World War. Jokes were cracked about the Studebaker that was "going both ways," but everyone watched it do it. The company looked in fine shape in 1946. But less than two decades later the proud name of Studebaker would be forever stilled in the American automobile industry.

1902-1912

STUDEBAKER — ELECTRIC: Studebaker Bros. Manufacturing Co. built a complete line of electric-powered cars and trucks from 1902-1912. The first models evolved from the firm's horsedrawn buggies while later models were more sophisticated. The two-passenger runabout was a single seat, buggy-type vehicle with leather fenders, bar-lever steering, chain drive and a leather dashboard. The victoria was basically the same vehicle with a "French" front hood, coach lights and an optional folding top. The stanhope featured a curved tonneau-type body with a single seat. It had coach lamps, runningboards and an optional, canopy-type folding top.

Early models of 1902-1903 used wire spoke bicycle wheels, which were later replaced with wooden artillery spoke wheels. Single-seat models had one electric motor. The four-passenger surrey, a two-seat model of underslung design, had two motors, as did commercial vehicles. Commercials came as a light-duty electric delivery with a doorless, enclosed van-type body or in truck form with a variety of large wagon-type bodies having weight-carrying capacities of 1,000, 2,500 or 7,500 pounds. A five-ton rated stake body truck was available after 1906. In addition, commercial body building to customer specifications was provided on special order jobs.

Four-passenger electric coupes were added to the line at a later date. According to Floyd Clymer, these were available after 1906, although other sources place the introduction year as 1910. The coupes had what is called "phone booth" or "china closet" styling, with tall, five-window bodies, a flat windshield/dash panel, small hood, deck and fenders. Coach lamps were mounted at the front, on the beltline.

All models had similar tiller controls, full-elliptic rear springs and semi-elliptic front springs. Solid rubber tires were used on the surrey, other models having pneumatic tires on clincher-type detachable wheels. Two separate brakes were provided on all models. One worked on the rear axle drums, except on the surrey where it worked directly on the wheel hubs. The second brake worked on the countershaft(s) of the motor(s). Both were foot operated.

On runabouts and stanhopes the running gear frames were of tubular steel and independent of the body. On the victoria and the surrey, which were underslung, the running gear frames were integral with the framework of the body, which was reinforced with steel rocker plates for extra rigidity.

Controllers on all Studebaker electrics gave four speeds in either direction. Drive on most cars (if not all) was by chain. The motor was mounted so that it could be swung back and forth to allow chain adjustments. Photos suggest that some late models may have featured some type of enclosed drive system without chains.

For 1904, the stanhope came finished in rich shades of maroon or black in combination with dark green. The victoria was available in dark shades of green or maroon with matching cloth upholstery. The surrey was finished in Royal green with green leather upholstery and an optional canopy top was available.

Complete year-by-year data covering Studebaker electrics was not available at the time this catalog went to press. We have included representative model listings, prices and technical specifications. It must be understood that these may have changed slightly from one year to the next.

I.D. DATA: Serial number and engine number information for Studebaker electrics is not currently available.

Selected 1904-1910 Model Specifications

Model No.	Body Type & Seating	Factory Price	Shipping Weight	Prod. Total
NA	Rbt.-2P	NA	1350	Note 1
NA	Surrey w/o Top-4P	1800	NA	Note 1
NA	Surrey w/Top-4P	1850	NA	Note 1
1363	Stanhope w/o Top-2P	1100	1500	Note 1
1363	Stanhope w/Top-2P	1150	1525	Note 1
1396	Vic. w/o Top (Exide)-2P	1550	1575	Note 1
1396	Vic. w/Top (Exide)-2P	1600	1600	Note 1
1396	Vic. w/o Top (Edison)-2P	1725	1575	Note 1
1396	Vic. w/Top (Edison)-2P	1775	1600	Note 1
2019A	Delivery Wag.-2P	NA	NA	Note 1
17B	Cpe.-2P	2200	2450	Note 1
17D	Phae.-4P	NA	NA	Note 1
22F	Stanhope w/Top	NA	NA	Note 1
2012A	5-Ton Truck	NA	9700	Note 1

Note 1: A total of 1,841 Studebaker electric vehicles were built between 1902 and 1912.

Note 2: The above chart gives representative models, prices and weights for Studebaker electrics of various years and is not intended as a complete listing of all models available.

ENGINE: Runabout (1902): A single Westinghouse standard vehicle motor was used. It was rated 40 volts and 24 amperes. This was equivalent to approximately 1.7 NACC hp. The battery consisted of 24 cells with a total capacity of 96 amp./hrs. Top speed: 13 mph. Driving range: 40 miles per charge. **Victoria (1904):** The victoria and other single-seat, two-passenger models used one electric motor rated 50 volts and 30 amperes. The standard battery consisted of 24 Exide cells. The victoria was available with an optional 36-cell Edison battery. Top speed: 14 mph. Driving range: 40 miles per charge. **Surrey (1904):** The four-passenger surrey was equipped with two motors each rated 80 volts and 12 amperes. Top speed: 14 mph. Driving range: NA. **Coupe (1906-1910):** The four-passenger Model 17-B electric coupe used one Westinghouse electric motor rated 48 volts and 26 amperes. Batteries (weighing 970 pounds) were carried in separate front and rear trays. Top speed: 15 mph. Driving range: 35 miles per charge. **Commercial Vehicles:** Commercial vehicles of 1,000 pounds or over capacity had two electric motors rated 80 volts and 20 amperes. This was equivalent to approximately 4.3 NACC hp. The batteries consisted of 40 cells. They were divided into four separate trays containing 10 cells each. This allowed replacement of individual trays for recharging, without tying up all the remaining cells.

CHASSIS: Stanhope (1904): W.B.: 62 in. Tread: 54 in. Tires: 30 x 3 in. (detachable tires). Victoria (1904): W.B.: 69 in. Tread: 54 in. Tires: 30 x 3 in. (detachable tires). Surrey (1904): Tires: 36 x 3 in. (solid tires). Runabout (1902-1903): W.B.: 61 in. O.L.: 73 in. Tread: 53 in. Tires: 30 x 3 in. (detachable tires).

TECHNICAL: Extra-heavy roller chain transmission. Speeds: 4F/1R. Electric speed control device on seat at driver's left, plus reversing switch and removable "Key" switch. Chain-drive. Differential gear mounted on rear axle. Two separate braking systems. Wire spoke or wood artillery wheels; Archibald type wheels with solid rubber tires corresponding to load capacity on commercial vehicles.

OPTIONS: Folding canopy top ($50.00). Victoria with Edison battery (175.00 extra). Coach lights. Leather fenders. Headlight. Electric horn.

Note: Some of these accessories were standard equipment on most models.

HISTORICAL: Introduced January 1902. Innovations: First automobiles built by Studebaker Bros. Manufacturing Co.; later became Studebaker Corp. Production: A total of 1,841 Studebaker electrics were made in 10 years of production. Company Patriarch J.M. Studebaker was said to favor the electrics over gas-powered Studebaker automobiles. The first Studebaker electric was sold to F.W. Blees of Macon, Missouri, on February 12, 1902. It is believed that the second car made was purchased by Thomas Alva Edison. Studebaker advertised that its electrics "Can Be Run Any Day In The Year By Any Member Of The Family." The electrics were marketed concurrently with Studebaker-Garford gasoline automobiles from 1903-1911.

1903

STUDEBAKER-GARFORD — MODEL A — TWO: This seems to be a car that the Studebaker history books overlooked. According to a 1904 edition of *Cycle and Automobile Trade Journal,* it was brought out in late 1903 and carried over into the following season with some changes. The journal described it as "a remarkably satisfactory little touring car." The only details given about the model are sketchy ones. It was noted that the car used an eight horsepower, double-opposed horizontal engine and incorporated a mechanical lubrication system with a chain-driven pump. Otherwise, it was said to be "similar to the (1904) Model C in many other respects." The body had provisions for a detachable tonneau and could be quickly transformed into a runabout. Finish was in maroon or royal green with upholstery in dark green leather. No other details about this model are readily available.

I.D. DATA: Serial number and engine number information is not available.

Model A, 2-cyl.

Model No.	Body Type & Seating	Factory Price	Shipping Weight	Prod. Total
A	Tonneau Tr.-5P	NA	NA	NA

ENGINE: The only information available about the Model A engine is that it was a two-cylinder, horizontally-opposed powerplant developing 8 N.A.C.C. hp.

CHASSIS: The Model A was described as being "similar to the Model C (of 1904) in many other respects." Additional chassis data is not available.

DRIVETRAIN: The Model A was similar to the 1904 Model C in drivetrain layout.

OPTIONS: Information not available.

HISTORICAL: Introduced late 1903. First gasoline-powered automobiles to bear the Studebaker nameplate. They had chassis built by the Garford Co. of Elyria, Ohio. The chassis were then shipped to the Studebaker factory, in South Bend, Indiana, where bodies were installed. *The Studebaker Century* by Asa E. Hall and Richard M. Langworth says that the first gas-powered Studebakers were built in 1904 and does not mention the Model A. *Studebaker: The Complete Story* by William A. Cannon and Fred K. Fox also does not mention the Model A and specifically dates the sale of the first gas-powered Studebaker-Garford to July 22, 1904. In fact, the only mention of the 1903 Model A is in the 1904 edition of *Cycle and Automobile Trade Journal* from which the above information was taken. It is possible these cars were Generals (refer to General of Cleveland, Ohio) and that only Studebakers from 1904 were manufactured by Garford.

1904

STUDEBAKER-GARFORD — MODELS A/B — TWO: According to *Cycle and Automobile Trade Journal* the mysterious Studebaker-Garford Model A gasoline-powered touring car was again available with "numerous 1904 improvements and refinements." No additional details are known, except that body and chassis specifications were the same as in 1903 and carried over into the new Model B is also a somewhat mysterious vehicle that Studebaker historians have overlooked. It was a gasoline-powered delivery wagon that used the same chassis as the Model A. *Cycle and Automobile Trade Journal* noted that "a very elegant little delivery wagon body" was used in place of the tonneau body. It had a carrying capacity of 500 pounds. The Model B was finished in maroon with black pin striping. It weighed 1,550 pounds and sold for $1,100. No other details or specifications are available.

STUDEBAKER-GARFORD — MODEL C — TWO: The new Model C is the car generally recognized as being the "first" gasoline-powered Studebaker. It was a medium-sized touring car for five persons featuring a body with a detachable rear tonneau. The frame was of armoured wood. The short hood had vertical louvers. The steering wheel was on the right-hand side with brake and gear selector levers outside the body. The body was finished in dark maroons or dark blue or in Royal green striped with yellow. Upholstery was in dark, matching shades of leather. Headlights, cowl lamps, fenders and a 10-gallon gas tank were among standard equipment features. A canopy top added $150 to the basic price.

I.D. DATA: [Models A/B] Serial number and engine number information not available. [Model C] Serial number and engine number information not available.

Model A, 2-cyl.

Model No.	Body Type & Seating	Factory Price	Shipping Weight	Prod. Total
A	Tonneau Tr.-5P	NA	NA	NA
Model B, 2-cyl.				
B	Delivery Wagon-2P	1100	1550	NA
Model C, 2-cyl.				
C	Tonneau Tr.-5P	1600	1800	NA

Note 1: Add $175 for canopy top.

ENGINE: [Models A/B] Two. Horizontally-opposed. N.A.C.C. H.P.: 8. [Model C] Two. Horizontally-opposed; under center type. B & S: 5 x 5-1/2 in. Disp.: 215.9 cu. in. N.A.C.C. H.P.: 16. Valve lifters: solid. Carb.: one-barrel.

CHASSIS: [Models A/B] Data not available. [Model C] W.B.: 82 in. Frt/RearTread: 56/56 in. Tires: 30 x 3-1/2 in.

TECHNICAL: [Models A/B] Layout similar to 1904 Model C. [Model C] Planetary transmission. Speeds: 2F/1R. Right-hand, outboard gear lever. Chain-drive. Spur differential on rear axle. Brakes: Two sets on rear hubs and differential. Artillery spoke wheels.

OPTIONS: Gas headlights. Kerosene side lamps. Canopy top ($175.00). Windshield. Horn.

HISTORICAL: Introduced January 1904. Innovations: New Model C touring car introduced. Officially claimed to be Studebaker's "first" gasoline automobile. The 1904 Studebaker-Garford models should not be confused with the later 1908 Garford Models A and B or 1909 Garford Model C, which were four-cylinder cars marketed under the Garford nameplate only. Studebaker officially credited Mr. H.D. Johnson, of South Bend, Ind., with the purchase of the "first" gas-powered Studebaker on July 22, 1904—a date that conflicts with the existence of the 1903 Model A Studebaker. The Studebaker-Garfords were actually marketed under only the Studebaker name in accordance with the contract between the two firms. However, the hyphenated name is preferred by Studebaker enthusiasts and historians today.

1905

STUDEBAKER-GARFORD — SERIES 15 HP — TWO: The Model C was carried over as the Model 9502 five-passenger touring car with detachable tonneau. It was now called a rear entrance touring car. There were virtually no changes in styling, finish or specifications although the price was lowered considerably. It was joined by a new Model 9502 five-passenger side entrance touring car. This model had a high, horizontal platform at the rear with a seat mounted on top of it. A door was used between the front and rear seat platforms. The new model came in either dark green or dark blue finish. Specifications of the two cars were otherwise identical.

STUDEBAKER-GARFORD — SERIES 20 HP — FOUR: New from Studebaker was a larger, four-cylinder touring car with a side entrance tonneau body and seating for five. Cataloged as Model 9503, this car had curved entranceways with doors at the rear. High-back, armchair style seats were of individual bucket type in the front and three-passenger "bench" type in the rear. Sweeping front fenders and higher rear fenders were used. This model came in either dark blue or dark green finish. A higher, rounder pressed steel dash, said to be of "pleasing design," was seen.

I.D. DATA: [Model 9502] Serial number and engine number information not available. [Model 9503] Serial number and engine number information not available.

Model 9502, 2-cyl.

Model No.	Body Type & Seating	Factory Price	Shipping Weight	Prod. Total
9502	Rear Entrance Tr.-5P	1250	1950	NA
9502	Side Entrance Tr.-5P	1350	1950	NA
Model 9503, 4-cyl.				
9503	Side Entrance Tr.-5P	3000	2100	NA

Note 1: A folding top of desired style was extra cost equipment.

ENGINE: [Model 9502] Engine specifications were the same as those of the 1904 Model C, except that the advertised horsepower rating was lowered to 15 hp. [Model 9503] Vertical. Cast enbloc. Four. Cast iron block. B & S: 3-7/8 x 4-1/2 in. Disp.: 212.3 cu. in. N.A.C.C. H.P.: 20. Valve lifters: mechanical. Carb.: Float feed: constant level type.

CHASSIS: [Model 9502] W.B.: 82 in. Frt/Rear Tread: 56-1/2/56-1/2 in. Tires: 30 x 3-1/2 in. [Model 9503] W.B.: 96 in. Frt/Rear Tread: 54/54 in. Tires 32 x 4 in.

TECHNICAL: [9502] Planetary transmission. Speeds: 2F/1R. Right-hand, outboard, gear selector. Chain drive. Rear wheel brakes. Artillery spoke wheels. [9503] Selecting sliding transmission. Speeds: 3F/1R. Right-hand, outboard, gear selector. Cone clutch. Bevel gear drive. Rear wheel brakes. Artillery spoke wheels.

OPTIONS: Folding top (of desired style). Gas headlights. Kerosene sidelamps. Windshield. Horn.

HISTORICAL: Introduced January 1905. Innovations: First four-cylinder Studebaker model released. Pressed steel frame construction on Model 9503. Selective sliding three-speed manual transmission in Model 9503. Garford continued to build Studebaker chassis in Ohio and ship them to South Bend for final assembly.

1906

STUDEBAKER-GARFORD — SERIES E — FOUR: Model 9503 was carried over, with lower prices, as the 1906 Series E touring car. It was again of side entrance design and the main styling changes were a two-inch longer wheelbase, the addition of runningboards and new colors. Finish was now available in maroon or pearl gray, as well as the dark blue and dark green used in 1905. A new model available in the same line was a town car of huge proportions with an open-sided driver's compartment. There was a glass center partition and the passenger compartment had five-windows along with paneled doors and rear. Finish colors on the town car were to owner specifications.

STUDEBAKER-GARFORD — SERIES F — FOUR: The new Series F Studebaker was a large, heavy five-passenger touring car with a wider rear tonneau and more massive doors. Finish was available in dark blue, maroon, dark green or pearl gray. A cape-style folding top was a popular extra-cost option.

STUDEBAKER-GARFORD — SERIES G — FOUR: The Series G five-passenger touring car was essentially a more powerful version of the Series F model. It had slightly fancier upholstery and sportier looking front fenders, plus a higher, squarer dashboard. A landau-style canopy top that covered only the rear compartment was available at extra cost. The foot brake on this model operated on the propeller shaft rather than the rear wheels and make-and-break magneto ignition was standard.

I.D. DATA: Serial number and engine number information not available.

Series E, 4-cyl.

Model No.	Body Type & Seating	Factory Price	Shipping Weight	Prod. Total
E-20	Side Entrance Tr.-5P	2600	2400	NA
E-20	Town Car-5P	4000	2750	NA

Note 1: Folding top optional on side entrance touring.

Series F, 4-cyl.

Model No.	Body Type & Seating	Factory Price	Shipping Weight	Prod. Total
F-28	Side Entrance Tr.-5P	3000	2700	NA

Note 2: A cape-style folding top was available.

Series G, 4-cyl.

Model No.	Body Type & Seating	Factory Price	Shipping Weight	Prod. Total
G-30	Side Entrance Tr.-5P	3700	2700	NA

Note 3: A folding canopy top was optional.

ENGINE: [Series E] Engine specifications were the same as on the 1905 Model 9503 except that the advertised horsepower rating was listed as 20 hp. [Series F] Vertical type. Cylinder cast enbloc. Four. Cast iron block. B & S: 4-3/8 x 4-3/4 in. Disp.: 285.6 cu. in. N.A.C.C. H.P.: 28. Jump spark ignition. Water-cooled via gear-driven pump, radiator and fan. Valve lifters: mechanical. Carb.: float feed; constant level type. [Series G] Vertical type. Cylinders cast in blocks of two.

Four. Cast iron block. B & S: 4-1/8 x 5-1/4 in. Disp.: 280.6 cu. in. N.A.C.C. H.P.: 30. Make-and-break ignition with magneto. Water-cooled via gear driven pump, radiator and fan. Valve lifters: mechanical. Carb.: float feed, constant level type.

CHASSIS: [Series E] W.B.: 98 in. Frt/Rear Tread: 54/54 in. Tires: (touring) 32 x 4 in. (town car) 32 x 4-1/2 in. [Series F] W.B.: 104 in. Frt/Rear Tread: 54/54 in. Tires: 34 x 4 in. [Series G] W.B.: 104 in. Frt/Rear Tread: 56/56 in. Tires: 34 x 4 in.

TECHNICAL: [All series] Sliding gear direct on high transmission. Speeds: 3F/1R. Right-hand outboard gear selector controls. Cone clutch. Bevel gear drive. Floating rear axle. Rear wheel mechanical brakes. Wood artillery spoke wheels.

OPTIONS: Folding top. Gas headlights. Kerosene side lamps. Horn. Windshield. Side curtains.

HISTORICAL: Introduced January 1906. Innovations: More powerful engines. First Studebaker town car. Longer wheelbases on new models. Make-and-break ignition with electric magneto introduced on G-30. The Model G-30 became the Garford Model A in 1908 when Studebaker took control of E-M-F and no longer needed Garford as its main chassis builder. However, some production of Studebaker-Garford cars continued through 1911. Garford was never able to build as many chassis as Studebaker could sell. Because of this, Studebaker formed associations with companies such as E-M-F of Detroit and Tincher Motor Car Co. of South Bend in hopes of achieving mergers that would provide additional production facilities.

1907-11

STUDEBAKER-GARFORD — 1907-1911 SERIES — FOURS: Year-by-year styling, finish and technical changes for the 1907-1911 Studebaker-Garford models are not available. The 1907 models were carried over from 1906, but had new alphabetical model designations. The first 40 hp Model B (Garford 40) was introduced in 1908. It had a T-head engine with cylinders cast in blocks of two. Bore and stroke was 4-3/4 x 5-1/4 inches giving a total displacement of 372.1 cu. in. A new 114-inch wheelbase was also used. The Model A of the same year was an improved version of the Model G of 1906-1907 with the same 30 hp, 280.6 cu. in. engine and 104-inch wheelbase. A Model H, with the same engine and wheelbase as the Model G, was also available in both 1907 and 1908.

For 1909, the Model A and Model B series were carried over with minimal change. The Model H was refined and renamed Model C. All-new was the 40 hp Model D. It had the 372.1 cu. in. engine, but a longer 117-1/2 inch wheelbase. In 1910, the Model H returned and was joined by a new Model M. The latter was merely an improved version of the Model L, which was last cataloged back in 1907. It revived the 285.6 cu. in./28 hp four-cylinder engine. Also available was the G-7, an improved variant of the Model D.

During 1911, the last year of Studebaker-Garford production, the G-7 was carried over as the G-8 with slightly higher prices. Also for 1911, there was a new G-10. It had a distinctive 116-inch wheelbase and a four-cylinder, 30 hp powerplant of 297.8 cu. in. (4-1/4 x 5-1/4 bore and stroke).

Interestingly, the 1908 Models A and B were also marketed under the Garford name. Studebaker soon halted this practice by enforcing its contract provisions. However, the contract terminated during calendar 1910 and, for 1911, the G-7 was available as a Studebaker or a Garford. The same is true of the 1911 G-8, which was sold under the Garford badge in 1912. The all-new G-10, however, appears to have been a Studebaker exclusive.

Even as the relationship between the two firms continued to deteriorate, Studebaker was expanding its own control over E-M-F, which it took over completely in 1910. E-M-F was merged into the new Studebaker Corporation on January 1, 1911, about the same time Garford broke out on its own. The non-Studebaker Garford automobiles were marketed until 1913, when Garford was absorbed into Willys-Overland. Studebaker, of course, survived well without Garford for the next 55 years or so.

1907

Model L, 4-cyl., 28 hp, 104" wb

Model No.	Body Type & Seating	Factory Price	Shipping Weight	Prod. Total
L	Rear Ent Tr-5P	3000	NA	NA
L	Limousine-7P	4000	NA	NA

Model G, 4-cyl., 30 hp, 104" wb

Model No.	Body Type & Seating	Factory Price	Shipping Weight	Prod. Total
G	Rear Ent Tr-5P	3700	NA	NA
G	Limousine-7P	4800	NA	NA

Model H, 4-cyl., 30 hp, 104" wb

H	Rear Ent Tr-5P	4000	NA	NA
H	Limousine-7P	5000	NA	NA

1908

Model H, 4-cyl., 30 hp, 104" wb

Model No.	Body Type & Seating	Factory Price	Shipping Weight	Prod. Total
H	Rear Ent Tr-5P	3500	NA	NA

Model A, 4-cyl., 30 hp, 104" wb

A	Tr	3500	NA	NA
A	Town Car-5P	4200	NA	NA
A	Rbt-2P	3500	NA	NA
A	Lan'let-5P	NA	NA	NA

Model B, 4-cyl., 40 hp, 114" wb

B	Tr-5P	4000	NA	NA
B	Rbt-2P	NA	NA	NA
B	Limo-7P	5000	NA	NA
B	Lan'let-5P	NA	NA	NA
B	Tourabout-4P	NA	NA	NA
B	Speed Car-3P	NA	NA	NA

1909

Model A, 4-cyl., 30 hp, 104" wb

Model No.	Body Type & Seating	Factory Price	Shipping Weight	Prod. Total
A	Tr-5P	3500	NA	NA
A	Twn Car-5P	NA	NA	NA
A	Rbt	NA	NA	NA
A	Lan'let-5P	NA	NA	NA

Model B, 4-cyl., 40 hp, 114" wb

B	Tr-5P	4000	NA	NA
B	Limo-7P	5000	NA	NA
B	Lan'let-5P	5000	NA	NA

Model C, 4-cyl., 30 hp, 104" wb

C	Tr-5P	NA	NA	NA

Model D, 4-cyl., 40 hp, 117.5" wb

D	Tr-5P	4000	NA	NA

1910

Model H, 4-cyl., 30 hp, 104" wb

Model No.	Body Type & Seating	Factory Price	Shipping Weight	Prod. Total
H	Tr-5P	NA	NA	NA

Model M, 4-cyl., 28 hp, 104" wb

M	Tr-5P	NA	NA	NA

Model G-7, 4-cyl., 40 hp, 117.5" wb

G-7	Tr-4/5P	3500	NA	NA
G-7	Tr-7P	3500	NA	NA
G-7	Limo (123" wb)	4750	NA	NA

1911

Model G-8, 4-cyl., 40 hp, 117.5" wb

Model No.	Body Type & Seating	Factory Price	Shipping Weight	Prod. Total
G-8	Limo-7P	4800	NA	NA
G-8	Lan'let-5P	4900	NA	NA
G-8	Tr-4/6/7P	3750	NA	NA
G-8	Rds-2P	3750	NA	NA

Model G-10, 4-cyl., 30 hp, 116" wb

G-10	Tr-5P	NA	NA	NA

NOTE: Studebaker-Garford association was discontinued after 1911 model year.

1913

STUDEBAKER — SA25 — FOUR: The 1913 Studebaker 25 came in two body styles, roadster and touring. They were the company's small four-cylinder models. Identifying features included a plain side hood and rear doors with wedge-shaped lower rear corners on the touring car. Cars in this line were the only Studebakers not equipped

1903 Studebaker, runabout (electric), HAC

1906 Studebaker, Model E-20, side entrance touring, HAC

1910 Studebaker, Model G-7, limousine (123-inch wheelbase), HAC

1915 Studebaker, Model SD-4, roadster, HAC

1904 Studebaker, Model C, tonneau touring, HAC

1909 Studebaker, Model D, touring, HAC

1913 Studebaker, Model SA25, touring, HAC

1919 Studebaker, Big Six (Series EG), touring, HAC

with electrical starting and lighting. Full-elliptical rear springs were featured. There were rear axle braces extending from the axle shaft housing to propeller shaft housing.

STUDEBAKER — AA35 — FOUR: The Studebaker 35 was the company's larger four-cylinder line. It offered three body styles, touring, coupe and sedan. The doors had rounded corners. The coupe featured leather upholstery and plate glass windows with Japanese leather dashboard trim and nickel-plated controls. The sedan had blue English broadcloth upholstery. Three-quarter elliptical rear springs were used. Radius rods extended from the rear axle to frame crossmembers.

STUDEBAKER — E — SIX: The 1913 Studebaker E-6 came in two body styles, touring and limousine. They were Studebaker's biggest cars. Under the extra-long hood was a long, six-cylinder engine with three blocks on a common crankcase. Each had two cylinders. Historians credit these as being the first mass production cars to have a six cast enbloc. Other features were three-quarter elliptical rear springs and radius rods bracing the axle to the frame. The coupe was equipped and trimmed similarly to the Model 35 coupe. The limousine offered broadcloth and Bedford cord upholstery with Turkish leather trim for the driver's compartment.

I.D. DATA: Series SA25 serial numbers were starting: 301501; ending: 315611. Engine numbers were starting: 25A-1; ending: 25A-15031. Series AA35 serial numbers were starting: 101501; ending: 110614. Engine numbers were starting: 35A-1; ending: 35A-10031. Series E serial numbers were starting: 600001 to 602800 and 602953 to 603002. Engine numbers: 6A-1 to 6A-3004.

Model 25, 4-cyl.

Model No.	Body Type & Seating	Factory Price	Shipping Weight	Prod. Total
25A	2-dr. Rds.-2P	875	NA	Note 1
25A	4-dr. Tr.-4P	885	NA	Note 1

Note 1: Total production was 15,000.

Model 35, 4-cyl.

35A	4-dr. Tr.-6P	1290	NA	Note 1
35A	2-dr. Cpe.-3P	1850	NA	Note 1
35A	4-dr. Sed.-4P	2050	NA	Note 1

Note 1: Total production was 10,000.

Model E, 6-cyl.

E-6	4-dr. Tr.-6P	1550	NA	Note 1
E-6	4-dr. Limo.-6P	2500	NA	Note 1

Note 1: Total production was 3,000.

ENGINE: [Model 25] L-head. Inline. Four (cast enbloc). Gray cast iron. B & S: 3-1/2 x 5 in. Disp.: 192.4 cu. in. Brake H.P.: 25. Net H.P.: 20 N.A.C.C. Valve lifters: solid. Carb.: Holley one-barrel sidedraft. [Model 35] L-head. Inline. Four (cast enbloc). Gray cast iron. B & S: 4-1/8 x 5 in. Brake H.P.: 35. Net H.P.: 27 N.A.C.C. Valve lifters: solid. Carb.: Holley one-barrel sidedraft. [Model E] L-head. Inline. Six (cast enbloc). Gray cast iron. B & S: 3-1/2 x 5 in. Disp.: 288.6 cu. in. Brake H.P.: 40. Net H.P.: 29 N.A.C.C. Valve lifters: solid. Carb.: Holley one-barrel sidedraft.

CHASSIS: [Series 25] W.B.: 102 in. Frt/Rear Tread: 56/56 in. [Series 35] W.B.: 115 in. Frt/Rear Tread: 56/56 in.

TECHNICAL: Selective sliding gear transmission (in unit with rear axle). Speeds: 3F/1R. Floor mounted gearshift controls. Clutch: Leather faced cone-type. External contracting rear wheel brakes. Twelve-spoke wood artillery wheels.

OPTIONS: Spare tire(s). Outside rear view mirror.

HISTORICAL: Introduced [25 and 35] December 1912; [E-6] January 1913. Innovations: First six cast enbloc. First exclusively Studebaker models. Calendar year production: 35,410. Model year production: 25,000. The president of Studebaker was Frederick Fish. Studebaker was the fourth largest American automaker.

1914

STUDEBAKER SC — SERIES 14 — FOUR: The cowl on 1914 Studebakers was redesigned to house the gas tank, which was moved from its former location under the front seat. A bead molding was added to the upper hood panel. The front fenders now had a beveled edge. Steering wheels were changed to the left side of the car, with transmission and emergency brake levers at the center.

STUDEBAKER EB — SERIES 14 — SIX: Changes on the Studebaker Six were similar to those on the fours. The Sixes had a longer wheelbase and longer hoods. The six-cylinder touring was a seven-passenger model with auxiliary folding seats in the rear passenger compartment. A distinctive model in this line was the five-passenger sedan. It was equipped with heavy plate glass windows, coachlights on the side and double body beltline moldings.

I.D. DATA: [Model SC] The serial numbers for 1914 four-cylinder domestic SC models were 403001 to 420515. Cars built for export had serial numbers 400001 to 400407. Engine numbers were 4B-1 to 4B-18050. [Model EB] Serial numbers for 1914 sixes were 605001 to 612450. Engine numbers were 6B-4001 to 6B-11620. No export versions of the Studebaker six were built this year.

Model SC, 4-cyl.

Model No.	Body Type & Seating	Factory Price	Shipping Weight	Prod. Total
SC-4	4-dr. Tr.-5P	1050	NA	Note 1
SC-4	2-dr. Lan. Rds.-2P	1200	NA	Note 1

Note 1: Total production was 17,976.

Model EB, 6-cyl.

EB-6	4-dr. Tr.-7P	1575	NA	Note 1
EB-6	2-dr. Lan. Rds.-3P	1800	NA	Note 1
EB-6	2-dr. Sed.-5P	2250	NA	Note 1

Note 1: Total production was 7,625.

ENGINE: [Model SC] L-head. Inline. Four (cast enbloc). Gray cast iron. B & S: 3-1/2 x 5 in. Disp.: 192.4 cu. in. Brake H.P.: 25. N.A.C.C. H.P.: 20. Valve lifters: solid. Carb.: Holley one-barrel sidedraft. [Model EB] L-head. Inline. Six (cast enbloc). Gray cast iron. B & S: 3-1/2 x 5 in. Disp.: 288.6 cu. in. Brake H.P.: 40. N.A.C.C. H.P.: 29. Valve lifters: solid. Carb.: Holley one-barrel.

CHASSIS: [Model SC-4] W.B.: 108.3 in. Frt/Rear Tread: 56/56 in. [Model EB-6] W.B.: 121.3 in. Frt/Rear Tread: 56/56 in.

TECHNICAL: Selective sliding gear transmission. Speeds: 3F/1R. Floor mounted gearshift controls. Clutch: Leather faced cone type full-floating. External contracting rear wheel brakes. Wood spoke artillery wheels.

OPTIONS: Spare tire(s). Outside rear view mirror.

HISTORICAL: Introduced [SC] October 1913-June 1914; [EB] October 1913-March 1915. Calendar year production: 35,000. Model year production: 25,601. Innovations: Improved carburetor feed system. Wagner two-unit starter/generator with six-volt battery. Centralized controls. Improved transmission. This was Frederick Fish's last year as president of Studebaker Corporation.

1915

STUDEBAKER — MODEL SD — SERIES 15 — FOUR: The 1915 Studebaker four looked much the same as the 1914 model. One obvious change was the relocation of the gas filler cap from the cowl to the right side of the instrument panel. Cowl lights were no longer used because the headlights had dimmer bulbs incorporated. Available models were a roadster and a touring car.

STUDEBAKER — MODEL EC — SERIES 15 — SIX: The 1915 Studebaker six looked much the same as the 1914 model. An obvious change was the relocation of the gas filler cap from the cowl to the right side of the instrument panel. Cowl lights were no longer used because the headlights had dimmer bulbs. Closed cars were not marketed.

I.D. DATA: [Model SD] The serial numbers for 1915 four-cylinder domestic SD models were 423001 to 447419. Cars built for export had serial numbers 449001 to 449443. Engine numbers were 4C-20001 to 4C-44931. [Model EC] Serial numbers for 1915 six-cylinder domestic EC models were 500001 to 504483 and 613001 to 617155. Export car serial numbers were 603001 to 603183. Engine numbers were 6C-12001 to 6C-20787.

Model SD, 4-cyl.

Model No.	Body Type & Seating	Factory Price	Shipping Weight	Prod. Total
SD-4	2-dr. Rds.-2P	985	NA	Note 1
SD-4	4-dr. Tr.-4P	985	NA	Note 1

Note 1: Total production was 24,849.

Model EC, 6-cyl.

Model No.	Body Type & Seating	Factory Price	Shipping Weight	Prod. Total
EC-6	4-dr. Tr.-5P	1389	NA	Note 1
EC-6	4-dr. Tr.-7P	1450	NA	Note 1

Note 1: Total production was 8,751.

ENGINE: [Model SD] L-head. Inline. Four (cast enbloc). Gray cast iron. B & S: 3-1/2 x 5 in. Disp.: 192.4 cu. in. Brake H.P.: 30. N.A.C.C. H.P.: 20. Valve lifters: solid. Carb.: Holley one-barrel. [Model EC] L-head. Inline. Six (cast enbloc). Gray cast iron. B & S: 3-1/2 x 5 in. Disp.: 288.6 cu. in. Brake H.P.: 40. N.A.C.C. H.P.: 29. Valve lifters: solid. Carb.: Holley one-barrel.

CHASSIS: [Model SD-4] W.B.: 108.3 in. Frt/Rear Tread: 56/56 in. Tires: 33 x 4 in. [Model EC-6] W.B.: 121.3 in. Frt/Rear Tread: 56/56 in.

TECHNICAL: Selective sliding gear transmission. Speeds: 3F/1R. Floor mounted gearshift controls. Leather faced cone clutch. Full-floating rear axle. External contracting rear wheel brakes. Wood spoke artillery wheels.

OPTIONS: Front bumper. Spare tire(s). Outside rear view mirror. "Fat Man" steering wheel.

HISTORICAL: Introduced [Model EC] July 1914-June 1915; [Model SD] June 1914-June 1915. Model year sales: 33,600. Innovations: Improved braking and steering systems. Gas tank stiffened and strengthened. Larger tires on SD four. Albert Erskine became president of Studebaker Corporation in 1915. Corporate profits exceeded $9 million. Frederick Fish became chairman of the board. John M. Studebaker was named honorary president.

1916

STUDEBAKER — MODEL SF FOUR-FORTY — SERIES 16 & 17 — FOUR: New appearance features for 1916 Studebakers included smoother body lines and wider rear tonneaus for touring cars. The jump seats inside seven-passenger open cars folded into the floor instead of the back of the front seat. The landau roadster, with a blind quarter top with top irons, made a reappearance. It had oval shaped "opera" windows on each side. Colors for the year were dark Studebaker blue with white striping. The fenders, hood and runningboards were black. The wheels were finished in blue with black trim. Wheelbase increased to 112 inches.

Several changes occurred in the middle of the production run. A splash apron was added below the radiator. The fuel tank was moved to the rear of the chassis. A divided front seat replaced the contoured bench in touring cars. Vehicles having these changes were in Series 17 and were sold as first series 1917 models.

STUDEBAKER — MODEL ED-6 — SERIES 16 & 17 — SIX: The six-cylinder Studebaker for 1916 had the same appearance changes as seen on the fours. The sixes continued to feature a larger wheelbase and longer front end sheet metal. The wheelbase increased to 122 inches. Body styles were the same as for model SF, plus a four-passenger coupe, seven-passenger limousine and a sedan.

Cars produced late in the production run had the same running modifications as described for four-cylinder cars. These cars were sold as 1917 models. An all-weather car was one new model.

Serial Number Data:
Model SF Series 16 (domestic): 460001 to 474180.
Model SF Series 16 (export): 450001 to 453228.
Model SF Series 17 (domestic): 474181 to 500369. Also: 100000 to 109500.
Engine Numbers:
Model SF Series 16: 50001 to 67100.
Model SF Series 17: 67151 to 96000 and 1000 to 9579.
Serial Number Data:
Model ED Series 16 (domestic): 630001 to 637260.
Model ED Series 16 (export): 624001 to 624865.
Model ED Series 17 (domestic): 637261 to 655270. Also: 200000 to 207500.
Model ED Series 17 (export): 624866 to 626023. Also: 200000 to 207500.
Engine Numbers:
Model ED Series 16: 25001 to 33153.
Model ED Series 17: 33270 to 51279 and 1000 to 7248.

Model SF, 4-cyl.

Model No.	Body Type & Seating	Factory Price	Shipping Weight	Prod. Total
SF	2-dr. Rds.-3P	850	NA	Note 1
SF	4-dr. Tr.-7P	885	NA	Note 1
SF	2-dr. Lan. Rds.-3P	1150	NA	Note 1

(1917 only model)

Model No.	Body Type & Seating	Factory Price	Shipping Weight	Prod. Total
SF	4-dr. A/W Sed.-7P	1565	NA	Note 1

Note 1: Total Model SF production was 80,842 cars between June 1915 and April 1918.

Note 2: Prices for the 1917 series were as follows: two-door roadster ($850); four-door touring ($875) and landau roadster ($1,150).

Model ED, 6-cyl.

Model No.	Body Type & Seating	Factory Price	Shipping Weight	Prod. Total
ED	2-dr. Rds.-3P	1000	NA	Note 1
ED	2-dr. Lan. Rds.-3P	1350	NA	Note 1
ED	4-dr. Tr.-7P	1050	NA	Note 1
ED	2-dr. Cpe.-4P	1550	NA	Note 1
ED	2-dr. Sed.-5P	1675	NA	Note 1
ED	3-dr. Limo.-7P	2250	NA	Note 1

(1917 only model)

Model No.	Body Type & Seating	Factory Price	Shipping Weight	Prod. Total
ED	4-dr. A/W Sed.-7P	1675	NA	Note 1

Note 1: Total Model ED production was 60,712 cars between June 1915 and January 1918.

Note 2: Prices for the 1917 Series were as follows: two-door roadster ($1,060); two-door landau roadster ($1,350); four-door touring ($1,085); two-door coupe ($1,600); two-door sedan ($1,675) and three-door limousine ($2,500).

ENGINE: [Model SF] L-head. Inline. Four. Gray cast iron. B & S: 3-7/8 x 5 in. Disp.: 235.6 cu. in. Brake H.P.: 44. N.A.C.C. H.P.: 24. Valve lifters: solid. Carb.: Holley one-barrel. [Model ED] L-head. Inline. Six. Gray cast iron. B & S: 3-7/8 x 5 in. Disp.: 353.8 cu. in. Brake H.P.: 54. N.A.C.C. H.P.: 36. Valve lifters: solid. Carb.: Holley one-barrel.

CHASSIS: [Model SF] W.B.: 112 in. Frt/Rear Tread: 56/56 in. Tires: 34 x 4 in. [Model ED] W.B.: 122 in. Frt/Rear Tread: 56/56 in. Tires: 34 x 4 in.

TECHNICAL: Selective sliding transmission. Speeds: 3F/1R. Floor mounted gearshift controls. Leather faced cone-type clutch. Full-floating rear axle. External contracting rear wheel brakes. Wood spoke artillery wheels.

OPTIONS: Front bumper. Spare tire(s). Outside rear view mirror. "Fat Man" steering wheel.

HISTORICAL: Introduced June 1915. Model production: 141,554 (about 25,000 cars were built in the 16th series). Innovations: (Series 16) Cylinder bore size increased. Carburetion improved and relocated. Improved water and oil pump drive systems. Improved clutch. Stronger propeller shaft. Larger brakes with equalizer. Sturdier rear axle. (Series 17) Fuel tank in rear. Vacuum tank replaces gravity feed. All-weather car added and exclusive to Series 17. Albert Erskine continued as Studebaker's president.

1917

STUDEBAKER — MODEL SF — SERIES 18 — FOUR: The Model SF continued to be sold in the second part of the 1917 model year and the early part of the 1918 model year. Production continued until April 1918. Cars in the 18th series had some changes in body styles and seating arrangements. One characteristic change was that the front passenger seat in the touring car could be reversed to face towards the rear. The jump seats now folded and slid under the contoured bench seat at the rear of the tonneau. Roadsters and touring cars could be ordered in gun metal gray.

STUDEBAKER — MODEL ED — SERIES 18 — SIX: The limousine had a handsome new body of elegant design and furnishings. Changes in other models were about the same as on fours, which used virtually the same bodies. The sixes had the longer chassis and front end sheet metal again.

Serial Number Data:
Model SF Series 18 (domestic): 109501 to 133051.
Model SF Series 18 (export): 10001 to 12906.
Engine Numbers:
Model SF Series 18: 7249 to 34600.
Serial Number Data:
Model ED Series 18 (domestic): 207501 to 233495.
Model ED Series 18 (export): 20001 to 21334.
Engine Numbers:
Model ED Series 18: 9580 to 35966.

Model SF, 4-cyl.

Model No.	Body Type & Seating	Factory Price	Shipping Weight	Prod. Total
SF	2-dr. Rds.-3P	1025	NA	Note 1
SF	4-dr. Tr.-7P	1050	NA	Note 1
SF	2-dr. Lan. Rds.-3P	NA	NA	Note 1
SF	4-dr. A/W Sed.-7P	1250	NA	Note 1

Note 1: See 1916 production total.

Model ED, 6-cyl.

Model No.	Body Type & Seating	Factory Price	Shipping Weight	Prod. Total
ED	2-dr. Rds.-3P	1335	NA	Note 1
ED	2-dr. Lan. Rds.-3P	1550	NA	Note 1
ED	4-dr. Tr.-7P	1385	NA	Note 1
ED	2-dr. Cpe.-4P	1850	NA	Note 1
ED	2-dr. Sed.-5P	1850	NA	Note 1
ED	3-dr. Limo.-7P	2750	NA	Note 1
ED	4-dr. A/W Sed.-7P	1565	NA	Note 1

Note 1: See 1916 production total.

ENGINE: [Model SF] L-head. Inline. Four. Gray cast iron. B & S: 3-7/8 x 5 in. Disp.: 235.6 cu. in. Brake H.P.: 44. Net H.P.: 24. Valve lifters: solid. Carb.: Holley one-barrel. [Model ED] L-head. Inline. Six. Gray cast iron. B & S: 3-7/8 x 5 in. Disp.: 353.8 cu. in. Brake H.P.: 54. Net H.P.: 36. Valve lifters: solid. Carb.: Holley one-barrel.

CHASSIS: [Model SF] W.B.: 112 in. Frt/Rear Tread: 56/56 in. Tires: 34 x 4 in. [Model ED] W.B.: 122 in. Frt/Rear Tread: 56/56 in. Tires: 34 x 4 in.

TECHNICAL: Selective sliding transmission. Speeds: 3F/1R. Floor mounted gearshift controls. Leather faced cone-type clutch. Full-floating rear axle. External contracting rear wheel brakes. Wood spoke artillery wheels.

OPTIONS: Front bumper. Spare tire(s). Outside rear view mirror. "Fat Man" steering wheel. Runningboard luggage gates.

HISTORICAL: See 1916 notes.

1918-19

STUDEBAKER — "LIGHT FOUR" MODEL SH — SERIES 19 — FOUR: The Light Four of 1918 is a rare Studebaker model. It was built on a 112-inch wheelbase and came as a touring, sedan and roadster. Appearance changes included smoother, more gently rounded body lines and a low slung look to the entire car. The rear edge of the rear doors slanted diagonally upwards near the rear fender contours.

STUDEBAKER — "LIGHT SIX" MODEL EH — SERIES 19 — SIX: This car was introduced as a "Light Six" and later called the "Special Six." Low slung bodies with smoothly rounded hood and cowl feature lines made these handsome automobiles. The roadster had a rounded rear deck and a new model was the four-passenger "chummy" roadster on which the rear of the body swooped downward in a sharp curve. It had individual front bucket seats. Standard body colors were maroon or dark blue.

STUDEBAKER — "BIG SIX" MODEL EG — SERIES 19 — SIX: The Model EG Big Six came only as a touring. The top panel of the hood and the cowl curved across the car. The main body feature line began at the radiator and ran in a straight line across the length of the hood sides and fully along the body belt line. The hood side panels were higher than on previous Studebakers. There were 14 tall ventilating louvers on the rear half of the hood side panels. The headlight buckets had a curved rectangular shaped housing circular lenses.

SERIAL NUMBER DATA: [Model SH] Serial numbers were stamped on a plate attached to the left frame member under the front fender. U.S. serial numbers were 133101 to 141975. Canadian serial numbers were 12951 and up. Engine numbers were 4001 to 4999; 41001 to 45000 and A.F. 1001 to A.F. 7950. [Model EH] Serial numbers were in the same location as on the "Light Four." Starting: 233501 to 257464. Canadian numbers were 21351 to 23256. Engine numbers were stamped on the starter motor support. Engine numbers were 6001 to 6999; 61001 to 70000 and BF 1001 to BF 18000. [Model EG] Serial numbers were in the same locations as on other 1918-19 models. U.S. numbers were 290001 to 301050. Canadian numbers were 29001 to 30138. Engine numbers were in the same location as on other 1918-19 models. Engine numbers were 7001 to 7999; 71001 to 73600 and CF 1001 to CF 31253.

Model SH, 4-cyl.

Model No.	Body Type & Seating	Factory Price	Shipping Weight	Prod. Total
SH	2-dr. Rds.-2P	1050	NA	Note 1
SH	4-dr. Tr.-5P	995	NA	Note 1
SH	4-dr. Sed.-5P	1525	NA	Note 1

Note 1: Total production was 12,500 according to one source; 8,900 according to a second source.

Model EH, 6-cyl.

Model No.	Body Type & Seating	Factory Price	Shipping Weight	Prod. Total
EH	4-dr. Tr.-5P	1395	NA	Note 1
EH	4-dr. Clb. Rds.-4P	1395	NA	Note 1
EH	2-dr. Rds.-2P	1450	NA	Note 1
EH	4-dr. Sed.-5P	1950	NA	Note 1
EH	2-dr. Cpe.-4P	1950	NA	Note 1

Note 1: Total production was 25,801.

Note 2: The four-passenger "chummy" roadster was also called a club roadster as listed above.

Model EG, 6-cyl.

Model No.	Body Type & Seating	Factory Price	Shipping Weight	Prod. Total
EG	4-dr. Tr.-7P	1795	NA	11,757

ENGINE: [Model SH] L-head. Inline. Four. Cast iron block. B & S: 3-1/2 x 5 in. Disp.: 192.4 cu. in. Brake H.P.: 40 @ 2000 R.P.M. N.A.C.C. H.P.: 19.6. Valve lifters: solid. Carb.: Stromberg one-barrel (plain tube). [Model EH] L-head. Inline. Six. Cast iron block. B & S: 3-1/2 x 5 in. Disp.: 288.6 cu. in. Brake H.P.: 50 @ 2000 R.P.M. N.A.C.C. H.P.: 29.4. Valve lifters: solid. Carb.: Ball & Ball one-barrel. [Model EG] L-head. Inline. Six. Cast iron block. B & S: 3-7/8 x 5 in. Disp.: 353.8 cu. in. C.R.: 4.1:1. Brake H.P.: 60 @ 2000 R.P.M. N.A.C.C. H.P.: 36. Main bearings: four. Valve lifters: solid. Carb.: Ball & Ball one-barrel.

CHASSIS: [Model SH] W.B.: 112 in. Frt/Rear Tread: 56/56 in. Tires: 32 x 3.5 in. [Model EH] W.B.: 119 in. Frt/Rear Tread: 56/56 in. Tires: 32 x 4 in. [Model EG] W.B.: 120 in. Frt/Rear Tread: 56/56 in.

TECHNICAL: Selective sliding transmission. Speeds: 3F/1R. Floor mounted gearshift controls. Aluminum cone clutch with leather facing. Semi-floating rear axle. External contracting rear wheel brakes. Wood spoke artillery wheels.

Note: The rear axle transmission (transaxle) used on 1913-17 Studebakers was dropped this year on all models. Hotchkiss drive was adopted.

OPTIONS: Front bumper. Runningboard toolbox. Moto-meter. Spare tire(s). Spotlight(s). Outside rear view mirror. Runningboard luggage gate. Wire spoke wheels.

HISTORICAL: Introduced February 1918. Model year sales: 50,058. Model year production: (1918) 18,419; (1919) 35,051. Innovations: Transaxle eliminated. Aluminum cone clutch replaces pressed steel type. Redesigned frame narrowing at front. Hotchkiss drive. Underslung springs with bronze bushings. Detachable cylinder head on Big Six. Clutch brake. This year's models marked a complete break from Studebaker's E-M-F origins as all three lines of cars were completely new. Albert Erskine continued as president of the corporation. Production was held down by effects of World War I.

1920-21

STUDEBAKER LIGHT SIX — MODEL EJ — SERIES 20-21 — SIX: The Studebaker Light Six, Model EJ, was an all-new automobile. While the general size and appearance was somewhat similar to the earlier Light Six, detail changes created a more modern looking car. The radiator shell was flatter and had a square opening for the radiator core. It was finished in body color and decorated with a circular Studebaker badge. The hood was shorter and had vertical louvers along the length of the side panels. The new cowl panel had a gentle, upward sweep. Larger doors were seen. All cars in the EJ line were normally finished in black, which was the standard factory color. The main difference between 1920 (Series 20) and 1921 (Series 21) models was in body styles and factory prices.

STUDEBAKER SPECIAL SIX — MODEL EH — SERIES 20-21 — SIX: The Special Six Model EH had only a few changes from 1919 models. Torpedo-shaped cowl lights and exterior door handles on open cars were among the changes. The rear fender design was slightly different than on the earlier cars in this line. Standard body colors continued to be maroon or dark blue.

STUDEBAKER BIG SIX — MODEL EG — SERIES 20-21 — SIX: The appearance of the Model EG Big Six was refined for 1920 and slightly updated for 1921. In 1920, cowl lights were added and the windshield frame was redesigned. It now had a straighter bottom section and slanted vertical uprights with one-piece glass. For 1921, a reverse curve was added to the back edge of the rear fenders.

I.D. DATA: [Model EJ] Serial numbers were located on the left side of frame over front axle. Starting: 1000001. Ending: 1035002. Engine numbers were located on a brass plate on the right rear motor support. Engine numbers are not available. [Model EH] Serial numbers were located on the left side of frame over front axle. Starting: 257465. Ending: 290000. Also: 504501 to 535876. Engine numbers were located on a brass plate on right rear motor support. Starting: BG 17001. Ending: BG 19537. Also: BG 49243 to BG 85644. [Model EG] Serial numbers were stamped on a plate attached to the left frame member under the front fender. Starting: 315701. Ending: 335069. Engine numbers were stamped on the starter motor support. Starting: CG 10001. Ending: CG 31253. Body serial numbers were stamped on the body frame just inside the right front door or stamped on a small aluminum plate attached to the body sill or embossed on a plate attached to engine side of firewall.

Model EJ, 6-cyl.

Model No.	Body Type & Seating	Factory Price	Shipping Weight	Prod. Total
(1920)				
6EJ	4-dr. Tr.-5P	1485	2550	Note 1
6EJ	2-dr. Lan. Rds.-2P	1650	2670	Note 1
6EJ	4-dr. Sed.-5P	2150	2900	Note 1
(1921)				
6EJ	4-dr. Tr.-5P	1485	2550	Note 2
6EJ	2-dr. Rds.-2P	1750	2480	Note 2
6EJ	2-dr. Cpe. Rds.-2P	1650	2690	Note 2
6EJ	4-dr. Sed.-5P	2150	2900	Note 2

Note 1: About 7,000 Light Sixes were built in the (1920) Series 20.

Note 2: About 28,000 Light Sixes were built in the (1921) Series 21.

Model EH, 6-cyl.

Model No.	Body Type & Seating	Factory Price	Shipping Weight	Prod. Total
(1920)				
6EH	4-dr. Tr.-5P	1685	2995	Note 1
6EH	2-dr. Rds.-2P	1685	2895	Note 1
6EH	4-dr. Rds.-4P	1685	2940	Note 1
6EH	2-dr. Cpe.-4P	2435	3100	Note 1
6EH	4-dr. Sed.-5P	2685	3310	Note 1
(1921)				
6EH	4-dr. Tr.-5P	1750	3035	Note 2
6EH	4-dr. Rds.-4P	1750	3035	Note 2
6EH	2-dr. Rds.-2P	1750	2895	Note 2
6EH	2-dr. Cpe.-4P	2650	3255	Note 2
6EH	4-dr. Sed.-5P	2750	3290	Note 2

Note 1: Total production for Series 20 was 45,096 cars built between October 1919 and May 1921.

Note 2: Total production for Series 21 was 23,520 cars built between April 1921 and December 1921.

Model EG, 6-cyl.

Model No.	Body Type & Seating	Factory Price	Shipping Weight	Prod. Total
(1920)				
6EG	4-dr. Tr.-7P	2135	3175	14,970
(1921)				
6EG	4-dr. Tr.-7P	2150	3230	Note 1
6EG	2-dr. Cpe.-4P	NA	3451	Note 1
6EG	4-dr. Sed.-7P	NA	3665	Note 1

Note 1: Total production for Series 21 (1921) was 6,277.

Note 2: The 1920 Big Sixes were built between November 1919 and April 1921. The 1921 Big Sixes were built between April 1921 and December 1921.

ENGINE: [Model EJ] L-head. Inline. Six (Cast enbloc). Cast iron block (aluminum cylinder head). B & S: 3-1/8 x 4-1/2 in. Disp.: 207.1 cu. in. C.R.: 4.1:1. Brake H.P.: 40 @ 2000 R.P.M. N.A.C.C. H.P.: 23.44. Valve lifters: solid. Carb.: Stromberg one-barrel. [Model EH] L-head. Inline. Six (detachable cylinder head). Cast iron block. B & S: 3-1/2 x 5 in. Disp.: 288.6 cu. in. C.R.: 4.1:1. Brake H.P.: 50 @ 2000 R.P.M. N.A.C.C. H.P.: 29.04. Main bearings: four. Valve lifters: solid. Carb.: Stromberg one-barrel. [Model EG] L-head. Inline. Six. Cast iron block. B & S: 3-7/8 x 5 in. Disp.: 353.8 cu. in. C.R.: 4.1:1. Brake H.P.: 60 @ 2000 R.P.M. N.A.C.C. H.P.: 36.04. Main bearings: four. Valve lifters: solid. Carb.: Ball & Ball one-barrel.

CHASSIS: [Model EJ] W.B.: 112 in. Frt/Rear Tread: 56/56 in. Tires: 32 x 4 in. [Model EH] W.B.: 119 in. Frt/Rear Tread: 56/56 in. Tires: 32 x 4 in. [Model EG] W.B.: 126 in. Frt/Rear Tread: 56/56 in. Tires: 33 x 4.5 in.

TECHNICAL: Selective sliding transmission. Speeds: 3F/1R. Floor mounted gearshift controls. Clutch: (Light Six) single disc; (others) cone type. Shaft drive. Semi-floating rear axle. Overall ratio: [Model EJ] 4.55:1; [Model EH] 4.33:1 and [Model EG] 3.71:1. External contracting rear wheel brakes. Wood spoke artillery wheels.

OPTIONS: Front bumper. Budd wire spoke wheels. Spare tire(s). Outside rear view mirror. Moto-meter. Luggage rack. Toolbox (running-board type). Spotlight(s). Wind wings.

HISTORICAL: Introduced [EJ] April 1920; [EH] October 1919; [EG] November 1919. Innovations: [EJ] Improved valves. Single disc clutch. Transmission lock. Aluminum head. Positive feed oiling. Optional rear end ratios of 4.08:1 or 5.00:1; [EH] Detachable cylinder head. Alemite lubrication; [EG] Body refinements. Alemite lubrication. Calendar year sales: (1920) 47,981; (1921) 69,863. Calendar year production: (1920) N/A; (1921) 65,000. Model year sales: (1920) 51,474; (1921) 66,423. Model year production: (1920) 67,066; (1921) 36,797 approximate. Albert Erskine continued as president of Studebaker. A new plant was opened for manufacture of Light Sixes. The first car was turned out on April 30, 1920. Studebaker ended production of horsedrawn vehicles this year. The company was America's fourth-ranked automaker in 1921.

1922

STUDEBAKER LIGHT SIX — MODEL EJ — SERIES 22 — SIX: The Light Six, Model EJ, continued into 1922 with only minor change. Cowl lamps that resembled miniature coach lights were added. Also new was an air ventilator on the top of the cowl. Reverse curve style rear fenders were also adopted. A crankcase breather tube was a technical improvement.

STUDEBAKER SPECIAL SIX — MODEL EL — SERIES 22 — SIX: The 1922 Special Six had styling more like that of last year's Big Six, which was considered more modern. Obvious appearance changes included a more massive windshield frame with circular cowl lamps at the bottom corners. Touring cars had a one-piece windshield. Roadsters had a two-piece version with torpedo-shaped cowl lamps. Closed models had rectangular cowl lamps. A cowl ventilator was new for all body styles.

STUDEBAKER BIG SIX — MODEL EK — SERIES 22 — SIX: Several refinements were seen on the 1922 Studebaker Big Six Model EK. A one-piece windshield was used. New headlights were seen. A courtesy light was added to the left side of the cars for nighttime illumination.

I.D. DATA: [Model EJ] Serial numbers were located on the left side of the frame over front axle. Serial numbers were 1035003 and up. Engine numbers were located on a brass plate on the right rear motor support. Engine numbers are not available. [Model EL] Serial numbers were located on the left side of frame over front axle. Starting: 3000001. Ending: 3039122. Engine numbers were located on a brass plate on the right rear motor support. Engine numbers EL-1 and up were used. [Model EK] Serial numbers were stamped on a plate attached to left frame member under front fender. Starting: 2000001. Ending: 2017139. Engine numbers were stamped on the starter motor support. Engine numbers were EK-1 and up. The body serial numbering system was the same as 1920-21.

Model EJ, 6-cyl.

Model No.	Body Type & Seating	Factory Price	Shipping Weight	Prod. Total
6EJ	Chassis	NA	1195	Note 1
6EJ	2-dr. Rds.-3P	1125	2480	Note 1
6EJ	4-dr. Tr.-5P	1150	2550	Note 1
6EJ	2-dr. Cpe. Rds.-2P	1550	2690	Note 1
6EJ	4-dr. Sed.-5P	1850	2900	Note 1

Note 1: Total production was approximately 49,000 Light Sixes built in the (1922) Series 22.

Note 2: Prices on all models were gradually lowered. For example, the touring car dropped from $1,485 in 1921 to $1,150 in 1922.

Model EL, 6-cyl.

6EL	Chassis	NA	2500	Note 1
6EL	2-dr. Rds.-2P	1585	2920	Note 1
6EL	4-dr. Tr.-5P	1635	3155	Note 1
6EL	4-dr. Rds.-4P	1635	3085	Note 1
6EL	2-dr. Cpe.-4P	2450	3355	Note 1
6EL	4-dr. Sed.-5P	2550	3545	Note 1

Note 1: The Model EL Special Six was produced from November 1921 to July 1924 as a 1922-1923-1924 model. A total of 111,443 were built for the three years combined.

Model EK, 6-cyl.

6EK	Std. Chassis	NA	2543	Note 1
6EK	4-dr. Tr.-7P	1985	3310	Note 1
6EK	2-dr. Cpe.-4P	2850	3445	Note 1
6EK	4-dr. Sed.-7P	2950	3670	Note 1
6EK	Spl. Chassis	NA	NA	Note 1

Note 1: The Model EK Big Six was produced from November 1921 to July 1924 as a 1922-1923-1924 model. A total of 48,892 were built for the three years combined.

ENGINE: See 1921 engine data. There were no major specifications changes for 1922. Light Sixes after engine number 35810 had four ring pistons.

CHASSIS: [Model EJ] W.B.: 112 in. Frt/Rear Tread: 56/56 in. Tires: 32 x 4 in. [Model EL] W.B.: 119 in. Frt/Rear Tread: 56/56 in. Tires: 32 x 4 in. [Model EK] W.B.: 126 in. Frt/Rear Tread: 56/56 in. Tires: 33 x 4.5 in.

TECHNICAL: Selective sliding transmission. Speeds: 3F/1R. Floor mounted gearshift controls. Clutch: Single plate dry disc type. Shaft drive. Semi-floating rear axle. Overall ratio: [EJ] 4.55:1; [EH] 4.33:1; [EK] 3.71:1. External contracting rear wheel brakes. Wood spoke artillery wheels.

OPTIONS: Bumper(s). Budd wire spoke wheels. Spare tire(s). Outside rear view mirror. Moto-meter. Luggage rack. Toolbox (runningboard type). Spotlight(s). Wind wings.

HISTORICAL: Introduced [EJ] April 1920; [EL] November 1921; [EK] November 1921. Innovations: [EJ] Oil filler in distributor housing support. Four ring pistons. Fuse location moved from cowl box to lighting switch. [EL] New disc clutch. [EK] New disc clutch. Body refinements. Calendar year sales: approximately 98,000. Model year sales: 110,269. Model year production: 107,378. Total sales this year amounted to $133 million. Albert Erskine continued as company president.

1923

STUDEBAKER LIGHT SIX — MODEL EM — SERIES 23 — SIX: The new EM had nearly the same chassis as previous Studebaker Light Sixes. A new feature was an all-steel body. On open cars the cowl lamps were now set into the bottom corners of the windshield frame.

STUDEBAKER SPECIAL SIX — MODEL EL — SERIES 23 — SIX: All 1923 Special Sixes had one-piece windshields. Open styles had cowl lamps set into the lower corners with built-in visors at the top. Closed cars had glareproof visors. Automatic wipers and taillights were now standard equipment. Step plates and aluminum kick plates were added to the runningboards. Standard color was Studebaker blue for the main body. The hood was black and wheels were blue. Gold pin striping was used on the wheels and hood louvers. An all-walnut steering wheel with updated spark/throttle controls was also new.

STUDEBAKER BIG SIX — MODEL EK — SERIES 23 — SIX: There were big changes in the appearance of the 1923 Big Six. Nickel-plated radiator shells were used. Standard equipment included automatic wipers; stoplights; nickel-plated bumpers, moto-meter and disc wheels. Two new models were the five-passenger coupe and the five-passenger speedster. The former was similar to the two-door sedan while the latter carried dual side mounted spare tires, a rear mounted touring trunk and extra plated parts included bright metal grab handles and runningboard kick plates.

I.D. DATA: [Model EM] Serial numbers were located on the left side of frame over front axle. Starting: 1084001. Ending: 1131849. An overlap in 1923-1924 Light Six serial numbers stems from the fact that each body style had a different starting number as follows: (touring) — 1131728, (roadster) — 1131727, (sedan) — 1128270 and (coupe roadster) — 1131850. Engine numbers were located on a brass plate on the right rear motor support. Engine numbers are not available. [Model EL] Serial numbers were located on the left side of frame over front axle. Starting: 3039123. Ending: 3075316. Engine numbers were located on a brass plate on the right rear motor support. Engine numbers EL-1 and up were used. [Model EK] Serial numbers were stamped on a plate attached to the left frame member under front fender. Starting: 2027500. Ending: 2060000. Engine numbers were stamped on the starter motor support. Engine numbers were EK-1 and up. The body serial numbering system was the same as 1920-21.

Model EM, 6-cyl.

Model No.	Body Type & Seating	Factory Price	Shipping Weight	Prod. Total
6EM	Chassis	NA	1945	Note 1
6EM	2-dr. Rds.-2P	975	2510	Note 1
6EM	4-dr. Tr.-5P	975	2650	Note 1
6EM	2-dr. Cpe.-2P	1225	2730	Note 1
6EM	4-dr. Sed.-5P	1550	3030	Note 1

Note 1: The Model EM Light Six was produced from December 1922 to July 1924 as a 1923-1924 model. A total of 118,022 were built for the two years combined.

Model EL, 6-cyl.

Model No.	Body Type & Seating	Factory Price	Shipping Weight	Prod. Total
6EL	Chassis	NA	2510	Note 1
6EL	4-dr. Tr.-5P	1275	3200	Note 1
6EL	2-dr. Rds.-4P	1275	3405	Note 1
6EL	2-dr. Rds.-2P	1250	3015	Note 1
6EL	2-dr. Cpe.-4P	1875	3600	Note 1
6EL	4-dr. Sed.-5P	2050	3605	Note 1

Note 1: The Model EL Special Six was produced from November 1921 to July 1924 as a 1922-1923-1924 model. A total of 111,443 were built for the three years combined.

Model EK, 6-cyl.

Model No.	Body Type & Seating	Factory Price	Shipping Weight	Prod. Total
6EK	Chassis	NA	2543	Note 1
6EK	4-dr. Tr.-7P	1750	3625	Note 1
6EK	4-dr. Spds.-5P	1835	3725	Note 1
6EK	2-dr. Cpe.-5P	2550	3750	Note 1
6EK	2-dr. Cpe.-4P	2400	3730	Note 1
6EK	4-dr. Sed.-7P	2750	4090	Note 1

Note 1: The Model EK Big Six was produced from November 1921 to July 1924 as a 1922-1923-1924 model. A total of 48,892 were built for the three years combined.

ENGINE: See 1921 engine data for Light Six, Special Six and Big Six, respectively.

CHASSIS: [Model EM] W.B.: 112 in. Frt/Rear Tread: 56/56 in. Tires: 31 x 4 in. [Model EL] W.B.: 119 in. Frt/Rear Tread: 56/56 in. Tires: 32 x 4 in. [Model EK] W.B.: 126 in. Frt/Rear Tread: 56/56 in. Tires: 33 x 4.5 in.

TECHNICAL: See 1922 drivetrain data. The Light Six Model EM had the same chassis features as the Light Six Model EJ.

OPTIONS: Bumper(s). Budd wire spoke wheels. Disc wheels. Spare tire(s). Outside rear view mirror. Moto-meter. Luggage rack (rear mounted). Touring trunk. Spotlight(s). Wind wings.

HISTORICAL: Introduced [EM] December 1922; [EL] November 1921; [EK] November 1921. Innovations: [EM] Cast iron cylinder head. New engine block. New intake system. [EL] New windshield design. New sun visors. New controls. Stoplights. [EK] Nickel radiator. New speedster style. Disc wheels. Calendar year registrations: 94,023. Model year sales: 145,167. Model year production: 89,418. Studebaker Corporation's 1923 income was $18,342,223—the highest in its history.

1924

STUDEBAKER LIGHT SIX — MODEL EM — SERIES 24 — SIX: The 1924 Light Six got fancier. Standard equipment now included bumpers, balloon tires and nickel-plated radiator shells.

STUDEBAKER SPECIAL SIX — MODEL EL — SERIES 24 — SIX: A sharp crease line was added on the hood of 1924 Special Six models. A new nickel-plated radiator shell was also seen. The cowl housed a new type of inspection lamp and closed cars had courtesy lamps on the lower left-hand side of the cowl, above the runningboard. The touring was fitted with plated passenger grab handles. Another new feature was runningboard kick plates. Standard body colors changed to Studebaker blue or Princess Louise Lake maroon. Wood spoke wheels were standard equipment.

STUDEBAKER BIG SIX — MODEL EK — SERIES 24 — SIX: The 1924 Big Six was nearly identical to the all new 1923 model. No major changes were made until the 1925 model production started in mid-1924.

I.D. DATA: [Model EM] Serial numbers were on left side of frame over front axle. Starting: 1128270. Ending: 1202000. An overlap of 1923-1924 serial numbers stems from the fact that each body style had different starting numbers. (See 1923 serial number data.) Engine number on brass plate on right rear motor support. Engine numbers not available. [Model EV] Serial numbers were on left side of frame over front axle. Starting: 3075317. Ending: 3120000. Engine numbers on brass plate on right rear motor support. Engine numbers were EL-1 and up. [Model EK] Serial numbers were on left side of frame over front axle. Starting: 2027500. Ending: 2060000. Engine numbers on brass plate on right rear motor support. Engine numbers were EK-1 and up.

Model EM, 6-cyl.

Model No.	Body Type & Seating	Factory Price	Shipping Weight	Prod. Total
6EM	4-dr. Tr.-5P	995	2650	Note 1
6EM	2-dr. Rds.-3P	1025	2510	Note 1
6EM	2-dr. Cpe. Rds.-2P	975	2730	Note 1
6EM	4-dr. Cus. Tr.-5P	NA	2830	Note 1
6EM	4-dr. Sed.-5P	1485	3030	Note 1
6EM	2-dr. Cpe.-5P	1195	2955	Note 1

Note 1: The Model EM Light Six was produced from December 1922 to July 1924 as a 1923-1924 model. A total of 118,022 were built for the two years combined.

Model EL, 6-cyl.

Model No.	Body Type & Seating	Factory Price	Shipping Weight	Prod. Total
6EL	4-dr. Tr.-5P	1350	3305	Note 1
6EL	2-dr. Rds.-2P	1325	3065	Note 1
6EL	2-dr. Cpe.-5P	1895	3600	Note 1
6EL	4-dr. Sed.-5P	1985	3650	Note 1

Note 1: The Model EL Special Six was produced from November 1921 to July 1924 as a 1922-1923-1924 model. A total of 111,443 were built for the three years combined.

Model EK, 6-cyl.

Model No.	Body Type & Seating	Factory Price	Shipping Weight	Prod. Total
6EK	4-dr. Tr.-7P	1750	3630	Note 1
6EK	4-dr. Spds.-5P	1835	3745	Note 1
6EK	2-dr. Cpe.-5P	2495	3770	Note 1
6EK	4-dr. Sed.-7P	2685	4130	Note 1

Note 1: The Model EK Big Six was produced from November 1921 to July 1924 as a 1922-1923-1924 model. A total of 48,892 were built for the three years combined.

ENGINE: [Model EM] L-head. Inline. Six. Cast iron block. B & S: 3-1/8 x 4-1/2 in. Disp.: 207.1 cu. in. C.R.: 4.38:1. Brake H.P.: 40 @ 2000 R.P.M. N.A.C.C. H.P.: 23.44. Main bearings: four. Valve lifters: solid. Carb.: Stromberg one-barrel. [Model EL] L-head. Inline. Six. Cast iron block. B & S: 3-1/2 x 5 in. Disp.: 288.6 cu. in. C.R.: 4.1:1. Brake H.P.: 50-55 @ 2000 R.P.M. N.A.C.C. H.P.: 29.39. Main bearings: four. Valve lifters: solid. Carb.: Stromberg one-barrel. [Model EK] L-head. Inline. Six. Cast iron block. B & S: 3-7/8 x 5 in. Disp.: 353.8 cu. in. C.R.: 4.1:1. Brake H.P.: 60-65 @ 2000 R.P.M. N.A.C.C. H.P.: 36.04. Main bearings: four. Valve lifters: solid. Carb.: Ball & Ball.

CHASSIS: [Model EM] W.B.: 112 in. Frt/Rear Tread: 56/56 in. Tires: 31 x 4 in. [Model EL] W.B.: 119 in. Frt/Rear Tread: 56/56 in. Tires: 32 x 4 in. [Model EK] W.B.: 126 in. Frt/Rear Tread: 56/56 in. Tires: 33 x 4.5 in.

TECHNICAL: Selective sliding transmission. Speeds: 3F/1R. Floor mounted gearshift controls. Clutch: single plate dry disc. Shaft drive. Semi-floating rear axle. Overall ratio: (EM) 4.55:1; (EL) 4.33:1; (EK) 3.71:1. External contracting rear wheel brakes. Wood spoke artillery wheels.

OPTIONS: Front bumper. Rear bumper. Dual sidemounts (Big Six speedster). Sidemount cover(s). Moto-meter. Spare tire(s). Whitewall tires. Runningboard kick plates. Luggage rack. Touring trunk. Outside rear view mirror. Budd wire spoke wheels. Disc wheels. Spotlight. Wind wings. Balloon tires.

Note: Some accessories were standard equipment on specific models.

HISTORICAL: Introduced [EM] December 1922; [EL] November 1921; [EK] November 1921. Calendar year registrations: 94,700. Model year production: 159,782. Innovations: [EM] Cast iron head on all 1924 models. Stromberg OE-1 carburetor. More stylish trim. [EL] New styling. Nickel radiator shell. Balloon tires optional. Production of 1924 models was halted in July 1924 for changeover to 1925 specifications. At the 1924 New York Automobile Show, Studebaker displayed a 1918 Big Six that had traveled over 500,000 miles in 5-1/2 years. Studebaker announced it had 225 acres of plant space in 1924 and employed 23,000 workers.

1925-26

STUDEBAKER STANDARD SIX — MODEL ER — SERIES 25-26 — SIX: The Model ER Standard Six replaced the Light Six in August 1924 and was sold as a 1925-1926 model. It was a completely restyled line of cars. Appearance changes included a higher, shorter, more rounded hood with a trim band at its rear edge. The multiple vertical louvers on the hood sides were contained within a raised rectangular panel with rounded corners. The front fenders had heavier beading. The rear fenders curved outward at both the front and rear edges. Windshields on open cars were nearly vertical and had heavier frames. Drum type headlamps were used. A new radiator shell was thicker and rounder and nickel-plated. The Duplex models were open body cars with rigid, steel-reinforced tops and pull-down side curtains. Standard equipment included balloon tires, shock absorbers and heaters on all closed cars except the coupe-roadster. Upholstery was of fine quality Spanish leather in open cars and Angora mohair and wool in closed models. All closed cars also had robe rails, wool carpets and silk curtains. Lacquer finish was used on 1925 closed cars. Available colors were light Navajo gray or darker Seminole gray. Open cars for 1925 were finished in black enamel with ivory pin striping. There were numerous running production changes that restorers of today find confusing. Many new colors were added to the 1926 series.

STUDEBAKER SPECIAL SIX — MODEL EQ — SERIES 25-26 — SIX: The 1925 Special Six continued to feature a distinctive, fluted radiator shell. New models included a Duplex phaeton and Duplex roadster with rigid, steel-reinforced tops and pull-down side curtains. Drum style headlamps and heavier beaded front fenders were added. The hood side louver design was similar to that of the Standard Six, but the hood top panel was fluted to meet the radiator contours and had a crease along each upper edge. Other new models included a four-passenger victoria, five-passenger berline (small limousine), brougham sedan, country club coupe and five-passenger coach. A special model, intended for police departments, was called the Sheriff. It was essentially a Special Six touring car chassis with the Big Six engine installed.

STUDEBAKER BIG SIX — MODEL EP — SERIES 25-26 — SIX: The Big Six had the same basic styling changes as the Standard Six including the new radiator, hood line, hood side panels, front and rear fenders, more vertical windshields and heavier windshield frames. It was, of course, a larger, heavier, more powerful car. Duplex open bodies were available along with a special sport phaeton and new closed styles such as the brougham sedan and berline. Standard equipment included: extra balloon tire, tube and tire cover; bumpers front and rear; moto-meter with lock and winged radiator cap; lights controlled from switch on steering wheel; automatic ignition system; one-piece windshield; glareproof visor; automatic windshield cleaner; rearview mirror; cowl and dome lights; extension lamp; stop and taillight; clock; speedometer, gas gauge, oil pressure indicator, ammeter; step pads and runningboard kick plate. As on other 1925 Studebakers, four-wheel hydraulic brakes were a new extra-cost option.

I.D. DATA: [Model ER] Serial numbers were on left side of frame over front axle. Starting: (1925) 1202001; (1926) 1284001. Ending: (1925) 1284000; (1926) 1346100. Engine numbers on brass plate on right rear motor support. Starting: ER-202501. Ending: ER-350001. [Model EQ] Serial numbers were on left side of frame over front axle. Starting: (1925) 3120001; (1926) 3161002. Ending: (1925) 3161001; (1926) 3172932. Engine numbers on brass plate on right rear motor support. Engine numbers were EQ-1 and up. [Model EP] Serial numbers were on left side of frame over front axle. Starting: (1925) 2060001; (1926) 2073001. Ending: (1925) 2073000; (1926) 2102299. Engine numbers on brass plate on right rear motor support. Engine numbers were EP-1 and up.

Model ER, 6-cyl.

Model No.	Body Type & Seating	Factory Price	Shipping Weight	Prod. Total
ER/T	4-dr. Dplx. Phae.-5P	1145	2870	Note 1
ER/R	2-dr. Dplx. Rds.-3P	1125	2760	Note 1
ER/F	2-dr. Coach-5P	1195	2980	Note 1
ER/Q	2-dr. Cty. Clb. Cpe.-3P	1395	2945	Note 1
ER/J	2-dr. Spt. Rds.-3P	1235	2820	Note 1
ER/L	4-dr. Spt. Phae.-5P	NA	2930	Note 1
ER/S	4-dr. Sed.-5P	1595	3260	Note 1
ER/Q	2-dr. Cpe. Rds.-3P	1395	NA	Note 1
ER/B	4-dr. w/Sed.-5P	1600	3260	Note 1
ER/K	2-dr. Cpe.-5P	1495	3110	Note 1
ER/W	4-dr. Ber.-5P	1650	3280	Note 1

Note 1: Total production between August 1924 and August 1926 was 147,099.

Note 2: Add 200 pounds for four-wheel brakes.

Model EQ, 6-cyl.

EQ	2-dr. Dplx. Phae.-3P	1445	3475	Note 1
EQ	2-dr. Dplx. Rds.-3P	1395	3360	Note 1
EQ	2-dr. Vic.-4P	1750	3665	Note 1
EQ	4-dr. Sed.-5P	1895	3855	Note 1
EQ	4-dr. Ber.-5P	NA	3890	Note 1
EQ	4-dr. Brgm.-5P	2120	3785	Note 1
EQ	4-dr. Spt. Rds.-4P	1395	3480	Note 1
EQ	2-dr. Coach-5P	1445	3520	Note 1

Note 1: Total production between August 1924 and July 1926 was 53,780.

Note 2: Add 200 pounds for four-wheel brakes.

Model EP, 6-cyl.

EP	4-dr. Dplx. Phae.-7P	1795	3785	Note 1
EP	2-dr. Cpe.-5P	1645	4030	Note 1
EP	4-dr. Brgm.-5P	2325	4095	Note 1
EP	4-dr. Sed.-7P	2245	4150	Note 1
EP	4-dr. Ber.-7P	2045	4200	Note 1
EP	4-dr. Sed.-5P	2245	3785	Note 1
EP	4-dr. Spt. Phae.-5P	1795	3505	Note 1
EP	2-dr. Clb. Cpe.-5P	2045	3570	Note 1

Note 1: Total production between August 1924 and August 1926 was 40,216.

Note 2: Add 200 pounds for four-wheel brakes.

ENGINE: [Model ER] L-head. Inline. Six. Cast iron block. B & S: 3-3/8 x 4-1/2 in. Disp.: 241.6 cu. in. C.R.: 4.5:1. Brake H.P.: 50 @ 2200 R.P.M. N.A.C.C. H.P.: 27.34. Main bearings: four. Valve lifters: solid. Carb.: Stromberg one-barrel Model T1 or Model OE-1. [Model EQ] L-head. Inline. Six. Cast iron block. B & S: 3-1/2 x 5 in. Disp.: 288.6 cu. in. C.R.: 4.45:1. Brake H.P.: 65 @ 2400 R.P.M. N.A.C.C. H.P.: 29.40. Main bearings: four. Valve lifters: solid. Carb.: Stromberg one-barrel. [Model EP] L-head. Inline. Six. Cast iron block. B & S: 3-7/8 x 5 in. Disp.: 353.8 cu. in. C.R.: 4.45:1. Brake H.P.: 75 @ 2400 R.P.M. N.A.C.C. H.P.: 36.04. Main bearings: four. Valve lifters: solid. Carb.: Ball & Ball one-barrel.

CHASSIS: [Model ER] W.B.: 113 in. Tires: 31 x 5.25 in. (early); 30 x 5.25 in. (late). [Model EQ] W.B.: 120 in. Tires: 32 x 6.20 in. [Model EP] W.B.: 120-127 in. Tires: 34 x 7.30 in.

1925 Studebaker, Special Six (Series EQ), brougham, OCW

1927 Studebaker, President Big Six (Series ES), custom sedan, AA

1927 Studebaker, President Big Six (Series ES), custom victoria, AA

1928 Studebaker, Dictator Six (Series GE - second series), Royal sedan, AA

1928 Studebaker, Commander Six (Series GB), roadster, OCW

1927 Studebaker, Standard Six (Series EU), rumbleseat coupe, AA

1927 Studebaker, President Big Six (Series ES), limousine, AA

1927 Studebaker, Standard Six (Series EU), sport roadster, AA

1928 Studebaker, Commander Six (Series GB), five-passenger sedan, AA

1928-1/2 Studebaker, President Eight (Series FB), sedan, AA

TECHNICAL: Manual transmission (unit type). Speeds: 3F/1R. Floor mounted gearshift controls. Clutch: single plate dry disc. Shaft drive. Semi-floating rear axle. Overall ratio: (ER) 4.18:1, (EQ) 4.36:1, (EP) 4.36:1. Two-wheel mechanical brakes. Wood spoke artillery wheels.

OPTIONS: Front bumper. Rear bumper. Spare tire(s). Dual sidemounts. Sidemount cover(s). Moto-meter. Winged radiator cap. Runningboard kick plates. Heater. Clock. Cigar lighter. Outside rear view mirror. Touring trunk. Trunk rack. Spotlight. Cowl lamps. Balloon tires. Four-wheel hydraulic brakes ($75.00). Painted artillery wheels. Disc wheels. Special paint. Wind wings.

Note: Some accessories were standard equipment on specific models.

HISTORICAL: Introduced [all series] August 1924. Calendar year registrations: (1925) 107,732; (1926) 93,475. Model year production: (1925) 80,365; (1926) 158,463. Innovations: [ER] Full-pressure lubrication. Unit powerplant/transmission. New motor mounts. Improved emergency brake. Alemite lubrication. Optional four-wheel hydraulic brakes. [EQ] Full-pressure lubrication. Unit powerplant/transmission. Higher compression ratio. Improved crankshaft. Larger wheelbase. Optional four-wheel hydraulic brakes. [EP] Full-pressure lubrication. Unit powertrain. Improved crankshaft. Optional four-wheel hydraulic brakes. Ab Jenkins made many record setting runs in Studebaker models. Company paid largest dividend in history during 1925. Paul G. Hoffman was named vice-president in charge of sales in 1925. Harold S. Vance was named vice-president in charge of engineering and production in 1926. Barney Roos joined the company in 1926 as chief engineer.

1927

STUDEBAKER — STANDARD/DICTATOR — MODEL EU — SERIES 27 — SIX: Early in 1927, cars in this line were called Standard Sixes. In the middle of the summer, they were renamed Dictator Sixes. Appearance changes included new bullet-shaped headlights, double bar bumpers with a fluted design and nickel plating, disc wheels and a new Atlanta hood ornament. Closed cars had French style roof visors. Double bead moldings set off the belt line. The lower molding continued across the upper side of the hood to the radiator shell. Attractive two-tone paint schemes were available. Late production cars had chrome-plated bright metal parts. Sport models now included a two-passenger rumbleseat.

STUDEBAKER — SPECIAL SIX — MODEL EQ — SERIES 26-27 — SIX: Production of the Special Six ended in July 1926 and many sources do not show this car as a 1927 model. However, the January 1927 *MoToR Annual Show Number* does list the car as being available as a 1927 model. Also, NADA's Official Used Car Guide gives a range of serial numbers for 1927 Special Sixes. It can therefore be deduced that the model was marketed in early 1927 as a carryover series with few changes from 1926 specifications. Apparently, only four models were still offered. The Special Sixes were the only models still equipped with wood spoke artillery wheels. While other Studebakers had four-wheel mechanical brakes, the Special Sixes had two-wheel mechanical brakes with four-wheel hydraulic brakes as a $75 option.

STUDEBAKER — COMMANDER BIG SIX — MODEL EW — SERIES 27 — SIX: The Commander was Studebaker's slightly cheaper version of the former Big Six. The car was introduced in January 1927, but was not named Commander until about April. The Commander had a 120-inch wheelbase. Styling features included bullet-shaped headlights, double bar bumpers, French type visors, disc wheels and double bead body molding with the lower bead extending across the hoods. An Atlanta style hood mascot was added. Sport models had rumbleseats.

STUDEBAKER — PRESIDENT BIG SIX — MODEL ES — SERIES 27 — SIX: Extensive styling changes marked the new model ES Big Six "President," a custom designed Studebaker sedan. They included lower bodies, more rounded roofs and body panels, two-tone paint (in lacquer), double bead belt moldings with scallops front and rear, disc wheels, large acorn headlights, French style visors, double bar bumpers and luxury interior trim. Only a seven-passenger sedan was sold at first. It was painted Croatan green with an ebony belt line and Ivory striping, or Ebony black with Thistle green belt line and yellow striping. The former had mohair upholstery, the latter was trimmed with broadcloth. Models added later included a seven-passenger touring and a division window limousine with the driving compartment trimmed in leather. The Atlanta type hood mascot was used on all Presidents. Two wheelbases—120 and 127 inches—were available for mounting of these bodies. Standard equipment included nickel-plated bumpers; no-draft ventilating windshield; Watson stabilizers; engine thermometer; clock; hydrostatic gas gauge; coincidental lock; oil filter; Alemite chassis lubrication; automatic wiper; double rear vision mirror; vanity case smoking set; armrests; toggle grips; auto dome light; rear signal light, emergency lamp on extension cord; four-wheel mechanical brakes; disc wheels; balloon tires; cowl lights and twin beam acorn headlights. The limousine also had glass enclosure, leather upholstered driving compartment and auto-phone.

I.D. DATA: [Model EU] Serial numbers were located on left side of frame over front axle. Starting: 1346001. Ending: 1410000. Note: Cars with serial numbers above 1385940 were sold as first series 1928 models. In this book the 1927 specifications apply to all EU models, since all cars were built as 1927 models. Engine numbers were located on the right side of block. Starting: EU-1. Ending: EU-65800. [Model EQ] Serial numbers were located on left side of frame over front axle. Starting: 3173001. Ending: 3200000. Engine numbers were on the starter motor support. The 1927 engine numbers are not available. [Model EW] Serial numbers were on the left side of frame over front axle or on left door hinge pillar. Starting: 4000001. Ending: 4039800. Engine numbers were stamped on right side of crankcase opposite number one cylinder. Starting: EW-1. Ending: EW-40700. Body symbols/numbers were embossed on plate on engine side of firewall. [Model ES] Serial numbers were on a plate on left frame member under front fender. Starting: 2102301. Ending: 2114902. Engine numbers were on starter motor support. Engine numbers were ES-43301 and up. Body numbers were in the same locations as previous Big Six models.

Model EU, 6-cyl.

Model No.	Body Type & Seating	Factory Price	Shipping Weight	Prod. Total
EU	2-dr. Spt. Rds.-2/4P	1245	3000	Note 1
EU	4-dr. Tr.-5P	1165	3080	Note 1
EU	4-dr. Dplx. Tr.-5P	1195	3105	Note 1
EU	4-dr. Tr.-7P	1245	3090	Note 1
EU	2-dr. Bus. Cpe.-2P	1195	3120	Note 1
EU	2-dr. Spt. Cpe.-2/4P	1295	3165	Note 1
EU	2-dr. Vic.-4P	1295	3165	Note 1
EU	4-dr. Sed.(P)-5P	1195	3230	Note 1
EU	4-dr. Sed.(M)-5P	1295	3235	Note 1

Note 1: Total production between June 1926 and September 1927 was 65,333.

Note 2: The (P) sedan has plush upholstery; the (M) sedan has mohair upholstery.

Model EQ, 6-cyl.

Model No.	Body Type & Seating	Factory Price	Shipping Weight	Prod. Total
EQ	4-dr. Dplx. Phae.-5P	1480	3475	Note 1
EQ	2-dr. Coach-5P	1480	3520	Note 1
EQ	4-dr. Brgm.-5P	1830	3785	Note 1
EQ	2-dr. Spt. Rds.-4P	1630	3480	Note 1

Note 1: Total production between August 1924 and July 1926 was 53,780.

Note 2: The above cars were the only models listed in the 1927 *MoToR Annual Show Number.* The above weights are per 1925-1926 specifications.

Model EW, 6-cyl.

Model No.	Body Type & Seating	Factory Price	Shipping Weight	Prod. Total
EW	2-dr. Spt. Rds.-2/4P	1595	3485	Note 1
EW	2-dr. Bus. Cpe.-2P	1545	NA	Note 1
EW	2-dr. Spt. Cpe.-2/4P	1645	3510	Note 1
EW	4-dr. Sed.-5P	1585	3570	Note 1
EW	2-dr. Cus. Vic.-5P	1575	3705	Note 1
EW	2-dr. Dplx. Rds.-3P	1530	3445	Note 1
EW	4-dr. Spt. Phae.-4P	1610	3580	Note 1
EW	4-dr. Cus. Brgm.-5P	1785	3835	Note 1

Note 1: Total production between December 1926 and October 1927 was 40,668.

Model ES, 6-cyl.

Model No.	Body Type & Seating	Factory Price	Shipping Weight	Prod. Total
ES	4-dr. Cus. Sed.-7P	2245	4050	Note 1
ES	4-dr. Limo.-7P	2495	NA	Note 1
ES	4-dr. Dplx- Phae.-7P	1810	3720	Note 1

Note 1: Total production between June 1926 and September 1927 was broken out by wheelbase. The figures were 7,949 cars on the 120-inch wheelbase and 9,405 cars on the 127-inch wheelbase.

EU ENGINE: L-head. Inline. Six. Cast iron block. B & S: 3-3/8 x 4-1/2 in. Disp.: 242 cu. in. C.R.: 4.5:1. Brake H.P.: 50 @ 2200 R.P.M. N.A.C.C. H.P.: 27.3. Main bearings: four. Valve lifters: solid. Carb.: Stromberg one-barrel Model OE-1.

EQ ENGINE: L-head. Inline. Six. Cast iron block. B & S: 3-1/2 x 5 in. Disp.: 289 cu. in. C.R.: 4.45:1. Brake H.P.: 65 @ 2400 R.P.M. N.A.C.C. H.P.: 29.4. Main bearings: four. Valve lifters: solid. Carb.: Stromberg one-barrel Model LS-2.

EW/ES ENGINE: L-head. Inline. Six. Cast iron block. B & S: 3-7/8 x 5 in. Disp.: 354 cu. in. C.R.: 4.45:1. Brake H.P.: 75 @ 2400 R.P.M. N.A.C.C. H.P.: 36. Main bearings: four. Valve lifters: solid. Carb.: Ball & Ball one-barrel Model SV33.

CHASSIS: [Series EU] W.B.: 113 in. Tires: 31 x 5.25 in. [Series EQ] W.B.: 120 in. Tires: 32 x 6.00 in. [Series EW] W.B.: 120 in. Tires: 32 x 6.00 in. [Series ES] W.B.: 120 or 127 in. Tires: 32 x 6.75 in.

TECHNICAL: Manual transmission (unit type). Speeds: 3F/1R. Floor shift controls. Clutch: Multiple dry disc. Shaft drive. Semi-floating rear axle. Overall ratio: (EU) 4.60:1/4.18:1; (EQ) 4.08:1/4.36:1; (EW) 3.69:1/4.08:1; (ES) 4.36:1. External contracting brakes. Four-wheel brakes standard on all models except Special Six. Disc wheels. Wheel rim size: (EU/EQ) 21 x 4.5 in.; (EW/ES) 21 x 5 in.

OPTIONS: Front bumper (opt. on three models). Rear bumper (opt. on three). Dual sidemounts. Sidemount cover(s). Hydraulic four-wheel brakes (on Special). Wind wings (std. on sport roadster). Heater. Clock (std. in President). Cigar lighter. Trunk rack (std. on two). Touring trunk. Wire wheels. Spotlight(s). Whitewalls. Special paint. Engine thermostat (opt. on some Specials). Smoking set (std. on seven). Vanity case (std. on President). Backing light. Shock absorbers (std. on eight). Spring covers. Spare tire (std. on three). Spare tire cover. Power tire pump.

HISTORICAL: Introduced (see notes in charts above). Calendar year registrations: 94,700. Model year production: 123,474. Innovations: New styling. Nickel-plated trim. Kelsey-Hayes disc wheels. No-draft ventilation on President. New radiator caps designed by Carl Mose. 1927 was Studebaker's "Diamond Jubilee" celebration year. Engineering staff moved to new facilities in South Bend, Indiana. Several famous record speed runs and endurance trials were undertaken by drivers of 1927 Studebaker Commanders.

1928

STUDEBAKER — DICTATOR — SERIES GE — SIX: The Model EU Dictator Six (see 1927 specifications) was sold as a 1928 Studebaker from July 1927 until the fall when new cars were introduced. The all-new series introduced the Dictator GE line that featured all-steel bodies, integral style sun visors, narrower front pillars, cowl lamps mounted on surcingles, unit group instrumentation and a new radiator design. Other appearance highlights were crowned fenders, new bumpers and beltline trim like that on last year's President. Kelsey-Hayes steel disc wheels were again standard. Other standard equipment included a tire lock; speedometer; hydrostatic gas gauge; engine thermometer; rearview mirror; stop light; windshield cleaner; front bumper; rear fender guards, and shock absorbers. Open models and coupes came with leather upholstery. The sedan had plush velvet seats and the sport coupe was trimmed in mohair. A spare rim was standard.

STUDEBAKER — COMMANDER — SERIES GB — SIX: The Commander GB was the new mid-sized, mid-priced line for the 1928 "Second Series" of Studebaker models introduced in the fall of 1927. Styling traits included all-steel bodies, integral sun visors and narrower front door pillars. Also seen was a flatter roof line, lower feature lines and distinctive belt line paneling on closed cars. Double bar bumpers of a more modern, non-fluted design were added. Budd steel disc wheels were standard fare. Other standard features were: a Stewart-Warner speedometer; hydrostatic gas gauge; coincidental lock; rearview mirror; stop light; automatic wiper; front bumper; rear fender guards; Gabriel shock absorbers; one spare disc wheel and a tire lock. Regal trimmed models also had: engine thermometers; cigar lighters; and a vanity case in the coupe. Roadsters and coupes were trimmed in leather. Other styles had mohair seats.

STUDEBAKER — PRESIDENT — SERIES ES — SIX: The President Six, Model ES, was carried over as a "First Series" 1928 Studebaker line until late fall. It was basically unchanged from the late 1927 offering. Features again included a no-draft ventilating windshield, gas gauge on instrument panel, oil filter, disc wheels and four-wheel mechanical brakes. Consult 1927 specifications for additional information.

STUDEBAKER — PRESIDENT — SERIES FA — EIGHT: Studebaker's big 1928 news was a big straight-eight series. The President Eight was a large, powerful, spacious car with outstanding acceleration and high maximum speed. Bodies on this model were full-visioned with extremely wide 28-inch doors. Interior furnishings included heavy 28-ounce broadcloth in two-tones on backs and cushions; single color headliners; deep tufted, form-fitting seats; double-deck, pillow-type seat springs; heavily upholstered armrests; two-tone walnut dash and garnish moldings; etched silver door medallions; Wilton velvet carpets and flap design door pockets. Standard equipment included chrome-plated, twin-beam headlights, opal iridescent dome and rear corner lights; combination tail/stop light; rearview mirror; auto wiper; coincidental ignition lock; no-draft ventilating windshield; speedometer; eight-day clock; electric gas gauge and dash thermometer. Styling innovations included an integral "cadet" style sun visor, all-steel body, full crown fenders and narrower radiator. A double bar bumper was of more modern design. There was an "8" emblem on the headlight tie-bar.

I.D. DATA: [Series GE] Serial numbers were on the left side of frame over front axle. Starting: 1410001. Ending: 1437600. Engine numbers were on right side of engine block. Starting: GE-1. Ending: GE-49700. [Series GB] Serial numbers in same location. Starting: 4039801. Ending: 4062100. Engine numbers in same location. Starting: GB-1. Ending: GB-8450. Body numbers embossed on firewall plate. [Series ES] Serial numbers and engine numbers were the same as 1927. [Series FB] Serial numbers were in the same location. Starting: 6000001. Ending: 6008600. Engine numbers on front of engine block. Starting: FB-1. Ending: FB-17775.

Model GE, 6-cyl.

Model No.	Body Type & Seating	Factory Price	Shipping Weight	Prod. Total
GE	2-dr. Royal Rds.-2/4P	1245	3000	Note 1
GE	4-dr. Royal Tr.-5P	1195	3030	Note 1
GE	4-dr. Dplx. Tr.-5P	1195	3085	Note 1
GE	4-dr. Royal Tr.-7P	1295	3050	Note 1
GE	2-dr- Bus. Cpe.-2P	1195	3095	Note 1
GE	2-dr. Royal Cpe.-2/4P	1295	3140	Note 1
GE	2-dr. Royal Vic.-4P	1295	3150	Note 1
GE	2-dr. Clb. Sed.-5P	1195	3190	Note 1
GE	4-dr. Sed.-5P	1265	3280	Note 1
GE	4-dr. Royal Sed.-5P	1395	3420	Note 1

Note 1: Total production between September 1927 and October 1928 was 48,339 units. This includes 1929 (Third Series) Model GE Dictators.

Model GB, 6-cyl.

Model No.	Body Type & Seating	Factory Price	Shipping Weight	Prod. Total
GB	2-dr. Regal Rds.-2/4P	1595	3340	Note 1
GB	2-dr. Cpe.-2P	1495	3395	Note 1
GB	2-dr. Regal Cpe.-2/4P	1625	3455	Note 1
GB	2-dr. Regal Cabr.-2/4P	1625	3425	Note 1
GB	2-dr. Vic.-4P	1495	3500	Note 1
GB	2-dr. Regal Vic.-4P	1625	3560	Note 1
GB	4-dr. Sed.-5P	1495	3560	Note 1
GB	4-dr. Clb. Sed.-5P	1435	3530	Note 1
GB	4-dr. Regal Sed.-5P	1625	3825	Note 1

Note 1: Total production October 1927 to June 1928 was 22,848.

Model ES, 6-cyl.

Model No.	Body Type & Seating	Factory Price	Shipping Weight	Prod. Total
ES	4-dr. Cus. Sed.-7P	1985	4032	Note 1
ES	4-dr. Limo.-7P	2250	4080	Note 1
ES	4-dr. Cus. Tr.-7P	1795	3805	Note 1

Note 1: See 1927 production total.

Model FA, 8-cyl.

Model No.	Body Type & Seating	Factory Price	Shipping Weight	Prod. Total
FA	4-dr. Tr.-7P	2285	3920	Note 1
FA	2-dr. State Cabr.-4P	2195	3980	Note 1
FA	4-dr. Sed.-5P	1985	4000	Note 1
FA	4-dr. State Sed.-5P	2250	4185	Note 1
FA	4-dr. Sed.-7P	2085	4040	Note 1
FA	4-dr. State Sed.-7P	2350	4225	Note 1
FA	4-dr. Limo.-7P	2450	4320	Note 1
FA	4-dr. State Ber.-7P	2350	4320	Note 1

Note 1: Total production December 1927 to October 1928 was 13,186.

ENGINE: [Series GE] L-head. Inline. Six. Cast iron block. B & S: 3-3/8 x 4-1/2 in. Disp.: 242 cu. in. C.R.: 4.5:1. Brake H.P.: 50 @ 2200 R.P.M. N.A.C.C. H.P.: 27.34. Main bearings: four. Valve lifters: solid. Carb.: Stromberg one-barrel Model T1. [Series GB/ES] L-head. Inline. Six. Cast iron block. B & S: 3-7/8 x 5 in. Disp.: 354 cu. in. C.R.: 4.25:1. Brake H.P.: 75 @ 2400 R.P.M. N.A.C.C. H.P.: 36.04. Main bearings: four. Valve lifters: solid. Carb.: Stromberg one-barrel Model TX2. [Series FA] L-head. Inline. Eight. Cast iron block. B & S: 3-3/8 x 4-3/8 in. Disp.: 312.5 cu. in. C.R.: 4.7:1. Brake H.P.: 100 @ 2600 R.P.M. N.A.C.C. H.P.: 36.45. Main bearings: five. Valve lifters: solid. Carb.: Schebler one-barrel Model 1-1/2 in.

CHASSIS: [Series GE] W.B.: 113 in. Tires: 30 x 5.50 in. [Series GB] W.B.: 120 in. Tires: 30 x 5.50 in. [Series ES] W.B.: 127 in. Tires: 32 x 6.75 in. [Series FA] W.B.: 131 in. Tires: 31 x 6.20 in.

TECHNICAL: Manual (unit type) transmission. Speeds: 3F/1R. Floor shift controls. Multiple dry disc clutch. Shaft drive. Semi-floating rear axle. Overall ratio: (GE) 4.60:1; (GB) 3.31:1; (FA) 4.30:1. Four-wheel brakes (except Special). President State has wire wheels; others have disc wheels. (Kelsey-Hayes on Dictator.) (Budd on Commander.)

OPTIONS: Backing light. Wind wings. Disc wheels (opt. on President). Dual sidemounts. Sidemount covers. Smoking set (opt. in 16 models). Vanity case (std. in victorias). Wire wheels (std. on President State models). Heater. Clock (std. in Commander and President). Cigar lighter (opt. on four). Trunk. Trunk rack. Whitewalls. Spotlight. Spring covers. Spare tire(s). Tire cover(s). Power tire pump.

HISTORICAL: Introduced: see chart notes. Calendar year registrations: 107,234. Model year production: 105,968. Innovations: First Studebaker Eight. Four-wheel Bendix self-energizing mechanical brakes standard on all Studebakers. Vibration dampener on new President Eight engine. Higher compression head on new Eight. AC fuel pump replaces vacuum feed system on all models. Torsion dampener-type clutch. New 20-inch wheel rims on Commanders. Dictator equipped with ball bearing spring shackles. Commander Club Sedan offers lowest price ever for a Big Six. Studebaker gained controlling interest in Pierce-Arrow Company with 1928 purchase of $2 million in stock.

1928-1/2

STUDEBAKER — DICTATOR — SERIES GE — SIX: Like other automakers, Studebaker held summer and winter new model introductions this year. Following standard practice, the "new" summer line offered little more than slightly re-worked 1928 cars that were sold as 1929 automobiles. Cars in the six-cylinder Dictator GE lineup had the following styling changes: higher radiators, new lower crown fenders, cadet sun visors, adjustable steering wheels and larger hubcaps. The new radiator had a deeper, more squared-off design and an "s" emblem was placed in front of it on the headlight tie-bar.

STUDEBAKER — COMMANDER — SERIES GH — SIX: The Commander GH was a new 1928-1/2 series composed of three models introduced in July 1928. These were the last Studebakers with the old 353.8 cu. in. Big Eight. New features included a higher radiator, redesigned crown fenders and lower bodies. The frontal appearance of these cars had a "military" look with the addition of cadet-style sun visors in place of the former overhanging type. The headlight tie-bar supported a globe-shaped emblem in the center of Commander models. It had the inscription "World's Champion" written on it.

STUDEBAKER — PRESIDENT — SERIES FB/FA — EIGHT: The Model FA President Eight was carried over into the early 1929 selling season with several changes. They included wider crown fenders, ball bearing spring shackles and an adjustable steering wheel. New body styles were added. They included a State cabriolet, tourer and State tourer. (Note: State models had six-wheel equipment with wire spoke rims.) Other 1928-1/2 styling changes were the addition of cadet-style visors, a new flat radiator cap and redesigned headlamps and cowl lights. These features closely resemble 1929 features, but the 1928-1/2 FAs have a distinctive 131-inch wheelbase. The FBs were a new line of 121-inch wheelbase President Eights also introduced in mid-1928 for the early 1929 sales year. Styling was much the same as for the FA. These cars came in colors of Autumn brown; Deauville sand; Duskblu burgundy; Suede gray; Damson Plum maroon; Spirea green and Port Wine red. Beltline moldings were done in contrasting tones of Ivory, Deauville sand or red. Both models had a larger displacement "FB" straight-eight engine. The headlight tie-bar emblem for Dictator models was an "8".

I.D. DATA: [Series GE] Serial numbers were in the same location. Starting: 1437601. Ending: 1460000. Engine numbers were on the right side of block. See 1928 engine numbers. [Series GH] Serial numbers were in the same location. Starting: 4062101. Ending: 4070500. Engine numbers were on the right side of the block. Engine numbers were GH-1 and up. [Series FB/FA] Serial numbers were in the same location. Starting: [FB] 7000001; [FA] 6008601. Ending: [FB] 7013500; [FA] 6013000. Engine numbers on front of block. Both models used the same engine number prefix. Starting: FB-1. Ending: FB-17775.

Model GE, 6-cyl.

Model No.	Body Type & Seating	Factory Price	Shipping Weight	Prod. Total
GE	4-dr. Tr.-5P	1265	3050	Note 1
GE	4-dr Tr.-7P	1325	3090	Note 1
GE	2-dr. Bus. Cpe.-2P	1265	3125	Note 1
GE	2-dr. Royal Cabr.-4P	1395	3430	Note 1
GE	2-dr. Royal Vic.-4P	1345	3210	Note 1
GE	2-dr. Clb. Sed.-5P	1185	3190	Note 1
GE	4-dr. Sed.-5P	1265	3280	Note 1
GE	4-dr. Royal Sed.-5P	1395	3420	Note 1

Note 1: For total production September 1927 to October 1928 see 1928 specifications. Cars built after June 1928 were sold as 1929 models.

Model GH, 6-cyl.

Model No.	Body Type & Seating	Factory Price	Shipping Weight	Prod. Total
GH	2-dr. Regal Vic.-5P	1625	3570	Note 1
GH	4-dr. Sed.-5P	1495	3670	Note 1
GH	4-dr. Regal Sed.-5P	1665	3800	Note 1

Note 1: Total production between June 1928 and October 1928 was 8,428.

President Model FB, 8-cyl.

Model No.	Body Type & Seating	Factory Price	Shipping Weight	Prod. Total
FB	2-dr. State Rds.-4P	1850	3535	Note 1
FB	2-dr. State Cabr.-4P	1850	3715	Note 1
FB	2-dr. State Vic.-4P	1850	3820	Note 1
FB	4-dr. Sed.-5P	1685	3760	Note 1
FB	4-dr. State Sed.-5P	1850	3900	Note 1

President Model FA (1928-1/2), 8-cyl.

Model No.	Body Type & Seating	Factory Price	Shipping Weight	Prod. Total
FA	4-dr. Tr.-7P	2285	3920	Note 2
FA	4-dr. State Tr.-7P	2485	4125	Note 2
FA	2-dr. State Cabr.-4P	2195	3980	Note 2
FA	4-dr. State Sed.-5P	2250	4185	Note 2
FA	4-dr. Sed.-5P	2085	4040	Note 2
FA	4-dr. State Sed.-7P	2350	4225	Note 2
FA	4-dr. Limo.-7P	2450	4320	Note 2

Note 1: Total production June 1928 to October 1928 was 13,186.

Note 2: For total production December 1927 to October 1928 see 1928 specifications. Cars built after June 1928 were sold as 1929 models.

GE ENGINE: L-head. Inline. Six. Cast iron block. B & S: 3-3/8 x 4-1/2 in. Disp.: 242 cu. in. C.R.: 4.41:1. Brake H.P.: 67 @ 2800 R.P.M. N.A.C.C. H.P.: 27.3. Main bearings: four. Valve lifters: solid. Carb.: Stromberg one-barrel Model UX2.

GH ENGINE: L-head. Inline. Six. Cast iron block. B & S: 3-7/8 x 5 in. Disp.: 354 cu. in. C.R.: 4.6:1 (4.7:1 on roadster). Brake H.P.: 85 @ 2800 R.P.M. N.A.C.C. H.P.: 36. Main bearings: four. Valve lifters: solid. Carb.: Ball & Ball one-barrel.

FB ENGINE: L-head. Inline. Eight. Cast iron block. B & S: 3-1/2 x 4-3/8 in. Disp.: 337 cu. in. C.R.: 4.9:1. Brake H.P.: 109 @ 3200 R.P.M. N.A.C.C. H.P.: 39.2. Main bearings: five. Valve lifters: solid. Carb.: Schebler one-barrel.

Note: The new "FB" engine was used in both FB and FA models produced after June 1928.

CHASSIS: [Series GE] W.B.: 113 in. Tires: 20 x 5.50 in. [Series GH] W.B.: 121 in. Tires: 30 x 5.50 in. [Series FB] W.B.: 121 in. Tires: 30 x 5.50 in. [Series FA] W.B.: 131 in. Tires: 31 x 6.20 in.

TECHNICAL: Unit type manual transmission. Speeds: 3F/1R. Floor shift controls. Multiple disc clutch. Shaft drive. Semi-floating rear axle. Overall ratio: [GE] 4.6:1; [GH] 3.31:1; [FB/FA] 4.1:1. Four-wheel mechanical brakes on all series. Wood spoke artillery wheels or wire spoke wheels standard depending on series.

OPTIONS: Front bumper. Rear guards. Whitewall tires. Dual sidemounts. Sidemount cover(s). Outside rear view mirror. Trunk rack. Touring rack. Heater. Clock. Cigar lighter. Spare tire. Wire spoke wheels. Pedestal sidemount mirrors. Spotlight(s). Special paint. Power tire pump. Disc wheels. Wind wings. Smoking set. Vanity case. Spring covers. Rear axle ratios.

HISTORICAL: Introduced: (see specification notes). Calendar year registrations: (1929) 82,839. Model year production: (1929) 57,790. Innovations: Larger displacement straight-eight. New fuel pump. New Fafnir spring shackles. Model identification on headlight tie-bar had "8" for Presidents, "World's Champion" globe for Commanders and "S" for Dictators. Dictator parking brake relocated to floorboard. In July 1928, four FB President models were taken to the Atlantic City, New Jersey, Speedway for an endurance run that broke all existing stock car speed and distance records. In November 1928, two more Presidents returned to Atlantic City for even more record-breaking runs. By the end of the year, these cars held 116 total stock car records in their size and displacement class. Studebakers achieved an all-time record for prewar sales in 1928 by selling $157 million worth of cars.

1929

STUDEBAKER — DICTATOR — SERIES GE — SIX: Production of the model GE Dictator had already ended by the time the "real" 1929 Studebakers were introduced in January 1929. Following standard practice, the cars built to 1928-1/2 specifications continued to be sold as long as the inventory lasted. There were probably a few running production changes. According to the January 1929 edition of *MoToR* there were only four models: sedan, cabriolet, Royal sedan and victoria sedan. Standard equipment included a Stewart-Warner speedometer; gasoline gauge; engine thermometer; coincidental lock; rearview mirror; Trico vacuum windshield wiper; stop and taillight, Lovejoy shock absorbers and tire lock. The standard sedan had wood spoke wheels and a spare rim was optional equipment. The cabriolet and Royal sedan had six wheel equipment standard. The victoria had wood spoke wheels and one spare rim as its standard equipment.

STUDEBAKER — COMMANDER — SERIES GJ — SIX: New Commander bodies were longer, lower and roomier. A double drop frame design permitted the extremely low lines. New features included safety glass windshields and adjustable driver's seats. Both the window reveals and belt panels were set off by new raised moldings. Chrome-plated trim highlighted the bodies. Deluxe models carried six wire wheels (five on roadster). A new brougham and convertible cabriolet had nickel-plated windshield frames. Standard equipment included a Stewart-Warner speedometer; gasoline gauge; engine thermometer; coincidental lock; New Haven clock; cigar lighter, rear view mirror, windshield wiper, trunk on the victoria, cabriolet and Regal sedan; tail and stop light; Lovejoy shock absorbers; wire wheels on roadsters, cabriolets and Regal sedan; wood spoke wheels on other models and spare tire lock. Double bar front bumpers and rear guards were optional at slight extra cost. The cadet sun visors were eliminated this year. Instead of a visor, the front window pillars on closed cars had a slight reverse curve that extended across the roof giving a slight visor-like effect. This was called a "French" windshield design.

STUDEBAKER — COMMANDER — SERIES FD — EIGHT: Appearancewise, the all-new Commander Eight was identical to the Commander Six. The headlight tie-bar emblem was used for differentiation. The Eight, of course, had the number "8" incorporated. Deluxe (Regal) models all carried six wire wheels except the roadster, which was fitted with five wire wheels. A clock was standard on all Commander Eights except the Regal roadster, sedan and victoria. A cigar lighter was optional on the same three models and standard on other Commander Eights. A trunk was standard on the convertible cabriolet, Regal sedan and brougham, optional on other models. Standard on all models was a speedometer, gas gauge, engine thermometer, tail and stop light; coincidental lock; rearview mirror; automatic wiper; Lovejoy shock absorbers and a tire lock.

STUDEBAKER — PRESIDENT — SERIES FH/FE — EIGHT: The new double drop frame was also used on 1929 Presidents, allowing lower and slightly wider bodies. Safety glass windshields were new. The doors were also wider. The new handling of window reveals and belt panels—with raised moldings—was also seen on Presidents. The FH cabriolet and FE brougham had nickel-plated windshield/window frames. Deluxe (State) models had six wire wheel equipment. The wheelbase was 125 inches on FHs and 135 inches on FEs. Cars in both lines used a new "FE" straight-eight engine with improved carburetion and slightly higher compression. Standard equipment on all Presidents included a speedometer; gas gauge; engine thermometer; coincidental lock; clock; cigar lighter; Trico vacuum wiper; tail and stop lamp; Houdaille twin-type hydraulic shock absorbers; spring covers, and tire lock. Kelsey-Hayes wood wheels and a single spare rim were standard on the sedans. Budd wire wheels with dual sidemounts were standard on victorias, cabriolets, broughams, limousines and all State sedans.

I.D. DATA: [Series GE] Serial and engine number same as 1928-1/2. [Series GJ] Serial numbers in same location. Starting: 4070501. Ending: 4081000. Engine numbers on right side of block. Starting: GJ-1 and up. [Series FD] Serial numbers in same location. Starting: 8000001. Ending: 8011000. Engine numbers were stamped on left side of block. Starting: FD-1 and up. [Series FE/FH] Serial numbers in same location. Starting: [FH] 7013501; [FE] 6013001. Ending: [FH] 7021000; [FE] 6016001. Engine numbers on right side of block. Starting: FE-1 and up.

Model GE, 6-cyl.

Model No.	Body Type & Seating	Factory Price	Shipping Weight	Prod. Total
GE	4-dr. Sed.-5P	1265	3280	Note 1
GE	2-dr. Cabr.-4P	1395	3280	Note 1
GE	4-dr. Royal Sed.-5P	1395	3415	Note 1
GE	2-dr. Vic. Sed.-5P	1345	3210	Note 1

Note 1: For total production September 1927 to October 1928 see 1928 specifications. Cars sold after January 1929 were considered 1929 "second series" models.

Model GJ, 6-cyl.

Model No.	Body Type & Seating	Factory Price	Shipping Weight	Prod. Total
GJ	2-dr. Rds.-2/4P	1375	2970	Note 1
GJ	2-dr. Regal Rds.-2/4P	1450	3000	Note 1
GJ	4-dr. Tr.-5P	1350	3070	Note 1
GJ	4-dr. Regal Tr.-5P	1450	3200	Note 1
GJ	4-dr. Tr.-7P	1410	3125	Note 1
GJ	4-dr. Regal Tr.-7P	1510	3275	Note 1
GJ	2-dr. Cpe.-2P	1350	3105	Note 1
GJ	2-dr. Spt. Cpe.-2/4P	1425	3160	Note 1
GJ	2-dr. Cabr.-2/4P	1495	3215	Note 1
GJ	2-dr. Vic.-4P	1375	3130	Note 1
GJ	4-dr. Sed.-5P	1375	3235	Note 1
GJ	4-dr. Regal Sed.-5P	1495	3335	Note 1
GJ	4-dr. Regal Brgm.-5P	1525	3415	Note 1

Note 1: Total production December 1928 to April 1930 was 16,019.

Model FD, 8-cyl.

Model No.	Body Type & Seating	Factory Price	Shipping Weight	Prod. Total
FD	2-dr. Regal Rds.-4P	1595	3040	Note 1
FD	4-dr. Tr.-5P	1495	3100	Note 1
FD	4-dr. Regal Tr.-5P	1595	3250	Note 1
FD	4-dr. Tr.-7P	1545	3125	Note 1
FD	4-dr. Regal Tr.-7P	1645	3275	Note 1
FD	2-dr. Bus. Cpe.-2P	1495	3140	Note 1
FD	2-dr. Spt. Cpe.-2/4P	1550	3195	Note 1
FD	2-dr. Regal Conv.-2/4P	1645	3240	Note 1
FD	2-dr. Vic.-4P	1525	3170	Note 1
FD	4-dr. Regal Brgm.-5P	1675	3440	Note 1
FD	4-dr. Sed.-5P	1525	3255	Note 1
FD	4-dr. Regal Sed.-5P	1645	3385	Note 1

Note 1: Total production December 1928 to June 1930 was 17,527.

Model FH, 8-cyl.

Model No.	Body Type & Seating	Factory Price	Shipping Weight	Prod. Total
FH	2-dr. Rds.-4P	1735	3770	Note 1
FH	2-dr. Cabr.-4P	1875	3970	Note 1
FH	2-dr. State Vic.-4P	1875	4015	Note 1
FH	4-dr. Sed.-5P	1735	4045	Note 1
FH	4-dr. State Sed.-5P	1875	4160	Note 1

Model FE, 8-cyl.

Model No.	Body Type & Seating	Factory Price	Shipping Weight	Prod. Total
FE	4-dr. Tr.-7P	1785	4065	Note 2
FE	4-dr. State Tr.-7P	2085	4210	Note 2
FE	4-dr. Brgm.-5P	2350	4360	Note 2
FE	4-dr. Sed.-7P	2175	4235	Note 2
FE	4-dr. State Sed.-7P	2350	4370	Note 2
FE	4-dr. Limo.-7P	2575	4385	Note 2

Note 1: Total production December 1928 to June 1930 was 17,527.

Note 2: Total production December 1928 to June 1930 was 8,740.

SERIES GE ENGINE: L-head. Inline. Six. Cast iron block. B & S: 3-3/8 x 4-1/2 in. Disp.: 242 cu. in. C.R.: 4.41:1. Brake H.P.: 67 @ 2800 R.P.M. N.A.C.C. H.P.: 27.3. Main bearings: four. Valve lifters: solid. Carb.: Stromberg one-barrel Model UX2.

SERIES GJ ENGINE: L-head. Inline. Six. Cast iron block. B & S: 3-3/8 x 4-5/8 in. Disp.: 248.3 cu. in. C.R.: 4.95:1. Brake H.P.: 74 @ 3000 R.P.M. N.A.C.C. H.P. 27.3. Main bearings: four. Valve lifters: solid. Carb.: Stromberg one-barrel Model UX2.

SERIES FD ENGINE: L-head. Inline. Eight. Cast iron block. B & S: 3-1/16 x 4-1/4 in. Disp.: 250.4 cu. in. C.R.: 5.05:1. Brake H.P.: 80 @ 3600 R.P.M. N.A.C.C. H.P.: 30.0. Main bearings: nine. Valve lifters: solid. Carb.: Stromberg one-barrel Model UX2.

Note: Top speed of the FD engine was 72 mph.

SERIES FH/FE ENGINE: L-head. Inline. Eight. Cast iron block. B & S: 3-1/2 x 4-3/8 in. Disp.: 337 cu. in. C.R.: (std.) 5.0:1; (opt.) 5.5:1 and 6.0:1. Brake H.P.: 114 @ 3200 R.P.M. N.A.C.C. H.P.: 39.2. Main bearings: five. Valve lifters: solid. Carb.: Stromberg two-barrel (duplex) Model UU2.

CHASSIS: [Series GE] W.B.: 113 in. Frt/Rear Tread: 57/57 in. Tires: 20 x 5.50 in. [Series GJ] W.B.: 120 in. Height: 69-5/16 in. Frt/Rear Tread: 58/58 in. Tires: 19 x 5.50 in. [Series FD] W.B.: 120 in. Height: 69-5/16 in. Frt/Rear Tread: 58/58 in. Tires: 19 x 5.50 in. [Series FH] W.B.: 125 in. Height: 71-5/16 in. Frt/Rear Tread: 59/59 in. Tires: 20 x 6.00 in., six-ply balloon. [Series FE] W.B.: 135 in. Height: 71-5/16 in. Frt/Rear Tread: 59/59 in. Tires: 19 x 6.50 in., six-ply balloon.

TECHNICAL: Unit-type manual transmission. Speeds: 3F/1R. Floor shift controls. Multiple-plate dry disc clutch (three plates on President; two on others). Shaft drive. Semi-floating rear axle. Overall ratio: [GE] 4.60:1; [GJ] 3.91:1; [FD] 4.36:1 or 3.91:1; [FH] 4.64:1; [FE] 4.78:1. Four-wheel mechanical brakes. Kelsey-Hayes wood spoke artillery wheels or Budd wire wheels.

OPTIONS: Front bumper. Rear guards. Whitewall tires. Dual sidemounts. Sidemount cover(s). Wind wings. Trunk rack. Touring trunk. Heater. Clock. Cigar lighter. Wire spoke wheels. Wood spoke wheels (on models with wire wheels std.). Outside rearview mirror. Spotlight(s). Smoking set. Vanity case. Backing lights. Stop light. Spring

1928-1/2 Studebaker, Commander Six (Series GH), Regal victoria, AA

1929 Studebaker, President Eight (Series FB - revised 1928 version), State roadster, AA

1929 Studebaker, President Eight (Series FE), touring, AA

1929 Studebaker, President Eight (Series FE), limousine, AA

1930 Studebaker, Dictator Eight (Series FC), rumbleseat coupe, AA

1930 Studebaker, Dictator Six (Series GL), club sedan, AA

1930 Studebaker, Commander Eight (Series FD), sedan, AA

1930 Studebaker, Commander Eight (Series FD), brougham, AA

1931 Studebaker, Six (Series 54 - revised, rebadged Erskine), roadster, AA

1931 Studebaker, Dictator Eight (Series 61), sport coupe, AA

covers (std. on President). Power tire pump. Tire cover. Pedestal-type sidemount mirrors. Special paint. High-compression heads (President). Rear axle ratios.

HISTORICAL: Introduced (see notes above). Calendar year registrations: (1929) 82,839. Model year production: (1929) 57,790. Innovations: Double drop frame. Duplex carburetion on President. Improved intake manifolding. Automatic choke. Larger brakes. Safer handbrake system. Improved rear axles. Houdaille shocks on President. Nine bearings in new Commander Eight. Studebaker claimed to be the world's predominant manufacturer of eight-cylinder automobiles this year. Several 1929 President Eights were used as "Official Cars" at the Indianapolis 500. Actress Mae West drove one of them.

1930

STUDEBAKER — DICTATOR — SERIES GL — SIX: The 1930 Dictator had a longer 115-inch wheelbase. A new double drop frame gave lower body lines. Hood louvers were grouped in a distinctive pattern of seven groupings, each with three vertical openings. A convex belt line panel was seen. The headlight tie-bar emblem was entirely eliminated on sixes. Standard equipment included a Stewart-Warner speedometer; gas gauge; thermometer; coincidental lock; shatterproof windshield, Trico wiper; tail and stop lamp; Kelsey-Hayes wood spoke wheels (except six wire wheels on Regal tourer and Regal sedan) and Lovejoy shock absorbers. Front and rear bumpers were said to be "standard," but were not included in list prices.

STUDEBAKER — DICTATOR — SERIES FC — EIGHT: The first eight-cylinder Dictator used the same body described above. Cars with serial numbers above 2122868 had a headlight tie-bar emblem with an "8" to identify the larger engine. Equipment features were the same as on the six-cylinder cars.

STUDEBAKER — COMMANDER — SERIES GJ — SIX: The Depression caused the Commander GJ to be carried over as a 1930 model. Specifications were unchanged. There were a few body style deletions and/or name changes. The standard roadster was dropped, the rumbleseat coupe was no longer called a sport coupe, the cabriolet was now a convertible cabriolet and the Regal brougham was downgraded to a standard brougham.

STUDEBAKER — COMMANDER — SERIES FD — EIGHT: A second carryover series was the Commander FD eight-cylinder line. Specifications were the same as in 1929. The seven-passenger standard and Regal touring cars were dropped, the business coupe was now called simply a coupe, the cabriolet became a convertible cabriolet and the Regal brougham was downgraded to a standard brougham. Two new models were both seven-passenger sedans—one standard and one with Regal equipment.

STUDEBAKER — PRESIDENT — SERIES FH/FE — EIGHT: In keeping with Studebaker's policy of no all-new 1930 models, the 125- and 135-inch wheelbase Presidents were carried over from 1929. There was, however, one change in the appearance of closed models; the visorless "French" style windshield design was used. The FH cabriolet was now a convertible cabriolet and the long-wheelbase FE line got two new body styles, a seven-passenger State limousine and a five-passenger State victoria. The latter car was introduced at the New York Automobile Show in January 1930.

STUDEBAKER — SERIES 53 — SIX: In 1927, Studebaker had introduced a small "companion" car called the Erskine. It was still available in 1930, but after May of that year the Erskine 53 was renamed the Studebaker 53. Features of the car included vertical hood louvers in groups of three, chrome-plated bright metal parts, a 114-inch wheelbase and a cadet style sun visor. The main changes in the new Studebaker were "S" logo hubcaps and a Studebaker radiator nameplate. A kit was available from dealers to allow owners to retrofit their 1930 Erskines with these Studebaker parts. Cars with serial numbers higher than 5083248 were considered Studebakers, according to National Automobile Dealer Association records.

I.D. DATA: [Series GL] Serial numbers were in the same location. Starting: 1460001. Ending: 1477293. Engine numbers were on the right side of block. Starting: GL-1. Ending: GL-18200. [Series FC] Serial numbers in same location. Starting: 2120001. Ending: 2134000. Engine numbers on left side of block. Engine numbers were FC-1 and up. [Series GJ] Serial numbers were in the same location. Starting: 4081001. Ending: 4086041. Engine numbers located on the right side of block. Engine numbers were GJ-1 and up. [Series FD] Serial numbers were in the same location. Starting: 8011001. Ending: 8025000. Engine numbers on left side of block. Engine numbers were FD-1 and up. [Series FH/FE] Serial numbers in same location. Starting: [FH] 7021001; [FE] 6016001. Ending: [FH] 7031000; [FE] 6022000. Engine numbers on front of engine block. Engine numbers were FE-1 and up. [Series 53] Serial numbers in same location. Starting: 5083248. Ending: 5085000. Engine numbers on right side of block. Engine numbers were E-001 and up.

Model GL, 6-cyl.

Model No.	Body Type & Seating	Factory Price	Shipping Weight	Prod. Total
GL	4-dr. Tr.-5P	1145	2955	Note 1
GL	4-dr. Regal Tr.-5P	1265	3075	Note 1
GL	2-dr. Cpe.-2P	1135	2915	Note 1
GL	2-dr. Spt. Cpe.-2/4P	1195	2980	Note 1
GL	4-dr. Brgm.-5P	1295	3250	Note 1
GL	2-dr. Clb. Sed.-5P	1095	2970	Note 1
GL	4-dr. Sed.-5P	1195	3080	Note 1
GL	4-dr. Regal Sed.-5P	1295	3200	Note 1

Note 1: Total production June 1929 to May 1930 was 17,561.

Model FC, 8-cyl.

Model No.	Body Type & Seating	Factory Price	Shipping Weight	Prod. Total
FC	4-dr. Tr.-5P	1285	2980	Note 1
FC	4-dr. Regal Tr.-5P	1385	3100	Note 1
FC	2-dr. Cpe.-2P	1255	2950	Note 1
FC	2-dr. Cpe.-2/4P	1315	3010	Note 1
FC	4-dr. Brgm.-5P	1415	3275	Note 1
FC	2-dr. Clb. Sed.-5P	1195	2990	Note 1
FC	4-dr. Sed.-5P	1295	3095	Note 1
FC	4-dr. Regal Sed.-5P	1415	3230	Note 1

Note 1: Total production May 1929 to August 1930 was 16,359.

Model GJ, 6-cyl.

Model No.	Body Type & Seating	Factory Price	Shipping Weight	Prod. Total
GJ	2-dr. Regal Rds.-2/4P	1495	3000	Note 1
GJ	4-dr. Tr.-5P	1395	3070	Note 1
GJ	4-dr. Regal Tr.-5P	1495	3200	Note 1
GJ	4-dr. Tr.-7P	1360	3095	Note 1
GJ	4-dr. Regal Tr.-7P	1460	3225	Note 1
GJ	2-dr. Cpe.-2P	1345	3105	Note 1
GJ	2-dr. Spt. Cpe.-2/4P	1425	3160	Note 1
GJ	2-dr. Conv. Cabr.-2/4P	1545	3215	Note 1
GJ	2-dr. Vic.-4P	1425	3130	Note 1
GJ	4-dr. Brgm.-5P	1575	3415	Note 1
GJ	4-dr. Sed.-5P	1525	3235	Note 1
GJ	4-dr. Regal Sed.-5P	1545	3335	Note 1

Note 1: Total production December 1928 to April 1930 was 16,019.

Model FD, 8-cyl.

Model No.	Body Type & Seating	Factory Price	Shipping Weight	Prod. Total
FD	2-dr. Regal Rds.-2/4P	1595	3040	Note 1
FD	4-dr. Tr.-5P	1395	3100	Note 1
FD	4-dr. Regal Tr.-5P	1595	3250	Note 1
FD	2-dr. Cpe.-2P	1495	3150	Note 1
FD	2-dr. Spt. Cpe.-2/4P	1545	3235	Note 1
FD	2-dr. Conv. Cabr.-2/4P	1695	3345	Note 1
FD	2-dr. Vic.-4P	1515	3200	Note 1
FD	4-dr. Brgm.-5P	1695	3540	Note 1
FD	4-dr. Sed.-5P	1515	3310	Note 1
FD	4-dr. Regal Sed.-5P	1695	3435	Note 1
FD	4-dr. Sed.-7P	1695	3355	Note 1
FD	4-dr. Regal Sed.-7P	1845	3470	Note 1

Note 1: Total production December 1928 to June 1930 was 24,639.

Model FH, 8-cyl.

Model No.	Body Type & Seating	Factory Price	Shipping Weight	Prod. Total
FH	2-dr. Rds.-2/4P	1795	3770	Note 1
FH	2-dr. Conv. Cabr.-2/4P	1975	3970	Note 1
FH	2-dr. State Vic.-4P	1975	4015	Note 1
FH	4-dr. Sed.-5P	1795	4045	Note 1
FH	4-dr. State Sed.-5P	1995	4160	Note 1

Model FE, 8-cyl.

Model No.	Body Type & Seating	Factory Price	Shipping Weight	Prod. Total
FE	4-dr. Tr.-7P	1845	4020	Note 2
FE	4-dr. State Tr.-7P	2145	4175	Note 2
FE	2-dr. State Vic.-5P	2295	4230	Note 2
FE	4-dr. Brgm.-5P	2395	4440	Note 2
FE	4-dr. Sed.-7P	2095	4305	Note 2
FE	4-dr. State Sed.-7P	2295	4435	Note 2
FE	4-dr. Limo.-7P	2595	4445	Note 2
FE	4 dr. State Limo.-7P	2795	4445	Note 2

Note 1: Total production December 1928 to June 1930 was 17,527.

Note 2: Total production December 1928 to June 1930 was 8,740.

Model 53, 6-cyl.

Model No.	Body Type & Seating	Factory Price	Shipping Weight	Prod. Total
53	4-dr. Tr.-5P	965	2840	Note 1
53	4-dr. Regal Tr.-5P	1065	2990	Note 1
53	2-dr. Bus. Cpe.-2P	895	2835	Note 1
53	2-dr. Regal Cpe.-2/4P	985	2890	Note 1
53	2-dr. Clb. Sed.-5P	935	2875	Note 1
53	4-dr. Sed.-5P	985	2950	Note 1
53	4-dr. Regal Sed.-5P	1085	3100	Note 1
53	4-dr. Lan. Sed.-5P	1125	3100	Note 1

Note 1: Total production November 1929 to November 1930 was 22,371.

SERIES GL ENGINE: L-head. Inline. Six. Cast iron block. B & S: 3-3/8 x 4-1/8 in. Disp.: 221 cu. in. C.R.: 4.8:1. Brake H.P.: 68 @ 3200 R.P.M. N.A.C.C. H.P.: 27.34. Main bearings: four. Valve lifters: solid. Carb.: Stromberg one-barrel Model UX2.

SERIES FC ENGINE: L-head. Inline. Eight. Cast iron block. B & S: 3-1/16 x 3-3/4 in. Disp.: 221 cu. in. C.R.: 5.0:1; (optional: 5.5:1). Brake H.P.: 70 @ 3200 R.P.M. N.A.C.C. H.P.: 30. Main bearings: nine. Valve lifters: solid. Carb.: Stromberg one-barrel Model UX2.

SERIES GJ ENGINE: L-head. Inline. Six. Cast iron block. B & S: 3-3/8 x 4-5/8 in. Disp.: 248.3 cu. in. C.R.: 4.8:1. Brake H.P.: 75 @ 3000 R.P.M. N.A.C.C. H.P.: 27.3. Main bearings: four. Valve lifters: solid. Carb.: Stromberg one-barrel Model UX2.

SERIES FD ENGINE: L-head. Inline. Eight. Cast iron block. B & S: 3-1/6 x 4-1/4 in. Disp.: 250.4 cu. in. C.R.: 5.10:1. Brake H.P.: 80 @ 3200 R.P.M. N.A.C.C. H.P.: 30.04. Main bearings: nine. Valve lifters: solid. Carb.: Stromberg one-barrel Model UX2.

SERIES FE ENGINE: L-head. Inline. Eight. Cast iron block. B & S: 3-1/2 x 4-3/8 in. Disp.: 337 cu. in. C.R.: 5.05:1. Brake H.P.: 115 @ 3200 R.P.M. N.A.C.C. H.P.: 39.2. Main bearings: five. Valve lifters: solid. Carb.: Stromberg two-barrel Model UU2.

SERIES "53" ENGINE: L-head. Inline. Six. Cast iron block. B & S: 3-1/4 x 4-1/8 in. Disp.: 205.3 cu. in. C.R.: 5.20:1. Brake H.P.: 70 @ 3200 R.P.M. N.A.C.C. H.P.: 25.4. Main bearings: four. Valve lifters: solid. Carb.: Schebler one-barrel Model S.

CHASSIS: [Series GL] W.B.: 115 in. Height: 69-7/16 in. Frt/Rear Tread: 58/58 in. Tires: 19 x 5.50 in. [Series FC] W.B.: 115 in. Height: 69-7/16 in. Frt/Rear Tread: 58/58 in. Tires: 19 x 5.50 in. [Series GJ] W.B.: 120 in. Height: 71-3/16 in. Frt/Rear Tread: 58/58 in. Tires: 19 x 5.50 in. [Series FD] W.B.: 120 in. Height: 71-3/16 in. Frt/Rear Tread: 58/58 in. Tires: 19 x 5.50 in. [Series FH] W.B.: 125 in. Height: 71-5/16 in. Frt/Rear Tread: 59/59 in. Tires: 20 x 6.00 in. [Series FE] W.B.: 135 in. Height: 71-7/8. Frt/Rear Tread: 59/59 in. Tires: 19 x 6.50 in. [Series "53"] W.B.: 114 in. Height: 69-1/4 in. Frt/Rear Tread: 58/58 in. Tires: 19 x 5.25 in.

TECHNICAL: Manual unit type transmission. Speeds: 3F/1R. Floor mounted gearshift controls. Multiple dry disc clutch. Semi-floating rear axle. Overall ratio: (GL) 4.78:1; (FC) 4.78:1; (GJ) 3.91:1; (FD) 4.36:1 or 3.91:1; (FH) 4.31:1; (FE) 4.64:1; (53) 4.78:1. External contracting four-wheel brakes. Wood spoke or wire wheels.

OPTIONS: Front bumper. Rear guards. Whitewalls. Dual sidemounts. Sidemount cover(s). Wind wings. Trunk rack. Trunk. Heater. Clock. Cigar lighter. Spare tire. Power tire pump. Stop lights. Spotlight(s). Outside rearview mirror. Wire wheels. Wood spoke wheels. Backing lights. Spring covers. Pedestal mirrors. Special paint. High compression head. Rear axle ratios. Smoking set. Vanity case.

HISTORICAL: Introduced: (see notes above). Calendar year registrations: 56,526. Model year production: 76,781. Innovations: Dictator Eight introduced. New Burgess power conserving mufflers. Automatic radiator shutters on Presidents. Valve spring dampeners on Presidents. Longer stroke Commander Six. Restyled Dictators with double drop frames. Improved Dictator emergency brake. Studebaker's profits dropped to $1.5 million in 1930, but the company still paid out $8 million in dividends.

1931

STUDEBAKER — SERIES 53/54 — SIX: The Series 53 Studebaker Six, which began life as an Erskine, was carried over into the first part of the 1931 selling season. Specifications were basically the same as before. The 1931 cars were those built from July 1930 to the end of series production in November 1930.

The Series 54 made its debut in January 1931 as the "new" Studebaker Six. Changes included a larger radiator cap and a vee-shaped radiator. Body styling was altered to make the six look more like other 1931 Studebakers, but cars in Series 54 had round headlights. A distinctive dual bar bumper was also seen. Standard equipment included a speedometer; gas gauge; thermometer ignition lock; windshield wiper; tail and stop light and Lovejoy shock absorbers. Twenty-nine inch wire spoke wheels were standard on the Regal tourer, Regal landau and Regal sedan; other models had 29-inch wood spoke wheels. New technical features included a fuel pump and four-point motor suspension.

STUDEBAKER — DICTATOR — SERIES FC/61 — EIGHT: The FC series Dictator Eight was carried over for the early part of the 1931 sales season. There were no basic changes from 1930 specifications. Cars built from July 1930 to August 1930 were sold as 1931 models.

The new 1931 Dictator Series 61 entered production in September 1930. It was also an eight-cylinder line. Wheelbase was reduced one inch. The body was restyled to look more like bigger Studebakers. The radiator shell was of a more rounded design with a thin molding run vertically down the center of the grille. This molding carried a Studebaker badge near its top. Slimmer headlight buckets were used and the headlights were slightly oval shaped. The hood sides no longer carried seven groups of three louvers inside a rectangular panel. Instead, there were 32 tall vertical louvers. Other new features included wider crown fenders with clearance lights on top of them, larger hubcaps and single bar bumpers. Cowl lights were eliminated. Standard equipment included a speedometer; gas gauge; thermometer; ignition lock; windshield wiper; tail and stop lamp; Lovejoy shock absorbers and 29-inch Kelsey-Hayes wheels. Wood spoke wheels were standard on all models, except the Regal sedan, which came with wire wheels. There was no Dictator Six in 1931.

STUDEBAKER — COMMANDER — SERIES 70 — EIGHT: Production of the all-new 1931 Commander Series 70 line began in July 1930 and continued to September 1931. New styling features included a vee-shaped radiator, larger, oval-shaped headlights and parking lights atop the front fenders. The new single bar bumper, of sturdier construction, had a vee-shaped dip in its center. The Commander wheelbase grew to 124 inches. Standard equipment included a speedometer, gasoline gauge, thermometer, ignition lock, non-shatterable glass (optional on Studebaker Six and Dictator), vacuum wiper, tail and stop light, and Lovejoy shock absorbers. Freewheeling was also standard. The Commander had Bendix four-wheel mechanical brakes, an adjustable steering wheel, carburetor intake silencer and starter controls on the instrument panel. Kelsey-Hayes 31-inch wood spoke wheels were standard on standard models. Wire spoke wheels were included on Commander Regals.

STUDEBAKER — PRESIDENT — SERIES 80/90 — EIGHT: The President Eight came in "short" (130 inch) and long (136 inch) wheelbase versions. New design features included a vee-shaped radiator, larger radiator cap, "veed" single bar bumper, parking lamps on front fenders and large, oval-shaped headlights. Standard equipment included freewheeling, ball bearing spring shackles, carburetor intake silencer, speedometer, gas gauge, thermometer, ignition lock, clock, cigar lighter, non-shatterable glass, windshield wiper, tail and stop light, Houdaille shock absorbers and spring covers. Kelsey-Hayes 31-inch wood spoke wheels were used on standard models. Kelsey-Hayes 31-inch wire spoke wheels were used on State models. An attractive new body style was the Model 80 four-seasons convertible roadster.

I.D. DATA: [Series 53/54] Serial number in same location. Starting: (53) 5085001; (54) 5096001. Ending: (53) 5095787; (54) 5120000. Engine number on front of block on Model 53; on left side of block on Model 54. Engine numbers were S-23001 and up. [Series FC/61] Serial number in same location. Starting: (FC) 2134001; (61) 9000001. Ending: (FC) 2136227; (61) 9015000. Engine number on left side of block. Engine numbers were (FC) FC-1 and up; (61) A-101 and up; [Series 70] Serial number in same location. Starting: 8025001. Ending: 8036000. Engine number on left side of block. Starting: C-101. Ending: C-12000. [Series 80/90] Serial number in same location. Starting: (80) 7031001; (90) 6022001. Ending: (80) 7037335; (90) 6025000. Engine number on front of block. Engine numbers were P-101 and up.

Model 53, 6-cyl.

Model No.	Body Type & Seating	Factory Price	Shipping Weight	Prod. Total
53	2-dr. Rds.-2P	895	2700	Note 1
53	4-dr. Tr.-5P	895	2840	Note 1
53	4-dr. Regal Tr.-5P	995	2990	Note 1
53	2-dr. Bus. Cpe.-2P	845	2790	Note 1
53	2-dr. Spt. Cpe.-2/4P	895	2840	Note 1
53	2-dr. Clb. Sed.-5P	845	2830	Note 1
53	4-dr. Sed.-5P	895	2930	Note 1
53	4-dr. Regal Sed.-5P	995	3075	Note 1
53	4-dr. Lan. Sed.-5P	995	3110	Note 1

Model 54, 6-cyl.

Model No.	Body Type & Seating	Factory Price	Shipping Weight	Prod. Total
54	2-dr. Rds.-2/4P	895	2700	Note 2
54	4-dr. Tr.-5P	895	2805	Note 2
54	4-dr. Regal Tr.-5P	970	2960	Note 2
54	2-dr. Bus. Cpe.-2P	845	2790	Note 2
54	2-dr. Spt. Cpe.-2/4P	895	2840	Note 2
54	4-dr. Sed.-5P	895	2930	Note 2
54	4-dr. Regal Sed.-5P	970	3075	Note 2

Note 1: Total production November 1929 to November 1930 was 22,371.

Note 2: Total production December 1930 to September 1931 was 23,917.

Dictator Model FC, 8-cyl.

Model No.	Body Type & Seating	Factory Price	Shipping Weight	Prod. Total
FC	4-dr. Tr.-5P	1285	2980	Note 1
FC	4-dr. Regal Tr.-5P	1385	3100	Note 1
FC	2-dr. Cpe.-2P	1255	2950	Note 1
FC	2-dr. Spt. Cpe.-2/4P	1315	3010	Note 1
FC	2-dr. Regal Brgm.-5P	1415	3275	Note 1

Model No.	Body Type & Seating	Factory Price	Shipping Weight	Prod. Total
FC	2-dr. Clb. Sed.-5P	1195	2990	Note 1
FC	4-dr. Sed.-5P	1295	3095	Note 1
FC	4-dr. Regal Sed.-5P	1415	3230	Note 1

Dictator Model 61, 8-cyl.

Model No.	Body Type & Seating	Factory Price	Shipping Weight	Prod. Total
61	2-dr. Cpe.-2P	1095	2905	Note 2
61	2-dr. Spt. Cpe.-2/4P	1150	2955	Note 2
61	4-dr. Sed.-5P	1150	3055	Note 2
61	4-dr. Regal Sed.-5P	1225	3195	Note 2

Note 1: Total production May 1929 to August 1930 was 16,359.

Note 2: Total production August 1930 to September 1931 was 14,141.

Commander Model 70, 8-cyl.

Model No.	Body Type & Seating	Factory Price	Shipping Weight	Prod. Total
70	2-dr. Cpe.-2/4P	1585	3400	Note 1
70	2-dr. Vic-4P	1585	3390	Note 1
70	2-dr. Regal Brgm.-5P	1685	3660	Note 1
70	4-dr. Sed.-5P	1585	3520	Note 1
70	4-dr. Regal Sed.-5P	1685	3660	Note 1

Note 1: Total production June 1930 to September 1931 was 10,823.

President Model 80, 8-cyl.

Model No.	Body Type & Seating	Factory Price	Shipping Weight	Prod. Total
80	2-dr. State Rds.-2/4P	1900	4130	Note 1
80	2-dr. Cpe.-2P	1850	3995	Note 1
80	2-dr. State Cpe.-2/4P	1950	4200	Note 1
80	4-dr. Sed.-5P	1850	4230	Note 1
80	4-dr. State Sed.-5P	1950	4385	Note 1

President Model 90, 8-cyl.

Model No.	Body Type & Seating	Factory Price	Shipping Weight	Prod. Total
90	4-dr. Tr.-7P	1850	4125	Note 2
90	4-dr. State Tr.-7P	2050	4265	Note 2
90	2-dr. State Vic.-4P	2250	4275	Note 2
90	2-dr. State Brgm.-5P	2250	4460	Note 2
90	4-dr. Sed.-7P	2150	4360	Note 2
90	4-dr. State Sed.-7P	2250	4520	Note 2
90	4-dr. State Limo.-7P	2550	4580	Note 2

Note 1: Total production June 1930 to September 1931 was 6,340.

Note 2: Total production June 1930 to September 1931 was 2,762.

ENGINE: [Standard Six] L-head. Inline. Six. Cast iron block. B & S: 3-1/4 x 4-1/8 in. Disp.: 205.2 cu. in. C.R.: 5.2:1. Brake H.P.: 70 @ 3200 R.P.M. N.A.C.C. H.P.: 25.4. Main bearings: four. Valve lifters: solid. Carb.: Schebler one-barrel Model TX5. Torque (compression) 104 lb.-ft. @ 1200 R.P.M. [Dictator Eight] L-head. Inline. Eight. Cast iron block. B & S: 3-1/16 x 3-3/4 in. Disp.: 221 cu. in. C.R.: (FC) 4.8:1; (61) 5.00:1, (opt. 61) 5.50:1. Brake H.P.: (FC) 70; (61) 81 @ 3200 R.P.M. N.A.C.C. H.P.: 30.4. Main bearings: nine. Valve lifters: solid. Carb.: Stromberg two-barrel Model UU2. Torque (compression) 104 lb.-ft. @ 1200 R.P.M. [Commander Eight] L-head. Inline. Eight. Cast iron block. B & S: 3-1/16 x 4-1/4 in. Disp.: 250.4 cu. in. C.R.: 5.20:1; (opt.) 5.50:1 or 6.00:1. Brake H.P.: 101 @ 3200 R.P.M. N.A.C.C. H.P.: 30.04. Main bearings: nine. Valve lifters: solid. Carb.: Stromberg two-barrel Model UU2. Torque (compression) 104 lb.-ft. @ 1200 R.P.M. [President Eight] L-head. Inline. Eight. Cast iron block. B & S: 3-1/2 x 4-3/8 in. Disp.: 337 cu. in. C.R.: 5.10:1; (opt.) 5.50:1 or 6.00:1. Brake H.P.: 122 @ 3200 R.P.M. N.A.C.C. H.P.: 39.2. Main bearings: nine. Valve lifters: solid. Carb.: Stromberg two-barrel Model UU2. Torque (compression) 104 lb.-ft. @ 1200 R.P.M.

CHASSIS: [Series 53] W.B.: 114 in. Height: 69-1/4 in. Frt/Rear Tread: 56.5/58 in. Tires: 19 x 5.25 in. [Series 54] W.B.: 114 in. Height: 69-1/4 in. Frt/Rear Tread: 56.5/58 in. Tires: 19 x 5.25 in. [Series FC] W.B.: 115 in. Height: 69-1/4 in. Frt/Rear Tread: 56.5/58 in. Tires: 19 x 5.50 in. [Series 61] W.B.: 114 in. Height: 69-1/4 in. Tires: 19 x 5.25 in. [Series 70] W.B.: 124 in. Height: 70-5/16 in. Frt/Rear Tread: 56.5/58 in. Tires: 19 x 6.00 in. [Series 80] W.B.: 122 in. Height: 71-5/8 in. Frt/Rear Tread: 56-5/8/59 in. Tires: 19 x 6.50 in. [Series 90] W.B.: 136 in. Height: 71-5/8 in. Frt/Rear Tread: 56-5/8/59 in. Tires: 19 x 6.50 in.

TECHNICAL: Manual transmission. Speeds: 3F/1R. Floor mounted gearshift controls. Clutch: Multiple dry disc. Semi-floating rear axle. Overall ratio: (53) 4.78:1; (54) 4.72:1; (FC, 61 and 70) 4.73:1; (80 and 90) 4.31:1. Bendix external expanding four-wheel mechanical brakes. Kelsey-Hayes wheels wood spoke on standard models and wire spoke on Regal and State models. Drivetrain option: freewheeling.

OPTIONS: Front bumper. Rear guards. Whitewall tires. Dual sidemounts. Sidemount cover(s). Backing light. Spring covers. Power tire pump. Heater. Clock (std. in President). Cigar lighter (std. in President). Wind wings. Outside rearview mirror. Pedestal mirrors. Spotlight. Trunk rack. Trunk. Wheel trim rings. Trippe lights. Special paint.

HISTORICAL: Introduced: (see preceding text). Calendar year registrations: 46,535. Model year production: 44,218. Innovations: Freewheeling. Improved steering gear. Improved brakes with cable control introduced at mid-year. Improved manifolding and carburetion on Commander/President. Silent gear transmission. Higher lift camshafts. On November 3, 1931, a President Model 80 set numerous stock car speed records at Muroc dry lake in California. In September 1931, Studebaker introduced its low-priced Rockne line.

1932

STUDEBAKER — SERIES 55 — SIX: Studebaker claimed that it had added 1-1/2 to 3 mph to the top speed of all its 1932 models by slanting the windshield and rounding the front body corners. Safety glass was now standard on all cars. A longer, 117-inch wheelbase was used for the cars in the six-cylinder Series 55 lineup. Visors over the windshield were eliminated. Also new was a single bar front bumper. A new, airplane-type instrument panel with circular gauges inside an oval panel was seen. A key operated automatic starter, freewheeling and Startix device were standard on all models. New models included the St. Regis brougham, Regal St. Regis brougham, convertible sedan and Regal convertible sedan. A 15-gallon fuel tank was used on sixes and Dictator Eights.

STUDEBAKER — DICTATOR — SERIES 62 — EIGHT: The 1932 Dictator Eights had a longer, 117-inch wheelbase. Styling features included a slanting windshield, vee-shaped radiator, oval headlights, single bar bumpers and one-piece crowned fenders. Standard equipment included a Stromberg carburetor, Delco-Remy ignition, mechanical Bendix brakes, safety glass, freewheeling, Startix device, synchromesh transmission and vacuum advance distributor. All Studebaker Eights carried standard front fender parking lights.

STUDEBAKER — COMMANDER — SERIES 71 — EIGHT: For 1932, the Commander had basically the same styling features as the less expensive models on a longer 125-inch wheelbase. Appearance features included a more streamlined all-steel body, vee-shaped radiator, sloping windshield with safety glass, wide one-piece fenders with parking lights and a new airplane-type instrument panel. Standard equipment included a synchromesh transmission, Houdaille automatic-ride shock absorbers, freewheeling, Startix automatic starting system, Stromberg carburetor, Delco-Remy ignition, rubber mounted four-point engine suspension and ball bearing spring shackles. A 17-gallon fuel tank was employed.

STUDEBAKER — PRESIDENT — SERIES 91 — EIGHT: The 1932 President came on only a single, 135-inch wheelbase. The roofline was streamlined by eliminating the visor and adding a sloped windshield. The radiator grille had more of a wedge-shaped look. It sloped sharply at its bottom. Steel artillery wheels were standard. Presidents had a clock and passaround cigar lighter with dual ash receivers in broughams and sedans. Standard equipment included a Stromberg carburetor; Delco-Remy ignition; mechanical Bendix brakes; synchromesh transmission; freewheeling; Startix device; inside sun visor; Ride Control; vacuum distributor; hydraulic shock absorbers; airplane-type instrument panel and metal spring covers.

I.D. DATA: [Series 55] Serial numbers were in the same location on the left side of frame over front axle. Starting: 5120001. Ending: 5133400. Engine numbers were on left side of block. Starting: S49001. Ending: S62821 (approx.). [Series 62] Serial numbers were in the same location. Starting: 9015001. Ending: 9020970. Engine numbers on left side of block. Starting: A15002. Ending: A21150 (approx.). [Series 71] Serial numbers were in the same locations. Starting: 8036001. Ending: 8040000. Engine numbers were on the left side of block. Starting: C12001. Ending: C15745 (approx.). [Series 91] Serial numbers were in the same location. Starting: 6025001. Ending: 6027400. Engine numbers were on the front of the block. Starting: P10001. Ending: P12440 (approx.).

Model 55, 6-cyl.

Model No.	Body Type & Seating	Factory Price	Shipping Weight	Prod. Total
55	2-dr. Conv. Rds.-2/4P	915	3035	Note 1
55	2-dr. Regal Conv. Rds.-2/4P	1020	3145	Note 1
55	2-dr. Cpe.-2P	840	3025	Note 1
55	2-dr. Regal Cpe.-2P	945	3115	Note 1
55	2-dr. Spt. Cpe.-2/4P	890	3080	Note 1
55	2-dr. Regal Spt. Cpe.-2/4P	995	3175	Note 1
55	2-dr. St. R. Brgm.-5P	915	3130	Note 1
55	2-dr. Regal St- R. Brgm.-5P	1020	3190	Note 1
55	4-dr. Conv. Sed.-5P	985	3210	Note 1
55	4-dr. Regal Conv. Sed.-5P	1000	3270	Note 1
55	4-dr. Sed.-5P	915	3170	Note 1
55	4-dr. Regal Sed.-5P	1020	3270	Note 1

1931 Studebaker, Dictator Eight (Series 61), Regal sedan, AA

1931 Studebaker, President Eight (Series 90), State tourer, AA

1932 Studebaker, President Eight (Series 91), State seven-passenger sedan, AA

1933 Studebaker, Six (Series 56), station wagon (with body by Cantrell), AA

1933 Studebaker, President Eight (Series 82), Regal St. Regis brougham, AA

1931 Studebaker, Commander Eight (Series 70), victoria, AA

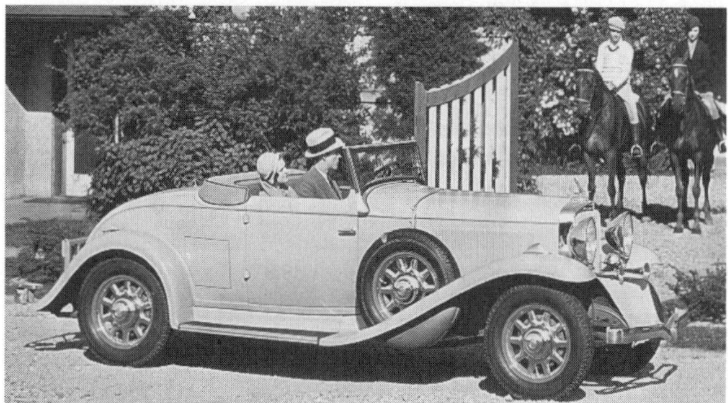
1932 Studebaker, Dictator Eight (Series 62), convertible roadster, AA

1932 Studebaker, President Eight (Series 91), State convertible sedan, AA

1933 Studebaker, Commander Eight (Series 73), Regal coupe, AA

1933 Studebaker, President Eight (Series 82), Regal sedan, AA

Note 1: Total production November 1931 to November 1932 was 13,647.

Model 62, 8-cyl.

Model No.	Body Type & Seating	Factory Price	Shipping Weight	Prod. Total
62	2-dr. Rds. Conv.-2/4P	1050	3115	Note 1
62	2-dr. Regal Rds. Conv.-2/4P	1155	3190	Note 1
62	2-dr. Cpe.-2P	980	3085	Note 1
62	2-dr. Regal Cpe.-2P	1085	3190	Note 1
62	2-dr. Spt. Cpe.-2/4P	1030	3160	Note 1
62	2-dr. Regal Spt. Cpt.-2P	1135	3265	Note 1
62	2-dr. St. R. Brgm.-5P	1050	3225	Note 1
62	2-dr. Regal St. R. Brgm.-5P	1155	3280	Note 1
62	4-dr. Conv. Sed.-5P	1125	3285	Note 1
62	4-dr. Regal Conv. Sed.-5P	1230	3345	Note 1
62	4-dr. Sed.-5P	1050	3240	Note 1
62	4-dr. Regal Sed-5P	1155	3345	Note 1

Note 1: Total production November 1931 to November 1932 was 6,021.

Model 71, 8-cyl.

Model No.	Body Type & Seating	Factory Price	Shipping Weight	Prod. Total
71	2-dr. Rds. Conv.-2/4P	1445	3480	Note 1
71	2-dr. Regal Rds. Conv.-2/4P	1550	3485	Note 1
71	2-dr. Spt. Cpe.-2/4P	1350	3415	Note 1
71	2-dr. Regal Spt. Cpe.-2/4P	1455	3520	Note 1
71	2-dr. St. R. Brgm.-5P	1445	3465	Note 1
71	2-dr. Regal St. R. Brgm.-5P	1550	3570	Note 1
71	4-dr. Conv. Sed.-5P	1560	3675	Note 1
71	4-dr. Regal Conv. Sed.-5P	1665	3680	Note 1
71	4-dr. Sed.-5P	1445	3545	Note 1
71	4-dr. Regal Sed.-5P	1550	3645	Note 1

Note 1: Total production November 1931 to November 1932 was 3,551.

Model 91, 8-cyl.

Model No.	Body Type & Seating	Factory Price	Shipping Weight	Prod. Total
91	2-dr. Rds. Conv.-2/4P	1750	4220	Note 1
91	2-dr. State Rds. Conv.-2/4P	1855	4200	Note 1
91	2-dr. Cpe.-2P	1595	NA	Note 1
91	2-dr. State Cpe.-2P	1700	NA	Note 1
91	2-dr. Spt.Cpe.-2/4P	1690	4255	Note 1
91	2-dr. State Spt. Cpe.-2/4P	1795	4235	Note 1
91	2-dr. St. R. Brgm.-5P	1750	4300	Note 1
91	2-dr. State St. R. Brgm.-5P	1855	4280	Note 1
91	4-dr. Conv. Sed.-5P	1880	4445	Note 1
91	4-dr. State Conv. Sed.-5P	1985	4425	Note 1
91	4-dr. Sed.-5P	1750	4260	Note 1
91	4-dr. State Sed.-5P	1855	4370	Note 1
91	4-dr. Sed.-7P	1890	4365	Note 1
91	4-dr. State Sed.-7P	1995	4475	Note 1
91	4-dr. Limo.-7P	1990	4525	Note 1
91	4-dr. State Limo.-7P	2095	4525	Note 1

Note 1: Total production November 1931 to December 1932 was 2,399.

ENGINE: [Six Engine] L-head. Inline. Cast iron block. B & S: 3-1/4 x 4-5/8 in. Disp.: 230 cu. in. C.R.: 5.0:1. Brake H.P.: 80 @ 3200 R.P.M. N.A.C.C. H.P.: 25.4. Main bearings: four. Valve lifters: solid. Carb.: Stromberg Model UUR-2 one-barrel. [Dictator Engine] L-head. Inline. Eight. Cast iron block. B & S: 3-1/16 x 3-3/4 in. Disp.: 221 cu. in. C.R.: 5.0:1. Brake H.P.: 85 @ 3200 R.P.M. N.A.C.C. H.P.: 30.04. Main bearings: nine. Valve lifters: solid. Carb.: Stromberg Model UUR-2 one-barrel. [Commander Engine] L-head. Inline. Eight. Cast iron block. B & S: 3-1/16 x 4-1/4 in. Disp.: 250.4 cu. in. C.R.: 5.15:1. Brake H.P.: 101 @ 3200 R.P.M. N.A.C.C. H.P.: 30.04. Main bearings: nine. Valve lifters: solid. Carb.: Stromberg Model UU-R one-barrel. [President Engine] L-head. Inline. Eight. Cast iron block. B & S: 3-1/2 x 4-3/8 in. Disp.: 337 cu. in. C.R.: 5.1:1. Brake H.P.: 122 @ 3200 R.P.M. N.A.C.C. H.P.: 39.2. Main bearings: nine. Valve lifters: solid. Carb.: Stromberg EE-22 two-barrel.

CHASSIS: [Series 55] W.B.: 117 in. Tires: 18 x 5.50 in. [Series 62] W.B.: 117 in. Tires: 18 x 5.50 in. [Series 71] W.B.: 125 in. Tires: 18 x 6.00 in. [Series 91] W.B.: 135 in. Tires: 18 x 6.50 in.

TECHNICAL: Synchromesh transmission. Speeds: 3F/1R. Floor mounted gearshift controls. Clutch: Single plate dry disc. Semi-floating rear axle. Overall ratio: (55) 4.27:1; (62) 4.73:1; (71) 4.73:1 and (91) 4.31:1. Bendix mechanical four-wheel brakes. Steel artillery spoke wheels. Drivetrain options: Freewheeling. Startix device. Silent second gear.

OPTIONS: Front bumper. Rear bumper. Outside rearview mirror. Dual sidemounts. Sidemount cover(s). Wire wheels. Pedestal mirrors. Radio. Heater. Clock. Cigar lighter. Radio antenna. Seat covers. Trippe lights. Spotlight(s). Parking lights (six). Trumpet horns. Trunk rack. Trunk. Whitewall tires. Chrome-plated spoke wheels. Power tire pump. Special paint.

HISTORICAL: Introduced November 1931. Calendar year registrations: 41,968 (including Rockne). Calendar year sales: 44,325 (including Rockne). Model year production: 47,950 (including Rockne). Innovations: Synchromesh transmission. Startix automatic starting system. Vacuum distributor. Higher, wider seats. Counterweighted crankshafts. Improved vibration dampening. Improved brakes. Drop center rims. Studebaker nearly merged with the White Motor Co. in October 1932. Failure to achieve the merger put Studebaker on the brink of bankruptcy.

1933

STUDEBAKER — SERIES 56 — SIX: For 1933, the vertical grille bars on all Studebakers were extended further downward and came to a rounded "vee" at the bottom. Front fenders were of a new, skirted design and the bottom of the leading edge of the rear fenders was given a more rounded contour. Oval-shaped headlights remained a Studebaker styling touch. The Six had larger sized tires and five more horsepower. The rear end styling was of a more streamlined "beavertail" design. Standard equipment on Series 56 models included a Stromberg carburetor, Delco-Remy ignition, mechanical brakes, ball bearing spring shackles, automatic choke, automatic starter, automatic heat control and automatic ride control. With the company in receivership, sales were low. The company's financial plight led to temporary discontinuance of the Dictator series.

STUDEBAKER — COMMANDER — SERIES 73 — EIGHT: Like other 1933 models, the Commander Eights had a more streamlined look with a radically sloped grille, skirted fenders, more sweeping rooflines and beavertail rear end styling. New standard equipment included a Stromberg downdraft carburetor, automatic choke and fully automatic spark advance. Other features highlighted in advertising were mechanical brakes, Delco-Remy ignition, ball bearing spring shackles, automatic ride control, automatic starter, safety glass and double inside sun visors. Ads also stressed that lubrication points were reduced to four fittings that required greasing at extended 2,500-mile intervals. Like the Studebaker Six, the Commander carried a 14-gallon fuel tank.

STUDEBAKER — PRESIDENT — SERIES 82 — EIGHT: Two President Eight series were offered in 1933. The 82 models were the smaller and less powerful of the two lines; virtually identical in size, performance and features to the 1932 Commander. Styling features included the more radical slant vee-type radiator, skirted fenders, double inside sun visors and beavertail rear styling. Standard equipment included a Stromberg carburetor, Delco-Remy ignition, Bendix vacuum-boosted power brakes, automatic choke, automatic starter, automatic manifold heat control, downdraft carburetion, ball bearing spring shackles, freewheeling and a 17-1/2 gallon fuel tank.

STUDEBAKER — PRESIDENT SPEEDWAY — SERIES 92 — EIGHT: The most expensive Studebaker line for 1933 was called the Speedway President series. These cars also had new slanting "vee" radiators, skirted fenders and beavertail rear ends. Double inside sun visors were featured. Gas filler caps were in the left rear fender. Standard equipment included a Stromberg carburetor, Delco-Remy ignition, mechanical power brakes, automatic starter, freewheeling, automatic ride control, ball bearing spring shackles and 20-1/2 gallon fuel tanks.

I.D. DATA: [Series 56] Serial numbers were in the same location on the left side of frame over front axle. Starting: 5133401. Ending: 5140262. Engine numbers were on the left side of engine block. Engine numbers were S63001 and up. [Series 73] Serial numbers were in the same location. Starting: 8040001. Ending: 8043781. Engine numbers were on the left side of the block. Engine numbers were C16101 and up. [Series 82] Serial numbers were in the same location. Starting: 7040001. Ending: 7041169. Engine numbers were on the side of the block. Engine numbers were B101 and up. [Series 92] Serial numbers were in the same location. Starting: 6027401. Ending: 6028017. Engine numbers were on the front of the block. Engine numbers were P12501 and up.

Model 56, 6-cyl.

Model No.	Body Type & Seating	Factory Price	Shipping Weight	Prod. Total
56	2-dr. Conv.-2/4P	915	3165	Note 1
56	2-dr. Regal Conv.-2/4P	1020	3260	Note 1
56	2-dr. Cpe.-2P	840	3160	Note 1
56	2-dr. Regal Cpe.-2P	945	3245	Note 1
56	2-dr. Spt. Cpe.-2/4P	890	3210	Note 1
56	2-dr. Regal Spt. Cpe.-2/4P	995	3300	Note 1
56	2-dr. St. R. Brgm.-5P	915	3300	Note 1
56	2-dr. Regal St. R. Brgm.-5P	1020	3375	Note 1
56	4-dr. Conv. Sed.-5P	1015	3380	Note 1
56	4-dr. Regal Conv. Sed.-5P	1120	3460	Note 1
56	4-dr. Sed.-5P	915	3310	Note 1
56	4-dr. Regal Sed.-5P	1020	3435	Note 1

Note 1: Total production November 1932 to July 1933 was 6,861.

Model 73, 8-cyl.

Model No.	Body Type & Seating	Factory Price	Shipping Weight	Prod. Total
73	2-dr. Rds. Conv.-2/4P	1095	3245	Note 1
73	2-dr. Regal Rds. Conv.-2/4P	1200	3335	Note 1
73	2-dr. Cpe.-2P	1000	3220	Note 1
73	2-dr. Regal Cpe.-2P	1105	3345	Note 1
73	2-dr. Spt. Cpe.-2/4P	1050	3275	Note 1
73	2-dr. Regal Spt. Cpe.-2/4P	1155	3405	Note 1
73	2-dr. St. R. Brgm.-5P	1075	3375	Note 1
73	2-dr. Regal St. R. Brgm-5P	1180	3475	Note 1
73	4-dr. Conv. Sed.-5P	1195	3475	Note 1
73	4-dr. Regal Conv. Sed.-5P	1300	3545	Note 1
73	4-dr. Sed.-5P	1075	3385	Note 1
73	4-dr. Regal Sed.-5P	1180	3500	Note 1

Note 1: Total production November 1932 to July 1933 was 3,841.

Model 82, 8-cyl.

Model No.	Body Type & Seating	Factory Price	Shipping Weight	Prod. Total
82	2-dr. State Rds. Conv.-2/4P	1490	3560	Note 1
82	2-dr. Cpe.-2/4P	1325	3520	Note 1
82	2-dr. State Cpe.-2/4P	1430	3600	Note 1
82	2-dr. St. R. Brgm.-5P	1385	3605	Note 1
82	2-dr. State St. R. Brgm.-5P	1490	3670	Note 1
82	4-dr. State Conv. Sed.-5P	1650	3745	Note 1
82	4-dr. Sed.-5P	1385	3640	Note 1
82	4-dr. State Sed.-5P	1490	3720	Note 1

Note 1: Total production November 1932 to July 1933 was 1,194.

Model 92, 8-cyl.

Model No.	Body Type & Seating	Factory Price	Shipping Weight	Prod. Total
92	2-dr. State Rds. Conv.-2/4P	1790	4285	Note 1
92	2-dr. StateCpe.-2/4P	1730	4335	Note 1
92	2-dr. State St. R. Brgm.-5P	1790	4400	Note 1
92	2-dr. State Conv. Sed.-5P	1960	4470	Note 1
92	4-dr. Sed.-5P	1685	4380	Note 1
92	4-dr. State Sed.-5P	1790	4465	Note 1
92	4-dr. Sed.-7P	1835	4470	Note 1
92	4-dr. State Sed.-7P	1940	4565	Note 1
92	4-dr. State Limo.-7P	2040	4605	Note 1

Note 1: Total production November 1932 to July 1933 was 635.

ENGINE: [Series 56] L-head. Inline. Six. Cast iron block. B & S: 3-1/4 x 4-5/8 in. Disp.: 230 cu. in. C.R.: 5.5:1. Brake H.P.: 85 @ 3200 R.P.M. N.A.C.C. H.P.: 25.4. Main bearings: four. Valve lifters: solid. Carb.: Stromberg two-barrel Model EE-22. [Series 73] L-head. Inline. Eight. Cast iron block. B & S: 3-1/16 x 4 in. Disp.: 235 cu. in. C.R.: 5.5:1. Brake H.P.: 100 @ 3800 R.P.M. N.A.C.C. H.P.: 30. Main bearings: nine. Valve lifters: solid. Carb.: Stromberg two-barrel Model EX-22. [Series 82] L-head. Inline. Eight. Cast iron block. B & S: 3-1/16 x 4-1/4 in. Disp.: 250 cu. in. C.R.: 5.0:1. Brake H.P.: 110 @ 3600 R.P.M. N.A.C.C. H.P.: 30. Main bearings: nine. Valve lifters: solid. Carb.: Stromberg two-barrel Model EE-22. [Series 92] L-head. Inline. Eight. Cast iron block. B & S: 3-1/2 x 4-3/8 in. Disp.: 337 cu. in. C.R.: 5.5:1. Brake H.P.: 132 @ 3400 R.P.M. N.A.C.C. H.P.: 39.2. Main bearings: nine. Valve lifters: solid. Carb.: Stromberg two-barrel Model EE-22.

CHASSIS: [Series 56] W.B.: 117 in. Tires: 17 x 5.50 in. [Series 73] W.B.: 117 in. Tires: 17 x 6.00 in. [Series 82] W.B.: 125 in. Tires: 17 x 6.50 in. [Series 92] W.B.: 135 in. Tires: 17 x 7.00 in.

TECHNICAL: Synchromesh manual transmission. Speeds: 3F/1R. Floor mounted gearshift controls. Clutch: single dry disc. Semi-floating rear axle. Overall ratio: (56 and 73) 4.36:1; (82) 4.73:1 and (92) 4.31:1. Vacuum boosted power mechanical brakes. Steel spoke artillery wheels. Drivetrain option: freewheeling.

OPTIONS: Front bumper. Rear bumper. Spare tire. Dual sidemounts. Sidemount cover(s). Outside rearview mirror. Pedestal mirrors. Radio. Heater. Clock. Cigar lighter. Radio antenna. Chrome-plated wheels. Wire spoke wheels. Spotlight(s). Fog lamps. Trippe lights. Trunk rack. Trunk. White pencil stripe tires. Special paint. Dual trumpet horns. Wind wings.

HISTORICAL: Introduced November 1932. Innovations: Downdraft carburetion. Power mechanical brakes. Improved chassis lubrication. Calendar year registrations: 36,242 (including Rockne). Model year sales: 43,024 (including Rockne). Model year production: 45,074 (including Rockne). Studebaker went into receivership on March 18, 1933. Two weeks later, Rockne sales activities were merged with those of the parent firm and Rockne production was transferred to South Bend. Studebaker divested itself of Pierce-Arrow. Officers of White Motor Co. were appointed receivers of the corporation.

1934

STUDEBAKER — DICTATOR — SERIES A — SIX: For 1934, the Dictator returned to the Studebaker lineup as a six-cylinder series. Styling features included a newly designed vee-type slanting radiator, aerodynamic streamlined bodies, more deeply skirted fenders, slanting hood louvers, single bar vee-shaped bumpers and a body belt molding that ran across the hood side and over the body, dropping sharply at the rear. There was a new instrument panel and front windows with integral wind wings. Closed models had streamlined trunks. Regal trim models featured six-wheel equipment. Standard equipment included a Stromberg carburetor, Autolite ignition, steeldraulic brakes, safety glass, freewheeling and automatic starter.

STUDEBAKER — DICTATOR — SERIES SPECIAL A — SIX: In January 1934, Studebaker announced a new "Year Ahead" series. The basic features were the same as those found on cars in the Dictator A series. However, there were five additional body styles including an aerodynamic sedan that looked like the famous Pierce Silver Arrow. These cars also had vacuum operated power brakes—previously limited to use on more expensive Studebakers. Safety glass was used in the windshield only to keep selling prices low.

STUDEBAKER — COMMANDER — SERIES B — EIGHT: The 1934 Commanders had more aerodynamic body contours, round headlights with bullet-shaped buckets, slanting vertical hood louvers (except horizontal louvers on Custom Land Cruiser sedan), vee-type slanting radiators, more deeply skirted fenders, single bar vee-shaped bumpers, front windows with integral wind wings and a body belt molding that sloped sharply at the rear. Regal equipment included two welled fenders and sidemounts. Regal and Custom models had streamlined trunks. Standard features included a Stromberg carburetor, Delco-Remy ignition, duo-power mechanical brakes, new instrument panel and X-frame. The Custom Land Cruiser came with fender skirts.

STUDEBAKER — PRESIDENT — SERIES C — EIGHT: More pronounced streamlining was also seen on 1934 Presidents. They featured recessed trunks, more rounded vee-shaped grilles, a wide vee bumper, built-in taillights, streamlined round headlights and all features found on Commanders. These cars were smaller and lighter than previous Presidents. They had a much smaller, less powerful straight-eight under their hoods.

I.D. DATA: [Series A] Serial numbers were in the same location on the left side of frame above front axle. Starting: 5145001 and up. Engine numbers were on the right side of engine block. Engine numbers were D101 and up. [Series Special A] Serial numbers were in the same location. Serial numbers were 5158151 and up. Engine numbers were on the right side of block. Engine numbers were DS101 and up. [Series B] Serial numbers were in the same location. Serial numbers were 8045001 and up. Engine numbers were on the right side of block. Engine numbers were 20001 and up. [Series C] Serial numbers were in the same location and began at 7045001 and up. Engine numbers were on the front of the block and began at B1401 and up.

Model A, 6-cyl.

Model No.	Body Type & Seating	Factory Price	Shipping Weight	Prod. Total
A	2-dr. Regal Cpe.-4P	875	2960	Note 1
A	2-dr. St. R. Sed.-5P	815	2850	Note 1
A	2-dr. Cus. St. R. Sed.-5P	865	2945	Note 1
A	4-dr. Sed.-5P	845	2920	Note 1
A	4-dr. Regal Sed.-5P	895	3015	Note 1

1933 Studebaker, President Speedway Eight (Series 92), Berline limousine, AA

1934 Studebaker, Dictator Six (Series A), roadster (with optional sidemounted tires), OCW

1934 Studebaker, Dictator Six (Series A), sedan, AA

1934 Studebaker, Dictator Six (Series A), coupe, AA

1935 Studebaker, President Eight (Series 1C), Regal sedan, OCW

1936 Studebaker, Dictator Six (Series 4A), coupe, AA

1936 Studebaker, President Eight (Series 2C), St. Regis cruising sedan, AA

1936 Studebaker, President Eight (Series 2C), cruising sedan (with optional sidemounted tires, metal tire covers and full wheel discs), AA

1937 Studebaker, Dictator Six (Series 6A), station wagon (with body by U.S.B.F.), AA

1937 Studebaker, President Eight (Series 3C), five-passenger coupe, AA

Note 1: Total production September 1933 to October 1934 was 45,851.

Model Special A, 6-cyl.

Model No.	Body Type & Seating	Factory Price	Shipping Weight	Prod. Total
Spl A	2-dr. Cpe.-2P	720	2790	Note 1
Spl A	2-dr. Regal Cpe.-2P	755	2855	Note 1
Spl A	2-dr. Cpe.-4P	775	2860	Note 1
Spl A	2-dr. Regal Cpe.-4P	805	2945	Note 1
Spl A	2-dr. St. R. Sed.-5P	745	2835	Note 1
Spl A	2-dr. Regal St. R. Sed.-5P	795	2930	Note 1
Spl A	4-dr. Sed.-5P	775	2905	Note 1
Spl A	4-dr. Regal Sed.-5P	825	3000	Note 1
Spl A	2-dr. St. R. Cus. Sed.-5P	795	2885	Note 1
Spl A	4-dr. Cus. Sed.-5P	825	2945	Note 1

Note 1: See Dictator A series total production above.

Model B, 8-cyl.

Model No.	Body Type & Seating	Factory Price	Shipping Weight	Prod. Total
B	2-dr. Rds. Conv.-4P	1025	3265	Note 1
B	2-dr. Regal Rds. Conv.-4P	1055	3345	Note 1
B	2-dr. Cpe.-2P	975	3215	Note 1
B	2-dr. Regal Cpe.-2P	1005	3300	Note 1
B	2-dr. Cpe.-4P	1025	3290	Note 1
B	2-dr. Regal Cpe.-4P	1055	3360	Note 1
B	2-dr. St. R. Sed.-5P	995	3245	Note 1
B	2-dr. Cus. St. Regal Sed.-5P	1045	3365	Note 1
B	4-dr. Sed.-5P	1025	3320	Note 1
B	4-dr. Regal Sed.-5P	1075	3445	Note 1
B	4-dr. Cus. Sed.-5P	1075	3370	Note 1
B	4-dr. Land Cruiser-5P	1220	NA	Note 1

Note 1: Total production September 1933 to October 1934 was 10,315.

Model C, 8-cyl.

Model No.	Body Type & Seating	Factory Price	Shipping Weight	Prod. Total
C	2-dr. Rds. Conv.-2/4P	1285	3445	Note 1
C	2-dr. Regal Rds. Conv.-2/4P	1315	3520	Note 1
C	2-dr. Cpe.-2P	1235	3380	Note 1
C	2-dr. Regal Cpe.-2P	1265	3480	Note 1
C	2-dr. Cpe.-4P	1285	3420	Note 1
C	2-dr. Regal Cpe.-4P	1315	3520	Note 1
C	4-dr. Sed.-5P	1285	3500	Note 1
C	4-dr. Regal Sed.-5P	1335	3630	Note 1
C	4-dr. Cus. Sed. 5P	1335	3560	Note 1
C	4-dr. Cus. Berl.-5P	1485	3610	Note 1
C	4-dr. Regal Berl.-5P	1485	3680	Note 1
C	4-dr. Ld. Cruiser Sed.-5P	1510	NA	Note 1

Note 1: Total production September 1933 to October 1934 was 3,698.

ENGINE: [Dictator Engine] L-head. Inline. Six. Cast iron block. (Aluminum cylinder head.) B & S: 3-1/4 x 4-1/8 in. Disp.: 205.3 cu. in. C.R.: 6.3:1. Brake H.P.: 88 @ 3600 R.P.M. N.A.C.C. H.P.: 25.35. Main bearings: four. Valve lifters: solid. Carb.: Stromberg one-barrel Model UR21. [Commander Engine] L-head. Inline. Eight. Cast iron block (aluminum cylinder head). B & S: 3-1/16 x 3-3/4 in. Disp.: 221 cu. in. C.R.: 6.3:1. Brake H.P.: 103 @ 3800 R.P.M. N.A.C.C. H.P.: 30. Main bearings: nine. Valve lifters: solid. Carb.: Stromberg one-barrel Model E-33. [President Engine] L-head. Inline. Eight. Cast iron block (aluminum cylinder head). B & S: 3-1/16 x 4-1/4 in. Disp.: 250.4 cu. in. C.R.: 6.3:1. Brake H.P.: 110 @ 3660 R.P.M. N.A.C.C. H.P.: 30. Main bearings: nine. Valve lifters: solid. Carb.: Stromberg two-barrel Model EE-22.

CHASSIS: [Series A & Spl. A] W.B.: 113 in. Tires: 17 x 5.50 in. [Series B] W.B.: 119 in. Tires: 17 x 6.00 in. [Series C] W.B.: 123 in. Tires: 17 x 6.50 in.

TECHNICAL: Synchromesh manual transmission. Speeds: 3F/1R. Floor mounted gearshift controls. Clutch: Single plate dry disc type. Semi-floating rear axle. Overall ratio: (Series A) 4.55:1; (Series B) 4.82:1 and (Series C) 4.70:1. Four-wheel steeldraulic brakes. Steel artillery spoke wheels. Drivetrain options: Freewheeling. Vacuum clutch. Overdrive.

OPTIONS: Front bumper. Rear bumper. Pin stripe. Whitewall tires. Dual sidemounts. Sidemount cover(s). Fender skirts. Bumper guards. Radio. Heater. Clock. Cigar lighter. Radio antenna. Seat covers. Two-tone finish. Spotlight(s). External trumpet horns. Wind wings.

HISTORICAL: Introduced October 1933. Innovations: Steeldraulic brakes on Commander and President. High compression aluminum cylinder heads. X-type frame. Clock-faced speedometer. Triple beam headlights. Improved body construction. Calendar year sales: 46,103. Calendar year registrations: 41,560. Model year production: 51,773. Studebaker was America's ninth ranked automaker in 1934. Paul G. Hoffman became Studebaker's president and launched a brilliant $10 million advertising campaign that put the company back on its feet. The Studebaker Rockne was no longer manufactured.

1935

STUDEBAKER — DICTATOR — SERIES 1A/2A — SIX: A longer, narrower grille with a rakish slant was used on 1935 Dictators. It was topped with a bird-in-flight hood ornament. Long, horizontal louvers graced the hood side panels. Longer, bullet-shaped headlight buckets were seen. The front bumper was no longer vee-shaped. It ran straight across the car, with a slight bow at its center. The Series 1A and 2A models were identical except for front axle design. The 1A models had a solid front axle. The 2A models had the new Independent Planar Wheel Suspension and cost $25 more on the coupe and $35 more on other standard body styles. On Dictator Regals the weight was 15 pounds higher and standard equipment included freewheeling, Startix, dual windshield wipers, dual sun visors, dual taillamps, robe rail and ash receivers. Front opening "suicide doors" were used on 1935 Studebakers. All 1935 Studebaker roadsters had roll-up windows and were really true convertibles.

STUDEBAKER — COMMANDER — SERIES 1B — EIGHT: Styling changes for 1935 Commanders were basically the same as those seen on Dictators. The Commander wheelbase was six inches longer. External trumpet horns were mounted below the front headlights on Commander models. Planar front wheel suspension was standard equipment. A cast iron cylinder head was standard, while the high compression aluminum head was optional.

STUDEBAKER — PRESIDENT — SERIES 1C — EIGHT: The 1935 President was virtually identical to the Commander in terms of its basic styling. The wheelbase was four inches longer. Presidents had a 17-1/2 gallon fuel tank, compared to 14-1/2 gallons on Dictators and Commanders. Although the two eight-cylinder lines used the same inline engine, the President had more horsepower due to its higher compression aluminum cylinder head. (Note: This feature was optional on Commanders.) Warner Gear automatic overdrive was standard equipment in Presidents. The cars in this series had a Flying Goddess-type hood mascot.

I.D. DATA: [Series 1A/2A] Serial numbers were stamped on a plate riveted to side member of frame under left front fender or to the left or right front door hinge pillar. Starting: 5500001. Ending: 5512000. Engine numbers were stamped on the left center of engine block above distributor. Starting: D-27501. Ending: D-62850. [Series 1B] Serial numbers were in the same location. Starting: 8103001. Ending: 8109000. Engine numbers were located on the left corner of engine above the water jacket cover. Starting: C-30501. Ending: C-36650. [Series 1C] Serial numbers were in the same location. Starting: 7101001. Ending: 7104000. Engine numbers were stamped on the left corner of block above water jacket cover. Starting: B-5501. Ending: B-7900.

Model 1A/Model 2A, 6-cyl.

Model No.	Body Type & Seating	Factory Price	Shipping Weight	Prod. Total
1A/2A	2-dr. Rds.-3/5P	745	2985	Note 1
1A/2A	2-dr. Regal Rds.-3/5P	775	3070	Note 1
1A/2A	2-dr. Cpe.-3P	695	2895	Note 1
1A/2A	2-dr. Regal Cpe.-3P	725	3005	Note 1
1A/2A	2-dr. Cpe.-3/5P	745	2995	Note 1
1A/2A	2-dr. Regal Cpe.-3/5P	775	3070	Note 1
1A/2A	2-dr. St. R. Sed.-5P	715	2965	Note 1
1A/2A	2-dr. Regal St. R. Sed.-5P	755	3085	Note 1
1A/2A	2-dr. Cus. St. R. Sed.-5P	740	3035	Note 1
1A/2A	4-dr. Sed.-6P	745	3030	Note 1
1A/2A	4-dr. Regal Sed.-6P	785	3160	Note 1
1A/2A	4-dr. Cus. Sed.-6P	770	3085	Note 1
1A/2A	4-dr. L. Cr. Sed.-5P	880	3100	Note 1
1A/2A	4-dr. Regal L. Cr. Sed.-5P	895	3220	Note 1

Note 1: The Series 1A Dictator was built December 1934 to September 1935; total production was 11,742. The Series 2A Dictator was built November 1934 to September 1935; total production was 23,550.

Note 2: Series 2A Dictators had serial numbers 5212001 to 5235000 and engine numbers D-27501 to D-62850. The three-passenger 2A coupe was $25 extra; the other standard 2A Dictators were $35 extra. Series 2A Regals were $40 extra.

Model 1B, 8-cyl.

Model No.	Body Type & Seating	Factory Price	Shipping Weight	Prod. Total
1B	2-dr. Rds.-3/5P	980	3510	Note 1
1B	2-dr. Regal Rds.-3/5P	1010	3570	Note 1
1B	2-dr. Cpe.-3P	925	3420	Note 1
1B	2-dr. Regal Cpe.-3P	960	3510	Note 1
1B	2-dr. R/S Cpe.-3/5P	980	3520	Note 1
1B	2-dr. Regal R/S Cpe.-3/5P	1010	3570	Note 1

Model No.	Body Type & Seating	Factory Price	Shipping Weight	Prod. Total
1B	2-dr. Regal St. R. Sed.-5P	1000	3620	Note 1
1B	2-dr. Cus. St. R. Sed.-5P	985	3550	Note 1
1B	4-dr. Regal Sed.-6P	1030	3685	Note 1
1B	4-dr. Cus. Sed.-6P	1015	3600	Note 1
1B	4-dr. L. Cr. Sed.-5P	1115	3625	Note 1
1B	4-dr. Regal L. Cr. Sed.-5P	1130	3720	Note 1

Note 1: Total production November 1934 to September 1935 was 6,085.

Model 1C, 8-cyl.

1C	2-dr. Rds.-3/5P	1295	3645	Note 1
1C	2-dr. Regal Rds.-3/5P	1325	3740	Note 1
1C	2-dr. Cpe.-3P	1245	3600	Note 1
1C	2-dr. Regal Cpe.-3P	1275	3685	Note 1
1C	2-dr. R/S Cpe.-3/5P	1295	3660	Note 1
1C	2-dr. Regal R/S Cpe.-3/5P	1325	3740	Note 1
1C	4-dr. Regal Sed.-6P	1345	3900	Note 1
1C	4-dr. Cus. Sed.-6P	1330	3790	Note 1
1C	4-dr. L. Cr.-5P	1430	3820	Note 1
1C	4-dr. Regal L. Cr.-5P	1445	3900	Note 1
1C	4-dr. Cus. Berl.-5P	1430	3900	Note 1
1C	4-dr. Regal Berl.-5P	1445	3970	Note 1

Note 1: Total production November 1934 to September 1935 was 2,305.

ENGINE: [Six-cylinder Engine] L-head. Inline. Cast iron block. B & S: 3-1/4 x 4-1/8 in. Disp.: 205.3 cu. in. C.R.: 6.3:1. Brake H.P.: 88 @ 3600 R.P.M. N.A.C.C. H.P.: 25.35. Main bearings: four. Valve lifters: solid. Carb.: Stromberg one-barrel Model EX-22. [Eight-cylinder Engine] L-head. Inline. Cast iron block. B & S: 3-1/16 x 4-1/2 in. Disp.: 250 cu. in. C.R.: (1B) 6.0:1; (1C) 6.5:1. Brake H.P.: (1B) 107 @ 3800 R.P.M.: (1C) 110 @ 3600 R.P.M. N.A.C.C. H.P.: (both) 30.01. Main bearings: nine. Valve lifters: solid. Carb.: (1B) Stromberg EE-11; (1C) same.

CHASSIS: [Series 1A/2A] W.B.: 114 in. Tires: 16 x 6.00 or 17 x 5.50 in. [Series 1B] W.B.: 120 in. Tires: 16 x 6.50 in. [Series 1C] W.B.: 124 in. Tires: 16 x 7.00 in.

TECHNICAL: Synchromesh transmission. Speeds: 3F/1R. Floor shift controls. Single plate dry disc clutch. Shaft drive. Semi-floating rear axle. Overall ratios: (1A) 4.11:1; (1B) 4.09:1; (1C) 4.09:1. Four-wheel hydraulic brakes. Steel artillery spoke wheels. Drivetrain options: free-wheeling. Overdrive was standard equipment on 1935 Presidents.

OPTIONS: Front bumper. Rear bumper. Whitewall tires. Dual sidemounts. Sidemount cover(s). Fender skirts. Bumper guards. Radio. Heater. Clock. Cigar lighter. Radio antenna. Seat covers. Outside rear view mirror. Spotlight(s). Pedestal sidemount mirrors. Wheel trim rings. Two-tone paint. Planar suspension on Dictators ($25-$40).

HISTORICAL: Introduced December 28, 1934. Innovations: Planar front wheel suspension. Automatic overdrive. Hydraulic brakes. Champion name for advertising and promotional purposes. Provision for radio mounting in all cars. Calendar year registrations: 39,573. Calendar year sales: 49,062. Model year production: 36,504. A 1935 Studebaker sedan, riding on the ties of the longest electric railway bridge in the world—near Berrien Springs, Michigan, traveled 60 mph in a promotion designed to highlight the advantages of Planar front wheel suspension. Studebaker was America's 11th ranked automaker this season.

1936

STUDEBAKER — DICTATOR — SERIES 3A/4A — SIX: There was no Commander series in 1936. The Dictators were on a new 116-inch wheelbase. Styling was much more conventional, but still attractive. Features included a die-cast grille, divided windshield, even longer bullet-shaped headlamps and hood trim with four, slim groupings of horizontal louvers with chrome spears on each end. New, free-standing, bullet-shaped taillights were seen. Studebaker returned to conventional front doors that were hinged at the A-pillar and opened from the rear. Planar front suspension was, again, a low-cost option.

STUDEBAKER — PRESIDENT — SERIES 2C — EIGHT: President styling changes were basically the same ones that Dictators had. The President wheelbase was nine inches longer. A distinctive hood ornament that was raised above the nose was used for Presidents. The hood side louvers, while of generally similar design, were full-length moldings. Planar front wheel suspension was standard equipment. Designer interior appointments were featured.

I.D. DATA: [Series 3A/4A] Serial numbers were in the same location on a plate riveted to side member of frame under left front fender or on left or right front hinge pillar. Starting: 5512001; (West Coast) 5850001. Ending: 5536000; (West Coast) 5852800. Series 4A models, with independent suspension, had serial numbers 5235001 to 5255000 for South Bend production and serial numbers 5800001 to 5802500 for West Coast production. Engine numbers were stamped on the left center of block above distributor. Starting: D-63001. Ending: D-112600. [Series 2C] Serial numbers were in the same location. Starting: 7104001; (West Coast) 7800001. Ending: 7111000; (West Coast) 7800800. Engine numbers were stamped on the left corner of block above water jacket cover. Starting: B-7901. Ending: B-15500.

Model 3A/Model 4A, 6-cyl.

Model No.	Body Type & Seating	Factory Price	Shipping Weight	Prod. Total
3A/4A	2-dr. Bus. Cpe.-3P	665	2910	Note 1
3A/4A	2-dr. Cus. Cpe.-3P	695	2965	Note 1
3A/4A	2-dr. Cus. Cpe.-5P	720	3020	Note 1
3A/4A	2-dr. Cus. St. R.-5P	725	3075	Note 1
3A/4A	2-dr. Cr. St. R.-5P	745	3080	Note 1
3A/4A	4-dr. Cus. Sed.-6P	755	3110	Note 1
3A/4A	4-dr. Cr. Sed.-6P	775	3120	Note 1

Note 1: Total production October 1935 to June 1936 included 26,634 Dictator 3As with conventional front axles and 22,029 Dictator 4As with independent front suspension.

Note 2: The "cruising" models (St. Regis cruising and cruising sedan) had built-in trunks. The "custom" sedans were slant-back models.

Model 2C, 8-cyl.

2C	2-dr. Cus. Cpe.-3P	965	3460	Note 1
2C	2-dr. Cus. Cpe.-5P	995	3515	Note 1
2C	2-dr. St. R. Cus.-5P	1015	3560	Note 1
2C	2-dr. St. R. Cr.-5P	1035	3570	Note 1
2C	4-dr. Cus. Sed.-6P	1045	3600	Note 1
2C	4-dr. Cus. Cr. Sed.-6P	1065	3615	Note 1

Note 1: Total production October 1935 to June 1936 was 7,297.

ENGINE: [Dictator Engine] L-head. Inline. Six. Cast iron block. B & S: 3-1/4 x 4-3/8 in. Disp.: 217.8 cu. in. C.R.: 6.3:1. Brake H.P.: 90 @ 3400 R.P.M. N.A.C.C. H.P.: 25.35. Main bearings: four. Valve lifters: solid. Carb.: Stromberg Model EX-23 one-barrel. [President Engine] L-head. Inline. Eight. Cast iron block. B & S: 3-1/16 x 4-1/6 in. Disp.: 250.4 cu. in. C.R.: 6.5:1. Brake H.P.: 115 @ 3600 R.P.M. N.A.C.C. H.P.: 30.01. Main bearings: nine. Valve lifters: solid. Carb.: Stromberg two-barrel Model EE-22.

CHASSIS: [Dictator Series 3A/4A] W.B.: 116 in. Tires: 16 x 6.00 in. [President Series 2C] W.B.: 125 in. Tires: 16 x 6.50 in.

TECHNICAL: Synchromesh manual transmission. Speeds: 3F/1R. Floor shift controls. Single plate dry disc clutch. Shaft drive. Semi-floating rear axle. Overall ratio: (all) 4.55:1. Four-wheel hydraulic brakes. Steel artillery spoke wheels. Drivetrain options: Vacuum clutch. Hill-holder. Freewheeling.

OPTIONS: Front bumper. Rear bumper. Whitewall tires. Dual sidemounts. Sidemount cover(s). Fender skirts. Bumper guards. Radio. Heater. Clock. Cigar lighter. Radio antenna. Seat covers. Dual taillights. Spotlight(s). Dual sun visors. Outside rearview mirror. Pedestal sidemount mirrors. Full wheel covers. Wheel trim ring(s). Independent front suspension, Dictator ($20).

HISTORICAL: Introduced November 2, 1935. Innovations: Hill-holder. Increased leg room. All-steel top construction. Eighteen-gallon fuel tank on all Studebakers. Roomier bodies. Designer interiors by Miss Helen Dryden. Improved engine mountings. Dictator engine moved forward by four inches. Calendar year registrations: 67,835. Calendar year sales: 85,026. Model year production: 63,664. A Dictator Six placed first in its class in California's National Gas Economy Classic by averaging 24.27 mpg. A President Eight was also first in its class with 20.34 mpg. Studebaker was America's ninth ranked manufacturer in 1936.

1937

STUDEBAKER — DICTATOR — SERIES 5A/6A — SIX: All 1937 Studebakers had new front end styling. Hoods were of one-piece construction. They were hinged at the cowl and raised from the front. The slanting, rounded radiator shell had horizontal grille bars. The top portion of the grille bars extended along the sides of the hood, forming ventilating louvers. A new feature, dual built-in warm air windshield defrosters, was available. A new flat type, 18-gallon gas tank, provided increased space in the trunk. A new safety feature was rotary door latches with safety catches. Standard equipment included a gas gauge, engine thermometer, Autolite ignition lock, George W. Borg clock, Casco cigar lighter, safety glass, one sun visor, dual windshield wipers, bumper, Houdaille shock absorbers, spring covers and Budd steel disc wheels. Planar front wheel suspension was used on the Series 6A models, which cost $20 more than similar body styles having a straight front axle. The two-door St. Regis cruising sedan and four-door cruising sedan were trunk-back body styles.

STUDEBAKER — PRESIDENT — SERIES 3C — EIGHT: Styling for Presidents was virtually identical to that used for Dictators. The President chassis had a 125-inch wheelbase. The Presidents had a Delco-Remy ignition system, instead of the Autolite system used in Dictators. Dual sun visors were standard, in addition to all other features included on Dictators. The "State" models, with deluxe equipment features, were $30 higher in price.

I.D. DATA: [Series 5A/6A] Serial numbers were in the same location, stamped on a plate riveted to frame side member under left front fender. Starting: 5536001; (West Coast) 5852801. Ending: 5581500; (West Coast) 5857400. Engine numbers were on the right center of block just below cylinder head. Starting: D-112601. Ending: D-201637. [Series 3C] Serial numbers were in the same location. Starting: 7111001; (West Coast) 7800801. Ending: 7119150; (West Coast) 7801750. Engine numbers were on the front of block between fan bracket and cylinder head. Starting: B-15501. Ending: B-24504.

Model 5A/Model 6A, 6-cyl.

Model No.	Body Type & Seating	Factory Price	Shipping Weight	Prod. Total
5A/6A	2-dr. Bus. Cpe.-3P	765	2695	Note 1
5A/6A	2-dr. Cus. Cpe.-3P	820	3005	Note 1
5A/6A	2-dr. Cus. Cpe.-5P	845	3045	Note 1
5A/6A	2-dr. Cus. St. R.-5P	850	3100	Note 1
5A/6A	2-dr. St. R.Cr.-6P	870	3100	Note 1
5A/6A	4-dr. Cus. Sed.-6P	880	3130	Note 1
5A/6A	4-dr. Cr. Sed.-6P	900	3140	Note 1

Note 1: Total production of Series 5A Dictators from August 1936 to July 1937 was 50,001. Total production of Series 6A Dictators from August 1936 to July 1937 was 39,001.

Model 3C, 8-cyl.

Model No.	Body Type & Seating	Factory Price	Shipping Weight	Prod. Total
3C	2-dr. Cus. Cpe.-3P	1085	3510	Note 1
3C	2-dr. Cus. Cpe.-5P	1115	3540	Note 1
3C	2-dr. Cus. St. R.-5P	1135	3600	Note 1
3C	2-dr. St. R. Cr.-5P	1155	3610	Note 1
3C	4-dr. Cus- Sed.-6P	1165	3620	Note 1
3C	4-dr. Cr. Sed.-6P	1185	3635	Note 1

Note 1: Total production August 1936 to July 1937 was 9,001.

Note 2: Add $30 to list price for cars with State equipment.

ENGINE: [Dictator Engine] L-head. Inline. Six. Cast iron block. B & S: 3-1/4 x 4-3/8 in. Disp.: 217.8 cu. in. C.R.: 6.0:1. Brake H.P.: 90 @ 3400 R.P.M. N.A.C.C. H.P.: 25.4. Main bearings: four. Valve lifters: solid. Carb.: Stromberg one-barrel Model EX-23. [President Engine] L-head. Inline. Eight. Cast iron block. B & S: 3-1/16 x 4-1/4 in. Disp.: 250.4 cu. in. C.R.: 6.5:1. Brake H.P.: 115 @ 3600 R.P.M. N.A.C.C. H.P.: 30.01. Main bearings: nine. Valve lifters: solid. Carb.: Stromberg two-barrel Model EE-1.

CHASSIS: [Series 5A/6A] W.B.: 116 in. Tires: 16 x 6.00 in. [Series 3C] W.B.: 125 in. Tires 16 x 6.50 in.

TECHNICAL: Synchromesh manual transmission. Speeds: 3F/1R. Floor mounted gearshift controls. Clutch: Borg & Beck single dry disc clutch. Hypoid rear axle. Overall ratio: (all) 4.55:1. Four-wheel hydraulic brakes. Steel disc wheels. Drivetrain options: Manual overdrive. Positive control automatic overdrive. Automatic Hill-Holder.

OPTIONS: Whitewall tires. Full wheel discs. Wheel trim rings. Dual sidemounts. Sidemount cover(s). Fender skirts. Bumper guards. Radio. Heater. Clock. Cigar lighter. Radio antenna. Seat covers. Parking lights. Spotlight(s). Sun roof. License plate frames. Special paint. State President equipment ($30.00). Dictator 6A Planar front wheel suspension ($20.00). Outside rearview mirror. Dual defroster system.

HISTORICAL: Introduced September 4, 1936. Innovations: Parking brake relocated. Built in defroster system. Rotary door latches. Hypoid rear axles. Direct action front shock absorbers on 6A and 3C models. New automatic overdrive option. Calendar year registrations: 70,048. Model year sales: 80,993. Model year production: 82,627. Some station wagons were built on the Dictator chassis by specialty body building firms. Studebaker made a small profit for the second year in-a-row. The company was America's 11th ranked automaker.

1938

STUDEBAKER — COMMANDER — SERIES 7A — SIX: All 1938 Studebakers had much smoother styling lines. The bodies were lower and six inches wider. Louvers were eliminated from the hood side panels. A chrome bead molding stretched from the grille to the rear deck. Seats were moved forward 5-1/2 inches and engines were moved forward 3-1/2 inches. The Dictator series was discontinued. Replacing it was the Studebaker/Commander Six. These cars had conventional, bullet-shaped headlight buckets on the front fender catwalks. A new instrument panel had square gauge clusters. In the center was a square-faced clock set into an ornate, rectangular trim panel decorated with horizontal moldings. A lower front tunnel was created by turning the transmission sideways. Planar suspension, safety glass, dual taillights, dual wipers and divided windshields were standard equipment. A single sun visor was featured. Also included at regular price was a speedometer, engine thermometer, Autolite ignition, Borg clock, Casco cigar lighter, two-way Houdaille shock absorbers, spring covers and Budd steel disc wheels. A new type of steering gear had triple tie rods. Vacuum gearshift was optional on all models. It had the gearshift lever housed in a bracket extending rearward from the center of the dash. (Note: These cars were introduced as the Studebaker Six and renamed Commander Six on December 3, 1937.)

STUDEBAKER — STATE COMMANDER — SERIES 8A — SIX: The State Commander was basically the same car as the base Commander, except that President-type headlamps were added. They were oblong shaped and tapered to a rounded back, which was faired into the fenders. Standard equipment for this line included everything used on the low-priced Commander plus a deluxe steering wheel, twin horns and Hill-Holder.

STUDEBAKER — STATE PRESIDENT — SERIES 4C — EIGHT: The difference in wheelbase between Presidents and Commanders was down to 5-1/2 inches this year. Styling changes for these models were similar to those used for State Commanders including the oblong-tapered headlamp fairings. Standard equipment included everything found on State Commanders plus/except Delco-Remy ignition, twin sun visors, larger tires and a different carburetor.

I.D. DATA: [Series 7A] Serial numbers were in the same location, stamped on a plate riveted to frame side member under left front fender. Starting: 5582001; (West Coast) 5857501. Ending: 5599146; (West Coast) 5859614. Engine numbers were on the right center of block just below cylinder head. Starting: H-101. Ending: H-42253. [Series 8A] Serial numbers were in the same location. Starting: 4090001; (West Coast) 4800001. Ending: 4109817; (West Coast) 4802235. Engine numbers were in the same location. Starting: H-101. Ending: H-42253. [Series 4C] Serial numbers were in the same location. Starting: 7120101; (West Coast) 7801801. Ending: 7125062; (West Coast) 7802311. Engine numbers were on the front of block between fan bracket and cylinder head. Starting: B-24601. Ending: B-30090.

Commander, 6-cyl.

Model No.	Body Type & Seating	Factory Price	Shipping Weight	Prod. Total
7A	2-dr. Bus. Cpe.-3P	875	3045	Note 1
7A	2-dr. Cus. Cpe.-3P	900	3060	Note 1
7A	2-dr. Clb. Sed.-6P	955	3140	Note 1
7A	4-dr. Cr. Sed.-6P	965	3190	Note 1
7A	4-dr. Conv. Sed.-6P	1315	3390	Note 1

Note 1: Total production September 1937 to July 1938 was 19,260.

State Commander, 6-cyl.

Model No.	Body Type & Seating	Factory Price	Shipping Weight	Prod. Total
8A	2-dr. Cus. Cpe.-3P	965	3095	Note 1
8A	2-dr. Clb. Sed.-6P	1030	3160	Note 1
8A	4-dr. Cr. Sed.-6P	1040	3215	Note 1
8A	4-dr. Conv. Sed.-6P	1365	3400	Note 1

Note 1: Total production August 1937 to July 1938 was 22,053.

President, 8-cyl.

Model No.	Body Type & Seating	Factory Price	Shipping Weight	Prod. Total
4C	2-dr. Cpe-3P	1120	3315	Note 1
4C	2-dr. Clb. Sed.-6P	1185	3400	Note 1
4C	4-dr. Cr. Sed.-6P	1195	3455	Note 1

State President, 8-cyl.

Model No.	Body Type & Seating	Factory Price	Shipping Weight	Prod. Total
4C	2-dr. Cpe.-3P	1130	3315	Note 1
4C	2-dr. Clb. Sed.-6P	1195	3400	Note 1
4C	4-dr. Cr. Sed.-6P	1205	3455	Note 1
4C	4-dr. Conv. Sed.-6P	1555	3640	Note 1

Note 1: Total production September 1937 to July 1938 was 5,474.

ENGINE: [Six-cylinder Engine] L-head. Inline. Cast iron block. B & S: 3-5/16 x 4-3/8 in. Disp.: 226.0 cu. in. C.R.: 6.0:1. Brake H.P.: 90 @ 3400 R.P.M. N.A.C.C. H.P.: 26.35. Main bearings: four. Valve lifters: solid. Carb.: Stromberg one-barrel Model BX026. [Eight-cylinder Engine] L-head. Inline. Cast iron block. B & S: 3-1/16 x 4-1/4 in. Disp.: 250.4 cu. in. C.R.: 6.0:1. Brake H.P.: 110 @ 3600 R.P.M. N.A.C.C. H.P.: 30.00. Main bearings: nine. Valve lifters: solid. Carb.: Stromberg two-barrel Model AA0161.

1937 Studebaker, President Eight (Series 3C), cruising sedan, AA

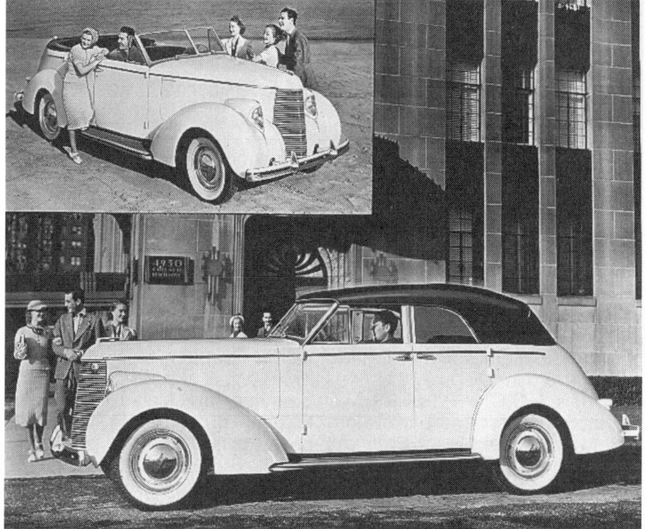

1938 Studebaker, President Eight (Series 4C), convertible sedan, AA

1939 Studebaker, Champion Custom Six (Series G), coupe, AA

1940 Studebaker, Champion Deluxe Six (Series 2-G), coupe (with singer/actress Judy Garland), AA

1938 Studebaker, Commander Six (Series 7A), cruising sedan, AA

1938 Studebaker, State Commander Six (Series 8A), club sedan, AA

1939 Studebaker, Champion Deluxe Six (Series G), cruising sedan, AA

1939 Studebaker, Commander Six (Series 9A), station wagon (with body by McVoy & Sons), AA

1940 Studebaker, Commander Deluxe Six (Series 10-A), cruising sedan (with optional Delux-Tone paint), AA

CHASSIS: [Series 7A] W.B.: 116-1/2 in. O.L.: 193-3/4 in. Frt/Rear Tread: 59.5/59.5 in. Tires: 6.00 x 16 in. [Series 8A] W.B.: 116-1/2 in. O.L.: 193-1/4 in. Frt/Rear Tread: 59.5/59.5 in. Tires: 6.00 x 16 in. [Series 4C] W.B.: 122 in. O.L.: 199-1/4 in. Frt/Rear Tread: 59.5/59.5 in. Tires: 6.50 x 16 in.

TECHNICAL: Synchromesh manual transmission. Speeds: 3F/1R. Floor mounted gearshift controls. Single disc dry plate clutch. Hypoid semi-floating rear axle. Overall ratio: (all) 4.55:1. Four-wheel hydraulic brakes. Budd steel disc wheels. Drivetrain options: Vacuum clutch. Hill-holder. Dash mounted transmission controls. Automatic overdrive.

OPTIONS: Whitewall tires. Full wheel discs. Wheel trim rings. Dual sidemounts. Sidemount cover(s). Fender skirts. Bumper guards. Radio. Heater. Clock. Cigar lighter. Radio antenna. Seat covers. Special paint. Spotlight(s). Deluxe steering wheel (in base Six). Dual horns (on base Six). "Miracle" shift lever. Outside rearview mirror. Dual sun visors (Commanders). Defroster. Front fender parking lights.

HISTORICAL: Introduced September 1937. Innovations: Optional dash mounted Miracle shift vacuum transmission control. Triple tie rod steering. Increased bore on six-cylinder engine. Five-inch wider front seat cushions. Low profile transmission mounting. Wider brake linings. Calendar year registrations: 41,504. Calendar year production: 92,200. Model year sales: 46,207. Model year production: 46,787. Studebaker was back in red ink this season despite moving to 10th position in domestic automobile sales. The reason for changing the Dictator name was negative associations with German dictator Adolf Hitler.

1939

STUDEBAKER — CHAMPION — SERIES G — SIX: The Champion was a new series for mid-1939. It featured horizontal radiator grille bars with vertical bars on each side. The side of the car was decorated with a long bead molding that ran from the rear quarter to the nose and two additional moldings below it on the hood side panels. Another chrome strip ran down the center of the hood and dropped to the grille. The front bumper was plain. Standard equipment on custom Champions included Planar front wheel suspension, steering column gearshift lever, variable ratio steering, speedometer, gas gauge, engine thermometer, Autolite ignition, Trico windshield wiper, bumpers, two-way Houdaille shock absorbers, spring covers, Budd steel disc wheels, single taillight, single sun visor and single horn. Custom models were the economy line and came without chrome inside door trim and with dashboards painted body color. Deluxe Champions also had front door armrests, dual wipers, dual sun visors, dual taillamps, rear seat ashtrays, ventilating quarter windows, broadcloth upholstery and chrome door sill panels.

STUDEBAKER — COMMANDER — SERIES 9A — SIX: The new Studebakers had a massive, but graceful hood that tapered to a prow-like front decorated with a vertical chrome strip. Flanking the hood were grilles with vertical chrome bars located in the front splash aprons. Headlamps and taillamps were flush with the fenders. The Studebaker name appeared in script on the center of the bumper and an attractive "S" emblem was placed just below the nose of the alligator style hood. A long chrome molding ran from the rear quarters to the nose, on the upper beltline. The hood side panels were decorated with two additional chrome strips running from the seam at the cowl, forward. They were about three-quarters of the length of the hood. Above these moldings, a Commander nameplate was positioned near the cowl. Standard equipment included: speedometer; gas gauge; engine thermometer; Autolite ignition; Borg clock; Casco cigar lighter; bumpers; guards; two-way Houdaille shock absorbers; spring covers; Budd disc wheels; twin taillights; dual inside sun visors; a single horn and dual windshield wipers; column mounted gearshift; Planar front wheel suspension and automatic Hill-Holder.

STUDEBAKER — STATE PRESIDENT — SERIES 5C — EIGHT: The State Presidents were larger and heavier than the Commanders, but looked about the same. The name President was on the hood sides, near the cowl seam (above the lower trim moldings). The bumper identification also read, "Studebaker President." Standard equipment included everything listed for Commanders plus/or except Delco-Remy ignition and dual horns. Also, the Houdaille shock absorbers, on cars in this line, were built into the independent front springing system.

I.D. DATA: [Series G] Serial numbers were in the same location on left front of frame. Starting: G-001; (West Coast) 800001. Ending: G-30400; (West Coast) 803600. Engine numbers were stamped on the left rear of engine near top of block or left front upper side of block. Starting: 001. Ending: 34100. [Series 9A] Serial numbers were in the same location. Starting: 4110001; (West Coast) 4802301. Ending: 4148500; (West Coast) 4807600. Engine numbers were in the same location. Starting: H-42501. Ending: H-87550. [Series 5C] Serial numbers were in the same location. Starting: 7125501; (West Coast) 7802501. Ending: 7133050; (West Coast) 7803250. Engine numbers were stamped on the left front corner of block above water jacket. Starting: B-30201. Ending: B-38500.

Model No.	Body Type & Seating	Factory Price	Shipping Weight	Prod. Total
Custom Champion, 6-cyl.				
G	2-dr. Cpe.-3P	660	2260	Note 1
G	2-dr. Clb. Sed.-6P	700	2330	Note 1
G	4-dr. Cr. Sed.-6P	740	2360	Note 1
Deluxe Champion, 6-cyl.				
G	2-dr. Cpe.-3P	720	2275	Note 1
G	2-dr. Clb. Sed.-6P	760	2345	Note 1
G	4-dr. Cr. Sed.-6P	800	2375	Note 1

Note 1: Total production January 1939 to July 1939 was 33,905.

Model No.	Body Type & Seating	Factory Price	Shipping Weight	Prod. Total
Commander, 6-cyl.				
9A	2-dr. Bus. Cpe.-3P	875	3045	Note 1
9A	2-dr. Cus. Cpe.-3P	900	3080	Note 1
9A	2-dr. Clb. Sed.-6P	955	3160	Note 1
9A	4-dr. Cr. Sed.-6P	965	3200	Note 1
9A	4-dr. Conv. Sed.-6P	1290	3400	Note 1
9A	4-dr. Sta. Wag.	—	—	Note 1

Note 1: Total production August 1938 to August 1939 was 43,724.

Model No.	Body Type & Seating	Factory Price	Shipping Weight	Prod. Total
President, 8-cyl.				
5C	2-dr. Cus. Cpe.-3P	1035	3300	Note 1
5C	2-dr. Clb. Sed.-6P	1100	3390	Note 1
5C	4-dr. Cr. Sed.-6P	1110	3440	Note 1
5C	4-dr. Conv. Sed.-6P	1460	3640	Note 1

Note 1 : Total production September 1938 to August 1939 was 8,205.

ENGINE: [Champion Six Engine] L-head. Inline. Cast iron block. B & S: 3 x 3-7/8 in. Disp.: 164.3 cu. in. C.R.: 6.5:1. Brake H.P.: 78 @ 4000 R.P.M. N.A.C.C. H.P.: 21.60. Main bearings: four. Valve lifters: solid. Carb.: Carter one-barrel Model WO. Torque: 128 lb.-ft. @ 1600 R.P.M. [Commander Six Engine] L-head. Inline. Cast iron block. B & S: 3-5/16 x 4-3/8 in. Disp.: 226 cu. in. C.R.: 6.0:1. Brake H.P.: 90 @ 3400 R.P.M. N.A.C.C. H.P.: 26.35. Main bearings: four. Valve lifters: solid. Carb.: Stromberg one-barrel Model BX026. Torque: 174 lb.-ft. @ 1200 R.P.M. [President Eight Engine] L-head. Inline. Cast iron block. B & S: 3-1/16 x 4-1/4 in. Disp.: 250.4 cu. in. C.R.: 6.0:1. Brake H.P.: 110 @ 3600 R.P.M. N.A.C.C. H.P.: 30.01. Main bearings: nine. Valve lifters: solid. Carb.: Stromberg two-barrel Model AA0161. Torque: 195 lb.-ft. @ 2000 R.P.M.

CHASSIS: [Series G] W.B.: 110 in. O.L.: 188-3/4 in. Height: 64-5/8 in. Frt/Rear Tread: 56-1/4/57 in. Tires: 16 x 5.50 in. [Series 9A] W.B.: 116.5 in. O.L.: 197.5 in. Height: 66-1/8 in. Frt/Rear Tread: 59-7/8/59-1/2 in. Tires: 16 x 6.00 in. [Series 5C] W.B.: 122 in. O.L.: 203 in. Height: 66-5/8 in. Frt/Rear Tread: 59-5/8/59-7/16 in. Tires: 16 x 6.50 in.

TECHNICAL: Synchromesh manual transmission. Speeds: 3F/1R. Steering column-mounted gearshift controls. Clutch: single disc dry plate type. Hypoid semi-floating rear axle. Overall ratio: (G) 4.56:1; (others) 4.55:1. Four-wheel hydraulic brakes. Budd steel disc wheels. Drivetrain options: Vacuum clutch. Hill-holder. Overdrive.

OPTIONS: Whitewall tires. Wheel trim rings. Dual sidemounts. Sidemount cover(s). Fender skirts. Bumper guards. Radio. Heater. Clock. Cigar lighter. Radio antenna. Seat covers. External sun shade. Spotlight(s). Fog lamps. Dual horns. Full wheel discs. Special paint. Outside rearview mirror. Climatizer central fresh air ventilating and heating system.

HISTORICAL: Introduced August 11, 1938 (except Champion). Champion introduced March 1939. Innovations: Column mount gearshift. New controlled overdrive. Climatizer ventilation system. Calendar year registrations: 84,660. Calendar year sales: 106,470. Calendar year production: 92,200. Model year production: 85,834. Studebaker placed a strong eighth in the 1939 U.S. auto sales race. A Studebaker Champion set an AAA record of 27.25 mpg in a 6,144 mile economy run from the San Francisco Golden Gate Exposition to the New York World's Fair.

1940

STUDEBAKER — CHAMPION — SERIES 2-G — SIX: The 1940 Champion had slight changes to front end styling. The center grille had more horizontal bars added. The bars were of a thinner design. Only two horizontal trim moldings were used on the hood, instead of three. Another new feature was the use of sealed beam headlights. Standard equipment on the low-priced Custom models included a speedometer, gasoline gauge, engine thermometer, windshield wipers, bumpers, Houdaille shock absorbers, spring covers, steel disc wheels, one taillight, one sun visor, one windshield wiper and single horn. Custom Deluxe models had twin wipers, taillights and horns, front door armrests, a Phantom steering wheel, horn ring, stainless steel lower body finishing strips and four bumper guards. Deluxe and DeLux-Tone models also had assist cords, rear seat ashtrays, robe rails, carpeted lower door panels and ventilating rear quarter windows (on cruising sedans). They also featured a two-tone interior. The Custom Champion had solid exterior and interior and the DeLux-Tone Champion had delux-tone exterior and interior.

STUDEBAKER — COMMANDER — SERIES 100-A — SIX: The 1940 Studebakers had more massive fenders and a greater degree of streamlining. The new Commander grille was of a large, lattice-bar design with low, chrome-plated ventilating grilles on both sides of the radiator. The model name appeared on the upper rear corner of the hood. Standard equipment included all found on Custom Champions, plus bumper guards, dual taillights, twin sun visors and two horns. A new, larger windshield was featured. Other new styling touches included sliding rear quarter windows, concealed gas filler caps and a hood lock operated via a lever on the steering column. Sedans in the new DeLux-Tone series had delux-tone exteriors and interiors. Coupes had solid exteriors and delux-tone interiors.

STUDEBAKER — PRESIDENT — SERIES 6-C — EIGHT: The President, for 1940, had styling similar to that of Commanders. The model name appeared on the upper rear corner of the hood. Standard equipment included all found on Commanders plus a clock, cigar lighter and dual horns. Presidents had a 122-inch wheelbase and larger 6.50 x 16-inch tires.

I.D. DATA: [Champion] Serial numbers were in the same locations on a plate riveted to the side member of the frame under the left front fender or on the right left front door hinge pillar. Starting: G-30501; (West Coast) G-803701. Ending: G-90069; (West Coast) G-811191. Engine numbers were stamped on the left rear of engine near top of block or left front upper side of block. Starting: 34101. Ending: 101169. [Commander] Serial numbers were in the same location. Starting: 4148501; (West Coast) 4807601. Ending: 4178797; (West Coast) 4811895. Engine numbers were in the same location. Starting: H-87601. Ending: H-122190. [President] Serial numbers were in the same location. Starting: 5582001; (West Coast) 5857501. Ending: 5599146; (West Coast) 5859614. Engine numbers were in the same location. Starting: H-101. Ending: H-42253.

Model No.	Body Type & Seating	Factory Price	Shipping Weight	Prod. Total
Champion Custom Line, 6-cyl.				
2-G	2-dr. Cpe.-3P	660	2290	Note 1
2-G	2-dr. OS Cpe.-5P	695	2335	Note 1
2-G	2-dr. Clb. Sed-5P	700	2360	Note 1
2-G	4-dr. Cr. Sed.-5P	740	2390	Note 1
Custom Deluxe Line, 6-cyl.				
2-G	2-dr. Cpe.-3P	690	2300	Note 1
2-G	2-dr. OS Cpe.-5P	725	2345	Note 1
2-G	2-dr. Clb. Sed.-5P	730	2370	Note 1
2-G	4-dr. Cr. Sed.-5P	770	2400	Note 1
Deluxe Line, 6-cyl.				
2-G	2-dr. Cpe.-3P	705	2315	Note 1
2-G	2-dr. OS Cpe.-5P	740	2360	Note 1
2-G	2-dr. Clb. Sed.-5P	745	2385	Note 1
2-G	4-dr. Cr. Sed.-5P	785	2415	Note 1
Delux-Tone Line, 6-cyl.				
2-G	2-dr. Cpe.-3P	720	2315	Note 1
2-G	2-dr. OS Cpe.-5P	755	2360	Note 1
2-G	2-dr. Clb. Sed.-5P	760	2385	Note 1
2-G	4-dr. Cr. Sed.-5P	800	2415	Note 1

Note 1: Total production August 1939 to June 1940 was 66,264.

Model No.	Body Type & Seating	Factory Price	Shipping Weight	Prod. Total
Commander Line, 6-cyl.				
10-A	2-dr. Cus. Cpe.-3P	895	3055	Note 2
10-A	2-dr. Clb. Sed.-6P	925	3135	Note 2
10-A	4-dr. Cr. Sed.-6P	965	3180	Note 2
Delux-Tone Commander, 6-cyl.				
10-A	2-dr. Cus. Cpe.-3P	935	3060	Note 2
10-A	2-dr. Clb. Sed.-6P	965	3140	Note 2
10-A	4-dr. Cr. Sed.-6P	1005	3185	Note 2

Note 2: Total production September 1939 to June 1940 was 34,477.

Model No.	Body Type & Seating	Factory Price	Shipping Weight	Prod. Total
State President Line, 8-cyl.				
6-C	2-dr. Cpe.-3P	1025	3280	Note 3
6-C	2-dr. Clb. Sed.-6P	1055	3370	Note 3
6-C	4-dr. Cr. Sed.-6P	1095	3420	Note 3
Delux-Tone Line, 8-cyl.				
6-C	2-dr. Cpe.-3P	1065	3285	Note 3
6-C	2-dr. Clb. Sed.-6P	1095	3375	Note 3
6-C	4-dr. Cr. Sed.-6P	1135	3425	Note 3

Note 3: Total production September 1939 to June 1940 was 6,444.

ENGINE: [Champion] L-head. Inline. Six. Cast iron block. B & S: 3 x 3-7/8 in. Disp.: 164.3 cu. in. C.R.: 6.50:1. Brake H.P.: 78 @ 4000 R.P.M. N.A.C.C. H.P.: 21.6. Main bearings: four. Valve lifters: solid. Carb.: Carter one-barrel Model WO. Torque: 128 lb.-ft. @ 1600 R.P.M. [Commander] L-head. Inline. Six. Cast iron block. B & S: 3-5/16 x 4-3/8 in. Disp.: 226 cu. in. C.R.: 6.0:1. Brake H.P.: 90 @ 3400 R.P.M. N.A.C.C. H.P.: 26.35. Main bearings: four. Valve lifters: solid. Carb.: Stromberg one-barrel Model BX026. Torque: 174 lb.-ft. @ 1200 R.P.M. [President] L-head. Inline. Eight. Cast iron block. B & S: 3-1/16 x 4-1/4 in. Disp.: 250.4 cu. in. C.R.: 6.0:1. Brake H.P.: 110 @ 3600 R.P.M. N.A.C.C. H.P.: 30.00. Main bearings: nine. Valve lifters: solid. Carb.: Stromberg two-barrel Model AA0161. Torque: 110 lb.-ft. @ 3600 R.P.M.

CHASSIS: [Series 2-G] W.B.: 110 in. O.L.: 188.75 in. Height: 64-5/8 in. Frt/Rear Tread: 56.25/57 in. Tires: 16 x 5.50 in. [Series 10-A] W.B.: 116.5 in. O.L.: 197.5 in. Height: 66-1/8 in. Frt/Rear Tread: 59-7/8/61 in. Tires: 16 x 6.00 in. [Series 6-C] W.B.: 122 in. O.L.: 203 in. Height: 66-5/8 in. Frt/Rear Tread: 59.75/61 in. Tires: 16 x 6.50 in.

TECHNICAL: Manual transmission. Speeds: 3F/1R. Column mounted gearshift controls. Clutch: (President) molded; (others) molded and woven. Shaft drive. Semi-floating rear axle. Overall ratio: (Champion) 4.56:1; (others) 4.55:1. Four-wheel hydraulic brakes. Budd steel disc wheels. Drivetrain options: Vacuum clutch. Hill-holder. Overdrive.

OPTIONS: Whitewall tires. Wheel trim rings. Outside rearview mirror. Parking lamps. Fender skirts. Bumper guards. Radio. Heater. Clock. Cigar lighter. Radio antenna. Seat covers. Spotlight(s). Two-tone paint. Special paint. Bumper wing guards. Master grille guard.

HISTORICAL: Introduced August/September 1939. Innovations: Pure air climatizer. Streamlined door handles. Sliding rear quarter windows on some models. Steering column hood lock. Improved door hinges. Delux-Tone two-tone models. Calendar year registrations: 102,281. Calendar year production: 117,091. Model year production: 120,543. Studebaker was America's eighth ranked automaker in 1940. A Champion model won first place in its class in the Gilmore Economy Run averaging 27-1/4 mpg during a cross-country trip at an average speed of 40 mph.

1941

STUDEBAKER — CHAMPION — SERIES 3-G — SIX — More streamlined bodies, designed by Raymond Loewy, were used on Champions this year. The cars were lower and longer, with a more massive front end appearance. Center grilles were eliminated. Low, die-cast grilles with multiple vertical bars were mounted in the front fender aprons on each side of the car. The nose was decorated with a large chrome emblem bearing the Studebaker "S" insignia. Twin chrome moldings ran from the hood peak to the upper rear quarters, tapering together as they moved back along the body. On DeLux-Tone models the area between the moldings were done in contrasting colors. Wider seats (54-1/4 inches front and 48 inches rear) were used in Champions. Standard equipment was the same as 1940, plus dual taillights. Custom Deluxe models also had dual wipers, sun visors and horns, front door armrests and chrome instrument board moldings. They had solid exterior finish and two-tone interiors. DeLux-Tone cars also had chrome door trim rings, ashtrays in the rear of club and cruising sedans and two-tone interiors and exteriors.

STUDEBAKER — COMMANDER — SERIES 11-A — SIX — The Commander had a longer wheelbase, wider doors, lower floors and reduction in overall height. Runningboards were eliminated. A new model with a familiar Studebaker name was the land cruiser, a sedan with rear quarter windows eliminated and reverse opening rear doors. A new grille and molding treatment was similar to that seen on Champions except that Commanders had a hood ornament. Customs were equipped the same as last year. DeLux-Tone cars also had chrome instrument board moldings and two-tone exteriors and interiors. Skyway models had chrome bands around all windows, chrome fender lights, two-tone instrument panels, two-tone exterior finish and bolster-type pleated upholstery.

STUDEBAKER — PRESIDENT — SERIES 7-C — EIGHT — Studebaker's fanciest series also had new Raymond Loewy styling with low, die-cast side grilles, increased glass area, air vents in the side of the cowl and longer, lower and wider lines. A mid-year model was a sedan-coupe with an innovative one-piece curved windshield. Custom models were quite plain. They had front fender lamps, but no other extraneous trim. DeLux-Tone cars had chrome instrument panel moldings and two-tone interiors and exteriors. Skyway models had wide chrome bands around all windows, chrome fender lights, two-tone instrument panels, two-tone exteriors (with tapering contrast band) and bolster-type pleated upholstery.

I.D. DATA: [Series 3-G] Serial numbers were in the same locations, on a plate riveted to side member of frame under left front fender or to left or right front door hinge pillars. Starting: G-90101; (West Coast) G-811201. Ending: G-165400; (West Coast) G-820902. Engine numbers were stamped on left rear of engine near top of block or left upper side of block near front. Starting: 101201. Ending: 186259. [Series 11-A] Serial numbers were in the same locations. Starting: 4178801; (West Coast) 4811901. Ending: 4216180; (West Coast) 4816518. Engine numbers were in the same location. Starting: H-122201. Ending: H-164222. [Series 7-C] Serial numbers were in the same locations. Starting: 7139101; (West Coast) 7803901. Ending: 7145407; (West Coast) 7804592. Engine numbers were located on the left corner of the block above water jacket cover. Starting: B-45001. Ending: B-52012.

Custom Line, 6-cyl.

Model No.	Body Type & Seating	Factory Price	Shipping Weight	Prod. Total
3-G	2-dr. Cpe.-3P	710	2370	Note 1
3-G	2-dr. Dbl. Date Cpe.-5P	750	2400	Note 1
3-G	2-dr. OS Cpe.-5P	750	2410	Note 1
3-G	2-dr. Clb. Sed.-5P	755	2450	Note 1
3-G	4-dr. Cr. Sed.-5P	795	2480	Note 1
Custom Deluxe Line, 6-cyl.				
3-G	2-dr. Cpe.-3P	745	2395	Note 1
3-G	2-dr. Dbl. Date Cpe.-5P	780	2435	Note 1
3-G	2-dr. OS Cpe.-5P	780	2425	Note 1
3-G	2-dr. Clb. Cpe.-5P	785	2470	Note 1
3 G	4-dr. Cr. Sed.-5P	825	2500	Note 1
DeLux-Tone Line, 6-cyl.				
3-G	2-dr. Cpe.-3P	780	2400	Note 1
3-G	2-dr. Dbl. Date Cpe.-5P	815	2440	Note 1
3-G	2-dr. OS Cpe.-5P	815	2430	Note 1
3-G	2-dr. Clb. Sed.-5P	820	2470	Note 1
3-G	4-dr. Cr. Sed.-5P	860	2500	Note 1

Note 1: Total production August 1940 to July 1941 was 84,910.

Custom Line, 6-cyl.

Model No.	Body Type & Seating	Factory Price	Shipping Weight	Prod. Total
11-A	2-dr. Sed. Cpe.-6P	990	3160	Note 2
11-A	4-dr. Cr. Sed.-6P	1010	3210	Note 2
11-A	4-dr. L. Cruiser-6P	1055	3230	Note 2
DeLux-Tone Line, 6-cyl.				
11-A	4-dr. Cr. Sed.-6P	1075	3225	Note 2
11-A	4-dr. L. Cruiser-6P	1120	3245	Note 2
Skyway Line, 6-cyl.				
11-A	2-dr. Sed. Cpe.-6P	1080	3200	Note 2
11-A	4-dr. Cr. Sed.-6P	1100	3240	Note 2
11-A	4-dr. L. Cruiser-6P	1130	3260	Note 2

Note 2: Total production August 1940 to July 1941 was 41,996.

Custom Line, 8-cyl.

Model No.	Body Type & Seating	Factory Price	Shipping Weight	Prod. Total
7-C	4-dr. Cr. Sed.-6P	1140	3450	Note 3
7-C	4-dr. L. Cruiser-6P	1185	3475	Note 3
DeLux-Tone Line, 8-cyl.				
7-C	4-dr. Cr. Sed.-6P	1205	3475	Note 3
7-C	4-dr. L. Cruiser-6P	1250	3500	Note 3
Skyway Line, 8-cyl.				
7-C	4-dr. Cr. Sed.-6P	1230	3500	Note 3
7-C	4-dr. L. Cruiser-6P	1260	3520	Note 3
7-C	2-dr. Sed. Cpe-6P	1210	3440	Note 3

Note 3: Total production August 1940 to July 1941 was 6,994.

ENGINE: [Champion] L-head. Inline. Six. Cast iron block. B & S: 3 x 4 in. Disp.: 170 cu. in. C.R.: 6.5:1. Brake H.P.: 80 @ 4000 R.P.M. N.A.C.C. H.P.: 21.6. Main bearings: four. Valve lifters: solid. Carb.: Carter one-barrel Model WA14965. [Commander] L-head. Inline. Six. Cast iron block. B & S: 3-5/16 x 4-3/8 in. Disp.: 226.2 cu. in. C.R.: 6.5:1. Brake H.P.: 94 @ 3600 R.P.M. N.A.C.C. H.P.: 26.35. Main bearings: four. Valve lifters: solid. Carb.: Stromberg one-barrel Model BXOV26. [President] L-head. Inline. Eight. Cast iron block. B & S: 3-1/16 x 4-1/4 in. Disp.: 250.4 cu. in. C.R.: 6.5:1. Brake H.P.: 117 @ 4000 R.P.M. N.A.C.C. H.P.: 30.00. Main bearings: nine. Valve lifters: solid. Carb.: Stromberg two-barrel Model AAV26.

CHASSIS: [Champion] W.B.: 110 in. Tires: 16 x 5.50 in. [Commander Series] W.B.: 119 in. Tires: 16 x 6.25 in. [President] W.B.: 124.5 in. Tires: 16 x 7.00 in.

TECHNICAL: Manual transmission. Speeds: 3F/1R. Column mounted gearshift controls. Clutch: (President) molded; (others) molded and woven. Shaft drive. Semi-floating rear axle. Overall ratio: (Champion) 4.56:1; (others) 4.55:1. Four-wheel hydraulic brakes. Budd steel disc wheels. Drivetrain options: Vacuum clutch. Hill-holder. Overdrive.

OPTIONS: Whitewall tires. Wheel trim rings. Outside rearview mirror. Parking lamps. Master grille guards. Fender skirts. Bumper guards. Radio. Heater. Clock. Cigar lighter. Radio antenna. Seat covers. External sun shade. Spotlight(s). Fender lamps. Full wheel discs. Front fender moldings. Front and rear fender wind split trim moldings. Two-tone paint. Fender skirt moldings. Bumper wing guards.

HISTORICAL: Introduced August 1940. Innovations: One-piece windshield on President sedan coupe. Engine and body mountings moved forward. Wider seats. Runningboards eliminated. Lower height with same headroom. Increased glass area. Improved manifolding and carburetion. Calendar year registrations: 114,331. Calendar year production: 119,325. Model year production: 133,900. Studebaker was ninth in U.S. auto sales this season. Sales climbed to over $100 million for the first time since 1929. The 1941 Champion had the largest production single model year in company history.

1942

STUDEBAKER — CHAMPION — SERIES 4-G — SIX: The 1942 Champions had extensive body styling changes. There were wider, more massive bumpers up front, with a built-in license plate assembly. The grille stretched completely across the front of the cars with large, round parking lamp assemblies at either side. Cross-hatching horizontal and vertical bars filled the grille on either side of a vertical center member. There was a large Studebaker emblem on the nose and a chrome hood ornament and molding along the center of the hood. Standard equipment included a speedometer, gas gauge, thermometer, ignition lock, wiper, spring covers, dual taillamps, one sun visor, a horn, double-acting shock absorbers and Budd steel disc wheels. Champion Deluxstyle equipment included dual wipers, dual sun visors, dual Airtone horns, front door armrests, front seat back garnish trim panel and ashtray, two courtesy lights, chrome sill moldings and solid exterior and interior colors and trim.

STUDEBAKER — COMMANDER — SERIES 12-A — SIX: The Commander also had the new, wide grille with narrow horizontal ribs supported by less obvious vertical members. Fog lamps in the grille were optional equipment. Parking lamps were on top of the front fenders. New, dual rear lamps included a flashing indicator as well as tail and stop lamps, mounted in a large, chrome-plated housing with ribbed side panels. The heavier, wraparound bumpers had a built-in license plate assembly in the center. Commander identification was stamped into the front of the bright metal hood molding. Standard equipment was the same as on Champions plus dual sun visors, horns and wipers. Autolite ignition was used for the Commander. Deluxstyle Commanders also had a front seat back garnish trim panel and ashtray, two automatic courtesy lights, stainless steel window reveal moldings, three chrome moldings on inside door panels and two-tone exterior and interior colors and trim. Skyway models also had bolster-type pleated upholstery, chrome bands around all side windows, white painted wheel discs and Lucite door hardware panels.

STUDEBAKER — PRESIDENT — SERIES 8-C — EIGHT: The President for 1942 had the same general styling characteristics as other Studebakers. Standard equipment for Custom models was the same as on Commanders. Deluxstyle models had the same upgraded trim features as Deluxstyle Commanders and Skyway upgrading was also similar to that of Skyway Commanders. On the President the starter, instead of being operated by a button on the dash, was brought into operation by the clutch pedal. President model identification was found at the front of the hood trim molding on Custom and Deluxstyle models. Skyway editions had a President nameplate at the rear of the hood near the cowl. A unique 1942 Studebaker feature was a steering column mounted radio station selector lever on cars equipped with factory radios.

I.D. DATA: [Champion] Serial numbers were in the same locations, stamped on a plate riveted to the frame side member under left front fender or on the left or right front hinge pillars. Starting: G-165501; (West Coast) G-821001. Ending: G-192583; (West Coast) G-823645. Engine numbers were stamped on the left rear of engine near top of block or left front upper side of block. Starting: 186301. Ending: 216050. [Commander] Serial numbers were in the same locations. Starting: 4216501; (West Coast) 4816601. Ending: 4232296; (West Coast) 4818305. Engine numbers were in the same locations. Starting: H-164301. Ending: H-181812. [President] Serial numbers were in the same locations. Starting: 7145501; (West Coast) 7804601. Ending: 7148659; (West Coast) 7804943. Engine numbers were stamped on the left corner of the block above water jacket. Starting: B-52101. Ending: B-55608.

Champion, 6-cyl.

Model No.	Body Type & Seating	Factory Price	Shipping Weight	Prod. Total
Custom				
4-G	2-dr. Cpe.-3P	744	2415	Note 1
4-G	2-dr. Dbl. Date. Cpe.-5P	769	2455	Note 1
4-G	2-dr. Clb. Sed.-5P	774	2495	Note 1
4-G	4-dr. Cr. Sed.-6P	804	2520	Note 1

1940 Studebaker, President Eight (Series 6-C), State club sedan (with optional Delux-Tone paint), AA

1941 Studebaker, President Eight (Series 7-C), Skyway sedan coupe, OCW

1942 Studebaker, Champion Custom Six (Series 4-G), club sedan, AA

1942 Studebaker, President Eight (Series 8-C), Deluxstyle land cruiser sedan (pre-ration model with whitewall tires), OCW

1947 Studebaker, Champion Deluxe (Series 6G), three-passenger coupe, AA

1941 Studebaker, Champion Custom Six (Series 3-G), cruising sedan, AA

1941 Studebaker, Commander Six (Series 11-A), land cruiser sedan (with optional Delux-Tone paint), OCW

1942 Studebaker, Commander Custom Six (Series 12-A), cruising sedan, AA

1946 Studebaker, Champion Skyway (Series 5G), cruising sedan, AA

1947 Studebaker, Champion Deluxe (Series 6G), sedan, AA

Deluxstyle

Model No.	Body Type & Seating	Factory Price	Shipping Weight	Prod. Total
4-G	2-dr. Cpe.-3P	779	2435	Note 1
4-G	2-dr. Dbl. Date. Cpe.-5P	804	2470	Note 1
4-G	2-dr. Clb. Sed.-5P	809	2520	Note 1
4-G	4-dr. Cr. Sed.-6P	839	2545	Note 1

Note 1: Total production August 1941 to January 1942 was 29,678.

Note 2: Production halted around January 1942 due to outbreak of World War II.

Commander, 6-cyl.

Model No.	Body Type & Seating	Factory Price	Shipping Weight	Prod. Total
Custom				
12-A	2-dr. Sed. Cpe.-6P	1025	3195	Note 3
12-A	4-dr. Cr. Sed.-6P	1045	3265	Note 3
12-A	4-dr. L. Cr.-6P	1080	3290	Note 3
Deluxstyle				
12-A	2-dr. Sed. Cpe.-6P	1070	3210	Note 3
12-A	4-dr. Cr. Sed.-6P	1090	3280	Note 3
12-A	4-dr. L. Cr.-6P	1125	3305	Note 3
Skyway				
12-A	2-dr. Sed. Cpe.-6P	1105	3240	Note 3
12-A	4-dr. Cr. Sed.-6P	1125	3300	Note 3
12-A	4-dr. L. Cr.-6P	1160	3315	Note 3

Note 3: Total production August 1941 to January 1942 was 17,500.

Note 4: Production halted around January 1942 due to outbreak of World War II.

President, 8-cyl.

Model No.	Body Type & Seating	Factory Price	Shipping Weight	Prod. Total
Custom				
8-C	2-dr. Sed. Cpe.-6P	1141	3440	Note 5
8-C	4-dr. Cr. Sed.-6P	1161	3485	Note 5
8-C	4-dr. L. Cr.-6P	1196	3510	Note 5
Deluxstyle				
8-C	2-dr. Sed. Cpe.-6P	1186	3455	Note 5
8-C	4-dr. Cr. Sed.-6P	1206	3500	Note 5
8-C	4-dr. L. Cr.-6P	1241	3515	Note 5
Skyway				
8-C	2-dr. Sed. Cpe.-6P	1221	3470	Note 5
8-C	4-dr. Cr. Sed.-6P	1241	3540	Note 5
8-C	4-dr. L. Cr.-6P	1276	3540	Note 5

Note 5: Total production August 1941 to January 1942 was 3,500.

Note 6: Production halted around January 1942 due to outbreak of World War II.

ENGINE: [Champion] L-head. Inline. Six. Cast iron block. B & S: 3 x 4 in. Disp.: 170 cu. in. C.R.: 6.5:1; (opt.) 7.0:1. Brake H.P.: 80 @ 4000 R.P.M. Taxable H.P.: 21.60. Main bearings: four. Valve lifters: solid. Carb.: Carter one-barrel Model 496S. Torque: 134 lb.-ft. @ 2000 R.P.M. [Commander] L-head. Inline. Six. Cast iron block. B & S: 3-5/16 x 4-3/8 in. Disp.: 226.2 cu. in. C.R.: 6.50:1; (opt.) 7.0:1. Brake H.P.: 94 @ 3600 R.P.M. Taxable H.P.: 26.35. Main bearings: four. Valve lifters: solid. Carb.: Stromberg one-barrel Model BXOV26. Torque: 176 lb.-ft. @ 1600 R.P.M. [President] L-head. Inline. Eight. Cast iron block. B & S: 3-1/16 x 4-1/4 in. Disp.: 250.4 cu. in. C.R.: 6.5:1; (opt.) 7.0:1. Brake H.P.: 117 @ 3800 R.P.M. Taxable H.P.: 30.0. Main bearings: nine. Valve lifters: solid. Carb.: Stromberg two-barrel Model AAV26. Torque: 200 lb.-ft. @ 2400 R.P.M.

CHASSIS: [Series 4-G] W.B.: 110 in. O.L.: 193 in. Frt/Rear Tread: 56-1/4/57 in. Tires: 16 x 5.50 in. [Series 12-A] W.B.: 119.5 in. O.L.: 210.25 in. Frt/Rear Tread: 58-1/4/60-5/16 in. Tires: 16 x 6.25 in. [Series 8-C] W.B.: 124.5 in. O.L.: 215-3/4 in. Frt/Rear Tread: 58-1/8/60-5/16 in. Tires: 15 x 7.00 in.

TECHNICAL: Warner Gear synchromesh transmission. Speeds: 3F/1R. Column mounted controls. (President) Inland woven and molded clutch; (others) Borg & Beck molded clutch. Shaft drive. Semi-floating rear axle. Overall ratio: (Champion) 4.1:1; (Commander) 4.09:1; (President) 4.09:1. Four-wheel Bendix hydraulic brakes. Budd steel disc wheels. Drivetrain options: Turbo-matic drive. Overdrive.

Note: Turbo-matic drive (available on Commander and President) consisted of a fluid coupling, an automatic vacuum-operated clutch and a conventional three-speed transmission with kick-down overdrive. It eliminated the clutch pedal and reduced gear shifting to a minimum. Gearshift lever positions were conventional, but second was called Traffic range and high was called Cruising range.

OPTIONS: Whitewall tires. Wheel trim rings. Full wheel discs. Front fender parking lights. Bumper wing tips. Fender skirts. Bumper guards. Radio. Heater. Clock. Cigar lighter. Radio antenna. Seat covers. External sun shade. Spotlight(s). Fog lamps. Climatizer. Turbo-matic drive.

HISTORICAL: Introduced September 1941. Innovations: Turbo-matic transmission. Dash controlled hood lock. Iron alloy pistons with Parco Lubrized surfaces. Larger clutch facing and vibration dampner on Champions. Clutch pedal starting. Calendar year registrations: 58,051. Calendar year sales: 9,285. Model year production: 47,678. Studebaker was America's eighth ranked automaker. Like other U.S. manufacturers, Studebaker became heavily involved in the war production effort after January 1942. The company built trucks, aircraft engines and "Weasels." The Weasel was a lightweight, tracked vehicle designed for troop transport and built in Arctic and amphibious models for special purpose applications.

STUDEBAKER 1946-1966

By VJ Day in 1945, the Studebaker company would look back over 93-1/2 years of producing road vehicles. Because of the successful Champion, which was introduced in 1939, and cost-plus war contracts, the Studebaker Corp. emerged from World War II in the best financial shape it had been in since 1929. The company, proud of its heritage, looked forward to the postwar years with great anticipation.

By Fred K. Fox

Anticipation and hope had always been the hallmark of the Studebaker organization. Two brothers, Henry and Clement Studebaker, set the company in motion in February 1852, when they opened a small blacksmith shop in South Bend, Ind. At first they only produced a few horse-drawn farm wagons, but with hard work and capital, and help from a third brother, John M. (who made a bundle building wheelbarrows for the goldminers of California), they propelled the company to international prominence. Not long after younger brothers Peter and Jacob joined the family organization, the Studebaker Brothers Manufacturing Co. proclaimed that it was the largest producer of horse-drawn vehicles in the world.

Studebaker produced its first salable automobile, an electric, in 1902. It entered the gasoline automobile business in 1904. In late 1910, Studebaker merged with EMF Corp. to form Studebaker Corp. In 1915, the first non-family member, Albert R. Erskine, became president of the corporation. During this period, Studebaker was, except for Ford, among the largest producers of automobiles in the country. Sales increases continued at a steady clip until the stock market crash in 1929.

Erskine felt that the Depression would be short-lived, so he continued to distribute large dividends. Erskine's misjudgment led Studebaker into receivership in 1933. Two resourceful Studebaker executives, Paul G. Hoffman and Harold S. Vance, pulled things together and saved the company. Hoffman and Vance guided the corporation through the Depression and introduced the successful Champion model. They were still directing the company in 1945, when automobile production resumed after World War II.

Hoffman was president. Vance acted as chairman of the board. Both men were responsible for Studebaker becoming the first established American automobile company to introduce a new postwar styling. A striking new car and a healthy seller's market helped Studebaker establish new sales and profit records during the late-1940s.

Although Studebaker's image seemed rosy, it was during this period that the seeds of the company's eventual undoing were taking root. A pampered workforce and many outdated buildings resulted in poor productivity and high overhead. When the seller's market switched to a buyer's market, in the early-1950s, these problems started to eat away at the profits. If the company had fed more profits back into plant improvements and taken a hard labor stance, things would have been much better. By 1953, the automobile division was operating in the red. Hoffman, who had left the company in 1948 to take a government position, returned in 1953. But neither he nor Vance could stop the flow of red ink.

Low-slung new styling in 1953, a takeover by Packard in 1954, and help from Curtiss-Wright in 1956, just prolonged what most insiders felt was a hopeless cause. The formation of the Studebaker-Packard Corp. brought in James Nance as chief executive officer. Two years later, under the guidance of Curtiss-Wright, Harold Churchill was selected as Studebaker-Packard's new president. This was a wise choice. Churchill, an engineer, was a loyal Studebaker man who had been with the corporation since 1926. He was determined to see that the company survived.

In late 1958, Churchill introduced the Lark. This compact car proved to be a big success during its first year. Churchill wanted to use 1959 profits to keep Studebaker in the forefront of small car development. However, the board of directors preferred using most of the profits for diversification. This difference of opinion resulted in the early 1961 replacement of Churchill with Sherwood Egbert.

Egbert, working within the constrictions of the board, also hoped to save the automotive division. His efforts fostered the creation of the Gran Turismo Hawk and the Avanti. Egbert's achievements, although commendable, did not help Studebaker's position. It was again on the negative side of the profit scale. The Packard name was dropped in 1962.

In late 1963, Egbert stepped down because of failing health. Studebaker's directors voted to close most of the South Bend, Ind., facility. Production was then centralized at the Hamilton plant, in Ontario, Canada. President of the Hamilton division was Gordon Grundy. He tried his best to operate the Canadian facility in the black. He did manage to make small profits, but not enough to satisfy the board of directors. Because of the board's dissatisfaction, the Canadian plant was closed in March 1966.

By early 1966, the corporation's other diversified holdings, including STP, represented a majority of Studebaker's sales. These other companies kept Studebaker going. In mid-1967, the Studebaker Corp. purchased the Wagner Electric Corp. and in November 1967 Studebaker combined with the Worthington Corp. to form Studebaker-Worthington. In the fall of 1979, the Studebaker-Worthington Corp. was absorbed by the smaller McGraw-Edison Co. of Illinois. Cooper Industries took over McGraw-Edison in 1985.

Nathan Altman and Leo Newman, two South Bend businessmen, revived the Avanti after Studebaker left town. In 1965, they created the Avanti Motor Corp. Avanti was sold several times before it, too, succumbed due to lack of sales.

1946

SKYWAY CHAMPION — MODEL 5G — The Champion, which had been Studebaker's lowest-priced model from 1939 to 1942, was the only Studebaker series produced for the 1946 model year. Production only lasted from December 1945 to March 1946. It was used as a filler between the end of World War II and the introduction of Studebaker's dramatic new 1947 models. Skyway trim, which was limited to Commanders and Presidents in 1942, was made standard on 1946 Champions. The main Skyway Champion styling features were clean sides combined with wide horizontally grooved moldings on the rocker panels and the lower edges of the front and rear fenders. These moldings were not used on 1942 Champions. Two-tone options were listed in early literature, but current knowledge indicates that only a few prototypes were painted two-tone. A model identification script was located in the center of the instrument panel.

STUDEBAKER I.D. NUMBERS: Serial number located on left front door lock pillar post. Engine number on top left side of front corner of cylinder block. The serial numbers for the 1946 Skyway Champion were G-193001 to G-212279. The engine numbers were 216501 to 235776. All were produced in the South Bend, Ind., plant.

SKYWAY CHAMPION SERIES

Model No.	Body/Style No.	Body Type & Seating	Factory Price	Shipping Weight	Prod. Total
5G	W7	4-dr Sed-6P	1097	2566	10,525
5G	F7	2-dr Sed-5P	1046	2541	5,000
5G	Q10	2-dr Cpe-5P	1044	2491	1,285
5G	Q8	2-dr Cpe-3P	1002	2456	2,465

ENGINE:

STUDEBAKER SIX: L-head. Cast iron block. Displacement: 169.6 cid. Bore and stroke: 3 x 4 inches. Compression ratio: 6.5:1. Brake hp: 80 at 4000 rpm. Four main bearings. Solid valve lifters. Carburetor: Carter Model WE-532S one-barrel.

CHASSIS FEATURES: Wheelbase: 110 inches. Overall length: 197.8 inches. Front tread: 56.25 inches. Rear tread: 57 inches. Tires: 5.50 x 16 tube type.

OPTIONS: Hill Holder. Directional signals. Fender lamps. Skyway eight-tube push-button radio or Liberator six-tube manual tuning radio. Internally controlled cowl radio antenna. Front and rear winguards (bumper extensions). Fog lights. Spotlight. Package compartment light. Underhood light. Climatizer heater/defroster. Two-tone Mattex seat covers. Cigar lighter. Electric clock. Locking gas tank cap. Plastic whitewall wheel discs. Stainless steel wheel trim rings. Chrome license plate frames. Exhaust extensions. Front gravel deflectors. Rear fender pebble deflectors. Automatic windshield cleaner. Glare-proof interior rearview mirror. Exterior rearview mirror. Visor vanity mirror. Transparent plastic grille cover (for cold weather). Tire chains. Wet oil bath air cleaner. Fram oil filter. A three-speed manual transmission with column-mounted gearshift was standard. Overdrive was available at $54.67 extra. A 7.0:1 compression ratio was optional.

HISTORICAL FOOTNOTES: Body style W7 was called a Cruising Sedan. Body style F7 was called a Club Sedan. Body style Q10 was called a Double Dater. Body style Q8 was a business coupe.

1947

CHAMPION — MODEL 6G — The Deluxe Champion was Studebaker's low-priced model. The Regal Deluxe trim version featured stainless steel windshield trim and stainless steel rocker panel moldings. The Deluxe version did not feature these items. The Champion's stainless steel grille was suspended in the radiator opening. The horizontal taillights were divided into two sections. A model identification script was located in the center of the instrument panel. All-new styling by Raymond Loewy and Virgil Exner featured front fenders flush with body. The 1947 Champion was introduced in May 1946.

STUDEBAKER I.D. NUMBERS: Serial number located on left front door lock pillar post. Engine number on top left side of front corner of cylinder block. [CHAMPION] The serial numbers for the 1947 Champions were G-212501 to G-314500 (South Bend) and G-824001 to G-827300 (Los Angeles). Champion engine numbers were 236001 to 342000 for both plants. [COMMANDER]: The serial numbers for the 1947 Commanders were 4232501 to 4287000 (South Bend) and 4818501 to 4820500 (Los Angeles). The Commander engine numbers were H-182001 to H-239000 for both plants.

CHAMPION SERIES

Model No.	Body/Style No.	Body Type & Seating	Factory Price	Shipping Weight	Prod. Total
DELUXE LINE					
6G	W3	4-dr Sed-6P	1478	2735	23,958
6G	F3	2-dr Sed-6P	1446	2685	10,860
6G	Q1	2-dr Cpe-3P	1378	2600	5,221
6G	C3	2-dr Cpe-5P	1472	2670	7,670
REGAL DELUXE LINE					
6G	W5	4-dr Sed-6P	1551	2760	30,000
6G	F5	2-dr Sed-6P	1520	2710	12,697
6G	Q2	2-dr Cpe-3P	1451	2620	3,379
6G	C5	2-dr Cpe-5P	1546	2690	9,061
6G	S2	2-dr Conv-5P	1902	2875	2,251

COMMANDER — MODEL 14A — For 1947, the Commander was Studebaker's top line model. The President, which had been Studebaker's prewar prestige model, was not returned to production until 1955. Regal Deluxe and Deluxe exterior trim variations were the same as on Champions. Except for the Land Cruiser, all basic bodies were the same as Champions from the cowl back. The long wheelbase Land Cruiser, like the convertible, came only with Regal Deluxe trim. The Commander's stainless steel grille sections were set into a painted steel stamping. Taillights were divided into four sections. 'Black light' instrument illumination was standard on all Commanders and Champions. Model identifications were located on the front edge of the hood and the right side of the instrument panel.

COMMANDER SERIES

Model No.	Body/Style No.	Body Type & Seating	Factory Price	Shipping Weight	Prod. Total
DELUXE LINE					
14A	Q1	2-dr Cpe-3P	1661	3140	301
14A	C3	2-dr Cpe-5P	1755	3210	2,742
14A	W3	4-dr Sed-6P	1761	3265	3,485
14A	F3	2-dr Sed-6P	1729	3230	548
REGAL DELUXE LINE					
14A	W5	4-dr Sed-6P	1882	3280	13,539
14A	F5	2-dr Sed-6P	1850	3245	2,159
14A	Q2	2-dr Cpe-3P	1781	3155	1,046
14A	C5	2-dr Cpe-5P	1876	3225	10,557
14A	S2	2-dr Conv-5P	2236	3420	1,503

LAND CRUISER (123" WHEELBASE)

Model No.	Body/Style No.	Body Type & Seating	Factory Price	Shipping Weight	Prod. Total
14A	Y5	4-dr Sed-6P	2043	3340	20,519

ENGINES:

(CHAMPION SIX) L-head. Cast iron block. Displacement: 169.6 cid. Bore and stroke: 3 x 4 inches. Compression ratio: 6.5:1. Brake hp: 80 at 4000 rpm. Four main bearings. Solid valve lifters. Carburetor: Carter Model WE-532S one-barrel.

(COMMANDER SIX) L-head. Cast iron block. Displacement: 226.2 cid. Bore and stroke: 3-5/16 x 4-3/8 inches. Compression ratio: 6.5:1. Brake hp: 94 at 3600 rpm. Four main bearings. Solid valve lifters. Carburetor: Stromberg Model BXOV-26 one-barrel.

CHASSIS FEATURES: Wheelbase: (Champion) 112 inches; (Commander, except Land Cruiser) 119 inches; (Land Cruiser) 123 inches. Overall length: (Champion) 192.7 inches; (Commander, except Land Cruiser) 204.4 inches; (Land Cruiser) 208.4 inches. Front tread: (Champion) 56.25 inches; (Commander) 55 inches. Rear tread: (Champion and Commander) 54 inches. Tires: (Champion) 5.50 x 15 tube type; (Commander) 6.50 x 15 tube type.

OPTIONS: Hill Holder. Directional signals. White sidewall tires. Skyway eight-tube push-button radio or Liberator six-tube manual tuning radio. Internally controlled cowl radio antenna. Climatizer heater/defroster or economy Quad-Duty heater. Champion hood ornament. Front fender ornaments. Strat-O-Lined or Universal exterior rearview mirror. Champion front and rear winguards (bumper extensions). Commander rear winguards (front winguards standard on Commander). Plastic whitewall wheel discs or stainless steel wheel trim rings. Chrome license plate frames. Exhaust extension. Fog lights. Spotlight. Underhood light. Champion Deluxe luggage compartment light. Champion package compartment light. Electric clock. Glare-proof interior rearview mirror. Visor vanity mirror. Cigarette lighter. Two-tone Mattex seat covers. Automatic windshield washer. Champion vacuum windshield wiper booster (standard on Commander). Locking gas cap. Rear ash receivers for Champion Deluxe two- and four-door sedans. Regal steering wheel for Deluxe trim models. Fram oil filter for Champions. Wet oil bath air cleaner. Tire chains. A three-speed manual transmission with column-mounted gearshift was standard on all models. Overdrive was available for $84.75 extra on Champions and $90.85 extra on Commanders. A 7.0:1 compression ratio was optional on both engines.

HISTORICAL FOOTNOTES: Body style Q was a business coupe. Starting in 1949, body style C was called a Starlight. The Starlight name is now applied retroactively to 1947 C bodies. The Y body (Land Cruiser) was a stretched W body. The Land Cruiser had vent windows in the rear doors.

1948

CHAMPION — MODEL 7G — The 1948 Champion continued with the same body style and trim offerings as in 1947. A single, full-width, horizontal stainless steel bar was added to the grille. A Champion script was affixed to the left front edge of the hood. Standard one-piece curved windshields on convertibles and five-passenger coupes were continued from 1947. All others had flat two-piece windshields.

STUDEBAKER I.D. NUMBERS: Serial number located on left front door lock pillar post. Engine number on top left side of front corner of cylinder block. [CHAMPION] The serial numbers for the 1948 Champions were G-314501 to G-399772 (South Bend); G-827301 to G-839550 (Los Angeles) and G-700001 and up (Canada). Engine numbers were 342001 to 439798 (South Bend and Los Angeles) and C-1001 and up (Canada). [COMMANDER] The serial numbers for the 1948 Commanders were 4287001 to 4360743 (South Bend) and 4820501 to 4832598 (Los Angeles). The engine numbers were H-239001 to H-324981 for both South Bend and Los Angeles plants.

CHAMPION SERIES

Model No.	Body/Style No.	Body Type & Seating	Factory Price	Shipping Weight	Prod. Total
DELUXE LINE					
7G	W3	4-dr Sed-6P	1635	2720	21,436
7G	F3	2-dr Sed-6P	1604	2675	10,203
7G	Q1	2-dr Cpe-3P	1535	2590	3,783
7G	C3	2-dr Cpe-5P	1630	2670	5,499
REGAL DELUXE LINE					
7G	W5	4-dr Sed-6P	1709	2725	30,494
7G	F5	2-dr Sed-6P	1677	2685	9,471
7G	Q2	2-dr Cpe-3P	1609	2615	823
7G	C5	2-dr Cpe-5P	1704	2690	8,982
7G	S2	2-dr Conv-5P	2059	2865	9,996

COMMANDER — MODEL 15A — The 1948 Commander continued with the same body style and trim offerings as in 1947, although production records indicate only one three-passenger coupe was produced. A wide horizontal trim strip was added to the front edge of the hood. Nylon upholstery was introduced as a standard feature on the Land Cruiser. The Land Cruiser, like the Champion/Commander five-passenger coupe and convertible, continued with a one-piece curved windshield. A gradual attempt was made to promote the Land Cruiser as a separate model.

COMMANDER SERIES

Model No.	Body/Style No.	Body Type & Seating	Factory Price	Shipping Weight	Prod. Total
DELUXE LINE					
15A	Q1	2-dr Cpe-3P	1856	—	0
15A	W3	4-dr Sed-6P	1956	3195	8,898
15A	F3	2-dr Sed-6P	1925	3165	1,440
15A	C3	2-dr Cpe-5P	1951	3150	2,913
REGAL DELUXE LINE					
15A	W5	4-dr Sed-6P	2077	3215	15,685
15A	F5	2-dr Sed-6P	2045	3175	1,661
15A	Q2	2-dr Cpe-3P	1977	—	1
15A	C5	2-dr Cpe-5P	2072	3165	11,528
15A	S2	2-dr Conv-5P	2431	3385	7,982
LAND CRUISER (123" WHEELBASE)					
15A	Y5	4-dr Sed-6P	2265	3280	35,731

ENGINES:

(CHAMPION SIX) L-head. Cast iron block. Displacement: 169.6 cid. Bore and stroke: 3 x 4 inches. Compression ratio: 6.5:1. Brake hp: 80 at 4000 rpm. Four main bearings. Solid valve lifters. Carburetor: Carter Model WE-532S or WE-661S one-barrel.

(COMMANDER SIX) L-head. Cast iron block. Displacement: 226.2 cid. Bore and stroke: 3-5/16 x 4-3/8 inches. Compression ratio: 6.5:1. Brake hp: 94 at 3600 rpm. Four main bearings. Solid valve lifters. Carburetor: Stromberg Model BXOV-26 one-barrel.

CHASSIS FEATURES: Wheelbase: (Champion) 112 inches; (Commander, except Land Cruiser) 119 inches; (Land Cruiser) 123 inches. Overall length: (Champion) 190.7 inches; (Commander, except Land Cruiser) 204.2 inches; (Land Cruiser) 208.2 inches. Front tread: (Champion) 56.25 inches; (Commander) 55 inches. Rear tread: (Champion and Commander) 54 inches. Tires: (Champion) 5.50 x 15 tube type; (Commander) 6.50 x 15 tube type.

OPTIONS: Hill Holder. Directional signals. White sidewall tires. Skyway eight-tube push-button radio or Starline six-tube push-button radio. Internally controlled cowl radio antenna. Climatizer heater/defroster or economy Quad-Duty heater. Front fender ornaments. Strat-O-Lined or Universal exterior rearview mirror. License plate frames. Plastic wheel discs or stainless wheel trim rings. Commander stainless wheel discs. Front and rear winguards (bumper extensions). Grille and trunk guards. Rear fender skirts. Exhaust deflector. Locking gas cap. Plastic top cover for convertibles. Rubber splash guards. Regal steering wheel for Deluxe models. Horn ring for Commander Deluxe models. Fog lights. Spotlight (internal or external control). Back-up light. Service light. Under hood light. Champion Deluxe luggage compartment light. Champion package compartment light. Cigarette lighter and front ashtray. Tell-Tale lights. Fabric, Mattex or plastic seat covers. Armrest covers. Door scuff pads. Select-O-Seat cushion springs. Exterior windshield sun visor. No-blo window deflector for rear doors. Door window awnings. Venetian shades. Breez-Bye Wind Rejector for convertibles. Rubber floor mats. Electric clock (standard on Land Cruiser). Glare-proof interior rearview mirror. Visor vanity mirror. Rear ash receivers for Champion Deluxe two- and four-door sedans. Automatic windshield washer. Studebaker Auto-Serv tissue dispenser. Custom luggage. Champion vacuum windshield wiper booster. Fram oil filter for Champions. Hydraulic bumper jack. Undercoating. Tire chains. A three-speed manual transmission with column-mounted gearshift was standard on all models. Overdrive was available for $84.75 extra on Champions and $90.85 extra on Commanders. A 7.0:1 compression ratio was optional on both engines.

HISTORICAL FOOTNOTES: Model year sales reached 166,069 units. Studebaker was ranked ninth on the industry sales chart. Body style Q was a business coupe. Starting in 1949, body style C was called a Starlight. The Starlight name is now applied retroactively to 1948 C bodies. The Y body (Land Cruiser) was a stretched W body. The Land Cruiser had vent windows in the rear doors.

1949

CHAMPION — MODEL 8G — The Champion continued as Studebaker's low-priced model. Body style and trim selections were the same as 1947 and 1948. Standard wraparound front and rear bumpers were introduced on all models. A second full-width horizontal stainless steel bar was added to the grille. The five-passenger (C body) coupe was christened the Starlight.

STUDEBAKER I.D. NUMBERS: Serial number located on left front door lock pillar post. Engine number on top left side of front corner of cylinder block. [CHAMPION] The serial numbers for the 1949 Champions were G-400501 to G-467959 (South Bend), G-839701 to G-851669 (Los Angeles) and G-703101 and up (Canada). The engine numbers were 441001 to 520550 (South Bend and Los Angeles) and C-4101 and up in Canada. [COMMANDER] The serial numbers for the 1949 Commanders were 4361001 to 4398473 (South Bend) and 4832701 to 4838950 (Los Angeles). The engine numbers were H-326001 to H-369772 for both South Bend and Los Angeles plants.

CHAMPION SERIES

Model No.	Body/Style No.	Body Type & Seating	Factory Price	Shipping Weight	Prod. Total
DELUXE LINE					
8G	Q1	2-dr Cpe-3P	1588	2645	1,642
8G	C3	2-dr Starlight Cpe-5P	1683	2705	5,917
8G	W3	4-dr Sed-6P	1688	2745	20,134
8G	F3	2-dr Sed-6P	1657	2720	10,359
REGAL DELUXE LINE					
8G	W5	4-dr Sed-6P	1762	2750	24,328
8G	F5	2-dr Sed-6P	1730	2725	5,618
8G	Q2	2-dr Cpe-3P	1662	2650	718
8G	C5	2-dr Starlight Cpe-5P	1757	2725	9,829
8G	S2	2-dr Conv-5P	2086	2895	7,035

COMMANDER — MODEL 16A — The Commander continued as Studebaker's top-line series. Except for the discontinuance of the Commander three-passenger business coupe (Q body), the body styles and trim selections were the same as 1947-48. Wraparound bumpers were made standard. Chrome and stainless steel overlays were added to the grille to cover up the painted areas. For the first time since 1938, the displacement of the Commander engine was increased.

COMMANDER SERIES

Model No.	Body/Style No.	Body Type & Seating	Factory Price	Shipping Weight	Prod. Total
DELUXE LINE					
16A	W3	4-dr Sed-6P	2019	3240	6,280
16A	F3	2-dr Sed-6P	1988	3215	1,418
16A	C3	2-dr Starlight Cpe-5P	2014	3200	2,712
REGAL DELUXE LINE					
16A	W5	4-dr Sed-6P	2140	3245	10,005
16A	F5	2-dr Sed-6P	2109	3220	934
16A	C5	2-dr Starlight Cpe-5P	2135	3205	6,278
16A	S2	2-dr Conv-5P	2467	3415	1,702
LAND CRUISER (123" WHEELBASE)					
16A	Y5	4-dr Sed-6P	2328	3325	14,390

ENGINES:

(CHAMPION SIX) L-head. Cast iron block. Displacement: 169.6 cid. Bore and stroke: 3 x 4 inches. Compression ratio: 6.5:1. Brake hp: 80 at 4000 rpm. Four main bearings. Solid valve lifters. Carburetor: Carter Model WE-715S one-barrel.

(COMMANDER SIX) L-head. Cast iron block. Displacement: 245.6 cid. Bore and stroke: 3-5/16 x 4-3/4 inches. Compression ratio: 6.5:1. Brake hp: 100 at 3400 rpm. Four main bearings. Solid valve lifters. Carburetor: Stromberg Model BXOV-26 one-barrel.

CHASSIS FEATURES: Wheelbase: (Champion) 112 inches; (Commander except Land Cruiser) 119 inches; (Land Cruiser) 123 inches. Overall length: (Champion) 191.9 inches; (Commander except Land Cruiser) 205.4 inches; (Land Cruiser) 209.4 inches. Front tread: (Champion) 56.25 inches; (Commander) 55 inches. Rear tread: (Champion and Commander) 54 inches. Tires: (Champion) 6.40 x 15 tube type; (Commander) 6.50 x 15 tube type.

OPTIONS: Hill Holder. Directional signals. White sidewall tires. Skyway eight-tube push-button radio or Starline six-tube push-button radio. Internally controlled vacuum-powered front fender radio antenna or internally controlled reel-type cowl radio antenna. Climatizer heater/defroster or economy Quad-Duty heater. Champion front fender ornaments. Start-O-Vu, Strat-O-Lined, Universal or Dor-Top exterior rearview mirror. License plate frames. Plastic wheel discs, stainless wheel discs or stainless wheel trim rings. Grille and trunk guards. Rear fender skirts. Exhaust deflector. Locking gas cap. Grease fitting Lubri-Caps. Door scuff pads. Rubber splash guards. Rubber floor mats. Regal horn ring for Deluxe models. Plastic top cover for convertibles. Fabric, Mattex or plastic seat covers. Select-O-Seat cushion springs. Armrest covers. Fog lights. Spotlight (internal or external control). Back-up light. Champion package compartment light. Underhood light. Champion Deluxe luggage compartment light. Service light. Cigarette lighter and front ashtray. Tell-Tale lights. Exterior windshield sun visor. Breez-Bye Wind Rejector for convertibles. No-blo wind deflector. Door window awnings. Venetian shades. Electric clock (standard on Land Cruiser). Glare-proof interior rearview mirror. Visor vanity mirror. Rear ash receivers for Champion Deluxe two- and four-door sedans. Robe rail for all models except Land Cruiser (standard on Land Cruiser). Safety child-proof rear door locks for four-door sedans. Automatic windshield washer. Champion vacuum windshield wiper booster. Tissue dispenser. Custom luggage. Fram oil filter for Champions. Hydraulic jack. Headbolt engine heater. Tire chains. Undercoating. A three-speed manual transmission with column-mounted gearshift was standard on all models. Overdrive was available for $91.55 extra on Champion and $97.85 extra on Commander. A 7.0:1 compression ratio was optional on both engines.

HISTORICAL FOOTNOTES: Model year sales totaled 118,435. Studebaker ranked eighth on the industry sales chart. Body style Q was a business coupe. The Y body (Land Cruiser) was a stretched W body. The Land Cruiser had vent windows in the rear doors.

1950

CHAMPION — MODEL 9G — A 'bullet-nose' front end and rear fenders that supported vertical taillights were new for 1950. The central body section was unchanged. The model identification was on the front fenders. Small headlight trim rings were used on Champions. Starting in midyear, these rings were chrome plated on Deluxe and Regal Deluxe trim lines. A low-priced Custom model was introduced at midyear. A new Automatic Drive was introduced as an option during midyear. A growing buyer's market reduced prices from 1949 and during the year they were reduced again. Available body types were the same as 1949. There was no hood ornament on Custom models. Stainless steel rocker panel moldings were standard on Regal Deluxe models.

STUDEBAKER I.D. NUMBERS: Serial number located on left front door lock pillar post. Engine number on top left side of front corner of cylinder block. [CHAMPION] The serial numbers for the 1950 Champions were G-468101 to G-686431 (South Bend), G-851801 to G-889014 (Los Angeles) and G-709401 and up (Canada). The beginning engine numbers were 521001 (South Bend and Los Angeles) and C-10501 in Canada. [COMMANDER] The serial numbers for the 1950 Commanders were 4398601 to 4461853 (South Bend) and 4839001 to 4848311 (Los Angeles). The beginning engine number was H-370001 for both South Bend and Los Angeles plants.

CHAMPION SERIES

Model No.	Body/Style No.	Body Type & Seating	Factory Price	Shipping Weight	Prod. Total
CUSTOM LINE					
9G	W1	4-dr Sed-6P	1519	2730	16,000
9G	F1	2-dr Sed-6P	1487	2695	19,593
9G	Q4	2-dr Cpe-3P	1419	2620	1,562
9G	C1	2-dr Starlight Cpe-5P	1514	2690	3,583
DELUXE LINE					
9G	W3	4-dr Sed-6P	1597	2750	46,027
9G	F3	2-dr Sed-6P	1565	2720	45,280
9G	Q1	2-dr Cpe-3P	1497	2635	2,082
9G	C3	2-dr Starlight Cpe-5P	1592	2705	19,028
REGAL DELUXE LINE					
9G	W5	4-dr Sed-6P	1676	2755	55,296
9G	F5	2-dr Sed-6P	1644	2725	21,976
9G	Q2	2-dr Cpe-3P	1576	2640	849
9G	C5	2-dr Starlight Cpe-5P	1671	2715	29,966
9G	S2	2-dr Conv-5P	1981	2900	9,362

COMMANDER — MODEL 17A — The 1950 Commander's 'bullet-nose' and rear fenders were the same as on Champions, while the front fenders and headlight trim rings were much larger. The bullet-nose piece was fully chrome plated on both Commanders and Champions. The model identification was on the front fenders. A Land Cruiser script was adjacent to the rear deck lid on that model. Body style and trim offerings were the same as in 1949. Standard chrome headlight trim rings and optional Automatic Drive were introduced as a running change. Prices were also reduced at midyear. On both Commanders and Champions a coil spring and A-arm arrangement replaced the former planar cross leaf spring independent front suspension system.

COMMANDER SERIES

Model No.	Body/Style No.	Body Type & Seating	Factory Price	Shipping Weight	Prod. Total
DELUXE LINE					
17A	W3	4-dr Sed-6P	1902	3255	11,440
17A	F3	2-dr Sed-6P	1871	3215	4,588
17A	C3	2-dr Starlight Cpe-5P	1897	3215	4,383

REGAL DELUXE LINE

Model No.	Body/Style No.	Body Type & Seating	Factory Price	Shipping Weight	Prod. Total
17A	W5	4-dr Sed-6P	2024	3265	14,832
17A	F5	2-dr Sed-6P	1992	3220	2,363
17A	C5	2-dr Starlight Cpe-5P	2018	3220	7,375
17A	S2	2-dr Conv-5P	2328	3375	2,867
LAND CRUISER (124" WHEELBASE)					
17A	Y5	4-dr Sed-6P	2187	3355	24,712

ENGINES:

(CHAMPION SIX) L-head. Cast iron block. Displacement: 169.6 cid. Bore and stroke: 3 x 4 inches. Compression ratio: 7.0:1. Brake hp: 85 at 4000 rpm. Four main bearings. Solid valve lifters. Carburetor: Carter Model WE-715S one-barrel.

(COMMANDER SIX) L-head. Cast iron block. Displacement: 245.6 cid. Bore and stroke: 3-5/16 x 4-3/8 inches. Compression ratio: 7.0:1. Brake hp: 102 at 3200 rpm. Four main bearings. Solid valve lifters. Carburetor: Stromberg Model BXOV-26 one-barrel or Carter Model WE-627SA one-barrel.

CHASSIS FEATURES: Wheelbase (Champion) 113 inches; (Commander except Land Cruiser) 120 inches; (Land Cruiser) 124 inches. Overall length: (Champion) 197.25 inches; (Commander except Land Cruiser) 207.9 inches; (Land Cruiser) 211.9 inches. Front tread: (Champion) 56.4 inches; (Commander) 55.5 inches. Rear tread: (Champion/Commander) 54 inches. Tires: (Champion) 6.40 x 15 tube type; (Commander) 7.60 x 15 tube type.

OPTIONS: Hill Holder. Directional signals. White sidewall tires. Stratoline eight-tube push-button radio, Starline six-tube push-button radio or Starline six-tube manual tuning radio. Internally controlled vacuum-powered front fender radio antenna or internally controlled reel-type cowl radio antenna. Climatizer heater/defroster. Champion front fender ornaments. Strat-O-Vu, Stratoline, Universal or Dor-Top exterior rearview mirror. Stratoline or Deluxe exhaust deflector. Rear fender skirts. License plate frames. Full chrome wheel covers or stainless wheel trim rings. Fabric or plastic seat covers. Armrest covers. Exterior windshield sun visor. No-blo wind deflector. Rubber floor mats (two types). Select-O-Seat cushion springs. Robe cord for all models except Land Cruiser. Grille and trunk guards. Plastic top cover for convertibles. Grease fitting Lubri-Caps. Door scuff pads. Rubber front fender splash guards. Locking gas cap. Trunk compartment mat for all models except Land Cruiser. Accelerator pedal cover and wear pad. Back-up lights. Fog lights. Spotlight (internal or external control). Parking brake warning light. Service light. Underhood light. Champion Custom/Deluxe luggage compartment light. Champion package compartment light. Standard or Drawmatic cigarette lighter. Cigarette lighter and front ash receiver. Tell-Tale light. Electric clock (standard on Land Cruiser). Glare-proof interior rearview mirror. Deluxe or standard vanity mirror. Tissue dispenser. Windshield washer. Safety child-proof rear door locks. Rear ash receivers for Champion Custom/Deluxe two- and four-door sedans. Custom luggage. Standard or Electro-Vac wiper booster for Champions. Fram oil filter for Champions. Headbolt engine heater. Winter transparent plastic grille cover. Cold weather Battery Vitalizer. Tire chains. Hydraulic jack. Undercoating. Pastel Sparkel Spray exterior finish treatment. Accessories specifically for the Champion Custom: extra interior sun visor, front door armrest, rear armrests (two- and four-door sedans), extra horn, hood ornament and interior courtesy light. A three-speed manual transmission with column-mounted gearshift was standard on all models. Overdrive was available for $92 extra on Champions and $98 extra on Commanders. Automatic Drive, starting in midyear, was available for $201 extra on all models. A 7.5:1 compression ratio was optional on both engines.

HISTORICAL FOOTNOTES: Model year sales totaled 320,884 units. Studebaker was ranked ninth on the industry sales chart. Body style Q was a business coupe. The Y body (Land Cruiser) was a stretched W body. The Land Cruiser had vent windows in the rear doors. The Land Cruiser continued with Regal Deluxe trim.

1951

CHAMPION — MODEL 10G — The Champion was continued as Studebaker's low-priced series. The outer edge of the "bullet-nose" section was painted body color and the center piece was made of plastic. One-piece curved windshields were standard on all body styles. The former two-piece rear window on two- and four-door sedans was replaced by a one-piece unit. The "Deluxe" term was deleted from the Regal Deluxe trim name. Painted headlight and taillight trim rings were used only on Custom models. Deluxe models had chrome headlight and taillight trim rings, but lacked the stainless steel rocker panel moldings that were standard on Regal models. The Champion and Commander wheelbases were identical. All fender and body panels were the same on Champions and Commanders for corresponding bodies. The model identification was located on the left front edge of the hood.

STUDEBAKER I.D. NUMBERS: Serial number located on left front door lock pillar post. Champion engine numbers were located on top left side front corner of cylinder block. Commander engine numbers were located on the top of the rear of the cylinder block next to the distributor. [CHAMPION] The serial numbers for 1951 were G-1000001 to G-1115017 (South Bend), G-889101 to G-907190 (Los Angeles) and G-724501 and up (Canada). The beginning engine numbers were 778001 and up (South Bend and Los Angeles) and C-25501 and up in Canada. [COMMANDER] The serial numbers for 1951 were 8110001 to 8216497 (South Bend), 8800001 to 8815942 (Los Angeles) and 8952001 and up (Canada). The beginning engine numbers were V-101 (South Bend and Los Angeles) and VC-101 (Canada).

CHAMPION SERIES

Model No.	Body/Style No.	Body Type & Seating	Factory Price	Shipping Weight	Prod. Total
CUSTOM LINE					
10G	W1	4-dr Sed-6P	1571	2690	9,972
10G	F1	2-dr Sed-6P	1540	2670	10,689
10G	Q4	2-dr Cpe-3P	1471	2585	2,429
10G	C1	2-dr Starlight Cpe-5P	1566	2650	2,781
DELUXE LINE					
10G	W3	4-dr Sed-6P	1649	2715	26,019
10G	F3	2-dr Sed-6P	1618	2690	18,591
10G	Q1	2-dr Cpe-3P	1549	2610	961
10G	C3	2-dr Starlight Cpe-5P	1644	2675	9,444
REGAL LINE					
10G	W5	4-dr Sed-6P	1728	2715	35,201
10G	F5	2-dr Sed-6P	1697	2690	8,931
10G	Q2	2-dr Cpe-3P	1628	2615	373
10G	C5	2-dr Starlight Cpe-5P	1723	2675	14,103
10G	S2	2-dr Conv-5P	2034	2890	4,742

COMMANDER — MODEL H — New for Commanders in 1951 was a V-8 overhead valve engine. The Deluxe trim name was discontinued and the Regal Deluxe became just the Regal. A new State name was used for top-line models. State models came standard with fender ornaments. Body selections were the same as in 1951, except that the Los Angeles plant produced one Commander business coupe. Bullet-nose, windshield and rear window changes were the same as on Champions. The grille on both Commanders and Champions was increased in size and moved forward so it was flush with the front sheet metal. The Commander and Champion had larger taillight lenses than in 1950. The model identification was located on the left front edge of the hood. The Land Cruiser name remained on the front fenders.

COMMANDER SERIES

Model No.	Body/Style No.	Body Type & Seating	Factory Price	Shipping Weight	Prod. Total
REGAL LINE					
H	W3	4-dr Sed-6P	1839	3070	29,603
H	F3	2-dr Sed-6P	1807	3050	8,034
H	Q1	2-dr Cpe-3P	—	—	1
H	C3	2-dr Starlight Cpe-5P	1833	3025	8,192
STATE LINE					
H	W5	4-dr Sed-6P	1939	3070	21,134
H	F5	2-dr Sed-6P	1907	3050	3,903
H	C5	2-dr Starlight Cpe-5P	1933	3025	11,637
H	S2	2-dr Conv-5P	2244	3245	3,770
LAND CRUISER (119" WHEELBASE)					
H	Y5	4-dr Sed-6P	2071	3165	38,055

ENGINES:

(CHAMPION SIX) L-head. Cast iron block. Displacement: 169.6 cid. Bore and stroke: 3 x 4 inches. Compression ratio: 7.0:1. Brake hp: 85 at 4000 rpm. Four main bearings. Solid valve lifters. Carburetor: Carter Model WE-715S one-barrel.

(COMMANDER V-8) Overhead valve. Cast iron block. Displacement: 232.6 cid. Bore and stroke: 3-3/8 x 3-1/4 inches. Compression ratio: 7.0:1. Brake hp: 120 at 4000 rpm. Five main bearings. Solid valve lifters. Carburetor: Stromberg Model AAUVB-26 two-barrel.

CHASSIS FEATURES: Wheelbase: (Champion/Commander except Land Cruiser) 115 inches; (Land Cruiser) 119 inches. Overall length: (Champion/Commander except Land Cruiser) 197.5 inches; (Land Cruiser) 201.5 inches. Front tread: 56.5 inches. Rear tread: 54 inches. Tires: (Champion) 6.40 x 15 tube type; (Commander) 7.10 x 15 tube type.

OPTIONS: Hill Holder. Directional signals. White sidewall tires. Stratoline eight-tube push-button radio. Starline six-tube push-button radio. Starline six-tube manual tuning radio. Internally controlled vacuum-powered front fender radio antenna or internally controlled reel-type cowl radio antenna. Climatizer heater/defroster. Champion and Regal Commander front fender ornaments. Strat-O-Vu, Stratoline or Universal exterior rearview mirror. Exhaust deflector. Rear fender skirts. Gas door guard. License plate frames. Full chrome wheel covers or stainless wheel trim rings. Fabric or plastic seat covers. Exterior windshield sun visor. Side window vent shades. No-blo wind deflector. Venetian shields. Select-O-Seat cushion springs. Robe cord for all models except Land Cruiser (standard on Land Cruiser). Grille and trunk guards. Plastic top cover for convertibles. Spark plug weather proofing kit. Rubber front fender splash guards. Door scuff pads. Locking gas cap. Rubber floor mats (two types). Accelerator pedal cover and wear pad. Back-up lights. Spotlight. Fog lights. Parking brake warning light. Underhood light. Glove compartment light. Service light. Luggage compartment light for all models except Land Cruiser (standard on Land Cruiser). Electric clock (standard on Land Cruiser). Standard or Drawmatic cigarette lighter. Glare-proof interior rearview mirror. Tissue dispenser. Standard or illuminated vanity mirror. Safety child-proof rear door locks. Windshield washer. Rear ash receiver for Champion Custom/Deluxe two- and four-door sedans. Custom luggage. Electric windshield wipers for Champions. Fram oil filter for all models except Land Cruiser (standard on Land Cruiser). Headbolt engine heater. Cold weather Battery Vitalizer. Tire chains. Hydraulic jack. Undercoating. Pastel Sparkel Spray exterior finish treatment. Accessories specifically for the Champion Custom: extra interior sun visor, front door armrests, rear armrests (two- and four-door sedans), extra horn, hood ornament and interior courtesy light. A three-speed manual transmission with column-mounted gearshift was standard on all models. Overdrive was available for $92 extra on Champions and $98 extra on Commanders. Automatic Drive was available for $201 extra on all models. A 7.5:1 compression ratio was optional on the Champion engine.

HISTORICAL FOOTNOTES: Model year sales reached 246,195 units. Studebaker remained ninth on the industry sales chart. Body style Q was a business coupe. The Y body (Land Cruiser) was a stretched W body. The Land Cruiser had vent windows in the rear doors. The Land Cruiser featured State trim.

1952

CHAMPION — MODEL 12G — The Champion body style and trim selections were the same as 1951, except that the business coupe (Q) was discontinued and a new two-door hardtop (K) was added. The 'bullet-nose' front end design was dropped and a horizontal grille, slightly similar to the upcoming 1953 design, was adopted. The grille molding bent down to form a 'V' in the center of the grille. Six vertical bars sloped back into the grille. Champions had an oblong emblem above the grille molding. The top one-third of each taillight was hooded. The central body sections, discounting the new hardtop, continued with the basic 1947 design. Rear fenders were unchanged from 1950-1951. The model identification was located on the left front edge of the hood. Two-tone finishes were available on hardtops.

STUDEBAKER I.D. NUMBERS: Serial number located on the front door lock pillar post. Effective with Champion serial number 8266501 and Commander serial number G-1160245 the location was moved to a plate attached to the left front door hinge pillar facing. Champion engine numbers were located on top left side front corner of cylinder block. Commander engine numbers were located on the top of the rear of the cylinder block next to the distributor. [CHAMPION] The serial numbers for 1952 were G-1115501 to G-1197180 (South Bend), G-907301 to G-917641 (Los Angeles) and G-735701 and up (Canada). The engine numbers were 911501 to 1000639 (South Bend and Los Angeles) and C-36722 and up for Canada. [COMMANDER] The serial numbers for 1952 were 8217001 to 8289877 (South Bend), 8816001 to 8826703 (Los Angeles) and 8954001 and up (Canada). The engine numbers were V-123001 to V-206512 (South Bend and Los Angeles) and VC-2036 and up for Canada.

CHAMPION SERIES

Model No.	Body/Style No.	Body Type & Seating	Factory Price	Shipping Weight	Prod. Total
CUSTOM LINE					
12G	W1	4-dr Sed-6P	1769	2695	6,400
12G	F1	2-dr Sed-6P	1735	2655	4,310
12G	C1	2-dr Starlight Cpe-5P	1763	2660	1,096
DELUXE LINE					
12G	W3	4-dr Sed-6P	1862	2720	24,542
12G	F3	2-dr Sed-6P	1828	2685	12,989
12G	C3	2-dr Starlight Cpe-5P	1856	2675	6,075
REGAL LINE					
12G	F5	2-dr Sed-6P	1913	2690	5,534
12G	W5	4-dr Sed-6P	1946	2725	20,566
12G	C5	2-dr Starlight Cpe-5P	1941	2695	6,183
12G	K2	2-dr Starliner HT-5P	2220	2860	12,119
12G	S2	2-dr Conv-5P	2273	2870	1,575

COMMANDER — MODEL 3H — The Commander styling changes were essentially the same as those for the Champion. A two-door hardtop was also added to the Commander lineup. Commanders had the same basic new grille as Champions, but a V-shaped Studebaker crest was mounted above the grille molding. Commander and Champion instrument panels were different. Since 1950, the Champion's instruments had been enclosed in a single enclosure, while the Commander's, since 1947, were held in three round dials. The model identification was located on the left front edge of the hood and on the deck lid. The Land Cruiser name was moved from the front fender to the deck lid. Front fender ornaments were standard on State models. Nineteen fifty-two marked the final year that the 1947 body styling was used. It was also the final year Studebaker used 'suicide' rear doors on four-door sedans.

COMMANDER SERIES

Model No.	Body/Style No.	Body Type & Seating	Factory Price	Shipping Weight	Prod. Total
REGAL LINE					
3H	W3	4-dr Sed-6P	2121	3085	22,037
3H	F3	2-dr Sed-6P	2086	3040	5,995
3H	C3	2-dr Starlight Cpe-5P	2115	3030	5,127
STATE LINE					
3H	W5	4-dr Sed-6P	2208	3075	9,998
3H	F5	2-dr Sed-6P	2172	3055	1,529
3H	C5	2-dr Starlight Cpe-5P	2202	3025	3,784
3H	K2	2-dr Starliner-5P	2488	3220	14,548
3H	S2	2-dr Conv-5P	2548	3230	1,715
LAND CRUISER (119" WHEELBASE)					
3H	Y5	4-dr Sed-6P	2365	3155	20,117

ENGINES:

(CHAMPION SIX) L-head. Cast iron block. Displacement: 169.6 cid. Bore and stroke: 3 x 4 inches. Compression ratio: 7.0:1. Brake hp: 85 at 4000 rpm. Four main bearings. Solid valve lifters. Carburetor: Carter Model WE-715S one-barrel.

(COMMANDER V-8) Overhead valve. Cast iron block. Displacement: 232.6 cid. Bore and stroke: 3-3/8 x 3-1/4 inches. Compression ratio: 7.0:1. Brake hp: 120 at 4000 rpm. Five main bearings. Solid valve lifters. Carburetor: Stromberg Model AAUVB-26 two-barrel.

CHASSIS FEATURES: Wheelbase: (Champion/Commander except Land Cruiser) 115 inches; (Land Cruiser) 119 inches. Overall length: (Champion/Commander except Land Cruiser) 197.5 inches; (Land Cruiser) 201.5 inches. Front tread: 56.5 inches. Rear tread: 54 inches. Tires: (Champion) 6.40 x 15 tube type; (Commander) 7.10 x 15 tube type.

OPTIONS: Hill Holder. Directional signals. White sidewall tires. Stratoline eight-tube push-button radio. Starline six-tube manual tuning radio. Internally controlled vacuum-powered front fender radio antenna or internally controlled reel-type cowl radio antenna. Climatizer heater/defroster. Fabric or plastic seat covers. Champion and Regal Commander front fender ornaments. Rear fender ornaments. Exhaust deflector. Starliner medallion. Rear fender skirts. "Automatic Drive" nameplate. Deluxe steering wheel. Full wheel covers or stainless wheel trim rings. Strat-O-Vu, Stratoline or Universal exterior rearview mirror. Gas door guard. License plate frames. Grille and trunk guards. Rubber floor mats. Plastic top cover for convertibles. Rubber front splash guards. Accelerator pedal cover and wear pad. Locking gas cap. Back-up lights. Spotlight. Fog lights. Parking brake warning light. Glove compartment light. Underhood light. Luggage compartment light for all models except Land Cruiser (standard on Land Cruiser). Electric clock (standard on Land Cruiser). Glare-proof interior rearview mirror. Tissue dispenser. Cigarette lighter. Windshield washer. Standard or illuminated vanity mirror. Safety child-proof rear door locks. Exterior windshield sun visor. Side window vent shades. No-blo wind deflector. Venetian shades. Select-O-Seat cushion springs. Custom luggage. Rear ash receiver for Champion Custom/Deluxe two- and four-door sedans. Sav-A-Battery caps. Fram oil filter for all models except Land Cruiser (standard on Land Cruiser). Electric windshield wipers for Champions. Fram radiator water filter. Headbolt engine heater. Cold weather Battery Vitalizer. Snow chains. Hydraulic jack. Undercoating. Accessories specifically for the Champion Custom: extra interior sun visor, front door armrests, rear armrests (two- and four-door sedans), extra horn, hood ornament and interior courtesy light. A three-speed manual transmission with column-mounted gearshift was standard on all models. Overdrive was available for $105 extra on Champions and $118 extra on Commanders. Automatic Drive was available for $231 extra on Champions and $243 extra on Commanders. A 7.5:1 compression ratio was optional on both engines.

HISTORICAL FOOTNOTES: Model year sales totaled 167,662. Studebaker maintained a ninth ranking on the industry sales chart. A Studebaker convertible was the official pace car of the Indianapolis 500-Mile race this year. A 1952 Commander State Starliner, Studebaker #7,130,874, was the final car built in Studebaker's first century

1948 Studebaker, Commander Regal Deluxe (Series 15A), convertible, OCW

1950 Studebaker, Commander Regal Deluxe (Series 16A), convertible, OCW

1952 Studebaker, Champion Deluxe (Series 12G), sedan, AA

1952 Studebaker, Commander State Starlight (Series 3H), coupe, AA

1953 Studebaker, Champion Regal Starliner (Series 14G), hardtop, AA

1950 Studebaker, Champion Regal Deluxe (Series 8G), convertible, AA

1950 Studebaker, Commander Land Cruiser (Series 16A), sedan, AA

1952 Studebaker, Champion Regal Starliner (Series 12G), hardtop, AA

1953 Studebaker, Champion Custom (Series 14G), sedan, AA

1953 Studebaker, Commander Regal (Series 4H), sedan, AA

(1852-1952). The Y body (Land Cruiser) was a stretched W body. The Land Cruiser had vent windows in the rear doors. The Land Cruiser featured State trim. The Starliner hardtop (K body) was based on the convertible (S) styling.

1953

CHAMPION — MODEL 14G — Studebaker introduced all-new bodies for 1953. The new sedans were shorter (except the Land Cruiser) and higher than the sporty Starliner hardtop (K) and Starlight coupe (C). The Starlight no longer featured the large wraparound four-piece rear window. The Starliner featured a single-piece rear window instead of the three-piece style used in 1952. The convertible was discontinued. Custom models continued with painted headlight and taillight trim rings. The Deluxe versions featured narrow stainless steel windshield moldings, while the Regal style had wide stainless steel windshield moldings. The instrument panel featured three circular instrument clusters covered by a single piece of glass. Plastic taillight lenses replaced the former glass ones. The grille had two front openings located above the bumper. They ran the full width of the cars, with a horizontal fin "floating" in each scoop-like opening. Parking lamps and directionals were mounted at each end. Model identification was on the left grille bar. Champions also had a hood ornament supplemented by the symbol 'S'. The Champion continued as the low-priced series.

STUDEBAKER I.D. NUMBERS: Serial number located on the front door lock pillar post. Effective with Champion serial number 8266501 and Commander serial number G-1160245 the location was moved to a plate attached to the left front door hinge pillar facing. Champion engine numbers were located on top left side front corner of cylinder block. Commander engine numbers were located on the top of the front of the cylinder block next to the oil filler tube mounting. [CHAMPION] Serial numbers for 1953 were G-1197501 to G-1270324 (South Bend), G-917701 to G-927156 (Los Angeles) and G-745101 and up (Canada). Engine numbers were G-1004001 and up (South Bend and Los Angeles) and C-46501 and up for Canada. [COMMANDER] Serial numbers for 1953 were 8290001 to 8353332 (South Bend), 8826801 to 8836505 (Los Angeles) and 8955401 and up (Canada). The beginning engine numbers were V-207001 (South Bend and Los Angeles) and VC-3501 (Canada).

CHAMPION SERIES

Model No.	Body/Style No.	Body Type & Seating	Factory Price	Shipping Weight	Prod. Total
CUSTOM					
14G	W1	4-dr Sed-6P	1767	2710	5,496
14G	F1	2-dr Sed-6P	1735	2690	3,983
DELUXE					
14G	W3	4-dr Sed-6P	1863	2735	17,180
14G	F3	2-dr Sed-6P	1831	2700	7,564
14G	C3	2-dr Starlight Cpe-5P	1868	2695	9,422
REGAL					
14G	W5	4-dr Sed-6P	1949	2745	17,897
14G	F5	2-dr Sed-6P	1917	2715	2,968
14G	C5	2-dr Starlight Cpe-5P	1995	2700	16,066
14G	K5	2-dr Starliner HT-5P	2116	2760	13,058

COMMANDER — MODEL 4H — Commanders, like Champions, received new 1953 bodies. For a given body type, the Champion and Commander bodies were identical. The State name was dropped and the Commander Deluxe identification was returned. Deluxe and Regal variations were the same as on Champions. The grille had two front openings located above the bumper. They ran the full width of the cars, with a horizontal fin "floating" in each scoop-like opening. Parking lamps and directionals were mounted at each end. Model identification was on the left grille bar. Champions also had a hood ornament supplemented by the symbol '8' as one of several V-8 emblems. During midyear, the tri-star emblems used on the hood and deck lid of early Commanders and Champions were replaced by large "V" emblems. The new instrument panel featured four hooded instrument pods. Model identification was on the left grille bar and on the deck lid of some, but not all examples.

COMMANDER SERIES

Model No.	Body/Style No.	Body Type & Seating	Factory Price	Shipping Weight	Prod. Total
DELUXE					
4H	W3	4-dr Sed-6P	2121	3075	10,065
4H	F3	2-dr Sed-6P	2089	3055	2,371
4H	C3	2-dr Starlight Cpe-5P	2127	3040	6,106
REGAL					
4H	W5	4-dr Sed-6P	2208	3095	7,454
4H	C5	2-dr Starlight Cpe-5P	2213	3040	14,752
4H	K5	2-dr Starliner HT-5P	2374	3120	19,236

LAND CRUISER

Model No.	Body/Style No.	Body Type & Seating	Factory Price	Shipping Weight	Prod. Total
4H	Y5	4-dr Sed-6P	2316	3180	15,981

ENGINES:

(CHAMPION SIX) L-head. Cast iron block. Displacement: 169.6 cid. Bore and stroke: 3 x 4 inches. Compression ratio: 7.0:1. Brake hp: 85 at 4000 rpm. Four main bearings. Solid valve lifters. Carburetor: Carter Model WE-989SA one-barrel.

(COMMANDER V-8) Overhead valve. Cast iron block. Displacement: 232.6 cid. Bore and stroke: 3-3/8 x 3-1/4 inches. Compression ratio: 7.0:1. Brake hp: 120 at 4000 rpm. Five main bearings. Solid valve lifters. Carburetor: Stromberg Model WWUVL-26 two-barrel.

CHASSIS FEATURES: Wheelbase: (sedans except Land Cruiser) 116.5 inches; (Land Cruiser, coupes and hardtops) 120.5 inches. Overall length: (sedans except Land Cruiser) 198.6 inches; (Land Cruiser) 202.6 inches; (coupes and hardtops) 201.9 inches. Front tread: 56.5 inches. Rear tread: 55.5 inches. Tires: (Champion) 6.40 x 15 tube type; (Commander) 7.10 x 15 tube type.

OPTIONS: Hill Holder. Hydraulic power steering ($134). (Mechanical power steering was mentioned in early publicity, but it was never put into production.) Directional signals. White sidewall tires. Stratoline eight-tube push-button radio. Starline six-tube manual tuning radio. Internally controlled reel-type cowl radio antenna. Auxiliary rear seat radio speaker. Climatizer heater/defroster. Fabric or plastic seat covers. Deluxe or Strat-O-Styled hood ornament. Front fender ornaments. Exhaust deflector. License plate frames (two styles). Gas door guard. "Automatic Drive" nameplate, Strat-O-Styled, Strat-O-Vu or Universal exterior rearview mirror. Rear fender skirts. Full wheel covers or wire wheel-type wheel covers. Front and rear winguards (bumper extensions). Rubber floor mats. Rubber front splash guards. Accelerator pedal cover and wear pad. Locking gas cap. Fog light bumperettes with or without the fog lights. Spotlight (with built-in rear mirror). Back-up lights. Parking brake warning light. Glove compartment light. Underhood light. Trunk light for all models except Land Cruiser (standard on Land Cruiser). Electric clock. Safety child-proof rear door locks. Glare-proof rearview mirror. Tissue dispenser. Cigarette lighter. Vanity mirror. Windshield washer. Exterior windshield sun visor. Side window vent shades. Custom luggage. Rear window defroster. Headbolt engine heater. Tire chains. Arctic wiper blades. Undercoating. Electric windshield wipers for Champions. Rear ash receiver for Champion Custom/Deluxe sedans. Fram oil filter for all models except Land Cruiser (standard on Land Cruiser). Fram radiator water filter. Crankcase ventilator. Accessories specifically for the Champion Custom: extra interior sun visor, front door armrests, rear armrests and rear seat ashtray. A three-speed manual transmission with column-mounted gearshift was standard on all models. Overdrive was available for $105 extra on Champions and $118 extra on Commanders. Automatic Drive was available for $231 extra on Champions and $243 extra on Commanders. A 7.5:1 compression ratio was optional on both engines.

HISTORICAL FOOTNOTES: Model year sales reached 151,576 units. Studebaker remained ranked ninth on the industry sales chart. The Y body (Land Cruiser) was a stretched W body. The Land Cruiser had vent windows in the rear doors. The Land Cruiser featured Regal trim.

1954

CHAMPION — MODEL 15G — Except for the addition of a new Conestoga two-door station wagon (D body), the body style offerings and trim identifications were the same as in 1953. Main exterior trim differences between Custom, Deluxe and Regal models remained unchanged. The addition of 10 vertical "teeth" in the grille and new flat-faced front bumper guards were the main exterior styling changes for 1954. Deluxes had chrome window trim. Regals had a rub molding extending from the front door panel to the rear fender. All Regal and Deluxe sedans and station wagons featured a standard 'air scoop' hood ornament. All new interior fabrics were color-keyed to the exterior paint scheme. The model identification remained on the left horizontal grille bar and for 1954, it was also placed on the deck lid handle of all body styles except the station wagon. Two-tone finishes were available on all models except the Custom line.

STUDEBAKER I.D. NUMBERS: Vehicle Identification Number located on left front door pillar. Champion engine number on top of left front corner of block. Commander engine number on top front of cylinder block near oil filler tube mounting. [CHAMPION] Serial numbers for 1954 were G-1274001 to G-1315831 (South Bend), G-927401 to G-932286 (Los Angeles) and G-753301 and up (Canada). The beginning engine numbers were 1090001 (South Bend and Los Angeles) and C-55782 (Canada). [COMMANDER] The beginning serial numbers for 1954 were 8354901 to 8380448 (South Bend), 8836801 to 8841029 (Los Angeles) and 8956751 and up (Canada). The beginning engine numbers were V-282501 (South Bend and Los Angeles) and VC-4941 (Canada).

CHAMPION SERIES

Model No.	Body/Style No.	Body Type & Seating	Factory Price	Shipping Weight	Prod. Total
CUSTOM					
15G	W1	4-dr Sed-6P	1801	2735	2,860
15G	F1	2-dr Sed-6P	1758	2705	2,653
DELUXE					
15G	F3	2-dr Sed-6P	1875	2730	4,449
15G	W3	4-dr Sed-6P	1918	2765	9,668
15G	C3	2-dr Starlight Cpe-5P	1972	2740	7,042
15G	D3	2-dr Sta Wag-6P	2187	2930	3,910
REGAL					
15G	W5	4-dr Sed-6P	2026	2780	7,286
15G	F5	2-dr Sed-6P	1983	2745	1,066
15G	C5	2-dr Starlight Cpe-5P	2080	2750	5,125
15G	K5	2-dr Starliner HT-5P	2241	2825	4,302
15G	D5	2-dr Sta Wag-6P	2295	2950	3,074

COMMANDER — MODEL 5H — For a given body type and trim line, the Commander exterior styling features were the same as on 1954 Champions. On the inside a single instrument visor replaced the four separate units used in 1953. A Commander Conestoga two-door station wagon was also introduced. Deluxes had chrome window trim. Regals had a rub molding extending from the front door panel to the rear fender. Land Cruisers had a folding rear seat armrest.

COMMANDER SERIES

Model No.	Body/Style No.	Body Type & Seating	Factory Price	Shipping Weight	Prod. Total
DELUXE					
5H	W3	4-dr Sed-6P	2179	3105	4,615
5H	F3	2-dr Sed-6P	2136	3075	1,086
5H	C3	2-dr Starlight Cpe-5P	2233	3085	2,868
5H	D3	2-dr Sta Wag-6P	2448	3265	1,912
REGAL					
5H	W5	4-dr Sed-6P	2287	3120	2,571
5H	C5	2-dr Starlight Cpe-5P	2341	3095	3,151
5H	K5	2-dr Starliner HT-5P	2502	3175	5,040
5H	D5	2-dr Sta Wag-6P	2556	3265	2,878
LAND CRUISER					
5H	Y5	4-dr Sed-6P	2438	3180	6,383

ENGINES:

(CHAMPION SIX) L-head. Cast iron block. Displacement: 169.6 cid. Bore and stroke: 3 x 4 inches. Compression ratio: 7.5:1. Brake hp: 85 at 4000 rpm. Four main bearings. Solid valve lifters. Carburetor: Carter Model WE-989SA, WE-2018S or WE-2190S one barrel.

(COMMANDER V-8) Overhead valve. Cast iron block. Displacement: 232.6 cid. Bore and stroke: 3-3/8 x 3-1/4 inches. Compression ratio: 7.5:1. Brake hp: 127 at 4000 rpm. Five main bearings. Solid valve lifters. Carburetor: Stromberg Model WWUVL-26 two-barrel.

CHASSIS FEATURES: Wheelbase: (station wagons and sedans except Land Cruiser) 116.5 inches; (Land Cruiser, coupes and hardtops) 120.5 inches. Overall length: (sedans except Land Cruiser) 198.6 inches; (Land Cruiser) 202.6 inches; (coupes and hardtops) 202.2 inches; (station wagons) 195.6 inches. Front tread: 56.5 inches. Rear tread: 55.5 inches. Tires: (Champion except station wagon) 6.40 x 15 tube type; (Champion station wagon) 6.70 x 15 tube type; (Commander) 7.10 x 15 tube type.

OPTIONS: Hill Holder. Hydraulic power steering ($134). Directional signals. White sidewall tires. Stratoline eight-tube push-button radio. Starline six-tube manual tuning radio. Internally controlled reel-type cowl radio antenna. Auxiliary rear seat speaker. Climatizer heater/defroster. Fabric or plastic seat covers. Front fender ornaments. Strat-O-Styled hood ornament for models without standard hood ornament. Exterior rearview mirror. Rear fender skirts. Full wheel covers, wire wheel-type wheel covers, wide stainless wheel trim rings or white painted metal trim rings. Imitation knock-off Sportster hubs. License plate frames. Gas door guard. Front and rear winguards (bumper extensions). Grille guard. Fog light bumperettes with or without the fog lights. Rubber floor mats. Rubber front splash guards. Accelerator pedal cover and wear pad. Locking gas cap. Spotlight (with built-in rearview mirror). Back-up lights. Parking brake warning light. Glove compartment light. Underhood light. Trunk light for all models except Land Cruiser and station wagons (standard on Land Cruiser). Electric clock (standard on Land Cruiser). Tissue dispenser. Vanity mirror. Exterior windshield sun visor. Side window vent shades. Glare-proof interior rearview mirror. Cigarette lighter. Safety child-proof rear door locks. Windshield washer. Custom luggage. Rear window defroster. Arctic wiper blades. Tire chains. Undercoating. Electric windshield wipers for Champions. Rear ash receiver for Champion Custom/Deluxe sedans. Fram oil filter (standard on Land Cruiser). Fram radiator water filter. Crankcase ventilator. Accessories specifically for the Champion Custom: extra interior sun visor, front door armrests, rear armrests and rear seat ashtrays. A three-speed manual transmission with column-mounted gearshift was standard on all models. Overdrive was available for $105 extra on Champions and $118 extra on Commanders. Automatic Drive was available for $216 extra on Champions and $227 extra on Commanders.

HISTORICAL FOOTNOTES: On June 22, 1954, Studebaker merged with Packard to become the Studebaker-Packard Corp. of America. This was the final year that the Land Cruiser name was used. Studebaker slipped to 11th rank on the industry sales chart as model year sales amounted to only 68,708 units. The Y body (Land Cruiser) was a stretched W body. The Land Cruiser had vent windows in the rear doors. The Land Cruiser featured Regal trim. A $60 ambulance conversion for the station wagon was introduced during midyear. Called the "Ambulet," it was available as a Champion or Commander with Deluxe (D7) or Regal (D9) trim. Numerous options, including a siren, red beacon light and cot, were available for the Ambulet.

1955

CHAMPION — MODEL 16G6 — The low-priced Champion series continued with the same body style and trim lines as in 1954, except for the deletion of the Regal two-door sedan. After Jan. 1, 1955, wraparound windshields were introduced on sedans and station wagons. Basic exterior trim differences between Custom, Deluxe and Regal models remained unchanged from 1954, except for the addition of wide 'butter knife' side trim on Regal sedans, coupes and hardtops. A massive horizontal chrome grille replaced the delicate 1953-1954 style. A hood ornament was standard on all models. Exterior model identification was limited to the deck lid handle. Starliner and Starlight names were discontinued. The Conestoga station wagon was still only available in two-door form.

STUDEBAKER I.D. NUMBERS: Vehicle Identification Number located on left front door pillar. Champion engine number on top of left front corner of block. Commander engine number on top front of cylinder block near oil filler tube mounting. [CHAMPION] Serial numbers were G-1316501 to G-1357374 (South Bend), G-932501 to G-936679 (Los Angeles) and G-758201 and up (Canada). The beginning engine numbers were 1138001 (South Bend and early Los Angeles), L-101 (late Los Angeles) and C-60501 (Canada). [COMMANDER] The serial numbers for 1955 Commanders with 224.3-cid engines were 8380601 to 8397200 (South Bend), 8841201 to 8843000 (Los Angeles) and 8957601 and up (Canada). The engine numbers for 1955 Commanders with the 224-cid engine were V-312701 and up (South Bend and Los Angeles) and VC-5701 and up (Canada). The serial numbers for 1955 Commanders with 259.2-cid engines were 8397201 to 8429407 (South Bend), 8843001 to 8849083 (Los Angeles) and 8958101 and up (Canada). The engine numbers for cars with the 259-cid engine were V-331101 and up (South Bend), VL-101 and up (Los Angeles) and VC-6201 and up (Canada). [PRESIDENT] The serial numbers for 1955 Presidents were 7150001 to 7170827 (South Bend), 7805001 to 7808480 (Los Angeles) and 7900001 and up (Canada). The beginning engine numbers were P-101 (South Bend and early Los Angeles), PL-101 (late Los Angeles) and PC-101 (Canada).

CHAMPION SERIES

Model No.	Body/Style No.	Body Type & Seating	Factory Price	Shipping Weight	Prod. Total
CUSTOM					
16G6	W1/2	4-dr Sed-6P	1783	2790	3,290
16G6	F1/2	2-dr Sed-6P	1741	2740	2,801
DELUXE					
16G6	W3/4	4-dr Sed-6P	1885	2805	13,621
16G6	F3/4	2-dr Sed-6P	1841	2780	7,666
16G6	C3	2-dr Cpe-5P	1875	2790	5,572
16G6	D3/4	2-dr Sta Wag-6P	2141	2980	3,517
REGAL					
16G6	W5/6	4-dr Sed-6P	1993	2815	7,406
16G6	C5	2-dr Cpe-5P	1975	2795	2,721
16G6	K5	2-dr HT-5P	2129	2865	2,408
16G6	D5/6	2-dr Sta Wag-6P	2312	2985	1,372

COMMANDER — MODEL 16G8 — The mid-range Commander series offered the same body styles and trim lines as the 1955 Champions. After Jan. 1, 1955, wraparound windshields were introduced on sedans and station wagons. As in the Champion line, Regal and State models had a belt molding extending from the headlamps to taillamps, widening at the edge of the rear door. Series designations were 'Commander' or 'President' in script on the rear fenders. Exterior model identification was also on the deck lid handle.

1954 Studebaker, Commander Deluxe (Series 5H), coupe (with optional two-tone paint), AA

1955 Studebaker, Commander Regal (Series 16G8), sedan, AA

1956 Studebaker, Champion Deluxe (Series 56G), sedan, AA

1956 Studebaker, Commander Parkview (Series 56B), station wagon, AA

1956 Studebaker, Golden Hawk (Series 56J), hardtop, AA

1954 Studebaker, Commander Deluxe Conestoga (Series 5H), station wagon, AA

1955 Studebaker, President Speedster (Series 6H), hardtop, AA

1956 Studebaker, Flight Hawk (Series 56G), coupe, AA

1956 Studebaker, President Classic (Series 56H), sedan, AA

1957 Studebaker, Scotsman (Series 57G), station wagon, AA

COMMANDER SERIES

Model No.	Body/Style No.	Body Type & Seating	Factory Price	Shipping Weight	Prod. Total
CUSTOM					
16G8	W1/2	4-dr Sed-6P	1919	3065	2,082
16G8	F1/2	2-dr Sed-6P	1873	3005	1,413
DELUXE					
16G8	W3/4	4-dr Sed-6P	2014	3075	16,768
16G8	F3/4	2-dr Sed-6P	1969	3045	6,834
16G8	D3/4	2-dr Sta Wag-6P	2274	3265	4,280
16G8	C3	2-dr Cpe-5P	1989	3065	6,975
REGAL					
16G8	C5	2-dr Cpe-5P	2094	3065	4,639
16G8	K5	2-dr HT-5P	2282	3150	3,296
16G8	D5/6	2-dr Sta Wag-6P	2445	3275	2,516
16G8	W5/6	4-dr Sed-6P	2127	3080	9,985

PRESIDENT — MODEL 6H — After an absence of 13 years, the top-line President series was returned. Basic President styling was the same as 1955 Champions and Commanders. The tri-level painted President Speedster hardtop was introduced in January 1955. State and Speedster styles featured the 'butter knife' side trim. Instrument panels were shared by all Champions, Commanders and Presidents (except the Speedster). The Speedster had an engine turned instrument panel. Almost every conceivable option was standard on the Speedster. After Jan. 1, 1955, wraparound windshields were introduced on sedans. The President State four-door sedan replaced the Land Cruiser. Model identification was on the deck lid handle and rear quarter panels. South Bend-built Speedsters had only 'Speedster' on quarter panels, while Los Angeles versions had both 'President' and 'Speedster' on these panels.

PRESIDENT SERIES

Model No.	Body/Style No.	Body Type & Seating	Factory Price	Shipping Weight	Prod. Total
DELUXE					
6H	Y3/Y4	4-dr Sed-6P	2311	3165	1,021
STATE					
6H	Y5/Y6	4-dr Sed-6P	2381	3220	14,634
6H	C5	2-dr Cpe-5P	2270	3110	3,327
6H	K5	2-dr HT-5P	2456	3175	3,468
6H	K7	2-dr Spds HT-5P	3253	3301	2,215

ENGINES:

(CHAMPION SIX) L-head. Cast iron block. Displacement: 185.6 cid. Bore and stroke: 3 x 4-3/8 inches. Compression ratio: 7.5:1. Brake hp: 101 at 4000 rpm. Four main bearings. Solid valve lifters. Carburetor: Carter Model WE-2108S one-barrel.

(COMMANDER V-8) [Early version] Overhead valve. Cast iron block. Displacement: 224.3 cid. Bore and stroke: 3-9/16 x 2-13/16 inches. Compression ratio: 7.5:1. Brake hp: 140 at 4500 rpm. Five main bearings. Solid valve lifters. Carburetor: Stromberg Model WW two-barrel. [Later version] Overhead valve. Cast iron block. Displacement: 259.2 cid. Bore and stroke: 3-9/16 x 3-1/4 inches. Compression ratio: 7.5:1. Brake hp: 162 at 4500 rpm. Five main bearings. Solid valve lifters. Carburetor: Stromberg Model WW two-barrel.

(PRESIDENT V-8) Overhead valve. Cast iron block. Displacement: 259.2 cid. Bore and stroke: 3-9/16 x 3-1/4 inches. Compression ratio: 7.5:1. Brake hp: 175 (early) and 185 (later) at 4500 rpm. Five main bearings. Solid valve lifters. Carburetor. Carter Model WCFB four-barrel.

CHASSIS FEATURES: Wheelbase: (station wagons and sedans except President) 116.5 inches; (President four-door sedans, coupes and hardtops) 120.5 inches. Overall length: (sedans except President) 202.2 inches; (President four-door sedan) 206.2 inches; (coupes and hardtops) 204.4 inches; (station wagons) 197.7 inches. Front tread: 56.7 inches. Rear tread: 55.7 inches. Tires: (Champion except station wagon) 6.40 x 15 tubeless; (Champion station wagon and all Commanders) 6.70 x 15 tubeless; (President) 7.10 x 15 tubeless.

OPTIONS: Hill Holder. Power steering ($108). Power brakes. Air conditioning for V-8-powered sedans ($567 midyear option). Power seats (midyear option). Power windows (midyear option). Directional signals. White sidewall tires. Stratoline eight-tube push-button radio or Starline six-tube manual tuning radio. Internally controlled reel-type cowl radio antenna. Auxiliary rear seat speaker. Climatizer heater/defroster. Fabric or plastic seat covers. Cushion toppers. Fender ornaments for models without standard fender ornaments. Exhaust deflectors (two styles). Exterior rearview mirror(s) (three styles). License plate frames. Door handle guards. Rear fender skirts. Gas door guard. Full wheel covers. Wire wheel-type wheel covers, or wide stainless wheel trim rings. Imitation knock-off Sportster hubs. Grille guard. Fog light bumperettes. Rubber floor mats. Front wheel splash guards. Accelerator pedal cover and wear pad. Locking gas cap. Spotlight (with built-in rearview mirror). Back-up lights. Glove compartment light. Underhood light. Trunk light (standard on President State sedan). Electric clock (standard on President). Tissue dispenser. Custom luggage. Vanity mirror. Exterior windshield sun visor. Side door vent shades. Glare-proof interior rearview mirror. Safety child-proof rear door locks. Windshield washer. 3-D Booster horn. Rear window defroster. Arctic wiper blades. Tire chains. Undercoating. Electric windshield wipers for Champions. Rear ash receivers. Fram oil filter (standard on President). Fram radiator water filter. Accessories specifically for the Champion/Commander Custom: front door armrests and rear armrests. A three-speed manual transmission with column-mounted gearshift was standard on all models except the Speedster. Automatic Drive or overdrive was standard on the Speedster. Overdrive was available for $115 extra on Champions and $118 on Commanders and Presidents. Automatic Drive was available for $216 extra on Champions and $227 extra on Commanders and Presidents. A power kit that featured a four-barrel carburetor (Carter WCFB) and dual exhaust was available for Commanders. The kit raised the 224-cid engine's power to 160 hp at 4500 rpm and the 259-cid engine's power to 182 hp at 4500 rpm.

HISTORICAL FOOTNOTES: Model year sales totaled 116,333. Studebaker dropped to 13th on the industry sales chart. The President four-door sedans (Y bodies) were stretched W bodies. The Y bodies had vent windows (fixed on President Deluxe) in the rear doors. An ambulance/emergency vehicle conversion for the station wagon was available. Called the Ambulet, it was available as a Champion or Commander with Deluxe (D7/D8) or Regal (D9/D10) trim. Numerous options, including a siren, red beacon light and cot, were available for the Ambulet. Early model sedans and station wagons with non-wraparound windshields used odd (1, 3, 5, 7, 9) trim number identification. Later model (after Jan. 1, 1955) sedans and station wagons with wraparound windshields used even (2, 4, 6, 8, 10) trim number identification.

1956

CHAMPION AND FLIGHT HAWK — SERIES 56G — The front and rear sections of all Studebaker sedans were greatly restyled in 1956. The station wagons, which had front ends like the sedans, were fitted with small fiberglass fins on the rear quarter panels. The coupes and hardtops were named Hawks and featured a square-shaped grille and flat-backed deck lid. Custom sedan models, which included the two-door sedanet, had horizontal side trim along the front two-thirds of the car. Deluxe sedans had full-length side trim. The rare Regal model, which was built mainly for sale outside the United States, had dual full-length side moldings. A new "Cyclops Eye" speedometer was introduced on sedans and station wagons. All models were switched from six-volt to twelve-volt electrical systems.

STUDEBAKER I.D. NUMBERS: Vehicle Identification Number located on left front door pillar. Champion engine numbers on top of left front corner of block. Commander engine numbers on top front of cylinder block near oil filler tube mounting. [CHAMPION/FLIGHT HAWK] Serial numbers were G-1357501 to G-1379117 (South Bend), G-936701 to G-938796 (Los Angeles) and G-763701 and up (Canada). The engine numbers were 1180251 and up (South Bend), L-3201 and up (Los Angeles) and C-66001 and up (Canada). [COMMANDER/POWER HAWK] Serial numbers were 8429601 to 8454060 (South Bend), 8849101 to 8852866 (Los Angeles) and 8960001 and up (Canada). The beginning engine numbers were V-363751 and up (South Bend), VL-6301 and up (Los Angeles) and VC-8101 and up (Canada). [PRESIDENT AND SKY HAWK] Serial numbers were 7171001 to 7188817 (South Bend), 7808501 to 7811699 (Los Angeles) and 7900601 and up (Canada). The beginning engine numbers were P-22001 (South Bend), PL-2701 (Los Angeles) and PC-601 (Canada). [GOLDEN HAWK] Serial numbers were 6030001 to 6033472 (South Bend) and 6800001 to 6800601 (Los Angeles). The beginning engine numbers were K-1001 (with overdrive) and S-1001 (with Twin Ultramatic).

CHAMPION/FLIGHT HAWK SERIES

Model No.	Body/Style No.	Body Type & Seating	Factory Price	Shipping Weight	Prod. Total
CUSTOM					
56G	W2	4-dr Sed-6P	1717	—	1,170
DELUXE					
56G	W4	4-dr Sed-6P	1996	2835	11,983
56G	F2	2-dr S'net-6P	1844	2780	3,097
56G	F4	2-dr Sed-6P	1946	2800	4,301
REGAL					
56G	W6	4-dr Sed-6P	—	—	1,180
FLIGHT HAWK					
56G	C3	2-dr Cpe-5P	1982	2780	4,389
56G	K7	2-dr HT-5P	—	—	560
PELHAM					
56G	D4	2-dr Sta Wag-6P	2232	3000	2,236

COMMANDER AND POWER HAWK — SERIES 56B — Styling changes were the same as those made on the Champions. Exterior trim variations were also the same as on Champions. The model identification was located on the front fenders of sedans and station wagons and all deck lids. The Commander continued as Studebaker's mid-range offering. The Power Hawk, like the Flight Hawk, was based on the original 1953 Starlight.

COMMANDER/POWER HAWK SERIES

Model No.	Body/Style No.	Body Type & Seating	Factory Price	Shipping Weight	Prod. Total
DELUXE					
56B	W4	4-dr Sed-6P	2125	3140	14,700
56B	F2	2-dr S'net-6P	1974	3085	1,523
56B	F4	2-dr Sed-6P	2076	3110	3,663
CUSTOM					
56B	W2	4-dr Sed-6P	1829	—	335
POWER HAWK					
56B	C3	2-dr Cpe-5P	2101	3095	7,095
PARKVIEW					
56B	D4	2-dr Sta Wag-6P	2354	3300	3,333

PRESIDENT AND SKY HAWK — SERIES 56H — The President series was limited to the top-line trim, which featured dual side trim moldings on sedans and station wagons. The President Classic had wide grooved, horizontal moldings just above the rocker panels. The model identification locations were the same as on Commanders and Champions. Except for the Golden Hawk model, the President series continued as Studebaker's top-line offering.

PRESIDENT/SKY HAWK SERIES

Model No.	Body/Style No.	Body Type & Seating	Factory Price	Shipping Weight	Prod. Total
PRESIDENT					
56H	W6	4-dr Sed-6P	2235	3210	6,822
56H	F6	2-dr Sed-6P	2188	3180	1,914
PRESIDENT CLASSIC					
56H	Y6	4-dr Sed-6P	2489	3295	8,507
SKY HAWK					
56H	K7	2-dr HT-5P	2477	3215	3,050
PINEHURST					
56H	D6	2-dr Sta Wag-6P	2529	3395	1,522

GOLDEN HAWK — MODEL 56J — The Golden Hawk, like the Sky Hawk and Flight Hawk hardtops, was based on the original 1953 Starliner body. Small upright fiberglass fins on the top of the rear fenders were a Golden Hawk exclusive among the four 1956 Hawk models. Like the President Classic, the Golden Hawk had wide grooved, horizontal moldings just above the rocker panels.

GOLDEN HAWK SERIES

Model No.	Body/Style No.	Body Type & Seating	Factory Price	Shipping Weight	Prod. Total
56J	K7	2-dr Gold Hawk HT-5P	3061	3360	4,071

ENGINES:

(CHAMPION AND FLIGHT HAWK SIX) L-head. Cast iron block. Displacement: 185.6 cid. Bore and stroke: 3 x 4-3/8 inches. Compression ratio: 7.8:1. Brake hp: 101 at 4000 rpm. Four main bearings. Solid valve lifters. Carburetor: Carter Model WE-2108S or WE-2417S one-barrel.

(COMMANDER AND POWER HAWK V-8) Overhead valve. Cast iron block. Displacement: 259.2 cid. Bore and stroke: 3-9/16 x 3-1/4 inches. Compression ratio: 7.8:1. Brake hp: 170 at 4500 rpm. Five main bearings. Solid valve lifters. Carburetor: Stromberg Model WW two-barrel.

(PRESIDENT AND SKY HAWK V-8) Overhead valve. Cast iron block. Displacement: 289 cid. Bore and stroke: 3-9/16 x 3-5/8 inches. Compression ratio: 7.8:1. Brake hp: 210 at 4500 rpm on Classic and Sky Hawk; 190 at 4500 rpm on others. Five main bearings. Solid valve lifters. Carburetor: Carter Model WCFB four-barrel on Classic and Sky Hawk. Stromberg Model WW two-barrel on all others.

(GOLDEN HAWK V-8) Packard engine. Overhead valve. Cast Iron block. Displacement: 352 cid. Bore and stroke: 4 x 3-1/2 inches. Compression ratio: 9.5:1. Brake hp: 275 at 4600 rpm. Five main bearings. Hydraulic valve lifters. Carburetor: Carter Model WCFB-23945 four-barrel.

CHASSIS FEATURES: Wheelbase: (station wagons and sedans except President Classic) 116.5 inches; (President Classic and Hawks) 120.5 inches. Overall length: (sedans except President Classic) 200.7 inches; (President Classic) 204.7 inches; (Hawks) 203.9 inches; (station wagons) 196.7 inches. Front tread: 56.7 inches. Rear tread: 55.7 inches. Tires: (Champion/Flight Hawk except station wagons) 6.40 x 15 tubeless; (Champion station wagon/Commander/President except Classic) 6.70 x 15 tubeless; (President Classic and Golden Hawk) 7.10 x 15 tubeless.

OPTIONS: Hill Holder. Power steering ($108). Power brakes. Air conditioning for V-8-powered sedans. Power seats. Power windows. Directional signals. White sidewall tires. Stratoline push-button radio. Starline manual tuning radio. Internally controlled reel-type cowl antenna or dual rear mounted antenna. Rear seat speaker. Regular full wheel covers or imitation spoke (not wire) wheel covers. Regal or Deluxe license plate frames. Imitation dual exhaust extension for sedan models with single exhaust. Exhaust extension for Hawks and station wagons. Rear bumper guards for sedans. Gas door guard. Door handle guards. Curb signals. Rubber floor mats. Rubber splash guards. Accelerator pedal cover and wear pad. Locking gas cap. Exterior rearview mirror. Glare-proof interior rearview mirror. Brake fluid safety reservoir. Windshield washer. Climatizer heater/defroster. Door-mounted front safety belts. Spotlight. Parking brake warning light. Glove compartment light (standard on Classic and Golden Hawk). Trunk and utility light. Underhood light. Back-up lights. Electric clock. Compass. Traffic light viewer. Cigarette lighter. Automatic transmission Anti-Creep. Station wagon luggage carrier. Cushion toppers. Vanity mirror. Tissue dispenser. Custom luggage. Station wagon air mattress. Fram oil filter for Champions and Commanders (standard on all others). Undercoating. A three-speed transmission with column-mounted gearshift was standard on all models except the Golden Hawk. Overdrive or Packard's Twin Ultramatic ($100 extra) was standard on the Golden Hawk. Overdrive was available for $108 extra on Champion/Flight Hawk, Commander/Power Hawk and Sky Hawk models. It was $118 extra on other President models. Flightomatic was available for $189 extra on all models except the Golden Hawk. An optional four-barrel carburetor (Carter Model WCFB) was available on Commanders, Power Hawks and W, F and D bodied Presidents. It increased the 259-cid V-8's power to 185 hp at 4500 rpm and the President's to 210 hp at 4500 rpm. The optional four-barrel carburetor was part of a power kit option that included dual exhaust. A 8.3:1 compression ratio was optional on Studebaker V-8 engines. A special order Commander Custom four-door police car was available with a 289-cid President engine.

HISTORICAL FOOTNOTES: Model year sales slumped to 69,593 units. Studebaker's California assembly plant was shuttered this year, leaving production taking place only in South Bend, Ind., and Canada. The President Classic four-door sedan (Y body) was a stretched W body. The Classic had vent windows in the rear doors. An ambulance/emergency vehicle conversion for the station wagons, called the Ambulet, was available as a Champion-D8 and a Commander-D8. The Custom four-door sedan (W2) was limited to police, taxi and export/Canadian sales. Except for one car, the Champion Regal (President trim) four-door sedan (56G-E6) was limited to export/Canadian sales.

1957

CHAMPION AND SILVER HAWK SIX — SERIES 57G — A new wraparound grille and larger taillights were the obvious changes for 1957 on sedans and station wagons. A four-door station wagon was introduced. Hawks were fitted with large canted metal fins on the rear fenders. Custom models had rubber moldings around the windshield and rear windows and single side trim moldings on the front two-thirds of the car. Deluxe versions featured bright metal moldings around the windshield and rear window and full-length side trim. Regal models (built only for sale outside the United States) had double side trim moldings on the rear quarter panels and single pieces on the front. A low-priced plain-Jane Scotsman line was introduced during midyear. The Scotsman had painted hubcaps and grille and no side trim moldings. The Scotsman was introduced as a Champion, but it was eventually referred to as a separate model like the Silver Hawk six. Except for the Scotsman and Silver Hawk, the model identification was on the front fenders. The Scotsman had no model identification and the Silver Hawk's nameplate was on the deck lid. In 1957, directional signals were made standard on all models.

STUDEBAKER I.D. NUMBERS: The Vehicle Identification Number is located on left front door pillar. Champion engine number on top of left front corner of block. Commander engine number on top front of cylinder block near oil filler tube mounting. [CHAMPION/SILVER HAWK SIX) Serial numbers were G-1379201 to G-1405239 (South Bend) and G-769101 and up (Canada). The beginning engine numbers were 1202101 (South Bend) and C-71401 (Canada). The Los Angeles plant was closed. [SCOTSMAN] Scotsman serial numbers were G-1393130 to G-1405239 and engine numbers began at 1213263 and up. [COMMANDER/SILVER HAWK 259] The serial numbers for the 1957 Commander and Silver Hawk 259s were 8454101 to 8471491 (South Bend) and 8962601 and up (Canada). The beginning engine numbers were V-390001 (South Bend) and VC-10701

(Canada). [PRESIDENT/SILVER HAWK 289] The serial numbers for the 1957 President and Silver Hawk 289s were 7188901 to 7209836 (South Bend) and 7901501 and up (Canada). The beginning engine numbers for 1957 Presidents and Silver Hawk 289s were P-39601 and up (South Bend) and PC-1501 and up (Canada). [GOLDEN HAWK] The serial numbers for the 1957 Golden Hawk were 6100001 to 6104354 (South Bend). The beginning engine number for the 1957 Golden Hawks was PS-1001.

CHAMPION/SILVER HAWK SIX SERIES

Model No.	Body/Style No.	Body Type & Seating	Factory Price	Shipping Weight	Prod. Total
SCOTSMAN					
57G	W1	4-dr Sed-6P	1826	2725	3,005
57G	F1	2-dr Sed-6P	1776	2680	2,943
57G	D1	2-dr Sta Wag-6P	1995	2875	3,400
CUSTOM					
57G	W2	4-dr Sed-6P	2049	2785	2,106
57G	F2	2-dr Sed-6P	2001	2755	1,751
57G	P2	4-dr Sta Wag-6P	—	—	25
DELUXE					
57G	W4	4-dr Sed-6P	2171	2810	8,313
57G	F4	2-dr Sed-6P	2123	2780	1,950
57G	P4	4-dr Sta Wag-6P	—	—	1
PELHAM					
57G	D4	2-dr Sta Wag-6P	2382	3015	1,120
REGAL					
57G	W6	4-dr Sed-6P	—	—	247
SILVER HAWK					
57G	C3	2-dr Cpe-5P	2142	2790	4,163
57G	K3	2-dr HT-5P	—	—	120

COMMANDER AND SILVER HAWK 259 — SERIES 57B — Styling changes and trim differences were the same as on Champions. Hawk models continued with the engine turned instrument panel concept introduced on the 1955 Speedster. Model identifications were in the same locations as on Champions. The Flight Hawk, Power Hawk and Sky Hawk models of 1956 were replaced by the various 1957 Silver Hawk models. Certain Silver Hawk models were limited to sales outside the United States. For instance, the Silver Hawk V-8 sold in the United States came with a 289-cid engine, while the Canadian version was fitted with a 259-cid engine.

COMMANDER/SILVER HAWK 259 SERIES

Model No.	Body/Style No.	Body Type & Seating	Factory Price	Shipping Weight	Prod. Total
CUSTOM					
57B	W2	4-dr Sed-6P	2173	3015	828
57B	F2	2-dr Sed-6P	2124	3075	530
DELUXE					
57B	W4	4-dr Sed-6P	2295	3140	10,285
57B	F4	2-dr Sed-6P	2246	3100	2,072
STATION WAGONS					
57B	D4	2-dr Park Sta Wag-6P	2505	3310	738
57B	P4	4-dr Prov Sta Wag-6P	2561	3355	3,995
SILVER HAWK					
57B	C3	2-dr Cpe-5P	—	—	1,180
57B	K3	2-dr HT-5P	—	—	248

PRESIDENT/SILVER HAWK 289/GOLDEN HAWK — SERIES 57H — Styling changes and trim differences were the same as on Champions. The Silver Hawk 289 came only as a pillared coupe. The Golden Hawk came only as a hardtop. Standard on the Golden Hawk was a belt-driven supercharger. Model identifications were in the same locations as on Champions.

PRESIDENT/SILVER HAWK 289/GOLDEN HAWK SERIES

Model No.	Body/Style No.	Body Type & Seating	Factory Price	Shipping Weight	Prod. Total
CUSTOM					
57H	W2	4-dr Sed-6P	—	—	74
57H	F2	2-dr Sed-6P	—	—	62
57H	P2	4-dr Wag-6P	—	—	6
DELUXE					
57H	W4	4-dr Sed-6P	—	—	33
57H	F4	2-dr Sed-6P	—	—	8
47H	D4	2-dr Sta Wag-6P	—	—	8
REGAL					
57H	W6	4-dr Sed-6P	2407	3205	3,127
57H	F6	2-dr Sed-6P	2358	3170	836
CLASSIC					
57H	Y6	4-dr Sed-6P	2539	3270	6,063
BROADMOOR					
57H	P6	4-dr Sta Wag-6P	2666	3415	1,530
SILVER HAWK					
57H	C3	2-dr Cpe-5P	2263	3185	9,607
GOLDEN HAWK					
57H	K7	2-dr HT-5P	3182	3400	4,356

ENGINES:

(CHAMPION/SILVER HAWK SIX) L-head. Cast iron block. Displacement: 185.6 cid. Bore and stroke: 3 x 4-3/8 inches. Compression ratio: 7.8:1. Brake hp: 101 at 4000 rpm. Four main bearings. Solid valve lifters. Carburetor: Carter Model WE or BBR1 one-barrel.

(COMMANDER/SILVER HAWK 259 V-8) Overhead valve. Cast iron block. Displacement: 259.2 cid. Bore and stroke: 3-9/16 x 3-1/4 inches. Compression ratio: 8.3:1. Brake hp: 180 at 4500 rpm. Five main bearings. Solid valve lifters. Carburetor: Stromberg Model WW two-barrel.

(PRESIDENT/SILVER HAWK 289 V-8) Overhead valve. Cast iron block. Displacement: 289 cid. Bore and stroke: 3-9/16 x 3-5/8 inches. Compression ratio: 8.3:1. Brake hp: 225 at 4500 rpm on Classic; 210 at 4500 rpm on all others. Five main bearings. Solid valve lifters. Carburetor: Carter Model WCFB four-barrel on Classic; Stromberg Model WW two-barrel on all others.

(GOLDEN HAWK V-8) Overhead valve. Cast iron block. Displacement: 289 cid. Bore and stroke: 3-9/16 x 3-5/8 inches. Compression ratio: 7.8:1. Brake hp: 275 at 4800 rpm. Five main bearings. Solid valve lifters. Carburetor: Stromberg Model WW two-barrel.

CHASSIS FEATURES: Wheelbase: (station wagons and sedans, except President Classic) 116.5 inches; (President Classic and Hawks) 120.5 inches. Overall length: (station wagons and sedans, except President Classic) 202.4 inches; (President Classic) 206.4 inches; (Hawks) 204 inches. Front tread: 56.7 inches. Rear tread: 55.7 inches. Tires: (Champion except station wagon) 6.40 x 15 tubeless; (Champion station wagon, Commander and President except Classic and Golden Hawk) 6.70 x 15 tubeless; (President Classic and Golden Hawk) 7.10 x 15 tubeless.

OPTIONS: [SCOTSMAN] Hill Holder. Rear-facing third seat for station wagons. Electric windshield wipers. Extra interior sun visor. Door armrests. A simple heater/defroster was standard on the Scotsman. A radio was not a listed option for Scotsmans. [OTHER MODELS] Power steering ($98). Hill Holder. Power brakes. Air conditioning for V-8-powered sedans. Power seats. Power windows. Rear-facing third seat for station wagons (midyear option; when third seat was ordered, Captive-Air tires were fitted since there was no room for a spare tire and wheel). White sidewall tires. Stratoline push-button radio. Starline manual tuning radio. Internally controlled reel-type cowl antenna or dual rear mounted antenna. Rear seat speaker. Regular full wheel covers or imitation spoke (not wire) wheel covers. License plate frames. Exhaust extensions or Stratoline exhaust deflectors. Exterior rearview mirrors (three types). Door edge guards. Gas door guard. Door handle guard. Front bumper guards. Locking gas cap. Curb signals. Rubber floor mats or carpet toppers. Rubber splash guards. Accelerator pedal cover and wear pad. Automatic transmission Anti-Creep. Brake fluid safety reservoir. Rear door safety locks. Windshield washer. Door mounted front safety belts. Climatizer heater/defroster. Spotlight. Parking brake warning light. Glove compartment light (standard on Classic and Golden Hawk). Trunk and utility light. Underhood light. Back-up lights. Seat toppers. Electric clock. Auto compass. Traffic light viewer. Cigarette lighter (standard on Presidents and Golden Hawks). Vanity mirror (illuminated or not). Tissue dispenser. Custom luggage. Roof luggage carrier for sedans and station wagons. Station wagon air mattress. Tripod jack. Fram oil filter (standard on 289-cid V-8). Undercoating. A three-speed manual transmission with column-mounted gearshift was standard on all models, except the Golden Hawk. Overdrive or Flightomatic ($119 extra); standard on the Golden Hawk. Overdrive was available for $100 extra on all other models. Flightomatic was available for $189 extra on all models other than the Golden Hawk and Scotsman. Flightomatic was not available on the Scotsman. An optional power kit that included a four-barrel carburetor (Carter Model WCFB) and dual exhaust was available on Commander (259-cid V-8) models and W, F, C, D and P President (289-cid V-8) models. The kit increased the 259-cid V-8's power to 195 hp at 4500 rpm and the 289-cid V-8's power to 225 hp at 4500 rpm. A Twin Traction limited slip differential was optional on all models. This type of differential was pioneered on Packard cars and light Studebaker trucks in 1956. Larger tire sizes were optional on most models.

HISTORICAL FOOTNOTES: Model year sales totaled only 63,101 units. For the third year in-a-row, Studebaker was ranked 13th on the industry sales chart. The President Classic four-door sedan (Y body) was a stretched W body. The Classic had vent windows in the rear doors. Except for the Scotsman, two-door sedans were called Club Sedans. An ambulance conversion for station wagons was available. Called the Ambulet, it was available as a Champion-D8, a Commander-D8 and President-D8. Heavy-duty two-door and four-door sedans and station wagons with Custom or Deluxe trim were utilized for emergency service vehicle use. They were available with '185' six or '259' V-8 engines. Special Commander Police Cruisers with President '289' V-8s were built. They were available as two-door or four-door sedans or station wagons with Custom or Deluxe trim. They were identified as 57Hs, so they are included in the President production figures. The following were limited to export/Canadian sales: Champion-W6, P2, Commander-C3 and K3. A few heavy-duty sedans with special "breathable Naugahyde" upholstery were sold as taxis.

1958

CHAMPION AND SILVER HAWK SIX — SERIES 58G — Canted metal rear quarter panel fins on regular Champion (not Scotsman) sedans and station wagons, plus dual headlight pods (with optional dual headlights) on the same body type were the main 1958 additions. Scotsman models had restyled round taillights, Studebaker lettering on the left rear quarter panel and a square mesh radiator grille. The Silver Hawk had new grille mesh in the side grille openings and small dual fins on the front fender-mounted parking lights. A large round Hawk emblem was placed in the lower center of the central Hawk grille. A long wheelbase Scotsman four-door sedan called the "Econ-O-Miler" was introduced. Model identification was on the rear fins, except on the Silver Hawk and Scotsman. The Scotsman had no model identification and the Silver Hawk nameplate was on the deck lid.

STUDEBAKER I.D. NUMBERS: The Vehicle Identification Number is located on the left front door pillar. Champion engine numbers are on top of the left front corner of block. Commander engine numbers are on top front of cylinder block near oil filler tube mounting. [CHAMPION/SILVER HAWK SIX] The beginning serial numbers were G-1405401 (South Bend) and G-772301 (Canada). The beginning engine numbers were 1228401 (South Bend) and C-74701 (Canada). [COMMANDER AND SILVER HAWK 259] The beginning serial numbers were 8471601 (South Bend) and 8965101 (Canada). The beginning engine numbers were V-407501 (South Bend) and VC-13301 (Canada). [PRESIDENT/SILVER HAWK 289/GOLDEN HAWK] The beginning serial numbers (including Marshals) were 7210001 (South Bend) and 7902001 (Canada). The beginning serial number for Golden Hawks was 6104501 (South Bend). The beginning engine numbers for Presidents (including Marshals) and Silver Hawk 289s were P-60701 (South Bend) and PC-2001 (Canada). The beginning engine number for Golden Hawks was PS-5501 (South Bend).

CHAMPION/SILVER HAWK SERIES

Model No.	Body/Style No.	Body Type & Seating	Factory Price	Shipping Weight	Prod. Total
SCOTSMAN					
58G	F1	2-dr Sed-6P	1795	2695	5,538
58G	W1	4-dr Sed-6P	1874	2740	7,654
58G	D1	2-dr Sta Wag-6P	2055	2870	7,680
SCOTSMAN ECON-O-MILER					
58G	Y1	4-dr Sed-6P	—	3030	1,118
CHAMPION					
58G	W4	4-dr Sed-6P	2253	2835	5,178
58G	F4	2-dr Sed-6P	2189	2795	1,455
58G	J4	2-dr HT Sed-6P	—	—	120
CHAMPION DELUXE					
58G	P4	4-dr Sta Wag-6P	—	—	12
SILVER HAWK					
58G	C3	2-dr Cpe-5P	2219	2810	2,442

COMMANDER AND SILVER HAWK 259 — SERIES 58B — Styling changes and trim differences were basically the same as on Champions, except that regular Commander sedans and station wagons came with standard dual headlights. A new two-door "sedan-size hardtop" was introduced in 1958. It was called a Starlight in most publicity announcements. Model identifications were in the same location as on Champions.

COMMANDER/SILVER HAWK 259 SERIES

Model No.	Body/Style No.	Body Type & Seating	Factory Price	Shipping Weight	Prod. Total
SCOTSMAN					
58B	W1	4-dr Sed-6P	1874	2735	37
58B	F1	2-dr Sed-6P	1795	2695	44
58B	D1	2-dr Sta Wag-6P	2055	2865	7
COMMANDER					
58B	W4	4-dr Sed-6P	2378	3185	6,771
58B	J4	2-dr HT Sed-6P	2493	3270	2,555
58B	P4	4-dr Prov Sta Wag-6P	2644	3420	2,412
SILVER HAWK					
58B	C3	2-dr Cpe-5P	2219	2795	367
58B	K3	2-dr HT-5P	—	—	56

PRESIDENT AND SILVER HAWK 289 AND GOLDEN HAWK — SERIES 58H — Styling changes were the same as on Commanders. Special President-powered Scotsman police cars, called Marshals, were introduced. A belt-driven supercharger was standard on the Golden Hawk. Model identifications were in the same locations as on Commanders.

PRESIDENT/SILVER HAWK/GOLDEN HAWK SERIES

Model No.	Body/Style No.	Body Type & Seating	Factory Price	Shipping Weight	Prod. Total
MARSHAL (POLICE)					
58H	W1	4-dr Sed-6P	—	3162	115
58H	F1	2-dr Sed-6P	—	—	152
58H	D1	2-dr Sta Wag-6P	—	—	70
PRESIDENT					
58H	J6	2-dr HT Sed-6P	2695	3355	1,171
58H	P4	4-dr Del Sta Wag-6P	—	—	1
58H	Y6	4-dr Sed-6P	2639	3365	3,570
SILVER HAWK					
58H	C3	2-dr Cpe-6P	2352	3210	4,485
GOLDEN HAWK					
58H	K7	2-dr HT-5P	3282	3470	878

ENGINES:

(CHAMPION/SILVER HAWK SIX) L-head. Cast iron block. Displacement: 185.6 cid. Bore and stroke: 3 x 4-3/8 inches. Compression ratio: 7.8:1. Brake hp: 101 at 4000 rpm. Four main bearings. Solid valve lifters. Carburetor: Carter Model WE or BBR1 one-barrel.

(COMMANDER/SILVER HAWK 259 V-8) Overhead valve. Cast iron block. Displacement: 259.2 cid. Bore and stroke: 3-9/16 x 3-1/4 inches. Compression ratio: 8.3:1. Brake hp: 180 at 4500 rpm. Five main bearings. Solid valve lifters. Carburetor: Stromberg Model WW two-barrel.

(PRESIDENT/SILVER HAWK 289 V-8) Overhead valve. Cast iron block. Displacement: 289 cid. Bore and stroke: 3-9/16 x 3-5/8 inches. Compression ratio: 8.3:1. Brake hp: 225 at 4500 rpm on President J6 and Y6; 210 at 4500 rpm on all others. Five main bearings. Solid valve lifters. Carburetor: Carter Model WCFB four-barrel on President J6 and Y6; Stromberg Model WW two-barrel on all others.

(GOLDEN HAWK SUPERCHARGED V-8) Overhead valve. Cast iron block. Displacement: 289 cid. Bore and stroke: 3-9/16 x 3-5/8 inches. Compression ratio: 7.8:1. Brake hp: 275 at 4800 rpm. Five main bearings. Solid valve filters. Carburetor: Stromberg Model WW two-barrel.

CHASSIS FEATURES: Wheelbase: (station wagons and sedans except Y bodies) 116.5 inches; (Y bodies and Hawks) 120.5 inches. Overall length: (station wagons and sedans except Y bodies) 202.4 inches; (President Y6 sedan and Econ-O-Miler Y1 sedan) 206.4 inches; (Hawks) 204 inches. Front tread: (with 15-inch wheels) 57.2 Inches; (with 14-inch wheels) 57.1 inches. Rear tread: (with 15-inch wheels) 56.2 inches; (with 14-inch wheels) 56.1 inches. Tires: Champion except station wagons and Econ-O-Miler) 6.40 x 15 tubeless; (Champion station wagon, Econ-O-Miler and Commander/President with W1, F1 and D1 bodies) 6.70 x 15 tubeless; (Provincial, Golden Hawk and President Y6 sedan) 8.00 x 14 tubeless; (all others) 7.50 x 14 tubeless.

OPTIONS: [SCOTSMAN] Hill Holder ($15). Rear-facing third seat for station wagons ($102). Electric windshield wipers ($12). Chrome hubcaps. Side moldings. Chrome headlamp rims. Chrome back-up lamps. Extra sun visor. Door armrests. Gas door guard. Door handle guards. Door edge guards. [OTHER MODELS] Power steering ($69). Hill Holder ($15). Power brakes ($38). Power windows ($102). Power seats ($45). Air conditioning ($325). Rear facing third seat for station wagons ($102). When this "Hideaway" third seat was ordered, Captive-Air tires were fitted since there was no room for a spare tire and wheel. White sidewall tires ($28). Transistor push-button Signal Seeking radio. Seven-tube transistor push-button radio ($80). Manual six-tube tuning tube radio ($61). Electric cowl antenna. Reel-type internally controlled antenna. Single deck lid antenna. Dual rear antenna. Rear seat speaker ($13). Regular full wheel covers ($17). Imitation spoke (not wire) wheel covers (15-inch only). License plate frames. Imitation deck lid

1957 Studebaker, Commander Deluxe (Series 57B), sedan, AA

1957 Studebaker, President Broadmoor (Series 57H), station wagon, AA

1959 Studebaker, Lark VI Deluxe (Series 59S), station wagon, AA

1960 Studebaker, Lark VIII Custom (Series 60V), sedan, AA

1960 Studebaker, Lark VIII Regal (Series 60V), station wagon (with optional roof rack), AA

1957 Studebaker, Silver Hawk (Series 57B), coupe, AA

1958 Studebaker, President Starlight (Series 58H), hardtop, AA

1959 Studebaker, Silver Hawk (Series 59V), coupe, AA

1960 Studebaker, Lark VIII Deluxe (Series 60V), convertible, AA

1961 Studebaker, Lark VI Regal (Series 61S), hardtop, AA

continental spare tire cover. Exhaust deflectors. Exterior rearview mirrors (two types). Front bumper guards. Locking gas cap. Curb signals. Gas door guards. Door handle guards. Door edge guards. Rubber floor mats or carpet toppers. Rubber splash guards. Accelerator pedal cover and wear pad. Automatic transmission Anti-Creep. Brake fluid safety reservoir. Windshield washer ($12). Rear door safety locks. Seat belts ($25). Spotlight. Back-up lights ($8). Trunk and utility light. Parking brake warning light. Glove compartment light (standard on regular Presidents and Golden Hawks). Electric clock ($16). Auto compass. Traffic light viewer. Vanity mirror (two types). Cigarette lighter (standard on regular Presidents and Golden Hawks). Roof luggage carrier for sedans and station wagons ($60). Seat toppers. Tissue dispenser. Tripod jack. Gasoline-fired Mini-Heat engine coolant heater. Fram oil filter (standard on '289' V-8s). Undercoating. A three-speed manual transmission with column-mounted gearshift was standard on all models except the Golden Hawk. Overdrive or Flightomatic ($78 extra) was standard on the Golden Hawk. Overdrive was available for $110 extra on all other models except the Econ-O-Miler taxi. Flightomatic was available for $189 extra on all models except the Econ-O-Miler and Scotsman Champion W1, F1 and D1 models. A heavy-duty water-cooled automatic was optional on the Econ-O-Miler taxi. An optional power kit, which included a four-barrel carburetor (Carter Model WCFB) and dual exhaust, was available on Commander ('259' V-8) models and W, F, C and D President ('289' V-8) models. The kit increased the '259' V-8's power to 196 hp at 4500 rpm and the '289' V-8's power to 225 hp at 4500 rpm. Twin-Traction was optional on all models at $35-$44. Optional tire and wheel sizes were available on most models.

HISTORICAL FOOTNOTES: Model year sales continued to slide with only 44,759 units sold. The Packard portion of the Studebaker-Packard Corp. ceased production of automobiles this year. The President Y6 and Econ-O-Miler Y1 four-door sedans were stretched W bodies. They had vent windows (fixed on Econ-O-Miler) in the rear doors. Most Econ-O-Milers were sold for taxi use. A kit was sold to convert Scotsman two-door station wagons into Panel Wagons. A special Scotsman two-door sedan with no rear seat was produced. It was called the Utility Sedan. The following were limited to export/Canadian sales: Champion-J4, P4, Commander-W1, F1, C3, K3 and D1.

1959

LARK VI AND SILVER HAWK SIX — SERIES 59S — All-new Lark compact models were introduced in 1959. Except for the Silver Hawk coupe, all of the former designs were discontinued. The 1959 Econ-O-Miler long wheelbase four-door sedan was based on the Lark. The central body section of the Lark was basically the 1958 Studebaker body, but the front and back sections were drastically shortened. Deluxe models had painted headlight moldings, no grille moldings and lacked padded instrument panels. Regal Larks had chrome moldings around the grille and headlights and a padded instrument panel. On sedans and station wagons the former "Cyclops-Eye" speedometer was replaced by a normal speedometer, although the central glovebox was retained. On Silver Hawk models the parking lights were relocated in the side grille. Lark model identification was below the deck lid on sedans and on the tailgate of station wagons. The Silver Hawk identification was on the rear fins. All models were available with only single headlights. The two-tone paint option was discontinued on everything except fleet cars.

STUDEBAKER I.D. NUMBERS: The Vehicle Identification Numbers were on the left front door hinge pillar. Six-cylinder engine numbers are on a pad at upper part of left-hand side of block. V-8 engine numbers are on a pad at upper left front of block. [LARK VI/SILVER HAWK SIX] The beginning serial numbers were 59S-1001 (South Bend) and 59SC-1001 (Canada). The beginning engine numbers were S-10001 (South Bend) and SC-10001 (Canada). [LARK VIII/SILVER HAWK V-8] The beginning serial numbers were 59V-1001 (South Bend) and 59VC-1001 (Canada). The beginning engine numbers were V-418701 (South Bend) and VC-14701 (Canada). Engines were stamped with a prefix followed by a production sequence number. Prefixes identified the engine as follows: S=six-cylinder; V=259-cid V-8; P=289-cid V-8.

LARK VI/SILVER HAWK SIX SERIES

Model No.	Body/Style No.	Body Type & Seating	Factory Price	Shipping Weight	Prod. Total
ECON-O-MILER					
59S	Y1	4-dr Sed-6P	—	2870	1,033
DELUXE					
59S	D4	2-dr Sta Wag-6P	2295	2805	13,227
59S	F4	2-dr Sed-6P	1925	2577	33,259
59S	W4	4-dr Sed-6P	1995	2605	26,566
REGAL					
59S	W6	4-dr Sed-6P	2175	2600	11,898
59S	J6	2-dr HT-6P	2275	2710	7,075
59S	D6	2-dr Sta Wag-6P	2455	2815	5,685
SILVER HAWK					
59S	C6	2-dr Cpe-6P	2360	2795	2,417

LARK VIII AND SILVER HAWK V-8 — SERIES 59V — Body style offerings and trim differences were the same as Series 59S models. Model identifications were also in the same locations. The 59V Deluxe models were limited to special order sales, Marshal sales, fleet sales and sales outside the United States. Both Lark VI and VIII models featured a black background Hawk emblem in the grille and on the tailgate of station wagons.

LARK VIII AND SILVER HAWK V-8 SERIES

Model No.	Body/Style No.	Body Type & Seating	Factory Price	Shipping Weight	Prod. Total
ECON-O-MILER					
59V	Y1	4-dr Sed-6P	—	3225	92
DELUXE					
59V	W4	4-dr Sed-6P	—	2925	1,367
59V	F4	2-dr Sed-6P	—	2899	550
59V	D4	2-dr Sta Wag-6P	—	3138	378
REGAL					
59V	W6	4-dr Sed-6P	2310	2924	14,530
59V	J6	2-dr HT-6P	2410	3034	7,996
59V	D6	2-dr Sta Wag-6P	2590	3148	7,419
SILVER HAWK					
59V	C6	2-dr Cpe-6P	2495	3140	5,371

ENGINES:

(LARK VI/SILVER HAWK SIX) L-head. Cast iron block. Displacement: 169.6 cid. Bore and stroke: 3 x 4 inches. Compression ratio: 8.3:1. Brake hp: 90 at 4000 rpm. Four main bearings. Solid valve lifters. Carburetor: Carter Model AS one-barrel.

(LARK VIII/SILVER HAWK V-8) Overhead valve. Cast iron block. Displacement: 259.2 cid. Bore and stroke: 3-9/16 x 3-1/4 inches. Compression ratio: 8.8:1. Brake hp: 180 at 4500 rpm. Five main bearings. Solid valve lifters. Carburetor: Stromberg Model WW two-barrel.

CHASSIS FEATURES: Wheelbase: (hardtop and sedans except Y1) 108.5 inches; (station wagons and Econ-O-Miler Y1) 113 inches; (Silver Hawk) 120.5 inches. Overall length: (hardtop and sedans except Y1) 175 inches; (station wagons) 184.5 inches; (Econ-O-Miler Y1) 179 inches; (Silver Hawk) 204 inches. Front tread: 57.4 inches. Rear tread: 56.6 inches. Tires: (Lark VI) 5.90 x 15 tubeless; (Lark VIII/Silver Hawk six and Econ-O-Miler six) 6.40 x 15 tubeless; (Silver Hawk V-8 and Econ-O-Miler V-8) 6.70 x 15 tubeless.

OPTIONS: Power steering for Series 59V models ($74). Air conditioning ($325). Power brakes ($38). Hill Holder ($15). Full reclining front seats ($26-$38). Rear facing third seat for station wagons ($124). When the "Hideaway" seat was ordered, Captive-Air tires were fitted, since there was no room for a spare tire and wheel. White sidewall tires. Tinted glass ($32). Transistor push-button Signal Seeking radio ($101). Transistor push-button radio ($80). Manual tuning tube radio ($61). Internally controlled reel-type crown antenna ($10). Single deck lid antenna ($9). Dual rear antenna ($17). Rear seat speaker ($13). Imitation deck lid continental spare tire cover. Exhaust deflectors. Exterior rearview mirrors (three types) ($5 and up). License plate frames. Bumper guards ($10). Gas door guards. Door handle guards. Locking gas cap. Rubber splash guards. Rubber front floor mats. Accelerator pedal cover and wear pad. Regular full wheel covers ($17). Imitation spoke (not wire) wheel covers. Windshield washer, manual ($9); electric ($12). Seat belts. Rear door safety locks. Compressed CO^2 can for fire fighting or tire inflation. Back-up lights. Spotlight. Glove compartment light. Electric clock. Tachometer for Silver Hawk V-8. Vanity mirror. Traffic light viewer. Cigarette lighter. Tissue dispenser. Touch-up paint applicator. Station wagon luggage carrier ($31). Tripod jack. Ice scraper and squeegee. Clear plastic seat covers. Climatizer heater/defroster. Undercoating. Oil filter. Special options for Deluxe models: Rear armrests. Second sun visor. Two-tone steering wheel with horn ring. Padded instrument panel. A Regal exterior trim kit was available for the Econ-O-Miler. A three-speed manual transmission with column-mounted gearshift was standard on all models. Overdrive was available for $110 extra on all models except the Econ-O-Miler taxi. Flightomatic was available for $200 extra on all models except the Econ-O-Miler. A heavy-duty water-cooled automatic was optional on the Econ-O-Miler taxi at $220. An optional power kit, which included a four-barrel carburetor (Carter Model WCFB) and dual exhaust, was available on all V-8s at $48 extra. The kit increased the '259' V-8's power to 195 hp at 4500 rpm. Twin-Traction was optional on all models at $35. Other tire sizes were optional. Lower compression ratios were available for exported cars.

HISTORICAL FOOTNOTES: Model year sales soared to 126,156 helping Studebaker to reach 10th on the industry sales chart. The Econ-O-Miler Y1 four-door sedan was a stretched W body. It had non-functional rear door vent windows. Most were sold as taxis, although some were sold outside the United States for private use. A kit was sold to convert Lark station wagons to Panel Wagons. A special Lark two-door sedan without a rear seat was offered. It was called the Utility Sedan.

1960

LARK VI AND HAWK SIX — SERIES 60S — The Lark styling was only slightly changed from 1959. A Lark emblem with a red background replaced the Hawk emblem used in the grille and on the station wagon tailgate. Mesh, instead of horizontal bars, was used in the small side grilles. Exterior trim differences between DeLuxe and Regal models were basically the same as in 1959. New in 1960 was a Lark convertible and a Lark four-door station wagon. The Econ-O-Miler was continued as a long-wheelbase, heavy-duty four-door sedan with Lark styling. The 'Silver' name was dropped from the Hawk's title. Hawks had imitation louvers on the front edge of the fins and red background Hawk emblems. The Hawk six was sold only outside North America. Lark model identification was on the back and also on the front fenders. The Hawk nameplate was on the rear fins.

STUDEBAKER I.D. NUMBERS: The Vehicle Identification Number is stamped on a plate on the left front door pillar. First two symbols indicate model year: 60=1960. Third symbol indicates engine: S=six-cylinder (169 cid); V=V-8 (259 cid); P=V-8 (289 cid). Fourth symbol (used on Canadian-built cars only) is a C for Canada. Following symbols indicate the production sequence at the assembly plant. Six-cylinder engine numbers located on a pad at upper left-hand front side of block. V-8 engine numbers located on a pad at upper left-hand front side of block. Engine numbers carried the engine codes as a prefix, followed by production sequence number. [LARK VI/HAWK SIX) Starting serial numbers were 60S-1001 (South Bend) and 60SC-1001 (Canada). The beginning engine numbers were S-106001 (South Bend) and SC-15501 (Canada). [LARK VIII/HAWK V-8]. Starting serial numbers were 60V-1001 (South Bend) and 60VC-1001 (Canada). The beginning 259-cid engine numbers were V-454701 (South Bend) and VC-16701 (Canada). The beginning 289-cid engine numbers were P-70501 (South Bend) and PC-2201 (Canada). Studebaker also attached a Body Number Plate to the cowl below the hood. It carried the company name, VIN (serial number), series code (first column of charts below), the Body/Style Number (second column of charts below), plus one of many interior trim codes too numerous to list here.

LARK VI/HAWK SIX SERIES

Model No.	Body/Style No.	Body Type & Seating	Factory Price	Shipping Weight	Prod. Total
ECON-O-MILER					
60S	Y1	4-dr Sed-6P	2393	2930	1,096
DELUXE					
60S	F4	2-dr Sed-6P	1976	2588	24,605
60S	W4	4-dr Sed-6P	2046	2592	22,534
60S	D4	2-dr Sta Wag-6P	2366	2763	3,497
60S	P4	4-dr Sta Wag-6P	2441	2792	5,420
REGAL					
60S	P6	4-dr Sta Wag-6P	2591	2836	1,925
60S	L6	2-dr Conv-6P	2621	2961	3,107
60S	J6	2-dr HT-6P	2296	2697	2,829
HAWK					
60S	C6	2-dr Cpe-6P	2383	2770	227

LARK VIII AND HAWK V-8 — SERIES 60V — Body style offerings and trim differences were the same as on Series 60S models. Model identifications were also in the same locations. The Hawk V-8 came standard with a 289-cid engine in the United States and Canada. For other countries, it came standard with a 259-cid engine. The '289' was optional on Hawk models in most of these countries.

LARK VIII/HAWK V-8 SERIES

Model No.	Body/Style No.	Body Type & Seating	Factory Price	Shipping Weight	Prod. Total
ECON-O-MILER					
60V	Y1	4-dr Sed-6P	2430	3225	215
DELUXE					
60V	F4	2-dr Sed-6P	2111	2921	8,102
60V	W4	4-dr Sed-6P	2181	2941	14,231
60V	D4	2-dr Sta Wag-6P	2501	3138	1,734
60V	P4	4-dr Sta Wag-6P	2576	3161	5,711
REGAL					
60V	W6	4-dr Sed-6P	2331	2966	11,410
60V	J6	2-dr HT-6P	2431	3033	4,565
60V	P6	4-dr Sta Wag-6P	2726	3183	5,741
60V	L6	2-dr Conv-6P	2756	3315	5,464
HAWK					
60V	C6	2-dr Cpe-6P	2650	3207	4,280

ENGINES:

(LARK VI/HAWK SIX) L-head. Cast iron block. Displacement: 169.6 cid. Bore and stroke: 3 x 4 inches. Compression ratio: 8.3:1. Brake hp: 90 at 4000 rpm. Four main bearings. Solid valve lifters. Carburetor: Carter Model AS one-barrel.

(LARK VIII/HAWK 259 V-8) Overhead valve. Cast iron block. Displacement: 259.2 cid. Bore and stroke. 3-9/16 x 3-1/4 inches. Compression ratio: 8.8:1. Brake hp: 180 at 4500 rpm. Five main bearings. Solid valve lifters. Carburetor: Stromberg Model WW two-barrel.

(HAWK 289 V-8) Overhead valve. Cast iron block. Displacement: 289 cid. Bore and stroke: 3-9/16 x 3-5/8 inches. Compression ratio: 8.8:1. Brake hp: 210 at 4500 rpm. Five main bearings. Solid valve lifters. Carburetor: Stromberg Model WW two-barrel.

CHASSIS FEATURES: Wheelbase: (hardtop, convertible and sedans except Y1) 108.5 inches; (station wagons and Econ-O-Miler Y1) 113 inches; (Hawk) 120.5 inches. Overall length: (hardtop, convertible and sedans except Y1) 175 inches; (station wagons) 184.5 inches; (Econ-O-Miler) 179 inches; (Hawk) 204 inches. Front tread: 57.4 inches. Rear tread: 56.6 inches. Tires: (Lark VI except convertible) 5.90 x 15 tubeless; (Lark VIII except convertible, Lark VI convertible, Hawk six and Econ-O-Miler six) 6.40 x 15 tubeless; (Hawk V-8, Lark VIII convertible and Econ-O-Miler V-8) 6.70 x 15 tubeless.

OPTIONS: Power steering for Series 60V models ($75). Air conditioning ($325). Power brakes ($38). Hill Holder ($15). Full reclining front seats ($26-$38). Headrests for reclining seats ($12). Individually adjustable front seats ($15). Rear facing third seat for station wagons ($124). When the Hideaway third seat was ordered, Captive-Air tires were fitted since there was no room for a spare tire and wheel. White sidewall tires ($28-$48). Tinted glass ($32). Transistor push-button radio ($64). Manual tuning tube radio ($57). Internally controlled reel-type cowl antenna ($10). Rear seat speaker ($13). Lark hood ornament. Bumper guards ($10). License plate frames. Station wagon cargo mat. Rubber splash guards. Exhaust deflector. Locking gas cap. Door handle guards. Regular full wheel covers ($16). Imitation spoke (not wire) wheel covers. Exterior rearview mirror (two types). Rubber front floor mats. Windshield washer (manual or electric) ($11). Front and rear seat belts. Rear door safety locks. Back-up lights. glovebox light. Spotlight. Electric clock. Tachometer for Hawk V-8 ($38). Station wagon luggage carrier ($54). Cigarette lighter ($4). Tissue dispenser. Cushion toppers. Clear plastic seat covers. Touch-up paint applicators. Climatizer heater/defroster ($71). Fram oil filter (standard on Hawk V-8) ($10). Gas line filter. Padded sun visors. Undercoating ($20). Special options for Deluxe models: Rear armrests. Second sun visor ($8). Padded instrument panel ($15). Two-tone steering wheel with horn ring ($7). Regal exterior trim kit (also available for Econ-O-Miler) ($36). A three-speed manual transmission with column-mounted gearshift was standard on all models. Overdrive was available for $110 extra on all models except the Econ-O-Miler taxi. Except for the Econ-O-Miler taxi, Flightomatic was available for $179 extra on six-cylinder models and $200 extra on V-8 models. A heavy-duty water-cooled automatic was optional on the Econ-O-Miler taxi and Marshals. An optional power kit, which included a four-barrel carburetor (Carter WCFB) and dual exhaust (except for the Hawk '289' V-8, which came standard with dual exhaust), was available on all V-8s for $44.95 extra. The kit increased the '259' V-8's power to 195 hp at 4500 rpm and the '289' V-8's power to 225 hp at 4500 rpm. Twin-Traction was optional on all models. Other tire sizes were optional on most models. Lower compression ratios were available for exported cars. A few Larks, mainly police Marshals, were special ordered with 289-cid V-8s.

HISTORICAL FOOTNOTES: Calendar year production of Studebakers amounted to 105,902. The Econ-O-Miler Y1 four-door sedan was a stretched W body. It had nonfunctional rear door vent windows. Most were sold as taxis, although some were sold outside the United States for private use. A kit was sold for $34.97 to convert two-door Lark station wagons into Panel Wagons. A special Lark two-door sedan with no rear seat was offered. It was called the Utility Sedan. Six-cylinder and V-8 Lark Marshals were available with W, F, Y, D and P bodies.

1961

LARK VI AND HAWK SIX — SERIES 61S — The Lark was slightly restyled in 1961. Regal models had standard dual headlights. Single headlights were standard on Deluxe models, although duals were an option. Rocker panel moldings were standard on Regal models. Rubber windshield and rear window moldings were standard on Deluxe models, although Regal stainless steel moldings were optional. Side trim on all Lark-related models, except the regular Y1 (heavy-duty, long-wheelbase four-door sedan) ran above the natural front fender contour line. The Y1 did not have side moldings as standard, although they were an option. A new Regal version of the Y body was introduced. It was called the Lark Cruiser and was marketed for private ownership. The six-cylinder Cruiser was only marketed outside North America. An extra fin-type trim molding and color band was added to the Hawk. The Hawk six was also sold only outside of North America. Lark model identification was on the back and also on the front fenders. The Hawk nameplate was on the rear fins. The six-cylinder engine was converted to overhead valves.

STUDEBAKER I.D. NUMBERS: The Vehicle Identification Number is stamped on a plate on the left front door pillar. First two symbols indicate model year: 61=1961. Third symbol indicates engine: S=six-cylinder (169 cid); V=V-8 (259 cid); P=V-8 (289 cid). Fourth symbol (used on Canadian-built cars only) was a C for Canada. Following symbols indicate the production sequence at the assembly plant. Six-cylinder engine numbers are on a pad at upper left-hand front side of block. V-8 engine numbers are on a pad at upper left-hand front side of block. Engine numbers carried the engine codes as a prefix, followed by production sequence number. [LARK VI/HAWK SIX]. Starting serial numbers were 61S-1001 (South Bend) and 61SC-1001 (Canada). The beginning engine numbers were S-172601 (South Bend) and SC-20101 (Canada). [LARK VIII/HAWK V-8]. Starting serial numbers were 61V-1001 (South Bend) and 61VC-1001 (Canada). The beginning 259-cid engine numbers were V-510401 (South Bend) and VC-18501 (Canada). The beginning 289-cid engine numbers were P-74701 (South Bend) and PC-2501 (Canada). Studebaker also attached a Body Number Plate to the cowl below the hood. It carried the company name, VIN (serial number), series code (first column of charts below), the Body/Style Number (second column of charts below), plus one of many interior trim codes too numerous to list here.

LARK VI/HAWK SIX SERIES

Model No.	Body/Style No.	Body Type & Seating	Factory Price	Shipping Weight	Prod. Total
HEAVY-DUTY					
61S	Y1	4-dr Sed-6P	2252	2943	1,108
DELUXE					
61S	F4	2-dr Sed-6P	1935	2661	12,571
61S	W4	4-dr Sed-6P	2005	2665	15,891
61S	D4	2-dr Sta Wag-6P	2290	2836	1,210
61S	P4	4-dr Sta Wag-6P	2370	2865	2,924
REGAL					
61S	W6	4-dr Sed-6P	2155	2692	3,802
61S	J6	2-dr HT-6P	2243	2770	1,870
61S	P6	4-dr Sta Wag-6P	2520	2870	693
61S	L6	2-dr Conv-6P	2554	3034	979
61S	Y6	4-dr Cruiser Sed-6P	—	—	24
HAWK					
61S	C6	2-dr Cpe-6P	—	—	266

LARK VIII AND HAWK V-8 — SERIES 61V — Body type and exterior trim selections were the same as the Series 61S models. Model identifications were also in the same locations. All Larks had a new instrument panel with the glove compartment on the far right. All left-hand drive Larks had swing brake and clutch (if fitted) pedals. The Hawk V-8 came standard with a 289-cid engine in the United States and Canada. For other countries, it came standard with a 259-cid engine. The '289' was optional in most of these countries.

LARK VIII/HAWK V-8 SERIES

Model No.	Body/Style No.	Body Type & Seating	Factory Price	Shipping Weight	Prod. Total
HEAVY-DUTY					
61V	Y1	4-dr Sed-6P	2389	3225	222
DELUXE					
61V	F4	2-dr Sed-6P	2070	2921	2,003
61V	W4	4-dr Sed-6P	2140	2941	7,343
61V	D4	2-dr Sta Wag-6P	2425	3112	1,177
61V	P4	4-dr Sta Wag-6P	2505	3161	1,815
REGAL					
61V	W6	4-dr Sed-6P	2290	2966	3,202
61V	J6	2-dr HT-6P	2378	3034	1,666
61V	P6	4-dr Sta Wag-6P	2655	3166	1,851
61V	L6	2-dr Conv-6P	2689	3315	1,002
61V	Y6	4-dr Cruiser-6P	2458	3001	5,232
HAWK					
61V	C6	2-dr Cpe-6P	2650	3207	3,663

ENGINES:

(LARK VI/HAWK SIX) Overhead valve. Cast iron block. Displacement: 169.6 cid. Bore and stroke: 3 x 4 inches. Compression ratio: 8.5:1. Brake hp: 112 at 4500 rpm. Four main bearings. Solid valve lifters. Carburetor: Carter Model AS one-barrel.

(LARK VIII/HAWK 259 V-8) Overhead valve. Cast iron block. Displacement: 259.2 cid. Bore and stroke: 3-9/16 x 3-1/4 inches. Compression ratio: 8.8:1. Brake hp: 180 at 4500 rpm. Five main bearings. Solid valve lifters. Carburetor: Stromberg Model WW two-barrel.

(LARK/PURSUIT MARSHAL/HAWK 289 V-8) Overhead valve. Cast iron block. Displacement: 289 cid. Bore and stroke: 3-9/16 x 3-5/8 inches. Compression ratio: 8.8:1. Brake hp: 210 at 4500 rpm. Five main bearings. Solid valve lifters. Carburetor: Stromberg Model WW two-barrel.

CHASSIS FEATURES: Wheelbase: (hardtop, convertible and sedans except Y bodies) 108.5 inches; (station wagons and Y bodies) 113 inches; (Hawk) 120.5 inches. Overall length: (hardtop, convertible and sedans except Y bodies) 175 inches; (station wagons) 184.5 inches; (Y bodies, Cruiser and Heavy-Duty sedan) 179 inches; (Hawk) 204 inches. Front tread: 57.4 inches. Rear Tread: 56.6 inches. Tires: (Lark VI except convertible) 6.00 x 15 tubeless; (Lark VIII except convertible, Lark VI convertible, Hawk six and Heavy-Duty sedan six) 6.50 x 15 tubeless; (Hawk V-8, Lark VIII convertible and Heavy-Duty sedan V-8) 6.70 x 15 tubeless.

OPTIONS: Power steering ($75). Air conditioning ($278-$325). Skytop sun roof ($185). Power brakes ($38). Hill Holder ($15). Full reclining front seats ($25-$47). Headrests for reclining seats ($12). Individually adjusted front seats (standard on North American Hawks) ($13-$35). Rear facing third seat for station wagons ($124 including Captive-Air tires and no spare). White sidewall tires ($28-$49). Tinted glass ($32). Transistor push-button radio ($64-$66). Manual tuning radio ($59). Internally controlled reel-type cowl antenna (now included with higher radio price). Rear seat speaker ($13). Lark hood ornament. Bumper guards ($10). Exterior rearview mirror (two types) ($5). Rubber splash guards. Exhaust deflectors. Locking gas cap. Rubber station wagon cargo mat. Rubber floor mats. License plate frames. Regular full wheel covers ($16). Imitation spoke (not wire) wheel covers. Front and rear seat belts ($13). Rear door safety locks. Windshield washer ($12). Automatic transmission Anti-Creep. Cushion toppers. Clear plastic seat covers. Tissue dispenser. Station wagon luggage rack ($54). Cigarette lighter (standard on Regal models) ($4). Electric clock (standard on Cruiser) ($16). Tachometer for Hawk V-8 ($54). Back-up lights. Glove compartment light. Spotlight. Climatizer heater/defroster ($71). Oil filter ($4 on some '289' V-8s; $10 on other V-8 models). Gas line filter. Touch-up paint applicators. Padded sun visors. Undercoating. Special options for Deluxe models: Regal windshield and rear window moldings ($20-$33). Dual headlights ($24). Rear ashtray. Second sun visor. Rear armrests. A Regal exterior trim kit was optional on Heavy-Duty sedans ($150). A three-speed manual transmission with column-mounted gearshift was standard on all models. Overdrive was available for $110 extra on all models except the Heavy-Duty sedan. Except for the Heavy-Duty sedan and Marshal, Flightomatic was available for $165 extra on six-cylinder models and $200 extra on V-8 models. A heavy-duty water-cooled automatic was optional on the Heavy-Duty sedan and Marshal. A new four-speed transmission with floor-mounted gearshift was optional on the Hawk V-8 at $188 extra. An optional four-barrel carburetor (Carter WCFB) was available for all V-8s at $21.52. The four-barrel increased the '259' V-8's power to 195 hp at 4500 rpm and the '289' V-8's power to 225 hp at 4500 rpm. The '259' V-8 dual exhaust kit was a separate $23.43 option. Dual exhaust were standard on '289' V-8 models. The '289' V-8 was optional on the Cruiser. The "Cruise" package included the 289-cid V-8, No. 44 axle, finned brake drums, heavy-duty radiator, oil filter and dual exhaust. Twin-Traction was optional on all models at $38.93. Other tire sizes were optional on most models. Lower compression ratios were available for export cars.

HISTORICAL FOOTNOTES: Calendar year production totaled 78,664 units. The Heavy-Duty sedan (Y1) and Lark Cruiser (Y6) featured stretched W bodies. They had rear door vent windows (not functional on Y1). Most domestic Heavy-Duty sedans were sold as taxis, although some were sold outside the United States for private use. A kit was sold, for $34.97, to convert two-door Lark station wagons to Panel Wagons. A special Lark two-door sedan with no rear seat was offered. It was called the Utility Sedan. Six-cylinder and V-8 Lark Marshals were available with W, F, Y, D and P bodies. The six-cylinder model was the City Marshal, the '259' V-8 was the Patrol Marshal and the '289' V-8 was the Pursuit Marshal. A limited production Studebaker Hawk, called the "Gran Turismo" and featuring a four-barrel carbureted V-8 coupled to a four-speed transmission as well as a dash plaque with the owner's name engraved on it, was offered (this model should not be confused with the Gran Turismo Hawks offered 1962-1964).

1962

LARK SIX AND GRAN TURISMO HAWK SIX — SERIES 62S — The Lark models were again restyled. Dual headlights were made standard on all Lark-type vehicles. Larks had round taillights. Regular Deluxe models had only rubber moldings around the windshield and rear windows. Regal models had stainless steel windshield and rear window moldings. The new Daytona hardtop and convertible models had special wide side moldings with the name Daytona on them. All four-door sedans used the long wheelbase Y body, although the Cruiser was the only one with rear door vent windows. Heavy-Duty Lark police and severe service four-door sedan, two-door sedan and four-door station wagon models were given their own model identifications. The two-door station wagon was discontinued. The new Gran Turismo Hawk had a squared roofline, no fins, and rocker panel moldings. The six-cylinder Gran Turismo Hawk and six-cylinder Cruiser were only sold outside North America. Lark and Cruiser nameplates were on the front fenders. On Hawks, the "Hawk" name was on the deck lid and the "Gran Turismo" script was on the doors.

STUDEBAKER I.D. NUMBERS: The Vehicle Identification Number is stamped on a plate on the left front door pillar. First two symbols indicate model year: 62=1962. Third symbol indicates engine: S=six-cylinder (169 cid); V=V-8 (259 cid); P=V-8 (289 cid). Fourth symbol (used on Canadian-built cars only) was a C for Canada. Following symbols indicate the production sequence at the assembly plant. Six-cylinder engine numbers located on a pad at upper left-hand front side of block. V-8 engine numbers located on a pad at upper left-hand front side of block. Engine numbers carried the engine codes as a prefix, followed by production sequence number. [LARK SIX/GT HAWK SIX] Starting serial numbers were 62S-1001 (South Bend) and 62SC-1001 (Canada). The beginning engine numbers were S-210901 (South Bend) and SC-24301 (Canada). [LARK EIGHT/GT HAWK V-8] Starting serial numbers were 62V-1001 (South Bend) and 62VF-1001 (Canada). The beginning 259-cid engine numbers were V-534910 (South Bend) and VC-19601 (Canada). The beginning 289-cid engine numbers were P-79801 (South Bend) and PC-2801 (Canada). Studebaker also attached a Body Number Plate to the cowl below the hood. It carried the company name, VIN (serial number), series code (first column of charts below) the Body/Style Number (second column of charts below), plus one of many interior trim codes too numerous to list here.

LARK/GRAN TURISMO HAWK SIXES

Model No.	Body/Style No.	Body Type & Seating	Factory Price	Shipping Weight	Prod. Total
TAXI					
62S	Y1	4-dr Taxi-6P	—	2970	Note 1
HEAVY-DUTY					
62S	F3	2-dr Sed-6P	—	2765	Note 1
62S	Y3	4-dr Sed-6P	—	2830	Note 1
62S	P3	4-dr Sta Wag-6P	—	2935	Note 1
DELUXE					
62S	Y4	4-dr Sed-6P	2040	2765	Note 1
62S	F4	2-dr Sed-6P	1935	2655	Note 1
62S	P4	4-dr Sta Wag-6P	2405	3000	Note 1
REGAL					
62S	Y6	4-dr Sed-6P	2190	2765	Note 1
62S	J6	2-dr HT-6P	2218	2765	Note 1
62S	P6	4-dr Sta Wag-6P	2555	3000	Note 1
62S	L6	2-dr Conv-6P	2589	3075	Note 1
DAYTONA					
62S	J8	2-dr HT-5P	2308	2765	Note 1
62S	L8	2-dr Conv-5P	2679	3075	Note 1
62S	Y8	4-dr Cruiser-6P	—	—	Note 1
GRAN TURISMO HAWK					
62S	K6	2-dr HT-5P	—	—	Note 1

NOTE 1: Complete production total breakouts are not available. The following figures are for both six-cylinder and V-8 models: (four-door sedans, except taxi) 49,961; (Style F two-door sedans) 19,196; (Style K Grand Turismo Hawk) 9,335; (Style J two-door hardtop coupe) 8,480; (Style P four-door station wagons) 10,522; (Style L convertibles) 2,681 and (Style Y1 taxicab) 2,212.

LARK V-8 AND GRAN TURISMO HAWK V-8 — SERIES 62V — Body type and exterior trim selections were the same as for Series 62S models. Eight-cylinder Lark sedans, hardtops and convertibles had V-8 emblems on the rear deck lid. Other model identifications were the same as on the Series 62S models. The Gran Turismo Hawk V-8 came standard with a 289-cid engine in the United States and Canada. For most other countries it came standard with a 259-cid engine. The '289' was optional in many of these countries.

LARK/GRAN TURISMO HAWK V-8S

Model No.	Body/Style No.	Body Type & Seating	Factory Price	Shipping Weight	Prod. Total
TAXI					
62V	Y1	4-dr Taxi-6P	—	3170	Note 1
HEAVY-DUTY					
62V	F3	2-dr Sed-6P	—	3005	Note 1
62V	Y3	4-dr Sed-6P	—	3070	Note 1
62V	P3	4-dr Sta Wag-6P	—	3175	Note 1
DELUXE					
62V	F4	2-dr Sed-6P	2070	2925	Note 1
62V	Y4	4-dr Sed-6P	2175	3020	Note 1
62V	P4	4-dr Sta Wag-6P	2540	3130	Note 1
REGAL					
62V	Y6	4-dr Sed-6P	2325	3020	Note 1
62V	J6	2-dr HT-6P	2353	3015	Note 1
62V	P6	4-dr Sta Wag-6P	2690	3130	Note 1
62V	L6	2-dr Conv-6P	2724	3305	Note 1
LARK DAYTONA					
62V	J8	2-dr HT-5P	2443	3015	Note 1
62V	L8	2-dr Conv-5P	2814	3305	Note 1
62V	Y8	4-dr Cruiser-6P	2493	3030	Note 1
GRAN TURISMO HAWK					
62V	K6	2-dr HT-5P	3095	3280	Note 1

NOTE 1: See Lark/Gran Turismo Hawk Six production note.

ENGINES:

(LARK/GRAN TURISMO HAWK SIX) Overhead valve. Cast iron block. Displacement: 169.6 cid. Bore and stroke: 3 x 4 inches. Compression ratio: 8.25:1. Brake hp: 112 at 4500 rpm. Four main bearings. Solid valve lifters. Carburetor: Carter Model AS one-barrel.

(LARK/GRAN TURISMO HAWK 259 V-8) Overhead valve. Cast iron block. Displacement: 259.2 cid. Bore and stroke: 3-9/16 x 3-1/4 inches. Compression ratio: 8.5:1. Brake hp: 180 at 4500 rpm. Five main bearings. Carburetor: Stromberg Model WW two-barrel.

(GRAN TURISMO HAWK/LARK PURSUIT MARSHAL 289 V-8) Cast iron block. Displacement: 289 cid. Bore and stroke: 3-9/16 x 3-5/8 inches. Compression ratio: 8.5:1. Brake hp: 210 at 4500 rpm. Five main bearings. Solid valve lifters. Carburetor: Stromberg Model WW two-barrel.

CHASSIS FEATURES: Wheelbase: (Lark hardtop, convertible and two-door sedans) 109 inches; (station wagons and four-door sedans) 113 inches; (Gran Turismo Hawk) 120.5 inches. Overall length: (Lark hardtop, convertible and two-door sedans) 184 inches; (four-door sedans) 188 inches; (station wagons) 187 inches; (Gran Turismo Hawk) 204 inches. Front tread: 57.4 inches. Rear tread: 56.6 inches. Tires: (Lark six except convertible) 6.00 x 15 tubeless; (Lark V-8 except convertible; Lark six convertible, GT Hawk six and taxi six) 6.50 x 15 tubeless; (GT Hawk V-8, Lark V-8 convertible and taxi V-8) 6.70 x 15 tubeless.

OPTIONS: Power steering ($77). Air conditioning ($278-$325). Skytop sun roof ($185). Power brakes ($42). Hill Holder (as in all years, available only for standard transmission with or without overdrive) ($15). Full reclining front seats ($26-$38). Head rests for reclining seats. Individually adjusted front seats (standard on North American GT Hawks and Lark Daytonas). Rear facing third seat for station wagons (including Captive-Air tires and no spare) ($124). White sidewall tires ($29-$49). Tinted glass ($32). All transistor push-button radio ($65-$69). Transistor manual tuning radio ($57-$62). Internally controlled reel-type cowl antenna (radio prices include antenna options). Rear seat speaker ($13). Lark Winguards (bumper extensions). Bumper guards (front and rear on Lark; front only on Hawk) ($10 each pair). Full wheel covers ($16). Rubber splash guards. Electric clock ($16). Exterior rearview mirror (two types) ($5). License plate frames. Locking gas cap. Door handle guards. Rubber front floor mats. Exhaust deflector. Seat belts ($12 each). Windshield washer ($12). Automatic transmission Anti-Creep. Rear door safety locks. Lark cushion toppers. Lark clear plastic seat covers. Padded sun visors ($58). Cigarette lighter for Deluxe models ($4). Tissue dispenser. Visor vanity mirror. Door utility packet (regular Lark models). Station wagon luggage rack ($40). Station wagon cargo mat. Station wagon rear deck cushion. Spotlight. Glove compartment light. Underhood light. Trunk light. Back-up lights for Deluxe models ($7). Climatizer heater/defroster. Oil filter (standard on '289' V-8 models) ($10). Fuel line filter. Touch-up paint applicators. Undercoating ($24). Regal trim kits for Deluxe, Heavy-Duty and taxi models. Special options for the Gran Turismo Hawk: Rear deck lid radio antenna ($59 with manual radio; $67 with push-button radio). Air-Flo or Aero strut wheel covers. Tachometer for V-8 models ($54). A three-speed manual transmission with column-mounted gearshift was standard on all models. Overdrive was available for $110 extra on all models except the taxi. Except for the taxi and Marshals, Flightomatic was available for $172 extra on six-cylinder models and $200 extra on V-8 models. A heavy-duty water-cooled automatic was optional on the taxi and Marshal models. A four-speed transmission with floor-mounted gearshift was optional on the Hawk V-8 and Lark Daytona V-8 for $188 extra. An optional four-barrel carburetor (Carter WCFB) was available for all V-8s at $22 extra. The four-barrel increased the '259' V-8's power to 195 hp at 4500 rpm and the '289' V-8's power to 225 hp at 4500 rpm. The '259' V-8 dual exhaust kit was a separate option at $23. Dual exhaust were standard on '289' V-8 models. The '289' V-8 was optional on all

Lark Series 62V models. Twin-Traction was optional on all models at $39. Other tire sizes were optional on most models. Lower compression ratios were available for export cars.

HISTORICAL FOOTNOTES: On April 26, 1962, the Packard half of the Studebaker-Packard Corp. name was dropped and the company was once again known as Studebaker Corp. Calendar year production totaled 102,387 units. A Studebaker Lark Daytona convertible was the official pace car of the Indianapolis 500-Mile race this year. Special Heavy-Duty W3, Y3 and P3 models were available for rural route mail carriers. Called the Rural Route Lark they offered some interesting options such as right-hand drive and Signal-Stat warning lights. The Lark Marshals were also based on the Heavy-Duty W3, Y3 and P3 models. The six-cylinder model was called the City Marshal, the '259' V-8 model the Patrol Marshal and the '289' V-8 model the Pursuit Marshal.

1963

SIX-CYLINDER — SERIES 63S — In 1963, the Lark-type Studebakers were only slightly restyled, but some major changes were made in their model identification. To give the Cruiser more identity, it was no longer classified as a Lark. The Regal, which for years had been a top-line model, was dropped down a notch. The Custom, which was once a low-priced trim offering, took over the former Regal position. The Daytona line was expanded to include the highest-priced version of the new sliding roof Wagonaire four-door station wagon. Then, in midyear, a bare bones Studebaker line called the Standard was introduced as Studebaker's new low-priced offering. The Standard had no side moldings. The Regal had one narrow molding per side. The Custom had check mark side moldings similar to what was used on 1962 Daytonas. The 1963 Daytona had side moldings that widened out at the back of the car. The 'Daytona' script was attached to the wide part of the molding. Cruiser side trim was the same as the Daytona, except it was fitted with a Cruiser script. All 1963 Lark-related models had a new, non-wraparound windshield and narrow window posts on sedans and station wagons. Changes on 1963 Gran Turismo Hawks were limited to trim alterations. Larger lettering on the deck lid overlay and closed-in side grilles were the most obvious. Daytona, Regal, Custom and Heavy-Duty models had Lark block lettering on the front fenders. The Standard had a Studebaker script in the same position. Gran Turismo model identifications were the same as in 1962. The Custom Wagonaire, the Cruiser six and the six-cylinder Gran Turismo Hawk were not available for domestic sale.

STUDEBAKER I.D. NUMBERS: The Vehicle Identification Number is stamped on a plate on the left front door pillar of Studebakers and top of right frame side member on Avantis. First two symbols indicate model year: 63=1963. Third symbol or group of symbols indicate engine: S=six-cylinder (169 cid); V=V-8 (259 cid); P=V-8 (289 cid); R=Avanti non-supercharged R1 V-8 (289 cid); RS=Avanti supercharged R2 V-8 (289 cid); R3S=Avanti supercharged R3 V-8 (304.5 cid). Extra symbol (used on Canadian-built cars only) was a C for Canada. Remaining symbols indicate the production sequence at the assembly plant. Six-cylinder engine numbers located on a pad at upper left-hand front side of block. V-8 engine numbers located on a pad at upper left-hand front side of block. Engine numbers carried the engine codes or Avanti R-RS-R3S codes as a prefix, followed by production sequence number. [LARK SIX/GT HAWK SIX] Starting serial numbers were 63S-1001 (South Bend) and 63SC-1001 (Canada). The beginning engine numbers were S-261201 (South Bend) and SC-29701 for Canada. [LARK EIGHT/GT HAWK V-8] Starting serial numbers were 63V-1001 (South Bend) and 63VF-1001 (Canada). The beginning 259-cid engine numbers were V-556601 (South Bend) and VC-21401 (Canada). The beginning 289-cid engine numbers were P-93601 (South Bend) and PC-3401 (Canada). [AVANTI] The beginning serial number was R-1001. The beginning unsupercharged (R1) engine number was R-1001. The beginning engine number for the optional supercharged (R2) engine was RS-1001. Studebaker also attached a Body Number Plate to the cowl below the hood. It carried the company name, VIN (serial number), series code (first column of charts below) the Body/Style Number (second column of charts below), plus one of many interior trim codes too numerous to list here.

SIX-CYLINDER SERIES — ALL LINES

Model No.	Body/Style No.	Body Type & Seating	Factory Price	Shipping Weight	Prod. Total
TAXICAB					
63S	Y1	4-dr Taxi-6P	2328	2970	Note 1
STANDARD LINE					
63S	F2	2-dr Sed-6P	1935	2610	Note 1
63S	Y2	4-dr Sed-6P	2040	2735	Note 1
63S	P2	4-dr Sta Wag-6P	2430	2945	Note 1
HEAVY-DUTY LINE					
63S	F3	2-dr Sed-6P	2096	2765	Note 1
63S	Y3	4-dr Sed-6P	2201	2830	Note 1
63S	P3	4-dr Sta Wag-6P	2591	2935	Note 1
REGAL LINE					
63S	F4	2-dr Sed-6P	2055	2610	Note 1
63S	Y4	4-dr Sed-6P	2160	2750	Note 1
63S	P4	4-dr Sta Wag-6P	2550	3200	Note 1
CUSTOM LINE					
63S	Y6	4-dr Sed-6P	2285	2750	Note 1
63S	F6	2-dr Sed-6P	2180	2610	Note 1
63S	P6	4-dr Sta Wag-6P	—	3200	Note 1
LARK DAYTONA					
63S	J8	2-dr HT-5P	2308	2775	Note 1
63S	P8	4-dr Wag Sta Wag-6P	2700	3245	Note 1
63S	L8	2-dr Conv-5P	2679	3020	Note 1
63S	Y8	4-dr Cruiser-6P	—	—	Note 1
GRAN TURISMO HAWK					
63S	K6	2-dr HT-5P	—	—	Note 1

NOTE 1: Complete production total breakouts are not available. The following figures are for both six-cylinder and V-8 models: (four-door sedans, except taxi) 40,113; (two-door Style F sedans) 17,401; (Style K Grand Turismo Hawk) 4,634; (Style J two-door hardtop coupe) 3,763; (Style P four-door station wagon) 11,915; (Style L convertibles) 1,015 and (Style Y1 taxicab) 1,170.

EIGHT-CYLINDER — SERIES 63V — Body type and exterior trim selections were the same as for Series 63S models. Most Lark-related models had V-8 emblems in the grille and on the rear deck lid. The domestic Gran Turismo Hawks and Cruisers came standard with 289-cid V-8s, but in most other countries they came with 259-cid V-8s. The Custom Wagonaire was not available for domestic sale.

EIGHT-CYLINDER SERIES — ALL LINES

Model No.	Body/Style No.	Body Type & Seating	Factory Price	Shipping Weight	Prod. Total
TAXICAB LINE					
63V	Y1	4-dr Taxi-6P	2465	3170	Note 1
STANDARD LINE					
63V	F2	2-dr Sed-6P	2070	2875	Note 1
63V	Y2	4-dr Sed-6P	2175	2935	Note 1
63V	P2	4-dr Sta Wag-6P	2565	3195	Note 1
HEAVY-DUTY LINE					
63V	F3	2-dr Sed-6P	2231	3005	Note 1
63V	Y3	4-dr Sed-6P	2336	3070	Note 1
63V	P3	4-dr Sta Wag-6P	2726	3175	Note 1
REGAL LINE					
63V	F4	2-dr Sed-6P	2190	2875	Note 1
63V	Y4	4-dr Sed-6P	2295	2970	Note 1
63V	P4	4-dr Sta Wag-6P	2685	3450	Note 1
CUSTOM LINE					
63V	F6	2-dr Sed-6P	2315	2875	Note 1
63V	Y6	4-dr Sed-6P	2420	2970	Note 1
63V	P6	4-dr Sta Wag-6P	—	3450	Note 1
LARK DAYTONA/CRUISER					
63V	J8	2-dr HT-5P	2443	2975	Note 1
63V	P8	4-dr Wag Sta Wag-6P	2835	3490	Note 1
63V	L8	2-dr Conv-5P	2814	3240	Note 1
63V	Y8	4-dr Cruiser-6P	2595	3030	Note 1
GRAN TURISMO HAWK					
63V	K6	2-dr HT-5P	3095	3230	Note 1

NOTE 1: See Six-Cylinder Series Production Total note.

AVANTI — MODEL 63R — The Avanti was Studebaker's fiberglass-bodied sport coupe. It was the first completely new body styling Studebaker had introduced since 1953. Smooth lines, an under-the-bumper radiator air intake and a wedge-shaped design were the Avanti's hallmarks. Model identification was on the front, just to the left of the right headlight. A Studebaker script was on the deck lid. Supercharged versions had a "supercharged" nametag on each front fender. The Avanti body sat on a modified Lark Daytona convertible chassis. All 1963 Avantis had round headlight enclosures.

AVANTI SERIES

Model No.	Body/Style No.	Body Type & Seating	Factory Price	Shipping Weight	Prod. Total
R	Q	2-dr Spt Cpe-5P	4445	3148	3,834

ENGINES:

(63S SIX) Overhead valve. Cast iron block. Displacement: 169.6 cid. Bore and stroke: 3 x 4 inches. Compression ratio: 8.25:1. Brake hp: 112 at 4500 rpm. Four main bearings. Solid valve lifters. Carburetor: Carter Model RBS or AS one-barrel.

(63V 259 V-8) Overhead valve. Cast iron block. Displacement: 259.2 cid. Bore and stroke: 2-9/16 x 3-1/4 inches. Compression ratio: 8.5:1. Brake hp: 180 at 4500 rpm. Five main bearings. Solid valve lifters. Carburetor: Stromberg Model WW two-barrel.

(HAWK/CRUISER/MARSHAL 289 V-8) Overhead valve. Cast iron block. Displacement: 289 cid. Bore and stroke: 3-9/16 x 3-5/8 inches. Compression ratio: 8.5:1. Brake hp: 210 at 4500 rpm. Five main bearings. Solid valve lifters. Carburetor: Stromberg Model WW two-barrel.

(AVANTI R1 V-8) Overhead valve. Cast iron block. Displacement: 289 cid. Bore and stroke: 3-9/16 x 3-5/8 inches. Compression ratio: 10.25:1. Brake hp: 240. Five main bearings. Solid valve lifters. Carburetor: Carter Model AFB four-barrel. (The Avanti V-8 was a $73 option on Cruiser sedans; a $157 option on Hawks and a $208 option on other V-8 models.)

(AVANTI SUPERCHARGED R2 V-8) Overhead valve. Cast iron block. Displacement: 289 cid. Bore and stroke: 3-9/16 x 3-5/8 inches. Compression ratio: 9.0:1. Brake hp: 289. Five main bearings. Solid valve lifters. Carburetor: Carter Model AFB four-barrel. (The supercharger was a separate $210 option on Avantis and other Studebakers with the Avanti V-8.)

CHASSIS FEATURES: Wheelbase: (two-door sedans, Daytona hardtop, Daytona convertible and Avanti) 109 inches; (four-door sedans and station wagons) 113 inches; (Gran Turismo Hawk) 120-1/2 inches. Overall length: (two-door sedans, Daytona hardtop and Daytona convertible) 184 inches; (four-door sedans) 188 inches; (station wagons) 187 inches; (Gran Turismo Hawk) 204 inches; (Avanti) 192 inches. Front tread: 57.4 inches. Rear tread: 56.6 inches. Tires: (All six-cylinder models except convertible and station wagon) 6.00 x 15 tubeless; (all V-8 models except Cruiser, convertible, station wagon and GT Hawk plus six-cylinder convertible and station wagon) 6.50 x 15 tubeless; (Cruiser, GT Hawk, Avanti, V-8 convertible and station wagon) 6.70 x 15 tubeless.

OPTIONS: Power brakes ($45). Skytop sun roof (hardtops and sedans only) ($185). Headrests. Reclining seats. Individually adjusted front seats (standard on some models). All transistor manual tuning radio ($57-$62). Internally controlled reel-type cowl antenna (antenna options included in various radio package prices). Winguards for models without wraparound bumpers. Full wheel covers ($16). Rubber splash guards. Stratoline exterior rearview mirror. Bumper guards. Electric clock ($16). Tachometer for GT Hawk and Avanti Lark-type cars ($54). Exhaust deflector. Safety rear door locks. Clear plastic seat covers or cushion toppers for Lark-type vehicles. Padded sun visors. Tissue dispenser. Cigarette lighter for low-priced models. Spotlight. Day-Night interior rearview mirror. Auto compass. Back-up lights for low-priced models ($8). Glovebox light. Trunk light. Climatizer heater/defroster ($80-$88). Fuel line filter. Undercoating. Special station wagon options: Luggage rack ($43). Car-Go-Pak. Power rear window ($33). Cargo mat. Tailgate step. Rear-facing third seat (including Captive-Air tires and no spare). Rear deck cushions. Special options for the Gran Turismo Hawk: Rear deck lid radio antenna. Air-Flo or Aero Strut wheel covers. Door handle guards. Visor vanity mirror. A convenience group and side moldings were available for low-priced models. (Note: some options were slightly lower-priced for Avantis.) Power Holder ($15). Air conditioning (not available with R2 engines). Sidewall tires ($32-$49). Tinted glass ($32). All transistor AM/FM push-button radio (added midyear). Rear seat speaker (the only speaker on most GT Hawks) ($13). Strato-vue rearview mirror. License plate frames. Locking gas cap. Rubber floor mats. Seat belts ($10). Automatic transmission Anti-Creep. Windshield washer ($14). Underhood light. Touch-up paint applicators. Power door windows were also optional on the Avanti ($75). A three-speed manual transmission with column-mounted gearshift was standard on all models except the Avanti. The Avanti came standard with a three-speed manual transmission with floor-mounted gearshift. Overdrive was available for $110 extra on all models except the taxi, Avanti and Avanti-powered V-8 models. Except for the Avanti, taxi, Heavy-Duty and Avanti-powered V-8s, Flightomatic was available for $180 extra on six-cylinder models and $210 extra on V-8 models. A heavy-duty water-cooled automatic was optional on the taxi and Heavy-Duty models. A floor shift-operated Power-Shift automatic was optional on most V-8 models. A four-speed manual transmission with floor-mounted gearshift was optional on all V-8 models except the taxi and Standard. Avanti R1 and R2 engines were optional on all V-8 models except the Standard and taxi. The regular '289' V-8 was optional on all V-8s that it was not standard on, except the Standard. A four-barrel carburetor (Carter AFB) was optional on all regular V-8s at $21.52. The four-barrel increased the '259' V-8's power to 195 hp at 4500 rpm and the '289' V-8's power to 225 hp at 4500 rpm. During midyear, R1 and R2 Super Hawk and Super Lark packages were introduced. They included numerous Avanti suspension and powertrain features. Twin-Traction was $39 option on all models. Disc brakes, standard on the Avanti, were optional on all other models at $102. Other tire sizes were optional on most models. Lower compression ratios were available for export cars.

HISTORICAL FOOTNOTES: Calendar year production slipped to 67,918 units. Special Heavy-Duty W3, Y3 and P3 models were available for rural route mail carriers. Called the Rural Route Lark, they offered interesting options, such as right-hand drive and Signal-Stat warning lights. The Lark Marshals were also based on the Heavy-Duty W3, Y3 and P3 models. The six-cylinder model was called the City Marshal, the 259-cid V-8 model the Patrol Marshal and the 289-cid V-8 model the Pursuit Marshal. The midyear Standard was sold for private use, but its main market was fleet sales. A fixed roof option was available on the Standard Wagonaires and certain export Wagonaires. Sadly, the last official day of production (1964 models) at the South Bend, Ind., assembly plant was Dec. 9, 1963. All subsequent Studebaker production occurred in Canada.

1964

SIX-CYLINDER — SERIES 64S/SERIES S — In 1964, the Lark name was de-emphasized and was actually only being used in connection with the early Challenger and Commander models. Several new model names and a squared-up design were the major changes for 1964. The Challenger, which was only sold domestically, replaced the 1963 Standard line. The Challenger had no side moldings and single headlights (duals were optional). Challenger sedans had Lark emblems on the upper rear quarter panels. The Commander replaced the 1963 Regal line. The Commander had narrow side moldings and single headlights (duals optional). Commander sedans had circled "S" emblems on the upper rear quarter panels. The 1964 Daytona line was expanded to include a four-door sedan. The Daytona and Cruiser had wide side moldings and standard dual headlights. The Cruiser had wide metal moldings across the back of the deck lid. Taxi and Heavy-Duty models were similar to Challengers in exterior trim. The Gran Turismo Hawk had a new, smooth deck lid and slightly restyled imitation side grilles. All models, except the Challenger, taxi and Heavy-Duty, had a standard circled "S" hood ornament. Challenger, Commander, Daytona and Cruiser models had model identifications on the front fenders. Taxis and Heavy-Duty models had Studebaker on the front fenders. Gran Turismo Hawk model identifications were the same as 1962-1963. The 1964 model year was like two years in one. The 'first' part revolved around cars built before the South Bend plant was closed in December 1963. The second part evolved when all production was centralized in Canada after Jan. 1, 1964. After the South Bend plant was closed, taxicabs, Challengers, Heavy-Duty models, Gran Turismo Hawks, Avantis and Studebaker trucks were discontinued. A new Special Commander two-door sedan and Canadian Cruiser were introduced in January 1964. During the early period, the six-cylinder Gran Turismo Hawk, Cruiser and Daytona models were limited to sales in certain countries outside the United States. After Jan. 1, 1964, the Cruiser six was still not available in North America.

STUDEBAKER I.D. NUMBERS: The Vehicle Identification Number is stamped on a plate on left front door pillar on Studebaker and top of right frame side member on Avanti. First two symbols indicate model year: 64=1964. Following symbol or group of symbols indicate engine: S=six-cylinder (169 cid); V=V-8 (259 cid); P=V-8 (289 cid); R=Avanti V-8 (289 cid/240 hp); RS=Avanti supercharged V-8 (289 cid/289 hp); R3S=Avanti R3 supercharged V-8 (304.5 cid/335 hp). An extra symbol used on Canadian-built cars only was a C for Canada. Remaining symbols indicate the production sequence at the assembly plant. Six-cylinder engine numbers located on a pad at upper left-hand front side of block. V-8 engine numbers located on a pad at upper left-hand front side of block. Engine numbers carried the engine codes as a prefix. All 1964 engine numbers were based on a complex formula that took into account the type of engine and date of manufacture. Studebaker shop manuals and parts catalogs explain the formula. [64S FIRST SERIES] Starting serial numbers for early-1964 six-cylinder-powered Studebakers were 64S-1001 (South Bend) and 64SC-1001 (Canada). [SC-10 SECOND SERIES] The beginning serial number for late-1964 (starting Jan. 2, 1964) six-cylinder-powered Studebakers was C-100001 and all were made in Canada. [64V FIRST SERIES] The beginning serial numbers for early-1964 V-8-powered Studebakers were 64V-1001 (South Bend) and 64VC-1001 (Canada). [VC-50 SECOND SERIES] The beginning serial number for late-1964 (starting Jan. 2, 1964) V-8-powered Studebakers was C-500001 and all were made in Canada. [AVANTI] The beginning serial number for 1964 Avantis was R-4835 and Avantis were all built in South Bend early in the model year. Studebaker also attached a Body Number Plate to the cowl below the hood. It carried the company name, VIN (serial number), series code (first column of charts below) the Body/Style Number (second column of charts below), plus one of many interior trim codes too numerous to list here.

1964 "FIRST SERIES" 64S SIX-CYLINDER

Model No.	Body/Style No.	Body Type & Seating	Factory Price	Shipping Weight	Prod. Total
TAXI					
64S	Y1	4-dr Taxi-6P	—	3060	428

1961 Studebaker, Hawk (Series 61V), coupe, AA

1962 Studebaker, Gran Turismo Hawk (Series 62V), hardtop, AA

1964 Studebaker, Avanti (Series 64R), sport coupe, AA

1964 Studebaker, Gran Turismo Hawk (Series 64V), hardtop (with optional vinyl Landau top), AA

1966 Studebaker, Commander (Series C-53), sedan, OCW

1962 Studebaker, Lark Regal (Series 62V), convertible, AA

1962 Studebaker, Lark Daytona Cruiser (Series 62V), sedan, AA

above and below, 1965 Studebaker, Daytona Wagonaire (Series C-51), station wagon, AA

1966 Studebaker, Cruiser (Series C-53), sedan, OCW

CHALLENGER

Model No.	Body/Style No.	Body Type & Seating	Factory Price	Shipping Weight	Prod. Total
64S	F2	2-dr Sed-6P	1935	2660	2,122
64S	Y2	4-dr Sed-6P	2040	2780	2,546
64S	P2	4-dr Sta Wag-6P	2430	3230	453
HEAVY-DUTY					
64S	F3	2-dr Sed-6P	—	2755	7
64S	Y3	4-dr Sed-6P	—	2850	18
64S	P3	4-dr Sta Wag-6P	2700	3295	9
COMMANDER					
64S	F4	2-dr Sed-6P	2055	2695	4,374
64S	Y4	4-dr Sed-6P	2160	2815	7,102
64S	P4	4-dr Sta Wag-6P	2550	3265	1,206
DAYTONA					
64S	Y8	4-dr Sed-6P	2310	2825	1,036
64S	P8	4-dr Sta Wag-6P	2700	3305	116
64S	L8	2-dr Conv-6P	2662	3090	55
GRAN TURISMO HAWK					
64S	K6	2-dr HT-5P	2958	3280	224

1964 "SECOND SERIES" SC-10 SIX-CYLINDER

Model No.	Body/Style No.	Body Type & Seating	Factory Price	Shipping Weight	Prod. Total
COMMANDER					
S	F4	2-dr Sed-6P	2055	2695	Note 1
S	P4	4-dr Sta Wag-6P	2550	3265	Note 1
S	Y4	4-dr Sed-6P	2160	2815	Note 1
COMMANDER SPECIAL					
S	F4 Sp.	2-dr Sed-6P	2185	2720	Note 1
DAYTONA					
S	Y8	4-dr Sed-6P	2310	2825	Note 1
S	P8	4-dr Sta Wag-6P	2700	3305	Note 1
S	L8	2-dr Conv-6P	2662	3090	Note 1

NOTE 1: Production Totals for "First" and "Second" Series combined.

EIGHT-CYLINDER MODELS — SERIES 64V — Styling and model identifications were the same as for the 1964 six-cylinder models. Most V-8 models had '8' emblems on the front fenders. Daytona sedans and hardtops had crossed checkered flag V-8 emblems on the upper rear quarter panels. Domestic Cruisers and Gran Turismo Hawks came standard with 289-cid V-8s.

1964 "FIRST SERIES" 64V V-8

Model No.	Body/Style No.	Body Type & Seating	Factory Price	Shipping Weight	Prod. Total
TAXI					
64V	Y1	4-dr Taxi-6P	—	3270	27
CHALLENGER					
64V	F2	2-dr Sed-6P	2070	2910	274
64V	Y2	4-dr Sed-6P	2175	3010	594
64V	P2	4-dr Sta Wag-6P	2565	3480	286
HEAVY-DUTY					
64V	F3	2-dr Sed-6P	—	2955	153
64V	Y3	4-dr Sed-6P	—	3060	80
64V	P3	4-dr Sta Wag-6P	—	3505	13
COMMANDER					
64V	F4	2-dr Sed-6P	2190	2945	1,553
64V	Y4	4-dr Sed-6P	2295	3045	6,753
64V	P4	4-dr Sta Wag-6P	2685	3515	1,605
DAYTONA					
64V	Y8	4-dr Sed-6P	2445	3055	5,390
64V	J8	2-dr HT-6P	2443	3060	2,414
64V	P8	4-dr Sta Wag-6P	2835	3555	1,543
64V	L8	2-dr Conv-6P	2797	3320	647
CRUISER					
64V	Y9	4-dr Sed-6P	2595	3120	5,023
GRAN TURISMO HAWK					
64V	K6	2-dr HT-5P	2958	3280	1,548

1964 "SECOND SERIES" VC-50 V-8

Model No.	Body/Style No.	Body Type & Seating	Factory Price	Shipping Weight	Prod. Total
COMMANDER					
V	F4	2-dr Sed-6P	2190	2945	Note 1
V	Y4	4-dr Sed-6P	2295	3045	Note 1
V	P4	4-dr Sta Wag-6P	2685	3515	Note 1
COMMANDER SPECIAL					
V	F4 Sp.	2-dr Sed-6P	2320	2970	Note 1
DAYTONA					
V	Y8	4-dr Sed-6P	2445	3055	Note 1
V	J8	2-dr HT-6P	2443	3060	Note 1
V	P8	4-dr Sta Wag-6P	2835	3555	Note 1
V	L8	2-dr Conv-6P	2797	3320	Note 1
CRUISER					
V	Y9	4-dr Sed-6P	2595	3120	Note 1

NOTE 1: Production Totals for "First" and "Second" Series combined.

AVANTI — Studebaker made no effort to make a definite break between 1963 and 1964 Avantis. Most 1964s had round knobs on the console heater/defroster/vent levers. Early 1964s had round headlight enclosures, but about 750 of the 809 cars produced in 1964 had square headlight enclosures. All 1964 Avantis had woodgrain consoles, instrument panels and steering wheels. The basic body styling was the same as 1963. The last Studebaker Avanti was built in December 1963.

AVANTI SERIES

Model No.	Body/Style No.	Body Type & Seating	Factory Price	Shipping Weight	Prod. Total
R	Q	2-dr Spt Cpe-5P	4445	3195	809

ENGINES:

(64S and S SIX) Overhead valve. Cast iron block. Displacement: 169.6 cid. Bore and stroke: 3 x 4 inches. Compression ratio: 8.25:1. Brake hp: 112 at 4500 rpm. Four main bearings. Solid valve lifters. Carburetor: Carter Model RBS or AS one-barrel.

(64V 259 V-8) Overhead valve. Cast iron block. Displacement: 259.2 cid. Bore and stroke: 3-9/16 x 3-1/4 inches. Compression ratio: 8.5:1. Brake hp: 180 at 4500 rpm. Five main bearings. Solid valve lifters. Carburetor: Stromberg Model WW two-barrel.

(HAWK/CRUISER/MARSHAL 289 V-8) Overhead valve. Cast iron block. Displacement: 289 cid. Bore and stroke: 3-9/16 x 3-5/8 inches. Compression ratio: 8.5:1. Brake hp: 210 at 4500 rpm. Five main bearings. Solid valve lifters. Carburetor: Stromberg Model WW two-barrel.

(R1 UNSUPERCHARGED V-8) Overhead valve. Cast iron block. Displacement: 289 cid. Bore and stroke: 3-9/16 x 3-5/8 inches. Compression ratio: 10.25:1. Brake hp: 240. Five main bearings. Solid valve lifters. Carburetor. Carter Model AFB four-barrel.

(R2 SUPERCHARGED V-8) Overhead valve. Cast iron block. Displacement: 289 cid. Bore and stroke: 3-9/16 x 3-5/8 inches. Compression ratio: 9.0:1. Brake hp: 289. Five main bearings. Solid valve lifters. Carburetor: Carter Model AFB four-barrel. (This powerplant was optional at extra-cost.)

CHASSIS FEATURES: Wheelbase: (two-door sedans, Daytona hardtop, Daytona convertible and Avanti) 109 inches; (four-door sedans and station wagons) 113 inches; (Gran Turismo Hawk) 120.5 inches. Overall length: (two-door sedans, Daytona hardtop and Daytona convertible) 190 inches; (four-door sedans) 194 inches; (station wagons) 193 inches; (Gran Turismo Hawk) 204 inches; (Avanti) 192 inches. Front tread: 57.4 inches. Rear tread: 56.6 inches. Tires: (All six-cylinder models except convertibles and station wagons) 6.00 x 15 tubeless; (All V-8 models except Cruiser, convertible, station wagon and GT Hawk, plus six-cylinder convertible and station wagon) 6.50 x 15 tubeless; (Cruiser, GT Hawk, Avanti, V-8 convertible and station wagon) 6.70 x 15 tubeless.

OPTIONS: Power brakes. Head rests. Reclining seats. Individually adjusted front seats (standard on some models). Climatizer heater/defroster. Transistor AM manual tuning radio. The rear seat speaker was the only type available on GT Hawks—as in the past, the rear seat speaker was not available on convertibles or station wagons. Bumper guards. Regular full wheel covers. V-8 engine dress-up kit. Rear fender stone shields (standard on Cruiser). Front fender splash guards. Stratoline exterior rearview mirror. Electric clock. Tachometer for Avanti-powered GT Hawks and Lark-type vehicles. Exhaust deflectors. Rear door safety locks. Day-Night interior rearview mirror. Clear plastic seat covers or cushion toppers for Lark-type vehicles. Padded sun visors. Cigarette lighter. Auto compass. Tissue dispenser. Back-up lights for low-priced models. Glove compartment light. Trunk light. Spotlight. Fuel line filter. Undercoating. Trim kits for low-priced models. Special station wagon options: Rear-facing third seat (including Captive-Air tires and no spare). Car-Go-Pak. Luggage rack. Cargo mat. Safety Sta-Bar kit. Tailgate step. Cargo cover. Rear deck cushions. Special options for the Gran Turismo Hawk: Rear deck lid radio antenna. Aero Strut wheel covers. Door handle guards. Visor vanity mirror. Partial vinyl roof. Power steering. Hill Holder. Air conditioning (not available with R2/R3 engines). White sidewall tires. Tinted glass. Transistor AM/FM push-button radio. Transistor AM push-button radio. Rear seat speaker. Strato-Vue rearview mirror. License plate frames. Rubber floor mats. Locking gas cap. Seat belts. Windshield washer. Adjustable shock absorbers. Underhood light. Touch-up paint applicators. Special Avanti options: Tilt steering wheel. Power door windows. Wire spoke wheel discs. A three-speed manual transmission with column-mounted gearshift was standard on all models except the Avanti. The Avanti came standard with a three-speed manual transmission with floor-mounted gearshift. Overdrive was available for $111 extra on all models except the taxi, Avanti and Avanti-powered V-8 models. Except for the Avanti, taxi, Heavy-Duty and Avanti-powered V-8s, Flightomatic was available for $185 extra on six-cylinder models and $210 extra on V-8 models. A heavy-duty water-cooled automatic was optional on the taxi and Heavy-Duty models. A floor shift-operated Power-Shift automatic or four-speed manual transmission was optional on most V-8 models. Except for the taxi, Avanti engines were optional on all V-8 models. The regular '289' V-8 was optional on all V-8s on which it was not standard. A four-barrel carburetor was optional on all regular V-8s. The four-barrel increased the '259' V-8's power to 195 hp at 4500 rpm and the '289' V-8's power to 225 hp at 4500 rpm. Twin-Traction was optional on all models. Disc brakes, standard on the Avanti, were optional on all other models. Other tire sizes were optional on most models. Lower compression ratios were available for export cars. Special extra-cost 304.5-cid Avanti engines were introduced late in 1963. The supercharged R3 engine produced 335 hp. The unsupercharged R4 version, which had two four-barrel carburetors, produced 280 hp.

HISTORICAL FOOTNOTES: As of Jan. 1, 1964, all Studebaker production took place in Canada. Calendar year production amounted to only 19,748 units. Special Heavy-Duty W3, Y3 and P3 models were available for rural route mail carriers. Called the Rural Router, they offered many options, including right-hand drive. The Marshals were also based on the Heavy-Duty W3, Y3 and P3 models. The six-cylinder model was called the City Marshal, the 259-cid V-8 model the Patrol Marshal, and the 289-cid V-8 model the Pursuit Marshal. A fixed roof option was available on all Wagonaire station wagons. Only 10 salable new cars (nine Avantis and one Commander two-door sedan) were fitted at the factory with R3 engines. Only one salable new car, a Daytona hardtop, was fitted at the factory with an R4 engine.

1965

SIX-CYLINDER COMMANDER/CRUISER — SERIES S ("C-11") — The 1965 stylings were almost identical to the late-1964 offerings. The major change was the switch to heavy-duty Canadian-built engines. These General Motors-McKinnon engines were based on Chevrolet designs. Dual headlights were standard on all 1965 Studebakers. The wide moldings on the back of the deck lid on Cruisers were discontinued. A new horizontal molding on Daytona sedans and Cruisers was added below the deck lid opening. The six-cylinder Cruiser was now available in North America. Commanders continued with narrow side moldings, while Cruisers had wide moldings. The model identifications were on the front fenders and also on the back of Cruisers and Daytonas. A six-cylinder Daytona was not offered In 1965.

STUDEBAKER I.D. NUMBERS: The Vehicle Identification Number is located on the left front hinge pillar post. First two symbols indicate engine: 06=six-cylinder with standard transmission; 66=six-cylinder with automatic; 20=V-8 with standard transmission; 80=V-8 with automatic. Third symbol indicates model year: 5=1965. Last six symbols are the sequential production number at the Canadian factory starting at 110001 and up for six-cylinder cars and 510001 and up for V-8s. [SIX-CYLINDER] The beginning serial number for the 1965 S models was C-110001 (Canada). The beginning engine numbers were 06510001 with standard transmission and 66510001 with automatic transmission. [V-8] The beginning serial number for the 1965 models was C-510001 (Canada). The beginning engine numbers were 205420001 with standard transmission and 805420001 with automatic transmission.

COMMANDER/CRUISER SIX SERIES

Model No.	Body/Style No.	Body Type & Seating	Factory Price	Shipping Weight	Prod. Total
COMMANDER					
S	F4	2-dr Sed-6P	2125	2695	3,067
S	Y4	4-dr Sed-6P	2230	2815	4,319
S	P4	4-dr Sta Wag-6P	2620	3246	564

CRUISER

Model No.	Body/Style No.	Body Type & Seating	Factory Price	Shipping Weight	Prod. Total
S	Y9	4-dr Sed-6P	2470	2815	791

EIGHT-CYLINDER COMMANDER/DAYTONA/CRUISER — SERIES V ("C-51") — The Daytona was only available as a V-8 in 1965. The Daytona side trim was like that on the Cruiser. A new Daytona Sport Sedan, with standard vinyl roof, replaced the Daytona hardtop. Commander and Cruiser trim was like that on the six-cylinder models. Model identifications were in the same locations as on the 'S' models. The 1964-type '8' fender nameplates were continued.

COMMANDER/DAYTONA/CRUISER V-8 SERIES

Model No.	Body/Style No.	Body Type & Seating	Factory Price	Shipping Weight	Prod. Total
COMMANDER					
V	F4	2-dr Sed-6P	2265	2891	571
V	Y4	4-dr Sed-6P	2370	2991	4,344
V	P4	4-dr Sta Wag-6P	2760	3461	534
DAYTONA					
V	F8	2-dr Spt Sed-6P	2565	3006	1,626
V	P8	4-dr Sta Wag-6P	2890	3501	723

CRUISER

Model No.	Body/Style No.	Body Type & Seating	Factory Price	Shipping Weight	Prod. Total
V	Y9	4-dr Sed-6P	2610	3006	2,901

ENGINES:

(COMMANDER/CRUISER SIX) Overhead valve. Cast iron block. Displacement: 194 cid. Bore and stroke: 3-9/16 x 3-1/4 inches. Compression ratio: 8.5:1. Brake hp: 120 at 4400 rpm. Seven main bearings. Hydraulic valve lifters. Carburetor: Rochester Model BV one-barrel.

(COMMANDER/DAYTONA/CRUISER V-8) Overhead valve. Cast iron block. Displacement: 283 cid. Bore and stroke: 3-7/8 x 3 inches. Compression ratio: 9.25:1. Brake hp: 195 at 4800 rpm. Five main bearings. Hydraulic valve lifters. Carburetor: Rochester Model 2GV two-barrel.

CHASSIS FEATURES: Wheelbase: (two-door sedans) 109 inches; (four-door sedans and station wagons) 113 inches. Overall length: (two-door sedans) 190 inches; (four-door sedans) 194 inches; (station wagons) 193 inches. Front tread: 57.4 inches. Rear tread: 56.6 inches. Tires: 7 35 x 15 tubeless.

OPTIONS: Hill Holder. V-8 power steering. V-8 power drum brakes. Individual reclining seats. Whitewall tires. Horn ring for Commander models. Tinted glass. Climatizer heater/defroster. Commander back-up lights. Electric clock (standard on Cruiser). Seat belts. Engine block heater. Vanity tray. Transistor push-button AM/FM radio. Transistor AM push-button radio. Transistor AM manual tuning radio. Rear seat speaker. Air conditioning. Exterior rearview mirror (two types). License plate frames. Rubber floor mats. Locking gas cap. Exhaust deflector. Rear door safety locks. Padded sun visors. Day-Night interior rearview mirror. Windshield washer (standard on top-line models). Rear fender stone shield (standard on Cruiser). Regular or wire wheel covers. Front fender splash guards. Head rests. Auto Compass. Spotlight. Vanity tray light. Trunk light. Underhood light. Undercoating. Special station wagon options: Power rear window. Cargo mat. Cargo cover. Rear deck cushions. Luggage rack. Tailgate step. Safety Sta-Bar kit. A three-speed manual transmission with column-mounted gearshift was standard on all models. Overdrive was available for $110 extra. Automatic was available for $172 extra on six-cylinder models and $200 extra on V-8 models. Twin-Traction ($39). Disc brakes, and transistor ignition (made standard on Daytona Sport Sedan) optional on all models. 7.25 x 15 tires were optional on all models.

HISTORICAL FOOTNOTES: Calendar year production totaled 18,588 Studebakers, all assembled in Canada. A midyear heavy-duty version of the Commander six-cylinder four-door sedan (S-Y4) was promoted for taxi, police and fleet car sales. It was listed as an option package instead of a separate model. The Wagonaire station wagon was only available with a sliding top during 1965.

1966

SIX-CYLINDER — SERIES S ("C-13") — Standard single headlights, a new grille and low side moldings were the main styling changes made by Studebaker during its last year of automotive production. "Refreshaire" vents above the taillights on sedans were Studebaker's last engineering achievement. Six-cylinder Daytonas were again offered. The Wagonaire was made a model of its own. Cruisers and Daytonas had wide side moldings while Commanders and Wagonaires had narrow side moldings. Engine displacement nameplates were placed on the front fenders. Model identifications except for the Wagonaire were on the front fender and also below the deck lid on Cruisers and Daytonas. The Wagonaire had a Studebaker script on the front fenders and Wagonaire script on the tailgate.

STUDEBAKER I.D. NUMBERS: The Vehicle Identification Number is located on the left front hinge pillar post. First two symbols indicate engine: 06=six-cylinder with standard transmission; 66=six-cylinder with automatic; 20=V-8 with standard transmission; 80=V-8 with automatic. Third symbol indicates model year: 6=1966. Last six symbols are the sequential production number at the Canadian factory starting at C-130001 and up for six-cylinder cars and C-530001 and up for V-8s. [SIX-CYLINDER] The beginning serial number for the 1966 S models was C-130001 (Canada). The beginning 194-cid engine numbers were 01610001 with standard transmission and 61610001 with automatic transmission. The beginning 230-cid engine number was 656100001. [V-8] The beginning serial number for the 1966 V series was C-530001 (Canada). The beginning engine numbers were 176400001 with standard transmission and 776400001 with automatic transmission.

SIX-CYLINDER SERIES S

Model No.	Body/Style No.	Body Type & Seating	Factory Price	Shipping Weight	Prod. Total
COMMANDER					
S	Y4	4-dr Sed-6P	2319	2815	Note 1
S	F4	2-dr Sed-6P	2215	2695	Note 1
DAYTONA/WAGONAIRE					
S	F8	2-dr Spt Sed-6P	2443	2755	Note 1
S	P8	4-dr Sta Wag-6P	2664	3246	Note 1
CRUISER					
S	Y9	4-dr Sed-6P	2544	2815	Note 1

NOTE 1: Production Totals are combined with V-8 totals below.

EIGHT-CYLINDER — SERIES V ("C-53") — The Series V body style and trim offerings were the same as for the six-cylinder models. Model identifications were in the same locations as those on Series S models.

EIGHT-CYLINDER SERIES V

Model No.	Body/Style No.	Body Type & Seating	Factory Price	Shipping Weight	Prod. Total
COMMANDER					
V	Y4	4-dr Sed-6P	2456	2991	1,368
V	F4	2-dr Sed-6P	2352	2891	198
DAYTONA/WAGONAIRE					
V	F8	2-dr Spt Sed-6P	2581	3006	620
V	P8	4-dr Sta Wag-6P	2802	3501	618
CRUISER					
V	Y9	4-dr Sed-6P	2682	3066	1,844

ENGINES:

(S SERIES SIX) Overhead valve. Cast iron block. Displacement: 194 cid. Bore and stroke: 3-9/16 x 3-1/4 inches. Compression ratio: 8.5:1. Brake hp: 120 at 4400 rpm. Seven main bearings. Hydraulic valve lifters. Carburetor: Rochester Model BV one-barrel.

(V SERIES V-8) Overhead valve. Cast iron block. Displacement: 283 cid. Bore and stroke: 3-7/8 x 3 inches. Compression ratio: 9.25:1. Brake hp: 195 at 4800 rpm. Five main bearings. Hydraulic valve lifters. Carburetor: Rochester Model 2GV two-barrel.

CHASSIS FEATURES: Wheelbase (two-door sedans) 109 inches; (four-door sedans and station wagons) 113 inches. Overall length: (two-door sedans) 190 inches; (four-door sedans) 194 inches; (station wagons) 193 inches. Front tread: 57.4 inches. Rear tread: 56.6 inches. Tires: 7.35 x 15 tubeless.

OPTIONS: Hill Holder. V-8 power steering. Air conditioning. Reclining seats. White sidewall tires. Vinyl roof for Cruiser. Vanity tray. Horn ring for Commander and Wagonaire models. Tinted glass. Climatizer heater/defroster. Back-up lights. Electric clock (standard on Cruiser). Transistor AM/FM push-button radio. Transistor AM manual tuning radio. Rear seat speaker. Rubber floor mats. Seat belts. Front fender splash guards. Rear fender stone shields (standard on Cruiser). Regular or wire wheel covers. Auto compass. Padded sun visors. Exterior rearview mirror (two types). Exhaust deflector. Rear door safety locks. Day-Night interior rearview mirror. Bumper guards (standard on Cruiser). Underhood light. Trunk light. Vanity tray light. Locking gas cap. Commander chrome gas cap. Spotlight. Special station wagon options: Power rear window. Tailgate step. Cargo mat. Luggage rack. Rear deck cushions. Cargo cover. Safety Sta-Bar kit. A three-speed manual transmission with column-mounted gearshift was standard on all models. Overdrive was available for $113 extra. Automatic was available for $192 extra on six-cylinder models and $225 extra on V-8 models. A larger 230-cid six-cylinder engine with an 8.5:1 compression ratio and 140 hp at 4400 rpm was originally optional on six-cylinder series cars with automatic transmissions. It was later made optional on all six-cylinder series cars. Twin-Traction, disc brakes and transistor ignition (standard on Daytona Sport Sedan) optional on all models. 7.75 x 15 tires were optional on all models.

HISTORICAL FOOTNOTES: Calendar year production was a meager 2,045 Studebakers. A heavy-duty taxi option kit for the Commander four-door sedan was available. These converted models were called S-Y4T. A fixed top option was available for the Wagonaire station wagon during 1966. Production of Studebakers at the Hamilton, Ontario, Canada assembly plant ceased in March of 1966, ending 114 years of Studebaker tradition and 64 years of Studebaker automobile production.

Studebaker dealership's used car showroom filled with low-mileage "cream puffs" for sale during the height of the Great Depression. Banner in background reads: Studebaker - Smart to be seen in but smarter to buy.

STUTZ

STUTZ — Indianapolis, Indiana — (1911-1935) — Mention the word Stutz and the Pavlovian-like response invariably is Bearcat. Seldom has a car become so indelibly etched in memory via a single model. The first Stutz built, however, was not a Bearcat. It was the widely-advertised "Car That Made Good in a Day"—and the day was the Indianapolis 500 in May 1911. Having made several primeval efforts at building an automobile in his native Ohio, Harry C. Stutz had arrived in Indianapolis in 1903, where he seems never to have lacked for a job in the automobile field though he did leapfrog from one to another. He also came up with the design for a rear-axle-mounted transmission, and by 1910 he had his own firm, the Stutz Auto Parts Company, for its manufacture. The year following, in just five weeks' time, he built the car that was taken immediately to the Indy racetrack for the inaugural running of the 500. There the Stutz was driven by Gil Anderson to an 11th-place finish, which was not good for any prize money but was good for the slogan that was used for several years thereafter. Though 11th might not seem much to crow about, the Stutz had averaged 68.25 mph—every car ahead of it had considerably more cubic inches than its 389—and, had not so many pit stops been necessary for tire changes, the car undoubtedly would have finished even higher. It had been a good day for Stutz. Several weeks later it was announced that the Ideal Motor Car Company had been organized for manufacture of the car that had done so well at Indy. And indeed it was a duplicate: T-head 60 hp Wisconsin four-cylinder engine (only in 1917 did Stutz begin to manufacture its own powerplants), trans/axle setup (a feature that would endure into the 1920s), and right-hand steering wheel (not until 1922 would the company go over to left-hand drive and initially only on closed models). The new Stutz was offered as a roadster, toy tonneau and touring, each priced at $2,000. In 1912, a 60 hp six-cylinder line was added to the fours, and in both the famous Bearcat model was offered. In 1912, too, the Stutz was entered in 30 different racing contests and won 25 of them. Invariably the car was a stock (or nearly stock) Bearcat. A true sports car in the scant-body/scant-comfort idiom, the Bearcat was a hairy, masculine machine, though the story that Harry Stutz purposely designed his clutches with springs so stiff that a woman could not operate them is probably apocryphal. Not until 1915 were special Stutz race cars (with Wisconsin-built sohc 16-valve engines) campaigned, and they did extraordinarily well also. The "White Squadron," as the Stutz team was known, was the chief rival to the Mercer. In 1915, too, Cannon Ball Baker drove a four-cylinder Bearcat from San Diego to New York in a transcontinental-recordbreaking 11 days-7 hours-15 minutes; and the Stutz Motor Car Company (as the firm had been renamed in May 1913 in a merger of Ideal and Stutz Auto Parts) augmented its line that year with a light 23 hp roadster called the H.C.S. model and priced at $1,475, for those who could not afford a Bearcat. Stutz was acquitting itself nicely in the marketplace: 266 cars in 1912, 759 in 1913, 649 in 1914, 1,079 in 1915, 1,535 in 1916, 2,207 in 1917. But already trouble was brewing. Because increased sales had necessitated increased facilities, and because further expansion was needed for the manufacture of its own engines (the 16-valve T-head four, which would be the mainstay of production from model year 1917 through 1923), Stutz made the decision to go public. By 1916, a Wall Street stock speculator named Alan A. Ryan had bought controlling interest in Stutz; by 1919 Harry C. Stutz had left the company to build a new car called the H.C.S.; by 1921, Ryan had engineered the infamous corner on Stutz stock, by 1922, he was broke. Taking over control of Stutz now was Bethlehem Steel magnate Charles M. Schwab. A new ohv 70 hp six joined the Stutz line for 1923, but soon there would be no Bearcat. Nor would there be for a number of years following, because in 1925 Frederick E. Moskovics strode into the Stutz presidency intent upon revising the marque's image from hairy beast into sophisticated beauty. He succeeded. The new Stutz Vertical Eight, Safety Chassis arrived for the 1926 model year. Its engine was a nine-main-bearing sohc dual-ignition eight developing 92 (late 115) bhp at 3200 rpm. Its centrally lubricated chassis featured an underslung worm drive that allowed for low and intoxicatingly sensuous bodies. Many of these were Weymann fabric bodies, Stutz contracting to take Charles Weymann's entire American output during the spring of 1928. Because much about the new Stutz was more European than prevailing American practice, many of the new body styles were given chic European designations: Monte Carlo, Biarritz, Versailles. And this new beauty was fast too, a sedan capturing the Stevens Trophy Cup in 1927 after averaging 68.44 mph for 24 hours at Indy, the Black Hawk speedsters winning everything in sight to become the 1927 AAA Stock Car Champion. Early in 1928, following a two-way average of 106.53 mph at Daytona, the Black Hawk was America's fastest production car. True, a Black Hawk did lose the curious match race against a Hispano-Suiza at Indy that April, but the Hispano's sponsor, Charles Weymann, used a Stutz to enter Le Mans that year and in 1929. By that time the Stutz factory had quit racing itself, following the tragic death of Frank Lockhart in a land speed record attempt at Daytona with the Stutz Black Hawk Special the week after the Hispano match race. Though the Vertical Eight had been sensationally received, with more than $3 million in orders during the week of its introduction, matters were not easy within the company itself. The Stutz legal department was busy with lawsuits instigated by Weidely for breach of contract (apparently some of the last pre-Moskovics era engines were to have been built by Weidely, and the company alleged its subsequent receivership resulted when Stutz reneged), and by James Scripps-Booth for breach of confidence (Booth had approached Stutz with an underslung worm drive design and had been turned down prior to Moskovics' appearance on the scene with his own idea of the same concept). Despite the glory of the new Stutz, these were troubled years. In January 1929, shortly after the introduction of a new and cheaper six-cylinder car by Stutz called the Blackhawk (absorbed into the Stutz line in 1931), Moskovics resigned from the company. Fortunately Edgar S. Gorrell, a Moskovics man, was chosen to succeed him. And Gorrell retained Charles "Pop" Greuter in the engineering post that he had served so well since joining the company in 1925. The company, wisely, elected not to enter the multi-cylinder race. Instead, introduced for 1932 was a development of the Vertical Eight (now renamed SV-16): the new car, introduced the previous April, was the fabulous DV-32 (dual overhead camshaft, four valves per cylinder) with a commanding 156 bhp. And it was for this model that the legendary Bearcat name was revived in a speedster that was guaranteed to exceed 100 mph. Even faster was the Super Bearcat, the same car on a truncated wheelbase (116 inches versus the Bearcat's 134-1/2). But the Depression was now in full swing. The company really tried, slashing prices and introducing some cost-cutting measures (the substitution of a three-speed gearbox for the Warner four-speed used since 1929). Ironically, the production figure for 1921 of 3,860 cars, which had so alarmed Charles Schwab upon his takeover of Stutz, turned out to be the best ever for the marque. The Vertical Eight's introductory year of 1926 saw some 3,692 cars built. The figures for the late Twenties were: 2,906 in 1927, 2,403 in 1928, 2,320 in 1929. During the Thirties few more than 1,500 cars were produced. In 1934, just six Stutzes left the factory. In January 1935, the company announced that "it is not a part of the present program to continue manufacture and sale of the Stutz car." The present program was production instead of the Pak-Age-Car, a light delivery van. Stutzes continued to be bodied and marketed in England through 1935, and, astoundingly, in the United States a 1936 model was announced, which probably means there might have been some parts on hand with which to put together a new Stutz should anyone have asked. On April 3, 1937, the Stutz Motor Car Company admitted its insolvency in court. In 1939 the firm was liquidated.

1912

Model A, 4-cyl., 60 hp, 120" wb

Model No.	Body Type & Seating	Factory Price	Shipping Weight	Prod. Total
A	Rds-2P	2000	—	Note 1
A	Toy Ton-4P	2000	—	Note 1
A	Tr-5P	2000	—	Note 1
A	Bearcat-2P	2000	—	Note 1
A	Cpe-4P	2500	—	Note 1
Model A, 6-cyl., 70 hp, 124" wb				
A	Toy Ton-4P	2250	—	Note 1
A	Bearcat-2P	2125	—	Note 1
A	Tr-6P (130" wb)	2250	—	Note 1

Note 1: Stutz production for 1912 totaled 266 with no body style breakout available.

1913

Series B, 4-cyl., 60 hp, 120" wb

Model No.	Body Type & Seating	Factory Price	Shipping Weight	Prod. Total
B	Rds-2P	2000	—	Note 1
B	Bearcat-2P	2000	—	Note 1
B	Toy Ton-4P	2000	—	Note 1
B	Tr-4P (124" wb)	2000	—	Note 1
B	Tr-6P (124" wb)	2050	—	Note 1
Series B, 6-cyl., 70 hp, 124" wb				
B	Bearcat-2P	2125	—	Note 1
B	Toy Ton-4P	2250	—	Note 1
B	Tr-6P (130" wb)	2300	—	Note 1

Note 1: Stutz production for 1913 totaled 759 with no body style breakout available.

1914

Series 4E, 4-cyl., 50 hp, 120" wb

Model No.	Body Type & Seating	Factory Price	Shipping Weight	Prod. Total
4E	Rds-2P	2000	—	Note 1
4E	Bearcat-2P	2000	—	Note 1
4E	Tr-5P	2150	—	Note 1
Series 6E, 6-cyl., 55 hp, 130" wb				
6E	Rds-2P	2250	—	Note 1
6E	Tr-6P	2400	—	Note 1

Note 1: Stutz production for 1914 totaled 649 with no body style breakout available.

1915

Series H.C.S., 4-cyl., 35 hp, 108" wb

Model No.	Body Type & Seating	Factory Price	Shipping Weight	Prod. Total
H.C.S.	Rds-2P	1475	—	Note 1
Series 4F, 4-cyl., 50 hp, 120" wb				
4F	Rds-2P	2000	—	Note 1
4F	Bearcat-2P	2000	—	Note 1
4F	Cpe	2600	—	Note 1
4F	Bulldog	2250	—	Note 1
4F	Tr-5P	2275	—	Note 1
4F	Sed-5P	3675	—	Note 1
Series 6F, 6-cyl., 55 hp, 130" wb				
6F	Rds-2P	2500	—	Note 1
6F	Bearcat-2P	2500	—	Note 1
6F	Cpe	2850	—	Note 1
6F	Tr-5P	2275	—	Note 1
6F	Tr-6P	2400	—	Note 1
6F	Sed-5P	3800	—	Note 1

Note 1: Stutz production for 1915 totaled 1,079 with no body style breakout available.

1916

Series C, 4-cyl., 50 hp, 120" wb

Model No.	Body Type & Seating	Factory Price	Shipping Weight	Prod. Total
C	Rds-2P	2100	—	Note 1
C	Bearcat-2P	2000	—	Note 1
C	Bulldog-4P	2250	—	Note 1
C	Sed-5P	3695	—	Note 1
Bulldog Special, 4-cyl., 50 hp, 130" wb				
—	Tr-4P	2250	—	Note 1
—	Tr-5P	2300	—	Note 1

Note 1: Stutz production for 1916 totaled 1,535 with no body style breakout available.

1917

Series R, 4-cyl., 80 hp, 130" wb

Model No.	Body Type & Seating	Factory Price	Shipping Weight	Prod. Total
R	Rds-2P	2375	—	Note 1
R	Bulldog Spec-4P	2550	—	Note 1
R	Bulldog Spec-6P	2550	—	Note 1
R	Bearcat-2P (120" wb)	2300	—	Note 1

Note 1: Stutz production for 1917 totaled 2,207 with no body style breakout available.

1918

Series S, 4-cyl., 80 hp, 130" wb

Model No.	Body Type & Seating	Factory Price	Shipping Weight	Prod. Total
S	Rds-2P	2550	—	Note 1
S	Bulldog Spec-4P	2650	—	Note 1
S	Bulldog Spec-6P	2750	—	Note 1
S	Bearcat-2P (120" wb)	2550	—	Note 1

Note 1: Stutz production for 1918 totaled 1,873 with no body style breakout available.

1919

Series G, 4-cyl., 80 hp, 130" wb

Model No.	Body Type & Seating	Factory Price	Shipping Weight	Prod. Total
G	Tr-6P	2850	—	Note 1
G	Rds-2P	2750	—	Note 1
G	C.C. Tr-4P	2850	—	Note 1
G	Bearcat-2P (120" wb)	2750	—	Note 1

Note 1: Stutz production for 1919 totaled 1,544 with no body style breakout available.

1920

Series H, 4-cyl., 80 hp, 130" wb

Model No.	Body Type & Seating	Factory Price	Shipping Weight	Prod. Total
H	Rds-2P	3250	—	Note 1
H	Tr-4/5P	3350	—	Note 1
H	Tr-6/7P	3350	—	Note 1
H	Bearcat-2P (120" wb)	3250	—	Note 1

Note 1: Stutz production for 1920 totaled 2,786 with no body style breakout available.

1921

Series K, 4-cyl., 80 hp, 130" wb

Model No.	Body Type & Seating	Factory Price	Shipping Weight	Prod. Total
K	Rds-2P	3900	—	Note 1
K	Tr-4P	4000	—	Note 1
K	Tr-6P	4000	—	Note 1
K	Cpe-4P	5500	—	Note 1
K	Bearcat-2P (120" wb)	3900	—	Note 1

Note 1: Stutz production for 1921 totaled 3,860 with no body style breakout available.

1922

Series KLDH, 4-cyl., 80 hp, 130" wb

Model No.	Body Type & Seating	Factory Price	Shipping Weight	Prod. Total
—	Cpe-3P	4800	—	Note 1
—	Rds-2P	3250	—	Note 1
—	Tr-6P	3350	—	Note 1
—	Spt-4P	3350	—	Note 1
—	Bearcat (120" wb)	3250	—	Note 1

Note 1: Stutz production for 1922 totaled 769 with no body style breakout available.

1923

Six/6-90, 6-cyl., 75 hp, 120" wb

Model No.	Body Type & Seating	Factory Price	Shipping Weight	Prod. Total
6-90	Sed-5P	—	3500	Note 1
6-90	Rds-2P	—	—	Note 1
6-90	Phae-5P	—	—	Note 1
Speedway Four/KLDH, 4-cyl., 88 hp, 130" wb				
—	Tr-4P	2790	—	Note 1
—	Tr-6P	2640	—	Note 1
—	Sed-5P	4450	—	Note 1
—	Cpe-4P	3490	—	Note 1
—	Rds-2P	2450	—	Note 1
—	Bearcat-2P	—	—	Note 1

Note 1: Stutz production for 1923 totaled 1,602 with no body style breakout available.

1924

Special Six/6-90-2, 6-cyl., 75 hp, 120" wb

Model No.	Body Type & Seating	Factory Price	Shipping Weight	Prod. Total
6-90-2	Phae-5P	1995	—	Note 1
6-90-2	Rds-2P	1995	—	Note 1
6-90-2	Sed-5P	2550	3750	Note 1

1913 Stutz, Series B, touring, HAC

1918 Stutz, Series S, roadster, HAC

1919 Stutz, Bearcat (Series G), speedster, HAC

1920 Stutz, Series H, roadster, AA

1921 Stutz, Series K, close-coupled touring, HAC

1925 Stutz, Series 695, suburban, HAC

1926 Stutz, Vertical Eight (Series AA), five-passenger speedster, AA

1927 Stutz, Vertical Eight (Series AA), enclosed drive limousine (with body by LeBaron), AA

1927 Stutz, Vertical Eight (Series AA), landau limousine (with body by LeBaron), AA

1928 Stutz, Series BB, five-passenger sedan, HAC

Speedway Six/6-95, 6-cyl., 80 hp, 130" wb

Model No.	Body Type & Seating	Factory Price	Shipping Weight	Prod. Total
6-95	Rds-2P	2450	—	Note 1
6-95	Tr-6P	2640	—	Note 1
6-95	Cpe-4P	3490	—	Note 1
6-95	Sed-5P	—	—	Note 1
6-95	Sed Limo-7P	—	—	Note 1
6-95	Berl Limo-7P	—	—	Note 1
6-95	Phae-5P	—	—	Note 1
6-95	Phae-7P	—	—	Note 1
Speedway Four/KLDH, 4-cyl., 88 hp, 130" wb				
—	Tr-4P	2790	—	Note 1
—	Tr-6P	2640	—	Note 1
—	Sed-5P	4450	—	Note 1
—	Cpe-4P	3490	—	Note 1
—	Rds-2P	2450	—	Note 1

Note 1: Stutz production for 1924 totaled 2,167 with no body style breakout available.

Production Note: 1924 was the final year for the Stutz four-cylinder engine.

1925

Series 693-694, 6-cyl., 80 hp, 120" wb

Model No.	Body Type & Seating	Factory Price	Shipping Weight	Prod. Total
693-694	Phae-5P	2395	3640	Note 1
693-694	Tourabout-5P	3000	—	Note 1
693-694	Rds-2P	2395	3492	Note 1
693-694	Cpe-4P	3050	3940	Note 1
693-694	Sed-5P	3050	3929	Note 1
Series 695, 6-cyl., 80 hp, 130" wb				
695	Tourster-7P	3075	4152	Note 1
695	Sportster-5P	3035	4064	Note 1
695	Sub Sed-7P	3935	4622	Note 1
695	Spt Brgm-5P	3785	4305	Note 1
695	Berl Limo-7P	4035	4675	Note 1

Note 1: Stutz production for 1925 totaled 2,190 with no body style breakout available.

Production Note: 1925 was the final year for the Stutz six-cylinder engine.

1926

AA/Vertical Eight, 8-cyl., 92 hp, 131" wb

Model No.	Body Type & Seating	Factory Price	Shipping Weight	Prod. Total
AA-2	Spds-2P	3150	4175	Note 1
AA-4	Spds-2/4P	3160	4175	Note 1
AA-8	Vic Cpe-4P	3175	4273	Note 1
AA-6	Brgm-5P	3195	4390	Note 1
AA-5	Sed-5P	3195	4416	Note 1
AA-10	R/S Cpe-2/4P	3165	4200	Note 1
AA/Vertical Eight, 8-cyl., 92 hp, 145" wb				
AA-7	Sed-7P	3685	4656	Note 1
AA-9	Berl Limo-7P	3785	4731	Note 1

Note 1: Stutz production for 1926 totaled 3,692 with no body style breakout available.

Production Note: Stutz introduced its Safety Chassis in 1926.

1927

AA/Vertical Eight, 8-cyl., 92 hp, 131" wb

Model No.	Body Type & Seating	Factory Price	Shipping Weight	Prod. Total
AA	Spds-2P	3350	4058	Note 1
AA	Spds-2/4P	3360	4141	Note 1
AA	Cpe-2P	3365	4182	Note 1
AA	Vic Cpe-4P	3375	4176	Note 1
AA	Brgm-5P	3395	4334	Note 1
AA	Sed-5P	3395	4340	Note 1
AA/Vertical Eight, 8-cyl., 92 hp, 145" wb				
AA	Sed-7P	3885	4646	Note 1
AA	Berl Limo-7P	3985	4731	Note 1
Weymann Custom/AA, 8-cyl., 92 hp, 131" wb				
AA	Wey Cus Sed-5P	4665	4393	Note 1
Weymann Custom/AA, 8-cyl., 92 hp, 145" wb				
AA	Wey Cus Sed-7P	5185	4640	Note 1

Note 1: Stutz production for 1927 totaled 2,906 with no body style breakout available.

Production Note: Four custom-bodied Stutz automobiles are listed in 1927 automobile guides, but neither the body builder nor wheelbase are identified. The four are: Sed-5P, $3995 and weighing 4340 pounds; Vic Cpe-4P, $3925 and weighing 4176 pounds; Cpe-2P, $3915 and weighing 4182 pounds; and, Cab Cpe-2P, $3995 and weighing 4090 pounds.

1928

Series BB, 8-cyl., 110 hp, 131" wb

Model No.	Body Type & Seating	Factory Price	Shipping Weight	Prod. Total
BB	Spds-2P	3495	4478	Note 1
BB	Spds-2/4P	3595	4509	Note 1
BB	Spds TC (tonneau cowl)-4P	3845	4509	Note 1
BB	Black Hawk Spds-2P	4895	4302	Note 1
BB	Black Hawk Spds-4P	4945	4466	Note 1
BB	Vic Cpe-4P	3495	4679	Note 1
BB	Cpe-2P	3495	4649	Note 1
BB	Cpe-5P	3545	4713	Note 1
BB	Sed-5P	3570	4977	Note 1
BB	Brgm-5P	3570	4820	Note 1
BB	Cabr Cpe-2P	3695	4520	Note 1
BB	Clpsbl Sed-5P	3995	4955	Note 1
BB	Clpsbl Limo-5P	4095	4955	Note 1
BB	Clpsbl Limo-7P	4195	4955	Note 1
Series BB, 8-cyl., 110 hp, 145" wb				
BB	Spds-7P	3895	4748	Note 1
BB	Sed-7P	3895	5018	Note 1
BB	Sed Limo-7P	3995	5159	Note 1
Series BB/Weymann Custom, 8-cyl., 110 hp, 131" wb				
BB	Deauville-4P	4120	4557	Note 1
BB	Chantilly Sed-5P	4120	4393	Note 1
BB	Monaco Cpe-4P	4120	4475	Note 1
BB	Riv Sed-5P	4420	4575	Note 1
BB	Faucon Noir-2P	4895	4302	Note 1
BB	Biarritz Sed-5P	4495	4645	Note 1
Series BB/Weymann Custom, 8-cyl., 110 hp, 145" wb				
BB	Chamonix Sed-5P	4545	4640	Note 1
BB	Fontainbleau-7P	4745	4778	Note 1
BB	Aix Les Baines-7P	4995	4778	Note 1
BB	Versailles-7P	5295	4778	Note 1
Series BB/Salon Custom, 8-cyl., 110 hp, 145" wb				
BB	Prince of Wales-5P	6345	5014	Note 1
BB	Prince of Wales-7P	6345	5014	Note 1
BB	Trans Twn Car	6895	5044	Note 1

Note 1: Stutz production for 1928 totaled 2,403 with no body style breakout available.

1929

Model M, 8-cyl., 113 hp, 134-1/2" wb

Model No.	Body Type & Seating	Factory Price	Shipping Weight	Prod. Total
M	Spds-2P	3345	4395	Note 1
M	Spds-4P	3345	4835	Note 1
M	Torp Spds-2P	3695	4868	Note 1
M	Cpe-2P	3395	4449	Note 1
M	Cpe-5P	2995	4775	Note 1
M	Cabr Cpe-2P	3595	4550	Note 1
M	Spds TC-4P	3595	4875	Note 1
M	Sed-5P	3395	4918	Note 1
Model M, 8-cyl., 113 hp, 145" wb				
M	Spds-4P	3745	4670	Note 1
M	Spds-7P	3895	4750	Note 1
M	Spds TC-4P	3995	4670	Note 1
M	Cls Cpld Spds-4P	3995	4770	Note 1
M	Conv Sed-5P	3995	4670	Note 1
M	Cabr Cpe-2P	3995	4650	Note 1
M	Sed-5P	3855	4863	Note 1
M	Sed-7P	3895	5010	Note 1
M	Limo-7P	3995	5050	Note 1
Model M/Weymann Custom, 8-cyl., 113 hp, 134-1/2" wb				
M	Chantilly Sed-5P	3895	4480	Note 1
M	Monaco Cpe-5P	3955	4535	Note 1
M	Deauville-5P	3955	4520	Note 1
Model M/Weymann Custom, 8-cyl., 113 hp, 145" wb				
M	Biarritz-5P	4115	4645	Note 1
M	Fontainbleau-7P	4145	4778	Note 1
M	Aix Les Baines-7P	4245	4778	Note 1

1929 Stutz, Model M, two-passenger coupe, AA

1929 Stutz, Model M, club coupe, AA

1929 Stutz, Model M, cabriolet coupe, AA

1929 Stutz, Monte Carlo (Model M), limousine (with body by Weymann), AA

1929 Stutz, Model M, transformable town car (with body by LeBaron), AA

1930 Stutz, Longchamps (Model MA), four-passenger (with body by Weymann), OCW

1932 Stutz, SV-16, four-passenger speedster (with tonneau cover), AA

1932 Stutz, DV-32 Patrician (with body by Brunn), OCW

1932 Stutz, DV-32, five-passenger sedan (with body by LeBaron), AA

1933 Stutz, SV-16 (Model 21), five-passenger sedan, OCW

Model M/Salon Custom, 8-cyl., 113 hp, 145" wb

Model No.	Body Type & Seating	Factory Price	Shipping Weight	Prod. Total
M	Sed-5P	4595	4910	Note 1
M	Limo-5P	4795	4950	Note 1
M	Brgm-6P	4795	4935	Note 1
M	Brgm Limo-6P	4995	4975	Note 1
M	Sed-6P	4795	4930	Note 1
M	Sed Limo-6P	4995	5055	Note 1
M	Sed Limo-7P	4995	5055	Note 1
M	Trans Cabr-5P	5410	—	Note 1
M	Trans Twn Car-5P	5500	5000	Note 1
M	Trans Twn Car-7P	6895	5000	Note 1

Note 1: Stutz production for 1929 totaled 2,320 with no body style breakout available.

1930

Model MA, 8-cyl., 113 hp, 134-1/2" wb

Model No.	Body Type & Seating	Factory Price	Shipping Weight	Prod. Total
MA	Spds-2P	3450	4595	Note 1
MA	Spds-4P	3450	4700	Note 1
MA	Spds TC-4P	3700	4775	Note 1
MA	Torp Spds-2P	3450	4735	Note 1
MA	Cpe-2P	3295	4850	Note 1
MA	Cpe-5P	3495	4950	Note 1
MA	Cabr Cpe-2P	3595	4850	Note 1
MA	Sed-5P	3695	4918	Note 1

Model MA, 8-cyl., 113 hp, 145" wb

Model No.	Body Type & Seating	Factory Price	Shipping Weight	Prod. Total
MA	Spds-4P	3745	4870	Note 1
MA	Spds-7P	3775	4950	Note 1
MA	Spds TC-4P	3995	4905	Note 1
MA	Conv Sed-5P	4395	5000	Note 1
MA	Cabr Cpe-2P	3995	5010	Note 1
MA	Sed-5P	3855	5045	Note 1
MA	Sed-7P	3895	5210	Note 1
MA	Limo-7P	3995	5050	Note 1

Model MA/Weymann Custom, 8-cyl., 113 hp, 134-1/2" wb

Model No.	Body Type & Seating	Factory Price	Shipping Weight	Prod. Total
MA	Chantilly Sed-5P	3895	4680	Note 1
MA	Monaco Cpe-5P	3955	4735	Note 1
MA	Deauville-5P	3955	4735	Note 1
MA	Longchamps-4P	4145	—	Note 1
MA	Versailles-5P	4145	—	Note 1

Model MA/Weymann Custom, 8-cyl., 113 hp, 145" wb

Model No.	Body Type & Seating	Factory Price	Shipping Weight	Prod. Total
MA	Biarritz-5P	4115	5000	Note 1
MA	Fontainbleau-7P	4145	5000	Note 1
MA	Aix Les Baines-7P	4245	5050	Note 1
MA	Chaumont-5P	4545	—	Note 1
MA	Monte Carlo-5P	4695	—	Note 1

Model MA/Salon Custom, 8-cyl., 113 hp, 145" wb

Model No.	Body Type & Seating	Factory Price	Shipping Weight	Prod. Total
MA	Sed-5P	4795	5110	Note 1
MA	Limo-5P	4995	5150	Note 1
MA	Brgm-6P	4995	5135	Note 1
MA	Brgm Limo-6P	5195	5175	Note 1
MA	Sed-6P	4995	5130	Note 1
MA	Sed Limo-6P	5195	5255	Note 1
MA	Sed Limo-7P	5195	5255	Note 1
MA	Trans Cabr-5P	5610	5200	Note 1
MA	Trans Twn Car-5P	5700	5250	Note 1
MA	Trans Twn Car-7P	7495	5200	Note 1

Note 1: Stutz production for 1930 totaled 1,038 with no body style breakout available.

1931

Model LA, 6-cyl., 85 hp, 127-1/2" wb

Model No.	Body Type & Seating	Factory Price	Shipping Weight	Prod. Total
LA	Spds-2P	2585	4105	Note 1
LA	Spds-4P	2585	4165	Note 1
LA	Spds TC-4P	2785	4210	Note 1
LA	Cpe-2P	2245	4355	Note 1
LA	Cpe-5P	1995	4200	Note 1
LA	Cabr Cpe-2/4P	2445	4285	Note 1
LA	Sed-5P	2245	4320	Note 1

Model MA, 8-cyl., 113 hp, 134-1/2" wb

Model No.	Body Type & Seating	Factory Price	Shipping Weight	Prod. Total
MA/24	Spds-2P	3495	4595	Note 1
MA/25	Spds-4P	3495	4700	Note 1
MA/26	Spds TC-4P	3795	4775	Note 1
MA/28	Torp Spds-2P	3595	4735	Note 1
MA/23	Cpe-2P	3495	4850	Note 1
MA/22	Cpe-5P	3445	4950	Note 1
MA/27	Cabr Cpe-2P	3595	4840	Note 1
MA/21	Sed-5P	3695	4918	Note 1

Model MA/Weymann Custom, 8-cyl., 113 hp, 134-1/2" wb

Model No.	Body Type & Seating	Factory Price	Shipping Weight	Prod. Total
MA/32	Longchamps-4P	4145	—	Note 1
MA/36	Versailles-5P	4145	—	Note 1

Model MB/Salon Custom, 8-cyl., 113 hp, 145" wb

Model No.	Body Type & Seating	Factory Price	Shipping Weight	Prod. Total
MB/60	Sed-5P	4795	5110	Note 1
MB/64	Sed-6P	4995	5130	Note 1
MB/62	Brgm-6P	4995	5135	Note 1
MB/63	Brgm Limo-6P	5195	5175	Note 1
MB/65	Sed Limo-6P	5195	5255	Note 1
MB/66	Sed Limo-7P	5195	5255	Note 1
MB/67	Trans Cabr-5P	5610	5200	Note 1
MB/88	Trans Twn Car-5P	5700	5250	Note 1
MB/90	Trans Twn Car-7P	7495	5200	Note 1
MB/53	Chaumont-5P	4545	—	Note 1
MB/54	Monte Carlo-5P	4695	—	Note 1

Note 1: Stutz production for 1931 totaled 310 with no body style breakout available.

Production Note: The DV-32 was introduced in April 1931.

1932

Model LAA, 6-cyl., 85 hp, 127-1/2" wb

Model No.	Body Type & Seating	Factory Price	Shipping Weight	Prod. Total
LAA	Cpe-4P	1620	4200	Note 1
LAA	Cpe-5P	1620	4355	Note 1
LAA	Sed-5P	1620	4520	Note 1
LAA	Club Sed-5P	1620	4420	Note 1

Model SV-16, 8-cyl., 115 hp, 134-1/2" wb

Model No.	Body Type & Seating	Factory Price	Shipping Weight	Prod. Total
SV-16	Spds-2P	3495	4595	Note 1
SV-16	Spds-4P	3795	4775	Note 1
SV-16	Torp Spds-2P	3595	4620	Note 1
SV-16	Cpe-4P	2995	4850	Note 1
SV-16	Cpe-5P	2695	4950	Note 1
SV-16	Cabr Cpe-4P	3345	4840	Note 1
SV-16	Cont Cpe-3P	5775	—	Note 1
SV-16	Sed-5P	2995	4918	Note 1
SV-16	Club Sed-5P	3095	4918	Note 1
SV-16	Longchamps-4P	4345	4318	Note 1
SV-16	Versailles-5P	4395	4318	Note 1

Model SV-16, 8-cyl., 115 hp, 145" wb

Model No.	Body Type & Seating	Factory Price	Shipping Weight	Prod. Total
SV-16	Spds-7P	3895	4950	Note 1
SV-16	Sed-5P	3895	5045	Note 1
SV-16	Sed-6P	4595	5100	Note 1
SV-16	Sed-7P	3895	5210	Note 1
SV-16	Spt Sed-4P	7095	—	Note 1
SV-16	Conv Sed-5P	4395	5045	Note 1
SV-16	Conv Vic-4P	6400	—	Note 1
SV-16	Limo-7P	3995	5255	Note 1
SV-16	Sed Limo-6P	4995	5255	Note 1
SV-16	Sed Limo-7P	4995	—	Note 1
SV-16	Chaumont-5P	4745	4548	Note 1
SV-16	Brgm-6P	4795	5135	Note 1
SV-16	Monte Carlo-5P	4895	4547	Note 1
SV-16	Brgm Limo-6P	4995	5135	Note 1
SV-16	Trans Cabr-7P	5495	5200	Note 1
SV-16	Prnc of Wales-6P	6245	—	Note 1
SV-16	Tuxedo Cabr-5P	7095	—	Note 1
SV-16	Patrician Cpe-5P	7095	—	Note 1
SV-16	Trans Twn Car-7P	7495	5305	Note 1

Model DV-32, 8-cyl., 156 hp, 134-1/2" wb

Model No.	Body Type & Seating	Factory Price	Shipping Weight	Prod. Total
DV-32	Bearcat	5895	—	Note 1

Note: All other models same as SV-16, with prices $1,000 more than SV-16.

Model DV-32, 8-cyl., 156 hp, 145" wb

Note: All models same as SV-16, with prices $1,000 more than SV-16.

Model DV-32, 8-cyl., 156 hp, 116" wb

Model No.	Body Type & Seating	Factory Price	Shipping Weight	Prod. Total
DV-32	Super Bearcat	5895	—	Note 1

Note 1: Stutz production for 1932 totaled 206 with no body style breakout available.

1933

Model LAA, 6-cyl., 85 hp, 127-1/2" wb

Model No.	Body Type & Seating	Factory Price	Shipping Weight	Prod. Total
LAA	Sed-5P	1895	4520	Note 1
LAA	Club Sed-5P	1895	4420	Note 1
LAA	Cpe-4P	1895	4200	Note 1
LAA	Cpe-5P	1895	4355	Note 1
LAA	Cabr Cpe-4P	2185	4342	Note 1

Model SV-16, 8-cyl., 115 hp, 134-1/2" wb

Model No.	Body Type & Seating	Factory Price	Shipping Weight	Prod. Total
SV-16	Spds-2P	3095	4528	Note 1
SV-16	Spds-4P	3795	—	Note 1
SV-16	Torp Spds-2P	3195	—	Note 1
SV-16	Cpe-4P	2995	4750	Note 1

Model No.	Body Type & Seating	Factory Price	Shipping Weight	Prod. Total
SV-16	Cpe-5P	2695	5290	Note 1
SV-16	Cabr Cpe-4P	3195	4865	Note 1
SV-16	Sed-5P	2995	5320	Note 1
SV-16	Club Sed-5P	3095	5300	Note 1
SV-16	Versailles-5P	4395	4318	Note 1

Model SV-16, 8-cyl., 115 hp, 145" wb

Model No.	Body Type & Seating	Factory Price	Shipping Weight	Prod. Total
SV-16	Spds-4P	3895	4750	Note 1
SV-16	Sed-5P	3410	5346	Note 1
SV-16	Sed-6P	4745	5320	Note 1
SV-16	Sed-7P	3460	5520	Note 1
SV-16	Conv Sed-5P	3710	5386	Note 1
SV-16	Limo-7P	3660	5556	Note 1
SV-16	Brgm Limo-6P	4995	5410	Note 1
SV-16	Sed Limo-6P	4995	5430	Note 1
SV-16	Cabr Cpe-4P	3660	5015	Note 1
SV-16	Chaumont-5P	4745	4952	Note 1
SV-16	Brgm-6P	4795	5410	Note 1
SV-16	Monte Carlo-5P	4895	5120	Note 1
SV-16	Twn Car-7P	5495	5502	Note 1

Model DV-32, 8-cyl., 156 hp, 134-1/2" wb

Model No.	Body Type & Seating	Factory Price	Shipping Weight	Prod. Total
DV-32	Bearcat	5895	—	Note 1

Note: All other models same as SV-16, with prices $700 more than SV-16.

Model DV-32, 8-cyl., 156 hp, 145" wb

Note: All models same as SV-16, with prices $700 more than SV-16.

Model DV-32, 8-cyl., 156 hp, 116" wb

Model No.	Body Type & Seating	Factory Price	Shipping Weight	Prod. Total
DV-32	Super Bearcat	5895	—	Note 1

Note 1: Stutz production for 1933 totaled 80 with no body style breakout available.

1934

Model SV-16, 8-cyl., 115 hp, 134-1/2" wb

Model No.	Body Type & Seating	Factory Price	Shipping Weight	Prod. Total
SV-16	Spds-2P	3095	—	Note 1
SV-16	Spds-4P	3195	4528	Note 1
SV-16	Torp Spds-2P	3795	—	Note 1
SV-16	Cpe-4P	—	4750	Note 1
SV-16	Cpe-5P	3095	5290	Note 1
SV-16	Conv Cpe-4P	—	4865	Note 1
SV-16	Sed-5P	2995	5320	Note 1
SV-16	Club Sed-5P	3195	5300	Note 1
SV-16	Versailles-5P	—	4318	Note 1

Model SV-16, 8-cyl., 115 hp, 145" wb

Model No.	Body Type & Seating	Factory Price	Shipping Weight	Prod. Total
SV-16	Conv Cpe-4P	3710	5015	Note 1
SV-16	Sed-7P	3660	5520	Note 1
SV-16	Limo-7P	3660	5556	Note 1
SV-16	Chaumont-5P	4745	4950	Note 1
SV-16	Monte Carlo-5P	4895	5300	Note 1

Model DV-32, 8-cyl., 156 hp, 134-1/2" wb

Note: All models same as SV-16, with prices $700 more than SV-16.

Model DV-32, 8-cyl., 156 hp, 145" wb

Note: All models same as SV-16, with prices $700 more than SV-16.

Note 1: Stutz production for 1934 totaled six with no body style breakout available.

1935

Model SV-16, 8-cyl., 115 hp, 134-1/2" wb

Model No.	Body Type & Seating	Factory Price	Shipping Weight	Prod. Total
SV-16	Spds-2P	3195	4488	Note 1
SV-16	Cpe-2P	3095	4619	Note 1
SV-16	Sed-5P	3095	4745	Note 1

Model SV-16, 8-cyl., 115 hp, 145" wb

Model No.	Body Type & Seating	Factory Price	Shipping Weight	Prod. Total
SV-16	Sed-7P	3560	4980	Note 1

Model DV-32, 8-cyl., 156 hp, 134-1/2" wb

Note: All models same as SV-16, with prices $700 more than SV-16.

Model DV-32, 8-cyl., 156 hp, 145" wb

Note: All models same as SV-16, with prices $700 more than SV-16.

Note 1: Stutz production for 1935 totaled two with no body style breakout available.

Production Note: A 1936 Stutz was announced, but the automaker admitted insolvency in court one year later with no new models available for either year.

Built at the time when the Stutz Motor Car Co. was quickly fading from the automotive scene, the cars it produced, nonetheless, remained second to none from a design and engineering standpoint. One of Stutz Motor's parting shots was this 1933 DV-32 four-passenger speedster with tonneau cover, which cost almost $4,600 at the height of the Great Depression.

OVERLAND

OVERLAND — Terre Haute, Indiana (1903-1905)/Indianapolis, Indiana — (1905-1909)/Toledo, Ohio (1909-1926, 1939) — The name for the car was decided over a coffeebreak one day during the fall of 1902 by Charles Minshall, president of the Standard Wheel Company of Terre Haute, and Claude E. Cox, who had just graduated from the Ross Polytechnic Institute in town. The sum total of both these men's experience in the automobile field was Cox's senior thesis project for which he had devised a four-wheeler out of a motorized tricycle. This, Minshall believed, was sufficient acquaintanceship with motor matters for Cox to design an automobile and head Standard Wheel's new automobile department. With some trepidation, the young man proceeded and came up with an Overland that was a quite advanced little car for its day. Its water-cooled 5 hp single-cylinder engine was mounted up front under a hood, a two-speed planetary transmission controlled by a foot pedal was fitted, together with jump spark ignition and a two-way switch plug for changeover between the two dry batteries, the plug being removable for "carrying in the pocket when the machine is left standing on the street to prevent any unauthorized person from starting it." The prototype of the Overland was tested in Terre Haute on February 12, 1903, with about 12 more built that year. Production doubled in 1904, when a two-cylinder model was added, and Cox was already at work on a revised twin and new four, both incorporating a steering wheel and shaft drive, for 1905. By January of that year, the facilities in Terre Haute being cramped, Cox moved the Overland automobile department into an abandoned Standard Wheel plant in Indianapolis. Scarcely had he got down to business there when Minshall had a change of heart; thus far his automotive venture had made no profit, a situation he concluded was not likely to improve, so he decided to forget the whole thing. Fortunately for Claude Cox, a buggy manufacturer in Indianapolis who was a Standard Wheel customer and who earlier had tried to build an automobile himself was fascinated by the two new Overland models and offered to back Cox in their production. For 51 percent of the stock, David M. Parry put up all the money necessary to organize the Overland Auto Company on March 31, 1906, and hastily built a few additions to his Parry Manufacturing Company factory. Production began, and the Panic of 1907 arrived. So did John North Willys. An automobile dealer from Elmira (New York), Willys had contracted for the Overland company's entire output (47 cars) for 1906, and had sent in a hefty order for 500 cars, with a $10,000 deposit, for 1907. When no cars were delivered and correspondence from the factory ceased, Willys entrained for Indianapolis to find out what was going on. There he discovered Parry had lost everything including his house in the Panic (a few years later he would recoup sufficiently to build the Parry automobile), and that parts were on hand for less than three automobiles. Willys took over. For the year following, until he could secure factory facilities, he built the Overlands in a circus tent, some 465 cars in 1908, all of them 20/24 hp fours. In January 1909, aghast at the feverish pace Willys was setting, Claude Cox left the company in anger. Willys' production of Overlands that year was an incredible 4,907 cars, some of them a new 45 hp six. Also in 1909, Willys bought a controlling interest in the Marion Motor Car Company in Marion, Ohio; purchased the huge and idle factory in Toledo that had formerly seen production of the Pope-Toledo and into which he would now move his Overland; and brought together all his varied interests in a new organization called the Willys-Overland Company. Production in 1910 tripled to 15,598 cars. Fours only were produced, in a confusing and staggering array of models, from 1910 through 1914, some varieties were fitted with sliding gear transmissions by 1912. In 1915, left-hand drive was introduced, and a six was returned to the line. But the biggest news from Willys-Overland arrived in October 1917, when the company announced an Overland four to challenge the Model T Ford head-on with a price tag of less than $500 to include self-starter and electric lights. John North Willys was riding high. From 1912 through the World War I years, only Henry Ford outproduced him. From a 1912 output of 28,572 cars, Willys-Overland production soared to 140,111 by 1916, mostly Overlands, though a healthy percentage of Willys' new Willys-Knight car introduced in 1914 was included. From a net Overland profit of $1 million in 1908, the Willys-Overland coffers were augmented by a $10 million profit in 1915. Meanwhile, John North Willys had taken to buying things: companies such as Moline Plow (makers of the Stephens Salient Six in Illinois) and factories such as the gargantuan Duesenberg facility in Elizabeth (New Jersey), these purchases made in 1918 and 1919, respectively. In 1917, a merger with Curtiss had put Willys in the presidency of that East Coast aviation company. By now Willys had removed himself from Toledo to New York City from whence he managed the affairs of Willys Corporation, his new holding company. Back in Ohio he installed Clarence A. Earl, a former hardware manufacturing executive, to see to continuing fortuitous production, which alas Earl did not do. A disastrous strike in Toledo, in addition to wartime exigencies, delayed introduction of the Overland competitor to the Model T until October of 1919, and when finally it was introduced its price tag was $845 and the Ford in the meantime had been provided a self-starter, which made the new Overland really no competitor at all. A new line of Willys-Knight fours was moving well in the marketplace, and an interesting Willys six was being developed in the former Duesenberg plant, but none of this forestalled the financial disaster toward which Willys Corporation was plummeting when the postwar recession hit. In order to survive, Willys needed the help of a bank, and Chase in Manhattan offered same with the condition that former Buick President Walter Percy Chrysler be brought in to manage things. Chrysler agreed for a flat million-dollar-a-year salary; his first two acts on the job were to cut John North Willys' salary in half (to $75,000, which was clearly a power play) and to fire Clarence Earl (which he probably had coming, though he immediately found fresh employment with Benjamin Briscoe). Enamored neither of the low-priced field nor the sleeve-valve engine, Chrysler was not impressed with the Overland or the Willys-Knight, though he was intrigued by the Willys six being developed in the Duesenberg plant. After two years of instituting cost-cutting measures for Willys, Chrysler left to take on a similar salvage job for Maxwell-Chalmers. Through a clever maneuvering of Willys Corporation into receivership and himself back into the driver's seat at Willys-Overland, John North Willys had his company back. The Willys interest in Curtiss was disposed of. The former Duesenberg plant in Elizabeth was sold to Billy Durant, and through a curious set of circumstances, the Willys six that had been developed there would ultimately evolve into the first Chrysler. Meanwhile, John North Willys was back on the job in Toledo and doing phenomenally well in revitalizing his company via the two cars that Chrysler had pooh-poohed: the Willys-Knight and the Overland. Realizing by now that a head-on competitor to the Model T was not a viable idea, Willys revised the Overland four into a slightly larger and more powerful—and prettier—car to which he attached appealing model designations like Blue Bird and Red Bird, and equally attractive price tags in the $700 range. Willys-Overland sales soared: from nearly 50,000 cars in 1921 to over 150,000 in 1925. During that same period, the Willys-Overland treasury improved from a deficit of $20 million to a profit nearly approaching that figure. In 1925, an Overland six was added to the line, to be continued together with the Overland fours the following year. But these would be the last cars from the company to bear the Overland name for over a decade. In 1927, the Whippet arrived, superseding the Overland. The Whippet would be discontinued in 1931, all succeeding cars carrying the Willys name as the country plunged into the Great Depression and Willys-Overland into receivership again. The Overland name returned briefly in 1939 for a line of low-priced fours that evolved into the Willys Americar by 1941. But by that time the man who had saved the Overland from oblivion in 1907 was no longer there. John North Willys died in August 1935.

1903

Model 13 — 1-cyl.

Model No.	Body Type & Seating	Factory Price	Shipping Weight	Prod. Total
13	Rbt.-2P	595	—	11

1904

Model 13 — 1-cyl.

Model No.	Body Type & Seating	Factory Price	Shipping Weight	Prod. Total
13	Rbt.-2P	595	—	Note 1
Model 15 — 2-cyl., 6-1/2 hp, 72" wb				
15	Rbt.-2P	600	—	Note 1

Note 1: Overland production for 1904 totaled 23 with no body style breakout available.

1905

Model 15 — 2-cyl., 7 hp, 72" wb

Model No.	Body Type & Seating	Factory Price	Shipping Weight	Prod. Total
15	Rbt.-2P	600	—	Note 1
Model 17 — 2-cyl., 9 hp, 78" wb				
17	Rbt.-2P	750	—	Note 1
Model 18 — 4-cyl., 16 hp, 90" wb				
18	Side Ent. Tonn.-4P	1500	—	Note 1

Note 1: Overland production for 1905 totaled 36 with no body style breakout available.

1906

Model 16 — 2-cyl., 9 hp, 78" wb

Model No.	Body Type & Seating	Factory Price	Shipping Weight	Prod. Total
16	Rbt.-2P	1250	—	Note 1

Model 18 — 4-cyl., 16 hp, 90" wb

Model No.	Body Type & Seating	Factory Price	Shipping Weight	Prod. Total
18	Tonn.-4P	1250	—	Note 1

Note 1: Overland production for 1906 totaled 47 with no body style breakout available.

1907

Model 22 — 4-cyl., 16/18 hp, 86" wb

Model No.	Body Type & Seating	Factory Price	Shipping Weight	Prod. Total
22	Spl. Rbt.	1250	—	Note 1
22	Tr.-5P	1250	—	Note 1

Note 1: Overland production for 1907 totaled five with no body style breakout available.

1908

Model 24 — 4-cyl., 20/22 hp, 96" wb

Model No.	Body Type & Seating	Factory Price	Shipping Weight	Prod. Total
24	Rbt.	1250	—	Note 1
24	Tr.-5P	1250	—	Note 1

Note 1: Overland production for 1908 totaled 465 with no body style breakout available.

1909

Model 30 — 4-cyl., 30 hp, 108" wb

Model No.	Body Type & Seating	Factory Price	Shipping Weight	Prod. Total
30	Rds.-4P	1300	—	Note 1
30	Cpe -2P	1650	—	Note 1
30	Tonn.-5P	1400	—	Note 1

Model 31 — 4-cyl., 30 hp, 110" wb

Model No.	Body Type & Seating	Factory Price	Shipping Weight	Prod. Total
31	Tourist	1400	—	Note 1
31	Toy Tonn.	1400	—	Note 1
31	Taxi	1400	—	Note 1

Model 32 — 4-cyl., 30 hp, 110" wb, three-speed transmission

Model No.	Body Type & Seating	Factory Price	Shipping Weight	Prod. Total
32	Tr.-5P	1500	—	Note 1
32	Rds.-3P	1500	—	Note 1
32	Rds.-4P	1500	—	Note 1

Model 34 — 6-cyl., 35 hp, 116" wb

Model No.	Body Type & Seating	Factory Price	Shipping Weight	Prod. Total
34	Rds.-4P	2000	—	Note 1

Note 1: Overland production for 1909 totaled 4,907 with no body style breakout available.

1910

Model 38 — 4-cyl., 25 hp, 102" wb

Model No.	Body Type & Seating	Factory Price	Shipping Weight	Prod. Total
38	Rds.-2P	1000	—	Note 1
38	Rds.-3P	1000	—	Note 1
38	Rds.-4P	1000	—	Note 1
38	Toy Tonn.	1000	—	Note 1

Model 40 — 4-cyl., 35 hp, 112" wb

Model No.	Body Type & Seating	Factory Price	Shipping Weight	Prod. Total
40	Rds.-3P	1250	—	Note 1
40	Rds.-4P	1450	—	Note 1

Model 41 — 4-cyl., 35 hp, 112" wb

Model No.	Body Type & Seating	Factory Price	Shipping Weight	Prod. Total
41	Tr.-5P	1450	—	Note 1
41	C.C. Tr.-4P	1500	—	Note 1

Model 42 — 4-cyl., 35 hp, 112" wb

Model No.	Body Type & Seating	Factory Price	Shipping Weight	Prod. Total
42	Tr.-5P	1500	—	Note 1
42	C.C. Tr.-4P	1850	—	Note 1

Note 1: Overland production for 1910 totaled 15,598 with no body style breakout available.

1911

Model 45/46/47 — 4-cyl., 20 hp, 96" wb

Model No.	Body Type & Seating	Factory Price	Shipping Weight	Prod. Total
45	Rds.-2P	775	—	Note 1
46	Torp. Rds.-2P	850	—	Note 1
47	Tr.-5P	850	—	Note 1
—	Cpe.-3P (102" wb)	1250	—	Note 1

Model 49 — 4-cyl., 25 hp, 102" wb

Model No.	Body Type & Seating	Factory Price	Shipping Weight	Prod. Total
49	Tr.-5P	1095	—	Note 1

Model 50/51 — 4-cyl., 30 hp, 110" wb

Model No.	Body Type & Seating	Factory Price	Shipping Weight	Prod. Total
50	Torp. Rds.-2P	1250	—	Note 1
51	Fore-Door Tr.-5P	1250	—	Note 1

Model 52/53/54/55/56 — 4-cyl., 40 hp, 118" wb

Model No.	Body Type & Seating	Factory Price	Shipping Weight	Prod. Total
53	Torp. Rds.-2P	1600	—	Note 1
54	Torp. Rds.-4P	1675	—	Note 1
55	Fore-Door Tr.-5P	1300	—	Note 1
56	Tr.-7P	1350	—	Note 1
52	Limo.-7P	2750	—	Note 1

Note 1: Overland production for 1911 totaled 18,745 with no body style breakout available.

1912

Model 58 — 4-cyl., 25 hp, 96" wb

Model No.	Body Type & Seating	Factory Price	Shipping Weight	Prod. Total
58	Rds.-2P	850	—	Note 1

Model 59 — 4-cyl., 30 hp, 106" wb

Model No.	Body Type & Seating	Factory Price	Shipping Weight	Prod. Total
59	Rds.	900	—	Note 1
59	Tr.	900	—	Note 1
59	Dly.	900	—	Note 1
59	Cpe.	1250	—	Note 1

Model 60 — 4-cyl., 35 hp, 114" wb

Model No.	Body Type & Seating	Factory Price	Shipping Weight	Prod. Total
60	Tr.-4P	1200	—	Note 1
60	Tr.-5P	1200	—	Note 1

Model 61 — 4-cyl., 45 hp, 118" wb

Model No.	Body Type & Seating	Factory Price	Shipping Weight	Prod. Total
61	Rds.	1500	—	Note 1
61	Tr.-4P	1500	—	Note 1
61	Tr.-5P	1500	—	Note 1
61	Cpe.	2000	—	Note 1

Note 1: Overland production for 1912 totaled 28,572 with no body style breakout available.

1913

Model 69 — 4-cyl., 25.6 hp, 110" wb

Model No.	Body Type & Seating	Factory Price	Shipping Weight	Prod. Total
69	Tr.-5P	985	—	Note 1
69	Rds.-2P	985	—	Note 1
69	Tr.-4P	1010	—	Note 1
69	Cpe.-3P	1500	—	Note 1

Model 71 — 4-cyl., 30.6 hp, 114" wb

Model No.	Body Type & Seating	Factory Price	Shipping Weight	Prod. Total
71	Tr.-5P	1475	—	Note 1
71	Rds.-2P	1475	—	Note 1
71	Tr.-4P	1475	—	Note 1

Note 1: Overland production for 1913 totaled 37,422 with no body style breakout available.

1914

Model 79 — 4-cyl., 35 hp, 114" wb

Model No.	Body Type & Seating	Factory Price	Shipping Weight	Prod. Total
79	Rds.-2P	950	—	Note 1
79	Tr.-5P	950	—	Note 1
79	Cpe.-4P	1550	—	Note 1

Model 46 — 4-cyl., 35 hp

Model No.	Body Type & Seating	Factory Price	Shipping Weight	Prod. Total
46	Tr.-5P	1075	—	Note 1

Note 1: Overland production for 1914 totaled 48,461 with no body style breakout available.

1915

Model 81 — 4-cyl., 30 hp, 106" wb

Model No.	Body Type & Seating	Factory Price	Shipping Weight	Prod. Total
81	Tr.-5P	850	—	NA
81	Rds.-2P	795	—	NA
81	Pan. Dly.	895	—	NA
81	Ex. Dly.	850	—	NA

Model 80 — 4-cyl., 35 hp, 114" wb

Model No.	Body Type & Seating	Factory Price	Shipping Weight	Prod. Total
80	Tr.-5P	1075	—	NA
80	Rds.-2P	1050	—	NA
80	Cpe.-4P	1600	—	NA

Model 82 — 6-cyl., 45/50 hp, 125" wb

Model No.	Body Type & Seating	Factory Price	Shipping Weight	Prod. Total
82	Tr.-7P	1475	—	NA

Production Note: Beginning in 1915 through 1926, Overland production was combined with Willys with no breakout available. See Willys for combined production total.

1916

Model 75 — 4-cyl., 20/25 hp, 104" wb

Model No.	Body Type & Seating	Factory Price	Shipping Weight	Prod. Total
75	Tr.-5P	615	—	NA
75	Rds.-2P	595	—	NA

Model 83 — 4-cyl., 35 hp, 106" wb

Model No.	Body Type & Seating	Factory Price	Shipping Weight	Prod. Total
83	Tr.-5P	750	—	NA
83	Win. Top Tr.-5P	950	—	NA
83	Rds.-2P	725	—	NA
83	Win. Top Rds.	875	—	NA
83	Pan. Dly.	750	—	NA
83	Open Dly.	725	—	NA
83	Limo.	950	—	NA
83	Conv. Cpe.-2P	875	—	NA

Model 84 — 4-cyl., 40 hp, 114" wb

Model No.	Body Type & Seating	Factory Price	Shipping Weight	Prod. Total
84	Rds.	1095	—	NA
84	Tr.	1125	—	NA
84	Cpe.	1500	—	NA
84	Limo.	1750	—	NA

Model 86 — 6-cyl., 45/50 hp, 125" wb

Model No.	Body Type & Seating	Factory Price	Shipping Weight	Prod. Total
86	Tr.-7P	1145	—	NA

1917

Big Four 85 — 4-cyl., 35 hp, 112" wb

Model No.	Body Type & Seating	Factory Price	Shipping Weight	Prod. Total
85	Cpe.-3P	795	—	NA
85	Sed.-5P	795	—	NA
85	Conv. Cpe.-4P	1045	—	NA
85	Conv. Sed.-5P	1195	—	NA

Light Six 85 — 6-cyl., 35/40 hp, 116" wb

Model No.	Body Type & Seating	Factory Price	Shipping Weight	Prod. Total
85	Rds.-3P	970	—	NA
85	Tr.-5P	925	—	NA
85	Conv. Cpe.-4P	1125	—	NA
85	Conv. Sed.-5P	1325	—	NA

Model 88 — 6-cyl., 45/50 hp, 125" wb

Model No.	Body Type & Seating	Factory Price	Shipping Weight	Prod. Total
88	Tr.-7P	1385	—	NA

1918

Light Four 90 — 4-cyl., 32 hp, 106" wb

Model No.	Body Type & Seating	Factory Price	Shipping Weight	Prod. Total
90	Tr.-5P	795	—	NA
90	Rds.-2P	780	—	NA
90	Cty. Clb. Rds.	840	—	NA
90	Sed.-5P	1240	—	NA

Big Four 85 — 4-cyl., 35 hp, 112" wb

Model No.	Body Type & Seating	Factory Price	Shipping Weight	Prod. Total
85	Cpe.-3P	1285	—	NA
85	Sed.-5P	1485	—	NA

Light Six 85 — 6-cyl., 35/40 hp, 116" wb

Model No.	Body Type & Seating	Factory Price	Shipping Weight	Prod. Total
85	Rds.-3P	1115	—	NA
85	Tr.-5P	1130	—	NA
85	Tr. Sed.-5P	1620	—	NA
85	Tr. Cpe.-3P	1420	—	NA

1919

Light Four 90 — 4-cyl., 32 hp, 106" wb

Model No.	Body Type & Seating	Factory Price	Shipping Weight	Prod. Total
90	Tr.-5P	985	—	NA
90	Rds.-3P	985	—	NA
90	Sed.-5P	1495	—	NA

1920

Model 4 — 4-cyl., 27 hp, 100" wb

Model No.	Body Type & Seating	Factory Price	Shipping Weight	Prod. Total
4	Tr.-5P	845	1940	NA
4	Rds.-2P	845	—	NA
4	Sed.-5P	1495	2152	NA

1921

Model 4 — 4-cyl., 27 hp, 100" wb

Model No.	Body Type & Seating	Factory Price	Shipping Weight	Prod. Total
4	Tr.-5P	895	1940	NA
4	Rds.-2P	895	—	NA
4	Cpe.-3P	1425	—	NA
4	Sed.-5P	1475	2192	NA

1922

Model 4 — 4-cyl., 27 hp, 100" wb

Model No.	Body Type & Seating	Factory Price	Shipping Weight	Prod. Total
4	Tr.-5P	595	1940	NA
4	Rds.-3P	595	—	NA
4	Cpe.-3P	850	—	NA
4	Sed.-5P	895	2192	NA

1923

Model 91 — 4-cyl., 27 hp, 100" wb

Model No.	Body Type & Seating	Factory Price	Shipping Weight	Prod. Total
91	Tr.-5P	525	2020	NA
91	Rds.-2P	525	—	NA
91	Cpe.-2P	795	—	NA
91	Sed.-5P	875	2200	NA

Model 92 — 4-cyl., 30 hp, 106" wb

Model No.	Body Type & Seating	Factory Price	Shipping Weight	Prod. Total
92	Redbird-5P	750	2047	NA

1924

Model 91 — 4-cyl., 27 hp, 100" wb

Model No.	Body Type & Seating	Factory Price	Shipping Weight	Prod. Total
91	Tr.-5P	495	2040	NA
91	Rds.-2P	495	—	NA
91	Champ. Sed.-5P	695	—	NA
91	Sed.-5P	795	2209	NA

Model 92 — 4-cyl., 30 hp, 106" wb

Model No.	Body Type & Seating	Factory Price	Shipping Weight	Prod. Total
92	Redbird-5P	—	2047	NA
92	Blackbird	—	—	NA
92	Bluebird-5P	—	—	NA

1925

Model 91 — 4-cyl., 27 hp, 100" wb

Model No.	Body Type & Seating	Factory Price	Shipping Weight	Prod. Total
91	Tr.-5P	530	1910	NA
91	Rds.-2P	530	1834	NA
91	Cpe.-2P	695	2013	NA
91	Sed.-5P	850	2205	NA

Model 92 — 4-cyl., 30 hp, 106" wb

Model No.	Body Type & Seating	Factory Price	Shipping Weight	Prod. Total
92	Tr.-5P	725	2044	NA

Model 93 — 6-cyl., 38 hp, 113" wb

Model No.	Body Type & Seating	Factory Price	Shipping Weight	Prod. Total
93	Sed.-5P	825	2500	NA
93	Del. Sed.-5P	—	—	NA

1926

Model 91 — 4-cyl., 27 hp, 100" wb

Model No.	Body Type & Seating	Factory Price	Shipping Weight	Prod. Total
91	Tr.-5P	495	1919	NA
91	Cpe.-2P	625	2060	NA
91	Sed.-5P	595	2205	NA
91	Del. Sed.-5P	695	2205	NA

Model 92 — 4-cyl., 30 hp, 106" wb

Model No.	Body Type & Seating	Factory Price	Shipping Weight	Prod. Total
92	Tr.-5P	—	—	NA

Model 93 — 6-cyl., 38 hp, 113" wb

Model No.	Body Type & Seating	Factory Price	Shipping Weight	Prod. Total
93	Tr.-5P	825	—	NA
93	Sed.-5P	895	2443	NA
93	Del. Sed.-5P	1095	2584	NA
93	Cpe.-2P	—	—	NA

1909 Overland, Model 32, roadster, OCW

1913 Overland, Model 69, coupe, HAC

1914 Overland, Model 79, touring HAC

1916 Overland, Model 83, limousine, HAC

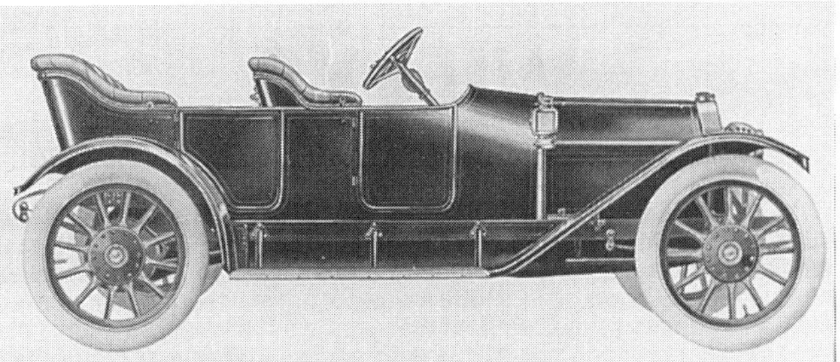
1912 Overland, Model 60, touring, HAC

1914 Overland, Model 79, roadster, HAC

1914 Overland, Model 79, coupe, HAC

1915 Overland, Model 80, coupe, HAC

1922 Overland, Model 4, touring, HAC

WILLYS

WILLYS-KNIGHT — Toledo, Ohio — (1914-1933)/WILLYS — (1916-1918, 1930-1942 et seq.) — Although John North Willys had been guiding the fortunes of the Overland company since 1907 (it was renamed Willys-Overland in 1909), it was not until 1914 that a car carried his name. Joining the Overland that year was the Willys-Knight, the sleeve-valve-engined car that was to endure longer than any other, with Willys-Overland ultimately producing more Knight-engined cars than virtually all other manufacturers in the world combined. Super salesman that he had been since his sporting goods store days in Elmira, New York, at the turn of the century, Willys doubtless was drawn to the Knight engine because of its novelty and the promotional advantages it promised, rather than any engineering features in its favor. John North Willys did not know a great deal about what made cars go, but he assuredly knew how to sell them. Already he had demonstrated that with the Overland; now he would become an unrelentingly ardent champion of the Knight. His first move had been made in this direction in 1913 with his outright purchase of the Edwards Motor Car Company, the drawings and factory equipment of which he moved from Long Island City (New York), together with H.J. Edwards himself, to Elyria (Ohio) and the former Garford plant that he owned. There the four-cylinder Willys-Knight was put into production as a relatively expensive $2,500-range car, which it remained for only a single year. By 1915, quantity production of a car in the $1,000 range was decided upon, with sleeve-valve engine manufacture only in Elyria thereafter, and Willys-Knight assembly integrated into the company's huge Toledo factory complex. A poppet-valve Willys Six (Continental engine) in the $1,300 range was introduced in late 1916 and remained for three seasons, and a $1,950 V-8 version of the Willys-Knight arrived in 1917 for a two-year stay. The flurry of Overland, Willys and Willys-Knight models now being offered by the company was bewildering, however, and not practical in view of the wartime shortages of material that would continue to plague manufacturers for some time after the Armistice. Thus, by 1919, the Willys-Overland Company decided to focus emphasis on but three cars: a low-priced Overland to compete with the Model T (which alas it would not), a Willys-Knight four in the $2,000 range (which, given the spiraling inflation of the period, would represent a fine buy, and by 1922 was down to $1,375), and a new Willys six that was then undergoing development in the former Duesenberg plant in Elizabeth, New Jersey (which would ultimately arrive on the marketplace, but not as a Willys). Rather like William C. Durant with General Motors, John North Willys had overextended himself. Buying the former Duesenberg plant had been but one of many company/factory purchases he made for his burgeoning empire, this one the most potentially interesting because of the six-cylinder car he ordered to be developed there for Willys Corporation (the holding company for all Willys' enterprises) by three former Studebaker engineers named Zeder, Skelton and Breer. In financial backwater in 1919, however, John North Willys was forced by Chase National Bank to accept outside management of his automobile business—and that management was in the person of former Buick President Walter Percy Chrysler. Chrysler remained in charge at Willys for just two years, ultimately leaving to perform a similar salvage operation at Maxwell-Chalmers. Thereafter John North Willys regained control of his Willys-Overland Company by a deft maneuvering of stock, and by moving the holding company of Willys Corporation into receivership. William C. Durant, now beginning his second empire, was high bidder for the former Duesenberg plant in Elizabeth at the auction sale, but the Willys Six that had been developed there was not of particular interest to him. It most certainly was, however, to Walter Chrysler; he had eyed the design covetously during his Willys days, and now that concept would be evolved into the first Chrysler. Meanwhile, never one to cry over spilled milk, John North Willys was back heartily on the job in Toledo directing production of two cars he still had: the Overland and the Willys-Knight, neither of which Chrysler had particularly cared for. But Chrysler had been wrong obviously, for what John North Willys accomplished now was nothing short of phenomenal. From less than 50,000 cars sold in 1921, Willys worked sales up to over 200,000 in 1925. From an indebtedness of $20 million, he worked up to a profit almost equaling that figure, also in 1925. Although the lower-priced Overlands accounted for the vast majority of the cars he sold, the Willys-Knight proved an immensely popular contender in the medium-priced field, 50,000 or more of them being sold annually. For the 1925 model year, the Lanchester vibration damper was introduced, as well as a new six-cylinder line of Willys-Knights. That year, Willys bought out the Stearns-Knight of Cleveland, and continued that higher-priced Knight-engined car in production until after the stock market crash. From 1926 forward, all Knights from Willys were sixes, including a brand-new lower-priced car called the Falcon-Knight, which was built for him by a friend in Elyria (and which would be absorbed into the Willys-Knight line in 1929). In the fall of 1926, he introduced another new car called the Whippet, which took off like a rocket. In the fall of 1929, believing all was well with his company, John North Willys relinquished his firm's presidency to former first Vice-President Linwood A. Miller; in March 1930, he became this nation's first ambassador to Poland. Two years later, with the Great Depression raging and at the request of President Hoover, he returned to manage his now-troubled company in Toledo. In his absence a poppet-valve Willys Six good for 65 hp and 72 mph had been introduced for 1930 in the $695-$850 range, followed later that year by an 80 hp Continental-engined eight at $1,245-$1,395. Freewheeling came in, and the Whippet went out for 1931; a synchronized transmission from Warner Gear arrived for 1932. Willys-Overland sales that year totaled just 26,444 cars. But already in development at the company was a new car that John North Willys believed would provide salvation. It was the Willys 77, in essence a developed version of the Whippet, a small 145.7-cubic inch four on a 100-inch wheelbase that the company could sell for under $500, the cheapest of any car in the United States except for the American Austin. All other model lines were dropped in 1933, as Willys-Overland moved into receivership that February, John North Willys believed his company could survive only in the lowest-priced field. Though its Willys 77's horsepower was only 48, its top speed was an impressive 75.1 mph, and the car became a favorite for Automobile Racing Club of America events where tweaked racing versions performed handsomely amid fields of Bugattis, Amilcars and MGs. A stock sedan ran 24 hours at Muroc's dry lake for a 65.5 mph average. Stressed in advertising during the Depression, of course, was the car's economy—as much as 30 mpg. Production continued under receivership, and finally a viable reorganization plan seemed to be coming together. But John North Willys was a spent man. In January 1935, he was elected Willys-Overland president; in May he suffered a heart attack; in August he was working from his bed when he died; in December the Willys reorganization was completed. Receivership ended in February 1936. In 1939, when the new Model 77 was given hydraulic brakes, it was given a new designation—or, rather, an old one; it was called an Overland. In 1941, the addition of hypoid final drive brought another new designation: Americar. The Americar was produced until shortly after Pearl Harbor. During World War II, together with the Ford Motor Co., Willys-Overland moved into manufacture of the jeep, which had been originated by American Bantam. Today, the company that John North Willys built survives as Jeep Corp., subsidiary of Chrysler Corp.

1915

Knight, Model K-19 — 4-cyl., 45 hp, 120" wb

Model No.	Body Type & Seating	Factory Price	Shipping Weight	Prod. Total
K-19	Rds.	2475	—	Note 1
K-19	Tr.	2475	—	Note 1
Knight, Model K-17 — 4-cyl., 45 hp, 120" wb				
K-17	Rds.	2750	—	Note 1
K-17	Tr.	2750	—	Note 1

Note 1: Production total of 91,904 includes Overland and Willys automobiles. No breakout by automaker or by body style is available.

1916

Knight, Model 84-4 — 4-cyl., 40 hp, 114" wb

Model No.	Body Type & Seating	Factory Price	Shipping Weight	Prod. Total
84-4	Rds-2P	1065	—	Note 1
84-4	Tr-5P	1095	—	Note 1
84-4	Cpe-4P	1500	—	Note 1
84-4	Limo-7P	1750	—	Note 1

Note 1: Production total of 140,111 includes Overland and Willys automobiles. No breakout by automaker or by body style is available.

1917

Knight, Model 88-4 — 4-cyl., 40 hp, 121" wb

Model No.	Body Type & Seating	Factory Price	Shipping Weight	Prod. Total
88-4	Tr-7P	1285	—	Note 1
88-4	Cpe-4P	1875	—	Note 1
88-4	Tr Sed-7P	1950	—	Note 1
88-4	Limo-7P	1950	—	Note 1
Model 88-6 — 6-cyl., 45 hp, 125" wb				
88-6	Tr-7P	1385	—	Note 1

Note 1: Production total of 130,988 includes Overland and Willys automobiles. No breakout by automaker or by body style is available.

1918

Willys 89 — 6-cyl., 45 hp, 120" wb

Model No.	Body Type & Seating	Factory Price	Shipping Weight	Prod. Total
89	Tr-7P	1295	—	Note 1
89	Clb Rds-4P	1295	—	Note 1
89	Conv Sed-6P	1975	—	Note 1
Knight, Model 88-4 — 4-cyl., 40 hp, 121" wb				
88-4	Tr-7P	1525	—	Note 1
88-4	Cpe-4P	2175	—	Note 1
88-4	Conv Sed-7P	2225	—	Note 1
88-4	Limo-7P	2375	—	Note 1
Knight, Model 88-8 — 8-cyl., 65 hp, 125" wb				
88-8	Rds-4P	2550	—	Note 1
88-8	Tr-7P	2000	—	Note 1
88-8	Conv Sed-7P	2700	—	Note 1
88-8	Limo-7P	2800	—	Note 1
88-8	Twn. Car-7P	2800	—	Note 1

Note 1: Production total of 88,753 includes Overland and Willys automobiles. No breakout by automaker or by body style is available.

1919

Willys 89 — 6-cyl., 45 hp, 120" wb

Model No.	Body Type & Seating	Factory Price	Shipping Weight	Prod. Total
89	Tr-7P	—	—	Note 1
89	Clb Rds-4P	—	—	Note 1
89	Sed-6P	—	—	Note 1
Knight, Model 88-4 — 4-cyl., 40 hp, 121" wb				
88-4	Tr-7P	—	—	Note 1
88-4	Cpe-4P	—	—	Note 1
88-4	Sed-7P	—	—	Note 1
88-4	Limo-7P	—	—	Note 1
Knight, Model 88-8 — 8-cyl., 65 hp, 125" wb				
88-8	Tr-7P	2750	—	Note 1
88-8	Cpe-4P	3425	—	Note 1
88-8	Tr Sed-7P	2750	—	Note 1
88-8	Limo-7P	3500	—	Note 1

Note 1: Production total of 80,853 includes Overland and Willys automobiles. No breakout by automaker or by body style is available.

1920

Knight, Model 20 — 4-cyl., 48 hp, 118" wb

Model No.	Body Type & Seating	Factory Price	Shipping Weight	Prod. Total
20	Tr-5P	1750	3040	Note 1
20	Cpe-4P	2650	—	Note 1
20	Sed-5P	2750	3160	Note 1
20	Limo-7P	2750	—	Note 1
Willys 89 — 6-cyl., 45 hp, 120" wb				
89	Clb Rds-4P	—	—	Note 1
89	Tr-7P	—	—	Note 1
89	Sed-6P	—	—	Note 1

Note 1: Production total of 105,025 includes Overland and Willys automobiles. No breakout by automaker or by body style is available.

1921

Knight, Model 20 — 4-cyl., 40 hp, 118" wb

Model No.	Body Type & Seating	Factory Price	Shipping Weight	Prod. Total
20	Rds-3P	2195	—	Note 1
20	Tr-5P	2195	3040	Note 1
20	Cpe-4P	2845	—	Note 1
20	Sed-5P	2945	3160	Note 1

Note 1: Production total of 48,016 includes Overland and Willys automobiles. No breakout by automaker or by body style is available.

1922

Knight, Model 20 — 4-cyl., 40 hp, 118" wb

Model No.	Body Type & Seating	Factory Price	Shipping Weight	Prod. Total
20	Rds-3P	1475	—	Note 1
20	Tr-5P	1525	3040	Note 1
20	Cpe-4P	2195	—	Note 1
20	Sed-5P	2395	3160	Note 1

Knight, Model 27 — 4-cyl., 118" wb

Model No.	Body Type & Seating	Factory Price	Shipping Weight	Prod. Total
27	Tr-7P	—	—	Note 1
27	Sed-7P	—	3160	Note 1

Note 1: Production total of 64,650 includes Overland and Willys automobiles. No breakout by automaker or by body style is available.

1923

Knight, Model 64— 4-cyl., 40 hp, 118" wb

Model No.	Body Type & Seating	Factory Price	Shipping Weight	Prod. Total
64	Rds-3P	1235	—	Note 1
64	Tr-5P	1235	2975	Note 1
64	Cpe-4P	1795	—	Note 1
64	Sed-5P	1950	3126	Note 1
Knight, Model 67 — 4-cyl., 40 hp, 124" wb				
67	Tr-7P	1435	3080	Note 1
67	Sed-7P	2195	3300	Note 1

Note 1: Production total of 119,785 includes Overland and Willys automobiles. No breakout by automaker or by body style is available.

1924

Knight, Model 64 — 4-cyl., 40 hp, 118" wb

Model No.	Body Type & Seating	Factory Price	Shipping Weight	Prod. Total
64	Rds-3P	—	—	Note 1
64	Tr-5P	1175	3000	Note 1
64	Cpe Sed-5P	1450	—	Note 1
64	Cpe-4P	1450	—	Note 1
64	Sed-5P	1795	3126	Note 1
Knight, Model 67 — 4-cyl., 40 hp, 124" wb				
67	Tr-7P	1435	—	Note 1
67	Sed-7P	2195	3300	Note 1

Note 1: Production total of 136,822 includes Overland and Willys automobiles. No breakout by automaker or by body style is available.

1925

Knight, Model 65 — 4 cyl., 40 hp, 118" wb

Model No.	Body Type & Seating	Factory Price	Shipping Weight	Prod. Total
65	Tr-5P	1195	2990	Note 1
65	Cpe-3P	1395	2955	Note 1
65	Cpe Sed-5P	1395	3062	Note 1
65	Sed-5P	1450	3090	Note 1
65	Brgm-5P	1595	3119	Note 1
Knight, Model 66 — 6-cyl., 60 hp, 126" wb				
66	Rds-2/4P	1750	3323	Note 1
66	Tr-5P	1750	3395	Note 1
66	Cpe Sed-5P	2095	3582	Note 1
66	Brgm-5P	2095	3672	Note 1
66	Cpe-4P	2195	3604	Note 1
66	Sed-5P	2295	3686	Note 1

Note 1: Production total of 157,662 includes Overland and Willys automobiles. No breakout by automaker or by body style is available.

1926

Knight, Model 66 — 6-cyl., 60 hp, 126" wb

Model No.	Body Type & Seating	Factory Price	Shipping Weight	Prod. Total
66	Rds-2/4P	1850	3351	Note 1
66	Cpe-4P	2195	3581	Note 1
66	Tr-5P	1750	3383	Note 1
66	Tr-7P	1950	3566	Note 1
66	Sed-5P	2295	3672	Note 1
66	Sed-7P	2495	3822	Note 1
Knight, Model 70 — 6-cyl., 53 hp, 113" wb				
70	Tr-5P	1295	2800	Note 1
70	2-dr Sed-5P	1395	2845	Note 1
70	4-dr Sed-5P	1495	2970	Note 1
70	Cpe-2P	1395	2730	Note 1
70	Rds-2/4P	1525	2860	Note 1

Note 1: Production total of 139,555 includes Overland and Willys automobiles. No breakout by automaker or by body style is available.

Production Note; 1926 was the final year for Overland. Production figures beginning in 1927 through 1931 include Whippet.

1927

Knight, Model 70A — 6-cyl., 52 hp, 113" wb

Model No.	Body Type & Seating	Factory Price	Shipping Weight	Prod. Total
70A	Rds-2/4P	1350	2965	Note 1
70A	Tr-5P	1295	2900	Note 1
70A	Cpe-2P	1295	2815	Note 1
70A	Cabr-2/4P	1395	2880	Note 1
70A	Sed-5P	1495	3105	Note 1
70A	Coach-5P	1295	3010	Note 1

Knight, Model 66A — 6-cyl., 65 hp, 126" wb

Model No.	Body Type & Seating	Factory Price	Shipping Weight	Prod. Total
66A	Spt Rds-2/4P	1950	3645	Note 1
66A	Cabr-2/4P	2295	3700	Note 1
66A	Tr-5P	1850	3684	Note 1
66A	Foursome Sed-4P	2295	3975	Note 1
66A	Sed-5P	2295	3975	Note 1

Knight, Model 66A — 6-cyl., 65 hp, 135" wb

Model No.	Body Type & Seating	Factory Price	Shipping Weight	Prod. Total
66A	Sed-7P	2850	4112	Note 1
66A	Tr-7P	2495	3943	Note 1
66A	Limo-7P	2950	4146	Note 1

Note 1: Production total of 139,406 includes Whippet and Willys automobiles. No breakout by automaker or by body style is available.

1928

Knight, Model 56 — 6-cyl., 45 hp, 109-1/2" wb

Model No.	Body Type & Seating	Factory Price	Shipping Weight	Prod. Total
56	Tr-5P	995	2710	Note 1
56	Cpe-2P	1045	2790	Note 1
56	2-dr Sed-5P	995	2816	Note 1
56	4-dr Sed-5P	1095	2885	Note 1

Knight, Model 70A — 6-cyl., 53 hp, 113" wb

Model No.	Body Type & Seating	Factory Price	Shipping Weight	Prod. Total
70A	Rds-2/4P	1350	2910	Note 1
70A	Tr-5P	1295	2951	Note 1
70A	Cpe-2P	1295	2767	Note 1
70A	Cpe-5P	1495	3127	Note 1
70A	Cabr-2/4P	1495	2916	Note 1
70A	Coach-5P	1295	3007	Note 1
70A	Sed-5P	1495	3187	Note 1

Knight, Model 66A — 6-cyl., 70 hp, 126" wb

Model No.	Body Type & Seating	Factory Price	Shipping Weight	Prod. Total
66A	Std Rds-2P	1750	3436	Note 1
66A	Rds-2/4P	1850	3486	Note 1
66A	Tr-5P	1850	3675	Note 1
66A	Cabr-2/4P	1995	3726	Note 1
66A	Foursome Sed-4P	2095	4012	Note 1
66A	Sed-5P	1995	4003	Note 1

Knight, Model 66A — 6-cyl., 70 hp, 135" wb

Model No.	Body Type & Seating	Factory Price	Shipping Weight	Prod. Total
66A	Cpe-5P	2295	3939	Note 1
66A	Sed-7P	2595	4112	Note 1
66A	Tr-7P	2285	3943	Note 1
66A	Limo-7P	2695	4146	Note 1

Note 1: Production total of 231,360 includes Whippet and Willys automobiles. No breakout by automaker or by body style is available.

1929

Knight, Series 56 — 6-cyl., 45 hp, 109-1/2" wb

Model No.	Body Type & Seating	Factory Price	Shipping Weight	Prod. Total
56	Tr-5P	945	2710	Note 1
56	Cpe-2/4P	995	2790	Note 1
56	Coach-5P	945	2816	Note 1
56	Sed-5P	1045	2858	Note 1

Knight, Series 70B — 6-cyl., 53 hp, 112-1/2" wb

Model No.	Body Type & Seating	Factory Price	Shipping Weight	Prod. Total
70B	Rds-2/4P	1045	2748	Note 1
70B	Tr-5P	1045	2778	Note 1
70B	Cpe-2P	1045	2891	Note 1
70B	DeL Cpe-2/4P	1145	2916	Note 1
70B	Coach-5P	1045	2903	Note 1
70B	Sed-5P	1145	3015	Note 1
70B	DeL Sed-5P	1195	3046	Note 1

Knight, Series 70B — 6-cyl., 53 hp, 115" wb

Model No.	Body Type & Seating	Factory Price	Shipping Weight	Prod. Total
70B	DeL Sed-5P	1265	3082	Note 1

Knight, Series 70A — 6-cyl., 53 hp, 113-1/2" wb

Model No.	Body Type & Seating	Factory Price	Shipping Weight	Prod. Total
70A	Rds-2P	1350	2910	Note 1
70A	Tr-5P	1295	2951	Note 1
70A	Cpe-2P	1295	2767	Note 1
70A	Cabr-2/4P	1495	2916	Note 1
70A	Coach-5P	1295	3007	Note 1
70A	Sed-5P	1495	3187	Note 1

Knight, Series 66A — 6-cyl., 70 hp, 126" wb

Model No.	Body Type & Seating	Factory Price	Shipping Weight	Prod. Total
66A	Rds-2P	1850	3486	Note 1
66A	Tr-5P	1850	3675	Note 1
66A	Cabr-2/4P	1995	3726	Note 1
66A	Foursome Sed-4P	2095	4012	Note 1
66A	Frsm DeL Sed-4P	2195	4128	Note 1
66A	Sed-5P	1995	4003	Note 1

Knight, Series 66A — 6-cyl., 70 hp, 135" wb

Model No.	Body Type & Seating	Factory Price	Shipping Weight	Prod. Total
66A	Tr-7P	2285	3943	Note 1
66A	Cpe-5P	2295	3939	Note 1
66A	Sed-7P	2595	4112	Note 1

Note 1: Production total of 112,983 includes Whippet and Willys automobiles. No breakout by automaker or by body style is available.

1930

Willys Six, Series 98B — 65 hp, 110" wb

Model No.	Body Type & Seating	Factory Price	Shipping Weight	Prod. Total
98B	Rds-2P	695	2360	Note 1
98B	Rds-2/4P	725	2497	Note 1
98B	Tr-5P	735	2434	Note 1
98B	Cpe-2P	695	2487	Note 1
98B	Cpe-2/4P	725	2538	Note 1
98B	Coach-5P	735	2566	Note 1
98B	Sed-5P	795	2641	Note 1
98B	DeL Sed-5P	850	2744	Note 1

Knight, Series 66B — 6-cyl., 87 hp, 120" wb

Model No.	Body Type & Seating	Factory Price	Shipping Weight	Prod. Total
66B	Rds-2/4P	1795	3592	Note 1
66B	Cpe-2/4P	1795	3815	Note 1
66B	Cpe-5P	1795	3866	Note 1
66B	Sed-5P	1795	3934	Note 1

Knight, Series 70B — 6-cyl., 53 hp, 112-1/2" wb

Model No.	Body Type & Seating	Factory Price	Shipping Weight	Prod. Total
70B	Rds-2/4P	975	2748	Note 1
70B	Tr-5P	975	2778	Note 1
70B	DeL Cpe-2/4P	1075	2883	Note 1
70B	Coach-5P	975	2900	Note 1
70B	Sed-5P	1075	2973	Note 1

Knight, Series 70B — 6-cyl., 53 hp, 115" wb

Model No.	Body Type & Seating	Factory Price	Shipping Weight	Prod. Total
70B	DeL. Sed	1195	3042	Note 1

Knight, Series 6-87 — 6-cyl., 55 hp, 112-1/2" wb

Model No.	Body Type & Seating	Factory Price	Shipping Weight	Prod. Total
87	Rds-2/4P	975	2718	Note 1
87	Tr-5P	975	2820	Note 1
87	Cpe-2/4P	1075	2922	Note 1
87	Coach-5P	975	2941	Note 1
87	Sed-5P	1075	2989	Note 1

Knight, Series 6-87 — 6-cyl., 55 hp, 115" wb

Model No.	Body Type & Seating	Factory Price	Shipping Weight	Prod. Total
87	Sed DeL-5P	1195	3118	Note 1

Note 1: Production total of 65,766 includes Whippet and Willys automobiles. No breakout by automaker or by body style is available.

Production Note: The Continental-engined Willys 8-80 was introduced in April 1930 and sold in the $1,245-$1,395 price range.

1931

Willys Six, Series 98B — 65 hp, 110" wb

Model No.	Body Type & Seating	Factory Price	Shipping Weight	Prod. Total
98B	Rds-5P	695	—	Note 1
98B	Rds-2/4P	725	2430	Note 1
98B	Tr-5P	735	—	Note 1
98B	Cpe-2P	695	—	Note 1
98B	Cpe-4P	725	—	Note 1
98B	Coach-5P	735	—	Note 1
98B	Sed-5P	795	2623	Note 1
98B	DeL Sed-5P	850	—	Note 1

Willys Six 97 — 6-cyl., 65 hp, 110" wb

Model No.	Body Type & Seating	Factory Price	Shipping Weight	Prod. Total
97	Rds-2P	495	2407	Note 1
97	Tr-5P	545	—	Note 1
97	Cpe-2P	565	2528	Note 1
97	Clb Sed-5P	675	2682	Note 1
97	Sed-5P	625	2670	Note 1

Willys Six 98D — 6-cyl., 65 hp, 113" wb

Model No.	Body Type & Seating	Factory Price	Shipping Weight	Prod. Total
98D	Vict Cpe-5P	795	2656	Note 1
98D	Sed-5P	795	2706	Note 1
98D	DeL Sed-5P	850	2791	Note 1
98D	DeL Vict Cpe-4P	850	2750	Note 1

Knight, Series 66B — 6-cyl., 87 hp, 120" wb

Model No.	Body Type & Seating	Factory Price	Shipping Weight	Prod. Total
66B	Rds-2/4P	1795	3515	Note 1
66B	Cpe-2/4P	1795	3745	Note 1

1914 Willys-Knight, Four, touring, HAC

1918 Willys-Knight, Six (Model 89), touring, HAC

1924 Willys-Knight, Four (Model 64), Country Club sport touring, OCW

1938 Willys, Four (Model 38), sedan, OCW

1948 Willys, Jeepster (Model 463), phaeton, OCW

1916 Willys-Knight, Six (Model K-19), touring, HAC

1920 Willys-Knight, Four (Model 20), coupe (with John North Willys), OCW

1927 Willys-Knight, Six (Model 66A), sedan, OCW

1940 Willys, Deluxe Four (Model 440), sedan, OCW

1949 Willys, Jeep (Model 633), station sedan, OCW

Model No.	Body Type & Seating	Factory Price	Shipping Weight	Prod. Total
66B	Cpe-5P	1795	3785	Note 1
66B	Sed-5P	1795	3868	Note 1

Knight, Series 6-87 — 6-cyl., 55 hp, 112-1/2" wb

Model No.	Body Type & Seating	Factory Price	Shipping Weight	Prod. Total
87	Rds-2/4P	975	2739	Note 1
87	Tr-5P	975	2768	Note 1
87	Cpe-2/4P	1075	2882	Note 1
87	Coach-5P	975	2884	Note 1
87	Sed-5P	1075	3001	Note 1

Knight, Series 6-87 — 6-cyl., 55 hp, 115" wb

Model No.	Body Type & Seating	Factory Price	Shipping Weight	Prod. Total
87	DeL Sed-5P	1195	3044	Note 1

Knight, Model 66D — 6-cyl., 87 hp, 121" wb

Model No.	Body Type & Seating	Factory Price	Shipping Weight	Prod. Total
66D	Vict Cpe-4P	1095	3482	Note 1
66D	Sed-5P	1095	3582	Note 1
66D	DeL Sed-5P	1195	3582	Note 1
66D	DeL Vict Cpe-4P	1195	3482	Note 1

Willys 8-80D — 8-cyl., 80 hp, 121" wb

Model No.	Body Type & Seating	Factory Price	Shipping Weight	Prod. Total
8-80D	Vict Cpe-4P	995	—	Note 1
8-80D	DeL Vict Cpe-4P	1095	—	Note 1
8-80D	Sed-5P	995	—	Note 1
8-80D	DeL Sed-5P	1095	3303	Note 1

Willys 8-80 — 8-cyl., 80 hp, 121" wb

Model No.	Body Type & Seating	Factory Price	Shipping Weight	Prod. Total
8-80	Cpe-2/4P	1245	3039	Note 1
8-80	DeL Cpe-2/4P	1345	3165	Note 1
8-80	Sed-5P	1295	3114	Note 1
8-80	DeL Sed-5P	1395	3239	Note 1

Note 1: Production total of 51,341 includes Whippet and Willys automobiles. No breakout by automaker or by body style is available.

1932

Willys Six 97 — 6-cyl., 65 hp, 110" wb

Model No.	Body Type & Seating	Factory Price	Shipping Weight	Prod. Total
97	Rds-2P	495	2407	Note 1
97	Cpe-5P	565	2648	Note 1
97	Sed-5P	675	2670	Note 1

Willys Six 98D — 6-cyl., 65 hp, 113" wb

Model No.	Body Type & Seating	Factory Price	Shipping Weight	Prod. Total
98D	Vict Cpe-4P	795	2656	Note 1
98D	Sed-5P	795	2706	Note 1

Willys 6-90 — (Silver Streak engine) 6-cyl., 65 hp, 113" wb

Model No.	Body Type & Seating	Factory Price	Shipping Weight	Prod. Total
90	Rds-2P	415	2570	Note 1
90	DeL Rds-4P	695	—	Note 1
90	Tr-5P	530	—	Note 1
90	Cpe-2P	530	2749	Note 1
90	Cpe-4P	645	—	Note 1
90	Sed 5P	610	2814	Note 1
90	Coach-5P	610	—	Note 1

Willys 8-80D — 8-cyl., 80 hp, 120" wb

Model No.	Body Type & Seating	Factory Price	Shipping Weight	Prod. Total
8-80D	Vict Cpe-4P	995	3100	Note 1
8-80D	Sed-5P	995	3131	Note 1

Willys 8-88— (Silver Streak engine) 8-cyl., 80 hp, 121" wb

Model No.	Body Type & Seating	Factory Price	Shipping Weight	Prod. Total
8-88	Rds-2P	730	2981	Note 1
8-88	Rds-4P	—	—	Note 1
8-88	DeL Rds-4P	—	—	Note 1
8-88	Cpe-2P	780	3148	Note 1
8-88	Cpe-4P	810	—	Note 1
8-88	Vict Cpe-4P	1030	3337	Note 1
8-88	Coach-5P	—	—	Note 1
8-88	Sed-5P	830	3250	Note 1
8-88	Tr-5P	—	—	Note 1
8-88	Cus Sed-5P	1030	—	Note 1

Knight, Model 95 Deluxe — (Silver Streak engine) 6-cyl., 60 hp, 113" wb

Model No.	Body Type & Seating	Factory Price	Shipping Weight	Prod. Total
95	Rds-2P	—	—	Note 1
95	Rds-4P	—	—	Note 1
95	Cpe-2P	745	2915	Note 1
95	Cpe-2/4P	775	2994	Note 1
95	Coach-5P	745	2982	Note 1
95	Sed-5P	795	3031	Note 1
95	Tr-5P	—	—	Note 1

Knight, Model 66D— (Silver Streak engine) 6-cyl., 87 hp, 121" wb

Model No.	Body Type & Seating	Factory Price	Shipping Weight	Prod. Total
66D	Vict Cpe-2P	1145	3664	Note 1
66D	Sed-5P	1295	3775	Note 1

Note 1:: Willys production totaled 25,898 with no body style breakout available.

Production Note: The Streamline series was introduced for the latter part of 1932.

1933

Willys 77 — 4-cyl., 48 hp, 100" wb

Model No.	Body Type & Seating	Factory Price	Shipping Weight	Prod. Total
77	Cpe-2P	395	2058	Note 1
77	Cus Cpe-2P	415	2072	Note 1
77	Cpe-2/4P	425	2072	Note 1
77	Cus Cpe-2/4P	445	2105	Note 1
77	Sed-4P	445	2136	Note 1
77	Cus Sed-4P	475	2156	Note 1

Willys 6-90A — 6-cyl., 65 hp, 113" wb

Model No.	Body Type & Seating	Factory Price	Shipping Weight	Prod. Total
6-90A	Rds-2P	535	2569	Note 1
6-90A	Cpe-2P	650	2781	Note 1
6-90A	Sed-5P	740	2913	Note 1

Willys 8-88A — 8-cyl., 80 hp, 121" wb

Model No.	Body Type & Seating	Factory Price	Shipping Weight	Prod. Total
8-88A	Cpe-2P	955	3217	Note 1
8-88A	Sed-5P	995	3368	Note 1

Knight, Model 66E — 6-cyl., 87 hp, 121" wb

Model No.	Body Type & Seating	Factory Price	Shipping Weight	Prod. Total
66E	Sed-5P	1420	3830	Note 1

Note 1: Willys production totaled 15,667 with no body style breakout available.

Production Note: 1933 was the final year for production of Willys six- and eight-cylinder engines until late in 1948 when the six was reintroduced in the Jeepster.

1934

Willys 77 — 4-cyl., 48 hp, 100" wb

Model No.	Body Type & Seating	Factory Price	Shipping Weight	Prod. Total
77	Cpe-2P	395	2058	Note 1
77	Cus Cpe-2P	415	2072	Note 1
77	Cpe-2/4P	425	2072	Note 1
77	Cus Cpe-2/4P	445	2105	Note 1
77	Sed-4P	450	2131	Note 1
77	Cus Sed-4P	475	2156	Note 1
77	Pan Dly	450	—	Note 1

Note 1: Willys production totaled 6,576 with no body style breakout available.

1935

Willys 77 — 4-cyl., 48 hp, 100" wb

Model No.	Body Type & Seating	Factory Price	Shipping Weight	Prod. Total
77	Cpe-2P	475	2034	Note 1
77	Sed-4P	495	2111	Note 1

Note 1: Willys production totaled 10,439 with no body style breakout available.

1936

Willys 77 — 4-cyl., 48 hp, 100" wb

Model No.	Body Type & Seating	Factory Price	Shipping Weight	Prod. Total
77	Cpe-2P	395	1970	Note 1
77	Sed-4P	415	2070	Note 1
77	DeL Sed-4P	445	2100	Note 1

Note 1: Willys production totaled 12,423 with no body style breakout available.

1937

Willys 37 — 4-cyl., 48 hp, 100" wb

Model No.	Body Type & Seating	Factory Price	Shipping Weight	Prod. Total
37	Cpe-2P	499	2146	Note 1
37	DeL Cpe-2P	579	—	Note 1
37	Sed-5P	538	2200	Note 1
37	DeL Sed-5P	589	2306	Note 1

Note 1: Willys production totaled 51,418 with no body style breakout available.

1938

Willys 38 — 4-cyl., 48 hp, 100" wb

Model No.	Body Type & Seating	Factory Price	Shipping Weight	Prod. Total
38	Std Cpe-2P	499	2145	Note 1
38	DeL. Cpe-2P	574	2155	Note 1
38	2-dr Clipper Sed-5P	539	2258	Note 1
38	Std Sed-5P	563	2247	Note 1
38	2-dr DeL Clpr Sed-5P	575	2258	Note 1
38	DeL Sed-5P	614	2263	Note 1
38	Cus Sed-5P	700	2336	Note 1

Note 1: Willys production totaled 13,012 with no body style breakout available.

1939

Overland/Model 39 — 4-cyl., 48 hp, 102" wb

Model No.	Body Type & Seating	Factory Price	Shipping Weight	Prod. Total
Speedway				
39	Cpe-2P	596	2137	Note 1
39	2-dr Sed-5P	616	2217	Note 1
39	4-dr Sed-5P	631	2249	Note 1
Deluxe				
39	Cpe-2P	646	2193	Note 1
39	2-dr Sed-5P	667	2262	Note 1
39	4-dr Sed-5P	689	2306	Note 1
Special				
39	Cpe-2P	610	2193	Note 1
39	2-dr Sed-5P	631	2262	Note 1
39	4-dr Sed-5P	646	2306	Note 1
Model 48 — 4-cyl., 48 hp, 100" wb				
48	Cpe-2P	524	2181	Note 1
48	2-dr Sed-5P	565	2258	Note 1
48	4-dr Sed-5P	586	2300	Note 1
Model 38 — 4-cyl., 48 hp, 100" wb				
38	Cpe-2P	499	2181	Note 1
38	2-dr Sed-5P	539	2258	Note 1
38	4-dr Sed-5P	563	2300	Note 1
38	DeL Cpe-2P	574	2181	Note 1
38	2-dr DeL Sed-5P	575	2258	Note 1
38	4-dr DeL Sed-5P	614	2300	Note 1

Note 1: Willys production totaled 14,734 with no body style breakout available.

Production Note: The Overland name was revived for a short time for a new, 1939 series with 102-inch wheelbase.

1940

Willys Speedway — 4-cyl., 61 hp, 102" wb

Model No.	Body Type & Seating	Factory Price	Shipping Weight	Prod. Total
440	Cpe-2P	529	2146	Note 1
440	4-dr Sed-5P	596	2238	Note 1
Willys Deluxe — 4 cyl., 61 hp, 102" wb				
440	Cpe-2P	641	2190	Note 1
440	4-dr Sed-5P	672	2255	Note 1
440	Sta Wag-6P	830	2124	Note 1

Note 1: Willys production totaled 21,418 with no body style breakout available.

1941

Willys (Americar)

Model No.	Body Type & Seating	Factory Price	Shipping Weight	Prod. Total
Speedway — 4-cyl., 63 hp, 104" wb				
441	Cpe-2P	634	2116	Note 1
441	4-dr Sed-5P	674	2230	Note 1
Deluxe — 4-cyl., 63 hp, 104" wb				
441	Cpe-2P	689	2135	Note 1
441	4-dr Sed-5P	720	2265	Note 1
441	Sta Wag-6P	916	2483	Note 1
Plainsman — 4-cyl., 63 hp, 104" wb				
441	Cpe-2P	740	2175	Note 1
441	4-dr Sed-5P	771	2305	Note 1

Note 1: Willys production totaled 22,102 with no body style breakout available.

1942

Willys (Americar)

Model No.	Body Type & Seating	Factory Price	Shipping Weight	Prod. Total
Speedway — 4-cyl., 63 hp, 104" wb				
442	Cpe-2P	695	2142	Note 1
442	4-dr Sed-5P	745	2261	Note 1
Deluxe — 4-cyl., 63 hp, 104" wb				
442	Cpe-2P	769	2184	Note 1
442	4-dr Sed-5P	795	2295	Note 1
442	Sta Wag-6P	978	2512	Note 1
Plainsman — 4-cyl., 63 hp, 104" wb				
442	Cpe-2P	819	2242	Note 1
442	4-dr Sed-5P	845	2353	Note 1

Note 1: Willys production totaled 3,829 with no body style breakout available.

WILLYS 1946-1955

Willys-Overland, of Toledo, Ohio, had a long history of making small cars prior to outbreak of World War II. When production of automobiles resumed, in 1945, the company temporarily abandoned the passenger car market, electing to sell civilian versions of its famous military jeep instead.

By John R. Smith

A wide choice of jeep-based vehicles was offered, ranging from those specially-equipped for agricultural use to fire trucks. Most were marketed as commercial vehicles, although the dual-purpose station wagon was often used as a passenger car by buyers preferring utility to style.

Willys had plans to return to the passenger car business, but not until the early 1950s. During the interim, the company decided to develop a totally new type of product that combined car and jeep features. It was called the Jeepster.

Production of the Jeepster began in May of 1948. It was essentially a four-passenger open car using the same chassis as the Jeep station wagon. Industrial designer Brooks Stevens was commissioned to do the overall styling, which incorporated a sporty look. Features included a jeep-like frontal treatment; angular front fenders (as used on the front of the station wagon); double-angled rear fenders and a body reflecting a number of European sports car traits, such as doors with cut-down upper edges. Standard equipment included bright front and rear bumpers with guards; dual sun visors; Deluxe steering wheel (with horn ring); luxury upholstery; chrome wheel trim rings; and manual transmission with overdrive.

The Jeepster was strictly a two-wheel-drive vehicle and sold for about $1,600 with a four-cylinder engine, manual folding top and plastic-windowed side curtains. Beginning in 1949, a six was offered as optional equipment. Slight styling changes were adopted for model year 1950, including the addition of five bright horizontal bars in the grille. Production of the Jeepster ended around June 1950, although sales seem to have gone on with reduced prices for about another year. After the model was gone, it caught on as a used car and was later revived, by Kaiser-Jeep Corp., in 1967.

One reason the Jeepster was dropped was due to Willys' re-entry into the passenger car field with the Aero sedan series of 1952. It consisted of a spartan two-door sedan named the Lark (with a 75 hp L-head six); plus the Wing and the Ace (same body style in richer trim) and the top-of-the-line Eagle two-door hardtop. The latter three cars were powered by a 90-hp version of the same engine, the extra output coming from a higher compression ratio and F-head engine. The F-head had overhead intake valves, but exhaust valves inside the block.

Kaiser took over Willys-Overland on April 28, 1953. The new line of cars was expanded by adding a four-door sedan in the Lark series and a next-step-up Falcon in two- or four-door form. Both Larks and Falcons used the L-head six, which was in its final year. It's also interesting to note that both of these names were used, years later, on compact models made by other companies. This was Willys' Golden Anniversary year. To commemorate the occasion, the wheel cover centers were finished in red and a gold 'W' was added to the grille.

For 1954, the Willys compact car line continued to grow with over 20 different varieties offered. Even a taxicab model was included. It's likely not all of these cars were produced concurrently, as midyear changes and model additions were quite common in the industry at this time. There was a new series of cars equipped with Kaiser's "Hurricane" (Continental Red Seal) six-cylinder engine. A handful of prototypes were even built with supercharged versions of this powerplant and a one-off convertible (which still exists today) was made by the Derham Body Co.

The last year for production of the Aero Willys was 1955, as Kaiser Industries was planning to abandon the U.S. passenger car market for good. Three nameplates were marketed this season: the Ace, Custom and Bermuda being advertised as "value leaders for 1955." *Motor Trend* magazine highlighted some of the new styling features such as toothier grilles; two-tone color treatments; more fashionable interiors; and padded dashboards.

At this point in time, Kaiser-Willys Division was selling about every Jeep it could make, but customers were not flocking to either brand's showrooms for passenger cars. The company operated on an international basis, however. It was involved in a diverse number of fields ranging from shipbuilding to aluminum mining. Management decided that the same cars could be produced and successfully marketed by branches of Kaiser Industries in South American countries.

By mid-1955, the Willys body dies were shipped to Brazil where a car close to the Aero Ace four-door was produced through 1962 as the Aero Willys 2600. A modernized version, bearing Aero Willys nameplates, was also sold in Brazil from 1963 to 1971. In character and size, this Itamaraty (President) model was the same type of car as the original with a trim upgrade by Brooks Stevens. It was even stretched into a limousine, the Itamaraty Executive.

The Itamaraty was the first Latin American car ever displayed at the Paris Auto Show (1963). In 1967, Willys-Overland de Brazil was sold to Ford. The Willys two- and four-door station wagon was also produced in Brazil and sold there by Ford through 1976. There was even a four-door variant, also designed by Brooks Stevens. Neither Brazilian model, however, should be confused with another called the Willys Interlagos Berlinette (1965-1967), which was actually a Renault marketed under the popular Willys badge. Only about a dozen Itamaraty models have been brought into the United States.

1946

WILLYS — (STATION WAGON) — For 1946, Willys introduced an all-steel, truck-like station wagon with a 134-cid four-cylinder engine. It used the same basic 104-inch wheelbase chassis as the prewar Willys Americar. It was significant in that it was the first true all-steel station wagon, though it was considered more truck than car. It was the only Willys civilian vehicle for the years 1946 and 1947. At first, all of these station wagons came with the front sheet metal painted maroon. The body was painted to resemble birch and mahogany paneling.

WILLYS I.D. NUMBERS: The Vehicle Identification Number is the same as the serial number. VIN locations: on a plate at the left of the driver's seat on the floor riser; on left door sill; on frame front cross member ahead of front spring hanger; on front frame cross member at center; on right side of cowl below hood; on inside of frame on left. Serial numbers for 1946 were 10001 to 16534. The engine number was the same as the serial number and was located on the top of the water pump boss, at the right front upper corner of the engine block.

WILLYS STATION WAGON SERIES

Model No.	Body/Style No.	Body Type & Seating	Factory Price	Shipping Weight	Prod. Total
446	46	2-dr Sta Wag-5P	1495	2898	6,533

NOTE 1: Price increased to $1,549 late in 1946.

ENGINE:

(FOUR) Inline. L-head. Cast iron block. Displacement: 134.2 cid. Bore and stroke: 3.13 x 4.38 inches. Compression ratio: 6.48:1. Brake hp: 63 at 4000 rpm. Carburetor: Carter WA1-613S one-barrel. Three main bearings. Solid valve lifters.

CHASSIS FEATURES: Wheelbase: 104 inches. Overall length: 174 Inches. Tires: 6.00 x 15 tube-type blackwall.

OPTIONS: Wheel trim rings. Front bumper guards. Rear bumper guards. Spotlight. Fog lamps. Three-speed manual transmission with overdrive was standard. Heavy-duty air cleaner.

HISTORICAL FOOTNOTES: The 1946 Willys were introduced in July 1946. Model year production peaked at 6,533 units. Calendar year sales of 6,533 cars were recorded. W.M. Canaday was the chief executive officer of Willys-Overland. Civilian Jeep production began in 1945. Station wagons and panel delivery trucks were added to the line during 1946. The four-wheel-drive Jeeps and two-wheel-drive panel trucks are considered commercial vehicles. Information about these models can be found in the *Standard Catalog Of Light-Duty American Trucks* by Krause Publications. A total of 71,455 Jeeps and one prototype model were assembled in calendar year 1946.

1947

WILLYS — (STATION WAGON) — 1947 Willys station wagons were identical to the 1946 models except for the smallest details.

WILLYS I.D. NUMBERS: The Vehicle Identification Number is the same as the serial number. VIN locations: on a plate at the left of the driver's seat on the floor riser; on left door sill; on frame front cross member ahead of front spring hanger; on front frame cross member at center; on right side of cowl below hood; on inside of frame on left. Serial numbers for 1947 were 16535 to 44045. The engine number was the same as the serial number and was located on the top of the water pump boss, at the right front upper corner of the engine block.

WILLYS STATION WAGON SERIES

Model No.		Body Type & Seating	Factory Price	Shipping Weight	Prod. Total
447	463	2-dr Sta Wag-5P	1616	2898	33,214

ENGINE:

(FOUR) Inline. L-head. Cast iron block. Displacement: 134.2 cid. Bore and stroke: 3.13 x 4.38 inches. Compression ratio: 6.48:1. Brake hp: 63 at 4000 rpm. Carburetor: Carter WA1-613S single-barrel. Three main bearings. Solid valve lifters.

CHASSIS FEATURES: Wheelbase: 104 inches. Overall length: 174 inches. Tires: 6.00 x 15 tube-type blackwall.

OPTIONS: Wheel trim rings. Front bumper guards. Rear bumper guards. Spotlight. Fog lamps. Three-speed manual transmission with overdrive was standard. Heavy-duty air cleaner.

HISTORICAL FOOTNOTES: The 1947 Willys models were introduced January 1947. Model year production peaked at 33,214 units. Calendar year sales of 33,214 cars were recorded this year. Two-wheel-drive and four-wheel-drive trucks appeared this season. Willys-Overland Motors, Inc. was headquartered at Toledo, Ohio.

1948

WILLYS — (ALL MODELS) — Production of 1948 Willys station wagons started in November 1947 and vehicles in this series were sold as both 1948 and 1949 models. As in 1946 and 1947, the 1948 station wagon utilized a grille with a vertical center divider and four vertical slots on either side of the center bar. The upscale Station Sedan was added in January 1948. On May 3, 1948, the Jeepster phaeton was introduced. The station wagon was little changed. The six-cylinder Station Sedan featured a fancier grille with a vertical molding and wider seats. A circular medallion was placed above the grille and a chrome molding graced the front center portion of the hood. On this model, the small upper bodyside panels just under the lower window frames were embossed with a basketweave trim pattern and painted a straw-like color. The Jeepster was an open touring car designed during World War II by Brooks Stevens. Its lines were borrowed from the jeep. It had an open compartment behind the cowl and a mechanically-operated soft top. The Jeepster and the Station Sedan helped to keep Willys-Overland in business. The station wagon came with a two-tone finish that gave the look of a "woodie."

WILLYS I.D. NUMBERS: The Vehicle Identification Number is the same as the serial number. VIN locations: on a plate at the left of the driver's seat on the floor riser; on left door sill; on frame front cross member ahead of front spring hanger; on front frame cross member at center; on right side of cowl below hood; on inside of frame on left. Serial numbers for early-series 1948 models were: Series 463 station wagon: 44046 to 79715; Series 663 station sedan: 10001 to 13118. Series VJ2 Jeepster: 65199 to 79715. The engine number was the same as the serial number and was located on the top of the water pump boss, at the right front upper corner of the engine block.

WILLYS SERIES

Model No.	Body/Style No.	Body Type & Seating	Factory Price	Shipping Weight	Prod. Total
STATION WAGON					
463	463	2-dr Sta Wag-5P	1645	2895	Note 1
STATION SEDAN					
663	663	2-dr Sta Wag-5P	1890	2900	Note 1
JEEPSTER					
463	VJ2	2-dr Phae-4P	1765	2468	10,326

NOTE 1: 22,309 station wagons and station sedans were built. No body style breakout available.

ENGINES:

(FOUR) Inline. L-head. Cast iron block. Displacement: 134.2 cid. Bore and stroke: 3.13 x 4.38 inches. Compression ratio: 6.48:1. Brake hp: 63 at 4000 rpm. Carburetor: Carter WA1-613S single-barrel. Three main bearings. Solid valve lifters.

(SIX) Inline. L-head. Cast iron block. Displacement: 148.5 cid. Bore and stroke: 3.00 x 3.50 inches. Compression ratio: 6.42:1. Brake hp: 72 at 4000 rpm. Carburetor: Carter WA1-645S single-barrel. Four main bearings. Solid valve lifters.

CHASSIS FEATURES: Wheelbase: (all models) 104 inches. Overall length: (station wagon) 174 inches; (station sedan) 175.8 inches; (Jeepster) 174.8 inches. Front tread: (all models) 55 inches. Rear tread: (all models) 57 inches. Tires: (November 1948 station wagon series) 6.70 x 15; (station sedan and later station wagons) 6.00 x 15; (Jeepster phaeton) 5.90 x 15.

OPTIONS: Front bumper guards. Rear bumper guards. Front grille guard. Wheel trim rings. Large wheel discs. Radio and antenna. License plate frames. White sidewall tires. Three-speed manual transmission with overdrive was standard. High-compression 7.0:1 cylinder head. Heavy-duty air cleaner was optional.

HISTORICAL FOOTNOTES: The 1948 Willys station wagon was introduced in November 1947. The station sedan six-cylinder models were introduced in January 1948. The four-cylinder Jeepster phaeton was added on May 3, 1948. Calendar year production of 32,635 cars was recorded. W.M. Canaday was the chief executive officer again this year. The most important event of the year was the introduction of the Jeepster phaeton. Willys also produced 104,632 non-passenger-type commercial vehicles this year. They included 63,170 Jeeps and 41,462 trucks. Willys was ranked as America's 16th largest automaker. The four-cylinder F-head engine was called the "Hurricane Four." The six-cylinder L-head engine was called the "Lightning Six."

1949

WILLYS — (ALL MODELS) — For 1949, Willys offered a new four-wheel-drive station wagon with a 104.5-inch wheelbase at midyear (July 1949). The regular station wagon and two versions of the Jeepster rounded out the four-cylinder line. The second Jeepster was introduced in January of 1948 and featured Willys' first F-head engine. Willys continued to sell the six-cylinder station sedan and station wagon and introduced a new six-cylinder Jeepster.

WILLYS I.D. NUMBERS: The Vehicle Identification Number is the same as the serial number. VIN locations: on a plate at the left of the driver's seat on the floor riser; on left door sill; on frame front cross member ahead of front spring hanger; on front frame cross member at center; on right side of cowl below hood; on inside of frame on left. Serial numbers for the cars in the late-1948/early-1949 styles were: (463 station wagon) 79716 to 106504; (663 station sedan) 13119 to 22769; (463 Jeepster) 79716 to 106504. Serial numbers for the vehicles introduced in July 1949 were: (four-cylinder station wagon) 10001 to 13186; (four-cylinder Jeepster) 10001 to 12698; (six-cylinder Jeepster) 10001 to 10654. The engine number was the same as the serial number and was located on the top of the water pump boss, at the right front upper corner of the engine block.

WILLYS SERIES

Model No.	Body/Style No.	Body Type & Seating	Factory Price	Shipping Weight	Prod. Total
SERIES STARTING NOVEMBER 1948					
(FOUR-CYLINDER)					
463	N/A	2-dr Sta Wag-5P	1595	2895	Note 1
463	N/A	2-dr Jeepster-4P	1495	2468	Note 1
(SIX-CYLINDER)					
633	N/A	2-dr Sta Wag-5P	1695	2890	Note 1
633	N/A	2-dr Sta Sed-5P	1745	2890	Note 1

SERIES STARTING JULY 1949

Model No.	Body/Style No.	Body Type & Seating	Factory Price	Shipping Weight	Prod. Total
(FOUR-CYLINDER)					
4x463	N/A	2-dr 4WD Wag-5P	1895	3136	Note1
VJ3	N/A	2-dr Jeepster-4P	1495	2468	Notes 1/2
(SIX-CYLINDER)					
VJ3	N/A	2-dr Jeepster-4P	1530	2392	Note 1

NOTE 1: 32,928 units were built for the 1949 calendar year, including 29,290 station wagons and station sedans; 3,638 Jeepsters.

NOTE 2: Model 463 Jeepster replaced by VJ-3 Jeepster four on Jan. 10, 1949.

ENGINES:

(FOUR) Inline. L-head. Cast iron block. Displacement: 134.2 cid. Bore and stroke: 3.13 x 4.38 inches. Compression ratio: 6.48:1. Brake hp: 63 at 4000 rpm. Carburetor: Carter WA1-613S single-barrel. Three main bearings. Solid valve lifters.

(SIX) Inline. L-head. Cast iron block. Displacement: 148.5 cid. Bore and stroke: 3.00 x 3.50 inches. Compression ratio: 6.42:1. Brake hp: 72 at 4000 rpm. Carburetor: Carter WA1-645S one-barrel. Four main bearings. Solid valve lifters.

CHASSIS FEATURES: Wheelbase: (Series 4x463 station wagon) 104.5 inches; (all other models) 104 inches. Overall length: (all models) 174.8 inches. Front tread: (Model 463) 55 inches; (all other models) 56 inches. Rear tread: (all models) 57 inches. Tires: (early Jeepster four) 5.90 x 15; (early series/others) 6.70 x 15; (late Jeepster four) 6.40 x 15; (others six and four) 6.70 x 15; (late 4x4 station wagon) 6.50 x 15.

OPTIONS: Front bumper guards. Rear bumper guards. Front grille guard. License plate frames. Large wheel discs. White sidewall tires. Wheel trim rings. Radio and antenna. Oversize tires. Special paint. Spotlights. Fog lights. Heater and defroster. Three-speed manual transmission was standard on Jeepsters. Overdrive transmission was standard on all models, except Jeepster. Four-cylinder 134.2 cid, 7.0:1 compression engine (no cost). Heavy-duty air cleaner was optional at extra cost.

HISTORICAL FOOTNOTES: The 1949 Willys were introduced November 1948; the VJ3-four Jeepster bowed Jan. 10, 1949, and the VJ3-six and 4x463 appeared in dealer showrooms July 1949. Model year production peaked at 32,928 units. Calendar year registrations of 28,576 cars were recorded. W.M. Canaday was the chief executive officer of Willys. The Jeepster continued to be sold with snap-on side curtains for weather protection. Roll-up side windows were not provided. The Milestone Car Society recognizes 1948 through 1951 Jeepsters as Milestone Cars. Willys-Overland also manufactured 31,595 civilian Jeeps and 18,342 other types of commercial vehicles during calendar year 1949.

1950

WILLYS — (ALL MODELS) — For 1950, Willys models were slightly restyled in the grille, with the vertical grille bars now being more pointed and divided by five horizontal bars. There was a new center-gauge dashboard design and new wraparound rear bumper The remainder of the body styling was unchanged from the previous year. Certain equipment formerly provided on both fours and sixes was now used with sixes only. This included dual wipers; front bumper guards and rails; wheel trim rings; rearview mirrors; cigar lighter and white sidewall tires.

WILLYS I.D. NUMBERS: The Vehicle Identification Number is the same as the serial number. VIN locations: on a plate at the left of the driver's seat on the floor riser; on left door sill; on frame front cross member ahead of front spring hanger; on front frame cross member at center; on right side of cowl below hood; on inside of frame on left. Series 463 station wagon serial numbers began at 106504 and went up to 112425; 4X463 station wagons began at 13186 and went up 17167; the VJ3-four Jeepsters began at 12698 and went up to 13190; the VJ3-six Jeepsters began at 10654 and went up to 11001; the 663-six station sedans began at 22769 and went up to 27786; and the 473-four station wagons and Jeepsters and the four-cylinder 4x473 four-wheel-drive station wagons began at 10001 and went up to 12045 in mixed production. 673-six station wagons and Jeepsters began at 10001 and went up to 17456 in mixed production. The engine number was the same as the serial number and was located on the top of the water pump boss, at the right front upper corner of the engine block.

WILLYS SERIES

Model No.	Body/Style No.	Body Type & Seating	Factory Price	Shipping Weight	Prod. Total
FIRST SERIES FOUR-CYLINDER					
450	463	2-dr Sta Wag-6P	1595	2895	Note 1
450	463x4	2-dr 4WD Sta Wag-6P	1895	3136	Note 1
450	VJ3-4	2-dr Jeepster-5P	1495	2468	Note 1
SECOND SERIES FOUR-CYLINDER					
450	473	2-dr Jeepster-5P	1390	2459	Note 1
450	473SW	2-dr Sta Wag-6P	1495	2818	Note 1
450	473X4	2-dr 4WD Sta Wag-6P	1990	3174	Note 1
FIRST SERIES SIX-CYLINDER					
650	663	2-dr Sta Wag-6P	1695	2895	Note 1
650	VJ3-6	2-dr Jeepster-5P	1530	2392	Note 1

SECOND SERIES SIX-CYLINDER

Model No.	Body/Style No.	Body Type & Seating	Factory Price	Shipping Weight	Prod. Total
650	673SW	2-dr Sta Wag-6P	1575	2831	Note 1
650	673VJ	2-dr Jeepster-5P	1490	2485	Note 1

NOTE 1: 38,052 units were built in calendar year 1950 including 5,834 Jeepsters and 32,218 station wagons.

ENGINES:

(FIRST SERIES 463/463x4/VJ-3 FOUR) Inline. L-head. Cast iron block. Displacement: 134.2 cid. Bore and stroke: 3.13 x 4.38 inches. Compression ratio: 6.48:1. Brake hp: 63 at 4000 rpm. Carburetor: Carter WA1-613S single-barrel. Three main bearings. Solid valve lifters.

(FIRST SERIES 663/VJ-3 SIX) Inline. L-head. Cast iron block. Displacement: 148.5 cid. Bore and stroke: 3.0 x 3.5 inches. Compression ratio: 6.42:1. Brake hp: 72 at 4000 rpm. Carburetor: Carter WA1-645S single-barrel. Four main bearings. Solid valve lifters.

(SECOND SERIES 473/473x4 FOUR) Inline. F-head. Cast iron block. Exhaust valves in engine block and intake valves in the cylinder head. Displacement: 134.2 cid. Bore and stroke: 3.13 x 4.38 inches. Compression ratio: 7.4:1. Brake hp: 72 at 4000 rpm. Carburetor: Carter WA1-613S single-barrel. Three main bearings. Solid valve lifters.

(SECOND SERIES 673 SIX) Inline. L-head. Cast iron block. Displacement: 161 cid. Bore and stroke: 3-1/8 x 3-1/2 inches. Compression ratio: 6.9:1. Brake hp: 75 at 4000 rpm. Carburetor: Carter WA1-645S single-barrel. Four main bearings. Solid valve lifters.

CHASSIS FEATURES: Wheelbase: (four-wheel-drive models) 104.5 inches; (conventional models) 104 inches. Overall length: (station wagon) 176.25 inches; (Jeepster) first series: 176.25 inches; second series 175.75 inches; (station sedan) 175.8 inches. Front tread: (all models) 55 inches. Rear tread: (all models) 57 inches. Tires: (Jeepster) first series: 5.90 x 15; second series: 6.40 x 15; (station wagon) 6.70 x 15.

OPTIONS: Front bumper guards. Rear bumper guards. Front grille guard. License plate frames. Large wheel discs. Wheel trim rings. White sidewall tires. Dual wipers on fours. Cigar lighter in fours. Special paint. Radio and antenna. Overdrive in Jeepster. Inside rearview mirror. Outside rearview mirror. Three-speed manual transmission was standard on Jeepsters. Overdrive transmission was standard, except on Jeepsters. Four-cylinder 134.2 cid, 7.8:1 high-compression engine (no cost). Heavy-duty air cleaner was optional at extra cost.

HISTORICAL FOOTNOTES: The 1950 Willys models were introduced in October 1949 and an expanded model range appeared in dealer showrooms after April 1950. Model year production peaked at 38,052 units. Calendar year registrations of 33,926 cars were recorded. W.M. Canaday was the chief executive officer of the company this year. Total output of the Jeepster was 5,834 units including 4,066 four-cylinder models and 1,778 six-cylinder models. Even with the 653 six-cylinder Jeepsters of 1949 thrown in, the total production of Jeepster sixes was below 2,500 cars. Willys-Overland Motors, Inc. also manufactured 26,624 civilian Jeeps and 22,282 other types of commercial vehicles this year. It was the last season for assemblies of Jeepster phaetons, although some such units built in calendar 1950 were sold as 1951 automobiles. Production of military jeeps resumed this year. In calendar year 1950, Willys built 2.8 percent (5,834) of all U.S. convertibles and 21.3 percent (32,218) of all station wagons made in the United States.

1951

WILLYS — (ALL MODELS) — 1951 Willys were identical to the second series 1950 models, which were introduced in April 1950.

WILLYS I.D. NUMBERS: The Vehicle Identification Number is the same as the serial number. VIN locations: on a plate at the left of the driver's seat on the floor riser; on left door sill; on frame front cross member ahead of front spring hanger; on front frame cross member at center; on right side of cowl below hood; on inside of frame on left. Serial numbers took the format 473-SW-451-AA1-10001. First symbol indicates type of engine: 4=four-cylinder; 6=six-cylinder, except four-wheel-drive models have the prefix 4x to indicate 4x4 system (i.e.: 4x473). Next two symbols (73) indicate series. Next two symbols indicate body type: SW=station wagon; VJ=Jeepster. Next symbol indicates engine type again, followed by a pair of symbols indicating model year: 51=1951. Next group of symbols is an alpha-numerical code: AA1=4x2 station wagon; FA1=4x4 station wagon; BA1=4x2 Jeepster. Beginning and ending serial numbers according to model were: (473-SW) 451-AA1-10001 to 451-AA1-25906; (4x473-SW) 451-FA1-10001 to 451-FA1-21854; (473-VJ) 451-BA1-10001 to 451-BA1-14086; (673-SW) 651-AA1-10001 to 651-AA1-18470; (673-VJ) 651-BA1-10001 to 651-BA1-11779. The engine number was the same as the serial number and was located on the top of the water pump boss, at the right front upper corner of the engine block.

WILLYS SERIES

Model No.	Body/Style No.	Body Type & Seating	Factory Price	Shipping Weight	Prod. Total
FOUR-CYLINDER					
451	473SW	2-dr Sta Wag-6P	1758	2818	Note 1
451	4X473	2-dr 2WD Wag-6P	2180	3174	Note 1
451	473VJ	2-dr Jeepster-5P	1426	2459	Note 2
SIX-CYLINDER					
651	673SW	2-dr Sta Wag-6P	1841	2831	Note 1
651	673VJ	2-dr Jeepster-5P	1529	2485	Note 2

NOTE 1: Total calendar year 1951 output was 28,226 units including 25,316 station wagons and 2,900 Aero Willys (1952 model).

NOTE 2: No Jeepsters were built in 1951 calendar year; only 1950 leftovers were sold.

ENGINES:

(FOUR) Inline. F-head. Cast iron block. Exhaust valves in engine block and intake valves in the cylinder head. Displacement: 134.2 cid. Bore and stroke: 3.13 x 4.38 inches. Compression ratio: 7.4:1. Brake hp: 72 at 4000 rpm. Carburetor: Carter YF-768S single-barrel. Three main bearings. Solid valve lifters.

(SIX) Inline. L-head. Cast iron block. Displacement: 161.1 cid. Bore and stroke: 3.13 x 3.50 inches. Compression ratio: 6.9:1. Brake hp: 75 at 4000 rpm. Carburetor: Zenith 39 single-barrel. Four main bearings. Solid valve lifters.

CHASSIS FEATURES: Wheelbase: (four-wheel-drive models) 104.5 inches; (conventional models) 104 inches. Overall length: (station wagon) 176.25 inches; (Jeepster) 176.25 inches; (four-wheel-drive) 175.8 inches. Front tread: (all models) 55 inches. Rear tread: (all models) 57 inches. Tires: (Jeepsters) 6.40 x 15; (4x2 station wagons) 6.70 x 15; (4x4 station wagon) 7.00 x 15.

OPTIONS: Front bumper guards. Rear bumper guards. Front grille guard. License frames. Large wheel discs. Wheel trim rings. White sidewall tires. Dual wipers on fours. Cigar lighter in fours. Special paint. Radio and antenna. Overdrive in Jeepster. Inside rearview mirror. Outside rearview mirror. Three-speed manual transmission was standard on Jeepsters. Overdrive transmission was standard, except on Jeepsters. Four-cylinder 134.2 cid, 7.8:1 high-compression engine (no cost). Heavy-duty air cleaner was optional at extra cost.

HISTORICAL FOOTNOTES: The 1951 Willys models were introduced in November 1950. Model year production peaked at 28,266 units. Calendar year registrations of 26,049 cars were recorded. W.M. Canaday was the chief executive officer of the company this year. The Jeepster was discontinued, although some leftover 1950-built units were sold as 1951 models. Willys-Overland Motors also built 76,571 civilian Jeeps and 20,244 other types of commercial vehicles in calendar year 1951. The company made 24,627 station wagons in the calendar year, which was 12.7 percent of the industry total. Overdrive was installed in 16,581 vehicles made in calendar year 1951.

1952

WILLYS — (ALL MODELS) — The big news for 1952 was the introduction of the Aero Willys line of passenger cars. The Aero was styled by designer Phil Wright and engineered by Clyde Paton. Frame-unitized welded chassis and body construction was featured. It had a clean design and provided good comfort and handling. Four separate models were offered in the Aero line. The Aero Lark was the base trim level and used the old 161 cid/75 hp six-cylinder flathead engine. The Aero Wing, Aero Ace and Aero Eagle hardtop used the overhead valve six-cylinder engine. Again there were two series of station wagons in 1952. The first series was a continuation of the 1951 edition. In April, the 475/685 series was introduced. The station wagons continued basically unchanged for 1952, except for a new chrome trim molding available for the sides of the hood. The little Jeepster phaeton was discontinued after the 1951 model year and would not return until the early 1960s.

WILLYS I.D. NUMBERS: The Vehicle Identification Number is the same as the serial number. VIN locations: on a plate at the left of the driver's seat on the floor riser; on left door sill; on frame front cross member ahead of front spring hanger; on front frame cross member at center; on right side of cowl below hood; on inside of frame on left. Serial numbers took the format 452-M1-10001. First symbol indicates type of engine: 4=four-cylinder; 6=six-cylinder. Second and third symbols indicate model year: 52=1952. Next group of symbols is an alpha-numerical code: KA2=Aero Lark; LA1=Aero Wing; MA1=Aero Ace; MC1=Aero Eagle; AA1=first se-

1950 Willys, Jeep (Model 450), station wagon, OCW

1951 Willys, Jeepster (Model 651), phaeton, OCW

1952 Willys, Aero Ace (Model 652), Custom sedan, OCW

1952 Willys, Aero Wing (Model 652), Super Deluxe sedan, OCW

1953 Willys, Aero Falcon (Model 675), Super Deluxe sedan, OCW

1954 Willys, Aero Ace Deluxe (Model 6-226), sedan, OCW

ries 4x2 station wagon; FA1=first series 4x4 station wagon; AA2=second series 4x2 station wagon; FA2=second series 4x4 station wagon. Beginning and ending serial numbers according to model were: (473-SW) 452-AA1-10001 to 452-AA1-10920; (673-SW) 652-AA1-10001 to 652-AA1-10652; (475) 452-AA2-10001 to 452-AA2-14277; (4x475) 452-FA2-10001 to 452-FA2-15683; (685) 652-AA2-10001 to 652-AA2-13709. (Lark) 652-KA2-1001 to 652-KA2-17561; (Wing) 652-LA1-1001 to 652-LA1-22820; (Ace) 652-MA1-1001 to 652-MA1-18706; (Eagle) 652-MC1-1001 to 652-MC1-11537. The engine number was the same as the serial number and was located on the top of the water pump boss, at the right front upper corner of the engine block.

WILLYS SERIES

Model No.	Body/Style No.	Body Type & Seating	Factory Price	Shipping Weight	Prod. Total
FIRST SERIES FOUR-CYLINDER					
452	473SW	2-dr Sta Wag-6P	1631	2818	Note 1
452	4X473	2-dr 4X4 Sta Wag	2092	3174	Note 1
FIRST SERIES SIX-CYLINDER					
652	673SW	2-dr Sta Wag-6P	1708	2831	Note 1
SECOND SERIES FOUR-CYLINDER					
652	475SW	2-dr Sta Wag-6P	1705	2818	Note 1
652	4X475	2-dr 4X4 Sta Wag	2134	3174	Note 1
SECOND SERIES SIX-CYLINDER					
652	685	2-dr Sta Wag-6P	1786	2850	Note 1
AERO LARK SIX-CYLINDER					
652	675	2-dr Del Sed-5P	1588	2487	7,474
AERO WING SIX-CYLINDER					
652	685	2-dr Sup Del Sed-5P	1825	2570	12,819
AERO ACE SIX-CYLINDER					
652	685	2-dr Cus Sed-5P	1904	2584	8,706
AERO EAGLE SIX-CYLINDER					
652	685	2-dr Cus HT-5P	1979	2575	2,364

NOTE 1: 48,845 Aero Willys and 12,890 station wagons were built in calendar year 1952.

ENGINES:

(473-SW/4x473-SW/475-SW/4x475-SW FOUR) Inline. F-head. Cast iron block. Exhaust valves in the engine block and intake valves in the cylinder head. Displacement: 134 2 cid. Bore and stroke: 3.13 x 4.38 inches. Compression ratio: 7.4:1. Brake hp: 72 at 4000 rpm. Carburetor: Carter YF-768S single-barrel. Three main bearings. Solid valve lifters.

(675 AERO LARK/673-SW SIX) Inline. L-head. Cast iron block. Displacement: 161.1 cid. Bore and stroke: 3.13 x 3.50 inches. Compression ratio: 6.9:1. Brake hp: 75 at 4000 rpm. Carburetor: Carter YS-924S single-barrel. Four main bearings. Solid valve lifters.

(685 STATION WAGON AND 685 AERO WING/ACE/EAGLE SIX) Inline. F-head. Cast iron block. Exhaust valves in the engine block and intake valves in the cylinder head. Displacement: 161.1 cid. Bore and stroke: 3.13 x 3.50 inches. Compression ratio: 7.6:1. Brake hp: 90 at 4200 rpm. Carburetor: Carter YS-924S single-barrel. Four main bearings. Solid valve lifters.

CHASSIS FEATURES: [STATION WAGON] Wheelbase: 104 inches; (4x473/4x475 station wagons) 104.5 inches. Overall length: 176.3 inches; (4x473/4x475 station wagons) 178 inches. Tires: (4x2) 6.70 x 15 tube-type blackwall; (4x4) 7.00 x 15. [AEROS] Wheelbase: 108 inches. Overall length: 180.8 inches. Tires: 5.90 x 15 tube-type blackwall.

OPTIONS: [STATION WAGON] Front bumper guards. Rear bumper guards. Front grille guard. License plate frames. Large wheel discs. Wheel trim rings. White sidewall tires. Dual wipers on fours. Cigar lighter in fours. Special paint. Radio and antenna. Inside rearview mirror. Outside rearview mirror. Three-speed manual overdrive transmission was standard. Four-cylinder 134.2 cid, 7.8:1 high-compression engine (no cost). Heavy-duty air cleaner was optional at extra cost. [AERO MODELS] Overdrive ($86.08). Electric clock. Cigar lighter. Hood ornament. Locking gas cap. Radio. Turn signals ($16.68). Windshield washers. Back-up lights. White sidewall tires. Radio ($76.54). Heater ($67.58). Continental kit ($149.95). Fender skirts ($24.95). Oil filter ($8.38). Airfoam seat cushion, per seat ($8.50). Full wheel discs ($16.14) and two-tone paint ($16.68).

HISTORICAL FOOTNOTES: The 1952 Willys Aero line was announced on Jan. 18, 1952. The Aero Ace was introduced March 5, 1952, and the Aero Lark on March 21. The 1952 second series Willys station wagons were introduced April 14, 1952. On March 19, the 1,000,000th Jeep was assembled. Annual registrations peaked at 41,016 units. Calendar year sales totals included 48,845 Aero Ace passenger cars and 12,890 station wagons for the private market. In addition, 119,371 Jeep trucks and 88,098 purpose-built Jeep commercial vehicles were made. Willys-Overland was ranked as America's 17th largest manufacturer of passenger cars this season, but was also the nation's fifth largest producer of motor vehicles. Approximately 36,000 Aero-type passenger cars were built to 1952 model specifications. Willys installed 29,268 optional overdrive transmissions this year. W.M. Canaday was president and board chairman of the firm, while the famed D.G. 'Barney' Roos was first vice-president. The Willys passenger cars were capable of up to 35 mpg fuel economy. The rear window on Aero Ace models was larger than on other styles. The Aero Ace with the F-head engine took second place among all cars in *Motor Trend* magazine's 1952 Engineering Achievement Award.

1953

WILLYS — (ALL MODELS) — Willys-Overland expanded the Aero line in 1953 and made only minor appearance changes from the 1952 models. These revisions included red-painted wheel cover emblems and a gold-plated 'W' in the center of the grille symbolizing the firm's 50th Anniversary. The Aero Wing was replaced with the Aero Falcon and a new four-door sedan was developed for the Lark, Falcon and Ace lines. The Eagle two-door hardtop continued to be the flagship of the line. The Lark series was the base trim level and included the word Lark on the trunk lid; the L-head four-cylinder engine; and rubber moldings around its two-piece windshield. The Falcon was the intermediate trim level and included the word Falcon on the trunk lid; the L-head four-cylinder engine; and chrome moldings around its two-piece windshield. The Ace was the top trim level and included the words Custom Ace on the trunk lid; the F-head four-cylinder engine; chrome moldings surrounding its one-piece windshield and a wraparound rear window. As in previous years, the Willys station wagons continued unchanged from the previous models. On April 28, 1953, Willys-Overland, Inc. was acquired by the Henry J. Kaiser Co. for approximately $60 million. The name was then changed to Willys Motors, Inc. The Toledo, Ohio-based Kaiser-Willys Sales Corp. sold the Kaiser-Frazer plant at Willow Run to General Motors. All production was shifted to the plant at Toledo.

WILLYS I.D. NUMBERS: The Vehicle Identification Number is the same as the serial number. VIN locations: on a plate at the left of the driver's seat on the floor riser; on left door sill; on frame front cross member ahead of front spring hanger; on front frame cross member at center; on right side of cowl below hood; on inside of frame on left. Serial numbers took the format 453-AA2-10001. First symbol indicates type of engine: 4=four-cylinder; 6=six-cylinder. Second and third symbols indicate model year: 53=1953. Next group of symbols is a series code: RBJ=Heavy-Duty Aero; KB1=Lark Deluxe four-door; KA1=Lark Deluxe two-door; PB1=Falcon Super four-door; PA1=Falcon Super two-door; MB1=Ace Custom four-door; MA1=Ace Custom two-door; MC1=Eagle two-door hardtop; AA2=4x2 station wagon; FA2=second series 4x4 station wagon. Beginning and ending serial numbers according to model were: (Aero Heavy-Duty) 653-RBJ-10001 to 653-RBJ-10187; (Aero Lark Deluxe four-door) 653-KB1-10001 to 653-KB1-17691; Aero Lark Deluxe two-door 653-KA1-10001 to 653-KA1-18205; (Aero Falcon Super Deluxe four-door) 653-PB1-10001 to 653-PB1-13470; Aero Falcon Super Deluxe two-door 653-PA1-10001 to 653-PA1-13054; (Aero Ace Custom four-door) 653-MB1-10001 to 653-MB1-17475; (Aero Ace Custom two-door) 653-MA1-10001 to 653-MA1-14988. The Aero Eagle two-door hardtop began at 653-MC1-1001 and went up to 653-MC1-17018. Model 475 station wagon models began at 453-AA2-10001 and went up to 453-AA2-14747. Model 4X475 station wagons began at 453-FA2-10001 and went up to 453-FA2-20631. Model 685 Deluxe station wagons began at 685-AA2-10001 and went up to 685-AA2-17548. The engine number was the same as the serial number and was located on the top of the water pump boss, at the right front upper corner of the engine block.

WILLYS SERIES

Model No.	Body/Style No.	Body Type & Seating	Factory Price	Shipping Weight	Prod. Total
FOUR-CYLINDER STATION WAGON					
475SW	AA2	2-dr Sta Wag-6P	1750	2818	4,764
4x475	FA2	2-dr 4X4 Sta Wag-6P	2134	3174	10,630
SIX-CYLINDER STATION WAGON					
685	AA2	2-dr Sta Wag-6P	1786	2850	7,547
WILLYS-AERO SERIES					
AERO HEAVY-DUTY LINE					
675	RBJ	4-dr Sed-5P	1680	2511	186
AERO LARK DELUXE					
675	KB1	4-dr Sed-5P	1580	2509	7,691
675	KB2	2-dr Sed-5P	1500	2487	8,205
AERO FALCON SUPER DELUXE					
675	PB1	4-dr Sed-5P	1700	2529	3,116
675	PB2	2-dr Sed-5P	1640	2507	3,054
AERO ACE CUSTOM					
685	MB1	4-dr Sed-5P	1870	2735	7,475
685	MB2	2-dr Sed-5P	1800	2585	4,958

AERO EAGLE

Model No.	Body/Style No.	Body Type & Seating	Factory Price	Shipping Weight	Prod. Total
685	MC1	2-dr HT Sed-5P	1979	2575	7,018

NOTE 1: 35,128 Aeros and 5,417 station wagons were built in calendar year 1953.

NOTE 2: 41,703 Aeros and 22,941 station wagons were built in model year 1953.

ENGINES:

(475/4x475 FOUR) Inline. F-head. Cast iron block. Exhaust valves in the engine block and intake valves in the cylinder head. Displacement: 134.2 cid. Bore and stroke: 3.13 x 4.38 inches. Compression ratio: 7.4:1. Brake hp: 72 at 4000 rpm. Carburetor: Carter YF-924S single-barrel. Three main bearings. Solid valve lifters.

(HEAVY-DUTY AND AERO LARK 675 SIX) Inline. L-head. Cast iron block. Displacement: 161.1 cid. Bore and stroke: 3.13 x 3.50 inches. Compression ratio: 6.9:1. Brake hp: 75 at 4000 rpm. Carburetor: Carter YS-924S single-barrel. Four main bearings. Solid valve lifters.

(AERO ACE/WING/EAGLE 685/685 STATION WAGON SIX) Inline. F-head. Cast iron block. Exhaust valves in the engine block and intake valves in the cylinder head. Displacement: 161.1 cid. Bore and stroke: 3.13 x 3.50 inches. Compression ratio: 7.6:1. Brake hp: 90 at 4400 rpm. Carburetor: Carter YS-924S single-barrel. Four main bearings. Solid valve lifters.

CHASSIS FEATURES: Wheelbase: (4x475 station wagons) 104.5 inches; (other models) 104 inches. Overall length: (station wagons) 176.25 inches; (other models) 180-7/8 inches. Tires: (4x475 station wagons) 7.00 x 15 inches; (4x2 station wagons) 6.70 x 15; (Lark) 5.90 x 15; (Wing/Ace/Eagle) 6.40 x 15.

OPTIONS: [STATION WAGON] Front bumper guards. Rear bumper guards. Front grille guard. License plate frames. Large wheel discs. Wheel trim rings. White sidewall tires. Dual wipers on fours. Cigar lighter in fours. Special paint. Radio and antenna. Inside rearview mirror. Outside rearview mirror. Three-speed manual overdrive transmission was standard. Four-cylinder 134.2 cid, 7.8:1 high-compression engine (no cost). Heavy-duty air cleaner was optional at extra cost. [AERO MODELS] Overdrive ($86.08). Electric clock. Cigar lighter. Hood ornament. Locking gas cap. Radio. Turn signals ($16.68). Windshield washers. Back-up lights. White sidewall tires. Radio ($76.54). Heater ($67.58). Continental kit ($149.95). Fender skirts ($24.95). Oil filter ($8.38). Airfoam seat cushion, per seat ($8.50). Full wheel discs ($16.14) and two-tone paint ($16.68).

HISTORICAL FOOTNOTES: The 1953 Willys Aero Eagle and Aero Lark were introduced on Dec. 15, 1952; Aero Falcon on Jan. 15, 1953; and the Aero Ace on Feb. 15, 1953. The Aero models were advertised as being "fresh out of the future." Willys' Golden Anniversary was celebrated Feb. 12, 1953. The company became a subsidiary of Kaiser Industries on April 28, 1953. Registrations of Willys models in 1953 peaked at 42,433 units. Calendar year sales of 40,563 cars were recorded, which included 35,146 Aeros and 5,417 Jeep station wagons. Nearly 18,000 vehicles, 4,703 hardtops and 13,260 station wagons, were built in California. Edgar F. Kaiser was the chief executive officer this year. Vice-President Barney Roos was gone. The new Aero Eagle hardtop coupe featured pillarless side window styling. *Motor Trend* magazine road tested a 1953 Willys Aero Ace with overdrive, an $80 option that was installed on 23,816 cars for the calendar year. The car covered the quarter-mile in 21.1 seconds during acceleration testing, which was slightly faster than average for cars in the under-$2,050 price class. The Ace was found to have a top speed of 82.6 mph and gave 24.9 mpg fuel economy. The operating cost per mile was estimated at 9.3 cents, which was slightly higher than the Chevrolet Two-Ten and Cadillac Sixty-Two. This figure included the cost of typical repairs on each model, but Willys lovers may have difficulty accepting the published results. *Auto Age* magazine test drove a 90-hp Lark Aero Wing in February 1953, recording a 0-to-60 mph time of 13 seconds and top speed of 90 mph. It delivered 23 mpg. A Borg-Warner strike, starting May 20, 1953, had a devastating effect on Willys sales and prompted the company, on July 15, to announce the availability of a new type of transmission—General Motors' Hydra-Matic—in many Willys models. On July 29, the Kaiser-Willys Sales Division was formed. Willys' sales placed it ninth in the American industry this season.

1954

WILLYS — (ALL MODELS) — At first glance, the 1954 Aero models appeared to be mostly the same as the 1953 models with larger taillights and revised interiors. The dash was more practical and less austere with vertical slots containing "airplane-type" levers for the controls. There was a new windshield wiper system with both arms moving in the same direction to overlap and eliminate a blind spot in the center. In March 1954, the Kaiser 226-cid L-head was made available, as an option, for the Ace and Eagle models. With the Kaiser engine the Aero was clocked at 85 mph by one magazine. It wasn't as much a high-top-end engine as one geared for good acceleration. Zero-to-60 mph was in the 13 second range. As an experiment, a few cars were fitted with the 140-hp Kaiser Manhattan engine featuring a Paxton centrifugal supercharger. With the supercharged engine, acceleration was comparable to that of a contemporary V-8 engine. The 1954 Aero models also handled much better than before, with the introduction of a new front suspension. It utilized threaded trunions, which were adjustable for wear. The kingpins and coil springs were longer, shock absorbers and A-arms were stronger and the steering idler arm was lengthened. A cross member connected left and right front suspension components to eliminate lateral torque and reduce toe-in variations. The Aero Willys was one of the best combinations of ride and handling offered by a domestic manufacturer in the 1950s. The Lark series was the base trim level Aero model for 1954 and included rubber moldings around the windshield and rear window; standard headlight trim and the six-cylinder F-head engine. The Ace was the top trim level of the Aero models and included all Lark trim, plus hooded headlight bezels; chrome windshield moldings; chrome rear window moldings; chrome trim around the top of the grille; and the big six-cylinder L-head engine. The top line Eagle hardtop featured all the Ace trim, plus 'W' medallions mounted on stainless steel rear window moldings. The Custom models included a continental spare tire mount as standard equipment. All models of the Aero line included new bumper guards; aluminum scuff plates; taillight assemblies; and chrome wheel covers as additions to the standard equipment listed in 1953. Once again, the Willys station wagon was largely unchanged from the previous year. New features included different two-tone paint treatments and a revised grille, with three horizontal bars instead of five. The Kaiser six 226-cid engine became an option.

WILLYS I.D. NUMBERS: The Vehicle Identification Number is the same as the serial number. VIN locations: on a plate at the left of the driver's seat on the floor riser; on left door sill; on frame front cross member ahead of front spring hanger; on front frame cross member at center; on right side of cowl below hood; on inside of frame on left. Serial numbers took the format 454-FA2-10001. First symbol indicates type of engine: 4=four-cylinder; 6=six-cylinder. Second and third symbols indicate model year: 54=1954. Next group of symbols is a series code: KB3=Lark Deluxe four-door; KA3=Lark Deluxe two-door; MB2=Aero Ace four-door; MA2=Aero Ace two-door; MC3=Aero Eagle two-door hardtop; MB1=Aero Ace Deluxe "226" four-door sedan; MA1=Aero Ace Deluxe "226" two-door sedan; MC1=Aero Eagle Deluxe "226" two-door hardtop; MC2=Aero Eagle Custom "226" two-door hardtop; FA2=4x2 station wagon; AA2=4x4 station wagon. Beginning and ending serial numbers according to model were: (Aero Lark Deluxe four-door) 654-KB3-10001 to 654-KB3-11482; Aero Lark Deluxe two-door 654-KA3-10001 to 654-KA3-11482; (Aero Ace four-door) 654-MB2-10001 to 654-MB2-11482; (Aero Ace two-door) 654-MA2-10001 to 654-MA2-11482; (Aero Eagle) 654-MC3-10001 to 654-MC3-11482, (four-cylinder 4x2 station wagon) 454-FA2-10001 to 454-FA2-5047; (4x2 station wagon with Willys six-cylinder) AA2-10001 to AA2-10945; (4x2 station wagon with Kaiser six-cylinder) 6-226-FA2-10001 to 6-226-FA2-12645. The engine number was the same as the serial number and was located on the top of the water pump boss, at the right front upper corner of the engine block.

WILLYS SERIES

Model No.	Body/Style No.	Body Type & Seating	Factory Price	Shipping Weight	Prod. Total
454	FA2	2-dr Sta Wag-6P	2134	3115	Note 1
654	AA2	2-dr Sta Wag-6P	1808	2381	Note 1
6-226	FA2	2-dr Del 4X4 Sta Wag-6P	2223	3278	Note 1

WILLYS AERO SERIES

Model No.	Body/Style No.	Body Type & Seating	Factory Price	Shipping Weight	Prod. Total
AERO LARK LINE					
654	KB3	4-dr Sed-5P	1670	2661	1,370
654	KA3	2-dr Sed-5P	1590	2623	1,482
AERO ACE LINE					
654	MB2	4-dr Sed-5P	1806	2709	1,195
654	MA2	2-dr Sed-5P	1735	2682	1,380
AERO EAGLE LINE					
654	MC3	2-dr HT-5P	1991	2778	84
AERO ACE DELUXE '226' LINE					
6-226	MB1	4-dr Sed-5P	1857	2778	586
6-226	MA1	2-dr Sed-5P	1786	2751	611
AERO EAGLE DELUXE '226' LINE					
6-226	MA1	2-dr HT-5P	2042	2847	660
AERO EAGLE CUSTOM '226' LINE					
6-226	MC2	2-dr HT-5P	2217	2904	499

NOTE 1: Calendar year output was 9,344 Aeros and 1,597 station wagons.

ENGINES:

(454 FOUR) Inline. F-head. Cast iron block. Exhaust valves in the engine block and intake valves in the cylinder head. Displacement: 134.2 cid. Bore and stroke: 3.13 x 4.38 inches. Compression ratio: 7.4:1. Brake hp: 72 at 4000 rpm. Carburetor: Carter YF-924S single-barrel. Three main bearings. Solid valve lifters.

(654 SIX) Inline. L-head. Cast iron block. Displacement: 161.1 cid. Bore and stroke: 3.13 x 3.50 inches. Compression ratio: 7.6:1. Brake hp: 90 at 4200 rpm. Carburetor: Carter YF-924S single-barrel. Four main bearings. Solid valve lifters.

(6-226 SIX) L-head. Cast iron block. Exhaust valves in the engine block and intake valves in the cylinder head. Displacement: 226.2 cid. Bore and stroke: 3.31 x 4.38 inches. Compression ratio: 7.3:1. Brake hp: 115 at 3650 rpm. Carburetor: Carter WBD two-barrel. Four main bearings. Solid valve lifters.

CHASSIS FEATURES: [STATION WAGON] Wheelbase: (654 four-wheel-drive station wagon) 104.5 inches; (other models) 104 inches. Overall length: (654 four-wheel-drive station wagon) 176.25 inches; (other models) 176.25 inches. Tires: (four-wheel-drive station wagons) 7.00 x 15; (other models) 6.70 x 15 tube-type blackwall. [AERO WILLYS] Wheelbase: 108 inches. Overall length: (with continental kit) 189.75 inches; (other models) 183 inches. Tires: (Eagles) 5.90 x 15 tube-type blackwall; (other models) 6.40 x 15 tube-type blackwall.

OPTIONS: [STATION WAGON] Front bumper guards. Rear bumper guards. Front grille guard. License plate frames. Large wheel discs. Wheel trim rings. White sidewall tires. Dual wipers on fours. Cigar lighter in fours. Special paint. Radio and antenna. Inside rearview mirror. Outside rearview mirror. Three-speed manual overdrive transmission was standard. Four-cylinder 134.2 cid, 7.8:1 high-compression engine (no cost). Heavy-duty air cleaner was optional at extra cost. [AERO WILLYS] Overdrive ($86). Hydra-Matic automatic transmission ($179). Power steering. Electric clock. Radio ($71). Heater ($63). Cigar lighter. Turn signals. Windshield washers. White sidewall tires, exchange price ($18).

HISTORICAL FOOTNOTES: The Aero series Willys models were introduced in February 1954. The Willys Aero Ace Deluxe, Eagle Custom and the Deluxe six station wagon appeared in dealer showrooms March 17, 1954. Registrations for 1954 peaked at just 17,002 units. Calendar year sales of 10,941 vehicles, including 9,344 passenger cars and 1,597 station wagons were recorded. Model year production of passenger car styles was approximately 8,220 units. Calendar year output included 1,619 two-door hardtops. Records show that 659 cars built in calendar year 1953 and 1,751 cars built in calendar year 1954 were equipped with Hydra-Matic transmission. This option was available, for the first time, in cars built to 1954 model specifications. *Motor Trend* magazine road tested a Willys Aero Ace in its July 1954 issue. This car, equipped with the '226' Kaiser engine, accelerated from 0-to-60 mph in 17.2 seconds and covered the standing start quarter-mile in 20.3 seconds with a terminal speed of 65 mph. It gave 17.7 mpg for the overall test. On April 14, 1954, Willys workers agreed to take a pay cut to help the firm in its attempt to stay competitive in the market. However, not even drastic steps such as closings of the Dowagiac, Mich., and Maywood assembly plants were enough to maintain Willys passenger cars past early 1955. An interesting feature of the Aero models was aircraft-type, push-pull dashboard control levers.

1955

WILLYS — (ALL MODELS) — By early 1955, Kaiser-Willys had decided to stop building passenger cars, but not before selling about 6,500 1955 models. No longer called Aeros, the line was divided into the Custom two- and four-door sedans and the Bermuda hardtop (as well as 659 Ace sedans). Engine options included the 161-cid and 226-cid six-cylinder engines. Prices were cut drastically in an effort to spark sales and the Bermuda was advertised as the nation's lowest-priced hardtop, but only 2,215 were built. Most were powered by the 226-cid Kaiser engine. Styling was much busier than in previous years and no single designer takes credit for it. New features included full-width grilles; chrome headlamp visors; chrome hood side moldings of a novel design; new two-tone color treatments and an especially wide selection of upholstery trims. The grille was an assembly of concave vertical chrome bars, rather than the simple unit used in previous models. A nicely styled hardtop station wagon was planned and the entire model line was scheduled for a sleek restyling for 1956, but neither plan was realized. As before, the Willys station wagon models were unchanged.

WILLYS I.D. NUMBERS: The Vehicle Identification Number is the same as the serial number. VIN locations: on a plate at the left of the driver's seat on the floor riser; on left door sill; on frame front cross member ahead of front spring hanger; on front frame cross member at center; on right side of cowl below hood; on inside of frame on left. Serial numbers were: (Custom two-door) 52467-10001 to 52467-10288; (Custom four-door) 52367-10001 to 52367-10288; (Bermuda two-door hardtop) 52567-10001 to 52567-12156; (6-226 station wagon) 54168-5001 to 54168-16513; (685 station wagon) 54727-10001 to 54727-11092. The engine number was the same as the serial number and was located on the top of the water pump boss, at the right front upper corner of the engine block.

WILLYS SERIES

Model No.	Body/Style No.	Body Type & Seating	Factory Price	Shipping Weight	Prod. Total
685	N/A	2-dr Sta Wag-6P	1997	2831	Note 1
6-226	N/A	2-dr 4WD Sta Wag-6P	2420	3278	Note 1
CUSTOM SERIES					
6-226	N/A	2-dr Sed-5P	1663	2751	288
6-226	N/A	4-dr Sed-5P	1725	2778	2,882
BERMUDA					
6-226	N/A	2-dr HT-5P	1795	2847	2,156
ACE					
6-226	N/A	4-dr Sed-5P	1856	2709	659

NOTE 1: Calendar 1955 production of station wagons was 12,240 units.

NOTE 2: Model year production of Aero Willys totaled 5,986 units.

NOTE 3: Calendar 1955 production of Aero Willys totaled 4,778 units.

NOTE 4: Calendar year production included 1,740 two-door hardtops.

ENGINES:

(454 FOUR) Inline. F-head. Cast iron block. Exhaust valves in the engine block and intake valves in the cylinder head. Displacement: 134.2 cid. Bore and stroke: 3.13 x 4.38 inches. Compression ratio: 7.4:1. Brake hp: 72 at 4000 rpm. Carburetor: Carter YF-924S single-barrel. Three main bearings. Solid valve lifters.

(6-226 SIX) L-head. Cast iron block. Exhaust valves in the engine block and intake valves in the cylinder head. Displacement: 226.2 cid. Bore and stroke: 3.31 x 4.38 inches. Compression ratio: 7.3:1. Brake hp: 115 at 3650 rpm. Carburetor: Carter WBD two-barrel. Four main bearings. Solid valve lifters.

CHASSIS FEATURES: [STATION WAGON] Wheelbase: (Model 6-226) 104.5 inches; (685 models) 104 inches. Overall length: 176.3 inches. Tires: (Model 6-226 station wagons) 6.40 x 15 tube-type blackwall; (other models) 6.70 x 15 tube-type blackwall. [AERO WILLYS] Wheelbase: 108 inches. Overall length: 189.8 inches with continental kit. Tires: 6.40 x 15 tube-type blackwall.

OPTIONS: [STATION WAGON] Front bumper guards. Rear bumper guards. Front grille guard. License plate frames. Large wheel discs. Wheel trim rings. White sidewall tires. Dual wipers on fours. Cigar lighter in fours. Special paint. Radio and antenna. Inside rearview mirror. Outside rearview mirror. Three-speed manual overdrive transmission was standard. Four-cylinder 134.2-cid, 7.8:1 high-compression engine (no cost). Heavy-duty air cleaner was optional at extra cost. [AERO WILLYS] Overdrive ($85). Dual-Range Hydra-Matic ($179). Electric clock. Radio. Heater. Cigar lighter. Turn signals. Windshield washers. White sidewall tires.

HISTORICAL FOOTNOTES: Kaiser-Willys withdrew as a carmaker in mid-1955, immediately after completing an order for 1,021 Kaisers for the Argentine market. The first 1955 Willys passenger car was assembled Nov. 2, 1954. The Bermuda hardtop and Custom four-door were introduced Jan. 6, 1955, and the two-door sedan was added to the line Feb. 16, 1955. Only 4,778 units were made between Jan. 1, 1955, and April 1955, when auto production ceased. Edgar F. Kaiser was the chief executive officer of the firm again. The Aero did get a new lease on life in South America. Its dies were eventually shipped to the former Kaiser subsidiary, Willys de Brasil, where a cleaned-up 1955 model (without the busy side moldings) was built with Willys F-head power. Production continued through 1962. In all, the Aero actually lasted over 10 years, which attests to its basically good design.

PRICING SECTION

Refer to page 3 for Condition Ratings

AUBURN

	6	5	4	3	2	1
1904						
Model A						
Tr	1150	3600	6000	12,000	21,000	30,000
1905						
Model B, 2-cyl.						
Tr	1100	3500	5800	11,600	20,300	29,000
1906						
Model C, 2-cyl.						
Tr	1100	3500	5800	11,600	20,300	29,000
1907						
Model D, 2-cyl.						
Tr	1100	3500	5800	11,600	20,300	29,000
1908						
Model G, 2-cyl., 24 hp						
Tr	1100	3500	5800	11,600	20,300	29,000
Model H, 2-cyl.						
Tr	1150	3600	6000	12,000	21,000	30,000
Model K, 2-cyl.						
Rbt	1150	3700	6200	12,400	21,700	31,000
1909						
Model G, 2-cyl., 24 hp						
Tr	1150	3600	6000	12,000	21,000	30,000
Model H, 2cyl.						
Tr	1150	3600	6000	12,000	21,000	30,000
Model K						
Rbt	1100	3500	5800	11,600	20,300	29,000
Model B, 4-cyl., 25-30 hp						
Tr	1100	3500	5800	11,600	20,300	29,000
Model C, 4-cyl.						
Tr	1150	3700	6200	12,400	21,700	31,000
Model D, 4-cyl.						
Rbt	1200	3850	6400	12,800	22,400	32,000
1910						
Model G, 2-cyl., 24 hp						
Tr	1050	3350	5600	11,200	19,600	28,000
Model H, 2-cyl.						
Tr	1100	3500	5800	11,600	20,300	29,000
Model K, 2-cyl.						
Rbt	1150	3600	6000	12,000	21,000	30,000
Model B, 4-cyl., 25-30 hp						
Tr	1150	3600	6000	12,000	21,000	30,000
Model C, 4-cyl.						
Tr	1100	3500	5800	11,600	20,300	29,000
Model D, 4-cyl.						
Rbt	1150	3600	6000	12,000	21,000	30,000
Model X, 4-cyl., 35-40 hp						
Tr	1150	3600	6000	12,000	21,000	30,000
Model R, 4-cyl.						
Tr	1150	3700	6200	12,400	21,700	31,000
Model S, 4-cyl.						
Rds	1150	3700	6200	12,400	21,700	31,000
1911						
Model G, 2-cyl., 24 hp						
Tr	1050	3350	5600	11,200	19,600	28,000
Model K, 2-cyl.						
Rbt	1100	3500	5800	11,600	20,300	29,000
Model L, 4-cyl., 25-30 hp						
Tr	1100	3500	5800	11,600	20,300	29,000
Model F, 4-cyl.						
Tr	1100	3500	5800	11,600	20,300	29,000
Model N, 4-cyl., 40 hp						
Tr	1150	3600	6000	12,000	21,000	30,000
Model Y, 4-cyl.						
Tr	1100	3500	5800	11,600	20,300	29,000
Model T, 4-cyl.						
Tr	1100	3500	5800	11,600	20,300	29,000
Model M, 4-cyl.						
Rds	1150	3600	6000	12,000	21,000	30,000
1912						
Model 6-50, 6-cyl.						
Tr	1150	3700	6200	12,400	21,700	31,000
Model 40H, 4-cyl., 35-40 hp						
Tr	1100	3500	5800	11,600	20,300	29,000
Model 40M, 4-cyl., 35-40 hp						
Rds	1100	3500	5800	11,600	20,300	29,000
Model 40N, 4-cyl., 35-40 hp						
Tr	1150	3600	6000	12,000	21,000	30,000
Model 35L, 4-cyl., 30 hp						
Tr	1050	3350	5600	11,200	19,600	28,000
Model 30L, 4-cyl., 30 hp						
Rds	1100	3500	5800	11,600	20,300	29,000
Tr	1150	3600	6000	12,000	21,000	30,000
1913						
Model 33M, 4-cyl., 33 hp						
Rds	1150	3600	6000	12,000	21,000	30,000
Model 33L, 4-cyl., 33 hp						
Tr	1150	3700	6200	12,400	21,700	31,000
Model 40A, 4-cyl., 40 hp						
Rds	1150	3700	6200	12,400	21,700	31,000
Model 40L, 4-cyl.						
Tr	1200	3850	6400	12,800	22,400	32,000
Model 45, 6-cyl., 45 hp						
Tr	1200	3850	6400	12,800	22,400	32,000
Model 45B, 6-cyl., 45 hp						
Rds	1150	3700	6200	12,400	21,700	31,000
T&C	1050	3350	5600	11,200	19,600	28,000

	6	5	4	3	2	1
Cpe	1000	3250	5400	10,800	18,900	27,000
Model 50, 6-cyl., 50 hp						
Tr	1250	3950	6600	13,200	23,100	33,000
1914						
Model 4-40, 4-cyl., 40 hp						
Rds	1050	3350	5600	11,200	19,600	28,000
Tr	1100	3500	5800	11,600	20,300	29,000
Cpe	900	2900	4800	9600	16,800	24,000
Model 4-41, 4-cyl., 40 hp						
Tr	1150	3600	6000	12,000	21,000	30,000
Model 6-45, 6-cyl., 45 hp						
Rds	1150	3600	6000	12,000	21,000	30,000
Tr	1150	3700	6200	12,400	21,700	31,000
Model 6-46, 6-cyl., 45 hp						
Tr	1200	3850	6400	12,800	22,400	32,000
1915						
Model 4-36, 4-cyl., 36 hp						
Rds	1050	3350	5600	11,200	19,600	28,000
Tr	1100	3500	5800	11,600	20,300	29,000
Model 4-43, 4-cyl., 43 hp						
Rds	1100	3500	5800	11,600	20,300	29,000
Tr	1150	3600	6000	12,000	21,000	30,000
Model 6-40, 6-cyl., 50 hp						
Rds	1150	3700	6200	12,400	21,700	31,000
Tr	1200	3850	6400	12,800	22,400	32,000
Cpe	950	3000	5000	10,000	17,500	25,000
Model 6-47, 6-cyl., 47 hp						
Rds	1150	3600	6000	12,000	21,000	30,000
Tr	1150	3700	6200	12,400	21,700	31,000
1916						
Model 4-38, 4-cyl., 38 hp						
Rds	1100	3500	5800	11,600	20,300	29,000
Tr	1150	3600	6000	12,000	21,000	30,000
Model 6-38						
Rds	1150	3600	6000	12,000	21,000	30,000
Tr	1150	3700	6200	12,400	21,700	31,000
Model 6-40, 6-cyl., 40 hp						
Rds	1200	3850	6400	12,800	22,400	32,000
Tr	1250	3950	6600	13,200	23,100	33,000
Model Union 4-36, 6-cyl., 36 hp						
Tr	1200	3850	6400	12,800	22,400	32,000
1917						
Model 6-39, 6-cyl., 39 hp						
Rds	1000	3250	5400	10,800	18,900	27,000
Tr	1050	3350	5600	11,200	19,600	28,000
Model 6-44, 6-cyl., 44 hp						
Rds	1050	3350	5600	11,200	19,600	28,000
Tr	1100	3500	5800	11,600	20,300	29,000
Model 4-36, 4-cyl., 36 hp						
Rds	1000	3100	5200	10,400	18,200	26,000
Tr	1000	3250	5400	10,800	18,900	27,000
1918						
Model 6-39, 6-cyl.						
Tr	950	3000	5000	10,000	17,500	25,000
Rds	950	3000	5000	10,000	17,500	25,000
Spt Tr	1000	3100	5200	10,400	18,200	26,000
Model 6-44, 6-cyl.						
Tr	950	3000	5000	10,000	17,500	25,000
Rds	950	3000	5000	10,000	17,500	25,000
Spt Tr	1000	3100	5200	10,400	18,200	26,000
Sed	650	2050	3400	6800	11,900	17,000
1919						
Model 6-39						
Tr	950	3000	5000	10,000	17,500	25,000
Rds	950	3000	5000	10,000	17,500	25,000
Cpe	550	1800	3000	6000	10,500	15,000
Sed	600	1900	3200	6400	11,200	16,000
1920						
Model 6-39, 6-cyl.						
Tr	950	3000	5000	10,000	17,500	25,000
Spt Tr	1000	3100	5200	10,400	18,200	26,000
Rds	1000	3100	5200	10,400	18,200	26,000
Sed	700	2150	3600	7200	12,600	18,000
Cpe	700	2300	3800	7600	13,300	19,000
1921						
Model 6-39						
Tr	950	3000	5000	10,000	17,500	25,000
Spt Tr	1000	3250	5400	10,800	18,900	27,000
Rds	1000	3250	5400	10,800	18,900	27,000
Cabr	1000	3250	5400	10,800	18,900	27,000
Sed	700	2150	3600	7200	12,600	18,000
Cpe	700	2300	3800	7600	13,300	19,000
1922						
Model 6-51, 6-cyl.						
Tr	1000	3250	5400	10,800	18,900	27,000
Rds	1050	3350	5600	11,200	19,600	28,000
Spt Tr	1050	3350	5600	11,200	19,600	28,000
Sed	700	2300	3800	7600	13,300	19,000
Cpe	750	2400	4000	8000	14,000	20,000
1923						
Model 6-43, 6-cyl.						
Tr	1050	3350	5600	11,200	19,600	28,000
Sed	700	2150	3600	7200	12,600	18,000
Model 6-63, 6-cyl.						
Tr	1100	3500	5800	11,600	20,300	29,000
Spt Tr	1150	3600	6000	12,000	21,000	30,000

	6	5	4	3	2	1
Brgm	700	2300	3800	7600	13,300	19,000
Sed	700	2150	3600	7200	12,600	18,000
Model 6-51, 6-cyl.						
Phae	1150	3600	6000	12,000	21,000	30,000
Tr	1100	3500	5800	11,600	20,300	29,000
Spt Tr	1150	3700	6200	12,400	21,700	31,000
Brgm	750	2400	4000	8000	14,000	20,000
Sed	700	2300	3800	7600	13,300	19,000
1924						
Model 6-43, 6-cyl.						
Tr	1050	3350	5600	11,200	19,600	28,000
Spt Tr	1100	3500	5800	11,600	20,300	29,000
Sed	700	2150	3600	7200	12,600	18,000
Cpe	700	2300	3800	7600	13,300	19,000
2d	700	2150	3600	7200	12,600	18,000
Model 6-63, 6-cyl.						
Tr	1100	3500	5800	11,600	20,300	29,000
Spt Tr	1150	3700	6200	12,400	21,700	31,000
Sed	700	2300	3800	7600	13,300	19,000
Brgm	750	2400	4000	8000	14,000	20,000
1925						
Model 8-36, 8-cyl.						
Tr	1300	4100	6800	13,600	23,800	34,000
2d Brgm	700	2150	3600	7200	12,600	18,000
4d Sed	700	2150	3600	7200	12,600	18,000
Model 6-43, 6-cyl.						
Phae	1200	3850	6400	12,800	22,400	32,000
Spt Phae	1250	3950	6600	13,200	23,100	33,000
Cpe	750	2400	4000	8000	14,000	20,000
4d Sed	700	2300	3800	7600	13,300	19,000
2d Sed	700	2150	3600	7200	12,600	18,000
Model 6-66, 6-cyl.						
Rds	1200	3850	6400	12,800	22,400	32,000
Brgm	650	2050	3400	6800	11,900	17,000
4d	700	2150	3600	7200	12,600	18,000
Tr	1250	3950	6600	13,200	23,100	33,000
Model 8-88, 8-cyl.						
Rds	1250	3950	6600	13,200	23,100	33,000
4d Sed 5P	700	2300	3800	7600	13,300	19,000
4d Sed 7P	700	2300	3800	7600	13,300	19,000
Brgm	700	2150	3600	7200	12,600	18,000
Tr	1250	3950	6600	13,200	23,100	33,000
1926						
Model 4-44, 4-cyl., 42 hp						
Tr	1150	3700	6200	12,400	21,700	31,000
Rds	1200	3850	6400	12,800	22,400	32,000
Cpe	900	2900	4800	9600	16,800	24,000
4d Sed	850	2750	4600	9200	16,100	23,000
Model 6-66, 6-cyl., 48 hp						
Rds	1300	4200	7000	14,000	24,500	35,000
Tr	1300	4100	6800	13,600	23,800	34,000
Brgm	850	2750	4600	9200	16,100	23,000
4d Sed	900	2900	4800	9600	16,800	24,000
Cpe	950	3000	5000	10,000	17,500	25,000
Model 8-88, 8-cyl., 88 hp, 129" wb						
Rds	1400	4450	7400	14,800	25,900	37,000
Tr	1350	4300	7200	14,400	25,200	36,000
Cpe	1000	3100	5200	10,400	18,200	26,000
Brgm	900	2900	4800	9600	16,800	24,000
5P Sed	900	2900	4800	9600	16,800	24,000
7P Sed	900	2950	4900	9800	17,200	24,500
Model 8-88, 8-cyl., 88 hp, 146" wb						
7P Sed	950	3000	5000	10,000	17,500	25,000
1927						
Model 6-66, 6-cyl., 66 hp						
Rds	1300	4200	7000	14,000	24,500	35,000
Tr	1300	4100	6800	13,600	23,800	34,000
Brgm	900	2900	4800	9600	16,800	24,000
Sed	950	3000	5000	10,000	17,500	25,000
Model 8-77, 8-cyl., 77 hp						
Rds	1350	4300	7200	14,400	25,200	36,000
Tr	1300	4200	7000	14,000	24,500	35,000
Brgm	950	3000	5000	10,000	17,500	25,000
Sed	950	3000	5000	10,000	17,500	25,000
Model 8-88, 8-cyl., 88 hp, 129" WB						
Tr	1450	4550	7600	15,200	26,600	38,000
Rds	1450	4700	7800	15,600	27,300	39,000
Cpe	1000	3250	5400	10,800	18,900	27,000
Brgm	900	2900	4800	9600	16,800	24,000
Sed	900	2900	4800	9600	16,800	24,000
Spt Sed	950	3000	5000	10,000	17,500	25,000
Model 8-88, 8-cyl., 88 hp, 146" wb						
7P Sed	950	3000	5000	10,000	17,500	25,000
Tr	1450	4700	7800	15,600	27,300	39,000
1928						
Model 6-66, 6-cyl., 66 hp						
Rds	1450	4700	7800	15,600	27,300	39,000
Cabr	1450	4550	7600	15,200	26,600	38,000
Sed	900	2900	4800	9600	16,800	24,000
Spt Sed	950	3000	5000	10,000	17,500	25,000
Model 8-77, 8-cyl., 77 hp						
Rds	1500	4800	8000	16,000	28,000	40,000
Cabr	1450	4700	7800	15,600	27,300	39,000
Sed	950	3000	5000	10,000	17,500	25,000
Spt Sed	1000	3100	5200	10,400	18,200	26,000
Model 8-88, 8-cyl., 88 hp						
Rds	1550	4900	8200	16,400	28,700	41,000
Tr	1500	4800	8000	16,000	28,000	40,000
Cabr	1500	4800	8000	16,000	28,000	40,000
Sed	950	3000	5000	10,000	17,500	25,000
Spt Sed	1000	3100	5200	10,400	18,200	26,000
Model 8-88, 8-cyl., 88 hp, 136" wb						
7P Sed	1000	3250	5400	10,800	18,900	27,000
SECOND SERIES						
Model 76, 6-cyl.						
Rds	1700	5400	9000	18,000	31,500	45,000
Cabr	1600	5150	8600	17,200	30,100	43,000
Sed	1000	3100	5200	10,400	18,200	26,000
Spt Sed	1000	3250	5400	10,800	18,900	27,000
Model 88, 8-cyl.						
Spds	3250	10,300	17,200	34,400	60,200	86,000
Rds	1950	6250	10,400	20,800	36,400	52,000
Cabr	1600	5150	8600	17,200	30,100	43,000
Sed	1000	3100	5200	10,400	18,200	26,000
Spt Sed	1000	3250	5400	10,800	18,900	27,000
Phae	1900	6000	10,000	20,000	35,000	50,000

	6	5	4	3	2	1
Model 115, 8-cyl.						
Spds	3450	11,050	18,400	36,800	64,400	92,000
Rds	2050	6600	11,000	22,000	38,500	55,000
Cabr	1850	5900	9800	19,600	34,300	49,000
Sed	1050	3350	5600	11,200	19,600	28,000
Spt Sed	1100	3500	5800	11,600	20,300	29,000
Phae	2000	6350	10,600	21,200	37,100	53,000
1929						
Model 76, 6-cyl.						
Rds	1800	5750	9600	19,200	33,600	48,000
Tr	1750	5500	9200	18,400	32,200	46,000
Cabr	1700	5400	9000	18,000	31,500	45,000
Vic	1150	3600	6000	12,000	21,000	30,000
Sed	1000	3100	5200	10,400	18,200	26,000
Spt Sed	1000	3250	5400	10,800	18,900	27,000
Model 88, 8-cyl.						
Spds	3750	12,000	20,000	40,000	70,000	100,000
Rds	2850	9100	15,200	30,400	53,200	76,000
Tr	2500	7900	13,200	26,400	46,200	66,000
Cabr	2550	8150	13,600	27,200	47,600	68,000
Vic	1200	3850	6400	12,800	22,400	32,000
Sed	1000	3100	5200	10,400	18,200	26,000
Spt Sed	1000	3250	5400	10,800	18,900	27,000
Phae	2150	6850	11,400	22,800	39,900	57,000
Model 115, 8-cyl.						
Spds	4350	13,900	23,200	46,400	81,200	116,000
Rds	3100	9850	16,400	32,800	57,400	82,000
Cabr	2550	8150	13,600	27,200	47,600	68,000
Vic	1250	3950	6600	13,200	23,100	33,000
Sed	1000	3100	5200	10,400	18,200	26,000
Spt Sed	1000	3250	5400	10,800	18,900	27,000
Phae	2950	9350	15,600	31,200	54,600	78,000
Model 6-80, 6-cyl.						
Tr	2150	6850	11,400	22,800	39,900	57,000
Cabr	2000	6350	10,600	21,200	37,100	53,000
Vic	1050	3350	5600	11,200	19,600	28,000
Sed	1000	3100	5200	10,400	18,200	26,000
Spt Sed	1000	3250	5400	10,800	18,900	27,000
Model 8-90, 8-cyl.						
Spds	4350	13,900	23,200	46,400	81,200	116,000
Tr	2950	9350	15,600	31,200	54,600	78,000
Cabr	2850	9100	15,200	30,400	53,200	76,000
Phae	3250	10,300	17,200	34,400	60,200	86,000
Vic	1250	3950	6600	13,200	23,100	33,000
Sed	1000	3250	5400	10,800	18,900	27,000
Spt Sed	1050	3350	5600	11,200	19,600	28,000
Model 120, 8-cyl.						
Spds	4900	15,600	26,000	52,000	91,000	130,000
Cabr	3100	9850	16,400	32,800	57,400	82,000
Phae	3250	10,300	17,200	34,400	60,200	86,000
Vic	1300	4200	7000	14,000	24,500	35,000
Sed	1050	3350	5600	11,200	19,600	28,000
7P Sed	1150	3600	6000	12,000	21,000	30,000
Spt Sed	1100	3500	5800	11,600	20,300	29,000
1930						
Model 6-85, 6-cyl.						
Cabr	2800	8900	14,800	29,600	51,800	74,000
Sed	1050	3350	5600	11,200	19,600	28,000
Spt Sed	1100	3500	5800	11,600	20,300	29,000
Model 8-95, 8-cyl.						
Cabr	2850	9100	15,200	30,400	53,200	76,000
Phae	2950	9350	15,600	31,200	54,600	78,000
Sed	1150	3600	6000	12,000	21,000	30,000
Spt Sed	1150	3700	6200	12,400	21,700	31,000
Model 125, 8-cyl.						
Cabr	2950	9350	15,600	31,200	54,600	78,000
Phae	3250	10,300	17,200	34,400	60,200	86,000
Sed	1150	3700	6200	12,400	21,700	31,000
Spt Sed	1200	3850	6400	12,800	22,400	32,000
1931						
Model 8-98, 8-cyl., Standard, 127" wb						
Spds	4150	13,200	22,000	44,000	77,000	110,000
Cabr	3000	9600	16,000	32,000	56,000	80,000
Phae	3300	10,550	17,600	35,200	61,600	88,000
Cpe	1200	3850	6400	12,800	22,400	32,000
2d Brgm	1100	3500	5800	11,600	20,300	29,000
5P Sed	1150	3600	6000	12,000	21,000	30,000
Model 8-98, 8-cyl., 136" wb						
7P Sed	1150	3700	6200	12,400	21,700	31,000
Model 8-98A, 8-cyl., Custom, 127"wb						
Spds	4350	13,900	23,200	46,400	81,200	116,000
Cabr	3600	11,500	19,200	38,400	67,200	96,000
Phae	3750	12,000	20,000	40,000	70,000	100,000
Cpe	1350	4300	7200	14,400	25,200	36,000
2d Brgm	1250	3950	6600	13,200	23,100	33,000
4d Sed	1300	4100	6800	13,600	23,800	34,000
Model 8-98, 8-cyl., 136" wb						
7P Sed	1350	4300	7200	14,400	25,200	36,000
1932						
Model 8-100, 8-cyl., Custom, 127" wb						
Spds	4750	15,100	25,200	50,400	88,200	126,000
Cabr	4000	12,700	21,200	42,400	74,200	106,000
Phae	4050	12,950	21,600	43,200	75,600	108,000
Cpe	1400	4450	7400	14,800	25,900	37,000
2d Brgm	1300	4100	6800	13,600	23,800	34,000
4d Sed	1300	4200	7000	14,000	24,500	35,000
Model 8-100, 8-cyl., 136" wb						
7P Sed	1450	4550	7600	15,200	26,600	38,000
Model 8-100A, 8-cyl., Custom Dual Ratio, 127" wb						
Spds	5250	16,800	28,000	56,000	98,000	140,000
Cabr	4900	15,600	26,000	52,000	91,000	130,000
Phae	5100	16,300	27,200	54,400	95,200	136,000
Cpe	1500	4800	8000	16,000	28,000	40,000
2d Brgm	1350	4300	7200	14,400	25,200	36,000
4d Sed	1400	4450	7400	14,800	25,900	37,000
Model 8-100A, 8-cyl., 136" wb						
7P Sed	1500	4800	8000	16,000	28,000	40,000
Model 12-160, 12-cyl., Standard						
Spds	5650	18,000	30,000	60,000	105,000	150,000
Cabr	5450	17,400	29,000	58,000	101,500	145,000
Phae	5650	18,000	30,000	60,000	105,000	150,000
Cpe	1750	5650	9400	18,800	32,900	47,000
2d Brgm	1350	4300	7200	14,400	25,200	36,000
4d Sed	1400	4450	7400	14,800	25,900	37,000
Model 12-160A, 12-cyl., Custom Dual Ratio						
Spds	6000	19,200	32,000	64,000	112,000	160,000

	6	5	4	3	2	1
Cabr	5800	18,600	31,000	62,000	108,500	155,000
Phae	6000	19,200	32,000	64,000	112,000	160,000
Cpe	2050	6600	11,000	22,000	38,500	55,000
2d Brgm	1550	4900	8200	16,400	28,700	41,000
4d Sed	1600	5050	8400	16,800	29,400	42,000
1933						
Model 8-101, 8-cyl., Standard, 127" wb						
Spds	3750	12,000	20,000	40,000	70,000	100,000
Cabr	2950	9350	15,600	31,200	54,600	78,000
Phae	3150	10,100	16,800	33,600	58,800	84,000
Cpe	1300	4100	6800	13,600	23,800	34,000
2d Brgm	1100	3500	5800	11,600	20,300	29,000
4d Sed	1150	3600	6000	12,000	21,000	30,000
Model 8-101, 8-cyl., 136" wb						
7P Sed	1150	3700	6200	12,400	21,700	31,000
Model 8-101A, 8-cyl., Custom Dual Ratio, 127" wb						
Spds	4350	13,900	23,200	46,400	81,200	116,000
Cabr	3250	10,300	17,200	34,400	60,200	86,000
Phae	3300	10,550	17,600	35,200	61,600	88,000
Cpe	1450	4550	7600	15,200	26,600	38,000
2d Brgm	1150	3700	6200	12,400	21,700	31,000
4d Sed	1200	3850	6400	12,800	22,400	32,000
Model 8-101A, 8-cyl., 136" wb						
7P Sed	1300	4100	6800	13,600	23,800	34,000
Model 8-105, 8-cyl., Salon Dual Ratio						
Spds	4500	14,400	24,000	48,000	84,000	120,000
Cabr	4000	12,700	21,200	42,400	74,200	106,000
Phae	3850	12,250	20,400	40,800	71,400	102,000
2d Brgm	1350	4300	7200	14,400	25,200	36,000
4d Sed	1300	4100	6800	13,600	23,800	34,000
Model 12-161, 12-cyl., Standard						
Spds	5100	16,300	27,200	54,400	95,200	136,000
Cabr	4900	15,600	26,000	52,000	91,000	130,000
Phae	5050	16,100	26,800	53,600	93,800	134,000
Cpe	1600	5050	8400	16,800	29,400	42,000
2d Brgm	1400	4450	7400	14,800	25,900	37,000
4d Sed	1450	4550	7600	15,200	26,600	38,000
Model 12-161A, 12-cyl., Custom Dual Ratio						
Spds	5450	17,400	29,000	58,000	101,500	145,000
Cabr	5250	16,800	28,000	56,000	98,000	140,000
Phae	5450	17,400	29,000	58,000	101,500	145,000
Cpe	1750	5500	9200	18,400	32,200	46,000
2d Brgm	1550	4900	8200	16,400	28,700	41,000
4d Sed	1650	5300	8800	17,600	30,800	44,000
Model 12-165, 12-cyl., Salon Dual Ratio						
Spds	5650	18,000	30,000	60,000	105,000	150,000
Cabr	5450	17,400	29,000	58,000	101,500	145,000
Phae	5650	18,000	30,000	60,000	105,000	150,000
2d Brgm	1650	5300	8800	17,600	30,800	44,000
4d Sed	1700	5400	9000	18,000	31,500	45,000
1934						
Model 652X, 6-cyl., Standard						
Cabr	2400	7700	12,800	25,600	44,800	64,000
2d Brgm	850	2750	4600	9200	16,100	23,000
4d Sed	900	2900	4800	9600	16,800	24,000
Model 652Y, 6-cyl., Custom						
Cabr	2850	9100	15,200	30,400	53,200	76,000
Phae	3000	9600	16,000	32,000	56,000	80,000
2d Brgm	1350	4300	7200	14,400	25,200	36,000
4d Sed	1300	4200	7000	14,000	24,500	35,000
Model 850X, 8-cyl., Standard						
Cabr	2950	9350	15,600	31,200	54,600	78,000
2d Brgm	1400	4450	7400	14,800	25,900	37,000
4d Sed	1350	4300	7200	14,400	25,200	36,000
Model 850Y, 8-cyl., Dual Ratio						
Cabr	5450	17,400	29,000	58,000	101,500	145,000
Phae	5650	18,000	30,000	60,000	105,000	150,000
2d Brgm	1600	5050	8400	16,800	29,400	42,000
4d Sed	1700	5400	9000	18,000	31,500	45,000
Model 1250, 12-cyl., Salon Dual Ratio						
Cabr	5650	18,000	30,000	60,000	105,000	150,000
Phae	5800	18,600	31,000	62,000	108,500	155,000
2d Brgm	1700	5400	9000	18,000	31,500	45,000
4d Sed	1750	5500	9200	18,400	32,200	46,000
1935						
Model 6-653, 6-cyl., Standard						
Cabr	2650	8400	14,000	28,000	49,000	70,000
Phae	3100	9850	16,400	32,800	57,400	82,000
Cpe	1350	4300	7200	14,400	25,200	36,000
2d Brgm	1300	4100	6800	13,600	23,800	34,000
4d Sed	1250	3950	6600	13,200	23,100	33,000
Model 6-653, 6-cyl., Custom Dual Ratio						
Cabr	2850	9100	15,200	30,400	53,200	76,000
Phae	3150	10,100	16,800	33,600	58,800	84,000
Cpe	1450	4550	7600	15,200	26,600	38,000
2d Brgm	1300	4200	7000	14,000	24,500	35,000
4d Sed	1300	4100	6800	13,600	23,800	34,000
Model 6-653, 6-cyl., Salon Dual Ratio						
Cabr	3100	9850	16,400	32,800	57,400	82,000
Phae	3300	10,550	17,600	35,200	61,600	88,000
Cpe	1450	4700	7800	15,600	27,300	39,000
2d Brgm	1350	4300	7200	14,400	25,200	36,000
4d Sed	1400	4450	7400	14,800	25,900	37,000
Model 8-851, 8-cyl., Standard						
Cabr	2850	9100	15,200	30,400	53,200	76,000
Phae	2850	9100	15,200	30,400	53,200	76,000
Cpe	1500	4800	8000	16,000	28,000	40,000
2d Brgm	1400	4450	7400	14,800	25,900	37,000
4d Sed	1450	4550	7600	15,200	26,600	38,000
Model 8-851, 8-cyl., Custom Dual Ratio						
Cabr	3000	9600	16,000	32,000	56,000	80,000
Phae	3100	9850	16,400	32,800	57,400	82,000
Cpe	1550	4900	8200	16,400	28,700	41,000
2d Brgm	1450	4550	7600	15,200	26,600	38,000
4d Sed	1450	4700	7800	15,600	27,300	39,000
Model 8-851, 8-cyl., Salon Dual Ratio						
Cabr	3250	10,300	17,200	34,400	60,200	86,000
Phae	3250	10,300	17,200	34,400	60,200	86,000
Cpe	1500	4800	8000	16,000	28,000	40,000
2d Brgm	1400	4450	7400	14,800	25,900	37,000
4d Sed	1450	4550	7600	15,200	26,600	38,000
Model 8-851, 8-cyl., Supercharged Dual Ratio						
Spds	6200	19,800	33,000	66,000	115,500	165,000
Cabr	3750	12,000	20,000	40,000	70,000	100,000
Phae	3850	12,250	20,400	40,800	71,400	102,000
Cpe	1600	5050	8400	16,800	29,400	42,000
2d Brgm	1450	4700	7800	15,600	27,300	39,000
4d Sed	1500	4800	8000	16,000	28,000	40,000

1936	6	5	4	3	2	1
Model 6-654, 6-cyl., Standard						
Cabr	2850	9100	15,200	30,400	53,200	76,000
Phae	2850	9100	15,200	30,400	53,200	76,000
Cpe	1400	4450	7400	14,800	25,900	37,000
2d Brgm	1350	4300	7200	14,400	25,200	36,000
4d Sed	1300	4200	7000	14,000	24,500	35,000
Model 6-654, 6-cyl., Custom Dual Ratio						
Cabr	3000	9600	16,000	32,000	56,000	80,000
Phae	3100	9850	16,400	32,800	57,400	82,000
Cpe	1450	4700	7800	15,600	27,300	39,000
2d Brgm	1350	4300	7200	14,400	25,200	36,000
4d Sed	1400	4450	7400	14,800	25,900	37,000
Model 6-654, 6-cyl., Salon Dual Ratio						
Cabr	4150	13,200	22,000	44,000	77,000	110,000
Phae	4200	13,450	22,400	44,800	78,400	112,000
Cpe	1500	4800	8000	16,000	28,000	40,000
2d Brgm	1400	4450	7400	14,800	25,900	37,000
4d Sed	1450	4550	7600	15,200	26,600	38,000
Model 8-852, 8-cyl., Standard						
Cabr	4500	14,400	24,000	48,000	84,000	120,000
Phae	4600	14,650	24,400	48,800	85,400	122,000
Cpe	1550	4900	8200	16,400	28,700	41,000
2d Brgm	1450	4550	7600	15,200	26,600	38,000
4d Sed	1450	4700	7800	15,600	27,300	39,000
Model 8-852, 8-cyl., Custom Dual Ratio						
Cabr	4650	14,900	24,800	49,600	86,800	124,000
Phae	4750	15,100	25,200	50,400	88,200	126,000
Cpe	1600	5150	8600	17,200	30,100	43,000
2d Brgm	1450	4700	7800	15,600	27,300	39,000
4d Sed	1500	4800	8000	16,000	28,000	40,000
Model 8-852, 8-cyl., Salon Dual Ratio						
Cabr	4750	15,100	25,200	50,400	88,200	126,000
Phae	4800	15,350	25,600	51,200	89,600	128,000
Cpe	1650	5300	8800	17,600	30,800	44,000
2d Brgm	1500	4800	8000	16,000	28,000	40,000
4d Sed	1550	4900	8200	16,400	28,700	41,000
Model 8, 8-cyl., Supercharged Dual Ratio						
Spds	6200	19,800	33,000	66,000	115,500	165,000
Cabr	4800	15,350	25,600	51,200	89,600	128,000
Phae	4900	15,600	26,000	52,000	91,000	130,000
Cpe	1750	5500	9200	18,400	32,200	46,000
2d Brgm	1550	4900	8200	16,400	28,700	41,000
4d Sed	1600	5050	8400	16,800	29,400	42,000

CORD

1930						
Series L-29, 8-cyl., 137.5" wb						
4d 5P Sed	3000	9600	16,000	32,000	56,000	80,000
4d 5P Brgm	3100	9850	16,400	32,800	57,400	82,000
2d 4P Conv 2-4 Pas	6400	20,400	34,000	68,000	119,000	170,000
4d Conv Sed	6550	21,000	35,000	70,000	122,500	175,000
1931						
Series L-29, 8-cyl., 137.5" wb						
4d 5P Sed	3100	9850	16,400	32,800	57,400	82,000
4d 5P Brgm	3150	10,100	16,800	33,600	58,800	84,000
2d 2-4P Cabr	6400	20,400	34,000	68,000	119,000	170,000
4d Conv Sed	6550	21,000	35,000	70,000	122,500	175,000
1932						
Series L-29, 8-cyl., 137.5" wb						
4d 5P Sed	3100	9850	16,400	32,800	57,400	82,000
4d 5P Brgm	3150	10,100	16,800	33,600	58,800	84,000
2d 2-4P Conv	6400	20,400	34,000	68,000	119,000	170,000
4d Conv Sed	6550	21,000	35,000	70,000	122,500	175,000
1933-34-35						
(Not Manufacturing)						
4d Phae	5200	16,550	27,600	55,200	96,600	138,000
1936						
Model 810, 8-cyl., 125" wb						
4d West Sed	2250	7200	12,000	24,000	42,000	60,000
4d Bev Sed	2350	7450	12,400	24,800	43,400	62,000
2d Sportsman	5200	16,550	27,600	55,200	96,600	138,000
2d Phae	5200	16,550	27,600	55,200	96,600	138,000
1937						
Model 812, 8-cyl., 125" wb						
4d West Sed	2250	7200	12,000	24,000	42,000	60,000
4d Bev Sed	2350	7450	12,400	24,800	43,400	62,000
2d Sportsman	5200	16,550	27,600	55,200	96,600	138,000
2d Phae	5200	16,550	27,600	55,200	96,600	138,000
Model 812, 8-cyl., 132" wb						
4d Cus Bev	2350	7450	12,400	24,800	43,400	62,000
4d Cus Berline	2400	7700	12,800	25,600	44,800	64,000

NOTE: Add 40 percent for S/C Models.

CHECKER

1960						
Checker Superba Std.						
Sed	350	1020	1700	3400	5950	8500
Sta Wag	350	1040	1700	3450	6000	8600
Checker Superba Spl.						
Sed	350	1040	1700	3450	6000	8600
Sta Wag	350	1040	1750	3500	6100	8700
1961						
Checker Superba						
Sed	350	1020	1700	3400	5950	8500
Sta Wag	350	1040	1700	3450	6000	8600
Checker Marathon						
Sed	350	1040	1700	3450	6000	8600
Sta Wag	350	1040	1750	3500	6100	8700
1962						
Checker Superba						
Sed	350	1020	1700	3400	5950	8500
Sta Wag	350	1040	1700	3450	6000	8600
Checker Marathon						
Sed	350	1040	1700	3450	6000	8600
Sta Wag	350	1040	1750	3500	6100	8700
1963						
Checker Superba						
Sed	350	1040	1700	3450	6000	8600
Sta Wag	350	1040	1750	3500	6100	8700
Checker Marathon						
Sed	350	1040	1700	3450	6000	8600
Sta Wag	350	1040	1750	3500	6100	8700
Limo	450	1080	1800	3600	6300	9000

	6	5	4	3	2	1
1964						
Checker Marathon						
Sed	350	1020	1700	3400	5950	8500
Sta Wag	350	1040	1700	3450	6000	8600
Limo	450	1090	1800	3650	6400	9100
Aerobus	350	1040	1750	3500	6100	8700
1965						
Marathon Series						
Sed	450	1050	1800	3600	6200	8900
DeL Sed	350	1020	1700	3400	5950	8500
Sta Wag	350	1040	1700	3450	6000	8600
Limo	450	1080	1800	3600	6300	9000
1966						
Marathon Series						
Sed	350	1020	1700	3400	5950	8500
DeL Sed	350	1040	1700	3450	6000	8600
Sta Wag	350	1040	1750	3500	6100	8700
Limo	450	1080	1800	3600	6300	9000
1967						
Marathon Series						
Sed	350	1020	1700	3400	5950	8500
Sta Wag	350	1040	1700	3450	6000	8600
1968						
Marathon Series						
Sed	350	1020	1700	3400	5950	8500
DeL Sed	350	1040	1700	3450	6000	8600
Sta Wag	350	1040	1750	3500	6100	8700
1969						
Marathon Series						
Sed	350	1020	1700	3400	5950	8500
DeL Sed	350	1040	1700	3450	6000	8600
Sta Wag	350	1040	1750	3500	6100	8700
Limo	450	1080	1800	3600	6300	9000
1970						
Marathon Series						
Sed	350	1020	1700	3400	5950	8500
Sta Wag	350	1040	1750	3500	6100	8700
DeL Sed	350	1040	1700	3450	6000	8600
Limo	450	1080	1800	3600	6300	9000
1971						
Marathon Series						
Sed	350	975	1600	3200	5600	8000
Sta Wag	350	1040	1750	3500	6100	8700
DeL Sed	350	1020	1700	3400	5950	8500
Limo	450	1080	1800	3600	6300	9000
NOTE: Add 5 percent for V8.						
1972						
Marathon Series						
Sed	350	975	1600	3200	5600	8000
Sta Wag	350	1040	1750	3500	6100	8700
DeL Sed	350	1020	1700	3400	5950	8500
NOTE: Add 5 percent for V8.						
1973						
Marathon Series						
Sed	350	975	1600	3200	5600	8000
Sta Wag	350	1040	1700	3450	6000	8600
DeL Sed	350	1020	1700	3400	5950	8500
NOTE: Add 5 percent for V8.						
1974						
Marathon Series						
Sed	350	975	1600	3200	5600	8000
Sta Wag	350	1040	1700	3450	6000	8600
DeL Sed	350	1020	1700	3400	5950	8500
NOTE: Add 5 percent for V8.						
1975						
Marathon Series						
Sed	350	900	1500	3000	5250	7500
Sta Wag	350	950	1500	3050	5300	7600
DeL Sed	350	950	1550	3100	5400	7700
1976						
4d Sed Marathon	350	880	1500	2950	5180	7400
4d Sed Marathon DeL	350	975	1600	3200	5500	7900
1977						
4d Sed Marathon	350	850	1450	2850	4970	7100
4d Sed Marathon DeL	350	950	1500	3050	5300	7600
1978						
4d Sed Marathon	350	850	1450	2850	4970	7100
4d Sed Marathon DeL	350	950	1500	3050	5300	7600
1979						
4d Sed Marathon	350	850	1450	2850	4970	7100
4d Sed Marathon DeL	350	950	1500	3050	5300	7600
1980						
4d Sed Marathon	350	860	1450	2900	5050	7200
4d Sed Marathon DeL	350	950	1550	3100	5400	7700
1981						
4d Sed Marathon	350	860	1450	2900	5050	7200
4d Sed Marathon DeL	350	950	1550	3100	5400	7700
1982						
4d Sed Marathon	350	860	1450	2900	5050	7200
4d Sed Marathon DeL	350	950	1550	3100	5400	7700

HUDSON

	6	5	4	3	2	1
1909						
Model 20, 4-cyl.						
2d Rds	1150	3700	6200	12,400	21,700	31,000
1910						
Model 20, 4-cyl.						
2d Rds	1150	3600	6000	12,000	21,000	30,000
4d Tr	1150	3600	6000	12,000	21,000	30,000
1911						
Model 33, 4-cyl.						
2d Rds	1150	3600	6000	12,000	21,000	30,000
2d Tor Rds	1150	3700	6200	12,400	21,700	31,000
4d Pony Ton	1200	3850	6400	12,800	22,400	32,000
4d Tr	1250	3950	6600	13,200	23,100	33,000
1912						
Model 33, 4-cyl.						
2d Rds	1300	4200	7000	14,000	24,500	35,000
2d Tor Rds	1350	4300	7200	14,400	25,200	36,000
4d Tr	1450	4550	7600	15,200	26,600	38,000
2d Cpe	1000	3100	5200	10,400	18,200	26,000
4d Limo	1100	3500	5800	11,600	20,300	29,000

	6	5	4	3	2	1
1913						
Model 37, 4-cyl.						
2d Rds	1200	3850	6400	12,800	22,400	32,000
2d Tor Rds	1250	3950	6600	13,200	23,100	33,000
4d Tr	1300	4100	6800	13,600	23,800	34,000
2d Cpe	950	3000	5000	10,000	17,500	25,000
4d Limo	1050	3350	5600	11,200	19,600	28,000
Model 54, 6-cyl.						
2d 2P Rds	1250	3950	6600	13,200	23,100	33,000
2d 5P Rds	1300	4100	6800	13,600	23,800	34,000
2d Tor Rds	1300	4200	7000	14,000	24,500	35,000
4d Tr	1350	4300	7200	14,400	25,200	36,000
4d 7P Tr	1400	4450	7400	14,800	25,900	37,000
2d Cpe	1000	3250	5400	10,800	18,900	27,000
4d Limo	1100	3500	5800	11,600	20,300	29,000
1914						
Model 40, 6-cyl.						
2d Rbt	1100	3500	5800	11,600	20,300	29,000
4d Tr	1150	3700	6200	12,400	21,700	31,000
2d Cabr	1150	3600	6000	12,000	21,000	30,000
Model 54, 6-cyl.						
4d 7P Tr	1200	3850	6400	12,800	22,400	32,000
1915						
Model 40, 6-cyl.						
2d Rds	1050	3350	5600	11,200	19,600	28,000
4d Phae	1150	3600	6000	12,000	21,000	30,000
4d Tr	1100	3500	5800	11,600	20,300	29,000
2d Cabr	1100	3500	5800	11,600	20,300	29,000
2d Cpe	700	2150	3600	7200	12,600	18,000
4d Limo	750	2400	4000	8000	14,000	20,000
4d Lan Limo	800	2500	4200	8400	14,700	21,000
Model 54, 6-cyl.						
4d Phae	1200	3850	6400	12,800	22,400	32,000
4d 7P Tr	1150	3700	6200	12,400	21,700	31,000
4d Sed	700	2300	3800	7600	13,300	19,000
4d Limo	850	2650	4400	8800	15,400	22,000
1916						
Super Six, 6-cyl.						
2d Rds	1000	3100	5200	10,400	18,200	26,000
2d Cabr	1000	3250	5400	10,800	18,900	27,000
4d Phae	1050	3350	5600	11,200	19,600	28,000
4d Tr Sed	650	2050	3400	6800	11,900	17,000
4d T&C	700	2150	3600	7200	12,600	18,000
Model 54, 6-cyl.						
4d 7P Phae	1150	3700	6200	12,400	21,700	31,000
1917						
Super Six, 6-cyl.						
2d Rds	900	2900	4800	9600	16,800	24,000
2d Cabr	950	3000	5000	10,000	17,500	25,000
4d 7P Phae	1000	3100	5200	10,400	18,200	26,000
4d Tr Sed	550	1800	3000	6000	10,500	15,000
4d T&C	700	2150	3600	7200	12,600	18,000
4d Twn Lan	650	2050	3400	6800	11,900	17,000
4d Limo Lan	700	2150	3600	7200	12,600	18,000
1918						
Super Six, 6-cyl.						
2d Rds	850	2650	4400	8800	15,400	22,000
2d Cabr	850	2750	4600	9200	16,100	23,000
4d 4P Phae	850	2750	4600	9200	16,100	23,000
4d 5P Phae	900	2900	4800	9600	16,800	24,000
2d 4P Cpe	550	1800	3000	6000	10,500	15,000
4d Tr Sed	600	1900	3200	6400	11,200	16,000
4d Sed	600	1900	3200	6400	11,200	16,000
4d Tr Limo	650	2050	3400	6800	11,900	17,000
4d T&C	650	2050	3400	6800	11,900	17,000
4d Limo	700	2150	3600	7200	12,600	18,000
4d Twn Limo	700	2150	3600	7200	12,600	18,000
4d Limo Lan	700	2150	3600	7200	12,600	18,000
4d F F Lan	700	2300	3800	7600	13,300	19,000
1919						
Super Six Series O, 6-cyl.						
2d Cabr	700	2300	3800	7600	13,300	19,000
4d 4P Phae	750	2400	4000	8000	14,000	20,000
4d 7P Phae	800	2500	4200	8400	14,700	21,000
2d 4P Cpe	450	1450	2400	4800	8400	12,000
4d Sed	400	1300	2200	4400	7700	11,000
4d Tr Limo	450	1450	2400	4800	8400	12,000
4d T&C	500	1550	2600	5200	9100	13,000
4d Twn Lan	500	1550	2600	5200	9100	13,000
4d Limo Lan	550	1700	2800	5600	9800	14,000
1920						
Super Six Series 10-12, 6-cyl.						
4d 4P Phae	750	2400	4000	8000	14,000	20,000
4d 7P Phae	800	2500	4200	8400	14,700	21,000
2d Cabr	600	1900	3200	6400	11,200	16,000
2d Cpe	400	1300	2200	4400	7700	11,000
4d Sed	400	1200	2000	4000	7000	10,000
4d Tr Limo	450	1450	2400	4800	8400	12,000
4d Limo	500	1550	2600	5200	9100	13,000
1921						
Super Six, 6-cyl.						
4d 4P Phae	750	2400	4000	8000	14,000	20,000
4d 7P Phae	800	2500	4200	8400	14,700	21,000
2d Cabr	600	1900	3200	6400	11,200	16,000
2d 4P Cpe	400	1200	2000	4000	7000	10,000
4d Sed	450	1080	1800	3600	6300	9000
4d Tr Limo	400	1200	2000	4000	7000	10,000
4d Limo	400	1300	2200	4400	7700	11,000
1922						
Super Six, 6-cyl.						
2d Spds	750	2400	4000	8000	14,000	20,000
4d Phae	700	2300	3800	7600	13,300	19,000
2d Cabr	600	1900	3200	6400	11,200	16,000
2d Cpe	450	1140	1900	3800	6650	9500
2d Sed	350	1020	1700	3400	5950	8500
4d Sed	350	1020	1700	3400	5950	8500
4d Tr Limo	400	1300	2200	4400	7700	11,000
4d Limo	400	1200	2000	4000	7000	10,000
1923						
Super Six, 6-cyl.						
2d Spds	750	2400	4000	8000	14,000	20,000
4d Phae	700	2300	3800	7600	13,300	19,000
2d Cpe	450	1140	1900	3800	6650	9500
2d Sed	350	1020	1700	3400	5950	8500
4d Sed	350	1020	1700	3400	5950	8500
4d 7P Sed	450	1080	1800	3600	6300	9000

1924	6	5	4	3	2	1
Super Six, 6-cyl.						
2d Spds	700	2300	3800	7600	13,300	19,000
4d Phae	700	2150	3600	7200	12,600	18,000
2d Sed	350	975	1600	3200	5600	8000
4d Sed	350	975	1600	3250	5700	8100
4d 7P Sed	350	1020	1700	3400	5950	8500
1925						
Super Six, 6-cyl.						
2d Spds	700	2300	3800	7600	13,300	19,000
4d Phae	700	2150	3600	7200	12,600	18,000
2d Sed	450	1140	1900	3800	6650	9500
4d Brgm	400	1200	2000	4000	7000	10,000
4d Sed	450	1140	1900	3800	6650	9500
4d 7P Sed	400	1200	2000	4000	7000	10,000
1926						
Super Six, 6-cyl.						
4d Phae	750	2400	4000	8000	14,000	20,000
2d Sed	400	1200	2000	4000	7000	10,000
4d Brgm	400	1300	2200	4400	7700	11,000
4d 7P Sed	400	1250	2100	4200	7400	10,500
1927						
Standard Six, 6-cyl.						
4d Phae	750	2400	4000	8000	14,000	20,000
2d Sed	450	1160	1950	3900	6800	9700
2d Spl Sed	400	1200	2000	4000	7000	10,000
4d Brgm	400	1250	2100	4200	7400	10,500
4d 7P Sed	400	1250	2100	4200	7400	10,500
Super Six						
2d Cus Rds	1250	3950	6600	13,200	23,100	33,000
4d Cus Phae	1300	4100	6800	13,600	23,800	34,000
2d Sed	400	1300	2200	4400	7700	11,000
4d Sed	450	1450	2400	4800	8400	12,000
4d Cus Brgm	600	1900	3200	6400	11,200	16,000
4d Cus Sed	650	2050	3400	6800	11,900	17,000
1928						
First Series, 6-cyl., (Start June, 1927)						
2d Std Sed	450	1140	1900	3800	6650	9500
4d Std Sed	450	1160	1950	3900	6800	9700
2d Sed	400	1200	2000	4000	7000	10,000
4d Sed	400	1250	2100	4200	7400	10,500
2d Rds	750	2400	4000	8000	14,000	20,000
4d Cus Phae	850	2750	4600	9200	16,100	23,000
4d Cus Brgm	450	1450	2400	4800	8400	12,000
4d Cus Sed	500	1550	2600	5200	9100	13,000
Second Series, 6-cyl., (Start Jan. 1928)						
2d Sed	400	1200	2000	4000	7000	10,000
4d Sed	400	1250	2100	4200	7400	10,500
2d RS Cpe	450	1450	2400	4800	8400	12,000
2d Rds	750	2400	4000	8000	14,000	20,000
4d EWB Sed	400	1250	2100	4200	7400	10,500
4d Lan Sed	400	1250	2100	4200	7400	10,500
2d Vic	400	1250	2100	4200	7400	10,600
4d 7P Sed	400	1300	2200	4400	7700	11,000
1929						
Series Greater Hudson, 6-cyl., 122" wb						
2d RS Rds	1300	4200	7000	14,000	24,500	35,000
4d Phae	1400	4450	7400	14,800	25,900	37,000
2d Cpe	550	1800	3000	6000	10,500	15,000
2d Sed	550	1700	2800	5600	9800	14,000
2d Conv	1200	3850	6400	12,800	22,400	32,000
2d Vic	550	1800	3000	6000	10,500	15,000
4d Sed	450	1450	2400	4800	8400	12,000
4d Twn Sed	450	1500	2500	5000	8800	12,500
4d Lan Sed	500	1550	2600	5200	9100	13,000
Series Greater Hudson, 6-cyl., 139" wb						
4d Spt Sed	700	2150	3600	7200	12,600	18,000
4d 7P Sed	750	2400	4000	8000	14,000	20,000
4d Limo	850	2650	4400	8800	15,400	22,000
4d DC Phae	1700	5400	9000	18,000	31,500	45,000
1930						
Great Eight, 8-cyl., 119" wb						
2d Rds	1450	4700	7800	15,600	27,300	39,000
4d Phae	1550	4900	8200	16,400	28,700	41,000
2d RS Cpe	750	2400	4000	8000	14,000	20,000
2d Sed	550	1800	3000	6000	10,500	15,000
4d Sed	600	1850	3100	6200	10,900	15,500
4d Conv Sed	1600	5050	8400	16,800	29,400	42,000
Great Eight, 8-cyl., 126" wb						
4d Phae	1650	5300	8800	17,600	30,800	44,000
4d Tr Sed	600	1850	3100	6200	10,900	15,500
4d 7P Sed	600	1900	3200	6400	11,200	16,000
4d Brgm	600	1900	3200	6400	11,200	16,000
1931						
Greater Eight, 8-cyl., 119" wb						
2d Rds	1650	5300	8800	17,600	30,800	44,000
4d Phae	1750	5500	9200	18,400	32,200	46,000
2d Cpe	550	1700	2800	5600	9800	14,000
2d Spl Cpe	600	2000	3300	6600	11,600	16,500
2d RS Cpe	650	2050	3400	6800	11,900	17,000
2d Sed	500	1550	2600	5200	9100	13,000
4d Sed	500	1600	2650	5300	9200	13,200
4d Twn Sed	550	1700	2800	5600	9800	14,000
Great Eight, l.w.b., 8-cyl., 126" wb						
4d Spt Phae	1800	5750	9600	19,200	33,600	48,000
4d Brgm	700	2300	3800	7600	13,300	19,000
4d Fam Sed	700	2300	3800	7600	13,300	19,000
4d 7P Sed	700	2200	3700	7400	13,000	18,500
4d Clb Sed	700	2200	3700	7400	13,000	18,500
4d Tr Sed	600	1900	3200	6400	11,200	16,000
4d Spl Sed	600	2000	3300	6600	11,600	16,500
1932						
(Standard) Greater, 8-cyl., 119" wb						
2d 2P Cpe	500	1600	2700	5400	9500	13,500
2d 4P Cpe	550	1700	2800	5600	9800	14,000
2d Spl Cpe	550	1800	3000	6000	10,500	15,000
2d Conv	1150	3700	6200	12,400	21,700	31,000
2d Sed	500	1550	2600	5200	9100	13,000
4d 5P Sed	500	1600	2700	5400	9500	13,500
4d Twn Sed	500	1650	2700	5400	9500	13,600
(Sterling) Series, 8-cyl., 132" wb						
4d Spl Sed	550	1800	3000	6000	10,500	15,000
4d Sub	550	1700	2800	5600	9800	14,000
Major Series, 8-cyl., 132" wb						
4d Phae	1250	3950	6600	13,200	23,100	33,000
4d Tr Sed	550	1800	3000	6000	10,500	15,000
4d Clb Sed	600	1850	3100	6200	10,900	15,500

	6	5	4	3	2	1
4d Brgm	600	2000	3300	6600	11,600	16,500
4d 7P Sed	600	1900	3200	6400	11,200	16,000
1933						
Pacemaker Super Six, 6-cyl., 113" wb						
2d Conv	850	2650	4400	8800	15,400	22,000
4d Phae	850	2750	4600	9200	16,100	23,000
2d Bus Cpe	400	1250	2100	4200	7400	10,500
2d RS Cpe	450	1400	2300	4600	8100	11,500
2d Sed	450	1080	1800	3600	6300	9000
4d Sed	450	1140	1900	3800	6650	9500
Pacemaker Standard, 8-cyl., 119" wb						
2d Conv	1000	3100	5200	10,400	18,200	26,000
2d RS Cpe	400	1250	2100	4200	7400	10,500
2d Sed	450	1140	1900	3800	6650	9500
4d Sed	450	1400	2300	4600	8100	11,500
Pacemaker Major, 8-cyl., 132" wb						
4d Phae	1050	3350	5600	11,200	19,600	28,000
4d Tr Sed	450	1400	2300	4600	8100	11,500
4d Brgm	450	1400	2300	4600	8100	11,500
2d Clb Sed	450	1450	2400	4800	8400	12,000
4d 7P Sed	450	1500	2500	5000	8800	12,500
1934						
Special, 8-cyl., 116" wb						
2d Conv	1100	3500	5800	11,600	20,300	29,000
2d Bus Cpe	400	1200	2050	4100	7100	10,200
2d Cpe	400	1250	2100	4200	7400	10,500
2d RS Cpe	450	1450	2400	4800	8400	12,000
2d Comp Vic	400	1300	2150	4300	7500	10,700
2d Sed	400	1250	2100	4200	7400	10,500
4d Sed	400	1200	2000	4000	7000	10,000
4d Comp Sed	400	1300	2200	4400	7700	11,000
DeLuxe Series, 8-cyl., 116" wb						
2d 2P Cpe	400	1250	2100	4200	7400	10,500
2d RS Cpe	450	1400	2300	4600	8100	11,500
2d Comp Vic	400	1300	2200	4400	7700	11,000
2d Sed	400	1300	2150	4300	7600	10,800
4d Sed	400	1250	2050	4100	7200	10,300
4d Comp Sed	400	1250	2100	4200	7400	10,600
Challenger Series, 8-cyl., 116" wb						
2d 2P Cpe	400	1250	2100	4200	7400	10,600
2d RS Cpe	450	1400	2350	4700	8300	11,800
2d Conv	1250	3950	6600	13,200	23,100	33,000
2d Sed	400	1250	2100	4200	7400	10,600
4d Sed	400	1300	2150	4300	7500	10,700
Major Series, 8-cyl., 123" wb						
(Special)						
4d Tr Sed	450	1450	2400	4800	8400	12,000
4d Comp Trs	450	1450	2450	4900	8500	12,200
(DeLuxe)						
4d Clb Sed	450	1500	2500	5000	8800	12,500
4d Brgm	450	1450	2450	4900	8500	12,200
4d Comp Clb Sed	450	1450	2400	4800	8500	12,100
1935						
Big Six, 6-cyl., 116" wb						
2d Conv	1150	3600	6000	12,000	21,000	30,000
2d Cpe	400	1250	2100	4200	7400	10,500
2d RS Cpe	400	1200	2000	4000	7000	10,000
4d Tr Brgm	400	1200	2000	4000	7000	10,000
2d Sed	450	1140	1900	3800	6650	9500
4d Sed	400	1200	2000	4000	7000	10,000
4d Sub Sed	400	1250	2100	4200	7300	10,400
Eight Special, 8-cyl., 117" wb						
2d Conv	1150	3700	6200	12,400	21,700	31,000
2d Cpe	400	1300	2150	4300	7500	10,700
2d RS Cpe	450	1400	2300	4600	8100	11,500
4d Tr Brgm	400	1200	2050	4100	7100	10,200
2d Sed	400	1200	2000	4000	7100	10,100
4d Sed	400	1250	2100	4200	7400	10,600
4d Sub Sed	400	1300	2150	4300	7500	10,700
Eight DeLuxe						
Eight Special, 8-cyl., 124" wb						
4d Brgm	400	1250	2100	4200	7400	10,600
4d Tr Brgm	400	1300	2150	4300	7500	10,700
4d Clb Sed	400	1250	2100	4200	7400	10,500
4d Sub Sed	400	1250	2100	4200	7400	10,600
Eight DeLuxe, 8-cyl., 117" wb						
2d 2P Cpe	400	1300	2150	4300	7600	10,800
2d RS Cpe	450	1400	2300	4600	8100	11,600
2d Conv	1200	3850	6400	12,800	22,400	32,000
4d Tr Brgm	400	1250	2050	4100	7200	10,300
2d Sed	400	1200	2050	4100	7100	10,200
4d Sed	400	1300	2150	4300	7500	10,700
4d Sub Sed	400	1300	2150	4300	7600	10,800
Eight Custom, 8-cyl., 124" wb						
4d Brgm	400	1300	2150	4300	7500	10,700
4d Tr Brgm	400	1300	2150	4300	7600	10,800
4d Sed	400	1250	2100	4200	7400	10,500
Sub Sed	400	1300	2150	4300	7600	10,800
Late Special, 8-cyl., 124" wb						
4d Brgm	400	1200	2050	4100	7100	10,200
4d Tr Brgm	400	1250	2050	4100	7200	10,300
4d Clb Sed	400	1200	2000	4000	7100	10,100
4d Sub Sed	400	1300	2150	4300	7600	10,800
Late DeLuxe, 8-cyl., 124" wb						
4d Brgm	400	1250	2050	4100	7200	10,300
4d Tr Brgm	400	1250	2100	4200	7300	10,400
4d Clb Sed	400	1200	2050	4100	7100	10,200
4d Sub Sed	400	1300	2200	4400	7600	10,900
1936						
Custom Six, 6-cyl., 120" wb						
2d Conv	1100	3500	5800	11,600	20,300	29,000
2d Cpe	400	1250	2100	4200	7400	10,500
2d RS Cpe	450	1450	2400	4800	8400	12,000
4d Brgm	400	1200	2000	4000	7000	10,000
4d Tr Brgm	400	1200	2000	4000	7100	10,100
4d Sed	400	1200	2000	4000	7000	10,000
4d Tr Sed	400	1250	2100	4200	7400	10,500
DeLuxe Eight, Series 64, 8-cyl., 120" wb						
2d Conv	1200	3850	6400	12,800	22,400	32,000
2d Cpe	400	1300	2150	4300	7500	10,700
2d RS Cpe	400	1250	2100	4200	7300	10,400
4d Brgm	400	1200	2050	4100	7100	10,200
4d Tr Brgm	400	1250	2050	4100	7200	10,300
DeLuxe Eight, Series 66, 8-cyl., 127" wb						
4d Sed	400	1300	2150	4300	7500	10,700
4d Tr Sed	400	1300	2200	4400	7700	11,000
Custom Eight, Series 65, 120" wb						
2d 2P Cpe	400	1300	2150	4300	7600	10,800

	6	5	4	3	2	1
2d RS Cpe	450	1400	2300	4600	8100	11,500
2d Conv	1200	3850	6400	12,800	22,400	32,000
4d Brgm	400	1250	2050	4100	7200	10,300
4d Tr Brgm	400	1250	2100	4200	7300	10,400
Custom Eight, Series 67, 127" wb						
4d Sed	400	1250	2100	4200	7400	10,600
4d Tr Sed	400	1300	2150	4300	7500	10,700

1937

	6	5	4	3	2	1
Custom Six, Series 73, 6-cyl., 122" wb						
2d Conv	1150	3700	6200	12,400	21,700	31,000
2d Conv Brgm	1200	3850	6400	12,800	22,400	32,000
2d Bus Cpe	400	1250	2100	4200	7400	10,500
2d 3P Cpe	400	1300	2200	4400	7700	11,000
2d Vic Cpe	450	1400	2300	4600	8100	11,500
2d Brgm	400	1250	2100	4200	7400	10,500
2d Tr Brgm	400	1300	2150	4300	7500	10,700
4d Sed	400	1300	2200	4400	7700	11,000
4d Tr Sed	400	1350	2200	4400	7800	11,100
DeLuxe Eight, Series 74, 8-cyl., 122" wb						
2d Cpe	450	1450	2400	4800	8400	12,000
2d Vic Cpe	450	1500	2500	5000	8800	12,500
2d Conv	1150	3700	6200	12,400	21,700	31,000
2d Brgm	450	1500	2500	5000	8800	12,600
2d Tr Brgm	500	1500	2550	5100	8900	12,700
4d Sed	500	1500	2550	5100	8900	12,700
4d Tr Sed	500	1550	2550	5100	9000	12,800
2d Conv Brgm	1050	3350	5600	11,200	19,600	28,000
DeLuxe Eight, Series 76, 8-cyl., 129" wb						
4d Sed	500	1550	2600	5200	9100	13,000
4d Tr Sed	500	1600	2700	5400	9500	13,500
Custom Eight, Series 75, 8-cyl., 122" wb						
2d Cpe	450	1450	2400	4800	8400	12,000
2d Vic Cpe	450	1450	2450	4900	8500	12,200
2d Conv Cpe	1200	3850	6400	12,800	22,400	32,000
2d Brgm	450	1400	2350	4700	8300	11,800
2d Tr Brgm	450	1450	2400	4800	8400	12,000
4d Sed	450	1400	2350	4700	8300	11,800
4d Tr Sed	450	1450	2400	4800	8300	11,900
2d Conv Brgm	1250	3950	6600	13,200	23,100	33,000
Custom Eight, Series 77, 8-cyl., 129" wb						
4d Sed	450	1450	2400	4800	8400	12,000
4d Tr Sed	450	1450	2450	4900	8500	12,200

1938

	6	5	4	3	2	1
Standard Series 89, 6-cyl., 112" wb						
2d Conv	1150	3700	6200	12,400	21,700	31,000
2d Conv Brgm	1200	3850	6400	12,800	22,400	32,000
2d 3P Cpe	450	1450	2400	4800	8400	12,000
2d Vic Cpe	450	1500	2500	5000	8800	12,500
4d Brgm	450	1350	2300	4600	8000	11,400
4d Tr Brgm	450	1400	2300	4600	8100	11,500
4d Sed	450	1400	2300	4600	8100	11,600
4d Tr Sed	450	1400	2350	4700	8200	11,700
Utility Series 89, 6-cyl., 112" wb						
2d Cpe	450	1400	2300	4600	8100	11,500
2d Sed	400	1300	2150	4300	7600	10,800
2d Tr Sed	400	1300	2200	4400	7600	10,900
DeLuxe Series 89, 6-cyl., 112" wb						
2d Conv	1150	3600	6000	12,000	21,000	30,000
2d Conv Brgm	1150	3700	6200	12,400	21,700	31,000
2d 3P Cpe	500	1550	2600	5200	9100	13,000
2d Vic Cpe	500	1600	2700	5400	9500	13,500
4d Brgm	450	1450	2400	4800	8400	12,000
4d Tr Brgm	450	1450	2450	4900	8500	12,200
4d Sed	450	1500	2450	4900	8600	12,300
4d Tr Sed	450	1500	2500	5000	8700	12,400
Custom Series 83, 6-cyl., 122" wb						
2d Conv	1150	3700	6200	12,400	21,700	31,000
2d Conv Brgm	1200	3850	6400	12,800	22,400	32,000
2d 3P Cpe	500	1600	2700	5400	9500	13,500
2d Vic Cpe	550	1700	2800	5600	9800	14,000
4d Brgm	450	1500	2500	5000	8800	12,500
4d Tr Brgm	450	1500	2500	5000	8800	12,600
4d Sed	450	1500	2500	5000	8700	12,400
4d Tr Sed	450	1500	2500	5000	8800	12,500
4d DeLuxe Series 84, 8-cyl., 122" wb						
2d Conv	1150	3700	6200	12,400	21,700	31,000
2d Conv Brgm	1200	3850	6400	12,800	22,400	32,000
2d 3P Cpe	550	1700	2800	5600	9800	14,000
2d Vic Cpe	550	1750	2900	5800	10,200	14,500
4d Brgm	500	1600	2650	5300	9200	13,200
4d Tr Brgm	450	1500	2500	5000	8800	12,500
4d Tr Sed	450	1450	2400	4800	8400	12,000
4d Custom Series 85, 8-cyl., 122" wb						
2d 3P Cpe	550	1800	3000	6000	10,500	15,000
2d Vic Cpe	600	1850	3100	6200	10,900	15,500
4d Brgm	550	1700	2800	5600	9800	14,000
4d Tr Brgm	550	1750	2900	5800	10,200	14,500
4d Sed	500	1600	2700	5400	9500	13,500
4d Tr Sed	500	1650	2700	5400	9500	13,600
Country Club Series 87, 8-cyl., 129" wb						
4d Sed	550	1800	3000	6000	10,500	15,000
4d Tr Sed	550	1800	3050	6100	10,600	15,200

1939

	6	5	4	3	2	1
DeLuxe Series 112, 6-cyl., 112" wb						
2d Conv	1150	3600	6000	12,000	21,000	30,000
2d Conv Brgm	450	1500	2500	5000	8700	12,400
2d Trav Cpe	450	1450	2400	4800	8400	12,000
2d Utl Cpe	450	1500	2500	5000	8800	12,500
2d 3P Cpe	500	1500	2550	5100	8900	12,700
2d Vic Cpe	500	1550	2600	5200	9100	13,000
2d Utl Sed	450	1400	2300	4600	8100	11,500
4d Tr Brgm	450	1450	2400	4800	8300	11,900
4d Tr Sed	450	1450	2400	4800	8400	12,000
4d Sta Wag	900	2900	4800	9600	16,800	24,000
4d Pacemaker Series 91, 6-cyl., 118" wb						
2d 3P Cpe	500	1600	2700	5400	9500	13,500
2d Vic Cpe	550	1700	2800	5600	9800	14,000
4d Tr Brgm	500	1600	2650	5300	9200	13,200
4d Tr Sed	500	1550	2600	5200	9100	13,000
Series 92, 6-cyl., 118" wb						
2d Conv	1200	3850	6400	12,800	22,400	32,000
2d Conv Brgm	1250	3950	6600	13,200	23,100	33,000
2d 3P Cpe	550	1800	3000	6000	10,500	15,000
2d Vic Cpe	600	1850	3100	6200	10,900	15,500
4d Tr Brgm	550	1750	2900	5800	10,200	14,500
4d Tr Sed	550	1700	2800	5600	9800	14,000
Country Club Series 93, 6-cyl., 122" wb						
2d Conv	1250	3950	6600	13,200	23,100	33,000
2d Conv Brgm	1300	4100	6800	13,600	23,800	34,000
2d 3P Cpe	600	1850	3100	6200	10,900	15,500
2d Vic Cpe	600	1900	3200	6400	11,200	16,000
4d Tr Brgm	600	1850	3100	6200	10,900	15,500
4d Tr Sed	550	1800	3000	6000	10,500	15,000
Big Boy Series 96, 6-cyl., 129" wb						
4d 6P Sed	600	1900	3200	6400	11,200	16,000
4d 7P Sed	600	1950	3250	6500	11,400	16,300
Country Club Series 95, 8-cyl., 122" wb						
2d Conv	1300	4100	6800	13,600	23,800	34,000
2d Conv Brgm	1300	4200	7000	14,000	24,500	35,000
2d 3P Cpe	600	1900	3200	6400	11,200	16,000
2d Vic Cpe	600	2000	3300	6600	11,600	16,500
4d Tr Brgm	600	1900	3150	6300	11,100	15,800
4d Tr Sed	600	1850	3100	6200	10,900	15,500
Custom Series 97, 8-cyl., 129" wb						
4d 5P Tr Sed	600	1950	3250	6500	11,300	16,200
4d 7P Sed	600	2000	3300	6600	11,600	16,500

1940

	6	5	4	3	2	1
Traveler Series 40-T, 6-cyl., 113" wb						
2d Cpe	450	1450	2450	4900	8500	12,200
2d Vic Cpe	450	1500	2500	5000	8700	12,400
2d Tr Sed	450	1450	2400	4800	8400	12,000
4d Tr Sed	450	1450	2400	4800	8500	12,100
DeLuxe Series, 40-P, 6-cyl., 113" wb						
2d 6P Conv	1000	3100	5200	10,400	18,200	26,000
2d Cpe	450	1500	2500	5000	8800	12,600
2d Vic Cpe	500	1500	2550	5100	8900	12,700
2d Tr Sed	450	1450	2450	4900	8500	12,200
4d Sed	450	1500	2450	4900	8600	12,300
Super Series 41, 6-cyl., 118" wb						
2d 5P Conv	1000	3250	5400	10,800	18,900	27,000
2d 6P Conv	1050	3350	5600	11,200	19,600	28,000
2d Cpe	550	1700	2800	5600	9800	14,000
2d Vic Cpe	550	1750	2900	5800	10,200	14,500
2d Tr Sed	450	1450	2400	4800	8400	12,000
4d Tr Sed	450	1450	2450	4900	8500	12,200
Country Club Series 43, 6-cyl., 125" wb						
4d 6P Sed	500	1550	2600	5200	9100	13,000
4d 7P Sed	500	1600	2700	5400	9500	13,500
Series 44, 8-cyl., 118" wb						
2d 5P Conv	1050	3350	5600	11,200	19,600	28,000
2d 6P Conv	1100	3500	5800	11,600	20,300	29,000
2d Cpe	600	1900	3200	6400	11,200	16,000
2d Vic Cpe	600	2000	3300	6600	11,600	16,500
2d Tr Sed	600	1850	3100	6200	10,900	15,600
4d Tr Sed	600	1900	3150	6300	11,000	15,700
DeLuxe Series 45, 8-cyl., 118" wb						
2d Tr Sed	600	1900	3150	6300	11,100	15,800
4d Tr Sed	600	1900	3200	6400	11,100	15,900
Country Club Eight Series 47, 8-cyl., 125" wb						
4d Tr Sed	600	1950	3200	6400	11,300	16,100
4d 7P Sed	600	1950	3250	6500	11,300	16,200
Big Boy Series 48, 6-cyl., 125" wb						
4d C-A Sed	550	1800	3000	6000	10,500	15,000
4d 7P Sed	550	1800	3050	6100	10,600	15,200

1941

	6	5	4	3	2	1
Utility Series 10-C, 6-cyl., 116" wb						
2d Cpe	450	1500	2500	5000	8800	12,500
2d Sed	450	1400	2300	4600	8100	11,500
Traveler Series 10-T, 6-cyl., 116" wb						
2d Cpe	500	1550	2600	5200	9100	13,000
2d Clb Cpe	500	1600	2700	5400	9500	13,500
2d Sed	450	1400	2350	4700	8200	11,700
4d Sed	450	1450	2400	4800	8300	11,900
DeLuxe Series 10-P, 6-cyl., 116" wb						
2d Conv	1000	3250	5400	10,800	18,900	27,000
2d Cpe	550	1700	2800	5600	9800	14,000
2d Clb Cpe	550	1750	2900	5800	10,200	14,500
2d Sed	450	1450	2400	4800	8500	12,100
4d Sed	450	1450	2450	4900	8500	12,200
Super Series 11, 6-cyl., 121" wb						
2d Conv	1100	3500	5800	11,600	20,300	29,000
2d Cpe	550	1750	2900	5800	10,200	14,500
2d Clb Cpe	550	1800	3000	6000	10,500	15,000
2d Sed	450	1500	2500	5000	8700	12,400
4d Sed	450	1500	2500	5000	8800	12,500
4d Sta Wag	1000	3250	5400	10,800	18,900	27,000
Commodore Series 12, 6-cyl., 121" wb						
2d Conv	1150	3600	6000	12,000	21,000	30,000
2d Cpe	550	1800	3050	6100	10,600	15,200
2d Clb Cpe	600	1850	3100	6200	10,800	15,400
2d Sed	500	1550	2600	5200	9100	13,000
4d Sed	500	1550	2600	5200	9200	13,100
Commodore Series 14, 8-cyl., 121" wb						
2d Conv	1150	3700	6200	12,400	21,700	31,000
2d Cpe	600	1850	3100	6200	10,900	15,500
2d Clb Cpe	600	1900	3150	6300	11,000	15,700
2d Sed	550	1750	2900	5800	10,200	14,600
4d Sed	550	1750	2950	5900	10,300	14,700
4d Sta Wag	1050	3350	5600	11,200	19,600	28,000
Commodore Custom Series 15, 8-cyl., 121" wb						
2d Cpe	600	1900	3150	6300	11,100	15,800
2d Clb Cpe	600	1900	3200	6400	11,200	16,000
Commodore Custom Series 17, 8-cyl., 128" wb						
4d Sed	550	1800	2950	5900	10,400	14,800
4d 7P Sed	550	1800	3000	6000	10,500	15,000
Big Boy Series 18, 6-cyl., 128" wb						
4d C-A Sed	550	1700	2850	5700	10,000	14,300
4d 7P Sed	550	1750	2900	5800	10,200	14,500

1942

	6	5	4	3	2	1
Traveler Series 20-T, 6-cyl., 116" wb						
2d Cpe	450	1500	2500	5000	8800	12,500
2d Clb Cpe	500	1500	2550	5100	8900	12,700
2d Sed	450	1400	2300	4600	8100	11,600
4d Sed	450	1400	2350	4700	8200	11,700
DeLuxe Series 20-P, 6-cyl., 116" wb						
2d Conv	1050	3350	5600	11,200	19,600	28,000
2d Cpe	500	1500	2550	5100	8900	12,700
2d Clb Cpe	500	1550	2600	5200	9100	13,000
2d Sed	450	1450	2400	4800	8400	12,000
4d Sed	450	1450	2400	4800	8500	12,100
Super Series 21, 6-cyl., 121" wb						
2d Conv	1100	3500	5800	11,600	20,300	29,000
2d Cpe	500	1550	2600	5200	9100	13,000
2d Clb Cpe	500	1600	2650	5300	9200	13,200
2d Sed	450	1500	2500	5000	8800	12,600
4d Sed	500	1500	2550	5100	8900	12,700

	6	5	4	3	2	1
4d Sta Wag	1100	3500	5800	11,600	20,300	29,000
Commodore Series 22, 6-cyl., 121" wb						
2d Conv	1150	3700	6200	12,400	21,700	31,000
2d Cpe	500	1600	2700	5400	9500	13,500
2d Clb Cpe	550	1700	2800	5600	9800	14,000
2d Sed	450	1500	2500	5000	8800	12,500
4d Sed	450	1500	2500	5000	8800	12,600
Commodore Series 24, 8-cyl., 121" wb						
2d Conv	1200	3850	6400	12,800	22,400	32,000
2d Cpe	550	1800	3000	6000	10,500	15,000
2d Clb Cpe	600	1850	3100	6200	10,900	15,500
2d Sed	550	1700	2850	5700	9900	14,200
4d Sed	550	1700	2850	5700	10,000	14,300
Commodore Custom Series 25, 8-cyl., 121" wb						
2d Clb Cpe	600	1850	3100	6200	10,900	15,600
Commodore Series 27, 8-cyl., 128" wb						
4d Sed	550	1750	2900	5800	10,200	14,500

1946-1947

	6	5	4	3	2	1
Super Series, 6-cyl., 121" wb						
2d Cpe	450	1450	2400	4800	8300	11,900
2d Clb Cpe	450	1450	2400	4800	8400	12,000
2d Conv	950	3000	5000	10,000	17,500	25,000
2d Sed	400	1300	2150	4300	7600	10,800
4d Sed	400	1300	2200	4400	7600	10,900
Commodore Series, 6-cyl., 121" wb						
2d Clb Cpe	450	1500	2500	5000	8800	12,600
4d Sed	450	1450	2400	4800	8400	12,000
Super Series, 8-cyl., 121" wb						
2d Clb Cpe	500	1500	2550	5100	8900	12,700
4d Sed	450	1450	2450	4900	8500	12,200
Commodore Series, 8-cyl., 121" wb						
2d Clb Cpe	500	1600	2650	5300	9300	13,300
2d Conv	1050	3350	5600	11,200	19,600	28,000
4d Sed	500	1550	2550	5100	9000	12,800

1948-1949

	6	5	4	3	2	1
Super Series, 6-cyl., 124" wb						
2d Cpe	450	1450	2400	4800	8400	12,000
2d Clb Cpe	450	1500	2450	4900	8600	12,300
2d Conv	1200	3850	6400	12,800	22,400	32,000
2d Sed	400	1350	2200	4400	7800	11,100
4d Sed	400	1300	2200	4400	7700	11,000
Commodore Series, 6-cyl., 124" wb						
2d Clb Cpe	500	1550	2600	5200	9100	13,000
2d Conv	1350	4300	7200	14,400	25,200	36,000
4d Sed	450	1500	2500	5000	8800	12,500
Super Series, 8-cyl., 124" wb						
2d Clb Cpe	500	1600	2700	5400	9500	13,500
2d Sed (1949 only)	450	1500	2500	5000	8800	12,600
4d Sed	450	1500	2500	5000	8800	12,500
Commodore Series, 8-cyl., 124" wb						
2d Clb Cpe	550	1700	2800	5600	9800	14,000
2d Conv	1450	4550	7600	15,200	26,600	38,000
4d Sed	500	1600	2700	5400	9500	13,500

1950

	6	5	4	3	2	1
Pacemaker Series 500, 6-cyl., 119" wb						
2d Bus Cpe	400	1300	2200	4400	7700	11,000
2d Clb Cpe	450	1450	2400	4800	8400	12,000
2d Conv	1300	4200	7000	14,000	24,500	35,000
2d Sed	400	1350	2200	4400	7800	11,100
4d Sed	400	1350	2250	4500	7800	11,200
DeLuxe Series 50A, 6-cyl., 119" wb						
2d Clb Cpe	500	1600	2650	5300	9200	13,200
2d Conv	1350	4300	7200	14,400	25,200	36,000
2d Sed	450	1400	2300	4600	8100	11,500
4d Sed	450	1400	2300	4600	8100	11,600
Super Six Series 501, 6-cyl., 124" wb						
2d Clb Cpe	500	1600	2700	5400	9500	13,500
2d Conv	1400	4450	7400	14,800	25,900	37,000
2d Sed	450	1450	2400	4800	8500	12,100
4d Sed	450	1450	2450	4900	8500	12,200
Commodore Series 502, 6-cyl., 124" wb						
2d Clb Cpe	550	1700	2800	5600	9800	14,000
2d Conv	1450	4550	7600	15,200	26,600	38,000
4d Sed	500	1550	2600	5200	9100	13,000
Super Series 503, 8-cyl., 124" wb						
2d Sed	500	1550	2600	5200	9100	13,000
2d Clb Cpe	550	1750	2900	5800	10,200	14,500
4d Sed	500	1500	2550	5100	8900	12,700
Commodore Series 504, 8-cyl., 124" wb						
2d Clb Cpe	550	1800	3000	6000	10,500	15,000
2d Conv	1500	4800	8000	16,000	28,000	40,000
4d Sed	500	1550	2600	5200	9100	13,000

1951

	6	5	4	3	2	1
Pacemaker Custom Series 4A, 6-cyl., 119" wb						
2d Cpe	450	1500	2500	5000	8800	12,500
2d Clb Cpe	500	1600	2700	5400	9500	13,500
2d Conv	1300	4200	7000	14,000	24,500	35,000
2d Sed	450	1450	2400	4800	8500	12,100
4d Sed	450	1450	2400	4800	8400	12,000
Super Custom Series 5A, 6-cyl., 124" wb						
2d Clb Cpe	550	1700	2800	5600	9800	14,000
2d Hlywd HT	700	2150	3600	7200	12,600	18,000
2d Conv	1350	4300	7200	14,400	25,200	36,000
2d Sed	450	1500	2500	5000	8800	12,500
4d Sed	500	1500	2550	5100	8900	12,700
Commodore Custom Series 6A, 6-cyl., 124" wb						
2d Clb Cpe	550	1750	2900	5800	10,200	14,500
2d Hlywd HT	700	2300	3800	7600	13,300	19,000
2d Conv	1400	4450	7400	14,800	25,900	37,000
4d Sed	550	1750	2900	5800	10,200	14,600
Hornet Series 7A, 6-cyl., 124" wb						
2d Clb Cpe	550	1800	3000	6000	10,500	15,000
2d Hlywd HT	750	2400	4000	8000	14,000	20,000
2d Conv	1450	4700	7800	15,600	27,300	39,000
4d Sed	550	1800	3000	6000	10,600	15,100
Commodore Custom Series 8A, 8-cyl., 124" wb						
2d Clb Cpe	600	1850	3100	6200	10,900	15,500
2d Hlywd HT	800	2500	4200	8400	14,700	21,000
2d Conv	1500	4800	8000	16,000	28,000	40,000
4d Sed	600	1850	3100	6200	10,900	15,600

1952

	6	5	4	3	2	1
Pacemaker Series 4B, 6-cyl., 119" wb						
2d Cpe	500	1500	2550	5100	8900	12,700
2d Clb Cpe	500	1550	2550	5100	9000	12,800
2d Sed	450	1500	2500	5000	8800	12,500
4d Sed	450	1500	2500	5000	8800	12,600
Wasp Series 5B, 6-cyl., 119" wb						
2d Clb Cpe	500	1550	2600	5200	9100	13,000
2d Hlywd HT	600	1900	3200	6400	11,200	16,000
2d Conv	1300	4200	7000	14,000	24,500	35,000
2d Sed	450	1500	2500	5000	8800	12,600
4d Sed	500	1500	2550	5100	8900	12,700
Commodore Series 6B, 6-cyl., 124" wb						
2d Clb Cpe	500	1600	2650	5300	9200	13,200
2d Hlywd HT	650	2050	3400	6800	11,900	17,000
2d Conv	1350	4300	7200	14,400	25,200	36,000
4d Sed	500	1550	2600	5200	9100	13,000
Hornet Series 7B, 6-cyl., 124" wb						
2d Clb Cpe	500	1600	2700	5400	9400	13,400
2d Hlywd HT	700	2150	3600	7200	12,600	18,000
2d Conv	1400	4450	7400	14,800	25,900	37,000
4d Sed	500	1550	2600	5200	9200	13,100
Commodore Series 8B, 8-cyl., 124" wb						
2d Clb Cpe	500	1600	2700	5400	9400	13,400
2d Hlywd HT	700	2300	3800	7600	13,300	19,000
2d Conv	1450	4550	7600	15,200	26,600	38,000
4d Sed	500	1550	2600	5200	9200	13,100

1953

	6	5	4	3	2	1
Jet Series 1C, 6-cyl., 105" wb						
4d Sed	400	1300	2200	4400	7700	11,000
Super Jet Series 2C, 6-cyl., 105" wb						
2d Clb Sed	450	1400	2300	4600	8100	11,500
4d Sed	450	1400	2300	4600	8100	11,600
Wasp Series 4C, 6-cyl., 119" wb						
2d Clb Cpe	450	1400	2350	4700	8300	11,800
2d Sed	450	1400	2300	4600	8100	11,500
4d Sed	450	1400	2300	4600	8100	11,600
Super Wasp Series 5C, 6-cyl., 119" wb						
2d Clb Cpe	450	1450	2400	4800	8400	12,000
2d Hlywd HT	600	1900	3200	6400	11,200	16,000
2d Conv	1300	4200	7000	14,000	24,500	35,000
2d Sed	450	1400	2300	4600	8100	11,600
4d Sed	450	1400	2350	4700	8200	11,700
Hornet Series 7C, 6-cyl., 124" wb						
2d Clb Cpe	500	1600	2700	5400	9500	13,500
2d Hlywd HT	650	2100	3500	7000	12,300	17,600
2d Conv	1450	4550	7600	15,200	26,600	38,000
4d Sed	500	1550	2600	5200	9100	13,000

1954

	6	5	4	3	2	1
Jet Series 1D, 6-cyl., 105" wb						
2 dr Utl Sed	400	1300	2200	4400	7700	11,000
2d Clb Sed	400	1350	2250	4500	7800	11,200
4d Sed	400	1350	2250	4500	7900	11,300
Super Jet Series 2D, 6-cyl., 105" wb						
2d Clb Sed	450	1400	2300	4600	8100	11,500
4d Sed	450	1400	2300	4600	8100	11,600
Jet Liner Series 3D, 6-cyl., 105" wb						
2d Clb Sed	450	1450	2400	4800	8400	12,000
4d Sed	450	1450	2400	4800	8500	12,100
Wasp Series 4D, 6-cyl., 119" wb						
2d Clb Cpe	450	1400	2300	4600	8100	11,500
2d Clb Sed	400	1350	2250	4500	7900	11,300
4d Sed	450	1350	2300	4600	8000	11,400
Super Wasp Series 5D, 6-cyl., 119" wb						
2d Clb Cpe	450	1400	2350	4700	8200	11,700
2d Hlywd HT	550	1800	3000	6000	10,500	15,000
2d Conv	1350	4300	7200	14,400	25,200	36,000
2d Clb Sed	450	1400	2300	4600	8100	11,600
4d Sed	450	1400	2300	4600	8100	11,500
Hornet Special Series 6D, 6-cyl., 124" wb						
2d Clb Cpe	500	1550	2600	5200	9100	13,000
2d Clb Sed	450	1450	2400	4800	8500	12,100
4d Sed	450	1500	2500	5000	8700	12,400
Hornet Series 7D, 6-cyl., 124" wb						
2d Clb Cpe	550	1700	2800	5600	9800	14,000
2d Hlywd HT	650	2050	3400	6800	11,900	17,000
2d Brgm Conv	1450	4700	7800	15,600	27,300	39,000
4d Sed	450	1500	2500	5000	8800	12,600
Italia, 6-cyl.						
2d	1200	3850	6400	12,800	22,400	32,000

1955

	6	5	4	3	2	1
Super Wasp, 6-cyl., 114" wb						
4d Sed	400	1250	2100	4200	7400	10,500
Custom Wasp, 6-cyl., 114" wb						
2d Hlywd HT	550	1800	3000	6000	10,500	15,000
4d Sed	400	1250	2100	4200	7400	10,600
Hornet Super, 6-cyl., 121" wb						
4d Sed	400	1300	2200	4400	7700	11,000
Hornet Custom, 6-cyl., 121" wb						
2d Hlywd HT	600	1900	3200	6400	11,200	16,000
4d Sed	450	1400	2300	4600	8100	11,500
Italia, 6-cyl.						
2d Cpe	1200	3850	6400	12,800	22,400	32,000

NOTE: Add 5 percent for V-8.
For Hudson Rambler prices see AMC.

1956

	6	5	4	3	2	1
Super Wasp, 6-cyl., 114" wb						
4d Sed	400	1200	2000	4000	7000	10,000
Super Hornet, 6-cyl., 121" wb						
4d Sed	400	1300	2200	4400	7700	11,000
Custom Hornet, 6-cyl., 121" wb						
2d Hlywd HT	650	2050	3400	6800	11,900	17,000
4d Sed	450	1450	2400	4800	8400	12,000
Hornet Super Special, 8-cyl., 114" wb						
2d Hlywd HT	700	2150	3600	7200	12,600	18,000
4d Sed	450	1450	2450	4900	8500	12,200
Hornet Custom, 8-cyl., 121" wb						
2d Hlywd HT	700	2300	3800	7600	13,300	19,000
4d Sed	450	1500	2500	5000	8800	12,500

NOTE: For Hudson Rambler prices see AMC.

1957

	6	5	4	3	2	1
Hornet Super, 8-cyl., 121" wb						
2d Hlywd HT	700	2150	3600	7200	12,600	18,000
4d Sed	500	1600	2700	5400	9500	13,500
Hornet Custom, 8-cyl., 121" wb						
2d Hlywd HT	700	2300	3800	7600	13,300	19,000
4d Sed	550	1750	2900	5800	10,200	14,500

NOTE: For Hudson Rambler prices see AMC.

ESSEX

1919	6	5	4	3	2	1
Model A (4-cyl.)						
2d Rds	500	1550	2600	5200	9100	13,000
4d Tr	450	1500	2500	5000	8800	12,500
4d Sed	400	1300	2200	4400	7700	11,000
1920						
4-cyl.						
2d Rds	500	1550	2600	5200	9100	13,000
4d Tr	450	1500	2500	5000	8800	12,500
4d Sed	400	1300	2200	4400	7700	11,000
1921						
4-cyl.						
2d Rds	500	1600	2700	5400	9500	13,500
4d Tr	450	1450	2400	4800	8400	12,000
2d Cabr	500	1550	2600	5200	9100	13,000
2d Sed	450	1140	1900	3800	6650	9500
4d Sed	450	1150	1900	3850	6700	9600
1922						
4-cyl.						
4d Tr	450	1450	2400	4800	8400	12,000
2d Cabr	500	1550	2600	5200	9100	13,000
2 dr Sed	450	1140	1900	3800	6650	9500
4d Sed	450	1150	1900	3850	6700	9600
1923						
4-cyl.						
2d Cabr	500	1550	2600	5200	9100	13,000
4d Phae	450	1450	2400	4800	8400	12,000
2d Sed	450	1080	1800	3600	6300	9000
1924						
Six, 6-cyl.						
4d Tr	500	1550	2600	5200	9100	13,000
2d Sed	450	1080	1800	3600	6300	9000
1925						
Six, 6-cyl.						
4d Tr	500	1550	2600	5200	9100	13,000
2d Sed	450	1050	1750	3550	6150	8800
1926						
Six, 6-cyl.						
4d Tr	500	1550	2600	5200	9100	13,000
2d Sed	450	1140	1900	3800	6650	9500
4d Sed	450	1150	1900	3850	6700	9600
1927						
Six, 6-cyl.						
4d Tr	550	1800	3000	6000	10,500	15,000
2d Sed	350	975	1600	3200	5600	8000
4d Sed	350	1000	1650	3300	5750	8200
Super Six, 6-cyl.						
2d BT Spds	850	2750	4600	9200	16,100	23,000
4d Tr	550	1800	3000	6000	10,500	15,000
2d 4P Spds	700	2300	3800	7600	13,300	19,000
2d Cpe	450	1140	1900	3800	6650	9500
2d Sed	350	1020	1700	3400	5950	8500
4d Sed	350	1040	1700	3450	6000	8600
4d DeL Sed	450	1080	1800	3600	6300	9000
1928						
First Series, 6-cyl.						
2d BT Spds	750	2400	4000	8000	14,000	20,000
2d 4P Spds	700	2300	3800	7600	13,300	19,000
2d Cpe	450	1130	1900	3800	6600	9400
2d Sed	350	1040	1700	3450	6000	8600
4d Sed	450	1050	1750	3550	6150	8800
Second Series, 6-cyl.						
2d Spt Rds	800	2500	4200	8400	14,700	21,000
4d Phae	750	2400	4000	8000	14,000	20,000
2d 2P Cpe	400	1200	2000	4000	7000	10,000
2d RS Cpe	400	1200	2050	4100	7100	10,200
2d Sed	350	1040	1700	3450	6000	8600
4d Sed	450	1050	1750	3550	6150	8800
1929						
Challenger Series, 6-cyl.						
2d Rds	1100	3500	5800	11,600	20,300	29,000
2d Phae	1050	3350	5600	11,200	19,600	28,000
2d 2P Cpe	450	1160	1950	3900	6800	9700
2d 4P Cpe	450	1190	2000	3950	6900	9900
2d Sed	450	1050	1800	3600	6200	8900
4d Sed	450	1130	1900	3800	6600	9400
2d RS Rds	1150	3600	6000	12,000	21,000	30,000
4d Phae	1100	3500	5800	11,600	20,300	29,000
2d Conv	1000	3250	5400	10,800	18,900	27,000
2d RS Cpe	400	1200	2000	4000	7000	10,000
4d Twn Sed	400	1200	2000	4000	7100	10,100
4d DeL Sed	400	1250	2050	4100	7200	10,300
1930						
First Series, Standard, 6-cyl.						
2d Rds	1250	3950	6600	13,200	23,100	33,000
2d Conv	1100	3500	5800	11,600	20,300	29,000
4d Phae	1150	3600	6000	12,000	21,000	30,000
2d 2P Cpe	450	1130	1900	3800	6600	9400
2d RS Cpe	400	1200	2000	4000	7000	10,000
2d Sed	950	1100	1850	3700	6450	9200
4d Std Sed	450	1120	1875	3750	6500	9300
4d Twn Sed	450	1130	1900	3800	6600	9400
Second Series, Standard, 6-cyl.						
2d RS Rds	1300	4200	7000	14,000	24,500	35,000
4d Phae	1300	4100	6800	13,600	23,800	34,000
4d Sun Sed	500	1550	2600	5200	9100	13,000
4d Tr	1200	3850	6400	12,800	22,400	32,000
2d 2P Cpe	450	1130	1900	3800	6600	9400
2d RS Cpe	400	1250	2100	4200	7300	10,400
2d Sed	350	975	1600	3200	5600	8000
4d Sed	350	975	1600	3250	5700	8100
4d Twn Sed	450	1080	1800	3600	6300	9000
4d DeL Sed	450	1130	1900	3800	6600	9400
4d Brgm	400	1200	2000	4000	7000	10,000
1931						
Standard, 6-cyl.						
2d BT Rds	1750	5650	9400	18,800	32,900	47,000
4d Phae	1150	3700	6200	12,400	21,700	31,000
2d RS Cpe	450	1450	2400	4800	8400	12,000
2d 2P Cpe	400	1300	2200	4400	7700	11,000
4d Sed	450	1130	1900	3800	6600	9400
2d Sed	450	1120	1875	3750	6500	9300
4d Tr Sed	450	1140	1900	3800	6650	9500
1932						
Pacemaker, 6-cyl.						
2d Conv	1050	3350	5600	11,200	19,600	28,000
4d Phae	1150	3600	6000	12,000	21,000	30,000
2d 2P Cpe	450	1450	2400	4800	8400	12,000
2d RS Cpe	500	1650	2800	5600	9700	13,900
2d Sed	450	1350	2300	4600	8000	11,400
4d Sed	450	1400	2300	4600	8100	11,500

TERRAPLANE

1933	6	5	4	3	2	1
Six, 6-cyl., 106" wb						
2d Rds	1050	3350	5600	11,200	19,600	28,000
4d Phae	1100	3500	5800	11,600	20,300	29,000
2d 2P Cpe	400	1200	2000	4000	7000	10,000
2d RS Cpe	450	1350	2300	4600	8000	11,400
2d Sed	400	1250	2100	4200	7300	10,400
4d Sed	400	1250	2100	4200	7400	10,600
Special Six, 6-cyl., 113" wb						
2d Spt Rds	1100	3500	5800	11,600	20,300	29,000
4d Phae	1150	3600	6000	12,000	21,000	30,000
2d Conv	1000	3250	5400	10,800	18,900	27,000
2d Bus Cpe	400	1350	2250	4500	7900	11,300
2d RS Cpe	450	1400	2300	4600	8100	11,600
2d Sed	400	1250	2100	4200	7400	10,600
4d Sed	400	1300	2150	4300	7600	10,800
DeLuxe Six, 6-cyl., 113" wb						
2d Conv	1050	3350	5600	11,200	19,600	28,000
2d 2P Cpe	400	1250	2100	4200	7400	10,500
2d RS Cpe	450	1450	2400	4800	8400	12,000
2d Sed	400	1300	2150	4300	7500	10,700
4d Sed	400	1300	2200	4400	7700	11,000
Terraplane, 8-cyl.						
2d 2P Rds	1100	3500	5800	11,600	20,300	29,000
2d RS Rds	1150	3600	6000	12,000	21,000	30,000
2d 2P Cpe	450	1400	2350	4700	8300	11,800
2d RS Cpe	500	1550	2600	5200	9100	13,000
2d Conv	1000	3250	5400	10,800	18,900	27,000
2d Sed	450	1400	2350	4700	8300	11,800
4d Sed	450	1450	2400	4800	8400	12,000
Terraplane DeLuxe Eight, 8-cyl.						
2d Conv	1100	3500	5800	11,600	20,300	29,000
2P Cpe	450	1450	2400	4800	8400	12,000
2d RS Cpe	500	1600	2700	5400	9500	13,500
2d Sed	450	1400	2350	4700	8300	11,800
4d Sed	450	1450	2400	4800	8400	12,000
1934						
Terraplane Challenger KS, 6-cyl., 112" wb						
2P Cpe	400	1250	2100	4200	7300	10,400
2d RS Cpe	450	1350	2300	4600	8000	11,400
2d Sed	450	1160	1950	3900	6800	9700
4d Sed	400	1200	2000	4000	7000	10,000
Major Line KU, 6-cyl.						
2P Cpe	400	1250	2100	4200	7400	10,500
2d RS Cpe	450	1400	2300	4600	8100	11,500
2d Conv	1050	3350	5600	11,200	19,600	28,000
2d Comp Vic	400	1250	2100	4200	7400	10,500
2d Sed	450	1080	1800	3600	6300	9000
4d Sed	400	1200	2000	4000	7100	10,100
4d Comp Sed	400	1250	2050	4100	7200	10,300
Special Line K, 8-cyl.						
2P Cpe	400	1300	2200	4400	7700	11,000
2d RS Cpe	450	1450	2400	4800	8400	12,000
2d Conv	1100	3500	5800	11,600	20,300	29,000
2d Comp Vic	400	1250	2100	4200	7400	10,600
2d Sed	400	1200	2000	4000	7000	10,000
4d Sed	400	1200	2000	4000	7100	10,100
4d Comp Sed	400	1250	2050	4100	7200	10,300
1935						
Special G, 6-cyl.						
2P Cpe	400	1250	2100	4200	7300	10,400
2d RS Cpe	400	1300	2150	4300	7500	10,700
4d Tr Brgm	400	1200	2050	4100	7100	10,200
2d Sed	400	1200	2000	4000	7100	10,100
4d Sed	400	1200	2050	4100	7100	10,200
4d Sub Sed	400	1250	2050	4100	7200	10,300
DeLuxe GU, 6-cyl., Big Six						
2d 2P Cpe	400	1250	2100	4200	7400	10,500
2d RS Cpe	400	1300	2200	4400	7700	11,000
2d Conv	1000	3100	5200	10,400	18,200	26,000
4d Tr Brgm	400	1250	2100	4200	7400	10,600
2d Sed	400	1250	2100	4200	7300	10,400
4d Sed	400	1250	2100	4200	7400	10,500
4d Sub Sed	400	1300	2150	4300	7500	10,700
1936						
DeLuxe 61, 6-cyl.						
2d Conv	1000	3100	5200	10,400	18,200	26,000
2d 2P Cpe	400	1200	2000	4000	7000	10,000
2d RS Cpe	400	1300	2200	4400	7700	11,000
4d Brgm	450	1150	1900	3850	6700	9600
4d Tr Brgm	400	1200	2000	4000	7000	10,000
4d Sed	450	1160	1950	3900	6800	9700
4d Tr Sed	450	1170	1975	3900	6850	9800
Custom 62, 6-cyl.						
2d Conv	1000	3250	5400	10,800	18,900	27,000
2d 2P Cpe	400	1250	2100	4200	7400	10,600
2d RS Cpe	450	1450	2400	4800	8400	12,000
4d Brgm	400	1250	2100	4200	7300	10,400
4d Tr Brgm	400	1250	2100	4200	7400	10,600
4d Sed	400	1250	2100	4200	7300	10,400
4d Tr Sed	400	1250	2100	4200	7400	10,500
1937						
DeLuxe 71, 6-cyl.						
2d Bus Cpe	400	1200	2000	4000	7000	10,000
2d 3P Cpe	400	1200	2000	4000	7100	10,100
2d Vic Cpe	400	1250	2100	4200	7300	10,400
2d Conv	950	3000	5000	10,000	17,500	25,000
4d Brgm	400	1200	2000	4000	7000	10,000
1938						
Terraplane Utility Series 80, 6-cyl., 117" wb						
2d 3P Cpe	450	1130	1900	3800	6600	9400
2d Sed	450	1090	1800	3650	6400	9100
4d Twn Sed	950	1100	1850	3700	6450	9200
4d Sed	450	1090	1800	3650	6400	9100
4d Tr Sed	950	1100	1850	3700	6450	9200
4d Sta Wag	550	1700	2800	5600	9800	14,000

	6	5	4	3	2	1
Terraplane Deluxe Series 81, 6-cyl., 117" wb						
2d 3P Conv	950	3000	5000	10,000	17,500	25,000
2d Conv Brgm	1000	3100	5200	10,400	18,200	26,000
2d 3P Cpe	450	1150	1900	3850	6700	9600
2d Vic Cpe	400	1300	2200	4400	7700	11,000
4d Brgm	450	1120	1875	3750	6500	9300
4d Tr Brgm	450	1090	1800	3650	6400	9100
4d Sed	950	1100	1850	3700	6450	9200
4d Tr Sed	450	1120	1875	3750	6500	9300
Terraplane Super Series 82, 6-cyl., 117" wb						
2d Conv	1000	3100	5200	10,400	18,200	26,000
2d Conv Brgm	950	3000	5000	10,000	17,500	25,000
2d Vic Cpe	400	1300	2200	4400	7700	11,000
4d Brgm	400	1250	2100	4200	7300	10,400
4d Tr Brgm	400	1200	2050	4100	7100	10,200
4d Sed	400	1250	2050	4100	7200	10,300
4d Tr Sed	400	1250	2100	4200	7300	10,400

KAISER

	6	5	4	3	2	1
1947-1948						
Special, 6-cyl.						
4d Sed	500	1550	2600	5200	9100	13,000
Custom, 6-cyl.						
4d Sed	500	1600	2700	5400	9500	13,500
1949-1950						
Special, 6-cyl.						
4d Sed	500	1650	2750	5500	9700	13,800
Traveler, 6-cyl.						
4d Sed	550	1700	2800	5600	9800	14,000
DeLuxe, 6-cyl.						
4d Sed	550	1700	2850	5700	10,000	14,300
4d Conv Sed	1450	4700	7800	15,600	27,300	39,000
Vagabond, 6-cyl.						
4d Sed	700	2150	3600	7200	12,600	18,000
Virginian, 6-cyl.						
4d Sed HT	1000	3100	5200	10,400	18,200	26,000
1951						
Special, 6-cyl.						
4d Sed	550	1700	2800	5600	9800	14,000
4d Trav Sed	550	1700	2850	5700	10,000	14,300
2d Sed	550	1700	2800	5600	9900	14,100
2d Trav Sed	550	1750	2900	5800	10,200	14,500
2d Bus Cpe	600	1900	3200	6400	11,200	16,000
DeLuxe						
4d Sed	550	1750	2900	5800	10,100	14,400
4d Trav Sed	550	1750	2900	5800	10,200	14,600
2d Sed	550	1750	2900	5800	10,200	14,500
2d Trav Sed	550	1750	2950	5900	10,300	14,700
2d Clb Cpe	700	2150	3600	7200	12,600	18,000
1952						
Kaiser DeLuxe, 6-cyl.						
4d Sed	550	1700	2800	5600	9800	14,000
Ta Sed	550	1750	2900	5800	10,200	14,500
2d Sed	550	1700	2800	5600	9800	14,000
2d Trav	550	1800	3000	6000	10,500	15,000
2d Bus Cpe	650	2100	3500	7000	12,300	17,500
Kaiser Manhattan, 6-cyl.						
4d Sed	600	1850	3100	6200	10,900	15,500
2d Sed	600	1900	3200	6400	11,200	16,000
2d Clb Cpe	700	2150	3600	7200	12,600	18,000
Virginian, 6-cyl.						
4d Sed	550	1750	2900	5800	10,200	14,500
2d Sed	550	1750	2900	5800	10,200	14,600
2d Clb Cpe	650	2050	3400	6800	11,900	17,000
1953						
Carolina, 6-cyl.						
2d Sed	550	1700	2850	5700	10,000	14,300
4d Sed	550	1700	2850	5700	9900	14,200
Deluxe						
2d Clb Sed	550	1750	2900	5800	10,200	14,500
4d Trav Sed	550	1750	2900	5800	10,200	14,600
4d Sed	550	1750	2900	5800	10,100	14,400
Manhattan, 6-cyl.						
2d Clb Sed	600	1900	3150	6300	11,000	15,700
4d Sed	600	1850	3100	6200	10,900	15,600
Dragon 4d Sed, 6-cyl.						
4d Sed	750	2400	4000	8000	14,000	20,000
1954						
Early Special, 6-cyl.						
4d Sed	600	1850	3100	6200	10,900	15,600
2d Clb Sed	600	1900	3150	6300	11,000	15,700
Late Special, 6-cyl.						
4d Sed	600	1850	3100	6200	10,900	15,500
2d Clb Sed	600	1850	3100	6200	10,900	15,600
Manhattan, 6-cyl.						
4d Sed	600	1900	3200	6400	11,200	16,000
2d Clb Sed	600	1950	3250	6500	11,300	16,200
Kaiser Darrin Spts Car, 6-cyl.						
2d Spt Car	1350	4300	7200	14,400	25,200	36,000
1955						
Manhattan, 6-cyl.						
4d Sed	600	2000	3300	6600	11,600	16,500
2d Clb Sed	600	2000	3300	6600	11,600	16,600

FRAZER

	6	5	4	3	2	1
1947-1948						
4d Sed	450	1500	2450	4900	8600	12,300
Manhattan, 6-cyl.						
4d Sed	500	1650	2700	5400	9500	13,600
1949-1950						
4d Sed	500	1550	2600	5200	9100	13,000
Manhattan, 6-cyl.						
4d Sed	550	1750	2900	5800	10,200	14,500
4d Conv Sed	1550	4900	8200	16,400	28,700	41,000
1951						
Manhattan, 6-cyl.						
4d Sed	550	1700	2800	5600	9800	14,000
4d Vag	600	1900	3200	6400	11,200	16,000
4d Sed HT	850	2650	4400	8800	15,400	22,000
4d Conv Sed	1450	4700	7800	15,600	27,300	39,000

RAMBLER

	6	5	4	3	2	1
1902						
One cylinder, 4 hp						
2P Rbt	1400	4450	7400	14,800	25,900	37,000
1903						
One cylinder, 6 hp						
2/4P Lt Tr	1350	4300	7200	14,400	25,200	36,000
1904						
Model E, 1-cyl., 7 hp, 78" wb						
Rbt	1200	3850	6400	12,800	22,400	32,000
Model G, 1-cyl., 7 hp, 81" wb						
Rbt	1250	3950	6600	13,200	23,100	33,000
Model H, 1-cyl., 7 hp, 81" wb						
Tonn	1250	3950	6600	13,200	23,100	33,000
Model J, 2-cyl., 16 hp, 84" wb						
Rbt	1300	4100	6800	13,600	23,800	34,000
Model K, 2-cyl., 16 hp, 84" wb						
Tonn	1300	4100	6800	13,600	23,800	34,000
Model L, 2-cyl., 16 hp, 84" wb						
Canopy Tonn	1300	4200	7000	14,000	24,500	35,000
1905						
Model G, 1-cyl., 8 hp, 81" wb						
Rbt	1200	3850	6400	12,800	22,400	32,000
Model H, 1-cyl., 8 hp, 81" wb						
Tr	1200	3850	6400	12,800	22,400	32,000
Type One, 2-cyl., 18 hp, 90" wb						
Tr	1250	3950	6600	13,200	23,100	33,000
Type Two, 2-cyl., 20 hp, 100" wb						
Surrey	1300	4100	6800	13,600	23,800	34,000
Limo	1350	4300	7200	14,400	25,200	36,000
1906						
Model 17, 2-cyl., 10/12 hp, 88" wb						
2P Rbt	1150	3700	6200	12,400	21,700	31,000
Type One, 2-cyl., 18/20 hp, 90" wb						
5P Surrey	1200	3850	6400	12,800	22,400	32,000
Type Two, 2-cyl., 20 hp, 100" wb						
5P Surrey	1250	3950	6600	13,200	23,100	33,000
Type Three, 2-cyl., 18/20 hp, 96" wb						
5P Surrey	1300	4100	6800	13,600	23,800	34,000
Model 14, 4-cyl., 25 hp, 106" wb						
5P Tr	1300	4200	7000	14,000	24,500	35,000
Model 15, 4-cyl., 35/40 hp, 112" wb						
5P Tr	1400	4450	7400	14,800	25,900	37,000
Model 16, 4-cyl., 35/40 hp, 112" wb						
5P Limo	1300	4100	6800	13,600	23,800	34,000
1907						
Model 27, 2-cyl., 14/16 hp, 90" wb						
2P Rbt	1150	3700	6200	12,400	21,700	31,000
Model 22, 2-cyl., 20/22 hp, 100" wb						
2P Rbt	1200	3850	6400	12,800	22,400	32,000
Model 21, 2-cyl., 20/22 hp, 100" wb						
5P Tr	1250	3950	6600	13,200	23,100	33,000
Model 24, 4-cyl., 25/30 hp, 108" wb						
5P Tr	1300	4100	6800	13,600	23,800	34,000
Model 25, 4-cyl., 35/40 hp, 112" wb						
5P Tr	1350	4300	7200	14,400	25,200	36,000
1908						
Model 31, 2-cyl., 22 hp, 106" wb						
Det Tonneau	1300	4100	6800	13,600	23,800	34,000
Model 34, 4-cyl., 32 hp, 112" wb						
3P Rds	1300	4200	7000	14,000	24,500	35,000
5P Tr	1350	4300	7200	14,400	25,200	36,000
1909						
Model 47, 2-cyl., 22 hp, 106" wb						
2P Rbt	1300	4100	6800	13,600	23,800	34,000
Model 41, 2-cyl., 22 hp, 106" wb						
5P Tr	1300	4200	7000	14,000	24,500	35,000
Model 44, 4-cyl., 34 hp, 112" wb						
5P Tr	1350	4300	7200	14,400	25,200	36,000
4P C.C. Tr	1400	4450	7400	14,800	25,900	37,000
Model 45, 4-cyl., 45 hp, 123" wb						
7P Tr	1600	5050	8400	16,800	29,400	42,000
4P C.C. Tr	1600	5150	8600	17,200	30,100	43,000
3P Rds	1550	4900	8200	16,400	28,700	41,000
1910						
Model 53, 4-cyl., 34 hp, 109" wb						
Tr	1450	4700	7800	15,600	27,300	39,000
Model 54, 4-cyl., 45 hp, 117" wb						
Tr	1550	4900	8200	16,400	28,700	41,000
Model 55, 4-cyl., 45 hp, 123" wb						
Tr	1600	5150	8600	17,200	30,100	43,000
Limo	1300	4100	6800	13,600	23,800	34,000
1911						
Model 63, 4-cyl., 34 hp, 112" wb						
Tr	1450	4550	7600	15,200	26,600	38,000
Rds	1400	4450	7400	14,800	25,900	37,000
Cpe	800	2500	4200	8400	14,700	21,000
Twn Car	850	2750	4600	9200	16,100	23,000
Model 64, 4-cyl., 34 hp, 120" wb						
Tr	1500	4800	8000	16,000	28,000	40,000
Toy Tonn	1550	4900	8200	16,400	28,700	41,000
Lan'let	1150	3700	6200	12,400	21,700	31,000
Model 65, 4-cyl., 34 hp, 128" wb						
Tr	1600	5050	8400	16,800	29,400	42,000
Toy Tonn	1600	5150	8600	17,200	30,100	43,000
Limo	1150	3700	6200	12,400	21,700	31,000
1912						
Four, 38 hp, 120" wb						
5P Cr Ctry Tr	1550	4900	8200	16,400	28,700	41,000
4P Sub Ctry Clb	1500	4800	8000	16,000	28,000	40,000
2P Rds	1500	4800	8000	16,000	28,000	40,000
4P Sed	800	2500	4200	8400	14,700	21,000
7P Gotham Limo	1000	3100	5200	10,400	18,200	26,000
Four, 50 hp, 120" wb						
Ctry Clb	1600	5050	8400	16,800	29,400	42,000
Valkyrie	1550	4900	8200	16,400	28,700	41,000
Four, 50 hp, 128" wb						
Morraine Tr	1650	5300	8800	17,600	30,800	44,000
Metropolitan	1700	5400	9000	18,000	31,500	45,000
Greyhound	1700	5400	9000	18,000	31,500	45,000
Knickerbocker	2200	6950	11,600	23,200	40,600	58,000
1913						
Four, 42 hp, 120" wb						
2/3P Cr Ctry Rds	1500	4800	8000	16,000	28,000	40,000
4/5P Cr Ctry Tr	1550	4900	8200	16,400	28,700	41,000

	6	5	4	3	2	1
4P Inside Drive Cpe	900	2900	4800	9600	16,800	24,000
7P Gotham Limo	1000	3250	5400	10,800	18,900	27,000

JEFFERY

	6	5	4	3	2	1
1914						
Four, 40 hp, 116" wb						
4d 5P Tr	1350	4300	7200	14,400	25,200	36,000
4d 5P Sed	600	1900	3200	6400	11,200	16,000
Four, 27 hp, 120" wb						
2d 2P Rds	1400	4450	7400	14,800	25,900	37,000
4d 4P/5P/7P Tr	1450	4550	7600	15,200	26,600	38,000
Six, 48 hp, 128" wb						
4d 5P Tr	1500	4800	8000	16,000	28,000	40,000
4d 6P Tr	1550	4900	8200	16,400	28,700	41,000
4d 7P Limo	950	3000	5000	10,000	17,500	25,000
1915						
Four, 40 hp, 116" wb						
4d 5P Tr	1500	4800	8000	16,000	28,000	40,000
2d 2P Rds	1450	4700	7800	15,600	27,300	39,000
2d 2P A/W	1050	3350	5600	11,200	19,600	28,000
4d 7P Limo	900	2900	4800	9600	16,800	24,000
4d 4P Sed	750	2400	4000	8000	14,000	20,000
Chesterfield Six, 48 hp, 122" wb						
4d 5P Tr	1700	5400	9000	18,000	31,500	45,000
2d 2P Rds	1600	5150	8600	17,200	30,100	43,000
2d 2P A/W	1600	5050	8400	16,800	29,400	42,000
1916						
Four, 40 hp, 116" wb						
4d 7P Tr	1650	5300	8800	17,600	30,800	44,000
4d 5P Tr	1600	5150	8600	17,200	30,100	43,000
4d 7P Sed	800	2500	4200	8400	14,700	21,000
4d 5P Sed	750	2400	4000	8000	14,000	20,000
2d 3P Rds	1550	4900	8200	16,400	28,700	41,000
Chesterfield Six, 48 hp, 122" wb						
4d 5P Tr	1800	5750	9600	19,200	33,600	48,000
1917						
Model 472, 4-cyl., 40 hp, 116" wb						
4d 7P Tr	1550	4900	8200	16,400	28,700	41,000
2d 2P Rds	1500	4800	8000	16,000	28,000	40,000
4d 7P Sed	750	2400	4000	8000	14,000	20,000
Model 671, 6-cyl., 48 hp, 125" wb						
4d 7P Tr	1700	5400	9000	18,000	31,500	45,000
2d 3P Rds	1650	5300	8800	17,600	30,800	44,000
4d 5P Sed	750	2400	4000	8000	14,000	20,000

NASH

	6	5	4	3	2	1
1918						
Series 680, 6-cyl.						
4d 7P Tr	1100	3500	5800	11,600	20,300	29,000
4d 5P Tr	1050	3350	5600	11,200	19,600	28,000
4d 4P Rds	1150	3600	6000	12,000	21,000	30,000
4d Sed	700	2300	3800	7600	13,300	19,000
2d Cpe	700	2300	3850	7700	13,400	19,200
1919						
Series 680, 6-cyl.						
2d Rds	1100	3500	5800	11,600	20,300	29,000
2d Spt Rds	1050	3350	5600	11,200	19,600	28,000
4d 5P Tr	1150	3600	6000	12,000	21,000	30,000
4d 7P Tr	1150	3700	6200	12,400	21,700	31,000
2d 4P Rds	1150	3600	6000	12,000	21,000	30,000
4d Sed	700	2150	3600	7200	12,600	18,000
2d Cpe	700	2200	3700	7400	13,000	18,500
1920						
Series 680, 6-cyl.						
4d 5P Tr	1050	3350	5600	11,200	19,600	28,000
2d Rds	1000	3250	5400	10,800	18,900	27,000
4d 7P Tr	1100	3500	5800	11,600	20,300	29,000
2d Cpe	700	2200	3700	7400	13,000	18,500
4d Sed	700	2150	3600	7200	12,600	18,000
4d Spt Tr	1150	3600	6000	12,000	21,000	30,000
1921						
Series 680, 6-cyl.						
4d 5P Tr	1000	3100	5200	10,400	18,200	26,000
2d Rds	1000	3250	5400	10,800	18,900	27,000
4d Spt Tr	1050	3350	5600	11,200	19,600	28,000
4d Tr	1000	3250	5400	10,800	18,900	27,000
2d Cpe	700	2200	3700	7400	13,000	18,500
4d Sed	650	2050	3400	6800	11,900	17,000
Series 40, 4-cyl.						
4d Tr	950	3000	5000	10,000	17,500	25,000
2d Rds	1000	3100	5200	10,400	18,200	26,000
2d Cpe	600	1900	3200	6400	11,200	16,000
4d Sed	550	1700	2800	5600	9800	14,000
2d Cabr	900	2900	4800	9600	16,800	24,000
1922						
Series 680, 6-cyl.						
4d 5P Tr	1000	3100	5200	10,400	18,200	26,000
4d 7P Tr	1000	3250	5400	10,800	18,900	27,000
4d 7P Sed	600	1900	3200	6400	11,200	16,000
2d Cpe	700	2150	3600	7200	12,600	18,000
2d Rds	1050	3350	5600	11,200	19,600	28,000
2d Spt	1100	3500	5800	11,600	20,300	29,000
4d 5P Sed	650	2050	3400	6800	11,900	17,000
Series 40, 4-cyl.						
4d Tr	950	3000	5000	10,000	17,500	25,000
2d Rds	1000	3100	5200	10,400	18,200	26,000
2d Cpe	650	2050	3400	6800	11,900	17,000
4d Sed	500	1550	2600	5200	9100	13,000
2d Cabr	750	2400	4000	8000	14,000	20,000
Ca'ole	550	1800	3000	6000	10,500	15,000
1923						
Series 690, 6-cyl., 121" wb						
2d Rds	1000	3250	5400	10,800	18,900	27,000
4d Tr	1050	3350	5600	11,200	19,600	28,000
4d Spt Tr	1100	3500	5800	11,600	20,300	29,000
4d Sed	450	1450	2400	4800	8400	12,000
2d Cpe	550	1800	3000	6000	10,500	15,000
Series 690, 6-cyl., 127" wb						
4d Tr	1050	3350	5600	11,200	19,600	28,000
4d Sed	450	1500	2500	5000	8800	12,500
2d Cpe	600	1850	3100	6200	10,900	15,500
Series 40, 4-cyl.						
4d Tr	1000	3100	5200	10,400	18,200	26,000
2d Rds	1000	3250	5400	10,800	18,900	27,000
4d Spt Tr	1050	3350	5600	11,200	19,600	28,000
Ca'ole	550	1700	2800	5600	9800	14,000
4d Sed	500	1550	2600	5200	9100	13,000
1924						
Series 690, 6-cyl., 121" wb						
2d Rds	1000	3250	5400	10,800	18,900	27,000
4d Tr	1000	3100	5200	10,400	18,200	26,000
4d Spl DeL	400	1200	2000	4000	7000	10,000
2d Cpe	450	1450	2400	4800	8400	12,000
4d Spl Sed	400	1300	2200	4400	7700	11,000
Series 690, 6-cyl., 127" wb						
4d 7P Tr	1050	3350	5600	11,200	19,600	28,000
4d 7P Sed	400	1250	2100	4200	7400	10,500
2d Vic	400	1300	2200	4400	7700	11,000
4 cyl.						
4d Tr	1000	3250	5400	10,800	18,900	27,000
2d Rds	1050	3350	5600	11,200	19,600	28,000
2d Cab	1000	3100	5200	10,400	18,200	26,000
4d 5P Sed	400	1300	2200	4400	7700	11,000
4d Sed	400	1200	2000	4000	7000	10,000
4d Spt Sed	450	1450	2400	4800	8400	12,000
2d Cpe	500	1550	2600	5200	9100	13,000
1925						
Advanced models, 6-cyl.						
4d Tr	900	2900	4800	9600	16,800	24,000
4d 7P Tr	950	3000	5000	10,000	17,500	25,000
4d Sed	450	1450	2400	4800	8400	12,000
2d Vic Cpe	500	1550	2600	5200	9100	13,000
4d 7P Sed	450	1500	2500	5000	8800	12,500
2d Rds	950	3000	5000	10,000	17,500	25,000
2d Cpe	450	1450	2400	4800	8400	12,000
2d Sed	400	1200	2000	4000	7000	10,000
Special models, 6-cyl.						
4d Tr	850	2750	4600	9200	16,100	23,000
4d Sed	400	1300	2200	4400	7700	11,000
2d Rds	900	2900	4800	9600	16,800	24,000
2d Sed	400	1300	2150	4300	7600	10,800
Light six, (Ajax), 6-cyl.						
4d Tr	700	2300	3800	7600	13,300	19,000
4d Sed	400	1200	2000	4000	7000	10,000
1926						
Advanced models, 6-cyl.						
4d 5P Tr	900	2900	4800	9600	16,800	24,000
4d 7P Tr	950	3000	5000	10,000	17,500	25,000
2d Sed	400	1200	2000	4000	7000	10,000
4d Sed	400	1200	2050	4100	7100	10,200
4d 7P Sed	400	1250	2100	4200	7400	10,500
2d Cpe	400	1300	2200	4400	7600	10,900
2d Rds	950	3000	5000	10,000	17,500	25,000
2d Vic Cpe	500	1550	2600	5200	9100	13,000
Special models, 6-cyl.						
2d Rds	850	2750	4600	9200	16,100	23,000
2d Sed	400	1250	2100	4200	7400	10,500
4d 7P Sed	400	1300	2150	4300	7500	10,700
2d Cpe	400	1300	2200	4400	7700	11,000
4d Sed	400	1250	2100	4200	7400	10,600
2d Spl Rds	1000	3100	5200	10,400	18,200	26,000
Light Six (formerly Ajax)						
4d Tr	700	2150	3600	7200	12,600	18,000
2d Sed	400	1250	2100	4200	7400	10,500
1927						
Standard, 6-cyl.						
4d Tr	750	2400	4000	8000	14,000	20,000
2d Cpe	450	1400	2300	4600	8100	11,500
2d Sed	400	1250	2100	4200	7400	10,600
4d Sed	450	1150	1900	3850	6700	9600
4d DeL Sed	400	1300	2150	4300	7500	10,700
Special, 6-cyl.						
(Begin September 1926)						
2d Rds	800	2500	4200	8400	14,700	21,000
4d Tr	750	2400	4000	8000	14,000	20,000
2d Cpe	450	1450	2400	4800	8400	12,000
2d Sed	400	1300	2200	4400	7700	11,000
4d Sed	400	1350	2250	4500	7800	11,200
(Begin January 1927)						
4d Cav Sed	450	1400	2300	4600	8100	11,500
4d Sed	450	1350	2300	4600	8000	11,400
2d RS Cab	650	2050	3400	6800	11,900	17,000
2d RS Rds	750	2400	4000	8000	14,000	20,000
Advanced, 6-cyl.						
(Begin August 1926)						
2d Rds	900	2900	4800	9600	16,800	24,000
4d 5P Tr	850	2750	4600	9200	16,100	23,000
4d 7P Tr	900	2900	4800	9600	16,800	24,000
2d Cpe	500	1550	2600	5200	9100	13,000
2d Vic	550	1700	2800	5600	9800	14,000
2d Sed	400	1300	2200	4400	7700	11,000
4d Sed	400	1350	2250	4500	7800	11,200
4d 7P Sed	450	1400	2300	4600	8100	11,500
(Begin January 1927)						
2d RS Cpe	550	1800	3000	6000	10,500	15,000
4d Spl Sed	450	1400	2300	4600	8100	11,500
4d Amb Sed	450	1400	2350	4700	8200	11,700
1928						
Standard, 6-cyl.						
4d Tr	700	2150	3600	7200	12,600	18,000
2d Cpe	450	1450	2400	4800	8400	12,000
2d Conv Cabr	800	2500	4200	8400	14,700	21,000
2d Sed	400	1250	2100	4200	7400	10,500
4d Sed	400	1250	2100	4200	7400	10,600
4d Lan Sed	400	1300	2150	4300	7500	10,700
Special, 6-cyl.						
4d Tr	650	2100	3500	7000	12,200	17,400
2d RS Rds	700	2300	3800	7600	13,300	19,000
2d Cpe	450	1450	2400	4800	8400	12,000
2d Conv Cabr	850	2750	4600	9200	16,100	23,000
2d Vic	550	1800	3000	6000	10,500	15,000
2d Sed	500	1550	2600	5200	9100	13,000
4d Sed	500	1600	2650	5300	9200	13,200
4d Cpe	500	1600	2700	5400	9500	13,500
Advanced, 6-cyl.						
4d Spt Tr	1000	3100	5200	10,400	18,200	26,000
4d Tr	950	3000	5000	10,000	17,500	25,000
2d RS Rds	1000	3250	5400	10,800	18,900	27,000

	6	5	4	3	2	1
2d Cpe	500	1550	2600	5200	9100	13,000
2d Vic	500	1600	2700	5400	9500	13,500
2d Sed	400	1350	2250	4500	7900	11,300
4d Sed	450	1400	2300	4600	8100	11,600
4d Cpe	450	1450	2400	4800	8400	12,000
4d 7P Sed	450	1350	2300	4600	8000	11,400
1929						
Standard, 6-cyl.						
4d Sed	400	1200	2050	4100	7100	10,200
4d Tr	850	2750	4600	9200	16,100	23,000
2d Cabr	650	2050	3400	6800	11,900	17,000
2d Sed	400	1200	2050	4100	7100	10,200
2P Cpe	400	1200	2000	4000	7100	10,100
4P Cpe	400	1250	2100	4200	7300	10,400
4d Lan Sed	400	1250	2050	4100	7200	10,300
Special, 6-cyl.						
2d Sed	400	1300	2200	4400	7700	11,000
2d 2P Cpe	450	1400	2300	4600	8100	11,500
2d 4P Cpe	450	1450	2400	4800	8400	12,000
2d Rds	1050	3350	5600	11,200	19,600	28,000
4d Sed	400	1300	2200	4400	7700	11,000
2d Cabr	850	2650	4400	8800	15,400	22,000
2d Vic	450	1350	2300	4600	8000	11,400
Advanced, 6-cyl.						
2d Cpe	450	1450	2400	4800	8400	12,000
2d Cabr	1000	3100	5200	10,400	18,200	26,000
2d Sed	450	1350	2300	4600	8000	11,400
4d 7P Sed	450	1400	2300	4600	8100	11,500
4d Amb Sed	450	1400	2350	4700	8300	11,800
4d Sed	450	1400	2300	4600	8100	11,500
1930						
Single, 6-cyl.						
2d Rds	800	2500	4200	8400	14,700	21,000
4d Tr	750	2400	4000	8000	14,000	20,000
2P Cpe	450	1400	2300	4600	8100	11,500
2d Sed	400	1300	2200	4400	7700	11,000
4P Cpe	450	1500	2500	5000	8700	12,400
2d Cabr	750	2400	4000	8000	14,000	20,000
4d Sed	400	1350	2200	4400	7800	11,100
4d DeL Sed	400	1350	2250	4500	7900	11,300
4d Lan'let	450	1450	2400	4800	8400	12,000
Twin-Ign, 6-cyl.						
2d Rds	1150	3700	6200	12,400	21,700	31,000
4d 7P Tr	1150	3600	6000	12,000	21,000	30,000
4d 5P Tr	1100	3500	5800	11,600	20,300	29,000
2d 2P Cpe	450	1450	2400	4800	8400	12,000
2d 4P Cpe	450	1450	2450	4900	8500	12,200
2d Sed	400	1300	2200	4400	7700	11,000
2d Cabr	850	2650	4400	8800	15,400	22,000
2d Vic	550	1800	3000	6000	10,500	15,000
4d Sed	450	1500	2500	5000	8700	12,400
4d 7P Sed	500	1500	2550	5100	8900	12,700
Twin-Ign, 8-cyl.						
2d Sed	550	1750	2900	5800	10,100	14,400
2d 2P Cpe	650	2100	3500	7000	12,300	17,500
2d 4P Cpe	700	2150	3600	7200	12,600	18,000
2d Vic	750	2400	4000	8000	14,000	20,000
2d Cabr	1500	4800	8000	16,000	28,000	40,000
4d Sed	550	1750	2900	5800	10,200	14,500
4d Amb Sed	600	1850	3100	6200	10,900	15,500
4d 7P Sed	550	1800	3000	6000	10,500	15,000
4d 7P Limo	600	1900	3200	6400	11,200	16,000
1931						
Series 660, 6-cyl.						
4d 5P Tr	950	3000	5000	10,000	17,500	25,000
2d 2P Cpe	450	1500	2500	5000	8800	12,500
2d 4P Cpe	500	1500	2550	5100	8900	12,700
2d Sed	450	1450	2400	4800	8400	12,000
4d Sed	450	1450	2400	4800	8400	12,000
Series 870, 8-cyl.						
2d 2P Cpe	550	1800	3000	6000	10,500	15,000
2d 4P Cpe	550	1800	3050	6100	10,600	15,200
4d Conv Sed	1900	6000	10,000	20,000	35,000	50,000
2d Sed	550	1700	2850	5700	9900	14,200
4d Spl Sed	550	1750	2900	5800	10,100	14,400
Series 880 - Twin-Ign, 8-cyl.						
2d 2P Cpe	650	2050	3400	6800	11,900	17,000
2d 4P Cpe	650	2100	3500	7000	12,300	17,500
4d Conv Sed	2000	6350	10,600	21,200	37,100	53,000
2d Sed	550	1800	3000	6000	10,500	15,000
4d Twn Sed	600	1850	3100	6200	10,900	15,500
Series 890 - Twin-Ign, 8-cyl.						
4d 7P Tr	1700	5400	9000	18,000	31,500	45,000
2d 2P Cpe	850	2750	4600	9200	16,100	23,000
2d 4P Cpe	900	2900	4800	9600	16,800	24,000
2d Cabr	1900	6000	10,000	20,000	35,000	50,000
2d Vic	750	2400	4000	8000	14,000	20,000
2d Sed	700	2150	3600	7200	12,600	18,000
4d Amb Sed	700	2300	3800	7600	13,300	19,000
4d 7P Sed	750	2400	4000	8000	14,000	20,000
4d 7P Limo	850	2650	4400	8800	15,400	22,000
1932						
Series 960, 6-cyl.						
4d 5P Tr	1150	3700	6200	12,400	21,700	31,000
2d 2P Cpe	500	1550	2600	5200	9100	13,000
2d 4P Cpe	500	1600	2700	5400	9500	13,500
2d Sed	400	1200	2000	4000	7000	10,000
4d Sed	400	1200	2050	4100	7100	10,200
Series 970, 8-cyl., 116.5" wb						
2d 2P Cpe	600	1900	3200	6400	11,200	16,000
2d 4P Cpe	600	2000	3300	6600	11,600	16,500
4d Conv Sed	2050	6500	10,800	21,600	37,800	54,000
2d Sed	500	1600	2700	5400	9500	13,500
4d Spl Sed	500	1650	2750	5500	9600	13,700
Series 980 - Twin-Ign, 8-cyl., 121" wb						
2d 2P Cpe	900	2900	4800	9600	16,800	24,000
2d 4P Cpe	950	3000	5000	10,000	17,500	25,000
4d Conv Sed	1950	6250	10,400	20,800	36,400	52,000
4d Sed	800	2500	4200	8400	14,700	21,000
4d Twn Sed	850	2650	4400	8800	15,400	22,000
Series 990 - Twin-Ign, 8-cyl., 124"-133" wb						
4d 7P Tr	1800	5750	9600	19,200	33,600	48,000
2d 2P Cpe	1000	3100	5200	10,400	18,200	26,000
2d 4P Cpe	1000	3250	5400	10,800	18,900	27,000
2d Cabr	1900	6000	10,000	20,000	35,000	50,000
2d Vic	1000	3100	5200	10,400	18,200	26,000
2d Sed	850	2650	4400	8800	15,400	22,000

	6	5	4	3	2	1
4d Spl Sed	900	2900	4800	9600	16,800	24,000
4d Amb Sed	950	3000	5000	10,000	17,500	25,000
4d 7P Sed	900	2900	4800	9600	16,800	24,000
4d Limo	1100	3500	5800	11,600	20,300	29,000
1933						
Standard Series						
2d Rds	900	2900	4800	9600	16,800	24,000
2d 2P Cpe	450	1400	2300	4600	8100	11,500
2d 4P Cpe	400	1300	2200	4400	7700	11,000
4d Sed	400	1200	2000	4000	7000	10,000
4d Twn Sed	400	1250	2100	4200	7400	10,500
Special Series, 8-cyl.						
2d Rds	1050	3350	5600	11,200	19,600	28,000
2d 2P Cpe	500	1600	2700	5400	9500	13,500
2d 4P Cpe	550	1700	2800	5600	9800	14,000
4d Sed	500	1550	2600	5200	9100	13,000
4d Conv Sed	1700	5400	9000	18,000	31,500	45,000
4d Twn Sed	500	1600	2700	5400	9500	13,500
Advanced Series, 8-cyl.						
2d Cabr	1300	4200	7000	14,000	24,500	35,000
2d 2P Cpe	550	1700	2800	5600	9800	14,000
2d 4P Cpe	550	1750	2900	5800	10,200	14,500
4d Sed	450	1450	2450	4900	8500	12,200
4d Conv Sed	1950	6250	10,400	20,800	36,400	52,000
2d Vic	550	1800	3000	6000	10,500	15,000
Ambassador Series, 8-cyl.						
2d Cabr	1700	5400	9000	18,000	31,500	45,000
2d Cpe	600	1900	3200	6400	11,200	16,000
4d Sed	550	1800	3000	6000	10,500	15,000
4d Conv Sed	2050	6600	11,000	22,000	38,500	55,000
2d Vic	1000	3250	5400	10,800	18,900	27,000
4d 142" Brgm	900	2900	4800	9600	16,800	24,000
4d 142" Sed	850	2650	4400	8800	15,400	22,000
4d 142" Limo	1050	3350	5600	11,200	19,600	28,000
1934						
Big Six, 6-cyl.						
2d Bus Cpe	450	1500	2500	5000	8800	12,500
2d Cpe	500	1550	2600	5200	9100	13,000
4d Brgm	450	1400	2300	4600	8100	11,500
2d Sed	400	1300	2200	4400	7700	11,000
4d Twn Sed	450	1400	2300	4600	8100	11,500
4d Tr Sed	450	1350	2300	4600	8000	11,400
Advanced, 8-cyl.						
2d Bus Cpe	500	1550	2600	5200	9100	13,000
2d Cpe	500	1600	2700	5400	9500	13,500
4d Brgm	500	1550	2600	5200	9100	13,000
2d Sed	500	1600	2700	5400	9500	13,500
4d Twn Sed	500	1600	2700	5400	9500	13,500
4d Tr Sed	500	1550	2600	5200	9100	13,000
Ambassador, 8-cyl.						
4d Brgm	500	1600	2700	5400	9500	13,500
2d Sed	500	1550	2600	5200	9100	13,000
4d Tr Sed	500	1600	2650	5300	9200	13,200
4d 7P Sed	550	1700	2800	5600	9800	14,000
4d Limo	600	1900	3200	6400	11,200	16,000
Lafayette, 6-cyl.						
2d Sed	400	1200	2000	4000	7000	10,000
4d Twn Sed	400	1200	2000	4000	7100	10,100
4d Brgm	400	1250	2050	4100	7200	10,300
2d Spl Cpe	450	1400	2300	4600	8100	11,500
2d Spl 4P Cpe	450	1450	2400	4800	8400	12,000
4d Spl Tr Sed	400	1250	2100	4200	7400	10,500
4d Spl Sed	400	1300	2150	4300	7500	10,700
4d Brgm	400	1300	2200	4400	7700	11,000
1935						
Lafayette, 6-cyl.						
2d Bus Cpe	400	1250	2100	4200	7400	10,500
2d Sed	450	1160	1950	3900	6800	9700
4d Brgm	400	1200	2000	4000	7000	10,000
4d Tr Sed	450	1170	1975	3900	6850	9800
4d Twn Sed	450	1190	2000	3950	6900	9900
2d Spl Cpe	450	1400	2300	4600	8100	11,500
4d Spl 6W Sed	400	1250	2100	4200	7400	10,500
4d 6W Brgm	400	1250	2100	4200	7400	10,600
Advanced, 6-cyl.						
2d Vic	400	1300	2200	4400	7700	11,000
4d 6W Sed	400	1200	2000	4000	7000	10,000
Advanced, 8-cyl.						
2d Vic	500	1600	2650	5300	9200	13,200
4d 6W Sed	450	1450	2450	4900	8500	12,200
Ambassador, 8-cyl.						
2d Vic	500	1600	2700	5400	9500	13,500
4d 6W Sed	450	1500	2500	5000	8800	12,500
1936						
Lafayette, 6-cyl.						
2d Bus Cpe	400	1250	2100	4200	7400	10,500
2d Cpe	400	1300	2150	4300	7500	10,700
2d Cabr	700	2300	3800	7600	13,300	19,000
4d Sed	450	1140	1900	3800	6650	9500
2d Vic	400	1200	2000	4000	7000	10,000
4d Tr Sed	450	1150	1900	3850	6700	9600
400 Series, 6-cyl.						
2d Bus Cpe	400	1300	2150	4300	7500	10,700
2d Cpe	400	1300	2200	4400	7700	11,000
2d Vic	400	1250	2100	4200	7400	10,500
4d Tr Vic	400	1300	2200	4400	7700	11,000
4d Sed	450	1150	1900	3850	6700	9600
4d Tr Sed	450	1160	1950	3900	6800	9700
2d Spl Bus Cpe	400	1300	2200	4400	7700	11,000
2d Spl Cpe	450	1400	2300	4600	8100	11,500
2d Spl Spt Cabr	850	2750	4600	9200	16,100	23,000
2d Spl Vic	400	1250	2100	4200	7400	10,500
2d Spl Tr Vic	400	1300	2200	4400	7700	11,000
4d Spl Sed	450	1150	1900	3850	6700	9600
4d Spl Tr Sed	450	1160	1950	3900	6800	9700
Ambassador Series, 6-cyl.						
2d Vic	450	1450	2400	4800	8400	12,000
4d Tr Sed	400	1300	2200	4400	7700	11,000
Ambassador Series, 8-cyl.						
4d Tr Sed	450	1450	2400	4800	8400	12,000
1937						
Lafayette 400, 6-cyl.						
2d Bus Cpe	450	1400	2300	4600	8100	11,500
2d Cpe	450	1450	2400	4800	8400	12,000
2d A-P Cpe	450	1450	2400	4800	8400	12,000
2d Cabr	700	2300	3800	7600	13,300	19,000
2d Vic Sed	400	1200	2000	4000	7000	10,000

	6	5	4	3	2	1
4d Tr Sed	400	1200	2000	4000	7100	10,100
Ambassador, 6-cyl.						
2d Bus Cpe	450	1450	2400	4800	8400	12,000
2d Cpe	450	1500	2500	5000	8800	12,500
2d A-P Cpe	500	1500	2550	5100	8900	12,700
2d Cabr	750	2400	4000	8000	14,000	20,000
2d Vic Sed	400	1300	2200	4400	7700	11,000
4d Tr Sed	400	1350	2200	4400	7800	11,100
Ambassador, 8-cyl.						
2d Bus Cpe	500	1600	2700	5400	9500	13,500
2d Cpe	550	1700	2800	5600	9800	14,000
2d A-P Cpe	550	1750	2900	5800	10,100	14,400
2d Cabr	850	2650	4400	8800	15,400	22,000
2d Vic Sed	450	1500	2500	5000	8800	12,500
4d Tr Sed	450	1500	2500	5000	8800	12,600
1938						
Lafayette						
Master, 6-cyl.						
2d Bus Cpe	400	1250	2100	4200	7400	10,600
2d Vic	400	1250	2100	4200	7300	10,400
4d Tr Sed	450	1140	1900	3800	6650	9500
DeLuxe, 6-cyl.						
2d Bus Cpe	400	1300	2150	4300	7600	10,800
2d A-P Cpe	400	1300	2200	4400	7700	11,000
2d Cabr	650	2050	3400	6800	11,900	17,000
2d Vic	400	1250	2100	4200	7400	10,500
4d Tr Sed	450	1150	1900	3850	6700	9600
Ambassador, 6-cyl.						
2d Bus Cpe	400	1250	2100	4200	7400	10,500
2d A-P Cpe	400	1300	2200	4400	7700	11,000
2d Cabr	700	2150	3600	7200	12,600	18,000
2d Vic	400	1200	2000	4000	7000	10,000
4d Tr Sed	450	1090	1800	3650	6400	9100
Ambassador, 8-cyl.						
2d Bus Cpe	400	1300	2200	4400	7700	11,000
2d A-P Cpe	450	1400	2300	4600	8100	11,500
2d Cabr	750	2400	4000	8000	14,000	20,000
2d Vic	400	1350	2200	4400	7800	11,100
4d Tr Sed	400	1300	2200	4400	7700	11,000
1939						
Lafayette, 6-cyl.						
(Add 10 percent for DeLuxe)						
2d Bus Cpe	400	1250	2100	4200	7400	10,500
2d Sed	400	1200	2000	4000	7000	10,000
4d Sed	450	1090	1800	3650	6400	9100
4d Tr Sed	950	1100	1850	3700	6450	9200
2d A-P Cpe	450	1400	2300	4600	8100	11,500
2d A-P Cabr	800	2500	4200	8400	14,700	21,000
Ambassador, 6-cyl.						
2d Bus Cpe	450	1400	2300	4600	8100	11,600
2d A-P Cpe	450	1450	2400	4800	8400	12,000
2d A-P Cabr	850	2750	4600	9200	16,100	23,000
2d Sed	450	1160	1950	3900	6800	9700
4d Sed	450	1170	1975	3900	6850	9800
4d Tr Sed	400	1200	2000	4000	7000	10,000
Ambassador, 8-cyl.						
2d Bus Cpe	500	1600	2700	5400	9500	13,500
2d A-P Cpe	500	1650	2700	5400	9500	13,600
2d A-P Cabr	1100	3500	5800	11,600	20,300	29,000
2d Sed	450	1400	2300	4600	8100	11,500
4d Sed	450	1400	2300	4600	8100	11,600
4d Tr Sed	450	1400	2350	4700	8200	11,700
1940						
DeLuxe Lafayette, 6-cyl.						
2d Bus Cpe	450	1400	2300	4600	8100	11,500
2d A-P Cpe	450	1400	2300	4600	8100	11,600
2d A-P Cabr	1000	3100	5200	10,400	18,200	26,000
2d FBk	400	1200	2050	4100	7100	10,200
4d FBk	400	1250	2050	4100	7200	10,300
4d Trk Sed	400	1250	2100	4200	7300	10,400
Ambassador, 6-cyl.						
2d Bus Cpe	450	1500	2500	5000	8800	12,600
2d A-P Cpe	500	1550	2600	5200	9100	13,000
2d A-P Cabr	1200	3850	6400	12,800	22,400	32,000
2d FBk	450	1400	2300	4600	8100	11,600
4d FBk	450	1400	2350	4700	8200	11,700
4d Trk Sed	450	1400	2350	4700	8300	11,800
Ambassador, 8-cyl.						
2d Bus Cpe	550	1750	2900	5800	10,200	14,500
2d A-P Cpe	550	1750	2900	5800	10,200	14,600
2d A-P Cabr	1300	4200	7000	14,000	24,500	35,000
2d FBk	500	1550	2600	5200	9100	13,000
4d FBk	500	1550	2600	5200	9200	13,100
4d Trk Sed	500	1600	2650	5300	9200	13,200
1941						
Ambassador 600, 6-cyl.						
2d Bus Cpe	450	1450	2400	4800	8400	12,000
2d FBk	400	1250	2100	4200	7400	10,600
4d FBk	400	1300	2150	4300	7500	10,700
2d DeL Bus Cpe	450	1500	2500	5000	8800	12,600
4d DeL Brgm	450	1400	2300	4600	8100	11,500
2d DeL FBk	400	1300	2200	4400	7700	11,000
4d DeL FBk	400	1350	2200	4400	7800	11,100
4d Tr Sed	400	1350	2250	4500	7800	11,200
Ambassador, 6-cyl.						
2d Bus Cpe	500	1650	2700	5400	9500	13,600
2d Spl Bus Cpe	500	1650	2750	5500	9600	13,700
2d A-P Cabr	1050	3350	5600	11,200	19,600	28,000
2d Brgm	450	1500	2500	5000	8700	12,400
4d Spl Sed	450	1500	2500	5000	8800	12,500
4d Spl FBk	450	1500	2500	5000	8700	12,400
4d DeL FBk	450	1500	2500	5000	8800	12,500
4d Tr Sed	450	1500	2500	5000	8800	12,600
Ambassador, 8-cyl.						
2d A-P Cabr	1150	3700	6200	12,400	21,700	31,000
2d DeL Brgm	500	1600	2700	5400	9500	13,500
4d Spl FBk	500	1650	2700	5400	9500	13,600
4d DeL FBk	500	1650	2750	5500	9600	13,700
4d Tr Sed	500	1650	2750	5500	9700	13,800
1942						
Ambassador 600, 6-cyl.						
2d Bus Cpe	450	1400	2350	4700	8200	11,700
2d Brgm	400	1250	2100	4200	7400	10,600
2d SS	400	1250	2100	4200	7400	10,500
4d SS	400	1250	2100	4200	7400	10,600
4d Tr Sed	400	1300	2150	4300	7500	10,700
Ambassador, 6-cyl.						
2d Bus Cpe	500	1550	2600	5200	9100	13,000
2d Brgm	450	1400	2350	4700	8300	11,800
2d SS	450	1400	2350	4700	8200	11,700
4d SS	450	1400	2350	4700	8300	11,800
4d Tr Sed	450	1450	2400	4800	8300	11,900
Ambassador, 8-cyl.						
2d Bus Cpe	450	1500	2500	5000	8800	12,500
2d Brgm	450	1450	2400	4800	8400	12,000
2d SS	450	1400	2350	4700	8300	11,800
4d SS	450	1450	2400	4800	8300	11,900
4d Tr Sed	450	1450	2400	4800	8400	12,000
1946						
600, 6-cyl.						
2d Brgm	400	1200	2000	4000	7100	10,100
4d Sed	400	1200	2000	4000	7000	10,000
4d Trk Sed	400	1250	2050	4100	7200	10,300
Ambassador, 6-cyl.						
2d Brgm	450	1400	2300	4600	8100	11,500
4d Sed	450	1400	2300	4600	8100	11,600
4d Trk Sed	450	1400	2350	4700	8200	11,700
4d Sub Sed	850	2750	4600	9200	16,100	23,000
1947						
600, 6-cyl.						
2d Brgm	400	1200	2000	4000	7100	10,100
4d Sed	400	1200	2000	4000	7000	10,000
4d Trk Sed	400	1250	2050	4100	7200	10,300
Ambassador, 6-cyl.						
2d Brgm	450	1400	2300	4600	8100	11,500
4d Sed	450	1400	2300	4600	8100	11,600
4d Trk Sed	450	1400	2350	4700	8200	11,700
4d Sub Sed	850	2750	4600	9200	16,100	23,000
1948						
600, 6-cyl.						
DeL Bus Cpe	450	1400	2350	4700	8300	11,800
4d Sup Sed	450	1150	1900	3850	6700	9600
4d Sup Trk Sed	450	1160	1950	3900	6800	9700
2d Sup Brgm	450	1160	1950	3900	6800	9700
4d Cus Sed	450	1170	1975	3900	6850	9800
4d Cus Trk Sed	450	1190	2000	3950	6900	9900
2d Cus Brgm	400	1200	2000	4000	7000	10,000
Ambassador, 6-cyl.						
4d Sed	400	1350	2250	4500	7800	11,200
4d Trk Sed	400	1350	2250	4500	7900	11,300
2d Brgm	400	1350	2250	4500	7900	11,300
4d Sub Sed	900	2900	4800	9600	16,800	24,000
Custom Ambassador, 6-cyl.						
4d Sed	450	1400	2300	4600	8100	11,500
4d Trk Sed	400	1300	2200	4400	7700	11,000
2d Brgm	450	1400	2300	4600	8100	11,500
2d Cabr	950	3000	5000	10,000	17,500	25,000
1949						
600 Super, 6-cyl.						
4d Sed	400	1300	2200	4400	7700	11,000
2d Sed	400	1350	2200	4400	7800	11,100
2d Brgm	400	1350	2250	4500	7800	11,200
600 Super Special, 6-cyl.						
4d Sed	400	1350	2200	4400	7800	11,100
2d Sed	400	1350	2250	4500	7800	11,200
2d Brgm	400	1350	2250	4500	7900	11,300
600 Custom, 6-cyl.						
4d Sed	400	1350	2250	4500	7900	11,300
2d Sed	450	1350	2300	4600	8000	11,400
2d Brgm	450	1400	2300	4600	8100	11,500
Ambassador Super, 6-cyl.						
4d Sed	450	1450	2400	4800	8500	12,100
2d Sed	450	1450	2450	4900	8500	12,200
2d Brgm	450	1500	2450	4900	8600	12,300
Ambassador Super Special, 6-cyl.						
4d Sed	450	1450	2450	4900	8500	12,200
2d Sed	450	1500	2450	4900	8600	12,300
2d Brgm	450	1500	2500	5000	8700	12,400
Ambassador Custom, 6-cyl.						
4d Sed	450	1500	2500	5000	8700	12,400
2d Sed	450	1500	2500	5000	8800	12,500
2d Brgm	450	1500	2500	5000	8800	12,600
1950						
Rambler Custom, 6-cyl.						
2d Conv Lan	550	1800	3000	6000	10,500	15,000
2d Sta Wag	450	1400	2300	4600	8100	11,500
Nash Super Statesman, 6-cyl.						
2d DeL Cpe	400	1350	2250	4500	7900	11,300
4d Sed	400	1350	2200	4400	7800	11,100
2d Sed	400	1350	2250	4500	7800	11,200
2d Clb Cpe	400	1350	2250	4500	7900	11,300
Nash Custom Statesman, 6-cyl.						
4d Sed	450	1350	2300	4600	8000	11,400
2d Sed	450	1400	2300	4600	8100	11,500
2d Clb Cpe	450	1400	2300	4600	8100	11,600
Ambassador, 6-cyl.						
4d Sed	450	1450	2400	4800	8400	12,000
2d Sed	450	1450	2450	4900	8500	12,200
2d Clb Cpe	450	1500	2450	4900	8600	12,300
Ambassador Custom, 6-cyl.						
4d Sed	450	1500	2500	5000	8700	12,400
2d Sed	450	1500	2500	5000	8800	12,500
2d Clb Cpe	450	1500	2500	5000	8800	12,600
1951						
Rambler, 6-cyl.						
2d Utl Wag	450	1400	2300	4600	8100	11,500
2d Sta Wag	450	1400	2350	4700	8200	11,700
2d Cus Clb Sed	450	1350	2300	4600	8000	11,400
2d Cus Conv	550	1800	3000	6000	10,500	15,000
2d Ctry Clb HT	500	1550	2600	5200	9100	13,000
2d Cus Sta Wag	450	1450	2400	4800	8400	12,000
Nash Statesman, 6-cyl.						
2d DeL Bus Cpe	450	1400	2300	4600	8100	11,500
4d Sup Sed	400	1350	2250	4500	7900	11,300
2d Sup	400	1350	2250	4500	7800	11,200
2d Sup Cpe	450	1400	2300	4600	8100	11,500
2d Cus Cpe	450	1400	2300	4600	8100	11,600
2d Cus	450	1400	2300	4600	8100	11,500
Ambassador, 6-cyl.						
4d Sup Sed	450	1450	2450	4900	8500	12,200
2d Sup	450	1450	2400	4800	8500	12,100
2d Sup Cpe	450	1500	2450	4900	8600	12,300
4d Cus Sed	450	1500	2500	5000	8700	12,400
2d Cus	450	1450	2450	4900	8500	12,200
2d Cus Cpe	450	1500	2450	4900	8600	12,300

Nash-Healey	6	5	4	3	2	1
Spt Rds	1200	3850	6400	12,800	22,400	32,000
1952-1953						
Rambler, 6-cyl.						
2d Utl Wag	450	1400	2300	4600	8100	11,500
2d Sta Wag	450	1400	2350	4700	8200	11,700
2d Cus Clb Sed	450	1400	2300	4600	8100	11,500
2d Cus Conv	550	1800	3000	6000	10,500	15,000
2d Cus Ctry Clb HT	500	1550	2600	5200	9100	13,000
2d Cus Sta Wag	450	1450	2400	4800	8400	12,000
Nash Statesman, 6-cyl.						
(Add 10 percent for Custom)						
2d Sed	450	1400	2350	4700	8200	11,700
4d Sed	450	1400	2300	4600	8100	11,600
2d Cus Ctry Clb	550	1700	2800	5600	9800	14,000
Ambassador, 6-cyl.						
(Add 10 percent for Custom)						
2d Sed	450	1450	2400	4800	8400	12,000
4d Sed	450	1450	2400	4800	8400	12,000
2d Cus Ctry Clb	550	1800	3000	6000	10,500	15,000
Nash-Healey						
2d Cpe (1953 only)	1350	4300	7200	14,400	25,200	36,000
2d Spt Rds	1500	4800	8000	16,000	28,000	40,000
1954						
Rambler, 6-cyl.						
2d DeL Clb Sed	450	1400	2300	4600	8100	11,500
2d Sup Clb Sed	450	1400	2300	4600	8100	11,600
2d Sup Ctry Clb HT	450	1500	2500	5000	8800	12,500
2d Sup Suburban Sta Wag	450	1400	2350	4700	8300	11,800
4d Sup Sed (108")	450	1400	2300	4600	8100	11,600
2d Cus Ctry Clb HT	500	1600	2700	5400	9500	13,500
2d Cus Conv	600	1900	3200	6400	11,200	16,000
2d Cus Sta Wag	450	1500	2500	5000	8800	12,500
4d Cus Sed (108")	450	1400	2350	4700	8200	11,700
4d Cus Wag (108)	450	1500	2500	5000	8800	12,600
2d Cus Wag (108")	500	1550	2600	5200	9100	13,000
Nash Statesman, 6-cyl.						
4d Sup Sed	400	1300	2200	4400	7700	11,000
2d Sup Sed	400	1350	2200	4400	7800	11,100
4d Cus Sed	400	1350	2250	4500	7800	11,200
2d Cus Ctry Clb HT	550	1800	3000	6000	10,500	15,000
Nash Ambassador, 6-cyl.						
(Add 5 percent for LeMans option).						
4d Sup Sed	450	1450	2450	4900	8500	12,200
2d Sup Sed	450	1500	2450	4900	8600	12,300
4d Cus Sed	450	1500	2500	5000	8800	12,500
2d Cus Ctry Clb HT	550	1800	3000	6000	10,500	15,000
Nash-Healey						
2d Cpe	1400	4500	7500	15,000	26,300	37,500
1955						
Rambler, 6-cyl.						
2d DeL Clb Sed	450	1400	2300	4600	8100	11,500
2d DeL Bus Sed	450	1350	2300	4600	8000	11,400
4d DeL Sed (108")	450	1400	2300	4600	8100	11,600
2d Sup Clb Sed	450	1400	2300	4600	8100	11,600
2d Sup Sta Wag	450	1350	2300	4600	8000	11,400
4d Sup Sed (108")	450	1400	2300	4600	8100	11,600
4d Sup Crs Ctry (108")	450	1450	2400	4800	8400	12,000
2d Cus Ctry Clb HT	550	1700	2800	5600	9800	14,000
4d Cus Sed (108")	450	1400	2350	4700	8200	11,700
4d Cus Crs Ctry (108")	500	1550	2600	5200	9100	13,000
Nash Statesman, 6-cyl.						
4d Sup Sed	450	1400	2300	4600	8100	11,500
4d Cus Sed	450	1400	2300	4600	8100	11,600
2d Cus Ctry Clb	550	1750	2900	5800	10,200	14,500
Nash Ambassador, 6-cyl.						
4d Sup Sed	450	1500	2500	5000	8800	12,600
4d Cus Sed	500	1500	2550	5100	8900	12,700
2d Cus Ctry Clb	600	1900	3200	6400	11,200	16,000
Nash Ambassador, 8-cyl.						
4d Sup Sed	500	1500	2550	5100	8900	12,700
4d Cus Sed	500	1550	2600	5200	9100	13,000
2d Cus Ctry Clb	600	1900	3200	6400	11,200	16,000
1956						
Rambler, 6-cyl.						
4d DeL Sed	400	1200	2050	4100	7100	10,200
4d Sup Sed	400	1250	2050	4100	7200	10,300
4d Sup Crs Ctry	400	1350	2200	4400	7800	11,100
4d Cus Sed	400	1350	2250	4500	7800	11,200
4d Cus HT	450	1450	2400	4800	8400	12,000
4d Cus Crs Ctry	450	1400	2300	4600	8100	11,600
4d HT Wag	450	1450	2400	4800	8400	12,000
Nash Statesman, 6-cyl.						
4d Sup Sed	450	1400	2300	4600	8100	11,500
Nash Ambassador, 6-cyl.						
4d Sup Sed	450	1450	2400	4800	8400	12,000
Nash Ambassador, 8-cyl.						
4d Sup Sed	450	1450	2450	4900	8500	12,200
4d Cus Sed	450	1500	2500	5000	8800	12,500
2d Cus HT	650	2050	3400	6800	11,900	17,000
1957						
Rambler, 6-cyl.						
4d DeL Sed	450	1120	1875	3750	6500	9300
4d Sup Sed	450	1140	1900	3800	6650	9500
4d Sup HT	400	1200	2000	4000	7000	10,000
4d Sup Crs Ctry	400	1200	2000	4000	7100	10,100
4d Cus Sed	450	1130	1900	3800	6600	9400
4d Cus Crs Ctry	400	1200	2050	4100	7100	10,200
Rambler, 8-cyl.						
4d Sup Sed	450	1140	1900	3800	6650	9500
4d Sup Crs Ctry Wag	400	1200	2050	4100	7100	10,200
4d Cus Sed	450	1150	1900	3850	6700	9600
4d Cus HT	400	1250	2050	4100	7200	10,300
4d Cus Crs Ctry Wag	400	1250	2100	4200	7300	10,400
4d Cus HT Crs Ctry	400	1300	2200	4400	7700	11,000
Rebel, 8-cyl.						
4d HT	500	1550	2600	5200	9100	13,000
Nash Ambassador, 8-cyl.						
4d Sup Sed	450	1400	2350	4700	8200	11,700
2d Sup HT	600	1900	3200	6400	11,200	16,000
4d Cus Sed	450	1450	2400	4800	8400	12,000
2d Cus HT	650	2050	3400	6800	11,900	17,000

AMC

1958-1959	6	5	4	3	2	1
American DeLuxe, 6-cyl.						
2d Sed	350	860	1450	2900	5050	7200
4d Sta Wag (1959 only)	350	870	1450	2900	5100	7300
American Super, 6-cyl.						
2d Sed	350	870	1450	2900	5100	7300
4d Sta Wag (1959 only)	350	880	1500	2950	5180	7400
Rambler DeLuxe, 6-cyl.						
4d Sed	350	860	1450	2900	5050	7200
4d Sta Wag	350	870	1450	2900	5100	7300
Rambler Super, 6-cyl.						
4d Sed	350	870	1450	2900	5100	7300
4d HT	350	900	1500	3000	5250	7500
4d Sta Wag	350	880	1500	2950	5180	7400
Rambler Custom, 6-cyl.						
4d Sed	350	950	1550	3100	5400	7700
4d HT	350	975	1600	3200	5500	7900
4d Sta Wag	350	900	1500	3000	5250	7500
Rebel Super V-8						
4d Sed DeL (1958 only)	350	950	1550	3100	5400	7700
4d Sed	350	950	1550	3150	5450	7800
4d Sta Wag	350	975	1600	3200	5500	7900
Rebel Custom, V-8						
4d Sed	350	975	1600	3200	5500	7900
4d HT	350	975	1600	3200	5600	8000
4d Sta Wag	350	975	1600	3200	5600	8000
Ambassador Super, V-8						
4d Sed	350	950	1550	3100	5400	7700
4d Sta Wag	350	950	1550	3150	5450	7800
Ambassador Custom, V-8						
4d Sed	350	950	1550	3150	5450	7800
4d Ht	350	975	1600	3200	5500	7900
4d Sta Wag	350	975	1600	3200	5500	7900
4d HT Sta Wag	350	975	1600	3250	5700	8100
1960						
American DeLuxe, 6-cyl.						
2d Sed	350	850	1450	2850	4970	7100
4d Sed	350	840	1400	2800	4900	7000
4d Sta Wag	350	860	1450	2900	5050	7200
American Super, 6-cyl.						
2d Sed	350	860	1450	2900	5050	7200
4d Sed	350	850	1450	2850	4970	7100
4d Sta Wag	350	870	1450	2900	5100	7300
American Custom, 6-cyl.						
2d Sed	350	870	1450	2900	5100	7300
4d Sed	350	860	1450	2900	5050	7200
4d Sta Wag	350	880	1500	2950	5180	7400
Rambler DeLuxe, 6-cyl.						
4d Sed	350	850	1450	2850	4970	7100
4d Sta Wag	350	860	1450	2900	5050	7200
Rambler Super, 6-cyl.						
4d Sed	350	860	1450	2900	5050	7200
4d 6P Sta Wag	350	870	1450	2900	5100	7300
4d 8P Sta Wag	350	880	1500	2950	5180	7400
Rambler Custom, 6-cyl.						
4d Sed	350	870	1450	2900	5100	7300
4d HT	350	880	1500	2950	5180	7400
4d 6P Sta Wag	350	880	1500	2950	5180	7400
4d 8P Sta Wag	350	900	1500	3000	5250	7500
Rebel Super, V-8						
Sed	350	880	1500	2950	5180	7400
4d 6P Sta Wag	350	900	1500	3000	5250	7500
4d 8P Sta Wag	350	950	1500	3050	5300	7600
Rebel Custom, V-8						
4d Sed	350	900	1500	3000	5250	7500
4d HT	350	950	1500	3050	5300	7600
4d 6P Sta Wag	350	950	1500	3050	5300	7600
4d 8P Sta Wag	350	950	1550	3100	5400	7700
Ambassador Super, V-8						
4d Sed	350	950	1500	3050	5300	7600
4d 6P Sta Wag	350	950	1550	3100	5400	7700
4d 8P Sta Wag	350	950	1550	3150	5450	7800
Ambassador Custom, V-8						
4d Sed	350	950	1550	3100	5400	7700
4d HT	350	975	1600	3200	5500	7900
6P Sta Wag	350	950	1550	3150	5450	7800
4d HT Sta Wag	350	975	1600	3200	5600	8000
4d 8P Sta Wag	350	975	1600	3200	5500	7900
1961						
American						
4d DeL Sed	350	840	1400	2800	4900	7000
2d DeL Sed	350	850	1450	2850	4970	7100
4d DeL Sta Wag	350	860	1450	2900	5050	7200
2d DeL Sta Wag	350	850	1450	2850	4970	7100
4d Sup Sed	350	850	1450	2850	4970	7100
2d Sup Sed	350	860	1450	2900	5050	7200
4d Sup Sta Wag	350	870	1450	2900	5100	7300
2d Sup Sta Wag	350	850	1450	2850	4970	7100
4d Cus Sed	350	850	1450	2850	4970	7100
2d Cus Sed	350	860	1450	2900	5050	7200
2d Cus Conv	450	1080	1800	3600	6300	9000
4d Cus Sta Wag	350	860	1450	2900	5050	7200
2d Cus Sta Wag	350	870	1450	2900	5100	7300
4d 400 Sed	350	860	1450	2900	5050	7200
2d 400 Conv	950	1100	1850	3700	6450	9200
Rambler Classic						
4d DeL Sed	350	840	1400	2800	4900	7000
4d DeL Sta Wag	350	850	1450	2850	4970	7100
4d Sup Sed	350	850	1450	2850	4970	7100
4d Sup Sta Wag	350	860	1450	2900	5050	7200
4d Cus Sed	350	860	1450	2900	5050	7200
4d Cus Sta Wag	350	870	1450	2900	5100	7300
4d 400 Sed	350	870	1450	2900	5100	7300
NOTE: Add 5 percent for V-8.						
Ambassador						
4d DeL Sed	350	850	1450	2850	4970	7100
4d Sup Sed	350	860	1450	2900	5050	7200
5d Sup Sta Wag	350	870	1450	2900	5100	7300
4d Sup Sta Wag	350	860	1450	2900	5050	7200
4d Cus Sed	350	870	1450	2900	5100	7300
5d Cus Sta Wag	350	900	1500	3000	5250	7500
4d Cus Sta Wag	350	880	1500	2950	5180	7400
4d 400 Sed	350	880	1500	2950	5180	7400
1962						
American						
4d DeL Sed	200	720	1200	2400	4200	6000

	6	5	4	3	2	1
2d DeL Sed	200	730	1250	2450	4270	6100
4d DeL Sta Wag	200	730	1250	2450	4270	6100
2d DeL Sta Wag	200	720	1200	2400	4200	6000
4d Cus Sed	200	730	1250	2450	4270	6100
2d Cus Sed	200	730	1250	2450	4270	6100
4d Cus Sta Wag	200	745	1250	2500	4340	6200
2d Cus Sta Wag	200	730	1250	2450	4270	6100
4d 400	200	730	1250	2450	4270	6100
2d 400	200	745	1250	2500	4340	6200
2d 400 Conv	950	1100	1850	3700	6450	9200
4d 400 Sta Wag	350	780	1300	2600	4550	6500
Classic						
4d DeL Sed	200	720	1200	2400	4200	6000
2d DeL	200	730	1250	2450	4270	6100
4d DeL Sta Wag	200	745	1250	2500	4340	6200
4d Cus Sed	200	750	1275	2500	4400	6300
2d Cus	350	770	1300	2550	4480	6400
4d Cus Sta Wag	200	750	1275	2500	4400	6300
5d Cus Sta Wag	350	770	1300	2550	4480	6400
4d 400 Sed	350	770	1300	2550	4480	6400
2d 400	350	780	1300	2600	4550	6500
4d 400 Sta Wag	350	790	1350	2650	4620	6600
NOTE: Add 5 percent for V-8.						
Ambassador						
4d Cus Sed	200	745	1250	2500	4340	6200
2d Cus Sed	200	750	1275	2500	4400	6300
4d Cus Sta Wag	350	800	1350	2700	4700	6700
4d 400 Sed	350	780	1300	2600	4550	6500
2d 400 Sed	350	790	1350	2650	4620	6600
4d 400 Sta Wag	350	800	1350	2700	4700	6700
5d 400 Sta Wag	350	820	1400	2700	4760	6800
1963						
American						
4d 220 Sed	200	670	1150	2250	3920	5600
2d 220 Sed	200	685	1150	2300	3990	5700
4d 220 Bus Sed	200	660	1100	2200	3850	5500
4d 220 Sta Wag	200	685	1150	2300	3990	5700
2 dr 220 Sta Wag	200	670	1150	2250	3920	5600
4d 330 Sed	200	685	1150	2300	3990	5700
2d 330 Sed	200	670	1150	2250	3920	5600
4d 330 Sta Wag	200	700	1200	2350	4130	5900
2d 330 Sta Wag	200	720	1200	2400	4200	6000
4d 440 Sed	200	700	1200	2350	4130	5900
2d 440 Sed	200	720	1200	2400	4200	6000
2d 440 HT	200	750	1275	2500	4400	6300
2d 440-H HT	350	840	1400	2800	4900	7000
2d 440 Conv	350	1020	1700	3400	5950	8500
4d 440 Sta Wag	200	730	1250	2450	4270	6100
Classic						
4d 550 Sed	200	660	1100	2200	3850	5500
2d 550 Sed	200	670	1150	2250	3920	5600
4d 550 Sta Wag	200	660	1100	2200	3850	5500
4d 660 Sed	200	660	1100	2200	3850	5500
2d 660 Sed	200	670	1150	2250	3920	5600
4d 660 Sta Wag	200	685	1150	2300	3990	5700
4d 770 Sed	200	700	1200	2350	4130	5900
2d 770 Sed	200	670	1200	2300	4060	5800
4d 770 Sta Wag	200	730	1250	2450	4270	6100
NOTE: Add 5 percent for V-8 models.						
Ambassador						
4d 800 Sed	200	670	1200	2300	4060	5800
2d 800 Sed	200	700	1200	2350	4130	5900
4d 880 Sta Wag	200	720	1200	2400	4200	6000
4d 880 Sed	200	700	1200	2350	4130	5900
2d 880 Sed	200	720	1200	2400	4200	6000
4d 880 Sta Wag	200	730	1250	2450	4270	6100
4d 990 Sed	200	720	1200	2400	4200	6000
2d 990 Sed	200	730	1250	2450	4270	6100
5d 990 Sta Wag	200	750	1275	2500	4400	6300
4d 990 Sta Wag	200	745	1250	2500	4340	6200
1964						
American						
4d 220 Sed	200	670	1150	2250	3920	5600
2d 220	200	685	1150	2300	3990	5700
4d 220 Sta Wag	200	670	1200	2300	4060	5800
4d 330 Sed	200	670	1200	2300	4060	5800
2d 330	200	700	1200	2350	4130	5900
4d 330 Sta Wag	200	700	1200	2350	4130	5900
4d 440 Sed	200	670	1200	2300	4060	5800
2d 440 HT	200	750	1275	2500	4400	6300
2d 440-H HT	350	840	1400	2800	4900	7000
2d Conv	350	1020	1700	3400	5950	8500
Classic						
4d 550 Sed	200	660	1100	2200	3850	5500
2d 550	200	670	1150	2250	3920	5600
4d 550 Sta Wag	200	685	1150	2300	3990	5700
4d 660 Sed	200	670	1150	2250	3920	5600
2d 660	200	685	1150	2300	3990	5700
4d 660 Sta Wag	200	670	1200	2300	4060	5800
4d 770 Sed	200	685	1150	2300	3990	5700
2d 770	200	670	1200	2300	4060	5800
2d 770 Ht	350	870	1450	2900	5100	7300
2d 770 Typhoon HT	350	1020	1700	3400	5950	8500
4d 770 Sta Wag	200	670	1200	2300	4060	5800
NOTE: Add 5 percent for V-8 models.						
Ambassador						
4d Sed	200	750	1275	2500	4400	6300
2d HT	350	820	1400	2700	4760	6800
4d 990H	350	840	1400	2800	4900	7000
4d Sta Wag	200	720	1200	2400	4200	6000
1965						
American						
4d 220 Sed	200	685	1150	2300	3990	5700
2d 220	200	670	1200	2300	4060	5800
4d 220 Sta Wag	200	670	1200	2300	4060	5800
4d 330 Sed	200	670	1200	2300	4060	5800
2 dr 330	200	720	1200	2400	4200	6000
4d 330 Sta Wag	200	730	1250	2450	4270	6100
4d 440 Sed	200	720	1200	2400	4200	6000
2d 440 HT	350	840	1400	2800	4900	7000
2d 440-H HT	350	860	1450	2900	5050	7200
2d Conv	350	1040	1700	3450	6000	8600
Classic						
4d 550 Sed	200	670	1150	2250	3920	5600
2d 550	200	685	1150	2300	3990	5700
4d 550 Sta Wag	200	685	1150	2300	3990	5700
4d 660 Sed	200	700	1200	2350	4130	5900
2d 660	200	720	1200	2400	4200	6000

	6	5	4	3	2	1
4d 660 Sta Wag	200	730	1250	2450	4270	6100
4d 770 Sed	200	700	1200	2350	4130	5900
2d 770 HT	200	745	1250	2500	4340	6200
2d 770-H HT	350	870	1450	2900	5100	7300
2d 770 Conv	350	1040	1750	3500	6100	8700
4d 770 Sta Wag	200	720	1200	2400	4200	6000
NOTE: Add 5 percent for V-8 models.						
Marlin						
2d FBk	350	900	1500	3000	5250	7500
Ambassador						
4d 880 Sed	200	720	1200	2400	4200	6000
2d 880	200	730	1250	2450	4270	6100
4d 880 Sta Wag	200	745	1250	2500	4340	6200
4d 990 Sed	200	730	1250	2450	4270	6100
2d 990 HT	200	750	1275	2500	4400	6300
2d 990-H HT	350	880	1500	2950	5180	7400
2d Conv	450	1050	1800	3600	6200	8900
4d Sta Wag	200	745	1250	2500	4340	6200
Marlin, V-8						
2d FBk	350	860	1450	2900	5050	7200
1966						
American						
4d 220 Sed	200	660	1100	2200	3850	5500
2d 220 Sed	200	670	1150	2250	3920	5600
4d 220 Wag	200	685	1150	2300	3990	5700
4d 440 Sed	200	670	1200	2300	4060	5800
2d 440 Sed	200	700	1200	2350	4130	5900
2d 440 Conv	200	670	1200	2300	4060	5800
4d 440 Wag	200	685	1150	2300	3990	5700
2d 440 HT	350	780	1300	2600	4550	6500
2d Rogue HT	350	900	1500	3000	5250	7500
Classic						
4d 550 Sed	200	670	1150	2250	3920	5600
2d 550 Sed	200	670	1150	2250	3920	5600
4d 550 Sta Wag	200	685	1150	2300	3990	5700
4d 770 Sed	200	670	1200	2300	4060	5800
2d 770 HT	200	745	1250	2500	4340	6200
2d 770 Conv	350	900	1500	3000	5250	7500
4d 770 Sta Wag	200	685	1150	2300	3990	5700
Rebel						
2d HT	350	900	1500	3000	5250	7500
Marlin						
2d FBk Cpe	350	900	1500	3000	5250	7500
Ambassador						
4d 880 Sed	200	700	1200	2350	4130	5900
2d 880 Sed	200	720	1200	2400	4200	6000
4d 880 Sta Wag	200	745	1250	2500	4340	6200
4d 990 Sed	200	730	1250	2450	4270	6100
2d 990 HT	350	840	1400	2800	4900	7000
2d 990 Conv	450	1080	1800	3600	6300	9000
4d 990 Sta Wag	200	700	1200	2350	4130	5900
DPL (Diplomat)						
2d DPL HT	350	950	1550	3150	5450	7800
1967						
American 220						
4d Sed	200	660	1100	2200	3850	5500
2d Sed	200	660	1100	2200	3850	5500
4d Sta Wag	200	670	1150	2250	3920	5600
American 440						
4d Sed	200	670	1150	2250	3920	5600
2d Sed	200	670	1150	2250	3920	5600
2d HT	200	720	1200	2400	4200	6000
4d Sta Wag	200	685	1150	2300	3990	5700
American Rogue						
2d HT	350	950	1500	3050	5300	7600
2d Conv	350	1020	1700	3400	5950	8500
Rebel 550						
4d Sed	200	660	1100	2200	3850	5500
2d Sed	200	660	1100	2200	3850	5500
4d Sta Wag	200	670	1150	2250	3920	5600
Rebel 770						
4d Sed	200	670	1150	2250	3920	5600
2d HT	200	720	1200	2400	4200	6000
4d Sta Wag	200	670	1150	2250	3920	5600
Rebel SST						
2d HT	200	745	1250	2500	4340	6200
2d Conv	350	1020	1700	3400	5950	8500
Rambler Marlin						
2d FBk Cpe	350	900	1500	3000	5250	7500
Ambassador 880						
4d Sed	200	685	1150	2300	3990	5700
2d Sed	200	685	1150	2300	3990	5700
4d Sta Wag	200	670	1200	2300	4060	5800
Ambassador 990						
4d Sed	200	720	1200	2400	4200	6000
2d HT	350	820	1400	2700	4760	6800
4d Sta Wag	200	730	1250	2450	4270	6100
Ambassador DPL						
2d HT	350	900	1500	3000	5250	7500
2d Conv	450	1080	1800	3600	6300	9000
1968						
American 220						
4d Sed	200	685	1150	2300	3990	5700
2d Sed	200	685	1150	2300	3990	5700
American 440						
4d Sed	200	670	1200	2300	4060	5800
4d Sta Wag	200	700	1200	2350	4130	5900
Rogue						
2d HT	350	975	1600	3200	5600	8000
Rebel 550						
4d Sed	200	685	1150	2300	3990	5700
2d Conv	350	1040	1750	3500	6100	8700
4d Sta Wag	200	660	1100	2200	3850	5500
2d HT	200	745	1250	2500	4340	6200
Rebel 770						
4d Sed	200	685	1150	2300	3990	5700
4d Sta Wag	200	670	1150	2250	3920	5600
2d HT	350	770	1300	2550	4480	6400
Rebel SST						
2d Conv	450	1050	1800	3600	6200	8900
2d HT	350	790	1350	2650	4620	6600
Ambassador						
4d Sed	200	670	1200	2300	4060	5800
2d HT	350	780	1300	2600	4550	6500
Ambassador DPL						
4d Sed	200	720	1200	2400	4200	6000
2d HT	350	800	1350	2700	4700	6700
4d Sta Wag	200	730	1250	2450	4270	6100

Ambassador SST	6	5	4	3	2	1
4d Sed	200	720	1200	2400	4200	6000
2d HT	350	840	1400	2800	4900	7000
Javelin						
2d FBk	350	1020	1700	3400	5950	8500
Javelin SST						
2d FsBk	400	1250	2100	4200	7400	10,500
NOTE: Add 20 percent for GO pkg. Add 30 percent for Big Bad pkg.						
AMX						
2d FBk	550	1700	2800	5600	9800	14,000
NOTE: Add 25 percent for Craig Breedlove Edit.						
1969						
Rambler						
4d Sed	200	670	1150	2250	3920	5600
2d Sed	200	670	1150	2250	3920	5600
Rambler 440						
4d Sed	200	685	1150	2300	3990	5700
2d Sed	200	685	1150	2300	3990	5700
Rambler Rogue						
2d HT	350	975	1600	3200	5600	8000
Rambler Hurst S/C						
2d HT	500	1550	2600	5200	9100	13,000
Rebel						
4d Sed	200	660	1100	2200	3850	5500
2d HT	200	720	1200	2400	4200	6000
4d Sta Wag	200	670	1150	2250	3920	5600
Rebel SST						
4d Sed	200	685	1150	2300	3990	5700
2d HT	200	745	1250	2500	4340	6200
4d Sta Wag	200	685	1150	2300	3990	5700
AMX						
2d FBk Cpe	550	1700	2800	5600	9800	14,000
NOTE: Add 25 percent for Big Bad Pkg.						
Javelin						
2d FBk Cpe	450	1080	1800	3600	6300	9000
Javelin SST						
2d FBk Cpe	400	1250	2100	4200	7400	10,500
NOTE: Add 20 percent for GO Pkg. Add 30 percent for Big Bad Pkg.						
Ambassador						
4d Sed	200	670	1200	2300	4060	5800
Ambassador DPL						
4d Sed	200	720	1200	2400	4200	6000
4d Sta Wag	200	720	1200	2400	4200	6000
2d HT	200	745	1250	2500	4340	6200
Ambassador SST						
4d Sed	200	670	1200	2300	4060	5800
2d HT	200	750	1275	2500	4400	6300
1970						
Hornet						
4d Sed	200	675	1000	2000	3500	5000
2d Sed	200	675	1000	2000	3500	5000
Hornet SST						
4d Sed	200	700	1050	2050	3600	5100
2d Sed	200	700	1050	2050	3600	5100
Rebel						
4d Sed	200	700	1050	2100	3650	5200
2d HT	200	720	1200	2400	4200	6000
4d Sta Wag	200	670	1150	2250	3920	5600
Rebel SST						
4d Sed	200	700	1075	2150	3700	5300
2d HT	350	780	1300	2600	4550	6500
4d Sta Wag	200	700	1050	2100	3650	5200
Rebel 'Machine'						
2d HT	450	1500	2500	5000	8800	12,500
AMX						
2d FBk Cpe	550	1700	2800	5600	9800	14,000
Gremlin						
2d Comm	200	700	1075	2150	3700	5300
2d Sed	200	650	1100	2150	3780	5400
Javelin						
2d FBk Cpe	350	975	1600	3200	5600	8000
Javelin SST						
2d FBk Cpe	450	1130	1900	3800	6600	9400
NOTE: Add 20 percent for GO pkg. Add 30 percent for Big Bad pkg.						
'Trans Am'						
2d FBk Cpe	400	1200	2000	4000	7000	10,000
'Mark Donohue'						
2d FBk Cpe	450	1140	1900	3800	6650	9500
Ambassador						
4d Sed	200	700	1075	2150	3700	5300
Ambassador DPL						
4d Sed	200	650	1100	2150	3780	5400
2d HT	200	660	1100	2200	3850	5500
4d Sta Wag	200	700	1075	2150	3700	5300
Ambassador SST						
4d Sed	200	660	1100	2200	3850	5500
2d HT	200	670	1150	2250	3920	5600
4d Sta Wag	200	650	1100	2150	3780	5400
1971						
Gremlin						
2d Sed	200	675	1000	2000	3500	5000
4d Sed	200	675	1000	2000	3500	5000
Hornet						
2d Sed	200	700	1050	2050	3600	5100
4d Sed	200	700	1050	2050	3600	5100
Hornet SST						
2d Sed	200	700	1050	2100	3650	5200
4d Sed	200	700	1050	2100	3650	5200
Hornet SC/360						
2d HT	350	975	1600	3200	5600	8000
Javelin						
2d HT	200	660	1100	2200	3850	5500
2d SST HT	200	720	1200	2400	4200	6000
NOTE: Add 10 percent for 401 V-8.						
Javelin AMX						
2d HT	350	900	1500	3000	5250	7500
NOTE: Add 15 percent for GO Pkg.						
Matador						
4d Sed	200	700	1050	2050	3600	5100
2d HT	200	660	1100	2200	3850	5500
4d Sta Wag	200	700	1050	2100	3650	5200
Ambassador DPL						
4d Sed	200	700	1050	2050	3600	5100
Ambassador SST						
4d Sed	200	700	1050	2100	3650	5200

	6	5	4	3	2	1
2d HT	200	650	1100	2150	3780	5400
4d Sta Wag	200	700	1075	2150	3700	5300
NOTE: Add 10 percent to Ambassador SST for Broughams.						
1972						
Hornet SST						
2d Sed	150	500	800	1600	2800	4000
4d Sed	150	550	850	1650	2900	4100
4d Sta Wag	150	550	850	1675	2950	4200
2d Gucci	200	675	1000	2000	3500	5000
4d DeL Wag	150	575	875	1700	3000	4300
4d 'X' Wag	150	550	850	1675	2950	4200
Matador						
4d Sed	150	550	850	1675	2950	4200
2d HT	150	575	900	1750	3100	4400
4d Sta Wag	150	575	875	1700	3000	4300
Gremlin						
2d Sed	150	550	850	1650	2900	4100
2d 'X' Sed	200	675	1000	2000	3500	5000
Javelin						
2d SST	200	675	1000	2000	3500	5000
2d AMX	200	720	1200	2400	4200	6000
2d Go '360'	350	840	1400	2800	4900	7000
2d Go '401'	350	975	1600	3200	5500	7900
2d Cardin	350	820	1400	2700	4760	6800
NOTE: Add 20 percent for 401 V-8. Add 25 percent for 401 Police Special V-8. Add 30 percent for GO Pkg.						
Ambassador SST						
4d Sed	150	550	850	1675	2950	4200
2d HT	150	575	900	1750	3100	4400
4d Sta Wag	150	575	875	1700	3000	4300
Ambassador Brougham						
NOTE: Add 10 percent to SST prices for Brougham.						
Gremlin V8						
2d	150	600	950	1850	3200	4600
Hornet V8						
2d	150	575	900	1750	3100	4400
4d	150	650	975	1950	3350	4800
2d HBk	150	600	900	1800	3150	4500
4d Sta Wag	150	575	900	1750	3100	4400
AMX V8						
2d HT	350	1000	1650	3300	5750	8200
NOTE: Add 15 percent for GO Pkg.						
Matador V8						
4d Sed	150	550	850	1675	2950	4200
2d HT	150	575	875	1700	3000	4300
Sta Wag	150	550	850	1675	2950	4200
Ambassador Brgm V8						
4d Sed	150	575	875	1700	3000	4300
2d HT	150	475	775	1500	2650	3800
4d Sta Wag	150	575	875	1700	3000	4300
1973						
Gremlin V8						
2d	150	600	900	1800	3150	4500
Hornet V8						
2d	150	500	800	1550	2700	3900
4d	150	475	775	1500	2650	3800
2d 2d HBk	150	500	800	1600	2800	4000
4d Sta Wag	150	500	800	1550	2700	3900
Javelin V8						
2d HT	200	675	1000	2000	3500	5000
AMX V8						
2d HT	350	975	1600	3200	5600	8000
Matador V8						
4d Sed	150	475	750	1475	2600	3700
2d HT	150	475	775	1500	2650	3800
4d Sta Wag	150	475	750	1475	2600	3700
Ambassador Brgm V8						
4d Sed	150	475	775	1500	2650	3800
2d HT	150	500	800	1550	2700	3900
4d Sta Wag	150	475	775	1500	2650	3800
1974						
Gremlin V8						
2d Sed	150	600	900	1800	3150	4500
Hornet						
4d Sed	125	400	700	1375	2400	3400
2d Sed	125	450	700	1400	2450	3500
2d HBk	125	450	750	1450	2500	3600
4d Sta Wag	125	450	700	1400	2450	3500
Javelin						
2d FBk	150	550	850	1675	2950	4200
Javelin AMX						
2d FBk	350	780	1300	2600	4550	6500
Matador						
4d Sed	125	380	650	1300	2250	3200
2d Sed	125	450	750	1450	2500	3600
4d Sta Wag	125	400	675	1350	2300	3300
Matador Brougham						
2d Cpe	150	475	750	1475	2600	3700
Matador 'X'						
2d Cpe	150	475	775	1500	2650	3800
Ambassador Brougham						
4d Sed	125	400	675	1350	2300	3300
4d Sta Wag	125	400	700	1375	2400	3400
NOTE: Add 10 percent for Oleg Cassini coupe. Add 12 percent for 'Go-Package'.						
1975						
Gremlin						
2d Sed	150	475	775	1500	2650	3800
Hornet						
4d Sed	125	450	700	1400	2450	3500
2d Sed	125	400	700	1375	2400	3400
2d HBk	125	450	700	1400	2450	3500
4d Sta Wag	125	450	700	1400	2450	3500
Pacer						
2d Sed	150	500	800	1550	2700	3900
Matador						
4d Sed	125	400	700	1375	2400	3400
2d Cpe	125	450	750	1450	2500	3600
4d Sta Wag	125	450	700	1400	2450	3500
1976						
Gremlin, V-8						
2d Sed	125	450	700	1400	2450	3500
2d Cus Sed	150	475	775	1500	2650	3800
Hornet, V-8						
4d Sed	125	370	650	1250	2200	3100
2d Sed	100	360	600	1200	2100	3000
2d HBk	125	380	650	1300	2250	3200

	6	5	4	3	2	1
4d Sptabt	125	400	675	1350	2300	3300
Pacer, 6-cyl.						
2d Sed	125	450	700	1400	2450	3500
Matador, V-8						
4d Sed	100	360	600	1200	2100	3000
2d Cpe	125	380	650	1300	2250	3200
4d Sta Wag	125	370	650	1250	2200	3100

NOTE: Deduct 5 percent for 6 cylinder.

1977

	6	5	4	3	2	1
Gremlin, V-8						
2d Sed	150	475	750	1475	2600	3700
2d Cus Sed	150	475	775	1500	2650	3800
Hornet, V-8						
4d Sed	125	380	650	1300	2250	3200
2d Sed	125	370	650	1250	2200	3100
2d HBk	125	400	675	1350	2300	3300
4d Sta Wag	125	400	700	1375	2400	3400
Pacer, 6-cyl.						
2d Sed	125	450	750	1450	2500	3600
4d Sta Wag	150	475	750	1475	2600	3700
Matador, V-8						
4d Sed	125	370	650	1250	2200	3100
2d Cpe	125	400	675	1350	2300	3300
4d Sta Wag	125	380	650	1300	2250	3200

NOTE: Deduct 5 percent for 6 cylinder.
Add 10 percent for AMX package.

1978

	6	5	4	3	2	1
Gremlin						
2d Sed	125	400	700	1375	2400	3400
2d Cus Sed	125	450	700	1400	2450	3500
Concord						
4d Sed	100	350	600	1150	2000	2900
2d Sed	100	330	575	1150	1950	2800
2d HBk	100	360	600	1200	2100	3000
4d Sta Wag	125	370	650	1250	2200	3100
Pacer						
2 dr Hatch	125	400	675	1350	2300	3300
4d Sta Wag	125	400	700	1375	2400	3400
AMX						
2 dr Hatch	125	450	750	1450	2500	3600
Matador						
4d Sed	100	330	575	1150	1950	2800
2d Cpe	100	360	600	1200	2100	3000
4d Sta Wag	100	350	600	1150	2000	2900

1979

	6	5	4	3	2	1
Spirit, 6-cyl.						
2d HBk	125	450	700	1400	2450	3500
2d Sed	125	400	700	1375	2400	3400
Spirit DL, 6-cyl.						
2d HBk	125	450	750	1450	2500	3600
2d Sed	125	450	700	1400	2450	3500
Spirit Limited, 6-cyl.						
2d HBk	150	475	750	1475	2600	3700
2d Sed	125	450	750	1450	2500	3600

NOTE: Deduct 5 percent for 4-cyl.

	6	5	4	3	2	1
Concord, V-8						
4d Sed	125	370	650	1250	2200	3100
2d Sed	100	360	600	1200	2100	3000
2d HBk	125	380	650	1300	2250	3200
4d Sta Wag	125	380	650	1300	2250	3200
Concord DL, V-8						
4d Sed	125	380	650	1300	2250	3200
2d Sed	125	370	650	1250	2200	3100
2d HBk	125	400	675	1350	2300	3300
4d Sta Wag	125	400	675	1350	2300	3300
Concord Limited, V-8						
4d Sed	125	400	675	1350	2300	3300
2d Sed	125	380	650	1300	2250	3200
4d Sta Wag	125	400	700	1375	2400	3400

NOTE: Deduct 5 percent for 6-cyl.

	6	5	4	3	2	1
Pacer DL, V-8						
2d HBk	125	400	700	1375	2400	3400
2d Sta Wag	125	450	700	1400	2450	3500
Pacer Limited, V-8						
2d HBk	125	450	700	1400	2450	3500
2d Sta Wag	125	450	750	1450	2500	3600

NOTE: Deduct 5 percent for 6-cyl.

	6	5	4	3	2	1
AMX, V-8						
2d HBk	150	475	750	1475	2600	3700

NOTE: Deduct 7 percent for 6-cyl.

1980

	6	5	4	3	2	1
Spirit, 6-cyl.						
2d HBk	150	500	800	1600	2800	4000
2d Cpe	150	500	800	1550	2700	3900
2d HBk DL	150	550	850	1650	2900	4100
2d Cpe DL	150	500	800	1600	2800	4000
2d HBk Ltd	150	575	875	1700	3000	4300
2d Cpe Ltd	150	550	850	1675	2950	4200

NOTE: Deduct 10 percent for 4-cyl.

	6	5	4	3	2	1
Concord, 6-cyl.						
4d Sed	125	450	750	1450	2500	3600
2d Cpe	125	450	700	1400	2450	3500
4d Sta Wag	150	475	750	1475	2600	3700
4d Sed DL	150	475	750	1475	2600	3700
2d Cpe DL	125	450	750	1450	2500	3600
4d Sta Wag DL	150	475	775	1500	2650	3800
4d Sed Ltd	150	500	800	1550	2700	3900
2d Cpe Ltd	150	475	775	1500	2650	3800
4d Sta Wag Ltd	150	500	800	1550	2700	3900
Pacer, 6-cyl.						
2d HBk DL	125	450	750	1450	2500	3600
2d Sta Wag DL	150	475	750	1475	2600	3700
2d HBk Ltd	150	475	775	1500	2650	3800
2d Sta Wag Ltd	150	500	800	1550	2700	3900
AMX, 6-cyl.						
2d HBk	150	550	850	1675	2950	4200
Eagle 4WD, 6-cyl.						
4d Sed	200	675	1000	2000	3500	5000
2d Cpe	200	675	1000	1950	3400	4900
4d Sta Wag	200	700	1050	2100	3650	5200
4d Sed Ltd	200	700	1050	2100	3650	5200
2d Cpe Ltd	200	700	1050	2050	3600	5100
4d Sta Wag Ltd	200	650	1100	2150	3780	5400

1981

	6	5	4	3	2	1
Spirit, 4-cyl.						
2d HBk	150	475	750	1475	2600	3700
2d Cpe	125	450	750	1450	2500	3600
2d HBk DL	150	500	800	1550	2700	3900
2d Cpe DL	150	475	775	1500	2650	3800
Spirit, 6-cyl.						
2d HBk	150	550	850	1650	2900	4100
2d Cpe	150	500	800	1600	2800	4000
2d HBk DL	150	575	875	1700	3000	4300
2d Cpe DL	150	550	850	1675	2950	4200
Concord, 6-cyl.						
4d Sed	150	475	750	1475	2600	3700
2d Cpe	125	450	750	1450	2500	3600
4d Sta Wag	150	475	775	1500	2650	3800
4d Sed DL	150	475	775	1500	2650	3800
2d Cpe DL	150	475	750	1475	2600	3700
4d Sta Wag DL	150	500	800	1550	2700	3900
4d Sed Ltd	150	500	800	1550	2700	3900
2d Cpe Ltd	150	475	775	1500	2650	3800
4d Sta Wag Ltd	150	500	800	1600	2800	4000

NOTE: Deduct 12 percent for 4-cyl.

	6	5	4	3	2	1
Eagle 50 4WD, 4-cyl.						
2d HBk SX4	200	675	1000	2000	3500	5000
2d HBk	200	675	1000	1950	3400	4900
2d HBk SX4 DL	200	700	1050	2100	3650	5200
2d HBk DL	200	700	1050	2050	3600	5100
Eagle 50 4WD, 6-cyl.						
2d HBk SX4	200	650	1100	2150	3780	5400
2d HBk	200	700	1075	2150	3700	5300
2d HBk SX4 DL	200	670	1150	2250	3920	5600
2d HBk DL	200	660	1100	2200	3850	5500

1982

	6	5	4	3	2	1
Spirit, 6-cyl.						
2d HBk	150	550	850	1675	2950	4200
2d Cpe	150	550	850	1650	2900	4100
2d HBk DL	150	575	900	1750	3100	4400
2d Cpe DL	150	575	875	1700	3000	4300

NOTE: Deduct 10 percent for 4-cyl.

	6	5	4	3	2	1
Concord, 6-cyl.						
4d Sed	150	475	775	1500	2650	3800
2d Cpe	150	475	750	1475	2600	3700
4d Sta Wag	150	500	800	1550	2700	3900
4d Sed DL	150	500	800	1550	2700	3900
2d Cpe DL	150	475	775	1500	2650	3800
4d Sta Wag DL	150	500	800	1600	2800	4000
4d Sed Ltd	150	500	800	1600	2800	4000
2d Cpe Ltd	150	500	800	1550	2700	3900
4d Sta Wag Ltd	150	550	850	1650	2900	4100

NOTE: Deduct 12 percent for 4-cyl.

	6	5	4	3	2	1
Eagle 50 4WD, 4-cyl.						
2d HBk SX4	200	700	1050	2050	3600	5100
2d HBk	200	675	1000	2000	3500	5000
2d HBk SX4 DL	200	700	1075	2150	3700	5300
2d HBk DL	200	700	1050	2100	3650	5200
Eagle 50 4WD, 6-cyl.						
2d HBk SX4	200	660	1100	2200	3850	5500
2d HBk	200	650	1100	2150	3780	5400
2d HBk SX4 DL	200	685	1150	2300	3990	5700
2d HBk DL	200	670	1150	2250	3920	5600
Eagle 30 4WD, 4-cyl.						
4d Sed	200	675	1000	1950	3400	4900
2d Cpe	150	650	975	1950	3350	4800
4d Sta Wag	200	675	1000	2000	3500	5000
4d Sed Ltd	200	675	1000	2000	3500	5000
2d Cpe Ltd	200	675	1000	1950	3400	4900
4d Sta Wag Ltd	200	700	1050	2100	3650	5200
Eagle 30 4WD, 6-cyl.						
4d Sed	200	700	1075	2150	3700	5300
2d Cpe	200	700	1050	2100	3650	5200
4d Sta Wag	200	660	1100	2200	3850	5500
4d Sed Ltd	200	660	1100	2200	3850	5500
2d Cpe Ltd	200	650	1100	2150	3780	5400
4d Sta Wag Ltd	200	685	1150	2300	3990	5700

1983

	6	5	4	3	2	1
Spirit, 6-cyl.						
2d HBk DL	150	575	875	1700	3000	4300
2d HBk GT	150	575	900	1750	3100	4400
Concord, 6-cyl.						
4d Sed	150	500	800	1550	2700	3900
4d Sta Wag	150	500	800	1600	2800	4000
4d Sed DL	150	500	800	1600	2800	4000
4d Sta Wag DL	150	550	850	1650	2900	4100
4d Sta Wag Ltd	150	575	875	1700	3000	4300
Alliance, 4-cyl.						
2d Sed	125	450	750	1450	2500	3600
4d Sed L	150	475	750	1475	2600	3700
2d Sed L	150	475	750	1475	2600	3700
4d Sed DL	150	475	775	1500	2650	3800
2d Sed DL	150	475	775	1500	2650	3800
4d Sed Ltd	150	500	800	1550	2700	3900
Eagle 50 4WD, 4-cyl.						
2d HBk SX4	200	700	1050	2100	3650	5200
2d HBk SX4 DL	200	650	1100	2150	3780	5400
Eagle 50 4WD, 6-cyl.						
2d HBk SX4	200	670	1150	2250	3920	5600
2d HBk SX4 DL	200	670	1200	2300	4060	5800
Eagle 30 4WD, 4-cyl.						
4d Sed	200	675	1000	2000	3500	5000
4d Sta Wag	200	700	1050	2100	3650	5200
4d Sta Wag Ltd	200	650	1100	2150	3780	5400
Eagle 30 4WD, 6-cyl.						
4d Sed	200	650	1100	2150	3780	5400
4d Sta Wag	200	670	1150	2250	3920	5600
4d Sta Wag Ltd	200	670	1200	2300	4060	5800

1984

	6	5	4	3	2	1
Alliance, 4-cyl.						
2d	150	475	750	1475	2600	3700
L						
4d	150	475	775	1500	2650	3800
2d	150	475	775	1500	2650	3800
DL						
4d	150	500	800	1550	2700	3900
2d	150	500	800	1550	2700	3900
Limited						
4d	150	500	800	1600	2800	4000
Encore, 4-cyl.						
2d Liftback	125	400	700	1375	2400	3400
S						
2d Liftback	125	450	700	1400	2450	3500
4d Liftback	125	450	700	1400	2450	3500

LS	6	5	4	3	2	1
2d Liftback	125	450	750	1450	2500	3600
4d Liftback	125	450	750	1450	2500	3600
GS						
2d Liftback	150	475	750	1475	2600	3700
Eagle 4WD, 4-cyl.						
4d Sed	200	700	1050	2050	3600	5100
4d Sta Wag	200	700	1075	2150	3700	5300
4d Sta Wag Ltd	200	660	1100	2200	3850	5500
Eagle 4WD, 6-cyl.						
4d Sed	200	660	1100	2200	3850	5500
4d Sta Wag	200	685	1150	2300	3990	5700
4d Sta Wag Ltd	200	700	1200	2350	4130	5900

1985

Alliance						
2d Sed	100	320	550	1050	1850	2600
4d Sed L	100	330	575	1150	1950	2800
2d Sed L	100	350	600	1150	2000	2900
Conv L	150	475	750	1475	2600	3700
4d Sed DL	125	380	650	1300	2250	3200
2d Sed DL	125	450	700	1400	2450	3500
Conv DL	150	550	850	1650	2900	4100
4d Ltd Sed	150	500	800	1550	2700	3900
Eagle 4WD						
4d Sed	200	670	1150	2250	3920	5600
4d Sta Wag	200	670	1200	2300	4060	5800
4d Ltd Sta Wag	200	720	1200	2400	4200	6000

1986

Encore 90						
2d HBk	125	450	700	1400	2450	3500
4d HBk	125	450	750	1450	2500	3600
Alliance						
2d Sed	125	450	750	1450	2500	3600
4d Sed	150	475	750	1475	2600	3700
Conv	200	660	1100	2200	3850	5500
Eagle						
4d Sed	200	685	1150	2300	3990	5700
4d Sta Wag	200	670	1200	2300	4060	5800
4d Ltd Sta Wag	200	720	1200	2400	4200	6000

NOTES: Add 10 percent for deluxe models.
Deduct 5 percent for smaller engines.

1987

2d Sed	150	500	800	1600	2800	4000
4d Sed	150	500	800	1600	2800	4000
2d HBk	150	550	850	1650	2900	4100
4d HBk	150	550	850	1650	2900	4100
2d Conv	350	820	1400	2700	4760	6800

NOTES: Add 10 percent for deluxe models.
Add 20 percent for GTA models.

Eagle						
4d Sed	350	780	1300	2600	4550	6500
4d Sta Wag	350	800	1350	2700	4700	6700
4d Sta Wag Ltd	350	830	1400	2950	4830	6900

PACKARD

1899

Model A, 1-cyl.
Rds — value not estimable

1900

Model B, 1-cyl.
Rds — value not estimable

1901

Model C, 1-cyl.
Rds — value not estimable

1902-03

Model F, 4-cyl.	6	5	4	3	2	1
Tr	2500	7900	13,200	26,400	46,200	66,000
1904						
Model L, 4-cyl.						
Tr	2250	7200	12,000	24,000	42,000	60,000
Model M, 4-cyl.						
Tr	2350	7450	12,400	24,800	43,400	62,000
1905						
Model N, 4-cyl.						
Tr	2050	6600	11,000	22,000	38,500	55,000
1906						
Model S, 4-cyl., 24 hp						
Tr	2050	6600	11,000	22,000	38,500	55,000
1907						
Model U, 4-cyl., 30 hp						
Tr	2150	6850	11,400	22,800	39,900	57,000
1908						
Model UA, 4-cyl., 30 hp						
Tr	2050	6600	11,000	22,000	38,500	55,000
Rds	1950	6250	10,400	20,800	36,400	52,000
1909						
Model UB UBS, 4-cyl., 30 hp						
Tr	2000	6350	10,600	21,200	37,100	53,000
Rbt	1600	5150	8600	17,200	30,100	43,000
Model NA, 4-cyl., 18 hp						
Tr	1700	5400	9000	18,000	31,500	45,000
1910-11						
Model UC UCS, 4-cyl., 30 hp						
Tr	2050	6600	11,000	22,000	38,500	55,000
Rbt	2000	6350	10,600	21,200	37,100	53,000
Model NB, 4-cyl., 18 hp						
Tr	1900	6000	10,000	20,000	35,000	50,000
1912						
Model NE, 4-cyl., 18 hp						
Tr	1700	5400	9000	18,000	31,500	45,000
Rbt	1750	5500	9200	18,400	32,200	46,000
Cpe	1150	3600	6000	12,000	21,000	30,000
Limo	1400	4450	7400	14,800	25,900	37,000
Imp Limo	1500	4800	8000	16,000	28,000	40,000
1911-12						
Model UE, 4-cyl., 30 hp						
Tr	2250	7200	12,000	24,000	42,000	60,000
Phae	2350	7450	12,400	24,800	43,400	62,000
Rbt	2400	7700	12,800	25,600	44,800	64,000
Cpe	1300	4200	7000	14,000	24,500	35,000
Brgm	1200	3850	6400	12,800	22,400	32,000
Limo	1500	4800	8000	16,000	28,000	40,000
Imp Limo	1600	5050	8400	16,800	29,400	42,000

1912

Model 12-48, 6-cyl., 36 hp	6	5	4	3	2	1
Tr	2850	9100	15,200	30,400	53,200	76,000
Phae	2650	8400	14,000	28,000	49,000	70,000
Rbt	2500	7900	13,200	26,400	46,200	66,000
Cpe	1600	5050	8400	16,800	29,400	42,000
Brgm	1450	4700	7800	15,600	27,300	39,000
Limo	1600	5050	8400	16,800	29,400	42,000
Imp Limo	1650	5300	8800	17,600	30,800	44,000
Model 1-38, 6-cyl., 38 hp						
Tr	2050	6600	11,000	22,000	38,500	55,000
Phae	2100	6700	11,200	22,400	39,200	56,000
4P Phae	2150	6850	11,400	22,800	39,900	57,000
Rbt	1900	6000	10,000	20,000	35,000	50,000
Cpe	1700	5400	9000	18,000	31,500	45,000
Imp Cpe	1750	5500	9200	18,400	32,200	46,000
Lan'let	1750	5650	9400	18,800	32,900	47,000
Imp Lan'let	1800	5750	9600	19,200	33,600	48,000
Limo	1900	6000	10,000	20,000	35,000	50,000
Imp Limo	2000	6350	10,600	21,200	37,100	53,000
1913						
Model 13-48, 6-cyl.						
Tr	2050	6600	11,000	22,000	38,500	55,000
1914						
Model 2-38, 6-cyl.						
Tr	1950	6250	10,400	20,800	36,400	52,000
Sal Tr	2000	6350	10,600	21,200	37,100	53,000
Spl Tr	2050	6500	10,800	21,600	37,800	54,000
Phae	2050	6600	11,000	22,000	38,500	55,000
4P Phae	2100	6700	11,200	22,400	39,200	56,000
Cpe	1700	5400	9000	18,000	31,500	45,000
Brgm	1500	4800	8000	16,000	28,000	40,000
4P Brgm	1500	4800	8000	16,000	28,000	40,000
2-38						
Lan'let	1600	5050	8400	16,800	29,400	42,000
Cabr Lan'let	1750	5650	9400	18,800	32,900	47,000
Limo	1500	4800	8000	16,000	28,000	40,000
Cabr Limo	1800	5750	9600	19,200	33,600	48,000
Imp Limo	1750	5500	9200	18,400	32,200	46,000
Sal Limo	1750	5650	9400	18,800	32,900	47,000
Model 14-48, 6-cyl.						
Tr	1900	6000	10,000	20,000	35,000	50,000
Model 4-48, 6-cyl., 48 hp						
Tr	1900	6100	10,200	20,400	35,700	51,000
Sal Tr	1900	6100	10,200	20,400	35,700	51,000
Phae	2050	6600	11,000	22,000	38,500	55,000
4P Phae	2100	6700	11,200	22,400	39,200	56,000
Cpe	1750	5500	9200	18,400	32,200	46,000
Brgm	1700	5400	9000	18,000	31,500	45,000
Sal Brgm	1750	5500	9200	18,400	32,200	46,000
Lan'let	1750	5650	9400	18,800	32,900	47,000
Cabr Lan'let	1900	6000	10,000	20,000	35,000	50,000
Limo	1750	5650	9400	18,800	32,900	47,000
Imp Limo	1850	5900	9800	19,600	34,300	49,000
Sal Limo	1900	6000	10,000	20,000	35,000	50,000
1915						
Model 3-38, 6-cyl.						
Tr	1900	6000	10,000	20,000	35,000	50,000
Sal Tr	1950	6250	10,400	20,800	36,400	52,000
Spl Tr	2050	6500	10,800	21,600	37,800	54,000
Phae	2050	6600	11,000	22,000	38,500	55,000
4P Phae	2050	6500	10,800	21,600	37,800	54,000
3-38 (38 hp)						
Brgm	1550	4900	8200	16,400	28,700	41,000
4P Brgm	1500	4800	8000	16,000	28,000	40,000
Cpe	1600	5050	8400	16,800	29,400	42,000
Lan'let	1700	5400	9000	18,000	31,500	45,000
Cabr Lan'let	1950	6250	10,400	20,800	36,400	52,000
Limo	1750	5650	9400	18,800	32,900	47,000
Limo Cabr	1900	6000	10,000	20,000	35,000	50,000
Imp Limo	1850	5900	9800	19,600	34,300	49,000
Sal Limo	1900	6100	10,200	20,400	35,700	51,000
Model 5-48, 6-cyl., 48 hp						
Tr	1900	6100	10,200	20,400	35,700	51,000
Sal Tr	1950	6250	10,400	20,800	36,400	52,000
Phae	2000	6350	10,600	21,200	37,100	53,000
4P Phae	2050	6500	10,800	21,600	37,800	54,000
Rbt	2200	6950	11,600	23,200	40,600	58,000
Cpe	1500	4800	8000	16,000	28,000	40,000
Brgm	1450	4700	7800	15,600	27,300	39,000
Sal Brgm	1500	4800	8000	16,000	28,000	40,000
Lan'let	1900	6000	10,000	20,000	35,000	50,000
Cabr Lan'let	2050	6500	10,800	21,600	37,800	54,000
Limo	2150	6850	11,400	22,800	39,900	57,000
Cabr Limo	2350	7450	12,400	24,800	43,400	62,000
Imp Limo	2350	7450	12,400	24,800	43,400	62,000
1916						
Twin Six, 12-cyl., 125" wb						
Tr	1900	6100	10,200	20,400	35,700	51,000
Sal Tr	1950	6250	10,400	20,800	36,400	52,000
Phae	2000	6350	10,600	21,200	37,100	53,000
Sal Phae	2050	6500	10,800	21,600	37,800	54,000
Rbt	1950	6250	10,400	20,800	36,400	52,000
Brgm	1500	4800	8000	16,000	28,000	40,000
Cpe	1550	4900	8200	16,400	28,700	41,000
Lan'let	1600	5150	8600	17,200	30,100	43,000
Limo	1650	5300	8800	17,600	30,800	44,000
Twin Six, 12-cyl., 135" wb						
Tr	2050	6500	10,800	21,600	37,800	54,000
Sal Tr	2050	6600	11,000	22,000	38,500	55,000
Phae	2050	6500	10,800	21,600	37,800	54,000
Sal Phae	2100	6700	11,200	22,400	39,200	56,000
Brgm	1600	5150	8600	17,200	30,100	43,000
Lan'let	1700	5400	9000	18,000	31,500	45,000
Sal Lan'let	1750	5500	9200	18,400	32,200	46,000
Cabr Lan'let	2000	6350	10,600	21,200	37,100	53,000
Limo	1750	5500	9200	18,400	32,200	46,000
Cabr Limo	2050	6500	10,800	21,600	37,800	54,000
Imp Limo	2000	6350	10,600	21,200	37,100	53,000
1917 Series II						
Twin Six, 12-cyl., 126" wb						
Tr	1750	5500	9200	18,400	32,200	46,000
Phae	1750	5650	9400	18,800	32,900	47,000
Sal Phae	1800	5750	9600	19,200	33,600	48,000
2P Rbt	1700	5400	9000	18,000	31,500	45,000
4P Rbt	1750	5500	9200	18,400	32,200	46,000
Brgm	1300	4100	6800	13,600	23,800	34,000
Cpe	1350	4300	7200	14,400	25,200	36,000

	6	5	4	3	2	1
Lan'let	1600	5150	8600	17,200	30,100	43,000
Limo	1650	5300	8800	17,600	30,800	44,000
Twin Six, 12-cyl., 135" wb						
Tr	1850	5900	9800	19,600	34,300	49,000
Sal Tr	1900	6000	10,000	20,000	35,000	50,000
Phae	1900	6100	10,200	20,400	35,700	51,000
Sal Phae	1950	6250	10,400	20,800	36,400	52,000
Brgm	1150	3600	6000	12,000	21,000	30,000
Lan'let	1550	4900	8200	16,400	28,700	41,000
Cabr Lan'let	1650	5300	8800	17,600	30,800	44,000
Limo	1600	5150	8600	17,200	30,100	43,000
Cabr Limo	1650	5300	8800	17,600	30,800	44,000
Imp Limo	1700	5400	9000	18,000	31,500	45,000
1918-1920						
Twin Six, 12-cyl., 128" wb						
Tr	1650	5300	8800	17,600	30,800	44,000
Sal Tr	1700	5400	9000	18,000	31,500	45,000
Phae	1750	5650	9400	18,800	32,900	47,000
Sal Phae	1850	5900	9800	19,600	34,300	49,000
Rbt	1800	5750	9600	19,200	33,600	48,000
2d Brgm	1200	3850	6400	12,800	22,400	32,000
Cpe	1300	4100	6800	13,600	23,800	34,000
Lan'let	1600	5050	8400	16,800	29,400	42,000
Limo	1650	5300	8800	17,600	30,800	44,000
Twin Six, 12-cyl., 136" wb						
Tr	1850	5900	9800	19,600	34,300	49,000
Sal Tr	1900	6100	10,200	20,400	35,700	51,000
Brgm	1250	3950	6600	13,200	23,100	33,000
Lan'let	1650	5300	8800	17,600	30,800	44,000
Limo	1700	5400	9000	18,000	31,500	45,000
Imp Limo	1750	5650	9400	18,800	32,900	47,000
1921-1922						
Single Six (1st Series), 116" wb						
5P Tr	1300	4100	6800	13,600	23,800	34,000
Rbt	1250	3950	6600	13,200	23,100	33,000
7P Tr	1300	4200	7000	14,000	24,500	35,000
Cpe	1100	3500	5800	11,600	20,300	29,000
Sed	1000	3250	5400	10,800	18,900	27,000
Single Six, 6-cyl., 126" wb						
Rbt	1350	4300	7200	14,400	25,200	36,000
Rds	1450	4550	7600	15,200	26,600	38,000
Tr	1400	4450	7400	14,800	25,900	37,000
Cpe	1150	3600	6000	12,000	21,000	30,000
5P Cpe	1100	3500	5800	11,600	20,300	29,000
Sed	1050	3350	5600	11,200	19,600	28,000
Limo Sed	1150	3700	6200	12,400	21,700	31,000
Single Six, 6-cyl., 133" wb						
Tr	1450	4550	7600	15,200	26,600	38,000
Sed	1050	3350	5600	11,200	19,600	28,000
Limo	1150	3700	6200	12,400	21,700	31,000
Single Eight, 8-cyl., 136" wb						
Rbt	1450	4550	7600	15,200	26,600	38,000
Spt Rds	1500	4800	8000	16,000	28,000	40,000
Cpe	1150	3600	6000	12,000	21,000	30,000
5P Cpe	1100	3500	5800	11,600	20,300	29,000
Sed	1000	3250	5400	10,800	18,900	27,000
Sed Limo	1150	3600	6000	12,000	21,000	30,000
Single Eight, 8-cyl., 143" wb						
Tr	1450	4700	7800	15,600	27,300	39,000
Sed	1100	3500	5800	11,600	20,300	29,000
Sed Limo	1200	3850	6400	12,800	22,400	32,000
Rds	1550	4900	8200	16,400	28,700	41,000
1923-24						
Single Six, 6-cyl., 126" wb						
Rbt	1200	3850	6400	12,800	22,400	32,000
Spt Rds	1300	4100	6800	13,600	23,800	34,000
Tr	1250	3950	6600	13,200	23,100	33,000
Sed	900	2900	4800	9600	16,800	24,000
Tr Sed	950	3000	5000	10,000	17,500	25,000
Limo Sed	1050	3350	5600	11,200	19,600	28,000
Single Six, 6-cyl., 133" wb						
Tr	1300	4200	7000	14,000	24,500	35,000
Sed	950	3000	5000	10,000	17,500	25,000
Sed Limo	1100	3500	5800	11,600	20,300	29,000
Single Eight, 8-cyl., 136" wb						
Tr	1500	4800	8000	16,000	28,000	40,000
Rbt	1600	5050	8400	16,800	29,400	42,000
Spt Rds	1700	5400	9000	18,000	31,500	45,000
Cpe	1050	3350	5600	11,200	19,600	28,000
5P Cpe	1000	3250	5400	10,800	18,900	27,000
Sed	1000	3100	5200	10,400	18,200	26,000
Sed Limo	1150	3600	6000	12,000	21,000	30,000
Single Eight, 8-cyl., 143" wb						
Tr	1600	5050	8400	16,800	29,400	42,000
Sed	1000	3250	5400	10,800	18,900	27,000
Clb Sed	1050	3350	5600	11,200	19,600	28,000
Sed Limo	1150	3700	6200	12,400	21,700	31,000
1925-26						
Single Six (3rd Series), 6-cyl., 126" wb						
Rbt	1300	4100	6800	13,600	23,800	34,000
Spt Rds	1400	4450	7400	14,800	25,900	37,000
Phae	1450	4550	7600	15,200	26,600	38,000
2P Cpe	1000	3100	5200	10,400	18,200	26,000
Cpe	950	3000	5000	10,000	17,500	25,000
5P Cpe	900	2900	4800	9600	16,800	24,000
Sed	850	2650	4400	8800	15,400	22,000
Sed Limo	1000	3250	5400	10,800	18,900	27,000
Single Six (3rd Series), 6-cyl., 133" wb						
Tr	1200	3850	6400	12,800	22,400	32,000
Sed	850	2750	4600	9200	16,100	23,000
Clb Sed	900	2900	4800	9600	16,800	24,000
Sed Limo	1050	3350	5600	11,200	19,600	28,000
1927						
Single Six (4th Series), 6-cyl., 126" wb						
Rds	1350	4300	7200	14,400	25,200	36,000
Phae	1400	4450	7400	14,800	25,900	37,000
Sed	900	2900	4800	9600	16,800	24,000
Single Six (4th Series), 6-cyl., 133" wb						
Tr	1400	4450	7400	14,800	25,900	37,000
Cpe	1000	3100	5200	10,400	18,200	26,000
Sed	950	3000	5000	10,000	17,500	25,000
Clb Sed	1000	3100	5200	10,400	18,200	26,000
Sed Limo	1100	3500	5800	11,600	20,300	29,000
Single Eight (3rd Series), 8-cyl., 136" wb						
Rbt	1650	5300	8800	17,600	30,800	44,000
Phae	1600	5150	8600	17,200	30,100	43,000
Sed	900	2900	4800	9600	16,800	24,000

	6	5	4	3	2	1
Single Eight (3rd Series), 8-cyl., 143" wb						
Tr	1750	5500	9200	18,400	32,200	46,000
Cpe	1050	3350	5600	11,200	19,600	28,000
Sed	950	3000	5000	10,000	17,500	25,000
Clb Sed	1000	3100	5200	10,400	18,200	26,000
Sed Limo	1100	3500	5800	11,600	20,300	29,000
1928						
Single Six (5th Series), 6-cyl., 126" wb						
Phae	1500	4800	8000	16,000	28,000	40,000
Rbt	1450	4700	7800	15,600	27,300	39,000
Conv	1300	4200	7000	14,000	24,500	35,000
RS Cpe	900	2900	4800	9600	16,800	24,000
Sed	850	2650	4400	8800	15,400	22,000
Single Six (5th Series), 6-cyl., 133" wb						
Phae	1750	5500	9200	18,400	32,200	46,000
7P Tr	1750	5650	9400	18,800	32,900	47,000
Rbt	1650	5300	8800	17,600	30,800	44,000
Sed	850	2750	4600	9200	16,100	23,000
Clb Sed	900	2900	4800	9600	16,800	24,000
Sed Limo	950	3000	5000	10,000	17,500	25,000
Standard, Single Eight (4th Series), 8-cyl., 143" wb						
Rds	1900	6000	10,000	20,000	35,000	50,000
Phae	1950	6250	10,400	20,800	36,400	52,000
Conv	1650	5300	8800	17,600	30,800	44,000
7P Tr	1900	6100	10,200	20,400	35,700	51,000
4P Cpe	850	2750	4600	9200	16,100	23,000
4P Cpe	900	2900	4800	9600	16,800	24,000
5P Cpe	950	3000	5000	10,000	17,500	25,000
Sed	850	2650	4400	8800	15,400	22,000
Clb Sed	850	2750	4600	9200	16,100	23,000
Sed Limo	950	3000	5000	10,000	17,500	25,000
Custom, Single Eight (4th Series), 8-cyl., 143" wb						
7P Tr	2350	7450	12,400	24,800	43,400	62,000
Phae	2350	7450	12,400	24,800	43,400	62,000
RDS	2250	7200	12,000	24,000	42,000	60,000
Conv Cpe	2050	6600	11,000	22,000	38,500	55,000
RS Cpe	950	3000	5000	10,000	17,500	25,000
7P Sed	900	2900	4800	9600	16,800	24,000
Sed	850	2750	4600	9200	16,100	23,000
Sed Limo	1000	3100	5200	10,400	18,200	26,000
1929						
Model 626, Standard Eight (6th Series), 8-cyl.						
Conv	2700	8650	14,400	28,800	50,400	72,000
Cpe	1150	3600	6000	12,000	21,000	30,000
Sed	950	3000	5000	10,000	17,500	25,000
Model 633, Standard Eight (6th Series), 8-cyl.						
Phae	3250	10,300	17,200	34,400	60,200	86,000
ROS	3400	10,800	18,000	36,000	63,000	90,000
7P Tr	3250	10,300	17,200	34,400	60,200	86,000
Cpe	1500	4800	8000	16,000	28,000	40,000
Sed	1000	3250	5400	10,800	18,900	27,000
Clb Sed	1050	3350	5600	11,200	19,600	28,000
Limo Sed	1300	4100	6800	13,600	23,800	34,000
Model 626, Speedster Eight (6th Series), 8-cyl.						
Phae	9000	28,800	48,000	96,000	168,000	240,000
Rds	9950	31,800	53,000	106,000	185,500	265,000
Model 640, Custom Eight (6th Series), 8-cyl.						
DC Phae	4750	15,100	25,200	50,400	88,200	126,000
7P Tr	4500	14,400	24,000	48,000	84,000	120,000
Rds	4500	14,400	24,000	48,000	84,000	120,000
Conv	4350	13,900	23,200	46,400	81,200	116,000
RS Cpe	2050	6600	11,000	22,000	38,500	55,000
4P Cpe	1700	5400	9000	18,000	31,500	45,000
Sed	1100	3500	5800	11,600	20,300	29,000
Clb Sed	1150	3600	6000	12,000	21,000	30,000
Limo	1250	3950	6600	13,200	23,100	33,000
Model 645, DeLuxe Eight (6th Series), 8-cyl.						
Phae	5250	16,800	28,000	56,000	98,000	140,000
Spt Phae	5250	16,800	28,000	56,000	98,000	140,000
7P Tr	5250	16,800	28,000	56,000	98,000	140,000
Rds	5250	16,800	28,000	56,000	98,000	140,000
RS Cpe	2250	7200	12,000	24,000	42,000	60,000
5P Cpe	1900	6000	10,000	20,000	35,000	50,000
Sed	1500	4800	8000	16,000	28,000	40,000
Clb Sed	1600	5050	8400	16,800	29,400	42,000
Limo	1750	5500	9200	18,400	32,200	46,000
1930						
Model 726, Standard 8 (7th Series), 8-cyl.						
Sed	1150	3700	6200	12,400	21,700	31,000
Model 733, Standard 8 (7th Series), 8-cyl., 134" wb						
Phae	4450	14,150	23,600	47,200	82,600	118,000
Spt Phae	4500	14,400	24,000	48,000	84,000	120,000
Rds	4450	14,150	23,600	47,200	82,600	118,000
7P Tr	4350	13,900	23,200	46,400	81,200	116,000
RS Cpe	2250	7200	12,000	24,000	42,000	60,000
4P Cpe	1300	4200	7000	14,000	24,500	35,000
Conv	3400	10,800	18,000	36,000	63,000	90,000
Sed	1400	4450	7400	14,800	25,900	37,000
Clb Sed	1450	4700	7800	15,600	27,300	39,000
Limo Sed	1600	5150	8600	17,200	30,100	43,000
Model 734, Speedster Eight (7th Series), 8-cyl.						
Boat	9750	31,200	52,000	104,000	182,000	260,000
RS Rds	9200	29,400	49,000	98,000	171,500	245,000
Phae	9400	30,000	50,000	100,000	175,000	250,000
Vic	4350	13,900	23,200	46,400	81,200	116,000
Sed	3400	10,800	18,000	36,000	63,000	90,000
Model 740, Custom Eight (7th Series), 8-cyl.						
Phae	4750	15,100	25,200	50,400	88,200	126,000
Spt Phae	4750	15,100	25,200	50,400	88,200	126,000
7P Tr	5250	16,800	28,000	56,000	98,000	140,000
Rds	6200	19,800	33,000	66,000	115,500	165,000
Conv	5250	16,800	28,000	56,000	98,000	140,000
RS Cpe	2650	8400	14,000	28,000	49,000	70,000
5P Cpe	1900	6000	10,000	20,000	35,000	50,000
Sed	1800	5750	9600	19,200	33,600	48,000
7P Sed	1850	5900	9800	19,600	34,300	49,000
Clb Sed	1900	6000	10,000	20,000	35,000	50,000
Limo	2050	6500	10,800	21,600	37,800	54,000
Model 745, DeLuxe Eight (7th Series)						
Phae	9000	28,800	48,000	96,000	168,000	240,000
Spt Phae	9400	30,000	50,000	100,000	175,000	250,000
Rds	8800	28,200	47,000	94,000	164,500	235,000
Conv	9550	30,600	51,000	102,000	178,500	255,000
7P Tr	8650	27,600	46,000	92,000	161,000	230,000
RS Cpe	2850	9100	15,200	30,400	53,200	76,000
5P Cpe	2500	7900	13,200	26,400	46,200	66,000
Sed	2050	6600	11,000	22,000	38,500	55,000
7P Sed	2150	6850	11,400	22,800	39,900	57,000

	6	5	4	3	2	1
Clb Sed	2200	7100	11,800	23,600	41,300	59,000
Limo	2550	8150	13,600	27,200	47,600	68,000
1931						
Model 826, Standard Eight (8th Series)						
Sed	1150	3700	6200	12,400	21,700	31,000
Model 833, Standard Eight (8th Series)						
Phae	4350	13,900	23,200	46,400	81,200	116,000
Spt Phae	4450	14,150	23,600	47,200	82,600	118,000
7P Tr	4300	13,700	22,800	45,600	79,800	114,000
Conv Sed	4900	15,600	26,000	52,000	91,000	130,000
Rds	4350	13,900	23,200	46,400	81,200	116,000
Conv	3600	11,500	19,200	38,400	67,200	96,000
RS Cpe	2250	7200	12,000	24,000	42,000	60,000
5P Cpe	2000	6350	10,600	21,200	37,100	53,000
7P Sed	1500	4800	8000	16,000	28,000	40,000
Clb Sed	1550	4900	8200	16,400	28,700	41,000
NOTE: Add 45 percent for 845 models.						
Model 840, Custom						
A/W Cabr	6200	19,800	33,000	66,000	115,500	165,000
A/W Spt Cabr	6400	20,400	34,000	68,000	119,000	170,000
A/W Lan'let	6550	21,000	35,000	70,000	122,500	175,000
A/W Spt Lan'let	6750	21,600	36,000	72,000	126,000	180,000
Dtrch Cv Sed	6950	22,200	37,000	74,000	129,500	185,000
Limo Cabr	6950	22,200	37,000	74,000	129,500	185,000
A/W Twn Car	6750	21,600	36,000	72,000	126,000	180,000
Dtrch Cv Vic	7150	22,800	38,000	76,000	133,000	190,000
Conv	7300	23,400	39,000	78,000	136,500	195,000
Spt Phae	7900	25,200	42,000	84,000	147,000	210,000
Phae	7700	24,600	41,000	82,000	143,500	205,000
Rds	7500	24,000	40,000	80,000	140,000	200,000
Tr	7300	23,400	39,000	78,000	136,500	195,000
Rs Cpe	2950	9350	15,600	31,200	54,600	78,000
5P Cpe	2250	7200	12,000	24,000	42,000	60,000
Sed	1900	6000	10,000	20,000	35,000	50,000
Clb Sed	2000	6350	10,600	21,200	37,100	53,000
Model 840, Individual Custom						
A/W Cabr	9550	30,600	51,000	102,000	178,500	255,000
A/W Spt Cabr	9750	31,200	52,000	104,000	182,000	260,000
A/W Lan'let	8250	26,400	44,000	88,000	154,000	220,000
A/W Spt Lan'let	8450	27,000	45,000	90,000	157,500	225,000
Dtrch Conv Sed	9200	29,400	49,000	98,000	171,500	245,000
Cabr Sed Limo	8450	27,000	45,000	90,000	157,500	225,000
A/W Twn Car	9000	28,800	48,000	96,000	168,000	240,000
Lan'let Twn Car	7900	25,200	42,000	84,000	147,000	210,000
Conv Vic	9400	30,000	50,000	100,000	175,000	250,000
Sed	2500	7900	13,200	26,400	46,200	66,000
Sed Limo	3000	9600	16,000	32,000	56,000	80,000
1932						
Model 900, Light Eight (9th Series)						
Rds	2350	7450	12,400	24,800	43,400	62,000
Cpe	1150	3700	6200	12,400	21,700	31,000
Cpe Sed	1100	3500	5800	11,600	20,300	29,000
Sed	1000	3250	5400	10,800	18,900	27,000
1932						
Model 901 Standard Eight (9th Series) 129" wb						
Sed	1000	3250	5400	10,800	18,900	27,000
Model 902 Standard Eight (9th Series) 136" wb						
Rds	4200	13,450	22,400	44,800	78,400	112,000
Phae	4500	14,400	24,000	48,000	84,000	120,000
Spt Phae	4750	15,100	25,200	50,400	88,200	126,000
RS Cpe	1900	6000	10,000	20,000	35,000	50,000
5P Cpe	1700	5400	9000	18,000	31,500	45,000
Sed	1150	3700	6200	12,400	21,700	31,000
7P Sed	1200	3850	6400	12,800	22,400	32,000
Clb Sed	1250	3950	6600	13,200	23,100	33,000
Limo	1300	4200	7000	14,000	24,500	35,000
Tr	4450	14,150	23,600	47,200	82,600	118,000
Conv Sed	4750	15,100	25,200	50,400	88,200	126,000
Conv Vic	4900	15,600	26,000	52,000	91,000	130,000
Model 903, DeLuxe Eight, 142" wb						
Conv	4900	15,600	26,000	52,000	91,000	130,000
Phae	4900	15,600	26,000	52,000	91,000	130,000
Spt Phae	5250	16,800	28,000	56,000	98,000	140,000
Conv Sed	5250	16,800	28,000	56,000	98,000	140,000
Conv Vic	5250	16,800	28,000	56,000	98,000	140,000
7P Tr	4000	12,700	21,200	42,400	74,200	106,000
RS Cpe	2500	7900	13,200	26,400	46,200	66,000
5P Cpe	2350	7450	12,400	24,800	43,400	62,000
Sed	1600	5050	8400	16,800	29,400	42,000
Clb Sed	1650	5300	8800	17,600	30,800	44,000
Model 904, DeLuxe Eight, 147" wb						
Sed	2350	7450	12,400	24,800	43,400	62,000
Limo	2700	8650	14,400	28,800	50,400	72,000
Model 904, Individual Custom, 147" wb						
Dtrch Conv Cpe	9550	30,600	51,000	102,000	178,500	255,000
Dtrch Cpe	6200	19,800	33,000	66,000	115,500	165,000
Cabr	9750	31,200	52,000	104,000	182,000	260,000
Spt Cabr	10,150	32,400	54,000	108,000	189,000	270,000
A/W Brgm	10,300	33,000	55,000	110,000	192,500	275,000
Dtrch Spt Phae	10,300	33,000	55,000	110,000	192,500	275,000
Dtrch Conv Sed	10,500	33,600	56,000	112,000	196,000	280,000
Spt Sed	6200	19,800	33,000	66,000	115,500	165,000
Limo Cabr	10,150	32,400	54,000	108,000	189,000	270,000
Dtrch Limo	7150	22,800	38,000	76,000	133,000	190,000
A-W Twn Car	10,500	33,600	56,000	112,000	196,000	280,000
Dtrch Conv Vic	10,900	34,800	58,000	116,000	203,000	290,000
Lan'let	6750	21,600	36,000	72,000	126,000	180,000
Spt Lan	7150	22,800	38,000	76,000	133,000	190,000
Twn Car Lan'let	7500	24,000	40,000	80,000	140,000	200,000
Model 905, Twin Six, (9th Series), 142" wb						
Conv	10,300	33,000	55,000	110,000	192,500	275,000
Phae	10,150	32,400	54,000	108,000	189,000	270,000
Spt Phae	9950	31,800	53,000	106,000	185,500	265,000
7P Tr	9550	30,600	51,000	102,000	178,500	255,000
Conv Sed	10,300	33,000	55,000	110,000	192,500	275,000
Conv Vic	10,500	33,600	56,000	112,000	196,000	280,000
RS Cpe	3600	11,500	19,200	38,400	67,200	96,000
5P Cpe	3400	10,800	18,000	36,000	63,000	90,000
Sed	2650	8400	14,000	28,000	49,000	70,000
Clb Sed	2700	8650	14,400	28,800	50,400	72,000
Model 906, Twin Six, 147" wb						
7P Sed	3400	10,800	18,000	36,000	63,000	90,000
Limo	4000	12,700	21,200	42,400	74,200	106,000
Model 906, Individual Custom, Twin Six, 147" wb						
Conv						value not estimable
Cabr						value not estimable
Dtrch Spt Phae						value not estimable
Dtrch Conv Vic						value not estimable

	6	5	4	3	2	1
Dtrch Sed						value not estimable
Dtrch Cpe						value not estimable
Lan'let						value not estimable
Twn Car Lan'let						value not estimable
A/W Twn Car						value not estimable
1933						
10th Series						
Model 1001, Eight, 127" wb						
Conv	4000	12,700	21,200	42,400	74,200	106,000
RS Cpe	1300	4200	7000	14,000	24,500	35,000
Cpe Sed	1250	3950	6600	13,200	23,100	33,000
Sed	1150	3700	6200	12,400	21,700	31,000
Model 1002, Eight, 136" wb						
Phae	5450	17,400	29,000	58,000	101,500	145,000
Conv Sed	5650	18,000	30,000	60,000	105,000	150,000
Conv Vic	5800	18,600	31,000	62,000	108,500	155,000
7P Tr	4900	15,600	26,000	52,000	91,000	130,000
RS Cpe	1700	5400	9000	18,000	31,500	45,000
5P Cpe	1400	4450	7400	14,800	25,900	37,000
Sed	1300	4200	7000	14,000	24,500	35,000
7P Sed	1350	4300	7200	14,400	25,200	36,000
Clb Sed	1400	4450	7400	14,800	25,900	37,000
Limo	1500	4800	8000	16,000	28,000	40,000
Model 1003, Super Eight, 135" wb						
Sed	1500	4800	8000	16,000	28,000	40,000
Model 1004, Super Eight, 142" wb						
Conv	6200	19,800	33,000	66,000	115,500	165,000
Phae	6400	20,400	34,000	68,000	119,000	170,000
Spt Phae	6950	22,200	37,000	74,000	129,500	185,000
Conv Vic	7300	23,400	39,000	78,000	136,500	195,000
Conv Sed	6950	22,200	37,000	74,000	129,500	185,000
7P Tr	6550	21,000	35,000	70,000	122,500	175,000
RS Cpe	2250	7200	12,000	24,000	42,000	60,000
5P Cpe	1900	6000	10,000	20,000	35,000	50,000
Sed	1300	4200	7000	14,000	24,500	35,000
Clb Sed	1400	4450	7400	14,800	25,900	37,000
Limo	1650	5300	8800	17,600	30,800	44,000
Fml Sed	1750	5650	9400	18,800	32,900	47,000
Model 1005, Twelve, 142" wb						
Conv	9200	29,400	49,000	98,000	171,500	245,000
Spt Phae	9400	30,000	50,000	100,000	175,000	250,000
Conv Sed	9400	30,000	50,000	100,000	175,000	250,000
Conv Vic	9550	30,600	51,000	102,000	178,500	255,000
RS Cpe	2950	9350	15,600	31,200	54,600	78,000
5P Cpe	2400	7700	12,800	25,600	44,800	64,000
Sed	1900	6000	10,000	20,000	35,000	50,000
Fml Sed	2000	6350	10,600	21,200	37,100	53,000
Clb Sed	2050	6500	10,800	21,600	37,800	54,000
Model 1006, Standard, 147" wb						
7P Sed	2850	9100	15,200	30,400	53,200	76,000
Limo	3100	9850	16,400	32,800	57,400	82,000
Model 1006, Custom Twelve, 147" wb, Dietrich						
Conv	9750	31,200	52,000	104,000	182,000	260,000
Conv Vic	10,150	32,400	54,000	108,000	189,000	270,000
Spt Phae	9950	31,800	53,000	106,000	185,500	265,000
Conv Sed	10,150	32,400	54,000	108,000	189,000	270,000
Cpe	3250	10,300	17,200	34,400	60,200	86,000
Fml Sed	3100	9850	16,400	32,800	57,400	82,000
Model 1006, LeBaron Custom, Twelve, 147" wb						
A/W Cabr						value not estimable
A/W Twn Car						value not estimable
Model 1006, Packard Custom, Twelve, 147" wb						
A/W Cabr						value not estimable
A/W Lan'let						value not estimable
Spt Sed						value not estimable
A/W Twn Car						value not estimable
Twn Car Lan'let						value not estimable
Limo						value not estimable
Lan'let Limo						value not estimable
A/W Cabr						value not estimable
A/W Twn Car						value not estimable
1934						
11th Series						
Model 1100, Eight, 129" wb						
Sed	1500	4800	8000	16,000	28,000	40,000
Model 1101, Eight, 141" wb						
Conv	4000	12,700	21,200	42,400	74,200	106,000
Phae	4200	13,450	22,400	44,800	78,400	112,000
Conv Vic	4300	13,700	22,800	45,600	79,800	114,000
Conv Sed	4350	13,900	23,200	46,400	81,200	116,000
RS Cpe	1900	6000	10,000	20,000	35,000	50,000
5P Cpe	1600	5050	8400	16,800	29,400	42,000
Sed	1500	4800	8000	16,000	28,000	40,000
Clb Sed	1550	4900	8200	16,400	28,700	41,000
Fml Sed	1600	5050	8400	16,800	29,400	42,000
Model 1102, Eight, 141" wb						
7P Sed	1600	5150	8600	17,200	30,100	43,000
Limo	1700	5400	9000	18,000	31,500	45,000
Model 1103, Super Eight, 135" wb						
Sed	1650	5300	8800	17,600	30,800	44,000
Model 1104, Super Eight, 142" wb						
Conv	4750	15,100	25,200	50,400	88,200	126,000
Phae	4800	15,350	25,600	51,200	89,600	128,000
Spt Phae	5250	16,800	28,000	56,000	98,000	140,000
Conv Vic	5250	16,800	28,000	56,000	98,000	140,000
Conv Sed	5250	16,800	28,000	56,000	98,000	140,000
RS Cpe	3000	9600	16,000	32,000	56,000	80,000
5P Cpe	2500	7900	13,200	26,400	46,200	66,000
Clb Sed	2400	7700	12,800	25,600	44,800	64,000
Fml Sed	2500	7900	13,200	26,400	46,200	66,000
Model 1105, Super Eight, Standard, 147" wb						
7P Sed	2700	8650	14,400	28,800	50,400	72,000
Limo	2850	9100	15,200	30,400	53,200	76,000
Model 1105, Dietrich, Super Eight, 147" wb						
Conv	5450	17,400	29,000	58,000	101,500	145,000
Conv Vic	6550	21,000	35,000	70,000	122,500	175,000
Conv Sed	6400	20,400	34,000	68,000	119,000	170,000
Cpe	3550	11,300	18,800	37,600	65,800	94,000
Spt Sed	3450	11,050	18,400	36,800	64,400	92,000
Model 1105, LeBaron, Super Eight, 147" wb						
Model 1106, Twelve, LeBaron, 135" wb						
Spds						value not estimable
Spt Phae						value not estimable
Model 1107, Twelve, 142" wb						
Conv						value not estimable
Phae						value not estimable
Spt Phae						value not estimable

	6	5	4	3	2	1
Conv Vic					value not estimable	
Conv Sed					value not estimable	
7P Tr					value not estimable	
RS Cpe					value not estimable	
5P Cpe					value not estimable	
Sed					value not estimable	
Clb Sed					value not estimable	
Fml Sed					value not estimable	
Model 1108, Twelve, Standard, 147" wb						
7P Sed	3250	10,300	17,200	34,400	60,200	86,000
Limo	3400	10,800	18,000	36,000	63,000	90,000
Model 1108, Twelve, Dietrich, 147" wb						
Conv					value not estimable	
Spt Phae					value not estimable	
Conv Sed					value not estimable	
Vic Conv					value not estimable	
Cpe					value not estimable	
Spt Sed					value not estimable	
Model 1108, Twelve, LeBaron, 147" wb						
Cabr					value not estimable	
Spt Phae					value not estimable	
A/W Twn Car					value not estimable	

1935

	6	5	4	3	2	1
120-A, 8 cyl., 120" wb						
Conv	1700	5400	9000	18,000	31,500	45,000
Bus Cpe	1050	3350	5600	11,200	19,600	28,000
Spt Cpe	1150	3600	6000	12,000	21,000	30,000
Tr Cpe	1150	3600	6000	12,000	21,000	30,000
Sed	750	2400	4000	8000	14,000	20,000
Clb Sed	850	2650	4400	8800	15,400	22,000
Tr Sed	800	2500	4200	8400	14,700	21,000
Series 1200, 8 cyl., 127" wb						
Sed	900	2900	4800	9600	16,800	24,000
Series 1201, 8 cyl., 134" wb						
Cpe Rds	2350	7450	12,400	24,800	43,400	62,000
Phae	2400	7700	12,800	25,600	44,800	64,000
Conv Vic	2700	8650	14,400	28,800	50,400	72,000
LeB A/W Cabr	3000	9600	16,000	32,000	56,000	80,000
RS Cpe	1800	5750	9600	19,200	33,600	48,000
5P Cpe	1750	5650	9400	18,800	32,900	47,000
Sed	1350	4300	7200	14,400	25,200	36,000
Fml Sed	1300	4200	7000	14,000	24,500	35,000
Clb Sed	1400	4450	7400	14,800	25,900	37,000
Series 1202, 8 cyl., 139" wb						
7P Sed	1700	5400	9000	18,000	31,500	45,000
Limo	1900	6000	10,000	20,000	35,000	50,000
Conv Sed	3400	10,800	18,000	36,000	63,000	90,000
LeB A/W Twn Car	3750	12,000	20,000	40,000	70,000	100,000
Series 1203, Super 8, 132" wb						
5P Sed	1800	5750	9600	19,200	33,600	48,000
Series 1204, Super 8, 139" wb						
Rds	3400	10,800	18,000	36,000	63,000	90,000
Phae	3450	11,050	18,400	36,800	64,400	92,000
Spt Phae	3600	11,500	19,200	38,400	67,200	96,000
Conv Vic	3550	11,300	18,800	37,600	65,800	94,000
RS Cpe	2350	7450	12,400	24,800	43,400	62,000
5P Cpe	2000	6350	10,600	21,200	37,100	53,000
Clb Sed	1700	5400	9000	18,000	31,500	45,000
Fml Sed	1650	5300	8800	17,600	30,800	44,000
LeB A/W Cabr	3400	10,800	18,000	36,000	63,000	90,000
Series 1205, Super 8, 144" wb						
Tr Sed	2550	8150	13,600	27,200	47,600	68,000
Conv Sed	3750	12,000	20,000	40,000	70,000	100,000
7P Sed	1900	6000	10,000	20,000	35,000	50,000
Limo	2150	6850	11,400	22,800	39,900	57,000
LeB A/W Twn Car	3600	11,500	19,200	38,400	67,200	96,000
Series 1207, V-12, 139" wb						
Rds	5650	18,000	30,000	60,000	105,000	150,000
Phae	5800	18,600	31,000	62,000	108,500	155,000
Spt Phae	6200	19,800	33,000	66,000	115,500	165,000
RS Cpe	3000	9600	16,000	32,000	56,000	80,000
5P Cpe	2800	8900	14,800	29,600	51,800	74,000
Clb Sed	2500	7900	13,200	26,400	46,200	66,000
Sed	2550	8150	13,600	27,200	47,600	68,000
Fml Sed	2650	8400	14,000	28,000	49,000	70,000
Conv Vic	5650	18,000	30,000	60,000	105,000	150,000
LeB A/W Cabr	5800	18,600	31,000	62,000	108,500	155,000
Series 1208, V-12, 144" wb						
Conv Sed	6950	22,200	37,000	74,000	129,500	185,000
7P Sed	2650	8400	14,000	28,000	49,000	70,000
Limo	3000	9600	16,000	32,000	56,000	80,000
LeB A/W Twn Car	6400	20,400	34,000	68,000	119,000	170,000

1936 14th Series

	6	5	4	3	2	1
Series 120-B, 8 cyl., 120" wb						
Conv	2050	6600	11,000	22,000	38,500	55,000
Conv Sed	2200	6950	11,600	23,200	40,600	58,000
Bus Cpe	1150	3600	6000	12,000	21,000	30,000
Spt Cpe	1150	3700	6200	12,400	21,700	31,000
Tr Cpe	1150	3600	6000	12,000	21,000	30,000
2d Sed	600	1900	3200	6400	11,200	16,000
Sed	650	2050	3400	6800	11,900	17,000
Clb Sed	700	2300	3800	7600	13,300	19,000
Tr Sed	700	2150	3600	7200	12,600	18,000
Series 1400, 8 cyl., 127" wb						
Sed	750	2400	4000	8000	14,000	20,000
Series 1401, 8 cyl., 134" wb						
Rds	3250	10,300	17,200	34,400	60,200	86,000
Phae	3300	10,550	17,600	35,200	61,600	88,000
Conv Vic	3700	11,750	19,600	39,200	68,600	98,000
LeB A/W Cabr	3400	10,800	18,000	36,000	63,000	90,000
RS Cpe	1700	5400	9000	18,000	31,500	45,000
5P Cpe	1600	5150	8600	17,200	30,100	43,000
Clb Sed	1400	4450	7400	14,800	25,900	37,000
Sed	1300	4200	7000	14,000	24,500	35,000
Fml Sed	1350	4300	7200	14,400	25,200	36,000
Series 1402, 8 cyl., 139" wb						
Conv Sed	4000	12,700	21,200	42,400	74,200	106,000
7P Tr	3850	12,250	20,400	40,800	71,400	102,000
7P Sed	1700	5400	9000	18,000	31,500	45,000
Bus Sed	1600	5150	8600	17,200	30,100	43,000
Limo	1900	6000	10,000	20,000	35,000	50,000
Bus Limo	1800	5750	9600	19,200	33,600	48,000
LeB Twn Car	3600	11,500	19,200	38,400	67,200	96,000
Series 1403, Super 8, 132" wb						
Sed	1600	5150	8600	17,200	30,100	43,000
Series 1404, Super 8, 139" wb						
Cpe Rds	3450	11,050	18,400	36,800	64,400	92,000
Phae	3750	12,000	20,000	40,000	70,000	100,000
Spt Phae	4000	12,700	21,200	42,400	74,200	106,000
Conv Vic	3850	12,250	20,400	40,800	71,400	102,000
LeB A/W Cabr	4000	12,700	21,200	42,400	74,200	106,000
RS Cpe	2350	7450	12,400	24,800	43,400	62,000
5P Cpe	2150	6850	11,400	22,800	39,900	57,000
Clb Sed	1950	6250	10,400	20,800	36,400	52,000
Fml Sed	1900	6000	10,000	20,000	35,000	50,000
Series 1405, Super 8, 144" wb						
7P Tr	4200	13,450	22,400	44,800	78,400	112,000
Conv Sed	4350	13,900	23,200	46,400	81,200	116,000
Series 1407, V-12, 139" wb						
Cpe Rds	5650	18,000	30,000	60,000	105,000	150,000
Phae	5800	18,600	31,000	62,000	108,500	155,000
Spt Phae	5800	18,600	31,000	62,000	108,500	155,000
LeB A/W Cabr	6000	19,200	32,000	64,000	112,000	160,000
Conv Vic	6000	19,200	32,000	64,000	112,000	160,000
RS Cpe	2850	9100	15,200	30,400	53,200	76,000
5P Cpe	2500	7900	13,200	26,400	46,200	66,000
Clb Sed	1900	6100	10,200	20,400	35,700	51,000
Sed	1750	5500	9200	18,400	32,200	46,000
Fml Sed	1700	5400	9000	18,000	31,500	45,000
Series 1408, V-12, 144" wb						
7P Tr	6000	19,200	32,000	64,000	112,000	160,000
Conv Sed	6200	19,800	33,000	66,000	115,500	165,000
7P Sed	1900	6000	10,000	20,000	35,000	50,000
Limo	2250	7200	12,000	24,000	42,000	60,000
LeB A/W Twn Car	6400	20,400	34,000	68,000	119,000	170,000

1937 15th Series

	6	5	4	3	2	1
Model 115-C, 6 cyl., 115" wb						
Conv	1500	4800	8000	16,000	28,000	40,000
Bus Cpe	950	3000	5000	10,000	17,500	25,000
Spt Cpe	1000	3250	5400	10,800	18,900	27,000
2d Sed	700	2150	3600	7200	12,600	18,000
Sed	650	2050	3400	6800	11,900	17,000
Clb Sed	700	2300	3800	7600	13,300	19,000
Tr Sed	700	2150	3600	7200	12,600	18,000
Sta Wag	1500	4800	8000	16,000	28,000	40,000
Model 120-C, 8 cyl., 120" wb						
Conv	1900	6000	10,000	20,000	35,000	50,000
Conv Sed	1950	6250	10,400	20,800	36,400	52,000
Bus Cpe	1200	3850	6400	12,800	22,400	32,000
Spt Cpe	1250	3950	6600	13,200	23,100	33,000
2d Sed	850	2650	4400	8800	15,400	22,000
Sed	800	2500	4200	8400	14,700	21,000
Clb Sed	850	2750	4600	9200	16,100	23,000
Tr Sed	850	2650	4400	8800	15,400	22,000
Sta Wag	1700	5400	9000	18,000	31,500	45,000
Model 120-CD, 8 cyl., 120" wb						
2d Sed	950	3000	5000	10,000	17,500	25,000
Clb Sed	1000	3250	5400	10,800	18,900	27,000
Tr Sed	1000	3100	5200	10,400	18,200	26,000
Model 138-CD, 8 cyl., 138" wb						
Tr Sed	1050	3350	5600	11,200	19,600	28,000
Tr Limo	1150	3700	6200	12,400	21,700	31,000
Model 1500, Super 8, 127" wb						
Sed	1000	3250	5400	10,800	18,900	27,000
Model 1501, Super 8, 134" wb						
Conv	3400	10,800	18,000	36,000	63,000	90,000
LeB A/W Cabr	3600	11,500	19,200	38,400	67,200	96,000
RS Cpe	2150	6850	11,400	22,800	39,900	57,000
5P Cpe	1900	6000	10,000	20,000	35,000	50,000
Clb Sed	1350	4300	7200	14,400	25,200	36,000
Tr Sed	1250	3950	6600	13,200	23,100	33,000
Fml Sed	1300	4100	6800	13,600	23,800	34,000
Vic	2700	8650	14,400	28,800	50,400	72,000
Model 1502, Super 8, 139" wb						
Conv Sed	3750	12,000	20,000	40,000	70,000	100,000
Bus Sed	1300	4200	7000	14,000	24,500	35,000
Tr Sed	1350	4300	7200	14,400	25,200	36,000
Tr Limo	1500	4800	8000	16,000	28,000	40,000
Bus Limo	1450	4700	7800	15,600	27,300	39,000
LeB A/W Twn Car	4150	13,200	22,000	44,000	77,000	110,000
Model 1506, V-12, 132" wb						
Tr Sed	1500	4800	8000	16,000	28,000	40,000
Model 1507, V-12, 139" wb						
Conv	5650	18,000	30,000	60,000	105,000	150,000
LeB A/W Cabr	5800	18,600	31,000	62,000	108,500	155,000
RS Cpe	2400	7700	12,800	25,600	44,800	64,000
5P Cpe	2350	7450	12,400	24,800	43,400	62,000
Clb Sed	1700	5400	9000	18,000	31,500	45,000
Fml Sed	1650	5300	8800	17,600	30,800	44,000
Tr Sed	1600	5150	8600	17,200	30,100	43,000
Conv Vic	5100	16,300	27,200	54,400	95,200	136,000
Model 1508, V-12, 144" wb						
Conv Sed	9000	28,800	48,000	96,000	168,000	240,000
Tr Sed	3000	9600	16,000	32,000	56,000	80,000
Tr Limo	3250	10,300	17,200	34,400	60,200	86,000
LeB A/W Twn Car	6950	22,200	37,000	74,000	129,500	185,000

1938 16th Series

	6	5	4	3	2	1
Model 1600, 6 cyl., 122" wb						
Conv	1400	4450	7400	14,800	25,900	37,000
Bus Cpe	800	2500	4200	8400	14,700	21,000
Clb Cpe	750	2400	4000	8000	14,000	20,000
2d Sed	550	1700	2800	5600	9800	14,000
Sed	550	1800	3000	6000	10,500	15,000
Model 1601, 8 cyl., 127" wb						
Conv	1700	5400	9000	18,000	31,500	45,000
Conv Sed	1750	5650	9400	18,800	32,900	47,000
Bus Cpe	1000	3250	5400	10,800	18,900	27,000
Clb Cpe	1050	3350	5600	11,200	19,600	28,000
2d Sed	750	2400	4000	8000	14,000	20,000
Sed	700	2300	3800	7600	13,300	19,000
Model 1601-D, 8 cyl., 127" wb						
Tr Sed	900	2900	4800	9600	16,800	24,000
Model 1601, 8 cyl., 139" wb						
Roll A/W Cabr	4150	13,200	22,000	44,000	77,000	110,000
Roll A/W Twn Car	4000	12,700	21,200	42,400	74,200	106,000
Roll Brgm	3600	11,500	19,200	38,400	67,200	96,000
Model 1602, 8 cyl., 148" wb						
Tr Sed	1150	3600	6000	12,000	21,000	30,000
Tr Limo	1300	4200	7000	14,000	24,500	35,000
Model 1603, Super 8, 127" wb						
Tr Sed	1350	4300	7200	14,400	25,200	36,000
Model 1604, Super 8, 134" wb						
Conv	3400	10,800	18,000	36,000	63,000	90,000
RS Cpe	1700	5400	9000	18,000	31,500	45,000
5P Cpe	1500	4800	8000	16,000	28,000	40,000

	6	5	4	3	2	1
Clb Sed	1000	3250	5400	10,800	18,900	27,000
Tr Sed	950	3000	5000	10,000	17,500	25,000
Fml Sed	1000	3100	5200	10,400	18,200	26,000
Vic	3250	10,300	17,200	34,400	60,200	86,000
Model 1605, Super 8, 139" wb						
Bus Sed	1300	4200	7000	14,000	24,500	35,000
Conv Sed	3750	12,000	20,000	40,000	70,000	100,000
Bus Limo	1900	6000	10,000	20,000	35,000	50,000
Model 1605, Super 8, Customs						
Bm A/W Cabr						value not estimable
Bm Tr Cabr						value not estimable
Roll A/W Cabr						value not estimable
Roll A/W Twn Car						value not estimable
Model 1607, V-12, 134" wb						
Conv Cpe	6950	22,200	37,000	74,000	129,500	185,000
2-4P Cpe	2400	7700	12,800	25,600	44,800	64,000
5P Cpe	2350	7450	12,400	24,800	43,400	62,000
Clb Sed	1900	6100	10,200	20,400	35,700	51,000
Conv Vic	6950	22,200	37,000	74,000	129,500	185,000
Tr Sed	1800	5750	9600	19,200	33,600	48,000
Fml Sed	1900	6000	10,000	20,000	35,000	50,000
Model 1608, V-12, 139" wb						
Conv Sed	7150	22,800	38,000	76,000	133,000	190,000
Tr Sed	2400	7700	12,800	25,600	44,800	64,000
Tr Limo	2550	8150	13,600	27,200	47,600	68,000
Model 1607-8, V-12, 139" wb						
Bm A/W Cabr						value not estimable
Bm Tr Cabr						value not estimable
Roll A/W Cabr						value not estimable
Roll A/W Twn Car						value not estimable

1939 17th Series

	6	5	4	3	2	1
Model 1700, 6 cyl., 122" wb						
Conv	1300	4200	7000	14,000	24,500	35,000
Bus Cpe	700	2300	3800	7600	13,300	19,000
Clb Cpe	750	2400	4000	8000	14,000	20,000
2d Sed	550	1700	2800	5600	9800	14,000
Tr Sed	550	1750	2900	5800	10,200	14,500
Sta Wag	1150	3700	6200	12,400	21,700	31,000
Model 1701, 8 cyl., 127" wb						
Conv	2200	6950	11,600	23,200	40,600	58,000
Conv Sed	2200	7100	11,800	23,600	41,300	59,000
Clb Cpe	850	2750	4600	9200	16,100	23,000
Bus Cpe	800	2500	4200	8400	14,700	21,000
2d Sed	650	2050	3400	6800	11,900	17,000
Sed	650	2050	3400	6800	11,900	17,000
Sta Wag	1200	3850	6400	12,800	22,400	32,000
Model 1702, 8-cyl., 148" wb						
Tr Sed	850	2650	4400	8800	15,400	22,000
Tr Limo	950	3000	5000	10,000	17,500	25,000
Model 1703, Super 8, 127" wb						
Tr Sed	1000	3250	5400	10,800	18,900	27,000
Conv	2350	7450	12,400	24,800	43,400	62,000
Conv Sed	2400	7700	12,800	25,600	44,800	64,000
Clb Cpe	1300	4200	7000	14,000	24,500	35,000
Model 1705, Super 8, 148" wb						
Tr Sed	1150	3600	6000	12,000	21,000	30,000
Tr Limo	1300	4200	7000	14,000	24,500	35,000
Model 1707, V-12, 134" wb						
Conv Cpe	6200	19,800	33,000	66,000	115,500	165,000
Conv Vic	6200	19,800	33,000	66,000	115,500	165,000
Roll A/W Cabr	4900	15,600	26,000	52,000	91,000	130,000
2-4P Cpe	2500	7900	13,200	26,400	46,200	66,000
5P Cpe	2250	7200	12,000	24,000	42,000	60,000
Sed	1900	6000	10,000	20,000	35,000	50,000
Clb Sed	1900	6100	10,200	20,400	35,700	51,000
Fml Sed	2150	6850	11,400	22,800	39,900	57,000
Model 1708, V-12, 139" wb						
Conv Sed						value not estimable
Bm Tr Cabr						value not estimable
Bm A/W Cabr						value not estimable
Tr Sed	2850	9100	15,200	30,400	53,200	76,000
Tr Limo	2950	9350	15,600	31,200	54,600	78,000
Roll A/W Twn Car						value not estimable

1940 18th Series

	6	5	4	3	2	1
Model 1800, 6 cyl., 122" wb, (110)						
Conv	1300	4200	7000	14,000	24,500	35,000
Bus Cpe	750	2400	4000	8000	14,000	20,000
Clb Cpe	800	2500	4200	8400	14,700	21,000
2d Sed	550	1700	2800	5600	9800	14,000
Sed	550	1700	2800	5600	9800	14,000
Sta Wag	1150	3600	6000	12,000	21,000	30,000
Model 1801, Std., 8 cyl., 127" wb, (120)						
Conv	1600	5050	8400	16,800	29,400	42,000
Conv Sed	1850	5900	9800	19,600	34,300	49,000
Bus Cpe	900	2900	4800	9600	16,800	24,000
Clb Cpe	950	3000	5000	10,000	17,500	25,000
2d Sed	700	2150	3600	7200	12,600	18,000
Clb Sed	700	2300	3800	7600	13,300	19,000
Sed	700	2150	3600	7200	12,600	18,000
Darr Vic	3750	12,000	20,000	40,000	70,000	100,000
Sta Wag	1250	3950	6600	13,200	23,100	33,000
Model 1801, DeLuxe, 8-cyl., 127" wb, (120)						
Conv	1700	5400	9000	18,000	31,500	45,000
Clb Cpe	950	3000	5000	10,000	17,500	25,000
Clb Sed	750	2400	4000	8000	14,000	20,000
Tr Sed	700	2300	3800	7600	13,300	19,000
Model 1803, Super 8, 127" wb, (160)						
Conv	2800	8900	14,800	29,600	51,800	74,000
Conv Sed	2950	9350	15,600	31,200	54,600	78,000
Bus Cpe	1000	3250	5400	10,800	18,900	27,000
Clb Cpe	1100	3500	5800	11,600	20,300	29,000
Clb Sed	1000	3250	5400	10,800	18,900	27,000
Sed	950	3000	5000	10,000	17,500	25,000
Model 1804, Super 8, 138" wb, (160)						
Sed	1050	3350	5600	11,200	19,600	28,000
Model 1805, Super 8, 148" wb, (160)						
Tr Sed	1100	3500	5800	11,600	20,300	29,000
Tr Limo	1150	3600	6000	12,000	21,000	30,000
Model 1806, Custom, Super 8, 127" wb, (180)						
Clb Sed	1300	4100	6800	13,600	23,800	34,000
Darr Conv Vic	4350	13,900	23,200	46,400	81,200	116,000
Model 1807, Custom, Super 8, 138" wb, (180)						
Darr Conv Sed	4500	14,400	24,000	48,000	84,000	120,000
Roll A/W Cabr	4150	13,200	22,000	44,000	77,000	110,000
Darr Spt Sed	3400	10,800	18,000	36,000	63,000	90,000
Fml Sed	1700	5400	9000	18,000	31,500	45,000
Tr Sed	1650	5300	8800	17,600	30,800	44,000
Model 1808, Custom, Super 8, 148" wb, (180)						
Roll A/W Twn Car	3400	10,800	18,000	36,000	63,000	90,000
Tr Sed	1700	5400	9000	18,000	31,500	45,000
Tr Limo	1750	5650	9400	18,800	32,900	47,000

1941 19th Series

	6	5	4	3	2	1
Model 1900, Std., 6 cyl., 122" wb, (110)						
Conv	1200	3850	6400	12,800	22,400	32,000
Bus Cpe	650	2050	3400	6800	11,900	17,000
Clb Cpe	700	2150	3600	7200	12,600	18,000
2d Sed	550	1700	2800	5600	9800	14,000
Tr Sed	550	1700	2800	5600	9800	14,000
Sta Wag	1450	4700	7800	15,600	27,300	39,000
Model 1900, Dlx., 6-cyl., 122" wb, (110)						
Conv	1400	4450	7400	14,800	25,900	37,000
Clb Cpe	750	2400	4000	8000	14,000	20,000
2d Sed	650	2050	3400	6800	11,900	17,000
Sed	550	1800	3000	6000	10,500	15,000
Sta Wag	1550	4900	8200	16,400	28,700	41,000
Model 1901, 8-cyl., 127" wb, (120)						
Conv	1500	4800	8000	16,000	28,000	40,000
Conv Sed	1600	5050	8400	16,800	29,400	42,000
Bus Cpe	850	2650	4400	8800	15,400	22,000
Clb Cpe	850	2750	4600	9200	16,100	23,000
2d Sed	700	2300	3800	7600	13,300	19,000
Sed	650	2050	3400	6800	11,900	17,000
Sta Wag	1750	5650	9400	18,800	32,900	47,000
DeL Sta Wag	1900	6000	10,000	20,000	35,000	50,000
Model 1903, Super 8, 127" wb, (160)						
Conv	2700	8650	14,400	28,800	50,400	72,000
DeL Conv	2800	8900	14,800	29,600	51,800	74,000
Conv Sed	2850	9100	15,200	30,400	53,200	76,000
DeL Conv Sed	2950	9350	15,600	31,200	54,600	78,000
Clb Cpe	950	3000	5000	10,000	17,500	25,000
Bus Cpe	900	2900	4800	9600	16,800	24,000
Sed	850	2750	4600	9200	16,100	23,000
Model 1904, Super 8, 138" wb, (160)						
Sed	1000	3250	5400	10,800	18,900	27,000
Model 1905, Super 8, 148" wb, (160)						
Tr Sed	1100	3500	5800	11,600	20,300	29,000
Tr Limo	1200	3850	6400	12,800	22,400	32,000
Model 1906, Custom, Super 8, 127" wb, (180)						
Darr Conv Vic	4000	12,700	21,200	42,400	74,200	106,000
Model 1907, Custom, Super 8, 138" wb, (180)						
Leb Spt Brgm	2650	8400	14,000	28,000	49,000	70,000
Roll A/W Cabr	3400	10,800	18,000	36,000	63,000	90,000
Darr Spt Sed	2850	9100	15,200	30,400	53,200	76,000
Tr Sed	1500	4800	8000	16,000	28,000	40,000
Fml Sed	1600	5050	8400	16,800	29,400	42,000
Model 1908, Custom, Super 8, 148" wb, (180)						
Roll A/W Twn Car	3300	10,550	17,600	35,200	61,600	88,000
Tr Sed	1700	5400	9000	18,000	31,500	45,000
LeB Tr Sed	1900	6000	10,000	20,000	35,000	50,000
Tr Limo	1950	6250	10,400	20,800	36,400	52,000
LeB Tr Limo	2250	7200	12,000	24,000	42,000	60,000
Series 1951, Clipper, 8 cyl., 127" wb						
Sed	600	1900	3200	6400	11,200	16,000

1942 20th Series

	6	5	4	3	2	1
Clipper Series -(6 cyl.)						
Series 2000, Special, 120" wb						
Bus Cpe	600	1900	3200	6400	11,200	16,000
Clb Sed	550	1800	3000	6000	10,500	15,000
Tr Sed	550	1700	2800	5600	9800	14,000
Series 2010, Custom, 120" wb						
Clb Sed	700	2150	3600	7200	12,600	18,000
Tr Sed	650	2050	3400	6800	11,900	17,000
Series 2020, Custom, 122" wb						
Conv	1350	4300	7200	14,400	25,200	36,000
Clipper Series -(8 cyl.)						
Series 2001, Special, 120" wb						
Bus Cpe	650	2050	3400	6800	11,900	17,000
Clb Sed	700	2150	3600	7200	12,600	18,000
Tr Sed	650	2050	3400	6800	11,900	17,000
Series 2011, Custom, 120" wb						
Clb Sed	800	2500	4200	8400	14,700	21,000
Tr Sed	750	2400	4000	8000	14,000	20,000
Series 2021, Custom, 127" wb						
Conv	1500	4800	8000	16,000	28,000	40,000
Super 8, 160 Series, Clipper, 127" wb, 2003						
Clb Sed	950	3000	5000	10,000	17,500	25,000
Tr Sed	900	2900	4800	9600	16,800	24,000
Super 8, 160, 127" wb, 2023						
Conv	2700	8650	14,400	28,800	50,400	72,000
Super 8, 160, 138" wb, 2004						
Tr Sed	1000	3250	5400	10,800	18,900	27,000
Super 8, 160, 148" wb, 2005						
7P Sed	1100	3500	5800	11,600	20,300	29,000
Limo	1150	3700	6200	12,400	21,700	31,000
Super 8, 160, 148" wb, 2055						
Bus Sed	1000	3250	5400	10,800	18,900	27,000
Bus Limo	1100	3500	5800	11,600	20,300	29,000
Super 8, 180, Clipper, 127" wb, 2006						
Clb Sed	1000	3100	5200	10,400	18,200	26,000
Tr Sed	950	3000	5000	10,000	17,500	25,000
Super 8, 180, Special, 127" wb, 2006						
Darr Conv Vic	4350	13,900	23,200	46,400	81,200	116,000
Super 8, 180, 138" wb, 2007						
Tr Sed	950	3000	5000	10,000	17,500	25,000
Fml Sed	1000	3250	5400	10,800	18,900	27,000
Roll A/W Cabr	3400	10,800	18,000	36,000	63,000	90,000
Super 8, 180, 148" wb, 2008						
Tr Sed	1200	3850	6400	12,800	22,400	32,000
Limo	1300	4200	7000	14,000	24,500	35,000
LeB Sed	1750	5650	9400	18,800	32,900	47,000
LeB Limo	1900	6100	10,200	20,400	35,700	51,000
Roll A/W Twn Car	3400	10,800	18,000	36,000	63,000	90,000

1946 21st Series

	6	5	4	3	2	1
Clipper, 6-cyl., 120" wb, 2100						
Clb Sed	550	1700	2800	5600	9800	14,000
Sed	500	1550	2600	5200	9100	13,000
Clipper, 6-cyl., 120" wb, 2130						
4d Taxi						value not estimable
Clipper, 8-cyl., 120" wb, 2101						
Tr Sed	500	1550	2600	5200	9100	13,000
Clipper, DeLuxe, 8-cyl., 120" wb, 2111						
Clb Sed	550	1800	3000	6000	10,500	15,000
Tr Sed	550	1700	2800	5600	9800	14,000
Clipper, Super 8, 127" wb, 2103						
Clb Sed	600	1900	3200	6400	11,200	16,000
Tr Sed	550	1800	3000	6000	10,500	15,000

	6	5	4	3	2	1
Clipper, Super 8, 127" wb, 2106 Custom						
Clb Sed	700	2150	3600	7200	12,600	18,000
Tr Sed	650	2050	3400	6800	11,900	17,000
Clipper, Super, 148" wb, 2126 Custom						
8P Sed	900	2900	4800	9600	16,800	24,000
Limo	1100	3500	5800	11,600	20,300	29,000

1947 21st Series

	6	5	4	3	2	1
Clipper, 6-cyl., 120" wb, 2100						
Clb Sed	550	1700	2800	5600	9800	14,000
Tr Sed	500	1550	2600	5200	9100	13,000
Clipper, DeLuxe, 8-cyl., 120" wb, 2111						
Clb Sed	550	1700	2800	5600	9800	14,000
Tr Sed	500	1550	2600	5200	9100	13,000
Clipper, Super 8, 127" wb, 2103						
Clb Sed	700	2150	3600	7200	12,600	18,000
Tr Sed	600	1900	3200	6400	11,200	16,000
Clipper, Super 8, 127" wb, 2106 Custom						
Clb Sed	800	2500	4200	8400	14,700	21,000
Tr Sed	700	2150	3600	7200	12,600	18,000
Clipper, Super 8, 148" wb, 2126 Custom						
7P Sed	900	2900	4800	9600	16,800	24,000
Limo	1100	3500	5800	11,600	20,300	29,000

1948 & Early 1949 22nd Series

	6	5	4	3	2	1
Series 2201, 8-cyl., 120" wb						
Clb Sed	500	1550	2600	5200	9100	13,000
Sed	450	1450	2400	4800	8400	12,000
Sta Sed	1450	4550	7600	15,200	26,600	38,000
Series 2211, DeLuxe, 8-cyl., 120" wb						
Clb Sed	550	1800	3000	6000	10,500	15,000
Tr Sed	550	1700	2800	5600	9800	14,000
Super 8, 120" wb, 2202						
Clb Sed	700	2150	3600	7200	12,600	18,000
Sed	650	2050	3400	6800	11,900	17,000
Super 8, 120" wb, 2232						
Conv	1450	4550	7600	15,200	26,600	38,000
Super 8, 141" wb, 2222						
Sed	850	2750	4600	9200	16,100	23,000
Limo	1050	3350	5600	11,200	19,600	28,000
Super 8, DeLuxe, 141" wb						
Sed	900	2900	4800	9600	16,800	24,000
Limo	1100	3500	5800	11,600	20,300	29,000
Custom 8, 127" wb, 2206						
Clb Sed	850	2750	4600	9200	16,100	23,000
Tr Sed	850	2650	4400	8800	15,400	22,000
Custom 8, 127" wb, 2233						
Conv	1500	4800	8000	16,000	28,000	40,000
Custom 8, 148" wb, 2226						
7P Sed	1100	3500	5800	11,600	20,300	29,000
Limo	1150	3600	6000	12,000	21,000	30,000

1949-1950 23rd Series

	6	5	4	3	2	1
Series 2301, 120" wb						
Clb Sed	550	1700	2800	5600	9800	14,000
Sed	500	1550	2600	5200	9100	13,000
Sta Sed	1450	4550	7600	15,200	26,600	38,000
2301 DeLuxe, 120" wb						
Clb Sed	550	1800	3000	6000	10,500	15,000
Sed	550	1700	2800	5600	9800	14,000
Super 8, 127" wb, 2302						
Clb Sed	650	2050	3400	6800	11,900	17,000
Sed	600	1900	3200	6400	11,200	16,000
Super 8, 2302 DeLuxe						
Clb Sed	700	2150	3600	7200	12,600	18,000
Sed	650	2050	3400	6800	11,900	17,000
Super 8, Super DeLuxe, 127" wb, 2332						
Conv	1450	4550	7600	15,200	26,600	38,000
Super 8, 141" wb, 2322						
7P Sed	950	3000	5000	10,000	17,500	25,000
Limo	1100	3500	5800	11,600	20,300	29,000
Custom 8, 127" wb, 2306						
Sed	850	2650	4400	8800	15,400	22,000
Custom 8, 127" wb, 2333						
Conv	1500	4800	8000	16,000	28,000	40,000

1951 24th Series

	6	5	4	3	2	1
200, Standard, 122" wb, 2401						
Bus Cpe	400	1300	2200	4400	7700	11,000
2d Sed	450	1400	2300	4600	8100	11,500
Sed	450	1450	2400	4800	8400	12,000
200, DeLuxe						
2d Sed	450	1450	2400	4800	8400	12,000
Sed	450	1500	2500	5000	8800	12,500
122" wb, 2402						
M.F HT	550	1800	3000	6000	10,500	15,000
Conv	1000	3100	5200	10,400	18,200	26,000
300, 127" wb, 2402						
Sed	500	1550	2600	5200	9100	13,000
Patrician, 400, 127" wb, 2406						
Sed	550	1800	3000	6000	10,500	15,000

1952 25th Series

	6	5	4	3	2	1
200, Std., 122" wb, 2501						
2d Sed	450	1400	2300	4600	8100	11,500
Sed	450	1450	2400	4800	8400	12,000
200, DeLuxe						
2d Sed	450	1500	2450	4900	8600	12,300
Sed	450	1500	2500	5000	8800	12,500
122" wb, 2531						
Conv	1000	3100	5200	10,400	18,200	26,000
M.F HT	600	1900	3200	6400	11,200	16,000
300, 122" wb, 2502						
Sed	500	1600	2700	5400	9500	13,500
Patrician, 400, 127" wb, 2506						
Sed	550	1800	3000	6000	10,500	15,000
Der Cus Sed	600	1900	3200	6400	11,200	16,000

1953 26th Series

	6	5	4	3	2	1
Clipper, 122" wb, 2601						
2d HT	550	1800	3000	6000	10,500	15,000
2d Sed	450	1450	2400	4800	8400	12,000
Sed	450	1450	2450	4900	8500	12,200
Clipper DeLuxe						
2d Sed	450	1500	2500	5000	8800	12,500
Sed	450	1500	2500	5000	8800	12,600
Cavalier, 127" wb, 2602						
Cav Sed	500	1550	2600	5200	9100	13,000
Packard 8, 122" wb, 2631						
Conv	1050	3350	5600	11,200	19,600	28,000
Carr Conv	1500	4800	8000	16,000	28,000	40,000
M.F HdTp	600	1900	3200	6400	11,200	16,000
Patrician, 127" wb, 2606						
Sed	600	1900	3200	6400	11,200	16,000
Der Fml Sed	700	2150	3600	7200	12,600	18,000
149" wb, 2626						
Exec Sed	650	2050	3400	6800	11,900	17,000
Corp Limo	700	2300	3800	7600	13,300	19,000

1954 54th Series

	6	5	4	3	2	1
Clipper, 122" wb, DeLuxe 5401						
2d HdTp	550	1800	3000	6000	10,500	15,000
Clb Sed	450	1450	2400	4800	8400	12,000
Sed	450	1450	2450	4900	8500	12,200
Clipper Super 5411						
Pan HT	600	1900	3200	6400	11,200	16,000
Clb Sed	500	1550	2600	5200	9100	13,000
Sed	500	1600	2650	5300	9200	13,200
Cavalier, 127" wb, 5402						
Sed	550	1700	2800	5600	9800	14,000
Packard 8, 122" wb, 5431						
Pac HT	650	2050	3400	6800	11,900	17,000
Conv	1050	3350	5600	11,200	19,600	28,000
Carr Conv	1500	4800	8000	16,000	28,000	40,000
Patrician, 127" wb, 5406						
Sed	550	1800	3000	6000	10,500	15,000
Der Cus Sed	650	2050	3400	6800	11,900	17,000
149" wb, 5426						
8P Sed	700	2150	3600	7200	12,600	18,000
Limo	700	2300	3800	7600	13,300	19,000

1955 55th Series

	6	5	4	3	2	1
Clipper, DeLuxe, 122" wb, 5540						
Sed	400	1200	2000	4000	7000	10,000
Clipper, Super, 5540						
Pan HT	550	1700	2800	5600	9800	14,000
Sed	400	1250	2100	4200	7400	10,500
Clipper Custom 5560 (352 cid V-8)						
Con HdTp	600	1900	3200	6400	11,200	16,000
Sed	400	1300	2200	4400	7700	11,000
Packard, 400, 127" wb, 5580						
"400" HT	950	3000	5000	10,000	17,500	25,000
Caribbean 5580						
Conv	1650	5300	8800	17,600	30,800	44,000
Patrician 5580						
Sed	650	2050	3400	6800	11,900	17,000

1956 56th Series

	6	5	4	3	2	1
Clipper, DeLuxe, 122" wb, 5640						
Sed	400	1250	2100	4200	7400	10,500
Clipper, Super, 5640						
HT	550	1800	3000	6000	10,500	15,000
Sed	400	1300	2200	4400	7700	11,000
Clipper, Custom, 5660						
Con HT	600	1900	3200	6400	11,200	16,000
Sed	450	1450	2400	4800	8400	12,000
Clipper Executive						
HT	650	2050	3400	6800	11,900	17,000
Sed	500	1550	2600	5200	9100	13,000
Packard, 400, 127" wb, 5680						
"400" HT	1000	3100	5200	10,400	18,200	26,000
Caribbean, 5688						
Conv	1700	5400	9000	18,000	31,500	45,000
HT	1100	3500	5800	11,600	20,300	29,000
Patrician, 5680						
Sed	600	1900	3200	6400	11,200	16,000

1957 57th L Series

	6	5	4	3	2	1
Clipper						
Sed	450	1140	1900	3800	6650	9500
Sta Wag	400	1200	2000	4000	7000	10,000

1958 58th L Series

	6	5	4	3	2	1
HT	500	1550	2600	5200	9100	13,000
Sed	350	1040	1750	3500	6100	8700
Sta Wag	450	1080	1800	3600	6300	9000
Hawk	900	2900	4800	9600	16,800	24,000

PIERCE-ARROW

1901

	6	5	4	3	2	1
1-cyl., 2-3/4 hp						
Motorette	1800	5750	9600	19,200	33,600	48,000
1-cyl., 3-3/4 hp						
Motorette	1900	6000	10,000	20,000	35,000	50,000

1902

	6	5	4	3	2	1
1-cyl., 3-1/2 hp, 58" wb						
Motorette	1900	6000	10,000	20,000	35,000	50,000

1903

	6	5	4	3	2	1
1-cyl., 5 hp						
Rbt	1950	6250	10,400	20,800	36,400	52,000
1-cyl., 6-1/2 hp						
Stanhope	2050	6500	10,800	21,600	37,800	54,000
2-cyl., 15 hp						
5P Tr	2200	6950	11,600	23,200	40,600	58,000

1904

	6	5	4	3	2	1
1-cyl., 8 hp, 70" wb						
Stanhope	1900	6000	10,000	20,000	35,000	50,000
2P Stanhope	1800	5750	9600	19,200	33,600	48,000
4 cyl., 24/28 hp, 93" wb						
5P Great Arrow Tr	2700	8650	14,400	28,800	50,400	72,000
2-cyl., 15 hp, 81" wb						
5P Tr	1700	5400	9000	18,000	31,500	45,000
4-cyl., 24/28 hp 93" wb						
Great Arrow Tr	2400	7700	12,800	25,600	44,800	64,000

1905

	6	5	4	3	2	1
1-cyl., 8 hp, 70" wb						
Stanhope	1450	4550	7600	15,200	26,600	38,000
Stanhope	1500	4800	8000	16,000	28,000	40,000
Great Arrow - 4-cyl., 24/28 hp, 100" wb						
5P Tonn	2350	7450	12,400	24,800	43,400	62,000
5P Canopy Tonn	2400	7700	12,800	25,600	44,800	64,000
5P Vic	2050	6600	11,000	22,000	38,500	55,000
5P Cape Tonn	2150	6850	11,400	22,800	39,900	57,000
Great Arrow - 4-cyl., 28/32 hp, 104" wb						
5P Tonn	2500	7900	13,200	26,400	46,200	66,000
5P Canopy Tonn	2400	7700	12,800	25,600	44,800	64,000
5P Vic	2350	7450	12,400	24,800	43,400	62,000
5P Cape Tonn	2400	7700	12,800	25,600	44,800	64,000
Great Arrow - 4-cyl., 28/32 hp, 109" wb						
7P Lan'let	1900	6000	10,000	20,000	35,000	50,000
7P Sub	1700	5400	9000	18,000	31,500	45,000
8P Opera Coach	1950	6250	10,400	20,800	36,400	52,000

	6	5	4	3	2	1
4-cyl., 24/28 hp, 100" wb						
Great Arrow Tr	2400	7700	12,800	25,600	44,800	64,000
Great Arrow Lan'let	2200	7100	11,800	23,600	41,300	59,000
Great Arrow Sub	2050	6600	11,000	22,000	38,500	55,000
4-cyl., 28/32 hp, 104" wb						
Great Arrow Opera Ch	2550	8150	13,600	27,200	47,600	68,000
1906						
Motorette - 1-cyl., 8 hp, 70" wb						
Stanhope	1150	3600	6000	12,000	21,000	30,000
Great Arrow - 4-cyl., 28/32 hp, 107" wb						
5P Tr	2500	7900	13,200	26,400	46,200	66,000
5P Vic	2050	6600	11,000	22,000	38,500	55,000
8P Open Coach	2650	8400	14,000	28,000	49,000	70,000
7P Sub	2550	8150	13,600	27,200	47,600	68,000
7P Lan'let	2350	7450	12,400	24,800	43,400	62,000
Great Arrow - 4-cyl., 40/45 hp, 109" wb						
7P Tr	2700	8650	14,400	28,800	50,400	72,000
8P Open Coach	2800	8900	14,800	29,600	51,800	74,000
7P Sub	2700	8650	14,400	28,800	50,400	72,000
7P Lan'let	2500	7900	13,200	26,400	46,200	66,000
1907						
Great Arrow - 4-cyl., 28/32 hp, 112" wb						
5P Tr	2800	8900	14,800	29,600	51,800	74,000
5P Limo	2500	7900	13,200	26,400	46,200	66,000
7P Sub	2550	8150	13,600	27,200	47,600	68,000
Great Arrow - 4-cyl., 40/45 hp, 124" wb						
7P Tr	2850	9100	15,200	30,400	53,200	76,000
7P Limo	2700	8650	14,400	28,800	50,400	72,000
7P Sub	2800	8900	14,800	29,600	51,800	74,000
Great Arrow - 6-cyl., 65 hp, 135" wb						
7P Tr	2850	9100	15,200	30,400	53,200	76,000
1908						
Great Arrow - 4-cyl., 30 hp, 112" wb						
Tr	2650	8400	14,000	28,000	49,000	70,000
Great Arrow - 4-cyl., 40 hp, 124" wb						
Tr	2850	9100	15,200	30,400	53,200	76,000
Sub	2700	8650	14,400	28,800	50,400	72,000
Great Arrow - 6-cyl., 40 hp, 130" wb						
Tr	3100	9850	16,400	32,800	57,400	82,000
Sub	2850	9100	15,200	30,400	53,200	76,000
Rds	3000	9600	16,000	32,000	56,000	80,000
Great Arrow - 6-cyl., 60 hp, 135" wb						
Tr	3400	10,800	18,000	36,000	63,000	90,000
Sub	3000	9600	16,000	32,000	56,000	80,000
Rds	3250	10,300	17,200	34,400	60,200	86,000
1909						
Model 24 - 4 cyl., 24 hp, 111-1/2" wb						
3P Rbt	1300	4200	7000	14,000	24,500	35,000
3P Vic Top Rbt	1400	4450	7400	14,800	25,900	37,000
2P Rbt	1300	4100	6800	13,600	23,800	34,000
4P Tr Car	1500	4800	8000	16,000	28,000	40,000
5P Lan'let	1450	4550	7600	15,200	26,600	38,000
5P Brgm	1450	4700	7800	15,600	27,300	39,000
Model 36 - 6-cyl., 36 hp, 119" wb						
5P Tr	1650	5300	8800	17,600	30,800	44,000
5P Cape Top Tr	1700	5400	9000	18,000	31,500	45,000
2P Rbt	1450	4700	7800	15,600	27,300	39,000
3P Rbt	1500	4750	7900	15,800	27,700	39,500
4P Tr	1600	5150	8600	17,200	30,100	43,000
5P Brgm	1500	4800	8000	16,000	28,000	40,000
5P Lan'let	1600	5050	8400	16,800	29,400	42,000
Model 40 - 4-cyl., 40 hp, 124" wb						
7P Sub	1900	6000	10,000	20,000	35,000	50,000
4P Tr Car	1850	5900	9800	19,600	34,300	49,000
7P Tr	1900	6000	10,000	20,000	35,000	50,000
7P Lan	1700	5400	9000	18,000	31,500	45,000
Model 48 - 6-cyl., 48 hp, 130" wb						
4P Tr	2150	6850	11,400	22,800	39,900	57,000
4P Cape Top Tr	2200	7100	11,800	23,600	41,300	59,000
2P Tr	2050	6600	11,000	22,000	38,500	55,000
3P Tr	2150	6850	11,400	22,800	39,900	57,000
7P Tr	2350	7450	12,400	24,800	43,400	62,000
7P Lan	2050	6600	11,000	22,000	38,500	55,000
7P Sub	2350	7450	12,400	24,800	43,400	62,000
Model 60 - 6-cyl., 60 hp, 135" wb						
7P Tr	2850	9100	15,200	30,400	53,200	76,000
7P Cape Top Tr	2950	9350	15,600	31,200	54,600	78,000
7P Sub	2950	9350	15,600	31,200	54,600	78,000
7P Lan	2650	8400	14,000	28,000	49,000	70,000
1910						
Model 36 - 6-cyl., 36 hp, 125" wb						
5P Lan'let	1650	5300	8800	17,600	30,800	44,000
4P Miniature Tonn	1600	5050	8400	16,800	29,400	42,000
5P Tr	1650	5300	8800	17,600	30,800	44,000
5P Brgm	1500	4800	8000	16,000	28,000	40,000
Rbt (119" wb)	1500	4800	8000	16,000	28,000	40,000
Model 48 - 6-cyl., 48 hp, 134-1/2" wb						
7P Lan'let	1900	6000	10,000	20,000	35,000	50,000
Miniature Tonn	1800	5750	9600	19,200	33,600	48,000
7P Tr	2050	6600	11,000	22,000	38,500	55,000
7P Sub	2050	6600	11,000	22,000	38,500	55,000
Rbt (128" wb)	1900	6000	10,000	20,000	35,000	50,000
Model 66 - 6-cyl., 66 hp, 140" wb						
7P Tr	2850	9100	15,200	30,400	53,200	76,000
4P Miniature Tonn	2650	8400	14,000	28,000	49,000	70,000
7P Sub	2850	9100	15,200	30,400	53,200	76,000
7P Lan'let	2650	8400	14,000	28,000	49,000	70,000
Rbt (133-1/2" wb)	2550	8150	13,600	27,200	47,600	68,000
1911						
Model 36T - 6-cyl., 38 hp, 125" wb						
5P Tr	2550	8150	13,600	27,200	47,600	68,000
3P Rbt	2400	7700	12,800	25,600	44,800	64,000
4P Miniature Tonn	2400	7700	12,800	25,600	44,800	64,000
5P Brgm	2150	6850	11,400	22,800	39,900	57,000
5P Lan'let	2350	7450	12,400	24,800	43,400	62,000
Model 48T - 6-cyl., 48 hp, 134-1/2" wb						
7P Tr	2800	8900	14,800	29,600	51,800	74,000
Rbt	2500	7900	13,200	26,400	46,200	66,000
Miniature Tonn	2550	8150	13,600	27,200	47,600	68,000
5P Close Coupled	2050	6600	11,000	22,000	38,500	55,000
5P Protected Tr	2500	7900	13,200	26,400	46,200	66,000
Sub	2700	8650	14,400	28,800	50,400	72,000
Lan	2700	8650	14,400	28,800	50,400	72,000
Model 66T - 6-cyl., 66 hp, 140" wb						
7P Tr	3100	9850	16,400	32,800	57,400	82,000
Rbt	2850	9100	15,200	30,400	53,200	76,000
Miniature Tonn	2950	9350	15,600	31,200	54,600	78,000
5P Protected Tr	2850	9100	15,200	30,400	53,200	76,000
Close Coupled	2500	7900	13,200	26,400	46,200	66,000
Sub	3000	9600	16,000	32,000	56,000	80,000
Lan	3000	9600	16,000	32,000	56,000	80,000
1912						
Model 36T - 6 cyl., 36 hp, 127-1/2" wb						
4P Tr	2500	7900	13,200	26,400	46,200	66,000
5P Tr	2500	7900	13,200	26,400	46,200	66,000
Brgm	2350	7450	12,400	24,800	43,400	62,000
Lan'let	2350	7450	12,400	24,800	43,400	62,000
Rbt (119" wb)	2400	7700	12,800	25,600	44,800	64,000
Model 48 - 6-cyl., 48 hp, 134-1/2" wb						
4P Tr	2700	8650	14,400	28,800	50,400	72,000
5P Tr	2700	8650	14,400	28,800	50,400	72,000
7P Tr	2800	8900	14,800	29,600	51,800	74,000
Brgm	2500	7900	13,200	26,400	46,200	66,000
Lan'let	2500	7900	13,200	26,400	46,200	66,000
Sub	2650	8400	14,000	28,000	49,000	70,000
Lan	2650	8400	14,000	28,000	49,000	70,000
Vestibule Sub	2550	8150	13,600	27,200	47,600	68,000
Rbt (128" wb)	2550	8150	13,600	27,200	47,600	68,000
Model 66 - 6-cyl., 66 hp, 140" wb						
4P Tr	3000	9600	16,000	32,000	56,000	80,000
5P Tr	3100	9850	16,400	32,800	57,400	82,000
7P Tr	3150	10,100	16,800	33,600	58,800	84,000
Sub	3100	9850	16,400	32,800	57,400	82,000
Lan	3000	9600	16,000	32,000	56,000	80,000
Vestibule Sub	3000	9600	16,000	32,000	56,000	80,000
Rbt (133-1/2" wb)	3000	9600	16,000	32,000	56,000	80,000
1913						
Model 38-C - 6-cyl., 38.4 hp, 119" wb						
3P Rbt	2050	6600	11,000	22,000	38,500	55,000
4P Tr	2150	6850	11,400	22,800	39,900	57,000
5P Tr	2200	7100	11,800	23,600	41,300	59,000
6P Brgm	2000	6350	10,600	21,200	37,100	53,000
6P Lan'let	2050	6500	10,800	21,600	37,800	54,000
Model 48-B - 6-cyl., 48.6 hp, 134-1/2" wb						
5P Tr	2700	8650	14,400	28,800	50,400	72,000
Rbt	2650	8400	14,000	28,000	49,000	70,000
4P Tr	2700	8650	14,400	28,800	50,400	72,000
7P Tr	2800	8900	14,800	29,600	51,800	74,000
Brgm	2050	6600	11,000	22,000	38,500	55,000
Lan'let	2150	6850	11,400	22,800	39,900	57,000
7P Sub	2350	7450	12,400	24,800	43,400	62,000
7P Lan	2200	7100	11,800	23,600	41,300	59,000
Vestibule Sub	2400	7700	12,800	25,600	44,800	64,000
Vestibule Lan	2400	7700	12,800	25,600	44,800	64,000
Model 66-A - 6-cyl., 60 hp, 147-1/2" wb						
7P Tr	3300	10,550	17,600	35,200	61,600	88,000
Rbt	3000	9600	16,000	32,000	56,000	80,000
4P Tr	3250	10,300	17,200	34,400	60,200	86,000
5P Tr	3250	10,300	17,200	34,400	60,200	86,000
Brgm	2650	8400	14,000	28,000	49,000	70,000
Lan'let	2650	8400	14,000	28,000	49,000	70,000
7P Sub	2850	9100	15,200	30,400	53,200	76,000
7P Lan	2850	9100	15,200	30,400	53,200	76,000
Vestibule Sub	2950	9350	15,600	31,200	54,600	78,000
Vestibule Lan	2950	9350	15,600	31,200	54,600	78,000
1914						
Model 38-C - 6-cyl., 38.4 hp, 132" wb						
5P Tr	2200	7100	11,800	23,600	41,300	59,000
4P Tr	2150	6850	11,400	22,800	39,900	57,000
7P Brgm	2000	6350	10,600	21,200	37,100	53,000
7P Lan'let	2050	6500	10,800	21,600	37,800	54,000
Vestibule Brgm	2050	6600	11,000	22,000	38,500	55,000
Vestibule Lan	2050	6600	11,000	22,000	38,500	55,000
3P Rbt (127-1/2" wb)	2150	6850	11,400	22,800	39,900	57,000
Model 48-B - 6-cyl., 48.6 hp, 142" wb						
4P Tr	2700	8650	14,400	28,800	50,400	72,000
5P Tr	2800	8900	14,800	29,600	51,800	74,000
7P Tr	2850	9100	15,200	30,400	53,200	76,000
7P Sub	2800	8900	14,800	29,600	51,800	74,000
7P Lan	2550	8150	13,600	27,200	47,600	68,000
Vestibule Sub	2500	7900	13,200	26,400	46,200	66,000
Vestibule Lan	2500	7900	13,200	26,400	46,200	66,000
Brgm	2500	7900	13,200	26,400	46,200	66,000
Lan	2550	8150	13,600	27,200	47,600	68,000
Vestibule Brgm	2550	8150	13,600	27,200	47,600	68,000
Vestibule Lan'let	2550	8150	13,600	27,200	47,600	68,000
3P Rbt (134-1/2 "wb)	2650	8400	14,000	28,000	49,000	70,000
Model 66-A - 6-cyl., 60 hp, 147-1/2" wb						
4P Tr	3150	10,100	16,800	33,600	58,800	84,000
5P Tr	3250	10,300	17,200	34,400	60,200	86,000
7P Tr	3300	10,550	17,600	35,200	61,600	88,000
7P Sub	3150	10,100	16,800	33,600	58,800	84,000
7P Lan	3000	9600	16,000	32,000	56,000	80,000
Vestibule Lan	3000	9600	16,000	32,000	56,000	80,000
7P Brgm	3000	9600	16,000	32,000	56,000	80,000
7P Lan	3000	9600	16,000	32,000	56,000	80,000
Vestibule Brgm	3100	9850	16,400	32,800	57,400	82,000
Vestibule Lan	3100	9850	16,400	32,800	57,400	82,000
3P Rbt	3100	9850	16,400	32,800	57,400	82,000
1915						
Model 38-C - 6-cyl., 38.4 hp, 134" wb						
5P Tr	2350	7450	12,400	24,800	43,400	62,000
4P Tr	2250	7200	12,000	24,000	42,000	60,000
2P Rbt	2150	6850	11,400	22,800	39,900	57,000
2P Cpe Rbt	2050	6600	11,000	22,000	38,500	55,000
7P Brgm	2050	6500	10,800	21,600	37,800	54,000
7P Lan'let	2050	6500	10,800	21,600	37,800	54,000
7P Sed	1900	6000	10,000	20,000	35,000	50,000
7P Brgm Lan'let	2050	6600	11,000	22,000	38,500	55,000
Vestibule Brgm	2150	6850	11,400	22,800	39,900	57,000
Vestibule Lan'let	2150	6850	11,400	22,800	39,900	57,000
Vestibule Brgm Lan'let	2150	6850	11,400	22,800	39,900	57,000
Model 48-B - 6-cyl., 48.6 hp, 142" wb						
5P Tr	2800	8900	14,800	29,600	51,800	74,000
4P Tr	2800	8900	14,800	29,600	51,800	74,000
7P Tr	2850	9100	15,200	30,400	53,200	76,000
2P Rbt	2700	8650	14,400	28,800	50,400	72,000
2P Cpe Rbt	2650	8400	14,000	28,000	49,000	70,000
Cpe	2550	8150	13,600	27,200	47,600	68,000
7P Sub	2500	7900	13,200	26,400	46,200	66,000
7P Lan	2500	7900	13,200	26,400	46,200	66,000
7P Brgm	2500	7900	13,200	26,400	46,200	66,000
Sub Lan	2500	7900	13,200	26,400	46,200	66,000
Vestibule Sub	2550	8150	13,600	27,200	47,600	68,000
Vestibule Lan	2550	8150	13,600	27,200	47,600	68,000
Vestibule Brgm	2500	7900	13,200	26,400	46,200	66,000

	6	5	4	3	2	1
Vestibule Sub Lan	2500	7900	13,200	26,400	46,200	66,000
Model 66-A - 6-cyl., 60 hp, 147-1/2" wb						
7P Tr	3300	10,550	17,600	35,200	61,600	88,000
4P Tr	3150	10,100	16,800	33,600	58,800	84,000
5P Tr	3250	10,300	17,200	34,400	60,200	86,000
2P Rbt	3100	9850	16,400	32,800	57,400	82,000
2P Cpe Rbt	3000	9600	16,000	32,000	56,000	80,000
7P Sub	3150	10,100	16,800	33,600	58,800	84,000
7P Lan	3150	10,100	16,800	33,600	58,800	84,000
7P Brgm	3150	10,100	16,800	33,600	58,800	84,000
7P Sub Lan	3150	10,100	16,800	33,600	58,800	84,000
Vestibule Lan	3250	10,300	17,200	34,400	60,200	86,000
Vestibule Sub	3250	10,300	17,200	34,400	60,200	86,000
Vestibule Brgm	3150	10,100	16,800	33,600	58,800	84,000
Vestibule Sub Lan	3250	10,300	17,200	34,400	60,200	86,000
1916						
Model 38-C - 6-cyl., 38.4 hp, 134" wb						
5P Tr	2400	7700	12,800	25,600	44,800	64,000
4P Tr	2400	7700	12,800	25,600	44,800	64,000
2P Rbt	2350	7450	12,400	24,800	43,400	62,000
3P Rbt	2350	7450	12,400	24,800	43,400	62,000
3P Cpe	1900	6000	10,000	20,000	35,000	50,000
2P Cpe	1900	6000	10,000	20,000	35,000	50,000
7P Brgm	1850	5900	9800	19,600	34,300	49,000
7P Lan'let	1850	5900	9800	19,600	34,300	49,000
7P Sed	1750	5650	9400	18,800	32,900	47,000
Brgm Lan'let	1900	6000	10,000	20,000	35,000	50,000
Vestibule Brgm	1950	6250	10,400	20,800	36,400	52,000
Vestibule Lan'let	1950	6250	10,400	20,800	36,400	52,000
Vestibule Brgm Lan'let	1950	6250	10,400	20,800	36,400	52,000
Model 48-B - 6-cyl., 48.6 hp, 142" wb						
7P Tr	2800	8900	14,800	29,600	51,800	74,000
4P Tr	2700	8650	14,400	28,800	50,400	72,000
5P Tr	2800	8900	14,800	29,600	51,800	74,000
2P Rbt	2700	8650	14,400	28,800	50,400	72,000
3P Rbt	2700	8650	14,400	28,800	50,400	72,000
2P Cpe	2350	7450	12,400	24,800	43,400	62,000
3P Cpe	2350	7450	12,400	24,800	43,400	62,000
7P Sub	2500	7900	13,200	26,400	46,200	66,000
7P Lan	2500	7900	13,200	26,400	46,200	66,000
7P Brgm	2400	7700	12,800	25,600	44,800	64,000
Sub Lan	2500	7900	13,200	26,400	46,200	66,000
Vestibule Sub	2500	7900	13,200	26,400	46,200	66,000
Vestibule Lan	2500	7900	13,200	26,400	46,200	66,000
Vestibule Brgm	2400	7700	12,800	25,600	44,800	64,000
Vestibule Sub Lan	2500	7900	13,200	26,400	46,200	66,000
Model 66-A - 6-cyl., 60 hp, 147-1/2" wb						
7P Tr	3250	10,300	17,200	34,400	60,200	86,000
4P Tr	3150	10,100	16,800	33,600	58,800	84,000
5P Tr	3150	10,100	16,800	33,600	58,800	84,000
2P Rbt	3100	9850	16,400	32,800	57,400	82,000
3P Rbt	3150	10,100	16,800	33,600	58,800	84,000
2P Cpe	2850	9100	15,200	30,400	53,200	76,000
3P Cpe	2850	9100	15,200	30,400	53,200	76,000
7P Sub	3000	9600	16,000	32,000	56,000	80,000
7P Lan	2950	9350	15,600	31,200	54,600	78,000
7P Brgm	2950	9350	15,600	31,200	54,600	78,000
Sub Lan	2950	9350	15,600	31,200	54,600	78,000
Vestibule Lan	2950	9350	15,600	31,200	54,600	78,000
Vestibule Sub	2950	9350	15,600	31,200	54,600	78,000
Vestibule Brgm	2950	9350	15,600	31,200	54,600	78,000
Vestibule Sub Lan	2950	9350	15,600	31,200	54,600	78,000
1917						
Model 38 - 6-cyl., 38.4 hp, 134" wb						
5P Tr	2050	6600	11,000	22,000	38,500	55,000
2P Rbt	2000	6350	10,600	21,200	37,100	53,000
3P Rbt	2000	6350	10,600	21,200	37,100	53,000
2P Cpe	1500	4800	8000	16,000	28,000	40,000
3P Cpe	1550	4900	8200	16,400	28,700	41,000
4P Tr	2050	6500	10,800	21,600	37,800	54,000
Brgm	1450	4700	7800	15,600	27,300	39,000
Lan'let	1450	4700	7800	15,600	27,300	39,000
Sed	1350	4300	7200	14,400	25,200	36,000
Vestibule Brgm	1500	4800	8000	16,000	28,000	40,000
Brgm Lan'let	1500	4800	8000	16,000	28,000	40,000
Vestibule Brgm Lan'let	1600	5050	8400	16,800	29,400	42,000
Fr Brgm	1600	5050	8400	16,800	29,400	42,000
Fr Brgm Lan'let	1600	5050	8400	16,800	29,400	42,000
Model 48 - 6-cyl., 48.6 hp, 142" wb						
7P Tr	2500	7900	13,200	26,400	46,200	66,000
2P Rbt	2350	7450	12,400	24,800	43,400	62,000
3P Rbt	2400	7700	12,800	25,600	44,800	64,000
2P Cpe	1900	6000	10,000	20,000	35,000	50,000
3P Cpe	1900	6000	10,000	20,000	35,000	50,000
5P Tr	2500	7900	13,200	26,400	46,200	66,000
4P Tr	2400	7700	12,800	25,600	44,800	64,000
Brgm	1850	5900	9800	19,600	34,300	49,000
Sub	1900	6000	10,000	20,000	35,000	50,000
Lan	1900	6000	10,000	20,000	35,000	50,000
Sub Lan	1900	6000	10,000	20,000	35,000	50,000
Vestibule Sub	1950	6250	10,400	20,800	36,400	52,000
Vestibule Lan	1950	6250	10,400	20,800	36,400	52,000
Vestibule Brgm	1900	6100	10,200	20,400	35,700	51,000
Vestibule Sub Lan	1950	6250	10,400	20,800	36,400	52,000
Model 66 - 6-cyl., 60 hp, 147-1/2" wb						
7P Tr	3250	10,300	17,200	34,400	60,200	86,000
2P Rbt	3100	9850	16,400	32,800	57,400	82,000
3P Rbt	3100	9850	16,400	32,800	57,400	82,000
2P Cpe	2850	9100	15,200	30,400	53,200	76,000
3P Cpe	2850	9100	15,200	30,400	53,200	76,000
4P Tr	3150	10,100	16,800	33,600	58,800	84,000
5P Tr	3150	10,100	16,800	33,600	58,800	84,000
Brgm	2550	8150	13,600	27,200	47,600	68,000
Sub	2650	8400	14,000	28,000	49,000	70,000
Lan	2650	8400	14,000	28,000	49,000	70,000
Sub Lan	2650	8400	14,000	28,000	49,000	70,000
Vestibule Sub	2650	8400	14,000	28,000	49,000	70,000
Vestibule Lan	2650	8400	14,000	28,000	49,000	70,000
Vestibule Brgm	2650	8400	14,000	28,000	49,000	70,000
Vestibule Sub Lan	2650	8400	14,000	28,000	49,000	70,000
1918						
Model 38 - 6-cyl., 38.4 hp, 134" wb						
5P Tr	2500	7900	13,200	26,400	46,200	66,000
2P Rbt	2400	7700	12,800	25,600	44,800	64,000
3P Rbt	2400	7700	12,800	25,600	44,800	64,000
2P Cpe	2050	6500	10,800	21,600	37,800	54,000
3P Cpe	2050	6500	10,800	21,600	37,800	54,000

	6	5	4	3	2	1
2P Conv Rds	2400	7700	12,800	25,600	44,800	64,000
3P Conv Rds	2400	7700	12,800	25,600	44,800	64,000
4P Rds	2500	7900	13,200	26,400	46,200	66,000
4P Tr	2400	7700	12,800	25,600	44,800	64,000
Brgm	2050	6600	11,000	22,000	38,500	55,000
Lan'let	2050	6600	11,000	22,000	38,500	55,000
Sed	1900	6000	10,000	20,000	35,000	50,000
Vestibule Brgm	1950	6250	10,400	20,800	36,400	52,000
Brgm Lan'let	1900	6100	10,200	20,400	35,700	51,000
Vestibule Lan'let	2050	6500	10,800	21,600	37,800	54,000
Vestibule Brgm Lan'let	2050	6500	10,800	21,600	37,800	54,000
Fr Brgm	2000	6350	10,600	21,200	37,100	53,000
Fr Brgm Lan'let	2050	6500	10,800	21,600	37,800	54,000
Twn Brgm	2000	6350	10,600	21,200	37,100	53,000
Model 48 - 6-cyl., 48.6 hp, 142" wb						
2P Rbt	2500	7900	13,200	26,400	46,200	66,000
4P Rbt	2500	7900	13,200	26,400	46,200	66,000
3P Rbt	2500	7900	13,200	26,400	46,200	66,000
2P Cpe	2150	6850	11,400	22,800	39,900	57,000
3P Cpe	2150	6850	11,400	22,800	39,900	57,000
2P Conv Rds	2500	7900	13,200	26,400	46,200	66,000
3P Conv Rds	2550	8150	13,600	27,200	47,600	68,000
4P Tr	2650	8400	14,000	28,000	49,000	70,000
5P Tr	2650	8400	14,000	28,000	49,000	70,000
Brgm	2350	7450	12,400	24,800	43,400	62,000
Sub	2350	7450	12,400	24,800	43,400	62,000
Lan	2350	7450	12,400	24,800	43,400	62,000
Sub Lan	2350	7450	12,400	24,800	43,400	62,000
Vestibule Sub	2350	7450	12,400	24,800	43,400	62,000
Vestibule Lan	2350	7450	12,400	24,800	43,400	62,000
Vestibule Brgm	2400	7700	12,800	25,600	44,800	64,000
Vestibule Sub Lan	2500	7900	13,200	26,400	46,200	66,000
Fr Brgm	2350	7450	12,400	24,800	43,400	62,000
7P Tr	2700	8650	14,400	28,800	50,400	72,000
7P Sub Lan	2500	7900	13,200	26,400	46,200	66,000
Model 66 - 6-cyl., 60 hp, 147-1/2" wb						
2P Rbt	3000	9600	16,000	32,000	56,000	80,000
3P Rbt	3000	9600	16,000	32,000	56,000	80,000
2P Cpe	2850	9100	15,200	30,400	53,200	76,000
3P Cpe	2850	9100	15,200	30,400	53,200	76,000
2P Con Rds	3000	9600	16,000	32,000	56,000	80,000
3P Con Rds	3100	9850	16,400	32,800	57,400	82,000
4P Tr	3150	10,100	16,800	33,600	58,800	84,000
5P Tr	3150	10,100	16,800	33,600	58,800	84,000
7P Tr	3250	10,300	17,200	34,400	60,200	86,000
Brgm	2650	8400	14,000	28,000	49,000	70,000
Sub	2700	8650	14,400	28,800	50,400	72,000
Lan	2700	8650	14,400	28,800	50,400	72,000
Sub Lan	2700	8650	14,400	28,800	50,400	72,000
Vestibule Lan	2850	9100	15,200	30,400	53,200	76,000
Vestibule Brgm	2850	9100	15,200	30,400	53,200	76,000
Vestibule Sub	2850	9100	15,200	30,400	53,200	76,000
Vestibule Sub Lan	2850	9100	15,200	30,400	53,200	76,000
1919						
Model 48-B-5 - 6-cyl., 48.6 hp, 142" wb						
7P Tr	2850	9100	15,200	30,400	53,200	76,000
2P Rbt	2550	8150	13,600	27,200	47,600	68,000
3P Rbt	2550	8150	13,600	27,200	47,600	68,000
4P Tr	2650	8400	14,000	28,000	49,000	70,000
4P Rds	2800	8900	14,800	29,600	51,800	74,000
5P Tr	2850	9100	15,200	30,400	53,200	76,000
2P Cpe	2250	7200	12,000	24,000	42,000	60,000
3P Cpe	2250	7200	12,000	24,000	42,000	60,000
2P Con Rds	2500	7900	13,200	26,400	46,200	66,000
3P Con Rds	2500	7900	13,200	26,400	46,200	66,000
Brgm	2250	7200	12,000	24,000	42,000	60,000
Brgm Lan'let	2250	7200	12,000	24,000	42,000	60,000
Fr Brgm	2350	7450	12,400	24,800	43,400	62,000
Fr Brgm Lan'let	2400	7700	12,800	25,600	44,800	64,000
Sub	2250	7200	12,000	24,000	42,000	60,000
Sub Lan	2250	7200	12,000	24,000	42,000	60,000
Vestibule Brgm	2350	7450	12,400	24,800	43,400	62,000
Vestibule Brgm Lan	2400	7700	12,800	25,600	44,800	64,000
Vestibule Sub	2350	7450	12,400	24,800	43,400	62,000
Vestibule Lan	2350	7450	12,400	24,800	43,400	62,000
Vestibule Sub Lan	2400	7700	12,800	25,600	44,800	64,000
1920						
Model 38 - 6 cyl., 38 hp, 134" wb						
2P & 3P Rbt	2050	6600	11,000	22,000	38,500	55,000
4P Tr	2100	6700	11,200	22,400	39,200	56,000
4P Rds	2150	6850	11,400	22,800	39,900	57,000
5P Tr	2200	6950	11,600	23,200	40,600	58,000
7P Tr	2250	7200	12,000	24,000	42,000	60,000
2P & 3P Cpe	1700	5400	9000	18,000	31,500	45,000
4P Sed	1150	3600	6000	12,000	21,000	30,000
7P Sed	1200	3850	6400	12,800	22,400	32,000
Brgm	1300	4200	7000	14,000	24,500	35,000
Fr Brgm	1400	4450	7400	14,800	25,900	37,000
Brgm Lan'let	1450	4550	7600	15,200	26,600	38,000
Tourer Brgm	1450	4700	7800	15,600	27,300	39,000
Vestibule Brgm	1500	4800	8000	16,000	28,000	40,000
Model 48 - 6-cyl., 48 hp, 142" wb						
2P & 4P Rbt	2200	6950	11,600	23,200	40,600	58,000
4P Tr	2250	7200	12,000	24,000	42,000	60,000
4P Rds	2250	7200	12,000	24,000	42,000	60,000
5P Tr	2350	7450	12,400	24,800	43,400	62,000
6P Tr	2500	7900	13,200	26,400	46,200	66,000
2P & 3P Cpe	1900	6000	10,000	20,000	35,000	50,000
5P Brgm	2050	6500	10,800	21,600	37,800	54,000
7P Fr Brgm	2050	6500	10,800	21,600	37,800	54,000
7P Sub	2100	6700	11,200	22,400	39,200	56,000
7P Vestibule Sub	2200	6950	11,600	23,200	40,600	58,000
7P Fr Sub	2100	6700	11,200	22,400	39,200	56,000
1921						
Model 38 - 6-cyl., 38 hp, 138" wb						
4P Tr	2100	6700	11,200	22,400	39,200	56,000
6P Tr	2100	6700	11,200	22,400	39,200	56,000
7P Tr	2200	6950	11,600	23,200	40,600	58,000
3P Rds	2200	6950	11,600	23,200	40,600	58,000
4P Cpe	1700	5400	9000	18,000	31,500	45,000
7P Brgm	1500	4800	8000	16,000	28,000	40,000
7P Limo	1600	5050	8400	16,800	29,400	42,000
6P Sed	1500	4800	8000	16,000	28,000	40,000
6P Vestibule Sed	1600	5050	8400	16,800	29,400	42,000
7P Lan	1650	5300	8800	17,600	30,800	44,000
1922						
Model 38 - 6-cyl., 38 hp, 138" wb						
4P Tr	2100	6700	11,200	22,400	39,200	56,000

	6	5	4	3	2	1
7P Tr	2200	6950	11,600	23,200	40,600	58,000
3P Rds	2100	6700	11,200	22,400	39,200	56,000
7P Brgm	1500	4800	8000	16,000	28,000	40,000
Cpe Sed	1500	4800	8000	16,000	28,000	40,000
3P Cpe	1700	5400	9000	18,000	31,500	45,000
4P Sed	1750	5500	9200	18,400	32,200	46,000
Lan'let	1500	4800	8000	16,000	28,000	40,000
Limo	1600	5050	8400	16,800	29,400	42,000
Fml Limo	1650	5300	8800	17,600	30,800	44,000
Vestibule Sed	1700	5400	9000	18,000	31,500	45,000
Sed	1650	5300	8800	17,600	30,800	44,000

1923

Model 38 - 6-cyl., 138" wb

	6	5	4	3	2	1
7P Tr	1900	6000	10,000	20,000	35,000	50,000
4P Tr	1800	5750	9600	19,200	33,600	48,000
2P Rbt	1700	5400	9000	18,000	31,500	45,000
3P Cpe	1450	4550	7600	15,200	26,600	38,000
4P Cpe Sed	1350	4300	7200	14,400	25,200	36,000
6P Brgm	1300	4200	7000	14,000	24,500	35,000
4P Sed	1200	3850	6400	12,800	22,400	32,000
7P Sed	1300	4100	6800	13,600	23,800	34,000
6P Lan'let	1500	4800	8000	16,000	28,000	40,000
7P Limo	1600	5050	8400	16,800	29,400	42,000
7P Encl Drive Limo	1650	5300	8800	17,600	30,800	44,000
7P Fml Limo	1700	5400	9000	18,000	31,500	45,000

1924

Model 33 - 6-cyl., 138" wb

	6	5	4	3	2	1
7P Tr	1900	6000	10,000	20,000	35,000	50,000
6P Tr	1800	5750	9600	19,200	33,600	48,000
4P Tr	1750	5500	9200	18,400	32,200	46,000
Rbt	1600	5050	8400	16,800	29,400	42,000
6P Brgm	1500	4800	8000	16,000	28,000	40,000
3P Cpe	1550	4900	8200	16,400	28,700	41,000
4P Cpe Sed	1550	4900	8200	16,400	28,700	41,000
4d 4P Sed	1450	4550	7600	15,200	26,600	38,000
7P Encl Drive Limo	1750	5650	9400	18,800	32,900	47,000
7P Fml Limo	1800	5750	9600	19,200	33,600	48,000
6P Lan'let	1850	5900	9800	19,600	34,300	49,000
7P Limo	1900	6000	10,000	20,000	35,000	50,000
7P Sed	1800	5750	9600	19,200	33,600	48,000
7P Fml Lan	1900	6000	10,000	20,000	35,000	50,000
7P Limo Lan	1900	6100	10,200	20,400	35,700	51,000
4P Sed Lan	1900	6000	10,000	20,000	35,000	50,000
3P Cpe Lan	2050	6600	11,000	22,000	38,500	55,000
7P Encl Drive Lan	2050	6600	11,000	22,000	38,500	55,000
7P Sed Lan	2050	6500	10,800	21,600	37,800	54,000

1925

Model 80 - 6-cyl., 130" wb

	6	5	4	3	2	1
7P Tr	1900	6000	10,000	20,000	35,000	50,000
4P Tr	1850	5900	9800	19,600	34,300	49,000
5P Sed	1400	4450	7400	14,800	25,900	37,000
4P Cpe	1600	5150	8600	17,200	30,100	43,000
7P Sed	1450	4550	7600	15,200	26,600	38,000
Encl Drive Limo	1700	5400	9000	18,000	31,500	45,000
2P Rbt	1750	5650	9400	18,800	32,900	47,000

Model 33 - 6-cyl., 138" wb

	6	5	4	3	2	1
2P Rbt	1950	6250	10,400	20,800	36,400	52,000
4P Tr	2000	6350	10,600	21,200	37,100	53,000
6P Tr	2050	6500	10,800	21,600	37,800	54,000
7P Tr	2050	6600	11,000	22,000	38,500	55,000
Brgm	1750	5650	9400	18,800	32,900	47,000
Cpe	1900	6000	10,000	20,000	35,000	50,000
4P Sed	1700	5400	9000	18,000	31,500	45,000
Cpe Sed	1700	5400	9000	18,000	31,500	45,000
Lan'let	1750	5650	9400	18,800	32,900	47,000
7P Sed	1750	5500	9200	18,400	32,200	46,000
Encl Drive Sed	1750	5650	9400	18,800	32,900	47,000
Limo	1900	6000	10,000	20,000	35,000	50,000
Lan	1850	5900	9800	19,600	34,300	49,000
Encl Drive Lan	1900	6100	10,200	20,400	35,700	51,000

1926

Model 80 - 6-cyl., 70 hp, 130" wb

	6	5	4	3	2	1
7P Tr	1900	6000	10,000	20,000	35,000	50,000
4P Tr	1750	5650	9400	18,800	32,900	47,000
2P Rds	1800	5750	9600	19,200	33,600	48,000
4P Cpe	2000	6350	10,600	21,200	37,100	53,000
7P Sed	1900	6000	10,000	20,000	35,000	50,000
7P Encl Drive Limo	2050	6600	11,000	22,000	38,500	55,000
5P Sed	1850	5900	9800	19,600	34,300	49,000
4P Cpe Lan	1750	5650	9400	18,800	32,900	47,000
5P Coach	1400	4450	7400	14,800	25,900	37,000

Model 33 - 6-cyl., 100 hp, 138" wb

	6	5	4	3	2	1
4P Tr	2500	7900	13,200	26,400	46,200	66,000
2P Rbt	2400	7700	12,800	25,600	44,800	64,000
6P Tr	2550	8150	13,600	27,200	47,600	68,000
7P Tr	2700	8650	14,400	28,800	50,400	72,000
6P Brgm	2250	7200	12,000	24,000	42,000	60,000
3P Cpe	1950	6250	10,400	20,800	36,400	52,000
4P Sed	1900	6000	10,000	20,000	35,000	50,000
4P Cpe Sed	1900	6100	10,200	20,400	35,700	51,000
4P Encl Drive Limo	2350	7450	12,400	24,800	43,400	62,000
7P Sed	2150	6850	11,400	22,800	39,900	57,000
6P Lan'let	2350	7450	12,400	24,800	43,400	62,000
7P Fr Limo	2350	7450	12,400	24,800	43,400	62,000
7P Sed Lan'let	2350	7450	12,400	24,800	43,400	62,000
4P Sed Lan'let	2350	7450	12,400	24,800	43,400	62,000
3P Cpe Lan'let	2400	7700	12,800	25,600	44,800	64,000
7P Limo	2400	7700	12,800	25,600	44,800	64,000
7P Encl Drive Limo	2500	7900	13,200	26,400	46,200	66,000
7P Encl Drive Lan'let	2550	8150	13,600	27,200	47,600	68,000

1927

Model 80 - 6-cyl., 70 hp, 130" wb

	6	5	4	3	2	1
7P Tr	2100	6700	11,200	22,400	39,200	56,000
4P Tr	2050	6600	11,000	22,000	38,500	55,000
2P Rds	2050	6500	10,800	21,600	37,800	54,000
4P Cpe	1800	5750	9600	19,200	33,600	48,000
7P Sed	1600	5050	8400	16,800	29,400	42,000
7P Encl Drive Limo	2050	6600	11,000	22,000	38,500	55,000
5P Sed	1550	4900	8200	16,400	28,700	41,000
2d 5P Coach	1600	5050	8400	16,800	29,400	42,000
4d 5P Coach	1700	5400	9000	18,000	31,500	45,000
4P Cpe	1850	5900	9800	19,600	34,300	49,000
2P Cpe	1750	5650	9400	18,800	32,900	47,000
4d 7P Coach	1750	5650	9400	18,800	32,900	47,000
7P Limo Coach	1950	6250	10,400	20,800	36,400	52,000

Model 36 - 6-cyl., 100 hp, 138" wb

	6	5	4	3	2	1
2P Rbt	2350	7450	12,400	24,800	43,400	62,000
4P Tr	2400	7700	12,800	25,600	44,800	64,000
7P Tr	2550	8150	13,600	27,200	47,600	68,000
3P Cpe	2200	7100	11,800	23,600	41,300	59,000
4d 4P Sed	1900	6000	10,000	20,000	35,000	50,000
4P Cpe Sed	1950	6250	10,400	20,800	36,400	52,000
4P Encl Drive Limo	2200	6950	11,600	23,200	40,600	58,000
7P Encl Drive Lan	2150	6850	11,400	22,800	39,900	57,000
7P Sed	2050	6600	11,000	22,000	38,500	55,000
7P Fr Lan	2100	6700	11,200	22,400	39,200	56,000
7P Sed Lan	2100	6700	11,200	22,400	39,200	56,000
4P Sed Lan	2050	6600	11,000	22,000	38,500	55,000
7P Encl Drive Limo	2200	7100	11,800	23,600	41,300	59,000
7P Fr Limo	2150	6850	11,400	22,800	39,900	57,000
4P Encl Drive Limo	2200	6950	11,600	23,200	40,600	58,000

1928

Model 81 - 6-cyl., 75 hp, 130" wb

	6	5	4	3	2	1
4P Rbt	2250	7200	12,000	24,000	42,000	60,000
4P Tr	2350	7450	12,400	24,800	43,400	62,000
4P Rds	2400	7700	12,800	25,600	44,800	64,000
5P Brgm	2050	6500	10,800	21,600	37,800	54,000
2P Cpe	2050	6600	11,000	22,000	38,500	55,000
5P Clb Sed	2050	6500	10,800	21,600	37,800	54,000
4P Cpe	2100	6700	11,200	22,400	39,200	56,000
5P Sed	1950	6250	10,400	20,800	36,400	52,000
Spt Sed Lan	2000	6350	10,600	21,200	37,100	53,000
Clb Sed Lan	2050	6500	10,800	21,600	37,800	54,000
7P Sed	2050	6500	10,800	21,600	37,800	54,000
4P Cpe DeL	2150	6850	11,400	22,800	39,900	57,000
7P Encl Drive Limo	2200	7100	11,800	23,600	41,300	59,000

Model 36 - 6-cyl., 100 hp, 138" wb

	6	5	4	3	2	1
4P Rbt	2850	9100	15,200	30,400	53,200	76,000
4P Tr	2950	9350	15,600	31,200	54,600	78,000
7P Tr	3000	9600	16,000	32,000	56,000	80,000
Encl Drive Limo	2650	8400	14,000	28,000	49,000	70,000
7P Sed	2400	7700	12,800	25,600	44,800	64,000
7P Encl Drive Lan'let	2650	8400	14,000	28,000	49,000	70,000
7P Sed Lan	2500	7900	13,200	26,400	46,200	66,000
3P Cpe	2500	7900	13,200	26,400	46,200	66,000
4P Cpe Sed	2500	7900	13,200	26,400	46,200	66,000
4P Encl Drive Sed	2700	8650	14,400	28,800	50,400	72,000
4P Sed	2250	7200	12,000	24,000	42,000	60,000
6P Encl Drive Limo	2850	9100	15,200	30,400	53,200	76,000
4P CC Sed	2550	8150	13,600	27,200	47,600	68,000
4P Sed Lan	2650	8400	14,000	28,000	49,000	70,000
4P Encl Drive Lan	2550	8150	13,600	27,200	47,600	68,000
6P Fml Limo	2850	9100	15,200	30,400	53,200	76,000
6P Fr Lan	2950	9350	15,600	31,200	54,600	78,000

1929

Model 125 - 8-cyl., 125 hp, 133" wb

	6	5	4	3	2	1
4P Rds	3400	10,800	18,000	36,000	63,000	90,000
4P Tr	3300	10,550	17,600	35,200	61,600	88,000
5P Brgm	2250	7200	12,000	24,000	42,000	60,000
4P Cpe	2550	8150	13,600	27,200	47,600	68,000
5P Sed	2350	7450	12,400	24,800	43,400	62,000
5P Twn Sed	2400	7700	12,800	25,600	44,800	64,000
7P Sed	2400	7700	12,800	25,600	44,800	64,000
7P Encl Drive Limo	2650	8400	14,000	28,000	49,000	70,000

Model 126 - 8-cyl., 125 hp, 143" wb

	6	5	4	3	2	1
7P Tr	3600	11,500	19,200	38,400	67,200	96,000
4P Conv Cpe	3700	11,750	19,600	39,200	68,600	98,000
7P Sed	2800	8900	14,800	29,600	51,800	74,000
7P Encl Drive Limo	2850	9100	15,200	30,400	53,200	76,000
4P Sed	2650	8400	14,000	28,000	49,000	70,000

1930

Model C - 8-cyl., 115 hp, 132" wb

	6	5	4	3	2	1
Clb Brgm	1900	6000	10,000	20,000	35,000	50,000
Cpe	1950	6250	10,400	20,800	36,400	52,000
Sed	1750	5650	9400	18,800	32,900	47,000

Model B - 8-cyl., 125 hp, 134" wb

	6	5	4	3	2	1
Rds	3750	12,000	20,000	40,000	70,000	100,000
Tr	3750	12,000	20,000	40,000	70,000	100,000
Spt Phae	4000	12,700	21,200	42,400	74,200	106,000
Conv Cpe	3700	11,750	19,600	39,200	68,600	98,000

Model B8-cyl., 125 hp, 139" wb

	6	5	4	3	2	1
5P Sed	2550	8150	13,600	27,200	47,600	68,000
Vic Cpe	2650	8400	14,000	28,000	49,000	70,000
7P Sed	2550	8150	13,600	27,200	47,600	68,000
Clb Sed	2650	8400	14,000	28,000	49,000	70,000
Encl Drive Limo	3000	9600	16,000	32,000	56,000	80,000

Model A - 8-cyl., 132 hp, 144" wb

	6	5	4	3	2	1
Tr	4150	13,200	22,000	44,000	77,000	110,000
Conv Cpe	4000	12,700	21,200	42,400	74,200	106,000
Sed	2850	9100	15,200	30,400	53,200	76,000
Encl Drive Limo	3600	11,500	19,200	38,400	67,200	96,000
Twn Car	3300	10,550	17,600	35,200	61,600	88,000

1931

Model 43 - 8-cyl., 125 hp, 134" wb

	6	5	4	3	2	1
Rds	3750	12,000	20,000	40,000	70,000	100,000
Tourer	3750	12,000	20,000	40,000	70,000	100,000
Cpe	2650	8400	14,000	28,000	49,000	70,000

Model 43 - 8-cyl., 125 hp, 137" wb

	6	5	4	3	2	1
5P Sed	1900	6000	10,000	20,000	35,000	50,000
Clb Sed	2050	6600	11,000	22,000	38,500	55,000
7P Sed	2150	6850	11,400	22,800	39,900	57,000
Encl Drive Limo	2250	7200	12,000	24,000	42,000	60,000

Model 42 - 8-cyl., 132 hp, 142" wb

	6	5	4	3	2	1
Rds	4150	13,200	22,000	44,000	77,000	110,000
Tourer	4150	13,200	22,000	44,000	77,000	110,000
Spt Tourer	4350	13,900	23,200	46,400	81,200	116,000
Conv Cpe	3850	12,250	20,400	40,800	71,400	102,000
5P Sed	2050	6600	11,000	22,000	38,500	55,000
Clb Sed	2200	6950	11,600	23,200	40,600	58,000
7P Sed	2150	6850	11,400	22,800	39,900	57,000
Clb Berl	2250	7200	12,000	24,000	42,000	60,000
Encl Drive Limo	2650	8400	14,000	28,000	49,000	70,000

Model 41 - 8-cyl., 132 hp, 147" wb

	6	5	4	3	2	1
Tr	4150	13,200	22,000	44,000	77,000	110,000
Conv Cpe	4150	13,200	22,000	44,000	77,000	110,000
Sed	2250	7200	12,000	24,000	42,000	60,000
Encl Drive Limo	2650	8400	14,000	28,000	49,000	70,000
Twn Car	2650	8400	14,000	28,000	49,000	70,000

1932

Model 54 - 8-cyl., 125 hp, 137" wb

	6	5	4	3	2	1
Conv Cpe Rds	3900	12,500	20,800	41,600	72,800	104,000
5P Tr	3750	12,000	20,000	40,000	70,000	100,000
Phae	3750	12,000	20,000	40,000	70,000	100,000
Brgm	2050	6500	10,800	21,600	37,800	54,000

	6	5	4	3	2	1
Cpe	2250	7200	12,000	24,000	42,000	60,000
5P Sed	2000	6350	10,600	21,200	37,100	53,000
Clb Sed	2050	6500	10,800	21,600	37,800	54,000
Clb Berl	2050	6600	11,000	22,000	38,500	55,000
Con Sed	3850	12,250	20,400	40,800	71,400	102,000
Model 54 8-cyl., 125 hp, 142" wb						
7P Tr	4000	12,700	21,200	42,400	74,200	106,000
7P Sed	2050	6600	11,000	22,000	38,500	55,000
Limo	2250	7200	12,000	24,000	42,000	60,000
Model 53 - 12-cyl., 140 hp, 137" wb						
Conv Cpe Rds	4150	13,200	22,000	44,000	77,000	110,000
5P Tr	4200	13,450	22,400	44,800	78,400	112,000
Phae	4150	13,200	22,000	44,000	77,000	110,000
Clb Brgm	2250	7200	12,000	24,000	42,000	60,000
Cpe	2350	7450	12,400	24,800	43,400	62,000
5P Sed	2150	6850	11,400	22,800	39,900	57,000
Clb Sed	2200	7100	11,800	23,600	41,300	59,000
Clb Berl	2500	7900	13,200	26,400	46,200	66,000
Con Sed	3850	12,250	20,400	40,800	71,400	102,000
Model 53 - 12-cyl., 140 hp, 142" wb						
7P Tr	4150	13,200	22,000	44,000	77,000	110,000
7P Sed	2500	7900	13,200	26,400	46,200	66,000
Limo	2700	8650	14,400	28,800	50,400	72,000
Model 51 - 12-cyl., 150 hp, 147" wb						
Cpe	2550	8150	13,600	27,200	47,600	68,000
Conv Vic Cpe	4350	13,900	23,200	46,400	81,200	116,000
Clb Sed	2550	8150	13,600	27,200	47,600	68,000
Conv Sed	3750	12,000	20,000	40,000	70,000	100,000
Encl Drive Limo	3100	9850	16,400	32,800	57,400	82,000
A/W Twn Brgm	3600	11,500	19,200	38,400	67,200	96,000
A/W Twn Cabr	3850	12,250	20,400	40,800	71,400	102,000
Encl Drive Brgm	3450	11,050	18,400	36,800	64,400	92,000
1933						
Model 836 - 8-cyl., 135 hp, 136" wb						
5P Clb Brgm	1750	5500	9200	18,400	32,200	46,000
5P Sed	1750	5650	9400	18,800	32,900	47,000
5P Clb Sed	1900	6100	10,200	20,400	35,700	51,000
7P Sed	1800	5750	9600	19,200	33,600	48,000
7P Encl Drive Limo	2050	6600	11,000	22,000	38,500	55,000
Model 1236 - 12-cyl., 160 hp, 136" wb						
5P Clb Brgm	1900	6100	10,200	20,400	35,700	51,000
5P Sed	1950	6250	10,400	20,800	36,400	52,000
5P Clb Sed	2100	6700	11,200	22,400	39,200	56,000
7P Sed (139")	2000	6350	10,600	21,200	37,100	53,000
7P Encl Drive Limo	2250	7200	12,000	24,000	42,000	60,000
Model 1242 - 12-cyl., 175 hp, 137" wb						
5P Tr	3600	11,500	19,200	38,400	67,200	96,000
5P Spt Phae	3850	12,250	20,400	40,800	71,400	102,000
7P Tourer (142")	3700	11,750	19,600	39,200	68,600	98,000
5P Clb Brgm	2000	6350	10,600	21,200	37,100	53,000
5P Sed	2050	6500	10,800	21,600	37,800	54,000
5P Clb Sed	2200	6950	11,600	23,200	40,600	58,000
5P Clb Berl	2250	7200	12,000	24,000	42,000	60,000
4P Cpe	1950	6250	10,400	20,800	36,400	52,000
4P Cus Rds	3900	12,500	20,800	41,600	72,800	104,000
5P Conv Sed	3600	11,500	19,200	38,400	67,200	96,000
7P Sed (142")	2050	6600	11,000	22,000	38,500	55,000
7P Encl Drive Limo	2500	7900	13,200	26,400	46,200	66,000
Model 1247 - 12-cyl., 175 hp, 142" wb						
5P Sed	2500	7900	13,200	26,400	46,200	66,000
5P Clb Sed	2550	8150	13,600	27,200	47,600	68,000
7P Sed (147")	2550	8150	13,600	27,200	47,600	68,000
5P Clb Berl	2550	8150	13,600	27,200	47,600	68,000
7P Encl Drive Limo	2700	8650	14,400	28,800	50,400	72,000
5P Conv Sed	3600	11,500	19,200	38,400	67,200	96,000
4P Cpe (147")	2850	9100	15,200	30,400	53,200	76,000
5P Conv Sed (147")	4350	13,900	23,200	46,400	81,200	116,000
5P Clb Sed (147")	2700	8650	14,400	28,800	50,400	72,000
Encl Drive Limo (147")	2850	9100	15,200	30,400	53,200	76,000
7P Twn Brgm (147")	2950	9350	15,600	31,200	54,600	78,000
7P Twn Car (147")	3100	9850	16,400	32,800	57,400	82,000
7P Twn Cabr (147")	4600	14,650	24,400	48,800	85,400	122,000
7P Encl Drive Brgm	3100	9850	16,400	32,800	57,400	82,000
1934						
Model 836A, 136" wb						
Clb Brgm	1800	5750	9600	19,200	33,600	48,000
Clb Brgm Salon	1900	6000	10,000	20,000	35,000	50,000
4d Sed	1900	6000	10,000	20,000	35,000	50,000
4d Sed Salon	1950	6250	10,400	20,800	36,400	52,000
Model 840A - 8-cyl., 139" wb						
Rds	2700	8650	14,400	28,800	50,400	72,000
Brgm	1950	6250	10,400	20,800	36,400	52,000
Sed	2000	6350	10,600	21,200	37,100	53,000
Clb Sed	2050	6500	10,800	21,600	37,800	54,000
Cpe	2150	6850	11,400	22,800	39,900	57,000
Model 840A - 8-cyl., 144" wb						
Silver Arrow	4350	13,900	23,200	46,400	81,200	116,000
Sed	2050	6600	11,000	22,000	38,500	55,000
Encl Drive Limo	2500	7900	13,200	26,400	46,200	66,000
Model 1240A - 12-cyl., 139" wb						
Rds	3450	11,050	18,400	36,800	64,400	92,000
Brgm	2050	6600	11,000	22,000	38,500	55,000
Sed	2100	6700	11,200	22,400	39,200	56,000
Clb Sed	2150	6850	11,400	22,800	39,900	57,000
Cpe	2250	7200	12,000	24,000	42,000	60,000
Model 1250A - 12-cyl., 144" wb						
Silver Arrow	4750	15,100	25,200	50,400	88,200	126,000
Sed	2250	7200	12,000	24,000	42,000	60,000
Encl Drive Limo	2700	8650	14,400	28,800	50,400	72,000
Model 1248A - 12-cyl., 147" wb						
Sed	2500	7900	13,200	26,400	46,200	66,000
Encl Drive Limo	2850	9100	15,200	30,400	53,200	76,000
1935						
Model 845 - 8-cyl., 140 hp, 138" wb						
Conv Rds	2650	8400	14,000	28,000	49,000	70,000
Clb Brgm	1900	6000	10,000	20,000	35,000	50,000
Cpe	2050	6600	11,000	22,000	38,500	55,000
5P Sed	1900	6100	10,200	20,400	35,700	51,000
Clb Sed	1950	6250	10,400	20,800	36,400	52,000
Model 845 - 8-cyl., 140 hp, 144" wb						
7P Sed	2000	6350	10,600	21,200	37,100	53,000
Encl Drive Limo	2250	7200	12,000	24,000	42,000	60,000
Silver Arrow	4350	13,900	23,200	46,400	81,200	116,000
Model 1245 - 12-cyl., 175 hp, 138" wb						
Conv Rds	3250	10,300	17,200	34,400	60,200	86,000
Clb Brgm	2050	6600	11,000	22,000	38,500	55,000
Cpe	2250	7200	12,000	24,000	42,000	60,000
5P Sed	2100	6700	11,200	22,400	39,200	56,000
Clb Sed	2150	6850	11,400	22,800	39,900	57,000

	6	5	4	3	2	1
Model 1245 - 12-cyl., 175 hp, 144" wb						
7P Sed	2350	7450	12,400	24,800	43,400	62,000
Encl Drive Limo	2500	7900	13,200	26,400	46,200	66,000
Silver Arrow	4750	15,100	25,200	50,400	88,200	126,000
Model 1255 - 12-cyl., 175 hp, 147" wb						
7P Sed	2500	7900	13,200	26,400	46,200	66,000
Encl Drive Limo	2700	8650	14,400	28,800	50,400	72,000
1936						
Deluxe 8 - 150 hp, 139" wb						
Cpe	1900	6000	10,000	20,000	35,000	50,000
Ctry Club Rds	2500	7900	13,200	26,400	46,200	66,000
Clb Sed	1700	5400	9000	18,000	31,500	45,000
5P Sed	1650	5300	8800	17,600	30,800	44,000
Clb Berl	1900	6000	10,000	20,000	35,000	50,000
Deluxe 8 - 150 hp, 144" wb						
7P Sed	1750	5650	9400	18,800	32,900	47,000
Limo	2050	6600	11,000	22,000	38,500	55,000
Metropolitan Twn Car	2250	7200	12,000	24,000	42,000	60,000
Conv Sed	2700	8650	14,400	28,800	50,400	72,000
Salon Twelve - 185 hp, 139" wb						
Cpe	2050	6600	11,000	22,000	38,500	55,000
Ctry Club Rds	2850	9100	15,200	30,400	53,200	76,000
Clb Sed	1850	5900	9800	19,600	34,300	49,000
5P Sed	1800	5750	9600	19,200	33,600	48,000
Clb Berl	2050	6600	11,000	22,000	38,500	55,000
Salon Twelve - 185 hp, 144" wb						
7P Sed	2000	6350	10,600	21,200	37,100	53,000
Limo	2250	7200	12,000	24,000	42,000	60,000
Metropolitan Twn Car	2500	7900	13,200	26,400	46,200	66,000
Conv Sed	3100	9850	16,400	32,800	57,400	82,000
7P Sed (147")	2250	7200	12,000	24,000	42,000	60,000
7P Encl Drive Limo	2550	8150	13,600	27,200	47,600	68,000
1937						
Pierce-Arrow 8 - 150 hp, 138" wb						
Cpe	1850	5900	9800	19,600	34,300	49,000
5P Sed	1600	5150	8600	17,200	30,100	43,000
Conv Rds	2500	7900	13,200	26,400	46,200	66,000
Clb Sed	1700	5400	9000	18,000	31,500	45,000
Clb Berl	1300	4200	7000	14,000	24,500	35,000
Fml Sed	1900	6100	10,200	20,400	35,700	51,000
Pierce-Arrow 8 - 150 hp, 144" wb						
7P Fml Sed	2050	6600	11,000	22,000	38,500	55,000
7P Sed	1950	6250	10,400	20,800	36,400	52,000
Limo	2250	7200	12,000	24,000	42,000	60,000
Conv Sed	2850	9100	15,200	30,400	53,200	76,000
Brunn Metro Twn Car	2500	7900	13,200	26,400	46,200	66,000
Twn Brgm	2350	7450	12,400	24,800	43,400	62,000
5P Encl Drive Limo (147")	2350	7450	12,400	24,800	43,400	62,000
Pierce-Arrow 12 - 185 hp, 139" wb						
Cpe	2000	6350	10,600	21,200	37,100	53,000
5P Sed	1750	5650	9400	18,800	32,900	47,000
Conv Rds	2850	9100	15,200	30,400	53,200	76,000
Clb Sed	1800	5750	9600	19,200	33,600	48,000
Clb Berl	1850	5900	9800	19,600	34,300	49,000
5P Fml Sed	2050	6600	11,000	22,000	38,500	55,000
Pierce-Arrow 12 - 185 hp, 144" wb						
7P Sed	1900	6000	10,000	20,000	35,000	50,000
Limo	2050	6600	11,000	22,000	38,500	55,000
Conv Sed	3450	11,050	18,400	36,800	64,400	92,000
Brunn Metro Twn Brgm	2850	9100	15,200	30,400	53,200	76,000
Pierce-Arrow 12 - 185 hp, 147" wb						
7P Sed	2250	7200	12,000	24,000	42,000	60,000
Encl Drive Limo	2550	8150	13,600	27,200	47,600	68,000
Metro Twn Car	2950	9350	15,600	31,200	54,600	78,000
1938						
Pierce-Arrow 8 - 150 hp, 139" wb						
5P Sed	1550	4900	8200	16,400	28,700	41,000
Clb Sed	1600	5150	8600	17,200	30,100	43,000
Cpe	1800	5750	9600	19,200	33,600	48,000
Conv Cpe	2500	7900	13,200	26,400	46,200	66,000
Clb Berl	1750	5650	9400	18,800	32,900	47,000
Fml Sed	1650	5300	8800	17,600	30,800	44,000
Pierce-Arrow 8 - 150 hp, 144" wb						
Brunn Metro Twn Brgm	2350	7450	12,400	24,800	43,400	62,000
7P Sed	2000	6350	10,600	21,200	37,100	53,000
Encl Drive Limo	2150	6850	11,400	22,800	39,900	57,000
Con Sed	2850	9100	15,200	30,400	53,200	76,000
Spl Sed	1950	6250	10,400	20,800	36,400	52,000
Fml Sed	2050	6600	11,000	22,000	38,500	55,000
Pierce-Arrow 12 - 185 hp, 139" wb						
5P Sed	2050	6600	11,000	22,000	38,500	55,000
Clb Sed	2150	6850	11,400	22,800	39,900	57,000
Cpe	2400	7700	12,800	25,600	44,800	64,000
Conv Cpe	3100	9850	16,400	32,800	57,400	82,000
Clb Berl	1900	6000	10,000	20,000	35,000	50,000
Fml Sed	1900	6000	10,000	20,000	35,000	50,000
Pierce-Arrow 12 - 185 hp, 144" wb						
Spl Sed	2250	7200	12,000	24,000	42,000	60,000
7P Sed	2350	7450	12,400	24,800	43,400	62,000
Encl Drive Limo	2700	8650	14,400	28,800	50,400	72,000
Conv Sed	3150	10,100	16,800	33,600	58,800	84,000
Brunn Metro Twn Brgm	2800	8900	14,800	29,600	51,800	74,000
Pierce-Arrow 12 - 147" wb						
7P Sed	2400	7700	12,800	25,600	44,800	64,000
Encl Drive Limo	2850	9100	15,200	30,400	53,200	76,000

STUDEBAKER

	6	5	4	3	2	1
1903						
Model A, 8 hp						
Tonn Tr	NA			Value inestimable		
1904						
Model A						
Tonn Tr	1050	3350	5600	11,200	19,600	28,000
Model B						
Dely Wagon	1000	3250	5400	10,800	18,900	27,000
Model C						
Tonn Tr	1100	3500	5800	11,600	20,300	29,000
1905						
Model 9502, 2-cyl.						
Rear Ent Tr	1150	3600	6000	12,000	21,000	30,000
Side Ent Tr	1150	3700	6200	12,400	21,700	31,000
Model 9503, 4-cyl.						
Side Ent Tr	1250	3950	6600	13,200	23,100	33,000

1906

	6	5	4	3	2	1
Model E, 20 N.A.C.C.H.P.						
Side Ent Tr	1100	3500	5800	11,600	20,300	29,000
Twn Car	1050	3350	5600	11,200	19,600	28,000
Model F, 28 N.A.C.C.H.P.						
Side Ent Tr	1150	3700	6200	12,400	21,700	31,000
Model G, 30 N.A.C.C.H.P.						
Side Ent Tr	1300	4100	6800	13,600	23,800	34,000

1907

	6	5	4	3	2	1
Model L, 4-cyl., 28 hp, 104" wb						
5P Rear Ent Tr	1300	4200	7000	14,000	24,500	35,000
Model G, 4-cyl., 30 hp, 104" wb						
5P Rear Ent Tr	1350	4300	7200	14,400	25,200	36,000
Model H, 4-cyl., 30 hp, 104" wb						
5P Rear Ent Tr	1350	4300	7200	14,400	25,200	36,000

1908

	6	5	4	3	2	1
Model H, 4-cyl., 30 hp, 104" wb						
5P Rear Ent Tr	1350	4300	7200	14,400	25,200	36,000
Model A, 4-cyl., 30 hp, 104" wb						
5P Tr	1350	4300	7200	14,400	25,200	36,000
5P Twn Car	1300	4200	7000	14,000	24,500	35,000
2P Rbt	1300	4100	6800	13,600	23,800	34,000
5P Lan'let	1350	4300	7200	14,400	25,200	36,000
Model B, 4-cyl., 40 hp, 114" wb						
5P Tr	1450	4550	7600	15,200	26,600	38,000
2P Rbt	1350	4300	7200	14,400	25,200	36,000
7P Limo	1400	4450	7400	14,800	25,900	37,000
5P Lan'let	1450	4550	7600	15,200	26,600	38,000
4P Trabt	1450	4700	7800	15,600	27,300	39,000
3P Speed Car	1400	4450	7400	14,800	25,900	37,000

1909

	6	5	4	3	2	1
Model A, 4-cyl., 30 hp, 104" wb						
5P Tr	1350	4300	7200	14,400	25,200	36,000
5P Twn Car	1300	4200	7000	14,000	24,500	35,000
Rbt	1300	4100	6800	13,600	23,800	34,000
5P Lan'let	1350	4300	7200	14,400	25,200	36,000
Model B, 4-cyl., 40 hp, 114" wb						
5P Tr	1450	4550	7600	15,200	26,600	38,000
7P Limo	1400	4450	7400	14,800	25,900	37,000
5P Lan'let	1450	4550	7600	15,200	26,600	38,000
Model C, 4-cyl., 30 hp, 104" wb						
5P Tr	1350	4300	7200	14,400	25,200	36,000
Model D, 4-cyl., 40 hp, 117.5" wb						
5P Tr	1450	4700	7800	15,600	27,300	39,000

1910

	6	5	4	3	2	1
Model H, 4-cyl., 30 hp, 104" wb						
5P Tr	1350	4300	7200	14,400	25,200	36,000
Model M, 4-cyl., 28 hp, 104" wb						
5P Tr	1300	4200	7000	14,000	24,500	35,000
Model G-7, 4-cyl., 40 hp, 117.5" wb						
4/5P Tr	1450	4550	7600	15,200	26,600	38,000
7P Tr	1450	4700	7800	15,600	27,300	39,000
Limo (123" wb)	1350	4300	7200	14,400	25,200	36,000

1911

	6	5	4	3	2	1
Model G-8, 4-cyl., 40 hp, 117.5" wb						
4d 7P Limo	1400	4450	7400	14,800	25,900	37,000
4d 5P Lan'let	1450	4550	7600	15,200	26,600	38,000
4d 4/6/7P Tr	1500	4800	8000	16,000	28,000	40,000
2d 2P Rds	1300	4200	7000	14,000	24,500	35,000
Model G-10, 4-cyl., 30 hp, 116" wb						
4d 5P Tr	1450	4550	7600	15,200	26,600	38,000

NOTE: Studebaker-Garford association was discontinued after 1911 model year.

1913

	6	5	4	3	2	1
Model SA-25, 4-cyl., 101" wb						
2d Rds	1000	3100	5200	10,400	18,200	26,000
4d Tr	1000	3250	5400	10,800	18,900	27,000
Model AA-35, 4-cyl., 115.5" wb						
4d Tr	1050	3350	5600	11,200	19,600	28,000
2d Cpe	850	2650	4400	8800	15,400	22,000
4d Sed	800	2500	4200	8400	14,700	21,000
Model E, 6-cyl., 121" wb						
4d Tr	1100	3500	5800	11,600	20,300	29,000
4d Limo	900	2900	4800	9600	16,800	24,000

1914

	6	5	4	3	2	1
Series 14, Model 1 SC, 4-cyl., 108.3" wb						
4d Tr	900	2900	4800	9600	16,800	24,000
2d Lan Rds	900	2900	4800	9600	16,800	24,000
Series 14, Model EB, 6-cyl., 121.3" wb						
4d Tr	950	3000	5000	10,000	17,500	25,000
4d Lan Rds	950	3000	5000	10,000	17,500	25,000
2d Sed	650	2050	3400	6800	11,900	17,000

1915

	6	5	4	3	2	1
Series 15, Model SD, 4-cyl., 108.3" wb						
2d Rds	900	2900	4800	9600	16,800	24,000
4d Tr	900	2900	4800	9600	16,800	24,000
Series 15, Model EC, 6-cyl., 121.3" wb						
4d 5P Tr	950	3000	5000	10,000	17,500	25,000
4d 7P Tr	1000	3100	5200	10,400	18,200	26,000

1916

	6	5	4	3	2	1
Model SF, 4-cyl., 112" wb						
2d Rds	850	2750	4600	9200	16,100	23,000
2d Lan Rds	900	2900	4800	9600	16,800	24,000
4d 7P Tr	950	3000	5000	10,000	17,500	25,000
4d A/W Sed	700	2300	3800	7600	13,300	19,000
Series 16 & 17, Model ED, 6-cyl., 121.8" wb						
2d Rds	900	2900	4800	9600	16,800	24,000
2d Lan Rds	950	3000	5000	10,000	17,500	25,000
4d 7P Tr	1000	3100	5200	10,400	18,200	26,000
2d Cpe	500	1550	2600	5200	9100	13,000
4d Sed	400	1300	2200	4400	7700	11,000
4d Limo	700	2300	3800	7600	13,300	19,000
4d A/W Sed	700	2300	3800	7600	13,300	19,000

NOTE: The All Weather sedan was available only in the Series 17.

1917 (Series 18)

	6	5	4	3	2	1
Series 18, Model SF, 4-cyl., 112" wb						
2d Rds	750	2400	4000	8000	14,000	20,000
2d Lan Rds	800	2500	4200	8400	14,700	21,000
4d 7P Tr	850	2650	4400	8800	15,400	22,000
4d A/W Sed	650	2050	3400	6800	11,900	17,000
Series 18, Model ED, 6-cyl., 121.8" wb						
2d Rds	800	2500	4200	8400	14,700	21,000
2d Lan Rds	850	2650	4400	8800	15,400	22,000
4d 7P Tr	850	2750	4600	9200	16,100	23,000
2d Cpe	450	1450	2400	4800	8400	12,000
4d Sed	400	1300	2200	4400	7700	11,000
4d Limo	550	1700	2800	5600	9800	14,000
4d A/W Sed	700	2300	3800	7600	13,300	19,000

1918-1919

	6	5	4	3	2	1
Series 19, Model SH, 4-cyl., 112" wb						
2d Rds	650	2050	3400	6800	11,900	17,000
4d Tr	650	2050	3400	6800	11,900	17,000
4d Sed	450	1140	1900	3800	6650	9500
Series 19, Model EH, 6-cyl., 119" wb						
4d Tr	700	2150	3600	7200	12,600	18,000
2d Clb Rds	700	2150	3600	7200	12,600	18,000
2d Rds	550	1700	2800	5600	9800	14,000
4d Sed	450	1150	1900	3850	6700	9600
2d Cpe	400	1200	2000	4000	7000	10,000
Series 19, Model EG, 6-cyl., 126" wb						
4d 7P Tr	750	2400	4000	8000	14,000	20,000

1920-21

	6	5	4	3	2	1
Model EJ, 6-cyl., 112" wb						
4d Tr	550	1700	2800	5600	9800	14,000
2d Lan Rds *	550	1800	3000	6000	10,500	15,000
2d Rds	550	1700	2850	5700	9900	14,200
2d Cpe Rds **	600	1850	3100	6200	10,900	15,500
4d Sed	450	1080	1800	3600	6300	9000
Model EH, 6-cyl., 119" wb						
4d Tr	550	1800	3000	6000	10,500	15,000
2d Rds	550	1800	3050	6100	10,600	15,200
4d Rds	600	1850	3100	6200	10,900	15,500
2d Cpe	400	1200	2000	4000	7000	10,000
4d Sed	450	1080	1800	3600	6300	9000
Model EG, Big Six						
4d 7P Tr	650	2050	3400	6800	11,900	17,000
2d Cpe **	400	1300	2200	4400	7700	11,000
4d 7P Sed	400	1200	2000	4000	7000	10,000

* 1920 Model only.
** 1921 Model only.

1922

	6	5	4	3	2	1
Model EJ, Light Six, 6-cyl., 112" wb						
2d Rds	550	1700	2800	5600	9800	14,000
4d Tr	500	1600	2700	5400	9500	13,500
2d Cpe Rds	550	1750	2900	5800	10,200	14,500
4d Sed	450	1140	1900	3800	6650	9500
Model EL, Special Six, 6-cyl., 119" wb						
2d Rds	550	1750	2900	5800	10,200	14,500
4d Tr	550	1700	2800	5600	9800	14,000
4d Rds	550	1800	3000	6000	10,500	15,000
2d Cpe	400	1300	2200	4400	7700	11,000
4d Sed	400	1200	2000	4000	7000	10,000
Model EK, Big Six, 6-cyl., 126" wb						
4d Tr	550	1800	3000	6000	10,500	15,000
2d Cpe	400	1250	2100	4200	7400	10,500
4d Sed	400	1200	2000	4000	7000	10,000
4d Spds	600	1900	3200	6400	11,200	16,000

1923

	6	5	4	3	2	1
Model EM, Light Six						
2d Rds	550	1700	2800	5600	9800	14,000
4d Tr	500	1600	2700	5400	9500	13,500
2d Cpe	400	1200	2000	4000	7000	10,000
4d Sed	450	1140	1900	3800	6650	9500
Model EL, Special Six						
4d Tr	550	1700	2800	5600	9800	14,000
2d 4P Cpe	400	1250	2100	4200	7400	10,500
2d Rds	550	1750	2900	5800	10,200	14,600
2d 5P Cpe	400	1300	2200	4400	7700	11,000
4d Sed	400	1200	2000	4000	7000	10,000
Model EK, Big Six						
4d Tr	600	1850	3100	6200	10,900	15,500
2d Spds	700	2150	3600	7200	12,600	18,000
2d 5P Cpe	450	1400	2300	4600	8100	11,500
2d 4P Cpe	450	1350	2300	4600	8000	11,400
4d Sed	400	1250	2100	4200	7400	10,500

1924

	6	5	4	3	2	1
Model EM, Light Six, 6-cyl., 112" wb						
4d Tr	500	1550	2600	5200	9100	13,000
2d Rds	500	1600	2700	5400	9500	13,500
2d Cpe Rds	550	1750	2900	5800	10,200	14,500
4d Cus Tr	550	1700	2800	5600	9800	14,000
4d Sed	350	1020	1700	3400	5950	8500
2d Cpe	450	1140	1900	3800	6650	9500
Model EL, Special Six, 6-cyl., 119" wb						
4d Tr	550	1700	2800	5600	9800	14,000
2d Rds	550	1750	2900	5800	10,200	14,500
2d Cpe	400	1300	2200	4400	7700	11,000
4d Sed	400	1200	2000	4000	7000	10,000
Model EK, Big Six, 6-cyl., 126" wb						
4d 7P Tr	650	2100	3500	7000	12,300	17,500
2d Spds	700	2150	3600	7200	12,600	18,000
2d Cpe	450	1400	2300	4600	8100	11,500
4d Sed	400	1200	2000	4000	7000	10,000

1925-1926

	6	5	4	3	2	1
Model ER, Standard Six, 6-cyl., 113" wb						
4d Dplx Phae	600	1900	3200	6400	11,200	16,000
2d Dplx Rds	600	2000	3300	6600	11,600	16,500
2d Coach	450	1050	1750	3550	6150	8800
2d Cty Clb Cpe	450	1450	2400	4800	8400	12,000
2d Spt Rds	600	1850	3100	6200	10,900	15,500
4d Spt Phae	550	1800	3000	6000	10,500	15,000
4d Sed	450	1080	1800	3600	6300	9000
2d Cpe Rds	600	1900	3200	6400	11,200	16,000
4d w/Sed	450	1140	1900	3800	6650	9500
4d Sed	450	1080	1800	3600	6300	9000
2d Cpe	400	1300	2200	4400	7700	11,000
4d Ber	400	1250	2100	4200	7400	10,500
Model EQ, Special Six 6-cyl., 120" - 127" wb						
4d Dplx Phae	700	2150	3600	7200	12,600	18,000
2d Dplx Rds	750	2350	3900	7800	13,700	19,500
2d Vic	400	1300	2150	4300	7600	10,800
4d Sed	400	1250	2100	4200	7400	10,500
4d Ber	450	1400	2300	4600	8100	11,500
2d Brgm	400	1300	2200	4400	7700	11,000
2d Spt Rds	700	2300	3800	7600	13,300	19,000
2d Coach	400	1200	2000	4000	7000	10,000
Model EP, Big Six, 6-cyl., 120" wb						
4d Dplx Phae	750	2400	4000	8000	14,000	20,000
2d Cpe	450	1450	2400	4800	8400	12,000
2d Brgm	450	1140	1900	3800	6650	9500
4d 7P Sed	450	1130	1900	3800	6600	9400
2d Ber	400	1300	2200	4400	7700	11,000
4d Sed	450	1140	1900	3800	6650	9500
4d Spt Phae	700	2300	3800	7600	13,300	19,000
2d Clb Cpe	950	1100	1850	3700	6450	9200

NOTE: Add 10 percent for 4 wheel brake option.

1927	6	5	4	3	2	1
Dictator, Model EU Standard, 6-cyl., 113" wb						
2d Spt Rds	850	2650	4400	8800	15,400	22,000
4d Tr	750	2450	4100	8200	14,400	20,500
4d Dplx Tr	800	2500	4200	8400	14,700	21,000
4d 7P Tr	750	2400	4000	8000	14,000	20,000
2d Bus Cpe	450	1400	2300	4600	8100	11,500
2d Spt Cpe	450	1450	2400	4800	8400	12,000
2d Vic	450	1140	1900	3800	6650	9500
4d (P) Sed	450	1080	1800	3600	6300	9000
4d (M) Sed	400	1200	2000	4000	7000	10,000
Special, Model EQ						
4d Dplx Phae	850	2750	4600	9200	16,100	23,000
2d Coach	400	1200	2000	4000	7000	10,000
2d Brgm	400	1300	2200	4400	7700	11,000
2d Spt Rds	900	2900	4800	9600	16,800	24,000
Commander, Model EW						
2d Spt Rds	950	3000	5000	10,000	17,500	25,000
2d Bus Cpe	450	1450	2400	4800	8400	12,000
2d Spt Cpe	450	1500	2500	5000	8800	12,500
4d Sed	400	1250	2100	4200	7400	10,500
2d Cus Vic	450	1400	2300	4600	8100	11,500
2d Dplx Rds	900	2900	4800	9600	16,800	24,000
4d Spt Phae	900	2900	4800	9600	16,800	24,000
2d Cus Brgm	400	1300	2150	4300	7500	10,700
President, Model ES						
4d Cus Sed	400	1250	2100	4200	7400	10,500
4d Limo	700	2150	3600	7200	12,600	18,000
4d Dplx Phae	850	2750	4600	9200	16,100	23,000
1928						
Dictator, Model GE						
2d Roy Rds	1300	4200	7000	14,000	24,500	35,000
4d Tr	1250	3950	6600	13,200	23,100	33,000
4d Dplx Tr	1300	4100	6800	13,600	23,800	34,000
4d 7P Roy Tr	1300	4200	7000	14,000	24,500	35,000
2d Bus Cpe	400	1250	2100	4200	7400	10,500
2d Roy Cpe	400	1300	2200	4400	7700	11,000
2d Roy Vic	400	1250	2100	4200	7400	10,500
2d Clb Sed	450	1160	1950	3900	6800	9700
4d Sed	950	1100	1850	3700	6450	9200
4d Roy Sed	450	1140	1900	3800	6650	9500
Commander, Model GB						
2d Reg Rds	1350	4300	7200	14,400	25,200	36,000
2d Cpe	450	1400	2300	4600	8100	11,500
2d Reg Cpe	450	1450	2400	4800	8400	12,000
2d Reg Cabr	400	1250	2100	4200	7400	10,500
2d Vic	400	1250	2100	4200	7400	10,500
2d Reg Vic	400	1300	2200	4400	7700	11,000
4d Sed	400	1250	2100	4200	7400	10,500
2d Clb Sed	400	1300	2150	4300	7500	10,700
4d Reg Sed	400	1200	2000	4000	7000	10,000
President Six, Model ES						
4d Cus Sed	400	1250	2100	4200	7400	10,500
4d Limo	600	1900	3200	6400	11,200	16,000
4d Cus Tr	850	2750	4600	9200	16,100	23,000
President Eight, Model FA						
4d 7P Tr	1150	3600	6000	12,000	21,000	30,000
2d Sta Cabr	1150	3700	6200	12,400	21,700	31,000
4d Sed	400	1350	2250	4500	7800	11,200
4d Sta Sed	450	1400	2300	4600	8100	11,500
4d 7P Sed	450	1400	2300	4600	8100	11,500
4d 7P Sta Sed	450	1450	2400	4800	8400	12,000
4d Limo	650	2050	3400	6800	11,900	17,000
4d Sta Ber	700	2150	3600	7200	12,600	18,000
1928-1/2						
Dictator, Model GE						
2d Tr	900	2900	4800	9600	16,800	24,000
2d 7P Tr	900	2950	4900	9800	17,200	24,500
2d Bus Cpe	400	1200	2000	4000	7000	10,000
2d Roy Cabr	1150	3600	6000	12,000	21,000	30,000
2d Roy Vic	400	1250	2100	4200	7400	10,500
2d Clb Sed	450	1160	1950	3900	6800	9700
4d Sed	450	1130	1900	3800	6600	9400
4d Roy Sed	400	1200	2000	4000	7000	10,000
Commander, Model GH						
2d Reg Vic	400	1300	2150	4300	7500	10,700
4d Sed	400	1200	2050	4100	7100	10,200
4d Reg Sed	400	1250	2100	4200	7300	10,400
President, Model FB						
2d Sta Rds	1150	3600	6000	12,000	21,000	30,000
2d Sta Cabr	1100	3500	5800	11,600	20,300	29,000
2d Sta Vic	400	1300	2150	4300	7600	10,800
4d Sed	400	1250	2100	4200	7300	10,400
4d Sta Sed	400	1250	2100	4200	7400	10,600
President, Model FA						
4d Tr	1150	3700	6200	12,400	21,700	31,000
4d Sta Tr	1200	3850	6400	12,800	22,400	32,000
2d Sta Cabr	1250	3950	6600	13,200	23,100	33,000
4d Sta Sed	450	1450	2400	4800	8400	12,000
4d Sed	450	1400	2350	4700	8300	11,800
4d 7P Sta Sed	450	1500	2500	5000	8800	12,500
4d Limo	700	2150	3600	7200	12,600	18,000
1929						
Dictator GE, 6-cyl., 113" wb						
4d 5P Tr	900	2900	4800	9600	16,800	24,000
4d 7P Tr	900	2900	4800	9600	16,800	24,000
2d Bus Cpe	400	1250	2100	4200	7400	10,500
2d Cabr	900	2900	4800	9600	16,800	24,000
2d Vic Ryl	400	1300	2200	4400	7700	11,000
Commander Six, Model GJ						
2d Rds	1450	4550	7600	15,200	26,600	38,000
2d Reg Rds	1450	4700	7800	15,600	27,300	39,000
4d Tr	1300	4100	6800	13,600	23,800	34,000
4d Reg Tr	1350	4300	7200	14,400	25,200	36,000
4d 7P Tr	1300	4100	6800	13,600	23,800	34,000
4d 7P Reg Tr	1350	4300	7200	14,400	25,200	36,000
2d Cpe	450	1400	2300	4600	8100	11,500
2d Spt Cpe	400	1300	2200	4400	7700	11,000
2d Cabr	1250	3950	6600	13,200	23,100	33,000
2d Vic	400	1250	2100	4200	7400	10,500
4d Sed	400	1200	2000	4000	7000	10,000
4d Reg Sed	400	1300	2200	4400	7700	11,000
4d Reg Brgm	450	1400	2300	4600	8100	11,500
Commander Eight, Model FD						
2d Reg Rds	1600	5050	8400	16,800	29,400	42,000
4d Tr	1400	4450	7400	14,800	25,900	37,000
4d Reg Tr	1450	4700	7800	15,600	27,300	39,000
4d 7P Tr	1400	4450	7400	14,800	25,900	37,000
4d 7P Reg Tr	1450	4700	7800	15,600	27,300	39,000

	6	5	4	3	2	1
2d Bus Cpe	500	1600	2700	5400	9500	13,500
2d Spt Cpe	550	1700	2800	5600	9800	14,000
2d Reg Conv	1400	4450	7400	14,800	25,900	37,000
2d Vic	450	1450	2400	4800	8400	12,000
2d Reg Brgm	500	1550	2600	5200	9100	13,000
4d Sed	450	1500	2500	5000	8800	12,500
4d Reg Sed	500	1550	2600	5200	9100	13,000
President Eight, Model FH, 125" wb						
2d Rds	1600	5150	8600	17,200	30,100	43,000
2d Cabr	1450	4700	7800	15,600	27,300	39,000
2d Sta Vic	550	1800	3000	6000	10,500	15,000
4d Sed	550	1700	2800	5600	9800	14,000
4d Sta Sed	550	1800	3000	6000	10,500	15,000
President Eight, Model FE, 135" wb						
4d 7P Tr	1450	4700	7800	15,600	27,300	39,000
4d 7P Sta Tr	1500	4750	7900	15,800	27,700	39,500
2d Brgm	550	1800	3000	6000	10,500	15,000
4d 7P Sed	550	1800	3000	6000	10,500	15,000
4d 7P Sta Sed	600	1900	3200	6400	11,200	16,000
4d 7P Limo	650	2050	3400	6800	11,900	17,000
1930						
Studebaker 53 Model, 6-cyl., 114" wb						
4d Tr	1250	3950	6600	13,200	23,100	33,000
4d Reg Tr	1300	4100	6800	13,600	23,800	34,000
2d Bus Cpe	450	1450	2400	4800	8400	12,000
2d Reg Cpe	450	1500	2500	5000	8800	12,500
2d Clb Sed	400	1300	2200	4400	7700	11,000
4d Sed	400	1200	2000	4000	7000	10,000
4d Reg Sed	400	1250	2100	4200	7400	10,500
4d Lan Sed	400	1200	2050	4100	7100	10,200
Dictator, 6 & 8 cyl., 115" wb						
4d Tr	1300	4100	6800	13,600	23,800	34,000
4d Reg Tr	1300	4200	7000	14,000	24,500	35,000
2d Cpe	450	1500	2500	5000	8800	12,500
2d Spt Cpe	500	1600	2700	5400	9500	13,500
2d Brgm	450	1400	2300	4600	8100	11,500
2d Clb Sed	400	1300	2200	4400	7700	11,000
4d Sed	400	1300	2200	4400	7700	11,000
4d Reg Sed	450	1400	2300	4600	8100	11,500
NOTE: Add $200. for Dictator 8-cyl.						
Commander 6 & 8 cyl., 120" wb						
Commander FD						
2d Reg Rds	1450	4550	7600	15,200	26,600	38,000
4d Tr	1350	4300	7200	14,400	25,200	36,000
4d Reg Tr	1400	4450	7400	14,800	25,900	37,000
4d 7P Tr	1350	4300	7200	14,400	25,200	36,000
4d 7P Reg Tr	1400	4450	7400	14,800	25,900	37,000
2d Cpe	550	1700	2800	5600	9800	14,000
2d Spt Cpe	550	1800	3000	6000	10,500	15,000
2d Conv Cabr	1350	4300	7200	14,400	25,200	36,000
2d Vic	450	1450	2400	4800	8400	12,000
2d Brgm	450	1500	2500	5000	8800	12,500
4d Sed	450	1450	2400	4800	8400	12,000
4d Reg Sed	500	1550	2600	5200	9100	13,000
NOTE: Add $200. for Commander 8-cyl.						
President FH Model						
2d Rds	1800	5750	9600	19,200	33,600	48,000
2d Conv Cabr	1600	5050	8400	16,800	29,400	42,000
2d Sta Vic	600	1900	3200	6400	11,200	16,000
4d Sed	550	1700	2800	5600	9800	14,000
4d Sta Sed	550	1800	3000	6000	10,500	15,000
President FE Model						
4d Tr	1700	5400	9000	18,000	31,500	45,000
4d Sta Tr	1750	5500	9200	18,400	32,200	46,000
2d Sta Vic	1050	3350	5600	11,200	19,600	28,000
2d Brgm	550	1800	3000	6000	10,500	15,000
4d Sed	600	1900	3200	6400	11,200	16,000
4d Sta Sed	650	2050	3400	6800	11,900	17,000
4d Limo	750	2400	4000	8000	14,000	20,000
4d Sta Limo	800	2500	4200	8400	14,700	21,000
1931						
Studebaker Six, Model 53, 114" wb						
2d Rds	1350	4300	7200	14,400	25,200	36,000
2d Tr	1200	3850	6400	12,800	22,400	32,000
2d Reg Tr	1250	3950	6600	13,200	23,100	33,000
2d Bus Cpe	400	1300	2200	4400	7700	11,000
2d Spt Cpe	450	1450	2400	4800	8400	12,000
2d Clb Sed	400	1200	2000	4000	7000	10,000
4d Sed	400	1200	2000	4000	7000	10,000
Model 61 Dictator, 8-cyl., 115" wb						
4d Reg Sed	400	1250	2100	4200	7300	10,400
4d Lan Sed	400	1250	2100	4200	7400	10,500
Series 54						
2d Rds	1600	5050	8400	16,800	29,400	42,000
4d Tr	1500	4800	8000	16,000	28,000	40,000
4d Rea Tr	1550	4900	8200	16,400	28,700	41,000
2d Bus Cpe	450	1500	2500	5000	8800	12,500
2d Spt Cpe	500	1550	2600	5200	9100	13,000
4d Sed	400	1300	2200	4400	7700	11,000
4d Reg Sed	450	1400	2300	4600	8100	11,500
Dictator Eight, Model FC						
4d Tr	1450	4700	7800	15,600	27,300	39,000
4d Reg Tr	1500	4800	8000	16,000	28,000	40,000
2d Cpe	500	1550	2600	5200	9100	13,000
2d Spt Cpe	500	1600	2700	5400	9500	13,500
2d Reg Brgm	450	1450	2400	4800	8400	12,000
2d Clb Sed	450	1400	2300	4600	8100	11,500
4d Sed	450	1450	2400	4800	8400	12,000
4d Reg Sed	450	1450	2450	4900	8500	12,200
Model 61						
2d Cpe	550	1700	2800	5600	9800	14,000
2d Spt Cpe	550	1800	3000	6000	10,500	15,000
4d Sed	450	1500	2500	5000	8800	12,500
4d Reg Sed	500	1550	2600	5200	9100	13,000
Commander Eight, Model 70						
2d Cpe	550	1750	2900	5800	10,200	14,500
2d Vic	550	1700	2800	5600	9800	14,000
2d Reg Brgm	550	1750	2900	5800	10,200	14,500
4d Sed	550	1750	2900	5800	10,200	14,500
4d Reg Sed	550	1800	3000	6000	10,500	15,000
President Eight, Model 80						
2d Sta Rds	2050	6600	11,000	22,000	38,500	55,000
2d Cpe	850	2750	4600	9200	16,100	23,000
2d Sta Cpe	950	3000	5000	10,000	17,500	25,000
4d Sed	650	2050	3400	6800	11,900	17,000
4d Sta Sed	700	2150	3600	7200	12,600	18,000
President Eight Model 90						
4d Tr	1800	5750	9600	19,200	33,600	48,000

	6	5	4	3	2	1
4d Sta Tr	1900	6000	10,000	20,000	35,000	50,000
2d Sta Vic	850	2650	4400	8800	15,400	22,000
2d Sta Brgm	850	2650	4400	8800	15,400	22,000
4d Sed	750	2400	4000	8000	14,000	20,000
4d Sta Sed	800	2500	4200	8400	14,700	21,000
4d Sta Limo	850	2750	4600	9200	16,100	23,000
1932						
Model 55, 6-cyl., 117" wb						
2d Conv Rds	1250	3950	6600	13,200	23,100	33,000
2d Reg Conv Rds	1400	4450	7400	14,800	25,900	37,000
2d Cpe	450	1500	2500	5000	8800	12,500
2d Reg Cpe	500	1500	2550	5100	8900	12,700
2d Spt Cpe	450	1500	2500	5000	8800	12,500
2d Reg Spt Cpe	500	1550	2600	5200	9100	13,000
2d St R Brgm	450	1400	2300	4600	8100	11,500
2d Reg St R Brgm	450	1400	2350	4700	8300	11,800
4d Conv Sed	1400	4450	7400	14,800	25,900	37,000
4d Reg Conv Sed	1450	4550	7600	15,200	26,600	38,000
4d Sed	400	1300	2200	4400	7700	11,000
4d Reg Sed	400	1350	2250	4500	7800	11,200
Model 62 Dictator, 8-cyl., 117" wb						
2d Conv Rds	1600	5050	8400	16,800	29,400	42,000
2d Reg Conv Rds	1600	5150	8600	17,200	30,100	43,000
2d Cpe	750	2400	4000	8000	14,000	20,000
2d Reg Cpe	800	2500	4200	8400	14,700	21,000
2d Spt Cpe	1000	3250	5400	10,800	18,900	27,000
2d Reg Spt Cpe	1050	3350	5600	11,200	19,600	28,000
2d St R Brgm	900	2900	4800	9600	16,800	24,000
2d Reg St R Brgm	950	3000	5000	10,000	17,500	25,000
4d Conv Sed	1400	4450	7400	14,800	25,900	37,000
4d Reg Conv Sed	1650	5300	8800	17,600	30,800	44,000
4d Sed	750	2400	4000	8000	14,000	20,000
4d Reg Sed	800	2500	4200	8400	14,700	21,000
Model 65 Rockne, 6-cyl., 110" wb						
2d 2P Cpe	450	1450	2400	4800	8400	12,000
4d 5P Sed	400	1300	2200	4400	7700	11,000
2d Sed	400	1250	2100	4200	7400	10,500
4d 5P Conv Sed	1300	4100	6800	13,600	23,800	34,000
2d Rds	1450	4550	7600	15,200	26,600	38,000
Model 71 Commander, 8-cyl.						
2d Rds Conv	1700	5400	9000	18,000	31,500	45,000
2d Reg Rds Conv	1750	5500	9200	18,400	32,200	46,000
2d Spt Cpe	1000	3100	5200	10,400	18,200	26,000
2d Reg Spt Cpe	1000	3250	5400	10,800	18,900	27,000
2d St R Brgm	1000	3100	5200	10,400	18,200	26,000
2d Reg St R Brgm	1000	3250	5400	10,800	18,900	27,000
4d Conv Sed	1650	5300	8800	17,600	30,800	44,000
4d Reg Conv Sed	1700	5400	9000	18,000	31,500	45,000
4d Sed	750	2400	4000	8000	14,000	20,000
4d Reg Sed	750	2450	4100	8200	14,400	20,500
Model 75 Rockne, 6-cyl., 114" wb						
2d 2P Cpe	450	1400	2300	4600	8100	11,500
2d 4P Cpe	400	1300	2200	4400	7700	11,000
4d 5P Sed	400	1300	2200	4400	7700	11,000
2d 2P DeL Cpe	450	1500	2500	5000	8800	12,500
2d 4P DeL Cpe	450	1450	2400	4800	8400	12,000
4d 5P DeL Sed	450	1450	2400	4800	8400	12,000
2d Rds	1500	4800	8000	16,000	28,000	40,000
4d Conv Sed	1450	4700	7800	15,600	27,300	39,000
Model 91 President, 8-cyl.						
2d Rds Conv	2250	7200	12,000	24,000	42,000	60,000
2d Sta Rds Conv	2350	7450	12,400	24,800	43,400	62,000
2d Cpe	1150	3600	6000	12,000	21,000	30,000
2d Sta Cpe	1150	3700	6200	12,400	21,700	31,000
2d Spt Cpe	1200	3850	6400	12,800	22,400	32,000
2d Sta Spt Cpe	1250	3950	6600	13,200	23,100	33,000
2d St R Brgm	1000	3250	5400	10,800	18,900	27,000
2d Sta St R Brgm	1050	3350	5600	11,200	19,600	28,000
4d Conv Sed	2200	7100	11,800	23,600	41,300	59,000
4d Sta Conv Sed	2250	7200	12,000	24,000	42,000	60,000
4d Sed	800	2500	4200	8400	14,700	21,000
4d Sta Sed	850	2650	4400	8800	15,400	22,000
4d Limo	950	3000	5000	10,000	17,500	25,000
4d Sta Limo	1000	3100	5200	10,400	18,200	26,000
4d 7P Sed	750	2400	4000	8000	14,000	20,000
4d 7P Sta Sed	800	2500	4200	8400	14,700	21,000
1933						
Model 10 Rockne, 6-cyl., 110" wb						
2d 4P Conv	1250	3950	6600	13,200	23,100	33,000
2d 4P DeL Conv Rds	1300	4100	6800	13,600	23,800	34,000
2d 2P Cpe	500	1550	2600	5200	9100	13,000
2d 5P Coach	400	1200	2000	4000	7000	10,000
2d 4P Cpe	450	1450	2400	4800	8400	12,000
2d 2P DeL Cpe	500	1550	2600	5200	9100	13,000
2d 5P Sed	400	1200	2000	4000	7000	10,000
2d 5P DeL Coach	400	1250	2100	4200	7400	10,500
4d 4P DeL Cpe	450	1450	2400	4800	8400	12,000
4d 5P DeL Sed	400	1200	2000	4000	7000	10,000
4d 5P Conv Sed	1400	4450	7400	14,800	25,900	37,000
4d 5P DeL Conv Sed	1450	4550	7600	15,200	26,600	38,000
Model 56 Studebaker, 6-cyl., 117" wb						
2d Conv	1450	4700	7800	15,600	27,300	39,000
2d Reg Conv	1500	4800	8000	16,000	28,000	40,000
2d Cpe	600	1900	3200	6400	11,200	16,000
2d Reg Cpe	650	2050	3400	6800	11,900	17,000
2d Spt Cpe	700	2150	3600	7200	12,600	18,000
2d Reg Spt Cpe	700	2300	3800	7600	13,300	19,000
2d St R Brgm	550	1800	3000	6000	10,500	15,000
2d Reg St R Brgm	600	1900	3200	6400	11,200	16,000
4d Conv Sed	1450	4550	7600	15,200	26,600	38,000
4d Reg Conv Sed	1450	4700	7800	15,600	27,300	39,000
4d Sed	500	1550	2600	5200	9100	13,000
4d Reg Sed	550	1700	2800	5600	9800	14,000
Model 73 Commander, 8-cyl.						
2d Rds Conv	1500	4800	8000	16,000	28,000	40,000
2d Reg Rds Conv	1550	4900	8200	16,400	28,700	41,000
2d Cpe	650	2050	3400	6800	11,900	17,000
2d Reg Cpe	700	2150	3600	7200	12,600	18,000
2d Spt Cpe	700	2300	3800	7600	13,300	19,000
2d Reg Spt Cpe	750	2400	4000	8000	14,000	20,000
2d St R Brgm	600	1900	3200	6400	11,200	16,000
2d Reg St R Brgm	650	2050	3400	6800	11,900	17,000
4d Conv Sed	1500	4800	8000	16,000	28,000	40,000
4d Reg Conv Sed	1550	4900	8200	16,400	28,700	41,000
4d Sed	600	1900	3200	6400	11,200	16,000
4d Reg Sed	650	2050	3400	6800	11,900	17,000
Model 82 President, 8-cyl.						
2d Sta Rds Conv	1600	5150	8600	17,200	30,100	43,000

	6	5	4	3	2	1
2d Cpe	650	2050	3400	6800	11,900	17,000
2d Sta Cpe	750	2400	4000	8000	14,000	20,000
2d St R Brgm	600	1900	3200	6400	11,200	16,000
2d Sta St R Brgm	650	2050	3400	6800	11,900	17,000
4d Sta Conv Sed	1600	5150	8600	17,200	30,100	43,000
4d Sed	650	2050	3400	6800	11,900	17,000
4d Sta Sed	700	2150	3600	7200	12,600	18,000
Model 92 President Speedway, 8-cyl.						
2d Sta Rds Conv	1650	5300	8800	17,600	30,800	44,000
2d Sta Cpe	750	2400	4000	8000	14,000	20,000
2d Sta St R Brgm	850	2650	4400	8800	15,400	22,000
4d Sta Conv Sed	1650	5300	8800	17,600	30,800	44,000
4d Sed	600	1900	3200	6400	11,200	16,000
4d Sta Sed	650	2050	3400	6800	11,900	17,000
4d 7P Sed	700	2150	3600	7200	12,600	18,000
4d 7P Sta Sed	700	2300	3800	7600	13,300	19,000
4d 7P Sta Limo	800	2500	4200	8400	14,700	21,000
1934						
Model Special A, Dictator						
2d Cpe	450	1450	2400	4800	8400	12,000
2d Reg Cpe	550	1700	2800	5600	9800	14,000
2d 4P Cpe	450	1450	2400	4800	8400	12,000
2d 4P Reg Cpe	500	1550	2600	5200	9100	13,000
2d St R Sed	400	1200	2000	4000	7000	10,000
2d Reg St R Sed	400	1250	2100	4200	7400	10,500
2d Sed	400	1200	2000	4000	7000	10,000
2d Reg Sed	400	1250	2100	4200	7400	10,500
4d Cus Reg St R	400	1300	2200	4400	7700	11,000
4d Cus Sed	450	1400	2300	4600	8100	11,500
Model A, Dictator						
2d Rdst	1300	4100	6800	13,600	23,800	34,000
2d Rds Regal	1300	4200	7000	14,000	24,500	35,000
2d Reg Cpe	600	1900	3200	6400	11,200	16,000
2d St R Sed	500	1550	2600	5200	9100	13,000
2d Cus St R Sed	400	1250	2100	4200	7400	10,500
4d Sed	400	1200	2000	4000	7000	10,000
4d Reg Sed	400	1250	2100	4200	7400	10,500
Model B, Commander						
2d Rds Conv	1300	4200	7000	14,000	24,500	35,000
2d Reg Rds Conv	1350	4300	7200	14,400	25,200	36,000
2d Cpe	600	1900	3200	6400	11,200	16,000
2d Reg Cpe	650	2050	3400	6800	11,900	17,000
2d 4P Cpe	550	1800	3000	6000	10,500	15,000
2d 4P Reg Cpe	600	1900	3200	6400	11,200	16,000
2d St R Sed	400	1300	2200	4400	7700	11,000
2d Cus St R Sed	450	1400	2300	4600	8100	11,500
4d Sed	400	1200	2000	4000	7000	10,000
4d Reg Sed	400	1250	2100	4200	7400	10,500
4d Cus Sed	400	1300	2150	4300	7500	10,700
4d L Cruise	400	1300	2200	4400	7700	11,000
Model C, President						
2d Rds Conv	1450	4550	7600	15,200	26,600	38,000
2d Reg Rds Conv	1450	4700	7800	15,600	27,300	39,000
2d Cpe	650	2050	3400	6800	11,900	17,000
2d Reg Cpe	700	2150	3600	7200	12,600	18,000
2d 4P Cpe	600	1900	3200	6400	11,200	16,000
2d 4P Reg Cpe	650	2050	3400	6800	11,900	17,000
2d Sed	450	1400	2300	4600	8100	11,500
2d Reg Sed	450	1450	2400	4800	8400	12,000
4d Cus Sed	450	1450	2400	4800	8400	12,000
4d Cus Berl	450	1500	2500	5000	8800	12,500
4d L Cruise	500	1600	2700	5400	9500	13,500
1935						
Model 1A, Dictator Six						
2d Rds	1250	3950	6600	13,200	23,100	33,000
2d Reg Rds	1300	4100	6800	13,600	23,800	34,000
2d Cpe	400	1300	2200	4400	7700	11,000
2d Reg Cpe	450	1450	2400	4800	8400	12,000
2d R/S Cpe	450	1500	2500	5000	8800	12,500
2d Reg R/S Cpe	500	1600	2700	5400	9500	13,500
2d St Reg	350	1040	1750	3500	6100	8700
2d Reg St Reg	450	1080	1800	3600	6300	9000
2d Cus St Reg	450	1120	1875	3750	6500	9300
4d Sed	350	1020	1700	3400	5950	8500
2d Reg Sed	450	1050	1750	3550	6150	8800
2d Cus Sed	450	1090	1800	3650	6400	9100
4d L Cr	450	1120	1875	3750	6500	9300
4d Reg L Cr	450	1140	1900	3800	6650	9500
Model 1B, Commander Eight						
2d Rds	1350	4300	7200	14,400	25,200	36,000
2d Reg Rds	1400	4450	7400	14,800	25,900	37,000
2d Cpe	450	1450	2400	4800	8400	12,000
2d Reg Cpe	500	1550	2600	5200	9100	13,000
2d R/S Cpe	500	1600	2700	5400	9500	13,500
2d Reg R/S Cpe	550	1700	2800	5600	9800	14,000
2d Reg St R	400	1200	2000	4000	7000	10,000
2d Cus St R	400	1200	2050	4100	7100	10,200
2d Reg Sed	400	1250	2050	4100	7200	10,300
2d Cus Sed	400	1250	2100	4200	7400	10,500
4d L Cr	400	1300	2200	4400	7700	11,000
4d Reg L Cr	400	1350	2250	4500	7900	11,300
Model 1C, President Eight						
2d Rds	1400	4450	7400	14,800	25,900	37,000
2d Reg Rds	1450	4550	7600	15,200	26,600	38,000
2d Cpe	550	1800	3000	6000	10,500	15,000
2d Reg Cpe	600	1900	3200	6400	11,200	16,000
2d R/S Cpe	600	2000	3300	6600	11,600	16,500
2d Reg R/S Cpe	650	2050	3400	6800	11,900	17,000
2d Reg Sed	400	1300	2200	4400	7700	11,000
2d Cus Sed	450	1450	2400	4800	8400	12,000
4d L Cr	500	1550	2600	5200	9100	13,000
4d Reg L Cr	550	1700	2800	5600	9800	14,000
4d Cus Berl	550	1800	3000	6000	10,500	15,000
4d Reg Berl	600	1850	3100	6200	10,900	15,500

NOTE: Add 10 percent for 2A Dictator models.

	6	5	4	3	2	1
1936						
Model 3A/4A, Dictator Six						
2d Bus Cpe	400	1200	2000	4000	7000	10,000
2d Cus Cpe	400	1300	2200	4400	7700	11,000
2d 5P Cus Cpe	450	1450	2400	4800	8400	12,000
2d Cus St R	950	1100	1850	3700	6450	9200
4d Cr St R	450	1140	1900	3800	6650	9500
2d Cus Sed	450	1140	1900	3800	6650	9500
4d Cr Sed	450	1170	1975	3900	6850	9800
Model 2C, President Eight						
2d Cus Cpe	500	1550	2600	5200	9100	13,000
2d 5P Cus Cpe	550	1700	2800	5600	9800	14,000
2d Cus St R	400	1350	2250	4500	7800	11,200
4d Cr St R	450	1400	2300	4600	8100	11,500

	6	5	4	3	2	1
4d Cus Sed	450	1450	2400	4800	8400	12,000
4d Cr Sed	500	1550	2600	5200	9100	13,000
NOTE: Add 10 percent for Model 4A Dictator Six.						
1937						
Model 5A/6A, Dictator Six						
2d Cpe Express	450	1450	2400	4800	8400	12,000
2d Bus Cpe	400	1300	2200	4400	7700	11,000
2d Cus Cpe	450	1450	2400	4800	8400	12,000
2d 5P Cus Cpe	450	1400	2300	4600	8100	11,500
2d Cus St R	450	1140	1900	3800	6650	9500
4d St R Cr	450	1130	1900	3800	6600	9400
4d Cus Sed	450	1130	1900	3800	6600	9400
4d Cr Sed	450	1160	1950	3900	6800	9700
Model 3C, President Eight						
2d Cus Cpe	500	1550	2600	5200	9100	13,000
2d 5P Cus Cpe	450	1500	2500	5000	8800	12,500
2d Cus St R	400	1350	2250	4500	7800	11,200
4d St R Cr	400	1350	2200	4400	7800	11,100
4d Cus Sed	400	1350	2200	4400	7800	11,100
4d Cr Sed	450	1350	2300	4600	8000	11,400
NOTE: Add 10 percent for Dictator 6A models.						
1938						
Model 7A, Commander Six						
2d Cpe Exp	400	1300	2200	4400	7700	11,000
2d Bus Cpe	400	1200	2000	4000	7000	10,000
2d Cus Cpe	400	1300	2200	4400	7700	11,000
2d Clb Sed	450	1150	1900	3850	6700	9600
4d Cr Sed	450	1170	1975	3900	6850	9800
4d Conv Sed	950	3050	5100	10,200	17,900	25,500
Model 8A, State Commander Six						
2d Cus Cpe	450	1400	2300	4600	8100	11,500
2d Clb Sed	450	1150	1900	3850	6700	9600
4d Cr Sed	450	1170	1975	3900	6850	9800
4d Conv Sed	1000	3200	5300	10,600	18,600	26,500
Model 4C, President Eight						
2d Cpe	450	1450	2400	4800	8400	12,000
2d Clb Sed	400	1300	2200	4400	7700	11,000
4d Cr Sed	450	1400	2300	4600	8100	11,500
Model 4C, State President Eight						
2d Cpe	500	1550	2600	5200	9100	13,000
2d Clb Sed	400	1350	2250	4500	7900	11,300
4d Cr Sed	450	1450	2400	4800	8400	12,000
4d Conv Sed	1100	3550	5900	11,800	20,700	29,500
1939						
Model G, Custom Champion Six						
2d Cpe	400	1300	2200	4400	7700	11,000
2d Clb Sed	400	1300	2150	4300	7500	10,700
4d Cr Sed	400	1300	2150	4300	7600	10,800
Model G, Deluxe Champion Six						
2d Cpe	500	1550	2600	5200	9100	13,000
2d Clb Sed	450	1400	2350	4700	8300	11,800
4d Cr Sed	450	1450	2400	4800	8400	12,000
Model 9A, Commander Six						
2d Cpe Express	600	1850	3100	6200	10,900	15,500
2d Bus Cpe	550	1700	2800	5600	9800	14,000
2d Cus Cpe	550	1800	3000	6000	10,500	15,000
2d Clb Sed	500	1650	2700	5400	9500	13,600
4d Cr Sed	500	1650	2750	5500	9600	13,700
4d Conv Sed	1200	3850	6400	12,800	22,400	32,000
Model 5C, State President Eight						
2d Cus Cpe	600	1900	3200	6400	11,200	16,000
2d Clb Sed	550	1800	3000	6000	10,500	15,000
4d Cr Sed	600	1850	3100	6200	10,900	15,500
4d Conv Sed	1300	4200	7000	14,000	24,500	35,000
1940						
Champion Custom						
2d Cpe	450	1500	2500	5000	8800	12,500
2d OS Cpe	500	1600	2700	5400	9500	13,500
2d Clb Sed	450	1450	2400	4800	8400	12,000
4d Cr Sed	450	1450	2400	4800	8500	12,100
Champion Custom Deluxe						
2d Cpe	550	1700	2800	5600	9800	14,000
2d OS Cpe	550	1750	2900	5800	10,200	14,500
2d Clb Sed	450	1450	2400	4800	8500	12,100
4d Cr Sed	450	1450	2450	4900	8500	12,200
Champion Deluxe						
2d Cpe	550	1750	2900	5800	10,200	14,500
2d OS Cpe	550	1800	3000	6000	10,500	15,000
2d Clb Sed	450	1450	2450	4900	8500	12,200
4d Cr Sed	450	1500	2450	4900	8600	12,300
Champion Deluxe-Tone						
2d Cpe	550	1700	2800	5600	9800	14,000
2d OS Cpe	550	1750	2900	5800	10,200	14,500
2d Clb Sed	450	1500	2450	4900	8600	12,300
4d Cr Sed	450	1500	2500	5000	8700	12,400
Commander						
2d Cus Cpe	550	1750	2900	5800	10,200	14,500
2d Clb Sed	450	1500	2500	5000	8800	12,600
4d Cr Sed	500	1500	2550	5100	8900	12,700
Commander Deluxe-Tone						
2d Cus Cpe	550	1800	3000	6000	10,500	15,000
2d Clb Sed	450	1500	2500	5000	8800	12,600
4d Cr Sed	500	1500	2550	5100	8900	12,700
State President						
2d Cpe	600	1850	3100	6200	10,900	15,500
2d Clb Sed	550	1700	2800	5600	9800	14,000
4d Cr Sed	550	1800	3000	6000	10,500	15,000
President Deluxe-Tone						
2d Cpe	600	1900	3200	6400	11,200	16,000
2d Clb Sed	550	1700	2850	5700	9900	14,200
4d Cr Sed	550	1800	3000	6000	10,500	15,000
1941						
Champion Custom						
2d Cpe	500	1550	2600	5200	9100	13,000
2d D D Cpe	500	1600	2700	5400	9500	13,500
2d OS Cpe	550	1700	2800	5600	9800	14,000
2d Clb Sed	500	1500	2550	5100	8900	12,700
4d Cr Sed	500	1550	2550	5100	9000	12,800
Champion Custom Deluxe						
2d Cpe	500	1600	2700	5400	9500	13,500
2d D D Cpe	500	1550	2600	5200	9100	13,000
2d OS Cpe	550	1750	2900	5800	10,200	14,500
2d Clb Sed	500	1550	2550	5100	9000	12,800
4d Cr Sed	500	1550	2600	5200	9100	13,000
Champion Deluxe-Tone						
2d Cpe	550	1700	2800	5600	9800	14,000
2d D D Cpe	550	1750	2900	5800	10,200	14,500
2d OS Cpe	550	1800	3000	6000	10,500	15,000
2d Clb Sed	500	1550	2550	5100	9000	12,800
4d Cr Sed	500	1550	2600	5200	9100	13,000
Commander Custom						
4d Sed Cpe	550	1800	3000	6000	10,500	15,000
2d Cr Cpe	600	1850	3100	6200	10,900	15,500
4d L Cruise	550	1800	3000	6000	10,500	15,000
Commander Deluxe-Tone						
4d Cr Sed	550	1850	3050	6100	10,700	15,300
4d L Cruise	600	1850	3100	6200	10,900	15,500
Commander Skyway						
4d Sed Cpe	650	2050	3400	6800	11,900	17,000
4d Cr Sed	600	1900	3200	6400	11,200	16,000
4d L Cruise	600	2000	3300	6600	11,600	16,500
President Custom						
4d Cr Sed	600	2000	3300	6600	11,600	16,500
4d L Cruise	650	2100	3500	7000	12,300	17,500
President Deluxe-Tone						
4d Cr Sed	650	2000	3350	6700	11,700	16,700
4d L Cruise	650	2100	3550	7100	12,400	17,700
President Skyway						
2d Sed Cpe	750	2400	4000	8000	14,000	20,000
4d Cr Sed	700	2300	3800	7600	13,300	19,000
4d L Cruise	750	2350	3900	7800	13,700	19,500
1942						
Champion Custom Series						
2d Cpe	400	1250	2100	4200	7400	10,500
2d D D Cpe	400	1300	2200	4400	7700	11,000
2d Clb Sed	400	1200	2000	4000	7000	10,000
4d Cr Sed	400	1200	2000	4000	7100	10,100
Champion Deluxstyle Series						
2d Cpe	400	1300	2200	4400	7700	11,000
2d D D Cpe	450	1400	2300	4600	8100	11,500
2d Clb Sed	400	1200	2000	4000	7100	10,100
4d Cr Sed	400	1200	2050	4100	7100	10,200
Commander Custom Series						
2d Sed Cpe	450	1400	2300	4600	8100	11,500
4d Cr Sed	400	1300	2150	4300	7500	10,700
4d L Cr	400	1300	2150	4300	7600	10,800
Commander Deluxstyle Series						
2d Sed Cpe	450	1500	2500	5000	8800	12,500
4d Cr Sed	400	1350	2250	4500	7900	11,300
4d L Cr	450	1400	2350	4700	8300	11,800
Commander Skyway Series						
2d Sed Cpe	550	1750	2900	5800	10,200	14,500
4d Cr Sed	500	1550	2550	5100	9000	12,800
4d L Cr	500	1650	2750	5500	9700	13,800
President Custom Series						
2d Sed Cpe	550	1750	2900	5800	10,200	14,500
4d Cr Sed	500	1550	2550	5100	9000	12,800
4d L Cr	500	1650	2750	5500	9700	13,800
President Deluxstyle Series						
2d Sed Cpe	600	1850	3100	6200	10,900	15,500
4d Cr Sed	500	1650	2750	5500	9700	13,800
4d L Cr	550	1800	2950	5900	10,400	14,800
President Skyway Series						
2d Sed Cpe	600	2000	3300	6600	11,600	16,500
4d Cr Sed	550	1800	2950	5900	10,400	14,800
4d L Cr	600	1900	3150	6300	11,100	15,800
1946						
Skyway Champion, 6-cyl., 109.5" wb						
2d 3P Cpe	450	1450	2400	4800	8400	12,000
2d 5P Cpe	450	1400	2300	4600	8100	11,500
2d Sed	400	1350	2250	4500	7800	11,200
4d Sed	450	1350	2300	4600	8000	11,400
1947-1949						
Champion, 6-cyl., 112" wb						
2d 3P Cpe	400	1200	2000	4000	7000	10,000
2d 5P Cpe Starlight	450	1350	2300	4600	8000	11,400
2d Sed	450	1160	1950	3900	6800	9700
4d Sed	450	1170	1975	3900	6850	9800
2d Conv	700	2300	3800	7600	13,300	19,000
Commander, 6-cyl., 119" wb						
2d 3P Cpe	400	1250	2100	4200	7300	10,400
2d 5P Cpe Starlight	450	1400	2350	4700	8300	11,800
2d Sed	400	1200	2000	4000	7100	10,100
4d Sed	400	1250	2050	4100	7200	10,300
2d Conv	750	2400	4000	8000	14,000	20,000
Land Cruiser, 6-cyl., 123" wb						
4d Ld Crs Sed	450	1400	2350	4700	8200	11,700
1950						
Champion, 6-cyl., 113" wb						
2d 3P Cpe	450	1350	2300	4600	8000	11,400
2d 5P Cpe Starlight	450	1500	2500	5000	8800	12,500
2d Sed	400	1350	2200	4400	7800	11,100
4d Sed	400	1350	2250	4500	7900	11,300
2d Conv	750	2400	4000	8000	14,000	20,000
Commander, 6-cyl., 120" - 124" wb						
2d 3P Cpe	450	1400	2300	4600	8100	11,500
2d 5P Cpe Starlight	450	1450	2400	4800	8400	12,000
2d Sed	400	1350	2250	4500	7900	11,300
4d Sed	450	1350	2300	4600	8000	11,400
2d Conv	800	2500	4200	8400	14,700	21,000
Land Cruiser, 6-cyl., 124" wb						
4d Ld Crs Sed	450	1450	2400	4800	8400	12,000
1951						
Champion Custom, 6-cyl., 115" wb						
4d Sed	450	1400	2300	4600	8100	11,600
2d Sed	450	1400	2300	4600	8100	11,500
2d 5P Cpe Starlight	450	1500	2500	5000	8800	12,500
2d 3P Cpe	400	1300	2150	4300	7600	10,800
Champion DeLuxe, 6-cyl., 115" wb						
4d Sed	400	1300	2150	4300	7500	10,700
2d Sed	400	1300	2150	4300	7600	10,800
2d 5P Cpe Starlight	500	1500	2550	5100	8900	12,700
2d 3P Cpe	400	1300	2200	4400	7700	11,000
Champion Regal, 6-cyl., 115" wb						
4d Sed	400	1300	2150	4300	7600	10,800
2d Sed	400	1300	2150	4300	7500	10,700
2d 5P Cpe Starlight	450	1450	2400	4800	8400	12,000
2d 3P Cpe	400	1300	2200	4400	7700	11,000
2d Conv	750	2400	4000	8000	14,000	20,000
Commander Regal, V-8, 115" wb						
4d Sed	400	1300	2200	4400	7700	11,000
2d Sed	400	1300	2200	4400	7600	10,900
5P Cpe Starlight	500	1550	2600	5200	9100	13,000

	6	5	4	3	2	1
Commander State, V-8, 115" wb						
4d Sed	450	1400	2300	4600	8100	11,500
2d Sed	450	1350	2300	4600	8000	11,400
5P Cpe Starlight	550	1700	2800	5600	9800	14,000
2d Conv	850	2650	4400	8800	15,400	22,000
Land Cruiser, V-8, 119" wb						
4d Sed	500	1550	2600	5200	9100	13,000

1952

	6	5	4	3	2	1
Champion Custom, 6-cyl., 115" wb						
4d Sed	400	1250	2100	4200	7400	10,600
2d Sed	400	1250	2100	4200	7400	10,500
2d 5P Cpe Starlight	450	1500	2500	5000	8800	12,500
Champion DeLuxe, 6-cyl., 115" wb						
4d Sed	400	1300	2150	4300	7500	10,700
2d Sed	400	1250	2100	4200	7400	10,600
2d 5P Cpe Starlight	450	1450	2400	4800	8400	12,000
Champion Regal, 6-cyl., 115" wb						
Sed	400	1300	2150	4300	7600	10,800
2d Sed	400	1300	2150	4300	7500	10,700
2d 5P Cpe Starlight	450	1500	2500	5000	8800	12,500
2d Star Cpe	500	1550	2600	5200	9100	13,000
2d Conv	700	2300	3800	7600	13,300	19,000
Commander Regal, V-8, 115" wb						
4d Sed	450	1400	2300	4600	8100	11,500
2d Sed	450	1350	2300	4600	8000	11,400
5P Cpe Starlight	550	1700	2800	5600	9800	14,000
Commander State, V-8, 115" wb						
4d Sed	450	1400	2300	4600	8100	11,600
2d Sed	450	1400	2300	4600	8100	11,500
2d Cpe Starlight	550	1750	2900	5800	10,200	14,500
2d Star HdTp	650	2050	3400	6800	11,900	17,000
2d Conv	850	2750	4600	9200	16,100	23,000
Land Cruiser, V-8, 119" wb						
2d Sed	500	1600	2700	5400	9500	13,500

1953-1954

	6	5	4	3	2	1
Champion Custom, 6-cyl., 116.5" wb						
4d Sed	450	1170	1975	3900	6850	9800
2d Sed	450	1150	1900	3850	6700	9600
Champion DeLuxe, 6-cyl., 116.5" - 120.5" wb						
4d Sed	400	1200	2000	4000	7000	10,000
2d Sed	450	1150	1900	3850	6700	9600
2d Cpe	550	1700	2800	5600	9800	14,000
2d Sta Wag	400	1350	2250	4500	7800	11,200
Champion Regal, 6-cyl., 116.5" - 120.5" wb						
4d Sed	400	1200	2000	4000	7000	10,000
2d Sed	450	1160	1950	3900	6800	9700
2d 5P Cpe	550	1800	3000	6000	10,500	15,000
2d HT	600	1900	3200	6400	11,200	16,000
2d Sta Wag (1954 only)	450	1400	2300	4600	8100	11,500
Commander DeLuxe, V-8, 116.5" - 120.5" wb						
4d Sed	400	1250	2100	4200	7400	10,500
2d Sed	400	1250	2100	4200	7300	10,400
2d Cpe	600	1900	3200	6400	11,200	16,000
Sta Wag (1954 only)	450	1450	2400	4800	8400	12,000
Commander Regal, V-8, 116.5" - 120.5" wb						
4d Sed	400	1300	2200	4400	7700	11,000
2d Cpe	600	2000	3300	6600	11,600	16,500
2d HT	700	2150	3600	7200	12,600	18,000
2d Sta Wag (1954 only)	450	1500	2450	4900	8600	12,300
Land Cruiser, V-8, 120.5" wb						
4d Sed	450	1400	2350	4700	8300	11,800
4d Reg Sed (1954 only)	450	1450	2400	4800	8400	12,000

1955

	6	5	4	3	2	1
Champion Custom, 6-cyl., 116.5" wb						
4d Sed	450	1160	1950	3900	6800	9700
2d Sed	450	1150	1900	3850	6700	9600
Champion DeLuxe, 6-cyl., 116.5" wb, 120.5" wb						
4d Sed	400	1200	2000	4000	7000	10,000
2d Sed	450	1160	1950	3900	6800	9700
2d Cpe	550	1700	2800	5600	9800	14,000
Champion Regal, 6-cyl., 116.5" wb, 120.5" wb						
4d Sed	400	1200	2000	4000	7100	10,100
2d Cpe	550	1800	3000	6000	10,500	15,000
2d HT	600	1900	3200	6400	11,200	16,000
2d Sta Wag	450	1400	2300	4600	8100	11,500
Commander Custom, V-8, 116.5" wb						
4d Sed	400	1250	2100	4200	7400	10,500
2d Sed	400	1250	2100	4200	7300	10,400
Commander DeLuxe, V-8, 116.5" - 120.5" wb						
4d Sed	400	1300	2150	4300	7500	10,700
2d Sed	400	1250	2100	4200	7400	10,600
2d Cpe	600	1900	3200	6400	11,200	16,000
Sta Wag	450	1450	2400	4800	8400	12,000
Commander Regal, V-8, 116.5" - 120.5" wb						
4d Sed	400	1300	2200	4400	7700	11,000
2d Cpe	600	1900	3200	6400	11,200	16,000
2d HT	650	2050	3400	6800	11,900	17,000
2d Sta Wag	450	1450	2400	4800	8400	12,000
President DeLuxe, V-8, 120.5" wb						
4d Sed	450	1400	2300	4600	8100	11,500
President State, V-8, 120.5" wb						
4d Sed	450	1450	2400	4800	8400	12,000
2d Cpe	650	2050	3400	6800	11,900	17,000
2d HT	700	2300	3800	7600	13,300	19,000
2d Spds HT	850	2650	4400	8800	15,400	22,000

NOTE: Deduct $200. for Champion models in all series.

1956

	6	5	4	3	2	1
Champion, 6-cyl., 116.5" wb						
4d Sed	450	1090	1800	3650	6400	9100
2d S'net	450	1080	1800	3600	6300	9000
2d Sed	450	1080	1800	3600	6300	9000
Flight Hawk, 6-cyl., 120.5" wb						
2d Cpe	550	1750	2900	5800	10,200	14,500
Champion Pelham, 6-cyl., 116.5" wb						
Sta Wag	400	1200	2000	4000	7000	10,000
Commander, V-8, 116.5" wb						
4d Sed	450	1170	1975	3900	6850	9800
2d S'net	450	1160	1950	3900	6800	9700
2d Sed	450	1170	1975	3900	6850	9800
Power Hawk, V-8, 120.5" wb						
2d Cpe	600	1850	3100	6200	10,900	15,500
Commander Parkview, V-8, 116.5" wb						
2d Sta Wag	450	1450	2400	4800	8400	12,000
President, V-8, 116.5" wb						
4d Sed	400	1250	2100	4200	7400	10,500
4d Classic	400	1300	2200	4400	7700	11,000
2d Sed	400	1250	2100	4200	7300	10,400
Sky Hawk, V-8, 120.5" wb						
2d HT	650	2050	3400	6800	11,900	17,000
President Pinehurst, V-8, 116.5" wb						
4d Sta Wag	450	1450	2400	4800	8400	12,000
Golden Hawk, V-8, 120.5" wb						
2d HT	850	2650	4400	8800	15,400	22,000

1957

	6	5	4	3	2	1
Champion Scotsman, 6-cyl., 116.5" wb						
4d Sed	450	1050	1800	3600	6200	8900
2d Sed	450	1050	1800	3600	6200	8900
2d Sta Wag	400	1200	2000	4000	7000	10,000
Champion Custom, 6-cyl., 116.5" wb						
4d Sed	450	1080	1800	3600	6300	9000
2d Clb Sed	450	1080	1800	3600	6300	9000
Champion DeLuxe, 6-cyl., 116.5" wb						
4d Sed	450	1090	1800	3650	6400	9100
2d Clb Sed	450	1050	1800	3600	6200	8900
Silver Hawk, 6-cyl., 120.5" wb						
2d Cpe	500	1600	2700	5400	9500	13,500
Champion Pelham, 6-cyl., 116.5" wb						
Sta Wag	450	1140	1900	3800	6650	9500
Commander Custom, V-8, 116.5" wb						
4d Sed	450	1090	1800	3650	6400	9100
2d Clb Sed	450	1080	1800	3600	6300	9000
Commander DeLuxe, V-8, 116.5" wb						
4d Sed	400	1200	2000	4000	7000	10,000
2d Clb Sed	400	1300	2150	4300	7600	10,800
Commander Station Wagons, V-8, 116.5" wb						
4d Park	450	1450	2400	4800	8400	12,000
4d Prov	450	1500	2500	5000	8800	12,500
President, V-8, 116.5" wb						
4d Sed	400	1300	2200	4400	7700	11,000
4d Classic	400	1300	2200	4400	7700	11,000
2d Clb Sed	400	1300	2150	4300	7600	10,800
Silver Hawk, V-8, 120.5" wb						
2d Cpe	650	2050	3400	6800	11,900	17,000
President Broadmoor, V-8, 116.5" wb						
4d Sta Wag	450	1500	2500	5000	8800	12,500
Golden Hawk, V-8, 120.5" wb						
2d Spt HT	850	2650	4400	8800	15,400	22,000

1958

	6	5	4	3	2	1
Champion Scotsman, 6-cyl., 116.5" wb						
4d Sed	350	950	1550	3100	5400	7700
2d Sed	350	950	1500	3050	5300	7600
4d Sta Wag	350	1020	1700	3400	5950	8500
Champion, 6-cyl., 116.5" wb						
4d Sed	350	950	1550	3150	5450	7800
2d Sed	350	950	1550	3100	5400	7700
Silver Hawk, 6-cyl., 120.5" wb						
2d Cpe	450	1450	2400	4800	8400	12,000
Commander, V-8, 116.5" wb						
4d Sed	450	1080	1800	3600	6300	9000
2d HT	400	1250	2100	4200	7400	10,500
4d Sta Wag	450	1140	1900	3800	6650	9500
President, V-8, 120.5" & 116.5" wb						
4d Sed	950	1100	1850	3700	6450	9200
2d HT	400	1300	2150	4300	7500	10,700
Silver Hawk, V-8, 120.5" wb						
2d Cpe	550	1800	3000	6000	10,500	15,000
Golden Hawk, V-8, 120.5" wb						
2d Spt HT	700	2300	3800	7600	13,300	19,000

1959-1960

	6	5	4	3	2	1
Lark DeLuxe, V-8, 108.5" wb						
4d Sed	350	975	1600	3200	5600	8000
2d Sed	350	975	1600	3200	5600	8000
4d Sta Wag (1960 only)	350	1000	1650	3350	5800	8300
2d Sta Wag	350	1020	1700	3400	5900	8400
Lark Regal, V-8, 108.5" wb						
4d Sed	350	1020	1700	3400	5950	8500
2d HT	400	1250	2100	4200	7400	10,500
2d Conv (1960 only)	600	1850	3100	6200	10,900	15,500
4d Sta Wag	350	1020	1700	3400	5950	8500

NOTE: Deduct 5 percent for 6 cyl. models.

	6	5	4	3	2	1
Hawk, V-8, 120.5" wb						
2d Spt Cpe	550	1700	2800	5600	9800	14,000

1961

	6	5	4	3	2	1
Lark DeLuxe, V-8, 108.5" wb						
4d Sed	350	950	1550	3150	5450	7800
2d Sed	350	975	1600	3200	5500	7900
Lark Regal, V-8, 108.5" wb						
4d Sed	350	975	1600	3200	5600	8000
2d HT	400	1200	2000	4000	7000	10,000
2d Conv	500	1600	2700	5400	9500	13,500
Lark Cruiser, V-8, 113" wb						
4d Sed	350	1000	1650	3300	5750	8200
Station Wagons, V-8, 113" wb						
4d DeL	350	950	1550	3150	5450	7800
2d	350	950	1550	3150	5450	7800
4d Reg	350	975	1600	3200	5500	7900
Hawk, 8-cyl., 120.5" wb						
2d Spt Cpe	550	1800	3000	6000	10,500	15,000

NOTE: Deduct 5 percent for 6 cyl. models.
First year for 4-speed Hawks.

1962

	6	5	4	3	2	1
Lark DeLuxe, V-8, 109" - 113" wb						
4d Sed	350	950	1550	3150	5450	7800
2d Sed	350	950	1550	3150	5450	7800
4d Sta Wag	350	1000	1650	3350	5800	8300
Lark Regal, V-8, 109" - 113" wb						
4d Sed	350	950	1550	3150	5450	7800
2d HT	400	1250	2100	4200	7400	10,500
2d Conv	450	1500	2500	5000	8800	12,500
4d Sta Wag	350	1020	1700	3400	5950	8500
Lark Daytona, V-8, 109" wb						
2d HT	400	1250	2100	4200	7400	10,500
2d Conv	500	1550	2600	5200	9100	13,000
Lark Cruiser, V-8, 113" wb						
4d Sed	400	1200	2000	4000	7000	10,000
Gran Turismo Hawk, V-8, 120.5" wb						
2d HT	600	1850	3100	6200	10,900	15,500

NOTE: Deduct 5 percent for 6 cyl. models.

1963

	6	5	4	3	2	1
Lark Standard, V-8, 109" - 113" wb						
4d Sed	350	950	1550	3150	5450	7800
2d Sed	350	950	1550	3150	5450	7800
4d Sta Wag	350	1020	1700	3400	5950	8500
Lark Regal, V-8, 109" - 113" wb						
4d Sed	350	950	1550	3150	5450	7800

	6	5	4	3	2	1
2d Sed	350	950	1550	3150	5450	7800
4d Sta Wag	350	1040	1750	3500	6100	8700
Lark Custom, V-8, 109" - 113" wb						
4d Sed	350	950	1550	3150	5450	7800
2d Sed	350	975	1600	3200	5500	7900
Lark Daytona, V-8, 109" - 113" wb						
2d HT	400	1200	2000	4000	7000	10,000
2d Conv	450	1500	2500	5000	8800	12,500
4d Sta Wag	400	1200	2000	4000	7000	10,000
Cruiser, V-8, 113" wb						
4d Sed	400	1200	2000	4000	7100	10,100
Gran Turismo Hawk, V-8, 120.5" wb						
2d HT	600	1850	3100	6200	10,900	15,500

NOTE: Deduct 5 percent for 6 cyl.
Add 10 percent for R1 engine option.
Add 20 percent for R2 engine option.
Add 30 percent for R3 engine option.

1964

	6	5	4	3	2	1
Challenger V-8, 109" - 113" wb						
4d Sed	350	975	1600	3200	5500	7900
2d Sed	350	975	1600	3200	5600	8000
4d Sta Wag	350	1000	1650	3300	5750	8200
Commander, V-8, 109" - 113" wb						
4d Sed	350	975	1600	3250	5700	8100
2d Sed	350	1000	1650	3300	5750	8200
4d Sta Wag	350	1020	1700	3400	5950	8500
Daytona, V-8, 109" - 113" wb						
4d Sed	350	1020	1700	3400	5950	8500
2d HT	450	1400	2300	4600	8100	11,500
2d Conv	450	1500	2500	5000	8800	12,500
4d Sta Wag	400	1250	2100	4200	7400	10,500
Cruiser, V-8, 113" wb						
4d Sed	400	1200	2050	4100	7100	10,200
Gran Turismo Hawk, V-8, 120.5" wb						
2d HT	600	1850	3100	6200	10,900	15,500

NOTE: Deduct 5 percent for 6 cyl. models.
Add 10 percent for R1 engine option.
Add 20 percent for R2 engine option.
Add 30 percent for R3 engine option.

1965

	6	5	4	3	2	1
Commander, V-8, 109" - 113" wb						
4d Sed	350	975	1600	3200	5600	8000
2d Sed	350	975	1600	3200	5500	7900
4d Sta Wag	350	1000	1650	3350	5800	8300
Daytona, V-8, 109" - 113" wb						
4d Spt Sed	350	1000	1650	3300	5750	8200
4d Sta Wag	350	1020	1700	3400	5950	8500
Cruiser, V-8, 113" wb						
4d Sed	350	1040	1750	3500	6100	8700

NOTE: Deduct 10 percent for 6 cyl. models.

1966

	6	5	4	3	2	1
Commander, V-8, 109" wb						
4d Sed	350	975	1600	3200	5600	8000
2d Sed	350	975	1600	3200	5500	7900
Daytona, V-8, 109" - 113" wb						
2d Spt Sed	350	1020	1700	3400	5950	8500
Cruiser, V-8, 113" wb						
4d Sed	350	1000	1650	3350	5800	8300
Wagonaire, V-8, 113" wb						
4d Sta Wag	350	1020	1700	3400	5950	8500

AVANTI

1963

	6	5	4	3	2	1
Avanti, V-8, 109" wb						
2d Spt Cpe	800	2500	4200	8400	14,700	21,000

NOTE: Add 20 percent for R2 engine option.

1964

	6	5	4	3	2	1
Avanti, V-8, 109" wb						
2d Spt Cpe	750	2400	4000	8000	14,000	20,000

NOTE: Add 20 percent for R2 engine option.
Add 40 percent for R4 engine option.
Add 60 percent for R3 engine option.

STUTZ

1912

	6	5	4	3	2	1
Series A, 4-cyl., 50 hp, 120" wb						
2P Rds	2700	8650	14,400	28,800	50,400	72,000
4P Toy Tonn	2650	8400	14,000	28,000	49,000	70,000
5P Tr	2650	8400	14,000	28,000	49,000	70,000
2P Bearcat	5250	16,800	28,000	56,000	98,000	140,000
4P Cpe	1900	6000	10,000	20,000	35,000	50,000
Series A, 6-cyl., 60 hp, 124" wb						
Touring - 6P (130" wb)						
6P Tr	2500	7900	13,200	26,400	46,200	66,000
4P Toy Tonn	2400	7700	12,800	25,600	44,800	64,000
2P Bearcat	5650	18,000	30,000	60,000	105,000	150,000

1913

	6	5	4	3	2	1
Series B, 4-cyl., 50 hp, 120" wb						
2P Rds	2700	8650	14,400	28,800	50,400	72,000
4P Toy Tonn	2650	8400	14,000	28,000	49,000	70,000
4P Tr (124" wb)	2650	8400	14,000	28,000	49,000	70,000
2P Bearcat	5250	16,800	28,000	56,000	98,000	140,000
6P Tr (124" wb)	2800	8900	14,800	29,600	51,800	74,000
Series B, 6-cyl., 60 hp, 124" wb						
2P Bearcat	5650	18,000	30,000	60,000	105,000	150,000
4P Toy Tonn	2650	8400	14,000	28,000	49,000	70,000
6P Tr (130" wb)	2850	9100	15,200	30,400	53,200	76,000

1914

	6	5	4	3	2	1
Model 4E, 4-cyl., 50 hp, 120" wb						
2P Rds	2650	8400	14,000	28,000	49,000	70,000
Bearcat	5450	17,400	29,000	58,000	101,500	145,000
5P Tr	2650	8400	14,000	28,000	49,000	70,000
Model 6E, 6-cyl., 55 hp, 130" wb						
2P Rds	2850	9100	15,200	30,400	53,200	76,000
6P Tr	2850	9100	15,200	30,400	53,200	76,000

1915

	6	5	4	3	2	1
Model H.C.S., 4-cyl., 23 hp, 108" wb						
2P Rds	1900	6000	10,000	20,000	35,000	50,000
Model 4F, 4-cyl., 36.1 hp, 120" wb						
2P Rds	2250	7200	12,000	24,000	42,000	60,000
Bearcat	5100	16,300	27,200	54,400	95,200	136,000
Cpe	1200	3850	6400	12,800	22,400	32,000
Bulldog	2200	6950	11,600	23,200	40,600	58,000
5P Tr	2350	7450	12,400	24,800	43,400	62,000
5P Sed	1100	3500	5800	11,600	20,300	29,000
Model 6F, 6-cyl., 38.4 hp, 130" wb						
2P Rds	2400	7700	12,800	25,600	44,800	64,000
Bearcat	5250	16,800	28,000	56,000	98,000	140,000
Cpe	1300	4200	7000	14,000	24,500	35,000
5P Tr	2500	7900	13,200	26,400	46,200	66,000
6P Tr	2500	7900	13,200	26,400	46,200	66,000
5P Sed	1150	3600	6000	12,000	21,000	30,000

1916

	6	5	4	3	2	1
Model C, 4-cyl., 36.1 hp, 120" wb						
2P Rds	2250	7200	12,000	24,000	42,000	60,000
Bearcat	4900	15,600	26,000	52,000	91,000	130,000
Bulldog	2500	7900	13,200	26,400	46,200	66,000
Sed	1100	3500	5800	11,600	20,300	29,000
Bulldog Special, 4-cyl., 36.1 hp, 130" wb						
4P Tr	2500	7900	13,200	26,400	46,200	66,000
5P Tr	2550	8150	13,600	27,200	47,600	68,000

1917

	6	5	4	3	2	1
Series R, 4-cyl., 80 hp, 130" wb						
2P Rds	2650	8400	14,000	28,000	49,000	70,000
4P Bulldog Spl	2500	7900	13,200	26,400	46,200	66,000
6P Bulldog Spl	2550	8150	13,600	27,200	47,600	68,000
Bearcat (120" wb)	5100	16,300	27,200	54,400	95,200	136,000

1918

	6	5	4	3	2	1
Series S, 4-cyl., 80 hp, 130" wb						
2P Rds	2650	8400	14,000	28,000	49,000	70,000
4P Bulldog Spl	2500	7900	13,200	26,400	46,200	66,000
6P Bulldog Spl	2550	8150	13,600	27,200	47,600	68,000
Bearcat (120" wb)	5100	16,300	27,200	54,400	95,200	136,000

1919

	6	5	4	3	2	1
Series G, 4-cyl., 80 hp, 130" wb						
6P Tr	2700	8650	14,400	28,800	50,400	72,000
2P Rds	2500	7900	13,200	26,400	46,200	66,000
4P C.C. Tr	2700	8650	14,400	28,800	50,400	72,000
Bearcat (120" wb)	5100	16,300	27,200	54,400	95,200	136,000

1920

	6	5	4	3	2	1
Series H, 4-cyl., 80 hp, 130" wb						
2P Bearcat (120" wb)	5100	16,300	27,200	54,400	95,200	136,000
2P Rds	2650	8400	14,000	28,000	49,000	70,000
4P/5P Tr	2700	8650	14,400	28,800	50,400	72,000
6P/7P Tr	2800	8900	14,800	29,600	51,800	74,000

1921

	6	5	4	3	2	1
Series K, 4-cyl., 80 hp, 130" wb						
2P Bearcat (120" wb)	5100	16,300	27,200	54,400	95,200	136,000
2P Rds	3400	10,800	18,000	36,000	63,000	90,000
4P Tr	2700	8650	14,400	28,800	50,400	72,000
6P Tr	2700	8650	14,400	28,800	50,400	72,000
4P Cpe	1500	4800	8000	16,000	28,000	40,000

1922

	6	5	4	3	2	1
Series K, 4-cyl., 80 hp, 130" wb						
3P Cpe	1500	4800	8000	16,000	28,000	40,000
2P Rds	2650	8400	14,000	28,000	49,000	70,000
Bearcat (120" wb)	5100	16,300	27,200	54,400	95,200	136,000
6P Tr	2700	8650	14,400	28,800	50,400	72,000
4P Spt	2850	9100	15,200	30,400	53,200	76,000

1923

	6	5	4	3	2	1
Special Six, 70 hp, 120" wb						
5P Sed	1300	4200	7000	14,000	24,500	35,000
5P Tr	2700	8650	14,400	28,800	50,400	72,000
Rds	2700	8650	14,400	28,800	50,400	72,000
Speedway Four, 88 hp, 130" wb						
6P Tr	2850	9100	15,200	30,400	53,200	76,000
Sportster	3000	9600	16,000	32,000	56,000	80,000
4P Cpe	1500	4800	8000	16,000	28,000	40,000
Sportsedan	1400	4450	7400	14,800	25,900	37,000
Rds	2650	8400	14,000	28,000	49,000	70,000
Bearcat	5250	16,800	28,000	56,000	98,000	140,000
Calif Tr	2950	9350	15,600	31,200	54,600	78,000
Calif Sptstr	2950	9350	15,600	31,200	54,600	78,000

1924

	6	5	4	3	2	1
Special Six, 70 hp, 120" wb						
5P Phae	2550	8150	13,600	27,200	47,600	68,000
Tourabout	2550	8150	13,600	27,200	47,600	68,000
2P Rds	2650	8400	14,000	28,000	49,000	70,000
Palanquin	2550	8150	13,600	27,200	47,600	68,000
5P Sed	1200	3850	6400	12,800	22,400	32,000
Speedway Four, 4-cyl., 88 hp, 130" wb						
2P Rds	2650	8400	14,000	28,000	49,000	70,000
2P Bearcat	5100	16,300	27,200	54,400	95,200	136,000
6P Tr	2700	8650	14,400	28,800	50,400	72,000
4P Cpe	1500	4800	8000	16,000	28,000	40,000

1925

	6	5	4	3	2	1
Models 693-694, 6-cyl., 70 hp, 120" wb						
5P Phae	2500	7900	13,200	26,400	46,200	66,000
5P Tourabout	2550	8150	13,600	27,200	47,600	68,000
2P Rds	2500	7900	13,200	26,400	46,200	66,000
4P Cpe	1450	4550	7600	15,200	26,600	38,000
5P Sed	1200	3850	6400	12,800	22,400	32,000
Model 695, 6-cyl., 80 hp, 130" wb						
7P Tourster	2550	8150	13,600	27,200	47,600	68,000
5P Sportster	2550	8150	13,600	27,200	47,600	68,000
7P Sub	1700	5400	9000	18,000	31,500	45,000
Sportbrohm	1650	5300	8800	17,600	30,800	44,000
7P Berline	1750	5500	9200	18,400	32,200	46,000

1926

	6	5	4	3	2	1
Vertical Eight, AA, 92 hp, 131" wb						
4P Spds	5100	16,300	27,200	54,400	95,200	136,000
5P Spds	5100	16,300	27,200	54,400	95,200	136,000
4P Vic Cpe	2050	6600	11,000	22,000	38,500	55,000
5P Brgm	1850	5900	9800	19,600	34,300	49,000
5P Sed	1500	4800	8000	16,000	28,000	40,000

1927

	6	5	4	3	2	1
Vertical Eight, AA, 92 hp, 131" wb						
4P Spds	5100	16,300	27,200	54,400	95,200	136,000
5P Spds	5100	16,300	27,200	54,400	95,200	136,000
2P Cpe	1900	6000	10,000	20,000	35,000	50,000
4P Cpe	1900	6000	10,000	20,000	35,000	50,000
5P Brgm	1850	5900	9800	19,600	34,300	49,000
5P Sed	1500	4800	8000	16,000	28,000	40,000
7P Berline	1850	5900	9800	19,600	34,300	49,000
7P Sed	1600	5050	8400	16,800	29,400	42,000

1928

	6	5	4	3	2	1
Series BB, 8-cyl., 115 hp, 131 & 135" wb						
2P Spds	5100	16,300	27,200	54,400	95,200	136,000

	6	5	4	3	2	1
4P Spds	5100	16,300	27,200	54,400	95,200	136,000
5P Spds	5250	16,800	28,000	56,000	98,000	140,000
7P Spds	5200	16,550	27,600	55,200	96,600	138,000
2P Black Hawk Spds	5450	17,400	29,000	58,000	101,500	145,000
4P Black Hawk Spds	5450	17,400	29,000	58,000	101,500	145,000
4P Vic Cpe	2050	6600	11,000	22,000	38,500	55,000
2P Cpe	1950	6250	10,400	20,800	36,400	52,000
5P Sed	1500	4800	8000	16,000	28,000	40,000
5P Brgm	1550	4900	8200	16,400	28,700	41,000
2P Cabr Cpe	3400	10,800	18,000	36,000	63,000	90,000
7P Sed	1600	5050	8400	16,800	29,400	42,000
7P Sed Limo	2250	7200	12,000	24,000	42,000	60,000
4P Deauville	2350	7450	12,400	24,800	43,400	62,000
5P Chantilly Sed	2350	7450	12,400	24,800	43,400	62,000
4P Monaco Cpe	2500	7900	13,200	26,400	46,200	66,000
5P Riv Sed	2500	7900	13,200	26,400	46,200	66,000
7P Biarritz Sed	2500	7900	13,200	26,400	46,200	66,000
5P Chamonix Sed	2550	8150	13,600	27,200	47,600	68,000
7P Fontainbleau	2550	8150	13,600	27,200	47,600	68,000
5P Aix Les Bains	2550	8150	13,600	27,200	47,600	68,000
7P Versailles	2650	8400	14,000	28,000	49,000	70,000
5P Prince of Wales	2650	8400	14,000	28,000	49,000	70,000
8P Prince of Wales	2700	8650	14,400	28,800	50,400	72,000
Transformable Twn Car	2850	9100	15,200	30,400	53,200	76,000
1929						
Model M, 8-cyl., 115 hp, 134-1/2" wb						
4P Spds	5100	16,300	27,200	54,400	95,200	136,000
7P Spds	5200	16,550	27,600	55,200	96,600	138,000
2P Speed Car	5250	16,800	28,000	56,000	98,000	140,000
5P Cpe	1950	6250	10,400	20,800	36,400	52,000
4P Cpe	1950	6250	10,400	20,800	36,400	52,000
2P Cabr	3600	11,500	19,200	38,400	67,200	96,000
5P Sed	1600	5050	8400	16,800	29,400	42,000
7P Sed	1600	5150	8600	17,200	30,100	43,000
5P Chantilly Sed	2350	7450	12,400	24,800	43,400	62,000
5P Monaco Cpe	2500	7900	13,200	26,400	46,200	66,000
5P Deauville	2350	7450	12,400	24,800	43,400	62,000
7P Limo	2350	7450	12,400	24,800	43,400	62,000
5P Sed	1900	6000	10,000	20,000	35,000	50,000
2P Cabr	3850	12,250	20,400	40,800	71,400	102,000
5P Biarritz	2500	7900	13,200	26,400	46,200	66,000
7P Fontainbleau	2550	8150	13,600	27,200	47,600	68,000
7P Aix Les Baines	2550	8150	13,600	27,200	47,600	68,000
5P Sed	2050	6600	11,000	22,000	38,500	55,000
5P Limo	2500	7900	13,200	26,400	46,200	66,000
6P Brgm	2500	7900	13,200	26,400	46,200	66,000
Brgm Limo	2550	8150	13,600	27,200	47,600	68,000
6P Sed	2050	6500	10,800	21,600	37,800	54,000
6P Sed Limo	2550	8150	13,600	27,200	47,600	68,000
7P Sed Limo	2550	8150	13,600	27,200	47,600	68,000
5P Transformable Cabr	3250	10,300	17,200	34,400	60,200	86,000
7P Trans Twn Car	3250	10,300	17,200	34,400	60,200	86,000
5P Trans Twn Car	3300	10,550	17,600	35,200	61,600	88,000
1930						
Model MA, 8-cyl., 115 hp, 134-1/2" wb						
2P Spds	5100	16,300	27,200	54,400	95,200	136,000
4P Spds	5100	16,300	27,200	54,400	95,200	136,000
2P Cpe	2050	6600	11,000	22,000	38,500	55,000
5P Cpe	2050	6600	11,000	22,000	38,500	55,000
Sed	1500	4800	8000	16,000	28,000	40,000
Cabr	3400	10,800	18,000	36,000	63,000	90,000
Longchamps	2500	7900	13,200	26,400	46,200	66,000
Versailles	2500	7900	13,200	26,400	46,200	66,000
Torpedo	2650	8400	14,000	28,000	49,000	70,000
Model MB, 8-cyl., 115 hp, 145" wb						
4P Spds	5250	16,800	28,000	56,000	98,000	140,000
7P Spds	5250	16,800	28,000	56,000	98,000	140,000
5P Sed	1600	5150	8600	17,200	30,100	43,000
7P Sed	1650	5300	8800	17,600	30,800	44,000
7P Limo	1900	6000	10,000	20,000	35,000	50,000
5P Sed	1750	5500	9200	18,400	32,200	46,000
Cabr	3450	11,050	18,400	36,800	64,400	92,000
Chaumont	2650	8400	14,000	28,000	49,000	70,000
Monte Carlo	2650	8400	14,000	28,000	49,000	70,000
5P Sed	2250	7200	12,000	24,000	42,000	60,000
5P Limo	2350	7450	12,400	24,800	43,400	62,000
Brgm	2250	7200	12,000	24,000	42,000	60,000
Brgm Limo	2500	7900	13,200	26,400	46,200	66,000
6P Sed	2250	7200	12,000	24,000	42,000	60,000
6P Sed Limo	2500	7900	13,200	26,400	46,200	66,000
7P Sed Limo	2550	8150	13,600	27,200	47,600	68,000
Transformable Cabr	3250	10,300	17,200	34,400	60,200	86,000
Transformable Twn Car	3250	10,300	17,200	34,400	60,200	86,000
Transformable Tr Cabr	3400	10,800	18,000	36,000	63,000	90,000
1931						
Model LA, 6-cyl., 85 hp, 127-1/2" wb						
4P Spds	4750	15,100	25,200	50,400	88,200	126,000
5P Cpe	1700	5400	9000	18,000	31,500	45,000
Sed	1450	4550	7600	15,200	26,600	38,000
4P Cpe	1750	5500	9200	18,400	32,200	46,000
Cabr Cpe	3000	9600	16,000	32,000	56,000	80,000
Model MA, 8-cyl., 115 hp, 134-1/2" wb						
4P Spds	4900	15,600	26,000	52,000	91,000	130,000
Torp	3450	11,050	18,400	36,800	64,400	92,000
4P Spds	5100	16,300	27,200	54,400	95,200	136,000
5P Cpe	1900	6000	10,000	20,000	35,000	50,000
4P Cpe	1900	6100	10,200	20,400	35,700	51,000
Cabr Cpe	3000	9600	16,000	32,000	56,000	80,000
Sed	1600	5050	8400	16,800	29,400	42,000
Longchamps	2050	6500	10,800	21,600	37,800	54,000
Versailles	2050	6500	10,800	21,600	37,800	54,000
Model MB, 8-cyl., 115 hp, 145" wb						
7P Spds	5100	16,300	27,200	54,400	95,200	136,000
5P Sed	1850	5900	9800	19,600	34,300	49,000
7P Sed	1900	6000	10,000	20,000	35,000	50,000
Limo	2250	7200	12,000	24,000	42,000	60,000
Cabr Cpe	3600	11,500	19,200	38,400	67,200	96,000
Conv Sed	4750	15,100	25,200	50,400	88,200	126,000
Chaumont	3600	11,500	19,200	38,400	67,200	96,000
Monte Carlo	3600	11,500	19,200	38,400	67,200	96,000
5P Sed	2250	7200	12,000	24,000	42,000	60,000
Brgm	2350	7450	12,400	24,800	43,400	62,000
7P Sed	2500	7900	13,200	26,400	46,200	66,000
Brgm Limo	2550	8150	13,600	27,200	47,600	68,000
6/7P Sed Limo	2650	8400	14,000	28,000	49,000	70,000
Transformable Cabr	3400	10,800	18,000	36,000	63,000	90,000
Transformable Twn Car	3250	10,300	17,200	34,400	60,200	86,000
Transformable Twn Cabr	3400	10,800	18,000	36,000	63,000	90,000

1932	6	5	4	3	2	1
Model LAA, 6-cyl., 85 hp, 127-1/2" wb						
Sed	1500	4800	8000	16,000	28,000	40,000
5P Cpe	2050	6600	11,000	22,000	38,500	55,000
4P Cpe	2050	6600	11,000	22,000	38,500	55,000
Clb Sed	1700	5400	9000	18,000	31,500	45,000
Model SV-16, 8-cyl., 115 hp, 134-1/2" wb						
4P Spds	4900	15,600	26,000	52,000	91,000	130,000
Torp	3250	10,300	17,200	34,400	60,200	86,000
5P Cpe	1900	6000	10,000	20,000	35,000	50,000
5P Sed	1700	5400	9000	18,000	31,500	45,000
4P Cpe	2050	6600	11,000	22,000	38,500	55,000
Clb Sed	1750	5650	9400	18,800	32,900	47,000
Cabr Cpe	3250	10,300	17,200	34,400	60,200	86,000
Longchamps	2050	6600	11,000	22,000	38,500	55,000
Versailles	2050	6600	11,000	22,000	38,500	55,000
6P Sed	1950	6250	10,400	20,800	36,400	52,000
Cont Cpe	2550	8150	13,600	27,200	47,600	68,000
Model SV-16, 8 cyl., 115 hp, 145" wb						
7P Spds	5450	17,400	29,000	58,000	101,500	145,000
7P Sed	3000	9600	16,000	32,000	56,000	80,000
5P Sed	2850	9100	15,200	30,400	53,200	76,000
Limo	3250	10,300	17,200	34,400	60,200	86,000
Conv Sed	4750	15,100	25,200	50,400	88,200	126,000
6P Sed	3100	9850	16,400	32,800	57,400	82,000
Chaumont	3600	11,500	19,200	38,400	67,200	96,000
Brgm	3250	10,300	17,200	34,400	60,200	86,000
Monte Carlo	3300	10,550	17,600	35,200	61,600	88,000
Brgm Limo	3400	10,800	18,000	36,000	63,000	90,000
7P Sed Limo	3400	10,800	18,000	36,000	63,000	90,000
6P Sed Limo	3400	10,800	18,000	36,000	63,000	90,000
Transformable Cabr	3600	11,500	19,200	38,400	67,200	96,000
Monte Carlo	3700	11,750	19,600	39,200	68,600	98,000
Prince of Wales	3700	11,750	19,600	39,200	68,600	98,000
Conv Vic	4150	13,200	22,000	44,000	77,000	110,000
Spt Sed	3250	10,300	17,200	34,400	60,200	86,000
Tuxedo Cabr	5100	16,300	27,200	54,400	95,200	136,000
Patrician Cpe	3400	10,800	18,000	36,000	63,000	90,000
Transformable Twn Car	5250	16,800	28,000	56,000	98,000	140,000
Model DV-32, 8-cyl., 156 hp, 134-1/2" wb						
Bearcat	6750	21,600	36,000	72,000	126,000	180,000
NOTE: All other models same as SV-16, with prices $1000 more than SV-16.						
Model DV-32, 8-cyl., 156 hp, 145" wb						
NOTE: All models same as SV-16, with prices $1000 more than SV-16.						
Model DV-32, 8-cyl., 156 hp, 116" wb						
Sup Bearcat	6750	21,600	36,000	72,000	126,000	180,000
1933						
Model LAA, 6-cyl., 85 hp, 127-1/2" wb						
5P Sed	1600	5050	8400	16,800	29,400	42,000
5P Cpe	1900	6000	10,000	20,000	35,000	50,000
4P Cpe	1900	6100	10,200	20,400	35,700	51,000
5P Clb Sed	1700	5400	9000	18,000	31,500	45,000
4P Cabr Cpe	2850	9100	15,200	30,400	53,200	76,000
Model SV-16, 8-cyl., 115 hp, 134-1/2" wb						
4P Spds	4150	13,200	22,000	44,000	77,000	110,000
2P Torp	3000	9600	16,000	32,000	56,000	80,000
4P Spds	4500	14,400	24,000	48,000	84,000	120,000
5P Cpe	2150	6850	11,400	22,800	39,900	57,000
5P Sed	1700	5400	9000	18,000	31,500	45,000
4P Cpe	2200	6950	11,600	23,200	40,600	58,000
5P Clb Sed	1750	5650	9400	18,800	32,900	47,000
4P Cabr Cpe	3000	9600	16,000	32,000	56,000	80,000
5P Versailles	2500	7900	13,200	26,400	46,200	66,000
Model SV-16, 8-cyl., 115 hp, 145" wb						
4P Spds	5250	16,800	28,000	56,000	98,000	140,000
5P Sed	2050	6600	11,000	22,000	38,500	55,000
7P Sed	2150	6850	11,400	22,800	39,900	57,000
7P Limo	2500	7900	13,200	26,400	46,200	66,000
4P Cabr Cpe	3600	11,500	19,200	38,400	67,200	96,000
5P Conv Sed	4900	15,600	26,000	52,000	91,000	130,000
6P Sed	2550	8150	13,600	27,200	47,600	68,000
5P Chaumont	2650	8400	14,000	28,000	49,000	70,000
6P Brgm	2650	8400	14,000	28,000	49,000	70,000
6P Sed	2550	8150	13,600	27,200	47,600	68,000
5P Monte Carlo	2700	8650	14,400	28,800	50,400	72,000
6P Brgm Limo	3250	10,300	17,200	34,400	60,200	86,000
6P Sed Limo	3000	9600	16,000	32,000	56,000	80,000
7P Twn Car	3400	10,800	18,000	36,000	63,000	90,000
5P Monte Carlo	3400	10,800	18,000	36,000	63,000	90,000
Series DV-32, 8-cyl., 156" wb						
NOTE: Same models as the SV-16 on the two chassis, with prices $700 more. Bearcat and Super Bearcat continued from 1932.						
1934						
Model SV-16, 8-cyl., 115 hp, 134-1/2" wb						
Spds	4500	14,400	24,000	48,000	84,000	120,000
Spds	4500	14,400	24,000	48,000	84,000	120,000
Torp	4150	13,200	22,000	44,000	77,000	110,000
4P Cpe	1900	6000	10,000	20,000	35,000	50,000
Conv Cpe	3250	10,300	17,200	34,400	60,200	86,000
Club Sed	2250	7200	12,000	24,000	42,000	60,000
5P Sed	2050	6600	11,000	22,000	38,500	55,000
5P Cpe	2250	7200	12,000	24,000	42,000	60,000
Versailles	2250	7200	12,000	24,000	42,000	60,000
Model SV-16, 8-cyl., 115 hp, 145" wb						
Conv Cpe	3400	10,800	18,000	36,000	63,000	90,000
7P Sed	2200	7100	11,800	23,600	41,300	59,000
Limo	2350	7450	12,400	24,800	43,400	62,000
Chaumont	2350	7450	12,400	24,800	43,400	62,000
Monte Carlo	2400	7700	12,800	25,600	44,800	64,000
Model DV-32, 8-cyl., 156 hp, 134-1/2" wb						
Spds	4900	15,600	26,000	52,000	91,000	130,000
Spds	4950	15,850	26,400	52,800	92,400	132,000
Torp	4800	15,350	25,600	51,200	89,600	128,000
4P Cpe	2250	7200	12,000	24,000	42,000	60,000
Conv Cpe	4750	15,100	25,200	50,400	88,200	126,000
Clb Sed	2200	7100	11,800	23,600	41,300	59,000
5P Sed	2200	6950	11,600	23,200	40,600	58,000
5P Cpe	2350	7450	12,400	24,800	43,400	62,000
Versailles	2500	7900	13,200	26,400	46,200	66,000
Model DV-32, 8-cyl., 156 hp, 145" wb						
Conv Cpe	4500	14,400	24,000	48,000	84,000	120,000
7P Sed	2250	7200	12,000	24,000	42,000	60,000
Limo	2650	8400	14,000	28,000	49,000	70,000
Chaumont	2650	8400	14,000	28,000	49,000	70,000
Monte Carlo	2700	8650	14,400	28,800	50,400	72,000
1935						
Model SV-16, 8-cyl., 134 & 145" wb						
2P Spds	3300	10,550	17,600	35,200	61,600	88,000

	6	5	4	3	2	1
2P Cpe	1950	6250	10,400	20,800	36,400	52,000
5P Sed	1600	5050	8400	16,800	29,400	42,000
7P Sed	1800	5750	9600	19,200	33,600	48,000
Model DV-32, 8-cyl., 134 & 145" wb						
2P Spds	3400	10,800	18,000	36,000	63,000	90,000
2/4P Cpe	2050	6600	11,000	22,000	38,500	55,000
5P Sed	1600	5050	8400	16,800	29,400	42,000
7P Limo	2050	6600	11,000	22,000	38,500	55,000

WILLYS

	6	5	4	3	2	1
1902-03						
Model 13, 1-cyl.						
2P Rbt	1150	3600	6000	12,000	21,000	30,000
1904						
Model 13, 1-cyl.						
2P Rbt	1050	3350	5600	11,200	19,600	28,000
1905						
Model 15, 2-cyl.						
2P Rbt	1050	3350	5600	11,200	19,600	28,000
Model 17, 2-cyl.						
2P Rbt	1050	3350	5600	11,200	19,600	28,000
Model 18, 4-cyl.						
5P Tr	1100	3500	5800	11,600	20,300	29,000
1906						
Model 16, 2-cyl.						
2P Rbt	1000	3250	5400	10,800	18,900	27,000
Model 18, 4-cyl.						
4P Tr	1050	3350	5600	11,200	19,600	28,000
1907						
Model 22, 4-cyl.						
2P Rbt	1000	3250	5400	10,800	18,900	27,000
1908						
Model 24, 4-cyl.						
2P Rds	1050	3350	5600	11,200	19,600	28,000
1909						
Model 30, 4-cyl.						
3P Rds	1000	3250	5400	10,800	18,900	27,000
4P Rds	1000	3250	5400	10,800	18,900	27,000
2P Cpe	950	3000	5000	10,000	17,500	25,000
Model 31, 4-cyl.						
4P Toy Tonn	1050	3350	5600	11,200	19,600	28,000
5P Tourist	1050	3350	5600	11,200	19,600	28,000
5P Taxi	1000	3250	5400	10,800	18,900	27,000
Model 32, 4-cyl.						
3P Rds	1000	3100	5200	10,400	18,200	26,000
4P Rds	1000	3250	5400	10,800	18,900	27,000
4P Toy Tonn	1000	3250	5400	10,800	18,900	27,000
5P Tr	1050	3350	5600	11,200	19,600	28,000
Willys, 6-cyl.						
3P Rds	1050	3350	5600	11,200	19,600	28,000
4P Rds	1050	3350	5600	11,200	19,600	28,000
Toy Tonn	1100	3500	5800	11,600	20,300	29,000
5P Tr	1100	3500	5800	11,600	20,300	29,000
1910						
Model 38, 4-cyl., 102" wb, 25 hp						
2P Rds	1000	3250	5400	10,800	18,900	27,000
3P Rds	1000	3250	5400	10,800	18,900	27,000
4P Rds	1050	3300	5500	11,000	19,300	27,500
Toy Tonn	1000	3250	5400	10,800	18,900	27,000
Model 40, 4-cyl., 112" wb, 40 hp						
3P Rds	1050	3350	5600	11,200	19,600	28,000
4P Rds	1050	3350	5600	11,200	19,600	28,000
Model 41, 4-cyl.						
5P Tr	1100	3500	5800	11,600	20,300	29,000
4P C.C. Tr	1100	3500	5800	11,600	20,300	29,000
Model 42, 4-cyl.						
5P Tr	1150	3600	6000	12,000	21,000	30,000
4P C.C. Tr	1150	3600	6000	12,000	21,000	30,000
1911						
Model 38, 4-cyl.						
4P Tr	950	3000	5000	10,000	17,500	25,000
2P Cpe	750	2400	4000	8000	14,000	20,000
Model 45, 4-cyl.						
2P Rds	1000	3100	5200	10,400	18,200	26,000
Model 46, 4-cyl.						
2P Torp	1000	3100	5200	10,400	18,200	26,000
Model 47, 4-cyl.						
Tr	1000	3250	5400	10,800	18,900	27,000
Model 49, 4-cyl.						
5P Tr	1000	3100	5200	10,400	18,200	26,000
4P Tr	1000	3250	5400	10,800	18,900	27,000
Model 50, 4-cyl.						
2P Torp	1150	3600	6000	12,000	21,000	30,000
Model 51, 4-cyl.						
4d 5P Tr	1100	3500	5800	11,600	20,300	29,000
5P Tr	1100	3500	5800	11,600	20,300	29,000
Model 52, 4-cyl.						
4d 5P Tr	1150	3600	6000	12,000	21,000	30,000
5P Tr	1150	3600	6000	12,000	21,000	30,000
Model 53, 4-cyl.						
2P Rds	1150	3700	6200	12,400	21,700	31,000
Model 54, 4-cyl.						
5P Tr	1150	3700	6200	12,400	21,700	31,000
Model 55, 4-cyl.						
4d 5P Tr	1150	3700	6200	12,400	21,700	31,000
5P Tr	1150	3700	6200	12,400	21,700	31,000
Model 56, 4-cyl.						
5P Tr	1200	3850	6400	12,800	22,400	32,000
1912						
Model 58R, 4-cyl., 25 hp						
Torp Rds	1000	3100	5200	10,400	18,200	26,000
Model 59R-T, 4-cyl., 30 hp						
Rds	1000	3250	5400	10,800	18,900	27,000
Tr	1050	3350	5600	11,200	19,600	28,000
Model 59C, 4-cyl., 30 hp						
Cpe	750	2400	4000	8000	14,000	20,000
Model 60, 4-cyl., 35 hp						
Tr	1100	3500	5800	11,600	20,300	29,000
Model 61, 4-cyl., 45 hp						
Rds	1300	4100	6800	13,600	23,800	34,000
4d Tr	1300	4200	7000	14,000	24,500	35,000
Tr	1300	4200	7000	14,000	24,500	35,000
Cpe	850	2750	4600	9200	16,100	23,000

	6	5	4	3	2	1
1913						
Model 69, 4-cyl., 30 hp						
Cpe	700	2300	3800	7600	13,300	19,000
Tr	1050	3350	5600	11,200	19,600	28,000
Rds	1000	3250	5400	10,800	18,900	27,000
4d Tr	1100	3500	5800	11,600	20,300	29,000
Model 71, 4-cyl., 45 hp						
Rds	1300	4100	6800	13,600	23,800	34,000
Tr	1300	4200	7000	14,000	24,500	35,000
5P Tr	1350	4300	7200	14,400	25,200	36,000
1914						
Model 79, 4-cyl., 35 hp						
Rds	1000	3250	5400	10,800	18,900	27,000
Tr	1050	3350	5600	11,200	19,600	28,000
Cpe	750	2400	4000	8000	14,000	20,000
Model 46, 4-cyl., 35 hp						
Tr	1100	3500	5800	11,600	20,300	29,000
1915						
Model 81, 4-cyl., 30 hp						
Rds	1050	3350	5600	11,200	19,600	28,000
Tr	1100	3500	5800	11,600	20,300	29,000
Willys-Knight K-19, 4-cyl., 45 hp						
Rds	1100	3500	5800	11,600	20,300	29,000
Tr	1150	3600	6000	12,000	21,000	30,000
Willys-Knight K-17, 4-cyl., 45 hp						
Rds	1150	3600	6000	12,000	21,000	30,000
Tr	1150	3700	6200	12,400	21,700	31,000
Model 80, 4-cyl., 35 hp						
Rds	950	3000	5000	10,000	17,500	25,000
Tr	900	2900	4800	9600	16,800	24,000
Cpe	750	2400	4000	8000	14,000	20,000
Model 82, 6-cyl., 45-50 hp						
7P Tr	1450	4550	7600	15,200	26,600	38,000
1916						
Model 75, 4-cyl., 20-25 hp						
Rds	700	2300	3800	7600	13,300	19,000
Tr	750	2400	4000	8000	14,000	20,000
Model 83, 4-cyl., 35 hp						
Rds	750	2400	4000	8000	14,000	20,000
Tr	800	2500	4200	8400	14,700	21,000
Model 83-B, 4-cyl., 35 hp						
Rds	800	2500	4200	8400	14,700	21,000
Tr	850	2650	4400	8800	15,400	22,000
Willys-Knight, 4-cyl., 40 hp (also Model 84)						
Rds	1000	3100	5200	10,400	18,200	26,000
Tr	1000	3250	5400	10,800	18,900	27,000
Cpe	600	1900	3200	6400	11,200	16,000
Limo	700	2150	3600	7200	12,600	18,000
Willys-Knight, 6-cyl., 45 hp (also Model 86)						
7P Tr	1300	4200	7000	14,000	24,500	35,000
1917-18						
Light Four 90, 4-cyl., 32 hp						
2P Rds	650	2050	3400	6800	11,900	17,000
5P Tr	700	2150	3600	7200	12,600	18,000
4P Ctry Clb	600	1900	3200	6400	11,200	16,000
5P Sed*	400	1200	2000	4000	7000	10,000
Big Four 85, 4-cyl., 35 hp						
3P Rds	700	2150	3600	7200	12,600	18,000
5P Tr	700	2300	3800	7600	13,300	19,000
3P Tr Cpe	550	1800	3000	6000	10,500	15,000
5P Tr Sed	400	1300	2200	4400	7700	11,000
Light Six 85, 6-cyl., 35-40 hp						
3P Rds	700	2300	3800	7600	13,300	19,000
5P Tr	750	2400	4000	8000	14,000	20,000
3P Tr Cpe	600	1900	3200	6400	11,200	16,000
5P Tr Sed	450	1450	2400	4800	8400	12,000
Willys 89, 6-cyl., 45 hp						
7P Tr	1000	3100	5200	10,400	18,200	26,000
4P Clb Rds	950	3000	5000	10,000	17,500	25,000
6P Sed	550	1700	2800	5600	9800	14,000
Willys-Knight 88-4, 4-cyl., 40 hp						
7P Tr	1100	3500	5800	11,600	20,300	29,000
4P Cpe	650	2050	3400	6800	11,900	17,000
7P Tr Sed	500	1550	2600	5200	9100	13,000
7P Limo	700	2150	3600	7200	12,600	18,000
Willys-Knight 88-8, 8-cyl., 65 hp						
7P Tr	1300	4100	6800	13,600	23,800	34,000
7P Sed	550	1700	2800	5600	9800	14,000
7P Limo	700	2150	3600	7200	12,600	18,000
7P Twn Car	700	2300	3800	7600	13,300	19,000

*This model offered 1917 only.

	6	5	4	3	2	1
1919						
Light Four 90, 4-cyl., 32 hp						
Rds	550	1700	2800	5600	9800	14,000
5P Tr	550	1800	3000	6000	10,500	15,000
Clb Rds	550	1800	3000	6000	10,500	15,000
5P Sed	400	1250	2100	4200	7400	10,500
Willys 89, 6-cyl., 45 hp						
7P Tr	1000	3100	5200	10,400	18,200	26,000
4P Clb Rds	950	3000	5000	10,000	17,500	25,000
6P Sed	400	1250	2100	4200	7400	10,500
Willys-Knight 88-4, 4-cyl., 40 hp						
7P Tr	900	2900	4800	9600	16,800	24,000
4P Cpe	450	1140	1900	3800	6650	9500
7P Sed	450	1140	1900	3800	6650	9500
7P Limo	450	1450	2400	4800	8400	12,000
Willys-Knight 88-8, 8-cyl., 65 hp						
7P Tr	1000	3250	5400	10,800	18,900	27,000
4P Cpe	400	1250	2100	4200	7400	10,500
7P Tr Sed	400	1200	2000	4000	7000	10,000
7P Limo	500	1550	2600	5200	9100	13,000
1920						
Model 4, 4-cyl., 100" wb, 27 hp						
2P Rds	700	2150	3600	7200	12,600	18,000
5P Tr	700	2300	3800	7600	13,300	19,000
Clb Rds	550	1700	2800	5600	9800	14,000
5P Sed	400	1200	2000	4000	7000	10,000
Model 89-6, Willys Six, 6-cyl.						
Clb Rds	700	2300	3800	7600	13,300	19,000
7P Tr	750	2400	4000	8000	14,000	20,000
6P Sed	400	1200	2000	4000	7000	10,000
Model 20 Willys-Knight, 4-cyl., 118" wb, 48 hp						
3P Rds	700	2300	3800	7600	13,300	19,000
5P Tr	750	2400	4000	8000	14,000	20,000
4P Cpe	400	1250	2100	4200	7400	10,500
5P Sed	400	1200	2000	4000	7000	10.000

1921

	6	5	4	3	2	1
Model 4, 4-cyl., 100" wb, 27 hp						
5P Tr	700	2150	3600	7200	12,600	18,000
2P Rds	700	2300	3800	7600	13,300	19,000
5P Sed	400	1250	2100	4200	7400	10,500
2P Cpe	400	1300	2150	4300	7600	10,800
Model 20 Willys-Knight, 4-cyl., 118" wb						
3P Rds	650	2050	3400	6800	11,900	17,000
5P Tr	700	2150	3600	7200	12,600	18,000
4P Cpe	450	1400	2300	4600	8100	11,500
5P Sed	400	1300	2200	4400	7700	11,000

1922

	6	5	4	3	2	1
Model 4, 4-cyl., 100" wb, 27 hp						
2P Rds	650	2050	3400	6800	11,900	17,000
5P Tr	700	2150	3600	7200	12,600	18,000
5P Sed	400	1250	2100	4200	7400	10,500
2P Cpe	400	1300	2150	4300	7500	10,700
Model 20 Willys-Knight, 4-cyl., 118" wb, 40 hp						
3P Rds	700	2300	3800	7600	13,300	19,000
5P Tr	750	2400	4000	8000	14,000	20,000
4P Cpe	400	1300	2200	4400	7700	11,000
5P Sed	400	1250	2100	4200	7400	10,500
Model 27 Willys-Knight, 4-cyl., 118" wb						
7P Tr	800	2500	4200	8400	14,700	21,000
7P Sed	400	1250	2100	4200	7400	10,500

1923-24

	6	5	4	3	2	1
Model 91, 4-cyl., 100" wb, 27 hp						
2P Rds	550	1700	2800	5600	9800	14,000
5P Tr	550	1700	2800	5600	9800	14,000
3P Cpe	400	1250	2100	4200	7400	10,500
5P Sed	400	1200	2000	4000	7000	10,000
Model 92, 4-cyl., 106" wb, 30 hp						
Redbird	950	3000	5000	10,000	17,500	25,000
Blackbird*	950	3000	5000	10,000	17,500	25,000
Bluebird*	950	3000	5000	10,000	17,500	25,000
Model 64 Willys-Knight, 4-cyl., 118" wb, 40 hp						
3P Rds	700	2300	3800	7600	13,300	19,000
5P Tr	750	2400	4000	8000	14,000	20,000
Ctry Clb	500	1550	2600	5200	9100	13,000
4P Cpe	400	1250	2100	4200	7400	10,500
5P Sed	400	1200	2000	4000	7000	10,000
Model 67 Willys-Knight, 4-cyl., 124" wb, 40 hp						
7P Tr	750	2400	4000	8000	14,000	20,000
7P Sed	400	1300	2200	4400	7700	11,000

*Model offered 1924 only.

1925

	6	5	4	3	2	1
Model 91, 4-cyl., 100" wb, 27 hp						
5P Tr	650	2050	3400	6800	11,900	17,000
2P Cpe	450	1400	2300	4600	8100	11,500
5P Tr Sed	400	1200	2000	4000	7000	10,000
5P Cpe Sed	400	1250	2050	4100	7200	10,300
5P DeL Sed	400	1250	2100	4200	7400	10,500
Model 92, 4-cyl., 106" wb, 30 hp						
Bluebird	800	2500	4200	8400	14,700	21,000
Model 93, 6-cyl., 113" wb, 38 hp						
5P Sed	400	1300	2150	4300	7600	10,800
DeL Sed	400	1300	2200	4400	7700	11,000
Model 65 Willys-Knight, 4-cyl., 124" wb, 40 hp						
5P Tr	700	2300	3800	7600	13,300	19,000
2P Cpe	450	1450	2400	4800	8400	12,000
Cpe Sed	450	1400	2300	4600	8100	11,500
Sed	400	1200	2000	4000	7000	10,000
Brgm	400	1300	2200	4400	7700	11,000
Model 66 Willys-Knight, 6-cyl., 126" wb, 60 hp						
Rds	750	2400	4000	8000	14,000	20,000
5P Tr	800	2500	4200	8400	14,700	21,000
Cpe Sed	450	1450	2400	4800	8400	12,000
Brgm	450	1500	2500	5000	8800	12,500
Cpe	450	1500	2500	5000	8800	12,500
Sed	450	1400	2300	4600	8100	11,500

1926

	6	5	4	3	2	1
Model 91, 4-cyl., 100" wb, 27 hp						
5P Tr	700	2150	3600	7200	12,600	18,000
2P Cpe	450	1400	2300	4600	8100	11,500
5P Sed	450	1170	1975	3900	6850	9800
2d Sed	450	1150	1900	3850	6700	9600
4P Cpe	450	1160	1950	3900	6800	9700
Model 92, 4-cyl., 100" wb, 30 hp						
5P Tr	700	2300	3800	7600	13,300	19,000
Model 93, 6-cyl., 113" wb, 38 hp						
5P Tr	750	2400	4000	8000	14,000	20,000
5P Sed	400	1200	2000	4000	7000	10,000
DeL Sed	400	1250	2100	4200	7400	10,500
2P Cpe	400	1200	2000	4000	7000	10,000
Model 66 Willys-Knight, 6-cyl., 126" wb, 60 hp						
Rds	900	2900	4800	9600	16,800	24,000
7P Tr	950	3000	5000	10,000	17,500	25,000
5P Tr	900	2900	4800	9600	16,800	24,000
4P Cpe	450	1400	2300	4600	8100	11,500
Sed	400	1300	2200	4400	7700	11,000
Model 70 Willys-Knight, 6-cyl., 113" wb, 53 hp						
5P Tr	950	3000	5000	10,000	17,500	25,000
Sed	400	1250	2100	4200	7400	10,500
2d Sed	400	1200	2000	4000	7000	10,000
Cpe	450	1400	2300	4600	8100	11,500
Rds	950	3000	5000	10,000	17,500	25,000

1927

	6	5	4	3	2	1
Model 70A Willys-Knight, 6-cyl., 113" wb, 52 hp						
Rds	850	2650	4400	8800	15,400	22,000
Tr	850	2750	4600	9200	16,100	23,000
Cpe	500	1550	2600	5200	9100	13,000
Cabr	800	2500	4200	8400	14,700	21,000
Sed	450	1400	2300	4600	8100	11,500
2d Sed	400	1300	2200	4400	7700	11,000
Model 66A Willys-Knight, 6-cyl., 126" wb, 65 hp						
Rds	1000	3100	5200	10,400	18,200	26,000
Tr	1000	3250	5400	10,800	18,900	27,000
Foursome	1000	3100	5200	10,400	18,200	26,000
Cabr	850	2750	4600	9200	16,100	23,000
5P Sed	450	1500	2500	5000	8800	12,500
7P Sed	500	1600	2700	5400	9500	13,500
Limo	550	1800	3000	6000	10,500	15,000

1928

	6	5	4	3	2	1
Model 56 Willys-Knight, 6-cyl., 109.5" wb, 45 hp						
Rds	800	2500	4200	8400	14,700	21,000
Tr	850	2650	4400	8800	15,400	22,000
Cpe	500	1600	2700	5400	9500	13,500
2d Sed	400	1300	2200	4400	7700	11,000
Sed	400	1350	2200	4400	7800	11,100
Model 70A Willys-Knight, 6-cyl., 113.5" wb, 53 hp						
Rds	850	2750	4600	9200	16,100	23,000
Tr	900	2900	4800	9600	16,800	24,000
Cpe	550	1800	3000	6000	10,500	15,000
5P Cpe	600	1850	3100	6200	10,900	15,500
Cabr	650	2050	3400	6800	11,900	17,000
2d Sed	450	1500	2500	5000	8800	12,500
Sed	500	1550	2600	5200	9100	13,000
Model 66A Willys-Knight, 6-cyl., 126" wb, 70 hp						
Rds	950	3000	5000	10,000	17,500	25,000
Tr	1000	3100	5200	10,400	18,200	26,000
Cabr	900	2900	4800	9600	16,800	24,000
Fml Sed	500	1600	2700	5400	9500	13,500
Sed	450	1450	2400	4800	8400	12,000
Model 66A Willys-Knight, 6-cyl., 135" wb, 70 hp						
7P Tr	1000	3250	5400	10,800	18,900	27,000
Cpe	650	2050	3400	6800	11,900	17,000
7P Sed	600	1850	3100	6200	10,900	15,500
Limo	600	1900	3200	6400	11,200	16,000

1929

(All Willys-Knight)

	6	5	4	3	2	1
Series 56, 6-cyl., 109.5" wb, 45 hp						
Rds	1000	3100	5200	10,400	18,200	26,000
Tr	800	2500	4200	8400	14,700	21,000
Cpe	500	1550	2600	5200	9100	13,000
2d Sed	450	1500	2500	5000	8800	12,500
Sed	500	1550	2600	5200	9100	13,000
Series 70A, 6-cyl., 113.2" wb, 53 hp						
Rds	1000	3250	5400	10,800	18,900	27,000
Tr	1050	3350	5600	11,200	19,600	28,000
Cpe	650	2050	3400	6800	11,900	17,000
Cabr	1000	3100	5200	10,400	18,200	26,000
2d Sed	500	1550	2600	5200	9100	13,000
Sed	500	1600	2700	5400	9500	13,500
Series 66A, 6-cyl., 126" wb, 70 hp						
Rds	1050	3350	5600	11,200	19,600	28,000
Tr	1100	3500	5800	11,600	20,300	29,000
Cabr	1000	3250	5400	10,800	18,900	27,000
Fml Sed	650	2050	3400	6800	11,900	17,000
DeL Fml Sed	650	2100	3500	7000	12,300	17,500
Sed	550	1800	3000	6000	10,500	15,000
Series 66A, 6-cyl., 135" wb, 70 hp						
7P Tr	1200	3850	6400	12,800	22,400	32,000
5P Cpe	750	2400	4000	8000	14,000	20,000
7P Sed	650	2050	3400	6800	11,900	17,000
Limo	700	2150	3600	7200	12,600	18,000
Series 70B, 6-cyl., 112.5" - 115" wb, 53 hp						
Rds	1000	3100	5200	10,400	18,200	26,000
Tr	1000	3250	5400	10,800	18,900	27,000
2P Cpe	600	1900	3200	6400	11,200	16,000
4P Cpe	550	1800	3000	6000	10,500	15,000
2d Sed	450	1500	2500	5000	8800	12,500
Sed	450	1500	2500	5000	8800	12,600
DeL Sed	500	1550	2600	5200	9100	13,000

1930

Willys Models

	6	5	4	3	2	1
Series 98B, 6-cyl., 110" wb, 65 hp						
Rds	1000	3250	5400	10,800	18,900	27,000
4P Rds	1050	3350	5600	11,200	19,600	28,000
5P Tr	1100	3500	5800	11,600	20,300	29,000
2P Cpe	500	1600	2700	5400	9500	13,500
4P Cpe	550	1800	3000	6000	10,500	15,000
2d Sed	450	1450	2400	4800	8400	12,000
Sed	450	1500	2500	5000	8800	12,500
DeL Sed	500	1550	2600	5200	9100	13,000

Willys-Knight Models

	6	5	4	3	2	1
Series 66B, 6-cyl., 120" wb, 87 hp						
Rds	1050	3350	5600	11,200	19,600	28,000
Tr	1100	3500	5800	11,600	20,300	29,000
2P Cpe	600	1900	3200	6400	11,200	16,000
5P Cpe	650	2050	3400	6800	11,900	17,000
Sed	550	1800	3000	6000	10,500	15,000

Series 70B, "See 1929 Series 70B"
Series 6-87, "See 1929 Series 56"

1931

Willys 98B, "See 1930 98B Series"

	6	5	4	3	2	1
Willys 97, 6-cyl., 110" wb, 65 hp						
Rds	950	3000	5000	10,000	17,500	25,000
Tr	1000	3100	5200	10,400	18,200	26,000
Cpe	550	1800	3000	6000	10,500	15,000
2d Sed	450	1500	2500	5000	8800	12,500
Clb Sed	500	1550	2600	5200	9100	13,000
Sed	450	1500	2500	5000	8800	12,500
Willys 98D, 6-cyl., 113" wb, 65 hp						
Vic Cpe	550	1700	2800	5600	9800	14,000
Sed	500	1550	2600	5200	9100	13,000

NOTE: Add 10 percent for DeLuxe Willys models.

Willys-Knight 66B, "See 1930 W-K 66B".
Willys-Knight 87, "See 1930 Series 6-87"

	6	5	4	3	2	1
Willys-Knight 66D, 6-cyl., 121" wb, 87 hp						
Vic Cpe	550	1700	2800	5600	9800	14,000
Sed	500	1550	2600	5200	9100	13,000
Cus Sed	500	1600	2700	5400	9500	13,500

NOTE: Add 10 percent for DeLuxe Willys-Knight models.

	6	5	4	3	2	1
Willys 8-80, 8-cyl., 120" wb, 80 hp						
Cpe	550	1700	2800	5600	9800	14,000
DeL Cpe	550	1750	2900	5800	10,200	14,500
Sed	450	1450	2400	4800	8400	12,000
DeL Sed	500	1600	2700	5400	9500	13,500
Willys 8-80D, 8-cyl., 120" wb, 80 hp						
Vic Cpe	500	1550	2600	5200	9100	13,000
DeL Vic Cpe	500	1600	2700	5400	9500	13,500
Sed	400	1300	2200	4400	7700	11,000
DeL Sed	450	1400	2300	4600	8100	11,500
Cus Sed	450	1450	2400	4800	8400	12,000

1932

Willys 97, "See 1931 Willys 97 Series"
Willys 98D, "See 1931 Willys 98D Series"

	6	5	4	3	2	1
Willys 90 (Silver Streak), 6-cyl., 113" wb, 65 hp						
2P Rds	950	3000	5000	10,000	17,500	25,000
4P Rds	950	3050	5100	10,200	17,900	25,500
Spt Rds	1000	3100	5200	10,400	18,200	26,000
5P Tr	1000	3100	5200	10,400	18,200	26,000
2P Cpe	550	1800	3000	6000	10,500	15,000
4P Cpe	600	1850	3100	6200	10,900	15,500

	6	5	4	3	2	1
Vic Cus	500	1550	2600	5200	9100	13,000
5P Sed	400	1250	2100	4200	7400	10,500
2d Sed	400	1300	2150	4300	7500	10,700
Spl Sed	450	1450	2400	4800	8400	12,000
Cus Sed	500	1600	2700	5400	9500	13,500
Willys 8-80D, "See 1931 Willys 8-80D"						
Willys 8-88 (Silver Streak), 8-cyl., 121" wb, 80 hp						
Rds	1000	3100	5200	10,400	18,200	26,000
Spt Rds	1000	3200	5300	10,600	18,600	26,500
2P Cpe	550	1700	2800	5600	9800	14,000
4P Cpe	550	1800	3000	6000	10,500	15,000
Vic Cus	550	1750	2900	5800	10,200	14,500
Sed	450	1500	2450	4900	8600	12,300
Spl Sed	500	1550	2550	5100	9000	12,800
Cus Sed	550	1700	2800	5600	9800	14,000
Willys-Knight 95 DeLuxe, 6-cyl., 113" wb, 60 hp						
2P Cpe	500	1600	2700	5400	9500	13,500
4P Cpe	550	1700	2800	5600	9800	14,000
Vic	500	1550	2600	5200	9100	13,000
2d Sed	450	1450	2400	4800	8400	12,000
Sed	450	1500	2500	5000	8800	12,500
Willys-Knight 66D, 6-cyl., 121" wb, 87 hp						
1st Series (start Oct. 1931)						
Vic	550	1800	3000	6000	10,500	15,000
DeL Vic	600	1850	3100	6200	10,900	15,500
Sed	500	1550	2600	5200	9100	13,000
DeL Sed	500	1600	2700	5400	9500	13,500
Cus Sed	550	1700	2800	5600	9800	14,000
2nd Series (start Jan. 1932)						
Vic Cus	550	1800	3000	6000	10,500	15,000
Cus Sed	600	1850	3100	6200	10,900	15,500
1933						
Willys 77, 4-cyl., 100" wb, 48 hp						
Cpe	550	1750	2900	5800	10,200	14,500
Cus Cpe	550	1800	3000	6000	10,500	15,000
4P Cpe	600	1850	3100	6200	10,900	15,500
4P Cus Cpe	600	1900	3200	6400	11,200	16,000
Sed	550	1700	2800	5600	9800	14,000
Cus Sed	550	1750	2900	5800	10,200	14,500
Willys 6-90A (Silver Streak), 6-cyl., 113" wb, 65 hp						
Rds	750	2400	4000	8000	14,000	20,000
4P Rds	750	2450	4100	8200	14,400	20,500
Spt Rds	800	2500	4200	8400	14,700	21,000
Cpe	500	1550	2600	5200	9100	13,000
Cus Cpe	500	1600	2700	5400	9500	13,500
2d Sed	450	1400	2300	4600	8100	11,500
Sed	450	1450	2400	4800	8400	12,000
Cus Sed	450	1500	2500	5000	8800	12,500
Willys 8-88A (Streamline), 8-cyl., 121" wb, 80 hp						
2P Cpe	500	1550	2600	5200	9100	13,000
Cus Cpe	550	1700	2800	5600	9800	14,000
Sed	450	1500	2500	5000	8800	12,500
Cus Sed	550	1700	2800	5600	9800	14,000
Willys-Knight 66E, 6-cyl., 121" wb, 87 hp						
Cus Sed	600	1850	3100	6200	10,900	15,500
1934						
Willys 77, 4-cyl., 100" wb, 48 hp						
Cpe	550	1800	3000	6000	10,500	15,000
Cus Cpe	600	1850	3100	6200	10,900	15,500
4P Cpe	600	1900	3150	6300	11,000	15,700
4P Cus Cpe	600	1900	3200	6400	11,200	16,000
Sed	550	1700	2800	5600	9800	14,000
Cus Sed	550	1750	2900	5800	10,200	14,500
Pan Dely	600	1900	3200	6400	11,200	16,000
1935						
Willys 77, 4-cyl., 100" wb, 48 hp						
Cpe	600	1850	3100	6200	10,900	15,500
Sed	500	1550	2600	5200	9100	13,000
1936						
Willys 77, 4-cyl., 100" wb, 48 hp						
Cpe	550	1800	3000	6000	10,500	15,000
Sed	500	1550	2600	5200	9100	13,000
DeL Sed	500	1600	2700	5400	9500	13,500
1937						
Willys 37, 4-cyl., 100" wb, 48 hp						
Cpe	550	1800	3000	6000	10,500	15,000
DeL Cpe	600	1850	3100	6200	10,900	15,500
Sed	550	1700	2800	5600	9800	14,000
DeL Sed	550	1750	2900	5800	10,200	14,500
1938						
Willys 38, 4-cyl., 100" wb, 48 hp						
Std Cpe	450	1500	2500	5000	8800	12,500
DeL Cpe	500	1550	2600	5200	9100	13,000
2d Clipper Sed	400	1300	2200	4400	7700	11,000
Std Sed	400	1300	2150	4300	7600	10,800
2d DeL Clipper Sed	400	1350	2250	4500	7800	11,200
DeL Sed	400	1300	2200	4400	7700	11,000
Cus Sed	400	1350	2250	4500	7800	11,200
1939						
Willys Std Speedway, 4-cyl., 102" wb, 48 hp						
Cpe	500	1600	2700	5400	9500	13,500
2d Sed	450	1400	2300	4600	8100	11,500
Sed	400	1300	2200	4400	7700	11,000
DelCpe	500	1650	2750	5500	9600	13,700
DeL 2d Sed	450	1400	2350	4700	8300	11,800
DeL 4d Sed	400	1350	2250	4500	7900	11,300
Spl Speedway Cpe	550	1700	2800	5600	9800	14,000
Spl Speedway 2d Sed	450	1450	2400	4800	8400	12,000
Spl Speedway 4d Sed	450	1400	2300	4600	8100	11,500
Model 48, 100" wb						
Cpe	550	1700	2850	5700	9900	14,200
2d Sed	450	1450	2450	4900	8500	12,200
4d Sed	450	1400	2300	4600	8100	11,600
Model 38, 100" wb						
Std Cpe	550	1700	2850	5700	9900	14,200
Std 2d Sed	450	1450	2450	4900	8500	12,200
Std 4d Sed	450	1400	2350	4700	8200	11,700

	6	5	4	3	2	1
DeL Cpe	550	1700	2850	5700	10,000	14,300
DeL 2d Sed	450	1500	2450	4900	8600	12,300
DeL 4d Sed	450	1400	2350	4700	8300	11,800
1940						
Willys Speedway, 4-cyl., 102" wb, 48 hp						
Cpe	500	1600	2700	5400	9500	13,500
Sed	450	1400	2350	4700	8200	11,700
Sta Wag	700	2150	3600	7200	12,600	18,000
DeLuxe, 4-cyl., 102" wb						
Cpe	450	1400	2300	4600	8100	11,600
Sed	400	1300	2200	4400	7700	11,000
Sta Wag	700	2300	3800	7600	13,300	19,000
1941						
Willys (Americar)						
Speedway Series, 4-cyl., 104" wb, 63 hp						
Cpe	500	1600	2700	5400	9500	13,500
Sed	450	1450	2400	4800	8400	12,000
DeLuxe, 4-cyl., 104" wb, 63 hp						
Cpe	550	1700	2800	5600	9800	14,000
Sed	450	1450	2400	4800	8400	12,000
Sta Wag	750	2400	4000	8000	14,000	20,000
Plainsman, 4-cyl., 104" wb, 63 hp						
Cpe	500	1650	2750	5500	9600	13,700
Sed	450	1400	2300	4600	8100	11,500
1946-47						
Willys 4-63, 4-cyl., 104" wb, 63 hp						
2d Sta Wag	400	1300	2200	4400	7700	11,000
1948						
Willys 4-63, 4-cyl., 104" wb, 63 hp						
2d Sta Wag	400	1300	2200	4400	7700	11,000
2d Jeepster	550	1700	2800	5600	9800	14,000
Willys 6-63, 6-cyl., 104" wb, 75 hp						
2d Sta Sed	450	1400	2300	4600	8100	11,500
2d Jeepster	550	1750	2900	5800	10,200	14,500
1949						
Willys 4X463, 4-cyl., 104.5" wb, 63 hp						
2d FWD Sta Wag	400	1200	2000	4000	7000	10,000
Willys VJ3, 4-cyl., 104" wb, 63 hp						
2d Phae	550	1700	2800	5600	9800	14,000
Willys 463, 4-cyl., 104" wb, 63 hp						
2d Sta Wag	400	1300	2200	4400	7700	11,000
Willys Six, 6-cyl., 104" wb, 75 hp						
2d Phae	550	1750	2900	5800	10,200	14,500
Willys Six, 6-cyl., 104" wb, 75 hp						
2d Sta Sed	450	1400	2350	4700	8300	11,800
2d Sta Wag	450	1400	2300	4600	8100	11,500
1950-51						
Willys 473SW, 4-cyl., 104" wb, 63 hp						
2d Sta Wag	400	1300	2200	4400	7700	11,000
Willys 4X473SW, 4-cyl., 104.5" wb, 63 hp						
2d FWD Sta Wag	400	1250	2100	4200	7400	10,500
Willys 473VJ, 4-cyl., 104" wb, 63 hp						
2d Phae	550	1750	2900	5800	10,200	14,500
NOTE: Add 10 percent for six cylinder models.						
1952						
Willys Aero, 6-cyl., 108" wb, 75 hp						
2d Lark	450	1080	1800	3600	6300	9000
2d Wing	950	1100	1850	3700	6450	9200
2d Ace	450	1150	1900	3850	6700	9600
2d HT Eagle	450	1400	2300	4600	8100	11,500
Willys Four, 4-cyl., 104"-104.5" wb, 63 hp						
2d FWD Sta Wag	450	1140	1900	3800	6650	9500
2d Sta Wag	400	1200	2000	4000	7000	10,000
Willys Six, 6-cyl., 104" wb, 75 hp						
2d Sta Wag	400	1250	2100	4200	7400	10,500
NOTE: Deduct 10 percent for standard models.						
1953						
Willys Aero, 6-cyl., 108" wb, 90 hp						
4d H.D. Aero	450	1170	1975	3900	6850	9800
4d DeL Lark	450	1120	1875	3750	6500	9300
2d DeL Lark	450	1140	1900	3800	6650	9500
4d Falcon	450	1150	1900	3850	6700	9600
2d Falcon	450	1140	1900	3800	6650	9500
4d Ace	450	1170	1975	3900	6850	9800
2d Ace	450	1150	1900	3850	6700	9600
2d HT Eagle	450	1450	2400	4800	8400	12,000
Willys Four, 4-cyl., 104"-104.5" wb, 72 hp						
2d FWD Sta Wag	450	1140	1900	3800	6650	9500
2d Sta Wag	400	1200	2000	4000	7000	10,000
Willys Six, 6-cyl., 104" wb, 90 hp						
2d Sta Wag	400	1250	2050	4100	7200	10,300
1954						
Willys, 6-cyl., 108" wb, 90 hp						
4d DeL Ace	450	1140	1900	3800	6650	9500
2d DeL Ace	950	1100	1850	3700	6450	9200
2d HT DeL Eagle	450	1450	2400	4800	8400	12,000
2d HT Cus Eagle	450	1500	2500	5000	8800	12,500
4d Lark	950	1100	1850	3700	6450	9200
2d Lark	450	1090	1800	3650	6400	9100
4d Ace	950	1100	1850	3700	6450	9200
2d Ace	450	1090	1800	3650	6400	9100
2d HT Eagle	450	1400	2350	4700	8300	11,800
Willys Four, 4-cyl., 104"-104.5" wb, 72 hp						
2d Sta Wag	400	1200	2000	4000	7000	10,000
Willys Six, 6-cyl., 104" wb, 90 hp						
2d FWD Sta Wag	450	1140	1900	3800	6650	9500
2d Sta Wag	400	1250	2050	4100	7200	10,300
1955						
Willys Six, 6-cyl., 108" wb, 90 hp						
4d Cus Sed	450	1170	1975	3900	6850	9800
2d Cus	400	1250	2050	4100	7200	10,300
2d HT Bermuda	500	1600	2700	5400	9500	13,500
Willys Six, 6-cyl., 104"-104.5" wb, 90 hp						
2d FWD Sta Wag	450	1140	1900	3800	6650	9500
2d Sta Wag	400	1200	2000	4000	7000	10,000